DERIVATIVES AND I

Basic Differentiation Rules

1. $\dfrac{d}{dx}[cu] = cu'$

2. $\dfrac{d}{dx}[u \pm v] = u' \pm v'$

3. $\dfrac{d}{dx}[uv] = uv' + vu'$

4. $\dfrac{d}{dx}\left[\dfrac{u}{v}\right] = \dfrac{vu' - uv'}{v^2}$

5. $\dfrac{d}{dx}[c] = 0$

6. $\dfrac{d}{dx}[u^n] = nu^{n-1}u'$

7. $\dfrac{d}{dx}[x] = 1$

8. $\dfrac{d}{dx}[|u|] = \dfrac{u}{|u|}(u'), \ u \neq 0$

9. $\dfrac{d}{dx}[\ln u] = \dfrac{u'}{u}$

10. $\dfrac{d}{dx}[e^u] = e^u u'$

11. $\dfrac{d}{dx}[\log_a u] = \dfrac{u'}{(\ln a)u}$

12. $\dfrac{d}{dx}[a^u] = (\ln a)a^u u'$

13. $\dfrac{d}{dx}[\sin u] = (\cos u)u'$

14. $\dfrac{d}{dx}[\cos u] = -(\sin u)u'$

15. $\dfrac{d}{dx}[\tan u] = (\sec^2 u)u'$

16. $\dfrac{d}{dx}[\cot u] = -(\csc^2 u)u'$

17. $\dfrac{d}{dx}[\sec u] = (\sec u \tan u)u'$

18. $\dfrac{d}{dx}[\csc u] = -(\csc u \cot u)u'$

19. $\dfrac{d}{dx}[\arcsin u] = \dfrac{u'}{\sqrt{1 - u^2}}$

20. $\dfrac{d}{dx}[\arccos u] = \dfrac{-u'}{\sqrt{1 - u^2}}$

21. $\dfrac{d}{dx}[\arctan u] = \dfrac{u'}{1 + u^2}$

22. $\dfrac{d}{dx}[\text{arccot } u] = \dfrac{-u'}{1 + u^2}$

23. $\dfrac{d}{dx}[\text{arcsec } u] = \dfrac{u'}{|u|\sqrt{u^2 - 1}}$

24. $\dfrac{d}{dx}[\text{arccsc } u] = \dfrac{-u'}{|u|\sqrt{u^2 - 1}}$

Basic Integration Formulas

1. $\displaystyle\int kf(u)\,du = k\int f(u)\,du$

2. $\displaystyle\int [f(u) \pm g(u)]\,du = \int f(u)\,du \pm \int g(u)\,du$

3. $\displaystyle\int du = u + C$

4. $\displaystyle\int u^n\,du = \dfrac{u^{n+1}}{n + 1} + C, \ n \neq -1$

5. $\displaystyle\int \dfrac{du}{u} = \ln|u| + C$

6. $\displaystyle\int e^u\,du = e^u + C$

7. $\displaystyle\int a^u\,du = \left(\dfrac{1}{\ln a}\right)a^u + C$

8. $\displaystyle\int \sin u\,du = -\cos u + C$

9. $\displaystyle\int \cos u\,du = \sin u + C$

10. $\displaystyle\int \tan u\,du = -\ln|\cos u| + C$

11. $\displaystyle\int \cot u\,du = \ln|\sin u| + C$

12. $\displaystyle\int \sec u\,du = \ln|\sec u + \tan u| + C$

13. $\displaystyle\int \csc u\,du = -\ln|\csc u + \cot u| + C$

14. $\displaystyle\int \sec^2 u\,du = \tan u + C$

15. $\displaystyle\int \csc^2 u\,du = -\cot u + C$

16. $\displaystyle\int \sec u \tan u\,du = \sec u + C$

17. $\displaystyle\int \csc u \cot u\,du = -\csc u + C$

18. $\displaystyle\int \dfrac{du}{\sqrt{a^2 - u^2}} = \arcsin \dfrac{u}{a} + C$

19. $\displaystyle\int \dfrac{du}{a^2 + u^2} = \dfrac{1}{a}\arctan \dfrac{u}{a} + C$

20. $\displaystyle\int \dfrac{du}{u\sqrt{u^2 - a^2}} = \dfrac{1}{a}\text{arcsec} \dfrac{|u|}{a} + C$

TRIGONOMETRY

Definition of the Six Trigonometric Functions

Right triangle definitions, where $0 < \theta < \pi/2$.

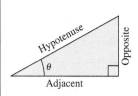

$$\sin\theta = \frac{\text{opp}}{\text{hyp}} \qquad \csc\theta = \frac{\text{hyp}}{\text{opp}}$$

$$\cos\theta = \frac{\text{adj}}{\text{hyp}} \qquad \sec\theta = \frac{\text{hyp}}{\text{adj}}$$

$$\tan\theta = \frac{\text{opp}}{\text{adj}} \qquad \cot\theta = \frac{\text{adj}}{\text{opp}}$$

Circular function definitions, where θ is any angle.

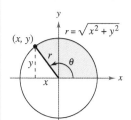

$$\sin\theta = \frac{y}{r} \qquad \csc\theta = \frac{r}{y}$$

$$\cos\theta = \frac{x}{r} \qquad \sec\theta = \frac{r}{x}$$

$$\tan\theta = \frac{y}{x} \qquad \cot\theta = \frac{x}{y}$$

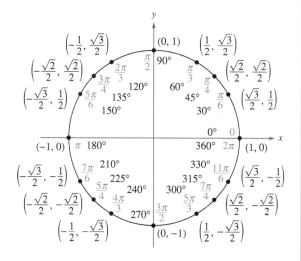

Reciprocal Identities

$$\sin x = \frac{1}{\csc x} \qquad \sec x = \frac{1}{\cos x} \qquad \tan x = \frac{1}{\cot x}$$

$$\csc x = \frac{1}{\sin x} \qquad \cos x = \frac{1}{\sec x} \qquad \cot x = \frac{1}{\tan x}$$

Quotient Identities

$$\tan x = \frac{\sin x}{\cos x} \qquad \cot x = \frac{\cos x}{\sin x}$$

Pythagorean Identities

$$\sin^2 x + \cos^2 x = 1$$

$$1 + \tan^2 x = \sec^2 x \qquad 1 + \cot^2 x = \csc^2 x$$

Cofunction Identities

$$\sin\left(\frac{\pi}{2} - x\right) = \cos x \qquad \cos\left(\frac{\pi}{2} - x\right) = \sin x$$

$$\csc\left(\frac{\pi}{2} - x\right) = \sec x \qquad \tan\left(\frac{\pi}{2} - x\right) = \cot x$$

$$\sec\left(\frac{\pi}{2} - x\right) = \csc x \qquad \cot\left(\frac{\pi}{2} - x\right) = \tan x$$

Even/Odd Identities

$$\sin(-x) = -\sin x \qquad \cos(-x) = \cos x$$

$$\csc(-x) = -\csc x \qquad \tan(-x) = -\tan x$$

$$\sec(-x) = \sec x \qquad \cot(-x) = -\cot x$$

Sum and Difference Formulas

$$\sin(u \pm v) = \sin u \cos v \pm \cos u \sin v$$

$$\cos(u \pm v) = \cos u \cos v \mp \sin u \sin v$$

$$\tan(u \pm v) = \frac{\tan u \pm \tan v}{1 \mp \tan u \tan v}$$

Double-Angle Formulas

$$\sin 2u = 2\sin u \cos u$$

$$\cos 2u = \cos^2 u - \sin^2 u = 2\cos^2 u - 1 = 1 - 2\sin^2 u$$

$$\tan 2u = \frac{2\tan u}{1 - \tan^2 u}$$

Power-Reducing Formulas

$$\sin^2 u = \frac{1 - \cos 2u}{2}$$

$$\cos^2 u = \frac{1 + \cos 2u}{2}$$

$$\tan^2 u = \frac{1 - \cos 2u}{1 + \cos 2u}$$

Sum-to-Product Formulas

$$\sin u + \sin v = 2\sin\left(\frac{u + v}{2}\right)\cos\left(\frac{u - v}{2}\right)$$

$$\sin u - \sin v = 2\cos\left(\frac{u + v}{2}\right)\sin\left(\frac{u - v}{2}\right)$$

$$\cos u + \cos v = 2\cos\left(\frac{u + v}{2}\right)\cos\left(\frac{u - v}{2}\right)$$

$$\cos u - \cos v = -2\sin\left(\frac{u + v}{2}\right)\sin\left(\frac{u - v}{2}\right)$$

Product-to-Sum Formulas

$$\sin u \sin v = \frac{1}{2}[\cos(u - v) - \cos(u + v)]$$

$$\cos u \cos v = \frac{1}{2}[\cos(u - v) + \cos(u + v)]$$

$$\sin u \cos v = \frac{1}{2}[\sin(u + v) + \sin(u - v)]$$

$$\cos u \sin v = \frac{1}{2}[\sin(u + v) - \sin(u - v)]$$

CALCULUS

for AP® 2e

with **CalcChat®** *and* **CalcView®**

Ron Larson
The Pennsylvania State University
The Behrend College

Paul Battaglia
Brentwood Academy

 CENGAGE

Australia • Brazil • Mexico • Singapore • United Kingdom • United States

AP® is a trademark registered by the College Board, which is not affiliated with, and does not endorse, this product.

Calculus for AP®
with CalcChat® and CalcView®
Second Edition
Ron Larson
Paul Battaglia

Product Director: Daniel Rogers

Product Manager: Raj Desai

Senior Product Marketing Manager: Sebastian Andino

Product Assistant: Jessica Livingston

Senior Content Project Manager: Jennifer Berry

Senior Content Developer: John Anderson

Manufacturing Planner: Doug Bertke

Senior IP Analyst: Diane Garrity

Senior Digital Delivery Lead: Mia Bryant

Digital Delivery Lead: Justin Karr

Text and Cover Designer: Larson Texts, Inc.

Cover Image: agsandrew/Shutterstock.com

Compositor: Larson Texts, Inc.

AP® is a trademark registered by the College Board, which is not affiliated with, and does not endorse, this product.

For product information and technology assistance, contact us at
Cengage Customer & Sales Support, 1-800-354-9706 or support.cengage.com.

For permission to use material from this text or product, submit all requests online at **www.cengage.com/permissions.**

ISBN: 978-0-357-43194-8

Cengage
200 Pier 4 Boulevard
Boston, MA 02210
USA

Cengage is a leading provider of customized learning solutions with employees residing in nearly 40 different countries and sales in more than 125 countries around the world. Find your local representative at **www.cengage.com.**

Cengage products are represented in Canada by Nelson Education, Ltd.

To learn more about Cengage platforms and services, register or access your online learning solution, or purchase materials for your course, visit **www.cengage.com.**

QR Code is a registered trademark of Denso Wave Incorporated.

Printed in the United States of America
Print Number: 05   Print Year: 2022

Contents

AP® is a trademark registered by the College Board, which is not affiliated with, and does not endorse, this product.

Appendices

*Available at the text-specific website LarsonCalculusforAP.com

Welcome to *Calculus for AP®* Second Edition. We are excited to offer you a new edition with even more resources that completely support the concepts and goals presented in the course frameworks for AP® Calculus AB and AP® Calculus BC.

Our main goals for this textbook are to provide you with the tools you need to understand calculus concepts and prepare you for the AP® Calculus Exams. We think you will find that this text, along with its resources, will help you to achieve these goals. Additionally, we are pleased and excited to offer you the companion websites listed below.

- **LarsonCalculusforAP.com** — companion website with resources to supplement your learning

- **CalcView.com** — video solutions to selected exercises

- **CalcChat.com** — worked-out solutions to odd-numbered exercises and access to online tutors

These websites will help enhance and reinforce your understanding of the material presented in this text and help you master calculus. Also, these websites are **free** to access, and you do **not** have to create an account to use them.

Features

UPDATED LarsonCalculusforAP.com

All website features have been updated based on the revisions to the text. Watch videos explaining mathematical concepts or proofs, explore examples, view three-dimensional graphs, review sample scoring for free-response questions, and much more.

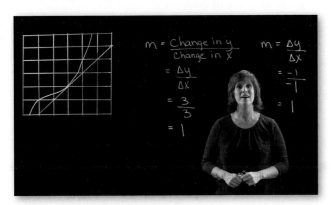

Video solutions of selected exercises are at CalcView.com.

UPDATED ⧉ CalcView®

The website CalcView.com contains video solutions of selected exercises. Watch instructors progress step-by-step through solutions, providing guidance to help you solve the exercises. The CalcView mobile app is available for free at the Apple® App Store® or Google Play™ store. The app features an embedded QR Code® reader that can be used to scan the on-page codes and go directly to the videos. You can also access the videos at CalcView.com.

UPDATED ⧉ CalcChat®

In the section and review exercises, be sure to notice the reference to CalcChat.com. This website provides free step-by-step solutions to all odd-numbered section and review exercises. Also, you can chat with a tutor, at no charge, during the hours posted at the site. Over the years, millions of students have visited this site for help. The CalcChat mobile app is available for free at the Apple® App Store® or Google Play™ store.

AP® is a trademark registered by the College Board, which is not affiliated with, and does not endorse, this product.

App store is a service mark of Apple Inc. Google Play is a trademark of Google Inc.
QR Code is a registered trademark of Denso Wave Incorporated.

NEW AP® Calculus AB and BC Mathematical Practices

The AP® Calculus AB and BC mathematical practices are well represented in the examples and exercises. According to the course frameworks for AP® Calculus AB and AP® Calculus BC, the mathematical practices "describe what a student should be able to do while exploring" calculus. To help you in your exploration of calculus, we have placed notes and exercises throughout the text highlighting these mathematical practices: *Implementing Processes, Connecting Representations, Justification,* and *Communication and Notation.* For more information on these practices (and their corresponding exercises), see page xi.

NEW AP® Calculus AB and BC Practice Exams

Located after Chapter 9, these exams will help you prepare for the AP® Calculus AB and BC Exams. The practice exams have questions modeled after the types of multiple-choice and free-response questions you will see on the AP® Exam.

NEW Error Analysis Exercises

The *Error Analysis* exercises appear in most sections. These exercises present a solution that contains a common error. You are asked to describe and then correct the error.

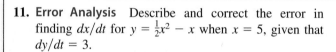

11. Error Analysis Describe and correct the error in finding dx/dt for $y = \frac{1}{2}x^2 - x$ when $x = 5$, given that $dy/dt = 3$.

$$\frac{dx}{dt} = (x - 1)\frac{dy}{dt} = (5 - 1)(3) = 12 \quad$$

NEW Exploring Concepts Exercises

The *Exploring Concepts* exercises appear in each section. These exercises will help you develop a deeper and clearer knowledge of calculus. Work through these exercises to build and strengthen your understanding of calculus concepts.

REVISED Table of Contents

Based on market research, feedback from users, and the updates to the course frameworks for AP® Calculus AB and AP® Calculus BC, we have made several changes to the table of contents.

- We renamed Section 3.7 *Linear Approximation and Differentials* to better reflect the content covered in the section.
- The Net Change Theorem has been moved from Section 4.4 *The Fundamental Theorem of Calculus* to new Section 4.5 *The Net Change Theorem.* This material was heavily rewritten and two new examples were added. Old Sections 4.5–4.7 are now Sections 4.6–4.8.

REVISED Chapter Openers

Each *Chapter Opener* highlights real-life applications used in the examples and exercises. For this edition, we also highlight the online help that is available at CalcView.com and CalcChat.com.

REVISED Examples

Many examples have been revised based on user feedback and the changes to the course frameworks for AP® Calculus AB and AP® Calculus BC. Here are a few instances where we made changes, but there are many more than those listed here.

- We rewrote some examples for clarity. (See Section P.3, Example 2; Section 1.3, Example 6; Section 1.6, Example 2; and Section 2.2, Example 11.)
- We added figures to show students how to check their work using technology. (See Section 1.3, Examples 2 and 3; Section 3.6, Example 6; and Section 6.3, Example 2.)
- We added new and revised examples showing functions represented by tables or graphs. (See Section 2.1, Examples 8 and 9; and Section 3.5, Examples 9 and 10.)
- We added a new particle motion example. (See Section 2.3, Example 10.)
- We added a new example that shows the derivation of the integration formula for $\ln x$. (See Section 7.2, Example 3.)

REVISED Side-By-Side Examples

Throughout the text, we present solutions to examples from multiple perspectives— algebraically, graphically, and numerically. The side-by-side format of this pedagogical feature helps you to see that a problem can be solved in more than one way and to see that different methods yield the same result. The side-by-side format also addresses many different learning styles. Many of these examples have been revised for clarity.

REVISED Algebra Reviews

Algebra Review notes appear throughout each chapter and offer algebraic support at point of use. This support is revisited in a two-page algebra review for each chapter in Appendix D, where additional details of example solutions with explanations are provided. Per user feedback, these examples have been revised in this edition to provide more algebraic help.

REVISED Insights

Throughout the book, *Insights* offer important information to help you prepare for the AP® Exam. These notes have been updated to reflect the changes in the new course frameworks for AP® Calculus AB and AP® Calculus BC.

> **Insight**
>
> On the AP® Exam, a Riemann sum is called a *left Riemann sum* when c_i is the left endpoint of $[x_{i-1}, x_i]$, a *right Riemann sum* when c_i is the right endpoint of $[x_{i-1}, x_i]$, and a *midpoint Riemann sum* when c_i is the midpoint of $[x_{i-1}, x_i]$.

REVISED Applications

Examples and exercises are included throughout the text to address the question, "When will I use this?" These applications are pulled from diverse sources, such as current events, world data, industry trends, and more, and relate to a wide range of interests. Understanding where calculus is used promotes better understanding of the material. We have updated the applications to use more current data and to include suggestions from our users.

REVISED Exercise Sets

The exercise sets have been carefully and extensively examined to ensure they are rigorous and relevant and to include topics our users have suggested. The exercises are organized and titled so you can better see the connection between examples and exercises, as well as the connection between exercises and the AP® Calculus AB and BC mathematical practices. (See page xi.) Multi-step, real-life exercises reinforce problem-solving skills and mastery of concepts by giving you the opportunity to apply the concepts in real-life situations. Per user feedback, we have added more particle motion problems.

REVISED Calculus AP® – Exam Preparation Questions

These questions appear in each section in Chapters 1–9 and are modeled after the types of questions you will encounter on the AP® Exam. These include multiple-choice and free-response questions. These questions have been updated to reflect the changes in the new course frameworks for AP® Calculus AB and AP® Calculus BC.

REVISED Section Projects

Projects appear in selected sections and encourage you to explore applications related to the topics you are studying. We have added new projects, revised others, and kept some of our favorites. All of these projects provide an interesting and engaging way for you and other students to work and investigate ideas collaboratively.

REVISED What You Need to Know

The *What You Need to Know* feature accompanies each set of AP® Exam Practice Questions appearing at the end of Chapters 1–9. This feature provides tips to help you prepare for the AP® Exam. These tips have been updated to reflect the changes in the new course frameworks for AP® Calculus AB and AP® Calculus BC.

REVISED AP® Exam Practice Questions

These questions appear at the end of Chapters 1–9 and are modeled after the types of questions you will encounter on the AP® Exam. These include multiple-choice and free-response questions. These questions have been updated to reflect the changes in the new course frameworks for AP® Calculus AB and AP® Calculus BC.

Section Objectives

At the beginning of each section, there is a list of learning objectives that provides you with the opportunity to preview what will be presented in the upcoming section.

Theorems

Theorems provide the conceptual framework for calculus. Theorems are clearly stated and separated from the rest of the text by boxes for quick visual reference. Key proofs often follow the theorem and can be found at LarsonCalculusforAP.com.

Proof Videos

Watch videos that explain the proofs of theorems in the text at LarsonCalculusforAP.com.

Definitions

As with theorems, definitions are clearly stated using precise, formal wording and are separated from the text by boxes for quick visual reference.

Remarks

These hints and tips reinforce or expand upon concepts, help you learn how to study mathematics, caution you about common errors, address special cases, or show alternative or additional steps to a solution of an example.

Explorations

Explorations provide unique challenges to study concepts that have not yet been formally covered in the text. They allow you to learn by discovery and introduce topics related to ones presently being studied. Exploring topics in this way encourages you to think outside the box.

Interactive Examples

Examples throughout the book are accompanied by *Interactive Examples* at LarsonCalculusforAP.com. These interactive examples allow you to explore calculus by manipulating functions or graphs and observing the results.

Technology and Technology Pitfall Notes

Throughout the text, *Technology* notes show you how to use technology to solve problems and explore concepts of calculus. *Technology Pitfall* notes point out some hidden difficulties of using technology.

How Do You See It?

The *How Do You See It?* exercise in each section presents a problem that you will solve by visual inspection using the concepts learned in the lesson. This exercise is excellent for classroom discussion.

Performance Tasks

Performance Tasks appear at the end of each chapter and ask you to demonstrate your knowledge and understanding of material in the chapter.

AP® Calculus AB and BC mathematical practices are embedded in the study of calculus and are intended to help students establish lines of reasoning that will enable them to apply calculus concepts to solve problems.

Mathematical Practice 1: Implementing Mathematical Processes

Determine expressions and values using mathematical procedures and rules.

- Reinforced throughout the text with *Implementing Processes* notes (see example at the right) and exercises.
- Side-by-side examples throughout this text demonstrate how to solve problems using different mathematical procedures.

Implementing Processes

Before differentiating functions involving radicals, rewrite the function with rational exponents.

Mathematical Practice 2: Connecting Representations

Translate mathematical information from a single representation or across multiple representations.

- Reinforced throughout the text with *Connecting Representations* notes and exercises (see example at the right).
- Students are provided ample opportunities to solve problems graphically, numerically, and analytically in the exercises as well as in the *Explorations*.
- Students identify mathematical information from graphical, numerical, analytical, or verbal representations, such as writing a definite integral given a graph.

105. Connecting Representations Give a geometric explanation of why

$$\int_0^{\pi/2} x \sin x \, dx \le \int_0^{\pi/2} x \, dx.$$

Verify the inequality by evaluating the integrals.

Mathematical Practice 3: Justification

Justify reasoning and solutions.

- Reinforced throughout the text with *Justification* notes and *Justifying* exercises (see example at the right).
- Students can confirm that solutions are accurate and appropriate. For example, students should verify answers to integration problems by differentiating.

97. Justifying Can you use Theorem 4.5 to find the area of the region bounded by the *x*-axis and the graphs of $y = 1/(x - 4)$, $x = 3$, and $x = 5$? Explain.

Mathematical Practice 4: Communication and Notation

Use correct notation, language, and mathematical conventions to communicate results or solutions.

- Reinforced throughout the text with *Communication and Notation* notes (see example at the left) and exercises.
- A variety of notations are used throughout the book so students become familiar with the different ways a concept can be presented.
- The connections between notations and definitions are explained throughout the text.
- Students are continually asked to interpret their results, explain their reasoning, and justify their answers in the problem-solving process.
- *Exploring Concepts, Writing, Think About It, Investigation, How Do You See It?, Error Analysis,* and *Proof* exercises require students to use clear, precise mathematical language in their solutions and explanations.

Communication and Notation

The unit for the area of a region defined by a rate of change is the unit for the rate of change multiplied by the unit for the independent variable. For instance, in Example 2, the unit for $v(t)$ is feet per second and the unit for t is seconds, so the unit for the area is

$$\frac{\text{feet}}{\text{second}} \cdot \text{second} = \text{feet}.$$

Go to www.collegeboard.org for more information about the AP® Calculus AB and BC mathematical practices.

Fast Track to a 5 Workbook (978-0-357-52033-8)
This AP® test preparation manual provides valuable test-taking strategies, review topics based on the course frameworks for AP® Calculus AB and AP® Calculus BC, and full-length diagnostic and practice exams. Keyed to this text, it helps students efficiently and effectively prepare for the AP® exam.

Student Solutions Manual (978-0-357-52034-5)
This guide offers step-by-step solutions for all odd-numbered exercises.

Instant Access Code: 978-0-357-52043-7
WebAssign® combines exceptional *Calculus for AP®* content with powerful online homework and assessment solutions. WebAssign® engages you with assignable learning resources, tutorial content, and an interactive eBook—MindTap, helping you to develop a deeper conceptual understanding of the subject matter.

LarsonCalculusforAP.com
Of the many features at this website, students have told us that the videos are the most helpful. Watch instructional videos presented by Dana Mosely, as he explains various calculus concepts. Watch proof videos presented by Bruce Edwards, as he explains various calculus theorems and their proofs. Use a QR Code® reader to scan the on-page codes ▦ near the theorems and go directly to the videos. Two other helpful features are the data downloads (editable spreadsheets so you do not have to enter the data) and the AP® Prep Solutions for the end-of-chapter AP® Exam Practice Questions.

CalcChat.com
This website provides free step-by-step solutions to all odd-numbered section and review exercises. Additionally, you can chat with a tutor, at no charge, during the hours posted at the site.

CalcView.com
This website has video solutions of selected exercises. Watch instructors progress step-by-step through solutions, providing guidance to help you solve the exercises. Use a QR Code® reader to scan the on-page codes ▦ and go directly to the videos.

AP® is a trademark registered by the College Board, which is not affiliated with, and does not endorse, this product.

QR Code is a registered trademark of Denso Wave Incorporated.

Teacher's Edition (978-0-357-52031-4)
The Teacher's Edition for *Calculus for AP®* is the complete student text that includes annotations for teachers, as well as wrap-around margins. In these margins, teachers will find notes from co-author Paul Battaglia—Chapter Planning Guides, Section Overviews, Essential Questions, Lesson Motivators, Teaching Strategies, Extra Examples, Common Errors, Mathematical Practice notes, Lesson Closers, Assignment Guides, Activities, Sample Grading Rubrics to the Performance Tasks, and answers to all exercises in the student edition. The Teacher's Edition also includes a correlation to the AP® Calculus AB and AP® Calculus BC curriculum framework and a pacing guide.

Complete Solutions Manual (978-0-357-52035-2)
This manual contains solutions to all exercises in the text. This can be found on the instructor companion site.

Teacher's Resource Guide (978-0-357-52032-1)
This robust manual contains an abundance of resources keyed to the *Calculus for AP®* text at the section and chapter level, including section objectives, teaching tips, and chapter projects.

Instant Access Code: 978-0-357-52043-7

WebAssign® combines exceptional *Calculus for AP®* content with the most powerful online homework solution. WebAssign® engages your students with assignable learning resources, tutorial content, and an interactive eBook—MindTap, helping you to develop a deeper conceptual understanding of the subject matter.

Cengage Learning Testing Powered by Cognero
This flexible online system offers additional AP® practice questions; allows you to author, edit, and manage test bank content; create multiple test versions in an instant; and deliver tests from your LMS, your classroom, or wherever you want. This is available online via *login.cengage.com*.

Instructor Companion Site
Everything you need for your course in one place! This collection of book-specific lecture and class tools is available online via *login.cengage.com*. Access and download PowerPoint presentations, the Solutions Manual, the Teacher's Resource Guide, and more.

LarsonCalculusforAP.com
In addition to its student resources, LarsonCalculusforAP.com also has resources to help teachers. Watch co-author Paul Battaglia discuss the key points and concepts of each section and provide teaching tips and strategies. Use the biographical sketches to show your students the history of calculus and the mathematicians who developed it.

MathGraphs.com
For exercises that ask students to draw on the graph, we have provided **free**, printable graphs at MathGraphs.com.

MathArticles.com
MathArticles.com provides you and your students with over 40 relevant articles from renowned math journals.

Acknowledgments

We would like to thank the many people who have helped us at various stages of *Calculus for AP®*. Their encouragement, criticisms, and suggestions have been invaluable.

Reviewers

Howard Alcosser, Diamond Bar High School, Yorba Linda, CA
Kaye Autrey, Greenville, SC
Tom Becvar, St. Louis University High School, St. Louis, MO
Jill Bell, Reagan High School, San Antonio, TX
Corey Boby, Bryant High School, Bryant, AR
Bob Brands, Skyview High School, Vancouver, WA
Robyn Bray, Wylie East High School, Wylie, TX
William Compton, Montgomery Bell Academy, Nashville, TN
Deborah Costello, Trinity Prep School, Winter Park, FL
James Epperson, The University of Texas at Arlington, Arlington, TX
Eliel Gonzalez, East Longmeadow High School, East Longmeadow, MA
Mark Howell, Gonzaga College High School, Washington, D.C.
Elizabeth Kana, Katy ISD, Katy, TX
Jon Kawamura, West Salem High School, Salem, OR
Mike Koehler, Blue Valley North High School, Overland Park, KS
Stephen Kokoska, Bloomsburg University, Bloomsburg, PA
Victor Levine, Madison Area Technical College, Madison WI
Guy Maudlin, Science Hill High School, Johnson City, TN
Lin McMullin, Ballston Lake, NY
Karen Miksch, National Math and Science Initiative, Dallas, TX
Susan Milhoan, Wylie High School, Wylie, TX
James Rahn, Ship Bottom, NJ
William Roloff, Lake Park High School, Roselle, IL
Dixie Ross, Pflugerville High School, Pflugerville, TX
Cesar Silva, Williams College, Williamstown, MA
Nancy Stephenson, St. Thomas High School, Houston, TX
Tom Tutor, Islesboro, ME
Suzanne Ross Walker, Greenville, RI
Michael White, Pennridge High School, Perkasie, PA
Peter Williams, North Oldham High School, Goshen, KY
Gladys Wood, Houston, TX
Patsy Young-Davis, Lake Mary, FL

We would like to thank the staff at Larson Texts, Inc., who assisted in preparing the manuscript, rendering the art package, typesetting, proofreading the pages and supplements, and developing the websites LarsonCalculusforAP.com, CalcView.com, and CalcChat.com.

On a personal level, we are grateful to our wives, Deanna Gilbert Larson and Janice Battaglia, for their love, patience, and support. Also, a special note of thanks goes out to R. Scott O'Neil.

If you have suggestions for improving this text, please feel free to write to us. Over the years we have received many useful comments from both teachers and students, and we value these very much.

Ron Larson
Paul Battaglia

Taking an AP® course can be exhilarating. Whether you are taking an AP® course at your school or you are working on the AP® curriculum independently, the stage is set for a great intellectual experience.

But sometime in the spring, when the examination begins to loom on a very real horizon, your AP® course can seem intimidating. It is a normal feeling to be nervous about the test; you are in good company.

The best way to deal with an AP® examination is to master it, not let it master you. You should think of this examination as a way to show off how much calculus you know. Attitude *does* help. But, no matter what type of math student you are, there is still a lot you can do to prepare for the exam. Focused review and practice time will help you master the examination so that you can walk in with confidence and earn a great score.

What's in *Calculus for AP®* that will help you prepare

As you work through the textbook, there are some things that you should do to get the most out of the text.

- As you read the sections,
    - read the notes about the AP® Calculus AB and BC mathematical practices: Implementing Processes, Connecting Representations, Justification, and Communication and Notation,
    - read the Remarks,
    - do the Explorations,
    - read the notes on Technology, and
    - take time to read the examples, especially the ones with multiple parts that try to represent various ways to look at similar problems and notice how different their solution methods might be.
- After finishing a section or the chapter, work through
    - the exercises about the AP® Calculus AB and BC mathematical practices: Implementing Processes, Connecting Representations, Justification, and Communication and Notation,
    - the True or False exercises to help you discern small differences in conceptual understanding,
    - the Think About It exercises and the Exploring Concepts exercises to help you improve your conceptual understanding and your ability to explain your thinking,
    - the How Do You See It? exercises to process the information—to help you compare methods and/or look at concepts,
    - the Review Exercises,
    - the Calculus AP®—Exam Preparation Questions,
    - the AP® Exam Practice Questions to practice your test-taking skills and understanding of the material you just studied, and
    - the AP® Practice Exams after Chapter 9 to help you prepare for the AP® Exam.

In calculus, reading the text is an essential part of the learning curve and will, in the end, save you time in understanding and mastering the material. There is more to the study of calculus than just being able to do some mathematics; you must understand the concepts and how they fit together. You will also learn to broaden your thinking as well as think logically if you allow yourself to try to see mathematics in a new way, not just as a set of algorithms.

AP® is a trademark registered by the College Board, which is not affiliated with, and does not endorse, this product.

How to get the most out of your Calculus class

- Know your advanced algebra skills:
  - Linear equations
  - Quadratics (factoring)
  - Functions (parent, transformations, piecewise, odd, even, domain, range)
  - Polynomials (zeros, end behavior)
  - Exponential and logarithmic curves
  - Rational and radical equations
  - Direct, inverse relations
  - Conics (for BC)
- Know your trigonometry:
  - Unit circle (0, 30, 45, 60, and 90 degrees and equivalent radian measures)
  - Symmetry around the unit circle
  - Basic identities
- Know basic sequences and series and when to apply which sequence or series formula.
- Have some knowledge of vectors (BC only).
- Know your calculator:
  - Four functions you should be able to do for the AP® test:
    - Plot the graph of a function in an appropriate window.
    - Find the zeros of a function (solving the equations numerically).
    - Calculate the derivative of a function numerically.
    - Calculate the definite integral numerically.
  - Know how to calculate the value of a function at a specific x: on the graph, 2nd calc, value; on the home screen, $y1$(value).
  - Graph your functions and analyze them as a comparison to the algebra you do. Note: You will not receive credit for a student-drawn graph. This step is to help you develop understanding of the function.

Remember that you have to analyze what the calculator gives you (e.g., how to know when a calculator has a "hole": try $1/(x - 2)$ and look for the value at $x = 2$).

Setting up a review schedule

The AP® Calculus courses are concerned with developing a student's understanding of the concepts while providing experiences with its methods and applications. Both the AB and BC courses require a depth of understanding. If you have been doing your homework steadily and keeping up with the course work, you are in good shape. Organize your notes, homework, and handouts from class by topic. For example, have a set of notes on pre-calculus topics (no longer tested on the AP® exam but essential to your success with calculus), limits, derivative rules and applications, integral rules and applications, series and sequences techniques and methods, and major theorems. If you can summarize the main information on a few pages, by topic, you will find reviewing much easier. Refer to these materials and this study guide as you begin to prepare for the exam. Use your textbook to get more detail as needed.

You will be much more comfortable going into the test if you understand how the test questions are designed and how best to approach them.

The multiple-choice questions often require deeper thinking than may at first be apparent. The free-response questions require a mastery of numerical, algebraic, and graphical approaches to problem solving, as well as an ability to verbally describe the meaning of the question/solution. You must actively do problems to gain understanding and excel in your performance. Athletes don't perform well just by reading books about their sport or by watching others. They must practice. So you, too, just like an athlete, must practice, practice, and practice if you want to do your best!

AP® information before the examination

In February

- Make sure that you are **registered** to take the test. Some schools take care of the paperwork and handle the fees for their AP® students, but check with your teacher or the AP® coordinator to make sure that you are registered. This is especially important if you have a documented disability and need test accommodations. If you are studying AP® independently, or if your school does not have an AP® coordinator, call AP® Services at the College Board at (888) 225-5427 (toll-free in the United States and Canada). You can also email *apstudents@info.collegeboard.org* for the name of the local AP® coordinator, who will help you through the registration process.
- Check on the eligibility of your **calculator.** Go online to

  https://apstudents.collegeboard.org/courses/ap-calculus-ab/calculator-policies

  early enough so that if you need a different calculator, you will have time to get one and to become familiar with it.

By Mid-March

- Begin your review process; set a schedule for yourself that you can follow.

Week before

- Review. Read through your notes. Concentrate on the broad outlines of the course, not the small details. Restudy any concept that you feel needs more attention.
- Begin to gather your materials together for the test.

Night before

- Put all of your **materials** in one place.
- Relax and get a good night's **rest** (this alone could improve your score because you will be able to think more clearly throughout the test).

Things to have on test day

- **Approved graphing calculator** with fresh batteries (you may have a second calculator as a backup, but it must also be a graphing calculator). The calculator must not have a typewriter-style (QWERTY) keyboard, nor can it be a non-graphing scientific calculator or on your phone. (*https://apstudents.collegeboard.org/courses/ ap-calculus-ab/calculator-policies*) Calculator memories are **not** cleared for the exam.

> ### Insight
> Be sure your calculator is set in **radian mode** (pi radians, or approximately three radians, is half the circle; 3 degrees is an angle just barely above the *x*-axis).

- #2 pencils (at least 2) with good erasers.
- A watch (to monitor your pace, but turn off the alarm if it has one).
- A bottle of water and a snack (fruit or power bar).
- Social Security number (if you choose to include it on the forms).
- The College Board school code.
- Photo identification and the admissions ticket.
- Comfortable clothes and a sweatshirt or sweater in case the room is cold.

Schools may have your admissions ticket at the testing site; a photo identification may not be needed at your own school, but check with your AP® coordinator prior to test day.

On the day of the examination, it is wise to eat a good breakfast. Studies show that students who eat a hot breakfast before testing get higher scores. Breakfast can give you the energy you need to power you through the test and more. You will spend some time waiting while everyone is seated in the right room for the right test. That's before the test has even begun. With a short break between Section I and Section II, the AP® Calculus exam can last almost four hours.

Now go get a 5!

To do well on the AP® Calculus examination,

- A student should understand and be able to work with the connections between the graphical, numerical, analytical, and verbal representations of functions.
- A student should be able to use derivatives to solve a variety of problems and understand the meaning of a derivative in terms of rate of change and local linearity.
- A student should use integrals to solve a variety of problems and should understand the meaning of a definite integral in terms of the limit of Riemann sums as well as the net accumulation of change.
- A student also needs to:
  - Understand both parts of the Fundamental Theorem of Calculus.
  - Communicate mathematics in written sentences.
  - Appropriately model a physical situation.
  - Use technology correctly and efficiently.
  - Determine the reasonableness of solutions and understand them in terms of units of measurement, size, and so on.

It is important to realize that a student who is in AP® Calculus is expected to have studied **all** of the prerequisite material. A student should have a mastery of functions and their properties and an understanding of algebra, graphs, and the language of domain, range, symmetry, periodicity, and so on. The student should also understand trigonometry and have a mastery of the basic values in the unit circle and the basic trigonometric identities.

Exam Format

The AP® Calculus examination currently consists of two major sections and each of those has two parts. All sections test proficiency on a variety of topics.

Multiple Choice: Section I has two sets of multiple-choice questions. Part A has 30 questions with an allotted time of 60 minutes and does not allow the use of a calculator. Part B has 15 questions and has 45 minutes allotted to it; this set contains some questions for which a graphing calculator would be needed to answer the questions. The multiple-choice section score is based on the number of questions answered correctly; no points will be deducted for incorrect answers and no points are awarded for unanswered questions.

Free Response: Section II has six free-response questions, and it is broken into two portions. Part A consists of two problems; some parts of some problems may require a graphing calculator and you will be allowed 30 minutes. Part B has four problems and you will be allowed 60 minutes; a calculator is not permitted during this time. Although you may continue working on Part A problems during this 60-minute session, you may no longer use a calculator. Thus, when working on Part A, you must be sure to answer the questions requiring a calculator during that first 30-minute period.

The grade for the examination is equally weighted between the multiple-choice and free-response sections of the exam. You can possibly earn a 5 on the exam even if you miss an entire free-response question. Students taking the BC exam will also receive an AB sub-score grade.

The free-response questions and solutions are published annually after the AP® Reading is completed and can be found at apcentral.collegeboard.com.

General AP® Test-Taking Strategies

Strategize the test question. Begin somewhere. Ask "What do I need?" and then "How do I get there?" Start with a clear definition; for a question about continuity, you need to have a clear definition of continuity to answer the question fully. (For example, see Question 6 of the 2003 AB Exam.)

- Know what the required tools on your calculator are and know how to access and use them:
    - Plot the graph of a function within a viewing window.
    - Find the zeros of a function (numerically solve equations).
    - Numerically calculate the derivative of a function.
    - Numerically calculate the value of a definite integral.
- Know the relationships between f, f', and f''.
- Know your differentiation and integration rules.
- Underline key components of the questions.
- Reread the question after you have answered it to be sure that you answered the question asked, that you haven't gone too far, or that you haven't contradicted yourself.
- Treat units carefully.
- Set the calculator to THREE decimal places and properly use the store key for intermediate steps (if you round too soon, your final answer will not be correct to the requisite three decimal places). If you choose to write your answer with more than three decimal places, only the first three places are read as your answer.

Strategies for the Multiple-Choice Section

Read the question carefully: Pressured for time, many students make the mistake of reading the questions too quickly or merely skimming them. By reading a question carefully, you may already have some idea about the correct answer. Careful reading is especially important in EXCEPT questions. After you solve the problem and have a solution, reread the question to be sure the answer you solved for actually answers the question. For example, you may have solved for where the maximum occurred (the x-value) but the question actually asks for the maximum value of f (the y-value), and thus you need one more step to complete the problem.

Eliminate any answer you know is wrong: You can write on the multiple-choice questions in the test book. As you read through the responses, draw a line through any answer you know is wrong. Do as much scratch work as is necessary in the exam book, but be sure to mark your solution choice on the answer sheet in the corresponding oval. In most math questions, it is generally better to NOT read through the possible answers until you have found what you think is the solution. There are times where you may have to look at the choices so that you have an idea of how to start or where you are going but generally they can lead you into incorrect assumptions.

Read all of the possible answers, then choose the most accurate response: AP® examinations are written to test your precise knowledge of a subject. Some of the responses may be partially correct, but there will only be one response that is completely true. *Be careful of absolute responses.* These answers often include the words *always* or *never*. They could be correct, but you should try to think of counterexamples to disprove them.

Skip tough questions: Skip them in the first go-through but be sure that you mark them in the margin so you can come back to them later if you possibly can. *Make sure you skip those questions on your answer sheet, too.*

There is no penalty for guessing: Thus, at the end, try to narrow down your choices by eliminating answers which you figure are not correct and make an educated guess. It is to your advantage to answer every question.

Additional Thoughts

- The exact numerical answer may not be among the choices given. You will have to choose the solution that best approximates the exact value.
- The domain of a function f is assumed to be the set of all real numbers x, where $f(x)$ is a real number, unless specified otherwise.
- f^{-1} or the prefix *arc-* indicates the inverse of a trigonometric function (e.g., $\cos^{-1} x = \arccos x$).

Types of Multiple-Choice Questions

All kinds of topics will be covered in the multiple-choice section; your skills and vocabulary will be tested as well as your ability to do multi-step problem solving. Terms like *average value, the definition of continuity, extremum (relative and absolute), the definition of a derivative in its two forms, differential equations, graphical interpretations,* and *slope fields* are just a sampling of terms that identify the kinds of problems you will see. Read through this text and do the practice problems to familiarize yourself with the way the questions are framed.

Multiple-choice questions will be formatted in two basic ways. You will find classic questions where there are just four choices for solutions. This is the most common type of problem; it requires you to read the question and select the most correct answer. Strategies for solving this type of problem include

- reading the question carefully,
- solving the problem and then interpreting your solution correctly to fit the question,
- eliminating known wrong answers, and
- on occasion, testing each solution to see which one is correct.

There will also be problems that could be called "list" and "group," where you may be asked "Which of the following is true about g?" They will give choices such as I, II, and III and the multiple-choice answers might appear as

   (A) None
   (B) I only
   (C) I and II only
   (D) I, II, and III

This kind of problem requires a clear understanding of some concept or definition. To approach this kind of question,

- eliminate known wrong answers,
- recall necessary theorems or definitions to help you interpret the question, and
- reread the problem to check your solution's accuracy.

Strategies for the Free-Response Section

- ALL work needs to be shown IN the test booklet.
- Scan all of the questions in the section you are working in. First solve the problems that you think you can do easily. You can mark and come back to the harder ones later. Most questions have multiple entry points. If you cannot answer part a, proceed to the next part, because part a is not always the easiest part.
- Show all of your work. Partial credit will be awarded for problems if the correct work is shown even if the answer is not present or is incorrect. Although not required, it can be helpful to the reader if you circle your final answer.
- Cross out incorrect answers with an "X" rather than spending time erasing. Crossed out or erased work will not be graded. However, don't cross out or erase work unless you have replaced it. Let the reader see what you tried; it may be worth some points.
- Be clear, neat, and organized in your work. If a reader cannot clearly understand your work, you may not receive full credit.

- Some free-response questions have several parts, such as a, b, c, and d. Attempt to solve each part. Even if your answer to "a" is incorrect, you still may be awarded points for the remaining parts of the question if the work is correct for those parts. Remember, the answers may not depend on an earlier response and that is why it is important to try each part. If you work with your incorrect answer (as long as it is reasonably derived) from a previous part, the reader will read with you in a later part (i.e., the reader will check your numerical answer on the basis of your incorrect input).

- Units are important in your answer. Keeping track of your units throughout calculations and performing unit cancellations, where possible, will help guide you to your answer. Points will be deducted for missing or incorrect units in the answer if the question asked that units be given.

- Don't just write equations or numbers in hopes of finding the correct answer. Extraneous or incorrect information could lead to a lower score. Don't make up work that is trivial, but do try the problem and the reader will read with you.

- You do not need to work the questions in order, but be sure the answer is entered in the correct section.

- When you use a table or a graph from one section (part a) in another part of the problem (part c, for example) be sure to refer to it in some way—state your use of it or draw an arrow back to it. If you inadvertently put a response in the wrong part of the problem, again, note it clearly to the reader.

- Show all your work.
    - Clearly label any functions [if the problem uses $g(x)$, don't call it $f(x)$]. If $g(x) =$ to some expression, use $g(x)$ in any problem in lieu of writing the expression. This helps to avoid a copy error.
    - Label your sign charts accurately, for example, f' or f'' for the derivative tests. However, these by themselves do not count as a justification. No credit is given for sign charts, but they can help develop your analysis and subsequent answer to the question. Do not use the pronoun "it" in your descriptions or solutions, specify which function or derivative or variable, etc. that you are using or the part of the question you are answering.
    - Label all graphs with appropriate notation including numeric intervals (by 1s or 10s, for example) and the names for the x- and y-axes (like distance and time).
    - Label all tables or other objects that you use to show your work.
    - Show standard mathematic (non-calculator) notation. For example, you must show the integral as $\int_1^3 (x + 2)\, dx$, not as fnInt $(x + 2, x, 1, 3)$.

Remember: You are not required to simplify your answer. It is best if you leave an answer in an un-simplified form to avoid making careless errors and to save time. For example, $y - 2.3 = -6(x + 5.4)$ would be an appropriate equation of a tangent line; there is no need to simplify it to slope-intercept form.

- Decimals require an accuracy of three decimal places in the solution. Thus be sure to understand how to carry (store in your calculator) the intermediate steps of a problem until you round to three decimal places at the end of the problem. If you do multiple calculations and each calculation is rounded to three decimal places prior to the next calculation, your final solution will not have the required accuracy. The third digit in the final solution can be rounded or truncated.

Scoring for Free-Response Questions

The free-response sections are graded on a scale of 0–9 with a dash (–) given for no work on the page. The chief reader is ultimately responsible for not only working through the solution and alternate solutions for each problem but is also responsible for assigning points on a 9-point scale to each problem. This varies from problem to problem based on how many parts are in the problem, as well as the difficulty or complexity of the particular question.

For example, in a problem that asks for units, units are generally assigned 1 point for the whole problem. In other words, if you do units correctly in part a, but incorrectly in part c, you would not be awarded the 1 point for units.

If a problem requires an explanation, or reasoning, it generally earns 1–2 points. In many cases, explanations can be in writing or with mathematical symbols.

In a typical area and volume problem, the integral is often worth 1 point and the answer is worth an additional 1 point. Sometimes the limits of integration are also worth 1 point. Thus, it is important that you at least start working on a problem because often some points can be earned for the setup, even if the solution is not there or is incorrect.

A "bald" answer is seldom awarded a point. A bald answer is one that has no supporting work or documentation, like "yes" or just a number.

To learn calculus and best prepare for the examination, read the text, take risks, ask questions, and look for the connections between the algebraic, numerical, and graphical approaches to similar problems. As much as possible, graph every problem to enhance your understanding of the concepts you are working with.

P Preparation for Calculus

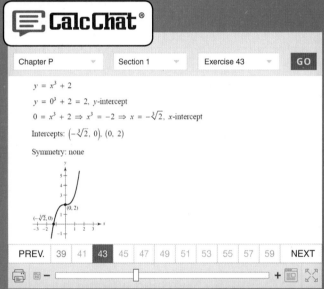

P.1 Gross Domestic Product *(Exercise 69, p. 11)*

P.3 Automobile Aerodynamics *(Exercise 82, p. 33)*

P.1   Graphs and Models

▶ Sketch the graph of an equation.
▶ Find the intercepts of a graph.
▶ Test a graph for symmetry with respect to an axis and the origin.
▶ Find the points of intersection of two graphs.
▶ Fit a mathematical model to a real-life data set.

The Graph of an Equation

Your study of calculus will be from multiple perspectives—*graphically, analytically, numerically,* and *verbally.* By using multiple perspectives, you will increase your understanding of core concepts.

For example, consider the equation $3x + y = 7$. The point $(2, 1)$ is a **solution point** of the equation because the equation is satisfied (is true) when 2 is substituted for x and 1 is substituted for y. This equation has many other solutions, such as $(1, 4)$ and $(0, 7)$. To find other solutions systematically, solve the original equation for y.

$$y = 7 - 3x \qquad \text{Analytic approach}$$

Then construct a **table of values** by substituting several values of x.

x	0	1	2	3	4
y	7	4	1	-2	-5

Numerical approach

From the table, you can see that $(0, 7)$, $(1, 4)$, $(2, 1)$, $(3, -2)$, and $(4, -5)$ are solutions of the original equation $3x + y = 7$. Like many equations, this equation has an infinite number of solutions. The set of all solution points is the **graph** of the equation, as shown in Figure P.1. Note that the sketch shown in Figure P.1 is referred to as the graph of $3x + y = 7$, even though it really represents only a *portion* of the graph. The entire graph would extend beyond the page. Using a verbal approach, you can say the graph of $3x + y = 7$ is a line that falls from left to right.

In this course, you will study many sketching techniques. The simplest is point plotting—that is, you plot points until the basic shape of the graph seems apparent.

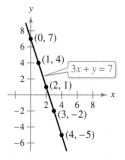

Graphical approach: $3x + y = 7$
Figure P.1

EXAMPLE 1   **Sketching a Graph by Point Plotting**

To sketch the graph of $y = x^2 - 2$, first construct a table of values. Next, plot the points shown in the table. Then connect the points with a smooth curve, as shown in the figure below. This graph is a *parabola*. (See Section 9.1 for more about parabolas and other conics.) Verbally, you can say the graph of $y = x^2 - 2$ is a curve that falls from left to right until it reaches its vertex at $(0, -2)$, then it rises from left to right.

x	-2	-1	0	1	2	3
y	2	-1	-2	-1	2	7

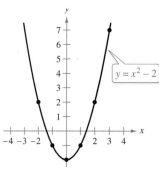

The parabola $y = x^2 - 2$

One disadvantage of point plotting is that to get a good idea about the shape of a graph, you may need to plot many points. With only a few points, you could badly misrepresent the graph. For instance, to sketch the graph of

$$y = \frac{1}{30}x(39 - 10x^2 + x^4)$$

you plot five points:

$$(-3, -3), \quad (-1, -1), \quad (0, 0), \quad (1, 1), \quad \text{and} \quad (3, 3)$$

as shown in Figure P.2(a). From these five points, you might conclude that the graph is a line. This, however, is not correct. By plotting several more points, you can see that the graph is more complicated, as shown in Figure P.2(b).

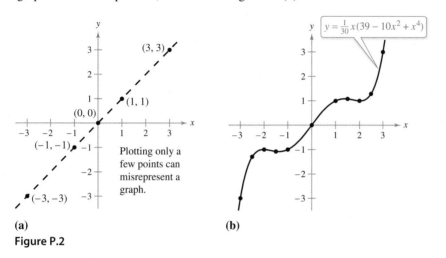

Plotting only a few points can misrepresent a graph.

(a)   (b)

Figure P.2

Technology

Graphing an equation has been made easier by technology. Even with technology, however, it is possible to misrepresent a graph badly. For instance, each of the graphing utility* screens in Figure P.3 shows a portion of the graph of

$$y = x^3 - x^2 - 25.$$

From the screen on the left, you might assume that the graph is a line. From the screen on the right, however, you can see that the graph is not a line. So, whether you are sketching a graph by hand or using a graphing utility, you must realize that different "viewing windows" can produce very different views of a graph. In choosing a viewing window, your goal is to show a view of the graph that fits well in the context of the problem.

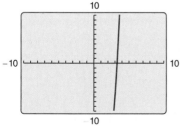

Graphing utility screens of $y = x^3 - x^2 - 25$

Figure P.3

Exploration

Comparing Graphical and Analytic Approaches   Use a graphing utility to graph each equation. In each case, find a viewing window that shows the important characteristics of the graph.

a. $y = x^3 - 3x^2 + 2x + 5$
b. $y = x^3 - 3x^2 + 2x + 25$
c. $y = -x^3 - 3x^2 + 20x + 5$
d. $y = 3x^3 - 40x^2 + 50x - 45$
e. $y = -(x + 12)^3$
f. $y = (x - 2)(x - 4)(x - 6)$

A purely graphical approach to this problem would involve a simple "guess, check, and revise" strategy. What types of things do you think an analytic approach might involve? For instance, does the graph have symmetry? Does the graph have turns? If so, where are they? As you proceed through Chapters 1, 2, and 3 of this text, you will study many new analytic tools that will help you analyze graphs of equations such as these.

---

*In this text, the term *graphing utility* refers to graphing calculators (such as the *TI-84 Plus* and *Desmos*) and computer graphing software (such as *Maple* and *Mathematica*).

Intercepts of a Graph

Two types of solution points that are especially useful in graphing an equation are those having zero as their x- or y-coordinate. Such points are called **intercepts** because they are the points at which the graph intersects the x- or y-axis. The point $(a, 0)$ is an **x-intercept** of the graph of an equation when it is a solution point of the equation. To find the x-intercepts of a graph, let y be zero and solve the equation for x. The point $(0, b)$ is a **y-intercept** of the graph of an equation when it is a solution point of the equation. To find the y-intercepts of a graph, let x be zero and solve the equation for y.

It is possible for a graph to have no intercepts, or it might have several. For instance, consider the four graphs shown in Figure P.4.

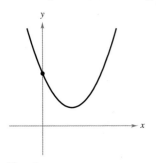

No x-intercepts
One y-intercept

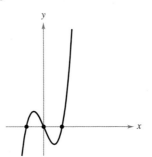

Three x-intercepts
One y-intercept

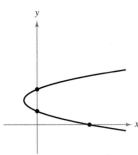

One x-intercept
Two y-intercepts
Figure P.4

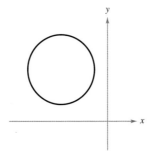

No intercepts

> **Communication and Notation**
>
> Some texts denote the x-intercept as the x-coordinate of the point $(a, 0)$ rather than the point itself. Unless it is necessary to make a distinction, when the term *intercept* is used in this text, it will mean either the point or the coordinate.

EXAMPLE 2   Finding x- and y-Intercepts

Find the x- and y-intercepts of the graph of $y = x^3 - 4x$.

Algebraic Solution

To find the x-intercepts, let y be zero and solve for x.

$$x^3 - 4x = 0 \qquad \text{Let } y \text{ be zero.}$$
$$x(x - 2)(x + 2) = 0 \qquad \text{Factor.}$$
$$x = 0 \qquad \text{Set first factor equal to zero.}$$
$$x - 2 = 0 \implies x = 2 \qquad \text{Set second factor equal to zero.}$$
$$x + 2 = 0 \implies x = -2 \qquad \text{Set third factor equal to zero.}$$

Because this equation has three solutions, you can conclude that the graph has three x-intercepts: $(0, 0)$, $(2, 0)$, and $(-2, 0)$. To find the y-intercepts, let x be zero. Doing this produces $y = 0$. So, the y-intercept is $(0, 0)$.

Graphical Solution

Use the *zero* or *root* feature of a graphing utility to find the intercepts of the graph of $y = x^3 - 4x$, as shown below. The x-intercepts are $(-2, 0)$, $(0, 0)$, and $(2, 0)$, and the y-intercept is $(0, 0)$.

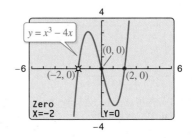

Symmetry of a Graph

Knowing the symmetry of a graph before attempting to sketch it is useful because you need only half as many points to sketch the graph. The three types of symmetry listed below can be used to help sketch the graphs of equations (see Figure P.5).

1. A graph is **symmetric with respect to the y-axis** if, whenever (x, y) is a point on the graph, then $(-x, y)$ is also a point on the graph. This means that the portion of the graph to the left of the y-axis is a mirror image of the portion to the right of the y-axis.

2. A graph is **symmetric with respect to the x-axis** if, whenever (x, y) is a point on the graph, then $(x, -y)$ is also a point on the graph. This means that the portion of the graph below the x-axis is a mirror image of the portion above the x-axis.

3. A graph is **symmetric with respect to the origin** if, whenever (x, y) is a point on the graph, then $(-x, -y)$ is also a point on the graph. This means that the graph is unchanged by a rotation of $180°$ about the origin.

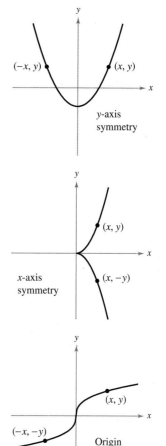

y-axis symmetry

x-axis symmetry

Origin symmetry

Figure P.5

Test for Symmetry

1. The graph of an equation in x and y is symmetric with respect to the y-axis when replacing x by $-x$ yields an equivalent equation.

2. The graph of an equation in x and y is symmetric with respect to the x-axis when replacing y by $-y$ yields an equivalent equation.

3. The graph of an equation in x and y is symmetric with respect to the origin when replacing x by $-x$ and y by $-y$ yields an equivalent equation.

The graph of a polynomial has symmetry with respect to the y-axis when each term has an even exponent (or is a constant). For instance, the graph of

$$y = 2x^4 - x^2 + 2$$

has symmetry with respect to the y-axis. Similarly, the graph of a polynomial has symmetry with respect to the origin when each term has an odd exponent, as illustrated in Example 3.

EXAMPLE 3 Testing for Symmetry

Test the graph of $y = 2x^3 - x$ for symmetry with respect to (a) the y-axis and (b) the origin.

Solution

a.

$y = 2x^3 - x$	Write original equation.
$y = 2(-x)^3 - (-x)$	Replace x by $-x$.
$y = -2x^3 + x$	Simplify. The result is *not* an equivalent equation.

Because replacing x by $-x$ does *not* yield an equivalent equation, you can conclude that the graph of $y = 2x^3 - x$ is *not* symmetric with respect to the y-axis.

b.

$y = 2x^3 - x$	Write original equation.
$-y = 2(-x)^3 - (-x)$	Replace x by $-x$ and y by $-y$.
$-y = -2x^3 + x$	Simplify.
$y = 2x^3 - x$	Equivalent equation

Because replacing x by $-x$ and y by $-y$ yields an equivalent equation, you can conclude that the graph of $y = 2x^3 - x$ is symmetric with respect to the origin, as shown in Figure P.6.

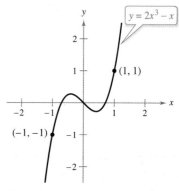

$y = 2x^3 - x$

$(1, 1)$

$(-1, -1)$

Origin symmetry

Figure P.6

EXAMPLE 4   Using Intercepts and Symmetry to Sketch a Graph

See LarsonCalculusforAP.com for an interactive version of this type of example.

Sketch the graph of $x - y^2 = 1$.

Solution

The graph is symmetric with respect to the x-axis because replacing y by $-y$ yields an equivalent equation.

$x - y^2 = 1$	Write original equation.
$x - (-y)^2 = 1$	Replace y by $-y$.
$x - y^2 = 1$	Equivalent equation

This means that the portion of the graph below the x-axis is a mirror image of the portion above the x-axis. To sketch the graph, first plot the x-intercept and the points above the x-axis. Then reflect in the x-axis to obtain the entire graph, as shown in Figure P.7.

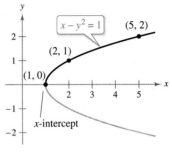

Figure P.7

Technology

Most graphing utilities are designed so that they most easily graph equations in which y is a function of x. (See Section P.3 for a definition of *function*.) To graph other types of equations, you may need to split the graph into two or more parts *or* you may need to use a different graphing mode. For instance, to graph the equation in Example 4, you can split it into two parts.

$y_1 = \sqrt{x - 1}$ Top portion of graph $y_2 = -\sqrt{x - 1}$ Bottom portion of graph

---

Points of Intersection

A **point of intersection** of the graphs of two equations is a point that satisfies both equations. One way to find all points of intersection of two graphs is by solving their equations simultaneously.

EXAMPLE 5   Finding Points of Intersection

Find all points of intersection of the graphs of $x^2 - y = 3$ and $x - y = 1$.

Algebraic Solution

To find the points of intersection analytically, solve both equations for y, set the two y-values equal to each other, and solve the resulting equation.

$y = x^2 - 3$	Solve first equation for y.
$y = x - 1$	Solve second equation for y.
$x^2 - 3 = x - 1$	Equate y-values.
$x^2 - x - 2 = 0$	Write in general form.
$(x - 2)(x + 1) = 0$	Factor.
$x = 2$ or -1	Solve for x.

The corresponding values of y are obtained by substituting $x = 2$ and $x = -1$ into either of the original equations. Doing this produces two points of intersection:

$(2, 1)$ and $(-1, -2)$.   Points of intersection

Graphical Solution

Begin by solving both equations for y. Then use a graphing utility to graph the equations $y_1 = x^2 - 3$ and $y_2 = x - 1$ in the same viewing window. Use the *intersect* feature to find the points of intersection of the graphs (see figure).

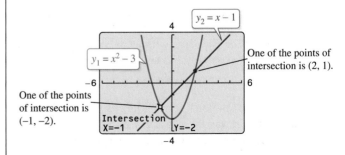

One of the points of intersection is $(2, 1)$.

One of the points of intersection is $(-1, -2)$.

Fitting Mathematical Models to Data

A basic premise of science is that much of the physical world can be described mathematically and that many physical phenomena are predictable. This scientific outlook was part of the scientific revolution that took place in Europe during the late 1500s. Two early publications connected with this revolution were *On the Revolutions of the Heavenly Spheres* by the Polish astronomer Nicolaus Copernicus and *On the Fabric of the Human Body* by the Belgian anatomist Andreas Vesalius. Each of these books was published in 1543, and each broke with prior tradition by suggesting the use of a scientific method rather than unquestioned reliance on authority.

One basic technique of modern science is gathering data and then describing the data with a **mathematical model**. For instance, the data in Example 6 are inspired by Leonardo da Vinci's famous drawing that indicates that a person's height and arm span are equal. In developing a mathematical model to represent actual data, you should strive for two (often conflicting) goals: simplicity and accuracy. That is, you want the model to be simple enough to be workable, yet accurate enough to produce meaningful results.

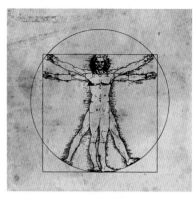

A computer graphics drawing based on the pen and ink drawing of Leonardo da Vinci's famous study of human proportions, called *Vitruvian Man*

EXAMPLE 6   Fitting a Linear Model to Data

A class of 28 people collected the data shown below, which represent their heights x and arm spans y (rounded to the nearest inch).

$(60, 61)$, $(65, 65)$, $(68, 67)$, $(72, 73)$, $(61, 62)$, $(63, 63)$, $(70, 71)$,

$(75, 74)$, $(71, 72)$, $(62, 60)$, $(65, 65)$, $(66, 68)$, $(62, 62)$, $(72, 73)$,

$(70, 70)$, $(69, 68)$, $(69, 70)$, $(60, 61)$, $(63, 63)$, $(64, 64)$, $(71, 71)$,

$(68, 67)$, $(69, 70)$, $(70, 72)$, $(65, 65)$, $(64, 63)$, $(71, 70)$, $(67, 67)$

Find a linear model to represent these data.

Solution

There are different ways to model these data with an equation. The simplest is to observe that x and y are about the same and list the model as simply $y = x$. A more careful analysis is to use a procedure from statistics called *least squares regression*. The least squares regression line for these data is

$$y = 1.006x - 0.23.$$ Least squares regression line

The graph of the model and the data are shown in Figure P.8. From this model, you can see that a person's arm span tends to be about the same as his or her height.

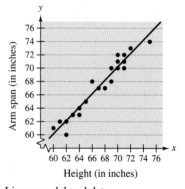

Linear model and data
Figure P.8

Technology

Many graphing utilities have built-in least squares regression programs. Typically, you enter the data into a graphing utility and then run the linear regression program. The program usually displays the slope and *y*-intercept of the best-fitting line and the *correlation coefficient r*. The correlation coefficient gives a measure of how well the data can be modeled by a line. The closer $|r|$ is to 1, the better the data can be modeled by a line. For instance, the correlation coefficient for the model in Example 6 is

$$r \approx 0.97$$ *r* is close to 1.

which indicates that the linear model is a good fit for the data. If the *r*-value is positive, then the variables have a positive correlation, as in Example 6. If the *r*-value is negative, then the variables have a negative correlation.

An equation that gives the height s of a falling object in terms of the time t is called a *position equation*. If air resistance is not considered, then the position of a falling object can be modeled by

$$s = -\tfrac{1}{2}gt^2 + v_0 t + s_0$$

where g is the acceleration due to gravity, v_0 is the initial velocity, and s_0 is the initial height. The value of g depends on where the object is dropped. On Earth, g is approximately 32 feet per second per second, or 9.8 meters per second per second.

To discover the value of g experimentally, you could record the heights of a falling object at several increments, as shown in Example 7.

EXAMPLE 7   Fitting a Quadratic Model to Data

A basketball is dropped from a height of about $5\tfrac{1}{4}$ feet. The height of the basketball is recorded 23 times at intervals of about 0.02 second. The results are shown in the table.

Time	0.0	0.02	0.04	0.06	0.08	0.099996
Height	5.23594	5.20353	5.16031	5.0991	5.02707	4.95146

Time	0.119996	0.139992	0.159988	0.179988	0.199984	0.219984
Height	4.85062	4.74979	4.63096	4.50132	4.35728	4.19523

Time	0.23998	0.25993	0.27998	0.299976	0.319972	0.339961
Height	4.02958	3.84593	3.65507	3.44981	3.23375	3.01048

Time	0.359961	0.379951	0.399941	0.419941	0.439941
Height	2.76921	2.52074	2.25786	1.98058	1.63488

Find a model to fit these data. Then use the model to predict the time when the basketball will hit the ground.

Solution

Begin by sketching a scatter plot of the data, as shown in Figure P.9. From the scatter plot, you can see that the data do not appear to be linear. It does appear, however, that they might be quadratic. To check this, enter the data into a graphing utility that has a quadratic regression program. You should obtain the model

$$s = -15.45t^2 - 1.302t + 5.2340. \qquad \text{Least squares regression quadratic}$$

Using this model, you can predict the time when the basketball hits the ground by substituting 0 for s and solving the resulting equation for t.

$$0 = -15.45t^2 - 1.302t + 5.2340 \qquad \text{Let } s = 0.$$

$$t = \frac{-b \pm \sqrt{b^2 - 4ac}}{2a} \qquad \text{Quadratic Formula}$$

$$t = \frac{-(-1.302) \pm \sqrt{(-1.302)^2 - 4(-15.45)(5.2340)}}{2(-15.45)} \qquad \text{Substitute } a = -15.45,\ b = -1.302,\ \text{and } c = 5.2340.$$

$$t \approx 0.54 \qquad \text{Choose positive solution.}$$

The solution is about 0.54 second. In other words, the basketball will continue to fall for about 0.1 second more before hitting the ground. (Note that the experimental value of g is $-\tfrac{1}{2}g = -15.45$, or $g = 30.90$ feet per second per second and the experimental value of s_0 is $s_0 = 5.234$ feet, which is close to the initial height of about $5\tfrac{1}{4}$ feet.) ∎

Insight

Although mathematical models are frequently used when examining real-life data, you are discouraged from using regression analysis on the AP® Exam. Refrain from trying to fit data presented in tabular form into an equation.

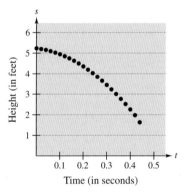

Scatter plot of data
Figure P.9

Algebra Review

For a review of using the Quadratic Formula to solve a quadratic equation, see the *Chapter P Algebra Review* on page A35.

What is mathematical modeling? This is one of the questions that is asked in the book *Guide to Mathematical Modelling*. Here is part of the answer.*

1. Mathematical modeling consists of applying your mathematical skills to obtain useful answers to real problems.

2. Learning to apply mathematical skills is very different from learning mathematics itself.

3. Models are used in a very wide range of applications, some of which do not appear initially to be mathematical in nature.

4. Models often allow quick and cheap evaluation of alternatives, leading to optimal solutions that are not otherwise obvious.

5. There are no precise rules in mathematical modeling and no "correct" answers.

6. Modeling can be learned only by *doing*.

EXAMPLE 8   Fitting a Trigonometric Model to Data

The number of hours of daylight on a given day on Earth depends on the latitude and the time of year. Here are the numbers of minutes of daylight at a location of 20°N latitude on the longest and shortest days of the year: June 21, 801 minutes; December 22, 655 minutes. Use these data to write a model for the amount of daylight d (in minutes) on each day of the year at a location of 20°N latitude. How could you check the accuracy of your model?

Solution

Here is one way to create a model. You can hypothesize that the model is a sine function whose period is 365 days. (See Appendix C.3 for a review of trigonometric functions.) Using the given data, you can conclude that the amplitude of the graph is $(801 - 655)/2$, or 73. So, one possible model is

$$d = 728 - 73 \sin\left(\frac{2\pi t}{365} + \frac{\pi}{2}\right).$$

In this model, t represents the number of each day of the year, with December 22 represented by $t = 0$. A graph of this model is shown in Figure P.10. To check the accuracy of this model, a table from the U.S. Naval Observatory was used to find the numbers of minutes of daylight on different days of the year at the location of 20°N latitude.

Date	Value of t	Actual Daylight	Daylight Given by Model
Dec 22	0	655 min	655 min
Jan 1	10	657 min	656 min
Feb 1	41	676 min	672 min
Mar 1	69	705 min	701 min
Apr 1	100	740 min	739 min
May 1	130	773 min	773 min
Jun 1	161	796 min	796 min
Jun 21	181	801 min	801 min
Jul 1	191	799 min	800 min
Aug 1	222	782 min	785 min
Sep 1	253	751 min	754 min
Oct 1	283	717 min	716 min
Nov 1	314	684 min	681 min
Dec 1	344	661 min	660 min

You can see that the model is fairly accurate.

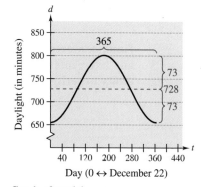

The amount of daylight received by locations on Earth varies with the time of year.

Graph of model
Figure P.10

---

* Text from Dilwyn Edwards and Mike Hamson, *Guide to Mathematical Modelling* (Boca Raton: CRC Press, 1990), p. 4.

P.1   Exercises

See *CalcChat.com* for tutorial help and worked-out solutions to odd-numbered exercises.

Matching In Exercises 1–4, match the equation with its graph. [The graphs are labeled (a), (b), (c), and (d).]

(a)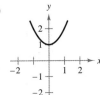

(b)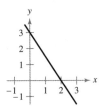

(c)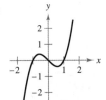

(d)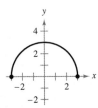

1. $y = -\frac{3}{2}x + 3$

2. $y = \sqrt{9 - x^2}$

3. $y = 1 + x^2$

4. $y = x^3 - x$

 Sketching a Graph by Point Plotting In Exercises 5–14, sketch the graph of the equation by point plotting.

5. $y = \frac{1}{2}x + 2$

6. $y = 5 - 2x$

7. $y = 4 - x^2$

8. $y = (x - 3)^2$

9. $y = |x + 1|$

10. $y = |x| - 1$

11. $y = \sqrt{x} - 6$

12. $y = \sqrt{x + 2}$

13. $y = \dfrac{2}{x}$

14. $y = \dfrac{1}{x + 3}$

 Approximating Solution Points In Exercises 15 and 16, use a graphing utility to graph the equation. Move the cursor along the curve to approximate the unknown coordinate of each solution point accurate to two decimal places.

15. $y = \sqrt{5 - x}$

    (a) $(2, y)$

    (b) $(x, 3)$

16. $y = x^5 - 5x$

    (a) $(-0.5, y)$

    (b) $(x, -4)$

 Finding Intercepts In Exercises 17–26, find any intercepts algebraically. Use a graphing utility to verify your results.

17. $y = 4x - 3$

18. $y = 2x^2 + 5$

19. $y = x^2 + x - 2$

20. $y^2 = x^3 - 4x$

21. $y = x\sqrt{16 - x^2}$

22. $y = (x - 1)\sqrt{x^2 + 1}$

23. $y = \dfrac{2 - \sqrt{x}}{5x + 1}$

24. $y = \dfrac{x^2 + 3x}{(3x + 1)^2}$

25. $x^2y - x^2 + 4y = 0$

26. $y = 2x - \sqrt{x^2 + 1}$

 Testing for Symmetry In Exercises 27–38, test for symmetry with respect to each axis and to the origin.

27. $y = x^2 - 6$

28. $y = x^2 - x$

29. $y^2 = x^3 - 8x$

30. $y = x^3 + x$

31. $xy = 4$

32. $xy^2 = -10$

33. $y = 5 - \sqrt{x + 4}$

34. $xy - \sqrt{16 - x^2} = 0$

35. $y = \dfrac{x}{x^2 + 1}$

36. $y = \dfrac{x^2}{x^2 + 1}$

37. $y = |x^3 + x|$

38. $|y| - x = 3$

 Using Intercepts and Symmetry to Sketch a Graph In Exercises 39–56, find any intercepts and test for symmetry. Then sketch the graph of the equation.

39. $y = 2 - 3x$

40. $y = \frac{2}{3}x + 1$

41. $y = 9 - x^2$

42. $y = 2x^2 + x$

43. $y = x^3 + 2$

44. $y = x^3 - 4x$

45. $y = x\sqrt{x + 5}$

46. $y = \sqrt{25 - x^2}$

47. $x = y^3$

48. $x = y^2 - 4$

49. $y = \dfrac{6}{x}$

50. $y = \dfrac{12}{x^2 + 1}$

51. $y = 6 - |x|$

52. $y = |6 - x|$

53. $y^2 - x = 25$

54. $x^2 + 4y^2 = 4$

55. $x + 3y^2 = 6$

56. $3x - 4y^2 = 8$

 Finding Points of Intersection In Exercises 57–60, find the points of intersection of the graphs of the equations. Use a graphing utility to verify your results.

57. $x + y = 8$

    $4x - y = 7$

58. $3x - 2y = -4$

    $4x + 2y = -10$

59. $x^2 + y = 15$

    $-3x + y = 11$

60. $x^2 + y^2 = 25$

    $-3x + y = 15$

 Finding Points of Intersection In Exercises 61 and 62, use a graphing utility to find the points of intersection of the graphs. Check your results analytically.

61. $y = \sqrt{x + 6}$

    $y = \sqrt{-x^2 - 4x}$

62. $y = -|2x - 3| + 6$

    $y = 6 - x$

63. Error Analysis Describe and correct the error in testing the graph of $y^2 + 1 = x$ for y-axis symmetry.

    $(-y)^2 + 1 = x \implies y^2 + 1 = x$

The graph of $y^2 + 1 = x$ is symmetric about the y-axis.

 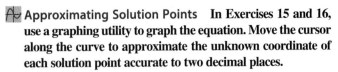

64. Error Analysis Describe and correct the error in finding the points of intersection of the graphs of $x + y = 1$ and $y + x^2 = x + 4$.

$$-x + 1 = -x^2 + x + 4$$

$$x^2 - 2x - 3 = 0$$

$$(x - 1)(x + 3) = 0$$

$$x = 1 \text{ or } -3$$

The points of intersection are $(1, 0)$ and $(-3, 4)$. ✗

65. Wages Each ordered pair gives the average weekly wage x (in dollars) for federal government workers and the average weekly wage y (in dollars) for state government workers for 2009 through 2017. *(Source: U.S. Bureau of Labor Statistics)*

$(1303, 937), (1331, 942), (1404, 966), (1410, 988),$
$(1402, 1010), (1458, 1042), (1498, 1075),$
$(1507, 1099), (1547, 1131)$

(a) Plot the data. From the graph, do the data appear to be approximately linear?

(b) Visually find a linear model for the data. Graph the model and use it to approximate y when $x = 1475$.

66. Quiz Scores The ordered pairs represent the scores on two consecutive 15-point quizzes for a class of 15 students.

$(7, 13), (9, 7), (14, 14), (15, 15), (10, 15), (9, 7), (11, 14),$
$(7, 14), \ (14, 11), \ (14, 15), \ (8, 10), \ (15, 9), \ (10, 11),$
$(9, 10), (11, 10)$

(a) Plot the data. From the graph, does the data appear to be approximately linear?

(b) If the data appear to be approximately linear, find a linear model for the data. If not, give some possible explanations.

67. Hooke's Law Hooke's Law states that the force F required to compress or stretch a spring (within its elastic limits) is proportional to the distance d that the spring is compressed or stretched from its original length. That is, $F = kd$, where k is a measure of the stiffness of the spring and is called the *spring constant.* The table shows the elongation d (in centimeters) of a spring when a force of F newtons is applied.

F	20	40	60	80	100
d	1.4	2.5	4.0	5.3	6.6

(a) Use the regression capabilities of a graphing utility to find a linear model for the data.

(b) Use a graphing utility to plot the data and graph the model. How well does the model fit the data? Explain.

(c) Use the model to estimate the elongation of the spring when a force of 55 newtons is applied.

68. Gross Domestic Product and Population The data show the gross domestic products x (in trillions of U.S. dollars) and the populations y (in millions) of 14 countries in a recent year. *(Source: Trading Economics)*

x	19.391	12.238	4.872	3.677	2.622
y	325.7	1390.1	126.7	82.9	66.2

x	2.597	2.583	1.935	1.653	1.531
y	1283.6	67.2	60.5	37.0	51.5

x	1.311	0.826	0.684	0.482
y	46.7	17.1	33.4	31.4

(a) Use the regression capabilities of a graphing utility to find a linear model for the data. What is the correlation coefficient?

(b) Use a graphing utility to plot the data and graph the model.

(c) Interpret the graph in part (b). Use the graph to identify the two points that differ most from the linear model.

(d) Delete the data for the two points identified in part (c). Fit a linear model to the remaining data and give the correlation coefficient.

69. MODELING DATA

The table shows the Gross National Product, or GNP, (in trillions of dollars) for the United States for selected years. *(Source: World Bank)*

Year	1987	1992	1997	2002	2007	2012	2017
GNP	4.7	6.5	8.6	11.1	14.6	16.6	19.6

(a) Use the regression capabilities of a graphing utility to find a mathematical model of the form

$$y = at^2 + bt + c$$

for the data. In the model, y represents the GNP (in trillions of dollars) and t represents the year, with $t = 7$ corresponding to 1987.

(b) Use a graphing utility to plot the data and graph the model. Compare the data with the model.

(c) Use the model to predict the GNP in the year 2029.

70. Modeling Data   The table shows the numbers of smartphones (in millions) in active use in the United States from 2012 through 2017. *(Source: CTIA-The Wireless Association)*

Year	2012	2013	2014	2015	2016	2017
Number	152	175	208	228	262	273

(a) Use the regression capabilities of a graphing utility to find a mathematical model of the form $y = at^2 + bt + c$ for the data. In the model, y represents the number of smartphones (in millions) and t represents the year, with $t = 12$ corresponding to 2012.

(b) Use a graphing utility to plot the data and graph the model. Compare the data with the model.

(c) Use the model to predict the number of smartphones in active use in the United States in the year 2029.

71. Break-Even Point   Find the sales necessary to break even $(R = C)$ when the cost C of producing x units is $C = 1.73x + 6500$ and the revenue R from selling x units is $R = 2.98x$.

72. Copper Wire   The resistance y in ohms of 1000 feet of solid copper wire at 68°F can be approximated by the model

$$y = \frac{10{,}370}{x^2}$$

where x is the diameter of the wire in mils (0.001 inch). Use a graphing utility to graph the model for $5 \le x \le 100$. By what factor is the resistance changed when the diameter of the wire is doubled?

73. Beam Strength   Students in a lab measured the breaking strength S (in pounds) of wood 2 inches thick, x inches wide, and 12 inches long. The results are shown in the table.

x	4	6	8	10	12
S	2370	5460	10,310	16,250	23,860

(a) Use the regression capabilities of a graphing utility to find a quadratic model for the data.

(b) Use a graphing utility to plot the data and graph the model.

(c) Use the model to approximate the breaking strength when $x = 2$.

(d) How many times greater is the breaking strength for a 4-inch-wide board than for a 2-inch-wide board?

(e) How many times greater is the breaking strength for a 12-inch-wide board than for a 6-inch-wide board? When the width of a board increases by a factor, does the breaking strength increase by the same factor? Explain.

74. Car Performance   The time t (in seconds) required to attain a speed of s miles per hour from a standing start for a Toyota Corolla is shown in the table. *(Source: Car & Driver)*

s	30	40	50	60	70	80	90
t	3.0	4.5	6.2	8.3	10.7	13.7	17.3

(a) Use the regression capabilities of a graphing utility to find a quadratic model for the data.

(b) Use a graphing utility to plot the data and graph the model.

(c) Use the graph in part (b) to state why the model is not appropriate for determining the times required to attain some of the speeds less than those shown in the table.

(d) Because the test began from a standing start, add the point $(0, 0)$ to the data. Fit a quadratic model to the revised data and graph the new model.

(e) Does the quadratic model in part (d) more accurately model the behavior of the car? Explain.

75. Engine Performance   A V8 car engine is coupled to a dynamometer, and the horsepower y is measured at different engine speeds x (in thousands of revolutions per minute). The results are $(1, 40)$, $(2, 85)$, $(3, 140)$, $(4, 200)$, $(5, 225)$, and $(6, 245)$.

(a) Use the regression capabilities of a graphing utility to find a cubic model for the data.

(b) Use a graphing utility to plot the data and graph the model.

(c) Use the model to approximate the horsepower when the engine is running at 4500 revolutions per minute.

76. Boiling Temperature   The table shows the temperatures T (in degrees Fahrenheit) at which water boils at selected pressures p (in pounds per square inch). *(Source: Standard Handbook for Mechanical Engineers)*

p	5	10	14.696 (1 atmosphere)	20
T	162.21	193.19	212.00	227.96

p	30	40	60	80	100
T	250.34	267.26	292.73	312.07	327.86

(a) Use the regression capabilities of a graphing utility to find a cubic model for the data.

(b) Use a graphing utility to plot the data and graph the model.

(c) Use the graph to estimate the pressure required for the boiling point of water to exceed 300°F.

(d) Explain why the model would not be accurate for pressures exceeding 100 pounds per square inch.

77. Particle Motion   The motion of an oscillating particle was measured by a motion detector. The data collected and the approximate maximum (positive and negative) displacements from equilibrium are shown in the figure. The displacement y is measured in centimeters, and the time t is measured in seconds.

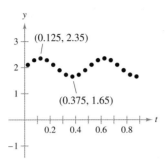

(a) Approximate the amplitude and period of the displacements.

(b) Find a model for the data without using a graphing utility.

(c) Use a graphing utility to graph the model in part (b). Compare the result with the data in the figure.

78. Temperature   The table shows the normal daily maximum temperatures for Miami M and Syracuse S (in degrees Fahrenheit) for month t, with $t = 1$ corresponding to January. *(Source: National Oceanic and Atmospheric Administration)*

t	1	2	3	4	5	6
M	76.4	78.1	80.3	83.2	87.0	89.5
S	31.5	34.2	43.2	57.2	68.8	77.5

t	7	8	9	10	11	12
M	90.9	91.0	89.3	86.2	81.7	77.9
S	81.6	80.0	72.2	60.0	48.4	36.4

(a) A model for Miami is

$M(t) = 83.90 + 7.42 \sin(0.4957t - 2.05)$

Find a model for Syracuse.

(b) Use a graphing utility to plot the data and graph the model for Miami. How well does the model fit?

(c) Use a graphing utility to plot the data and graph the model for Syracuse. How well does the model fit?

(d) Use the models to estimate the average annual maximum temperature in each city. Which term of the model did you use? Explain.

(e) What is the period of each model? Is it what you expected? Explain.

(f) Which city has a greater variability in temperature throughout the year? Which factor of the models determines this variability? Explain.

79. Using Solution Points   For what values of k does the graph of $y = kx^3$ pass through the point?

(a) $(1, 4)$ (b) $(-2, 1)$

(c) $(0, 0)$ (d) $(-1, -1)$

80. Using Solution Points   For what values of k does the graph of $y^2 = 4kx$ pass through the point?

(a) $(1, 1)$ (b) $(2, 4)$

(c) $(0, 0)$ (d) $(3, 3)$

EXPLORING CONCEPTS

Writing Equations   In Exercises 81 and 82, write an equation whose graph has the indicated property. (There may be more than one correct answer.) Explain how you obtained your answer.

81. The graph has intercepts at $x = -3$, $x = 5$, and $x = 6$.

82. The graph has intercepts at $x = -\frac{3}{2}$, $x = 4$, and $x = \frac{5}{2}$.

83. Justifying

(a) A graph is symmetric with respect to the x-axis and to the y-axis. Is the graph also symmetric with respect to the origin? Explain.

(b) A graph is symmetric with respect to one axis and to the origin. Is the graph also symmetric with respect to the other axis? Explain.

84.   HOW DO YOU SEE IT?   Use the graphs of the two equations to answer the questions below.

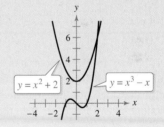

(a) What are the intercepts for each graph?

(b) Determine the symmetry for each graph.

(c) Determine the point of intersection of the two graphs.

True or False?   In Exercises 85 and 86, determine whether the statement is true or false. If it is false, explain why or give an example that shows it is false.

85. If $(3, -4)$ is a point on a graph that is symmetric with respect to the x-axis, then $(-3, -4)$ is also a point on the graph.

86. If $b^2 - 4ac = 0$ and $a \neq 0$, then the graph of $y = ax^2 + bx + c$ has only one x-intercept.

P.2   Linear Models and Rates of Change

▶ Find the slope of a line passing through two points.
▶ Write the equation of a line with a given point and slope.
▶ Interpret slope as a ratio or as a rate in a real-life application.
▶ Sketch the graph of a linear equation in slope-intercept form.
▶ Write equations of lines that are parallel or perpendicular to a given line.

The Slope of a Line

The **slope** of a nonvertical line is a measure of the number of units the line rises (or falls) vertically for each unit of horizontal change from left to right. Consider the two points

$$(x_1, y_1) \quad \text{and} \quad (x_2, y_2)$$

on the line in Figure P.11. As you move from left to right along this line, a vertical change of

$$\Delta y = y_2 - y_1 \qquad \text{Change in } y$$

units corresponds to a horizontal change of

$$\Delta x = x_2 - x_1 \qquad \text{Change in } x$$

units. (The symbol Δ is the uppercase Greek letter delta, and the symbols Δy and Δx are read "delta y" and "delta x.")

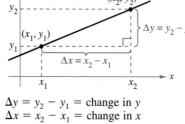

$\Delta y = y_2 - y_1 =$ change in y
$\Delta x = x_2 - x_1 =$ change in x
Figure P.11

Justification

When using the formula for slope, note that

$$\frac{y_2 - y_1}{x_2 - x_1} = \frac{-(y_1 - y_2)}{-(x_1 - x_2)}$$
$$= \frac{y_1 - y_2}{x_1 - x_2}.$$

So, it does not matter in which order you subtract *as long as* you are consistent and both "subtracted coordinates" come from the same point.

Definition of the Slope of a Line

The **slope** m of the nonvertical line passing through (x_1, y_1) and (x_2, y_2) is

$$m = \frac{\Delta y}{\Delta x} = \frac{y_2 - y_1}{x_2 - x_1}, \quad x_1 \neq x_2.$$

Slope is not defined for vertical lines.

Figure P.12 shows four lines: one has a positive slope, one has a slope of zero, one has a negative slope, and one has an "undefined" slope. In general, the greater the absolute value of the slope of a line, the steeper the line. For instance, in Figure P.12, the line with a slope of -5 is steeper than the line with a slope of $\frac{1}{5}$.

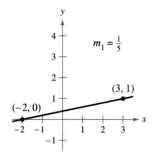

If m is positive, then the line rises from left to right.
Figure P.12

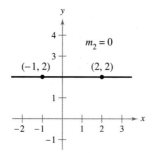

If m is zero, then the line is horizontal.

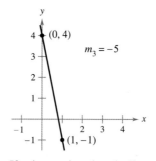

If m is negative, then the line falls from left to right.

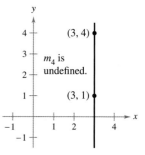

If m is undefined, then the line is vertical.

Equations of Lines

Any two points on a nonvertical line can be used to calculate its slope. This can be verified from the similar triangles shown in Figure P.13. (Recall that the ratios of corresponding sides of similar triangles are equal.)

If (x_1, y_1) is a point on a nonvertical line that has a slope of m and (x, y), is *any other* point on the line, then

$$\frac{y - y_1}{x - x_1} = m.$$

This equation in the variables x and y can be rewritten in the form $y - y_1 = m(x - x_1)$, which is the **point-slope form** of the equation of a line.

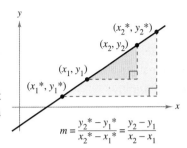

$$m = \frac{y_2{}^* - y_1{}^*}{x_2{}^* - x_1{}^*} = \frac{y_2 - y_1}{x_2 - x_1}$$

Any two points on a nonvertical line can be used to determine its slope.
Figure P.13

Point-Slope Form of the Equation of a Line

The **point-slope form** of the equation of the line that passes through the point (x_1, y_1) and has a slope of m is

$$y - y_1 = m(x - x_1).$$

Remember that only nonvertical lines have a slope. Consequently, vertical lines cannot be written in point-slope form.

Exploration

Investigating Equations of Lines   Use a graphing utility to graph each of the linear equations. Which point is common to all seven lines? Which value in the equation determines the slope of each line?

a. $y - 4 = -2(x + 1)$

b. $y - 4 = -1(x + 1)$

c. $y - 4 = -\frac{1}{2}(x + 1)$

d. $y - 4 = 0(x + 1)$

e. $y - 4 = \frac{1}{2}(x + 1)$

f. $y - 4 = 1(x + 1)$

g. $y - 4 = 2(x + 1)$

Use your results to write an equation of a line passing through $(-1, 4)$ with a slope of m.

EXAMPLE 1   **Finding an Equation of a Line**

Find an equation of the line that has a slope of 3 and passes through the point $(1, -2)$. Then sketch the line.

Solution

$$y - y_1 = m(x - x_1) \qquad \text{Point-slope form}$$
$$y - (-2) = 3(x - 1) \qquad \text{Substitute } -2 \text{ for } y_1, 1 \text{ for } x_1, \text{ and } 3 \text{ for } m.$$
$$y + 2 = 3x - 3 \qquad \text{Simplify.}$$
$$y = 3x - 5 \qquad \text{Solve for } y.$$

To sketch the line, first plot the point $(1, -2)$. Then, because the slope is $m = 3$, you can locate a second point on the line by moving one unit to the right and three units upward, as shown in Figure P.14.

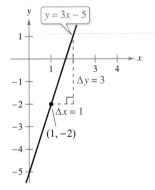

The line with a slope of 3 passing through the point $(1, -2)$
Figure P.14

Ratios and Rates of Change

The slope of a line can be interpreted as either a *ratio* or a *rate*. If the x- and y-axes have the same unit of measure, then the slope has no units and is a **ratio.** If the x- and y-axes have different units of measure, then the slope is a rate or **rate of change.** In your study of calculus, you will encounter applications involving both interpretations of slope.

EXAMPLE 2   Using Slope as a Ratio

The maximum recommended slope of a wheelchair ramp is $\frac{1}{12}$. A business installs a wheelchair ramp that rises to a height of 22 inches over a length of 24 feet, as shown in the figure. Is the ramp steeper than recommended?   *(Source: ADA Standards for Accessible Design)*

Solution

The length of the ramp is 24 feet or $12(24) = 288$ inches. The slope of the ramp is the ratio of its height (the rise) to its length (the run).

$$\text{Slope of ramp} = \frac{\text{rise}}{\text{run}}$$

$$= \frac{22 \text{ in.}}{288 \text{ in.}}$$

$$\approx 0.076$$

Because the slope of the ramp is less than $\frac{1}{12} \approx 0.083$, the ramp is not steeper than recommended. Note that the slope is a ratio and has no units.

EXAMPLE 3   Using Slope as a Rate of Change

The population of Utah was about 2,427,000 in 2005 and about 3,161,000 in 2018. Find the average rate of change of the population over this 13-year period. What will the population of Utah be in 2025?   *(Source: U.S. Census Bureau)*

Solution

Over this 13-year period, the average rate of change of the population of Utah was

$$\text{Rate of change} = \frac{\text{change in population}}{\text{change in years}}$$

$$= \frac{3,161,000 - 2,427,000}{2018 - 2005}$$

$$\approx 56,462 \text{ people per year.}$$

Assuming that the population of Utah continues to increase at this same rate for the next 7 years, the population in 2025 will be about

$$3,161,000 + 7(56,462) = 3,556,234 \text{ people.} \qquad \text{See Figure P.15.}$$

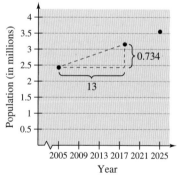

Population of Utah
Figure P.15

The rate of change found in Example 3 is an **average rate of change.** An average rate of change is always calculated over an interval. In this case, the interval is [2005, 2018]. In Chapter 2, you will study *instantaneous rates of change.*

Graphing Linear Models

Many problems in coordinate geometry can be classified into two basic categories.

1. Given a graph (or parts of it), find its equation.
2. Given an equation, sketch its graph.

For lines, you can solve problems in the first category by using the point-slope form. The point-slope form, however, is not especially useful for solving problems in the second category. The form that is better suited to sketching the graph of a line is the **slope-intercept** form of the equation of a line.

The Slope-Intercept Form of the Equation of a Line

The graph of the linear equation

$$y = mx + b \qquad \text{Slope-intercept form}$$

is a line whose slope is m and whose y-intercept is $(0, b)$.

EXAMPLE 4   Sketching Lines in the Plane

Sketch the graph of each equation.

a. $y = 2x + 1$

b. $y = 2$

c. $3y + x - 6 = 0$

Solution

a. Because $b = 1$, the y-intercept is $(0, 1)$. Because the slope is $m = 2$, you know that the line rises two units for each unit it moves to the right, as shown in Figure P.16(a).

b. By writing the equation $y = 2$ in slope-intercept form

$$y = (0)x + 2$$

you can see that the slope is $m = 0$ and the y-intercept is $(0, 2)$. Because the slope is zero, you know that the line is horizontal, as shown in Figure P.16(b).

c. Begin by writing the equation in slope-intercept form.

$$3y + x - 6 = 0 \qquad \text{Write original equation.}$$
$$3y = -x + 6 \qquad \text{Isolate } y\text{-term on the left.}$$
$$y = -\tfrac{1}{3}x + 2 \qquad \text{Slope-intercept form}$$

> **Algebra Review**
>
> For a review of rewriting equations in two variables, see the *Chapter P Algebra Review* on page A35.

In this form, you can see that the y-intercept is $(0, 2)$ and the slope is $m = -\tfrac{1}{3}$. This means that the line falls one unit for every three units it moves to the right, as shown in Figure P.16(c).

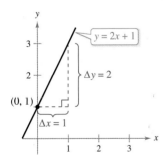

(a) $m = 2$; line rises

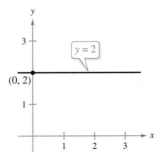

(b) $m = 0$; line is horizontal

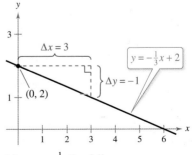

(c) $m = -\tfrac{1}{3}$; line falls

Figure P.16

Because the slope of a vertical line is not defined, its equation cannot be written in slope-intercept form. However, the equation of any line can be written in the **general form**

$$Ax + By + C = 0$$ General form of the equation of a line

where A and B are not *both* zero. For instance, the vertical line

$x = a$ Vertical line

can be represented by the general form

$x - a = 0.$ General form

Summary of Equations of Lines

1. General form: $Ax + By + C = 0$
2. Vertical line: $x = a$
3. Horizontal line: $y = b$
4. Slope-intercept form: $y = mx + b$
5. Point-slope form: $y - y_1 = m(x - x_1)$

Parallel and Perpendicular Lines

The slope of a line is a convenient tool for determining whether two lines are parallel or perpendicular, as shown in Figure P.17. Specifically, distinct nonvertical lines with the same slope are parallel, and nonvertical lines whose slopes are negative reciprocals are perpendicular.

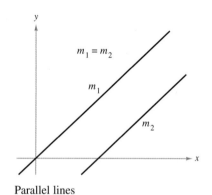

Parallel lines

Figure P.17

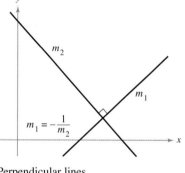

Perpendicular lines

Parallel and Perpendicular Lines

1. Two distinct nonvertical lines are **parallel** if and only if their slopes are equal—that is, if and only if

   $m_1 = m_2.$ Parallel ⟺ Slopes are equal.

2. Two nonvertical lines are **perpendicular** if and only if their slopes are negative reciprocals of each other—that is, if and only if

   $m_1 = -\dfrac{1}{m_2}.$ Perpendicular ⟺ Slopes are negative reciprocals.

Communication and Notation

In mathematics, the phrase "if and only if" is a way of stating two implications in one statement. For instance, the first statement at the left could be rewritten as the following two implications.

a. If two distinct nonvertical lines are parallel, then their slopes are equal.

b. If two distinct nonvertical lines have equal slopes, then they are parallel.

EXAMPLE 5 Finding Parallel and Perpendicular Lines

See LarsonCalculusforAP.com for an interactive version of this type of example.

Find the general forms of the equations of the lines that pass through the point $(2, -1)$ and are (a) parallel to and (b) perpendicular to the line $2x - 3y = 5$.

Solution

Begin by writing the linear equation $2x - 3y = 5$ in slope-intercept form.

$$2x - 3y = 5 \qquad \text{Write original equation.}$$
$$y = \tfrac{2}{3}x - \tfrac{5}{3} \qquad \text{Slope-intercept form}$$

So, the given line has a slope of $m = \tfrac{2}{3}$. (See Figure P.18.)

a. The line through $(2, -1)$ that is parallel to the given line also has a slope of $\tfrac{2}{3}$.

$$y - y_1 = m(x - x_1) \qquad \text{Point-slope form}$$
$$y - (-1) = \tfrac{2}{3}(x - 2) \qquad \text{Substitute.}$$
$$3(y + 1) = 2(x - 2) \qquad \text{Simplify.}$$
$$3y + 3 = 2x - 4 \qquad \text{Distributive Property}$$
$$2x - 3y - 7 = 0 \qquad \text{General form (See Figure P.18.)}$$

Note the similarity to the equation of the given line, $2x - 3y = 5$.

b. Using the negative reciprocal of the slope of the given line, you can determine that the slope of a line perpendicular to the given line is $-\tfrac{3}{2}$.

$$y - y_1 = m(x - x_1) \qquad \text{Point-slope form}$$
$$y - (-1) = -\tfrac{3}{2}(x - 2) \qquad \text{Substitute.}$$
$$2(y + 1) = -3(x - 2) \qquad \text{Simplify.}$$
$$2y + 2 = -3x + 6 \qquad \text{Distributive Property}$$
$$3x + 2y - 4 = 0 \qquad \text{General form (See Figure P.18.)}$$

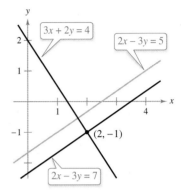

Lines parallel and perpendicular to $2x - 3y = 5$

Figure P.18

Technology Pitfall

The slope of a line will appear distorted if you use different tick-mark spacing on the x- and y-axes. For instance, the graphing utility screens in Figures P.19(a) and P.19(b) both show the lines $y = 2x$ and $y = -\tfrac{1}{2}x + 3$. These lines have slopes that are negative reciprocals, so they must be perpendicular. In Figure P.19(a), however, the lines do not appear to be perpendicular because the tick-mark spacing on the x-axis is not the same as that on the y-axis. In Figure P.19(b), the lines appear perpendicular because the tick-mark spacing on the x-axis is the same as on the y-axis. This type of viewing window is said to have a *square setting*.

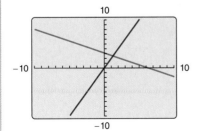

(a) Tick-mark spacing on the x-axis is not the same as tick-mark spacing on the y-axis.

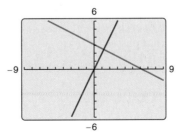

(b) Tick-mark spacing on the x-axis is the same as tick-mark spacing on y-axis.

Figure P.19

P.2   Exercises

See *CalcChat.com* for tutorial help and worked-out solutions to odd-numbered exercises.

Estimating Slope   In Exercises 1–4, estimate the slope of the line from its graph. To print an enlarged copy of the graph, go to *MathGraphs.com*.

1.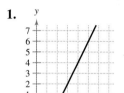

2.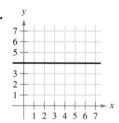

3.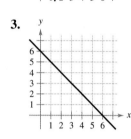

4.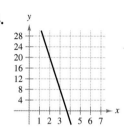

 Finding the Slope of a Line   In Exercises 5–10, plot the pair of points and find the slope of the line passing through them.

5. $(3, -4), (5, 2)$

6. $(0, 0), (-7, 14)$

7. $(4, 6), (4, 1)$

8. $(3, -5), (5, -5)$

9. $\left(-\frac{1}{2}, \frac{2}{3}\right), \left(-\frac{3}{4}, \frac{1}{6}\right)$

10. $\left(\frac{7}{8}, \frac{3}{4}\right), \left(\frac{5}{4}, -\frac{1}{4}\right)$

 Sketching Lines   In Exercises 11 and 12, sketch the lines through the point with the indicated slopes on the same set of coordinate axes.

Point			*Slopes*	

11. $(3, 4)$ (a) 1   (b) -2 (c) $-\frac{3}{2}$ (d) Undefined

12. $(-2, 5)$ (a) 3   (b) -3 (c) $\frac{1}{3}$ (d) 0

 Finding Points on a Line   In Exercises 13–16, use the point on the line and the slope of the line to find three additional points on the line.

13. $(6, 2), \; m = 0$

14. $(-4, 3), \; m$ is undefined.

15. $(1, 7), \; m = -3$

16. $(-2, -2), \; m = 2$

 Finding an Equation of a Line   In Exercises 17–22, find an equation of the line that passes through the point and has the indicated slope. Then sketch the line.

17. $(0, 3), \; m = \frac{3}{4}$

18. $(-5, -2), \; m = 3$

19. $(0, 0), \; m$ is undefined.

20. $(0, 4), \; m = 0$

21. $(2, -3), \; m = -2$

22. $(-2, 4), \; m = -\frac{3}{5}$

23. CONVEYOR DESIGN

A moving conveyor is built to rise 1 meter for each 3 meters of horizontal change.

(a) Find the slope of the conveyor.

(b) The conveyor runs between two floors in a factory. Find the length of the conveyor when the vertical distance between floors is 10 feet.

24. Modeling Data   The table shows the populations y (in millions) of the United States for 2013 through 2018. The variable t represents the time in years, with $t = 13$ corresponding to 2013.   *(Source: United Nations)*

t	13	14	15	16	17	18
y	315.5	317.7	319.9	322.2	324.5	326.8

(a) Plot the data by hand and connect adjacent points with a line segment.

(b) Use the slope of each line segment to determine the years when the population increased least rapidly.

(c) Find the average rate of change of the population of the United States from 2013 through 2018.

(d) Use the average rate of change of the population to predict the population of the United States in 2025.

 Finding the Slope and *y*-Intercept   In Exercises 25–30, find the slope and the *y*-intercept (if possible) of the line.

25. $y = 4x - 3$

26. $-x + y = 1$

27. $5x + y = 20$

28. $6x - 5y = 15$

29. $x = -1$

30. $y = 4$

 Sketching a Line in the Plane   In Exercises 31–38, sketch the graph of the equation.

31. $y = -4$

32. $x = 3$

33. $y = -2x + 1$

34. $y = \frac{1}{3}x - 1$

35. $y - 2 = \frac{3}{2}(x - 1)$

36. $y - 1 = 3(x + 4)$

37. $3x - y - 2 = 0$

38. $x + 2y + 6 = 0$

Finding an Equation of a Line   **In Exercises 39–46, find an equation of the line that passes through the points. Then sketch the line.**

39. $(4, 3), (0, -5)$

40. $(-2, -2), (1, 7)$

41. $(-5, 8), (4, 0)$

42. $(-3, 6), (1, 2)$

43. $(6, 3), (6, 8)$

44. $(1, -2), (3, -2)$

45. $\left(\frac{1}{2}, \frac{7}{2}\right), \left(0, \frac{3}{4}\right)$

46. $\left(\frac{7}{8}, \frac{3}{4}\right), \left(\frac{5}{4}, -\frac{1}{4}\right)$

47. Writing an Equation   Write an equation for the line that passes through the points (a, c) and $(0, b)$, $a \neq 0$.

48. Using Intercepts   Show that the line with intercepts $(a, 0)$ and $(0, b)$ has the following equation.

$$\frac{x}{a} + \frac{y}{b} = 1, \quad a \neq 0, b \neq 0$$

Writing an Equation in General Form   **In Exercises 49–54, use the result of Exercise 48 to write an equation of the line with the given characteristics in general form.**

49. x-intercept: $(2, 0)$

   y-intercept: $(0, 3)$

50. x-intercept: $\left(-\frac{2}{3}, 0\right)$

   y-intercept: $(0, -2)$

51. Point on line: $(-1, 2)$

   x-intercept: $(a, 0)$

   y-intercept: $(0, a)$

   $(a \neq 0)$

52. Point on line: $(3, -4)$

   x-intercept: $(a, 0)$

   y-intercept: $(0, a)$

   $(a \neq 0)$

53. Point on line: $(9, -2)$

   x-intercept: $(2a, 0)$

   y-intercept: $(0, a)$

   $(a \neq 0)$

54. Point on line: $\left(-\frac{2}{3}, -2\right)$

   x-intercept: $(a, 0)$

   y-intercept: $(0, -a)$

   $(a \neq 0)$

Finding Parallel and Perpendicular Lines   **In Exercises 55–62, write the general forms of the equations of the lines that pass through the given point and are (a) parallel to the given line and (b) perpendicular to the given line.**

Point	Line	Point	Line
55. $(-7, -2)$	$x = 1$	**56.** $(-1, 0)$	$y = -3$
57. $(-3, 2)$	$x + y = 7$	**58.** $(2, 5)$	$x - y = -2$
59. $(2, 1)$	$4x - 2y = 3$	**60.** $\left(\frac{5}{6}, -\frac{1}{2}\right)$	$7x + 4y = 8$
61. $(5, -3)$	$5x - 3y = 0$	**62.** $(-4, -5)$	$3x + 4y = 7$

63. Error Analysis   Describe and correct the error in finding an equation of the line that has a slope of $-\frac{5}{2}$ and passes through the point $(-1, 4)$.

$$y - (-1) = -\tfrac{5}{2}(x - 4)$$
$$y + 1 = -\tfrac{5}{2}x + 10$$
$$y = -\tfrac{5}{2}x + 9$$

64. Error Analysis   Describe and correct the error in finding the general form of the equation of the line that passes through the point $(2, -3)$ and is perpendicular to the line $y = -\frac{3}{4}x + 6$.

$$y - (-3) = -\tfrac{4}{3}(x - 2)$$
$$3(y + 3) = -4(x - 2)$$
$$3y + 9 = -4x + 8$$
$$4x + 3y + 1 = 0$$

Rate of Change   **In Exercises 65–68, you are given the dollar value of a product in 2019 and the rate at which the value of the product is expected to change during the next 5 years. Write a linear equation that gives the dollar value V of the product in terms of the year t. (Let $t = 0$ represent 2010.)**

	2019 Value	Rate
65.	$1850	$250 increase per year
66.	$156	$4.50 increase per year
67.	$17,200	$1600 decrease per year
68.	$524,000	$16,500 decrease per year

Collinear Points   **In Exercises 69 and 70, determine whether the points are collinear. (Three points are *collinear* if they lie on the same line.)**

69. $(0, 4), (7, -6), (-5, 11)$

70. $(-2, 1), (-1, 0), (2, -2)$

EXPLORING CONCEPTS

Justifying   **In Exercises 71 and 72, find the coordinates of the point of intersection of the given segments. Explain how you obtained your results.**

71.

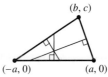

Perpendicular bisectors

72.

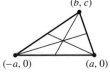

Medians

73. Analyzing a Line   A line is represented by the equation $ax + by = 4$.

(a) When is the line parallel to the x-axis? y-axis?

(b) Give values for a and b such that the line has a slope of $\frac{5}{8}$.

(c) Give values for a and b such that the line is perpendicular to $y = \frac{2}{5}x + 3$.

(d) Give values for a and b such that the line coincides with the graph of $5x + 6y = 8$.

74. **HOW DO YOU SEE IT?**   Several lines are shown in the figure below. (The lines are labeled a, b, c, d, e, and f.)

(a) Which lines have a positive slope?

(b) Which lines have a negative slope?

(c) Which lines appear parallel?

(d) Which lines appear perpendicular?

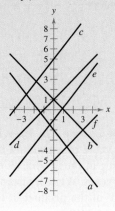

75. Choosing a Job   As a salesperson, you receive a monthly salary of $2000, plus a commission of 7% of sales. You are offered a new job at $2300 per month, plus a commission of 5% of sales.

(a) Write linear equations for your monthly wage W in terms of your monthly sales s for your current job and your job offer.

(b) Use a graphing utility to graph each equation and find the point of intersection. What does it signify?

(c) You think you can sell $20,000 worth of a product per month. Should you change jobs? Explain.

76. Straight-Line Depreciation   A small business purchases a piece of equipment for $875. After 5 years, the equipment will be outdated, having no value.

(a) Write a linear equation giving the value y of the equipment in terms of the time x (in years), $0 \le x \le 5$.

(b) Find the value of the equipment when $x = 2$.

(c) Estimate (to two-decimal-place accuracy) the time when the value of the equipment is $200.

77. Apartment Rental   A real estate office manages an apartment complex with 50 units. When the rent is $780 per month, all 50 units are occupied. However, when the rent is $825, the average number of occupied units drops to 47. Assume that the relationship between the monthly rent p and the demand x is linear. (*Note:* The term *demand* refers to the number of occupied units.)

(a) Write a linear equation giving the demand x in terms of the rent p.

(b) *Linear extrapolation*   Use a graphing utility to graph the demand equation and use the trace feature to predict the number of units occupied when the rent is raised to $855.

(c) *Linear interpolation*   Predict the number of units occupied when the rent is lowered to $795. Verify graphically.

78. Modeling Data   An instructor gives regular 20-point quizzes and 100-point exams in a mathematics course. Average scores for six students, given as ordered pairs (x, y), where x is the average quiz score and y is the average exam score, are $(18, 87)$, $(10, 55)$, $(19, 96)$, $(16, 79)$, $(13, 76)$, and $(15, 82)$.

(a) Use the regression capabilities of a graphing utility to find the least squares regression line for the data.

(b) Use a graphing utility to plot the points and graph the regression line in the same viewing window.

(c) Use the regression line to predict the average exam score for a student with an average quiz score of 17.

(d) Interpret the meaning of the slope of the regression line.

(e) The instructor adds 4 points to the average exam score of everyone in the class. Describe the changes in the positions of the plotted points and the change in the equation of the line.

79. Tangent Line   Find an equation of the line tangent to the circle $x^2 + y^2 = 169$ at the point $(5, 12)$.

80. Tangent Line   Find an equation of the line tangent to the circle $(x - 1)^2 + (y - 1)^2 = 25$ at the point $(4, -3)$.

81. Distance   Show that the distance between the point (x_1, y_1) and the line $Ax + By + C = 0$ is

$$\text{Distance} = \frac{|Ax_1 + By_1 + C|}{\sqrt{A^2 + B^2}}.$$

82. Distance   Use the result of Exercise 81 to write the distance d between the point $(3, 1)$ and the line $y = mx + 4$ in terms of m. Use a graphing utility to graph the equation. When is the distance 0? Explain the result geometrically.

Distance   In Exercises 83–86, use the result of Exercise 81 to find the distance between the point and line or between the lines.

83. Point: $(-2, 1)$ **84.** Point: $(2, 3)$
     Line: $x - y - 2 = 0$ Line: $4x + 3y = 10$

85. Line: $x + y = 1$ **86.** Line: $3x - 4y = 1$
     Line: $x + y = 5$ Line: $3x - 4y = 10$

True or False?   In Exercises 87–90, determine whether the statement is true or false. If it is false, explain why or give an example that shows it is false.

87. The lines represented by $ax + by = c_1$ and $bx - ay = c_2$ are perpendicular. Assume $a \ne 0$ and $b \ne 0$.

88. It is possible for two lines with positive slopes to be perpendicular to each other.

89. If a line contains points in both the first and third quadrants, then its slope must be positive.

90. The equation of any line can be written in general form.

P.3   Functions and Their Graphs

▶ Use function notation to represent and evaluate a function.
▶ Find the domain and range of a function.
▶ Sketch the graph of a function.
▶ Identify different types of transformations of functions.
▶ Classify functions and recognize combinations of functions.

Functions and Function Notation

A **relation** between two sets X and Y is a set of ordered pairs, each of the form (x, y), where x is a member of X and y is a member of Y. A **function** from X to Y is a relation between X and Y that has the property that any two ordered pairs with the same x-value also have the same y-value. The variable x is the **independent variable,** and the variable y is the **dependent variable.**

You can use functions to model many real-life situations. For instance, the area A of a circle is a function of the circle's radius r.

$$A = \pi r^2 \qquad \text{\small{\textit{A} is a function of \textit{r}.}}$$

In this case, r is the independent variable and A is the dependent variable.

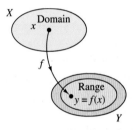

A real-valued function f of a real variable

Figure P.20

> #### Definition of a Real-Valued Function of a Real Variable
>
> Let X and Y be sets of real numbers. A **real-valued function f of a real variable x** from X to Y is a correspondence that assigns to each number x in X exactly one number y in Y.
>
> The **domain** of f is the set X. The number y is the **image** of x under f and is denoted by $f(x)$, which is called the **value of f at x.** The **range** of f is a subset of Y and consists of all images of numbers in X. (See Figure P.20.)

There are a variety of ways to specify functions. In this text, however, you will concentrate primarily on functions that are given by equations involving the dependent and independent variables. For instance, the equation

$$x^2 + 2y = 1 \qquad \text{\small{Equation in implicit form}}$$

defines y, the dependent variable, as a function of x, the independent variable. To **evaluate** this function (that is, to find the y-value that corresponds to a given x-value), it is convenient to isolate y on the left side of the equation.

$$y = \tfrac{1}{2}(1 - x^2) \qquad \text{\small{Equation in explicit form}}$$

Using f as the name of the function, you can write this equation as

$$f(x) = \tfrac{1}{2}(1 - x^2). \qquad \text{\small{Function notation}}$$

The original equation

$$x^2 + 2y = 1$$

implicitly defines y as a function of x. When you solve the equation for y, you are writing the equation in **explicit** form.

Function notation has the advantage of clearly identifying the dependent variable as $f(x)$ while at the same time telling you that x is the independent variable and that the function itself is "f." The symbol $f(x)$ is read "f of x." Function notation allows you to be less wordy. Instead of asking "What is the value of y that corresponds to $x = 3$?" you can ask "What is $f(3)$?"

In an equation that defines a function of x, the role of the variable x is simply that of a placeholder. For instance, the function

$$f(x) = 2x^2 - 4x + 1$$

can be described by the form

$$f(\boxed{}) = 2(\boxed{})^2 - 4(\boxed{}) + 1$$

where rectangles are used instead of x. To evaluate $f(-2)$, replace each rectangle with -2.

$$\begin{aligned} f(-2) &= 2(-2)^2 - 4(-2) + 1 &&\text{Substitute } -2 \text{ for } x. \\ &= 2(4) + 8 + 1 &&\text{Simplify.} \\ &= 17 &&\text{Simplify.} \end{aligned}$$

Although f is often used as a convenient function name with x as the independent variable, you can use other symbols. For instance, these three equations all define the same function.

$$\begin{aligned} f(x) &= x^2 - 4x + 7 &&\text{Function name is } f, \text{ independent variable is } x. \\ h(t) &= t^2 - 4t + 7 &&\text{Function name is } h, \text{ independent variable is } t. \\ g(s) &= s^2 - 4s + 7 &&\text{Function name is } g, \text{ independent variable is } s. \end{aligned}$$

EXAMPLE 1   Evaluating Functions

For the function f defined by $f(x) = x^2 + 7$, evaluate each expression.

a. $f(3a)$ **b.** $f(b - 1)$ **c.** $\dfrac{f(x + \Delta x) - f(x)}{\Delta x}$

Solution

a.
$$\begin{aligned} f(3a) &= (3a)^2 + 7 &&\text{Substitute } 3a \text{ for } x. \\ &= 9a^2 + 7 &&\text{Simplify.} \end{aligned}$$

b.
$$\begin{aligned} f(b - 1) &= (b - 1)^2 + 7 &&\text{Substitute } b - 1 \text{ for } x. \\ &= b^2 - 2b + 1 + 7 &&\text{Expand binomial.} \\ &= b^2 - 2b + 8 &&\text{Simplify.} \end{aligned}$$

c.
$$\begin{aligned} \frac{f(x + \Delta x) - f(x)}{\Delta x} &= \frac{[(x + \Delta x)^2 + 7] - (x^2 + 7)}{\Delta x} \\ &= \frac{x^2 + 2x\Delta x + (\Delta x)^2 + 7 - x^2 - 7}{\Delta x} \\ &= \frac{2x\Delta x + (\Delta x)^2}{\Delta x} \\ &= \frac{\Delta x(2x + \Delta x)}{\Delta x} \\ &= 2x + \Delta x, \quad \Delta x \neq 0 \end{aligned}$$

> **Connecting Representations**
>
> The expression in Example 1(c) is called a *difference quotient* and has a special significance in calculus. You will learn more about this in Chapter 2.

> **Algebra Review**
>
> For a review of evaluating algebraic expressions, see the *Chapter P Algebra Review* on page A34.

In calculus, it is important to specify the domain of a function or expression clearly. For instance, in Example 1(c), the two expressions

$$\frac{f(x + \Delta x) - f(x)}{\Delta x}$$

and

$$2x + \Delta x, \quad \Delta x \neq 0$$

are equivalent because $\Delta x = 0$ is excluded from the domain of each expression. Without a stated domain restriction, the two expressions would not be equivalent.

The Domain and Range of a Function

The domain of a function can be described *explicitly*, or it may be described *implicitly* by an equation used to define the function. The **implied domain** is the set of all real numbers for which the equation is defined, whereas an explicitly defined domain is one that is given along with the function. Below are two examples.

$$f(x) = \frac{1}{x^2 - 4}, \quad 4 \le x \le 5 \qquad \text{Explicitly defined domain: } \{x:\ 4 \le x \le 5\}$$

$$g(x) = \frac{1}{x^2 - 4} \qquad \text{Implied domain: } \{x:\ x \ne \pm 2\}$$

EXAMPLE 2   **Finding Domains and Ranges of Functions**

Find the domain and range of each function.

a. $f(x) = \sqrt{x - 1}$ **b.** $g(x) = \tan x$ **c.** $h(x) = \begin{cases} 1 - x, & x < 1 \\ \sqrt{x - 1}, & x \ge 1 \end{cases}$

Algebraic Solution

a. Because an expression under a radical cannot be negative, the domain of $f(x) = \sqrt{x - 1}$ is the set of all real numbers such that $x - 1 \ge 0$. So, the domain is the interval $[1, \infty)$. Because the value of a radical expression is never negative, the range of $f(x) = \sqrt{x - 1}$ is the set of all nonnegative real numbers. So, the range is the interval $[0, \infty)$.

b. You know from the identity $\tan x = \sin x / \cos x$ that the tangent function is undefined when $\cos x = 0$. (See Appendix C.3 for a review of trigonometric functions.) Because $\cos x$ is 0 for odd multiples of $\pi/2$, the domain of $g(x) = \tan x$ is the set of all x-values such that

$$x \ne \frac{\pi}{2} + n\pi, \quad \text{where } n \text{ is an integer.}$$

Note that $\tan x$ increases without bound as x approaches $\pi/2$ from the left and decreases without bound as x approaches $-\pi/2$ from the right. So, the range of $g(x) = \tan x$ is all real numbers, or the interval $(-\infty, \infty)$.

c. Because h is defined for $x < 1$ and $x \ge 1$, the domain is the set of all real numbers. So, the domain is the interval $(-\infty, \infty)$. On the portion of the domain for which $x \ge 1$, the function behaves as in Example 2(a). For $x < 1$, the values of $1 - x$ are positive. So, the range is the set of all nonnegative real numbers, or the interval $[0, \infty)$.

Graphical Solution

a. The y-coordinates of points on the graph extend from 0 upwards. So, the range is the set of all nonnegative real numbers.

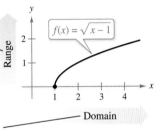

The x-coordinates of points on the graph extend from 1 to the right. So, the domain is the set of all real numbers greater than or equal to 1.

b. The y-coordinates of points on the graph extend both upwards and downwards. So, the range is the set of all real numbers.

The x-coordinates $\pi/2$, $-\pi/2$, $3\pi/2$, and $-3\pi/2$, and so on, are not in the domain. So, the domain is the set of all x-values such that

$$x \ne \frac{\pi}{2} + n\pi$$

where n is an integer.

c. The y-coordinates of points on the graph extend from 0 upwards. So, the range is the set of all nonnegative real numbers.

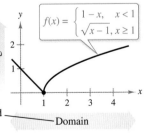

The x-coordinates of points on the graph extend to the left and to the right. So, the domain is the set of all real numbers.

A function from X to Y is **one-to-one** when to each y-value in the range there corresponds exactly one x-value in the domain. For instance, the function in Example 2(a) is one-to-one, whereas the functions in Examples 2(b) and 2(c) are not one-to-one. A function from X to Y is **onto** when its range consists of all of Y.

The Graph of a Function

The graph of the function $y = f(x)$ consists of all points $(x, f(x))$, where x is in the domain of f. In Figure P.21, note that

x = the directed distance from the y-axis

and

$f(x)$ = the directed distance from the x-axis.

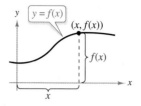

The graph of a function
Figure P.21

A vertical line can intersect the graph of a function of x at most *once*. This observation provides a convenient visual test, called the **Vertical Line Test,** for functions of x. That is, a graph in the coordinate plane is the graph of a function of x if and only if no vertical line intersects the graph at more than one point. For example, in Figure P.22(a), you can see that the graph does not define y as a function of x because a vertical line intersects the graph twice, whereas in Figures P.22(b) and P.22(c), the graphs do define y as a function of x.

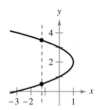

(a) Not a function of x

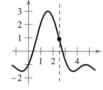

(b) A function of x

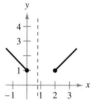

(c) A function of x

Figure P.22

Figure P.23 shows the graphs of eight basic functions. You should be able to recognize these graphs. (The graphs of the other four basic trigonometric functions are shown in Appendix C.3.)

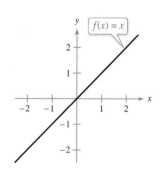

Identity function

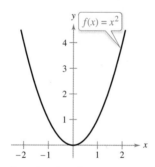

Squaring function

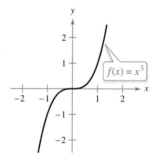

Cubing function

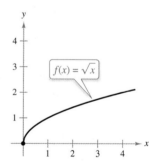

Square root function

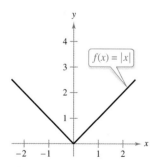

Absolute value function

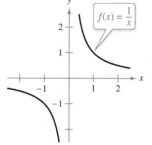

Rational function

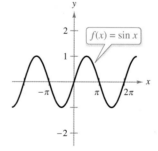

Sine function

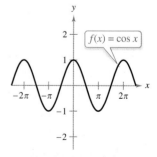

Cosine function

The graphs of eight basic functions
Figure P.23

Transformations of Functions

Some families of graphs have the same basic shape. For example, compare the graph of $y = x^2$ with the graphs of the four other quadratic functions shown in Figure P.24.

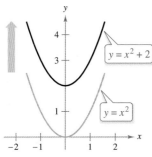

(a) Vertical shift upward

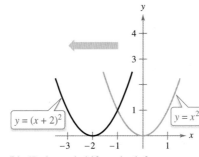

(b) Horizontal shift to the left

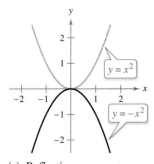

(c) Reflection

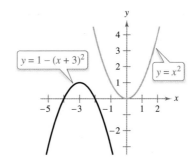

(d) Shift left, reflect, and shift upward

Figure P.24

Each of the graphs in Figure P.24 is a **transformation** of the graph of $y = x^2$. The three basic types of transformations illustrated by these graphs are vertical shifts, horizontal shifts, and reflections. Function notation lends itself well to describing transformations of graphs in the plane. For instance, using

$$f(x) = x^2 \qquad \text{Original function}$$

as the original function, the transformations shown in Figure P.24 can be represented by these equations.

a. $y = f(x) + 2$ Vertical shift up two units

b. $y = f(x + 2)$ Horizontal shift to the left two units

c. $y = -f(x)$ Reflection about the x-axis

d. $y = -f(x + 3) + 1$ Shift left three units, reflect about the x-axis, and shift up one unit

---

Basic Types of Transformations ($c > 0$)

Original graph:	$y = f(x)$
Horizontal shift c units to the **right:**	$y = f(x - c)$
Horizontal shift c units to the **left:**	$y = f(x + c)$
Vertical shift c units **downward:**	$y = f(x) - c$
Vertical shift c units **upward:**	$y = f(x) + c$
Reflection (about the x-axis):	$y = -f(x)$
Reflection (about the y-axis):	$y = f(-x)$
Reflection (about the origin):	$y = -f(-x)$

Classifications and Combinations of Functions

The modern notion of a function is derived from the efforts of many seventeenth- and eighteenth-century mathematicians. Of particular note was Leonhard Euler (1707–1783), who introduced the function notation $y = f(x)$. By the end of the eighteenth century, mathematicians and scientists had concluded that many real-world phenomena could be represented by mathematical models taken from a collection of functions called **elementary functions.** Elementary functions fall into three categories.

1. Algebraic functions (polynomial, radical, rational)
2. Trigonometric functions (sine, cosine, tangent, and so on)
3. Exponential and logarithmic functions

You can review the trigonometric functions in Appendix C.3. The other nonalgebraic functions, such as the inverse trigonometric functions and the exponential and logarithmic functions, are introduced in Sections P.4 and P.5.

The most common type of algebraic function is a polynomial function

$$f(x) = a_n x^n + a_{n-1} x^{n-1} + \cdots + a_2 x^2 + a_1 x + a_0$$

where n is a nonnegative integer. The numbers a_i are **coefficients,** with a_n the **leading coefficient** and a_0 the **constant term** of the polynomial function. If $a_n \neq 0$, then n is the **degree** of the polynomial function. The zero polynomial $f(x) = 0$ is not assigned a degree. It is common practice to use subscript notation for coefficients of general polynomial functions, but for polynomial functions of low degree, these simpler forms are often used. (Note that $a \neq 0$.)

> ### Connecting Representations
>
> Polynomial functions of the form $f(x) = x^n$ are sometimes referred to as *power functions*.

Zeroth degree:	$f(x) = a$	Constant function
First degree:	$f(x) = ax + b$	Linear function
Second degree:	$f(x) = ax^2 + bx + c$	Quadratic function
Third degree:	$f(x) = ax^3 + bx^2 + cx + d$	Cubic function

Although the graph of a nonconstant polynomial function can have several turns, eventually the graph will rise or fall without bound as x moves to the right or left. Whether the graph of

$$f(x) = a_n x^n + a_{n-1} x^{n-1} + \cdots + a_2 x^2 + a_1 x + a_0$$

eventually rises or falls can be determined by the function's degree (odd or even) and by the leading coefficient a_n, as indicated in Figure P.25. Note that the dashed portions of the graphs indicate that the **Leading Coefficient Test** determines *only* the right and left behavior of the graph.

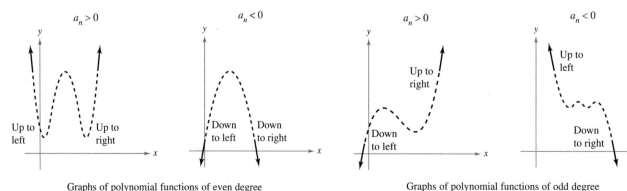

Graphs of polynomial functions of even degree   Graphs of polynomial functions of odd degree

The Leading Coefficient Test for polynomial functions

Figure P.25

Just as a rational number can be written as the quotient of two integers, a **rational function** can be written as the quotient of two polynomials. Specifically, a function f is rational when it has the form

$$f(x) = \frac{p(x)}{q(x)}, \quad q(x) \neq 0$$

where $p(x)$ and $q(x)$ are polynomials.

Polynomial functions and rational functions are examples of **algebraic functions.** An algebraic function of x is one that can be expressed as a finite number of sums, differences, multiples, quotients, and radicals involving x^n. For example,

$$f(x) = \sqrt{x + 1}$$

is algebraic. Functions that are not algebraic are **transcendental.** For instance, the trigonometric functions are transcendental.

There are various ways to combine two functions to create new functions. For example, given $f(x) = 2x - 3$ and $g(x) = x^2 + 1$, you can form the functions shown.

$(f + g)(x) = f(x) + g(x) = (2x - 3) + (x^2 + 1)$ Sum

$(f - g)(x) = f(x) - g(x) = (2x - 3) - (x^2 + 1)$ Difference

$(fg)(x) = f(x)g(x) = (2x - 3)(x^2 + 1)$ Product

$(f/g)(x) = \dfrac{f(x)}{g(x)} = \dfrac{2x - 3}{x^2 + 1}$ Quotient

You can combine two functions in yet another way, called **composition.** The resulting function is called a **composite function.**

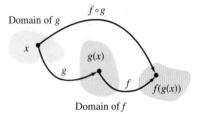

The domain of the composite function $f \circ g$

Figure P.26

Definition of Composite Function

Let f and g be functions. The function $(f \circ g)(x) = f(g(x))$ is the **composite** of f with g. The domain of $f \circ g$ is the set of all x in the domain of g such that $g(x)$ is in the domain of f. (See Figure P.26.)

The composite of f with g is generally not the same as the composite of g with f. This is shown in the next example.

EXAMPLE 3   Finding Composite Functions

See LarsonCalculusforAP.com for an interactive version of this type of example.

For $f(x) = 2x - 3$ and $g(x) = \cos x$, find each composite function.

a. $f \circ g$ **b.** $g \circ f$

Solution

a. $(f \circ g)(x) = f(g(x))$ Definition of $f \circ g$

$\qquad = f(\cos x)$ Substitute $\cos x$ for $g(x)$.

$\qquad = 2(\cos x) - 3$ Definition of $f(x)$

$\qquad = 2 \cos x - 3$ Simplify.

b. $(g \circ f)(x) = g(f(x))$ Definition of $g \circ f$

$\qquad = g(2x - 3)$ Substitute $2x - 3$ for $f(x)$.

$\qquad = \cos(2x - 3)$ Definition of $g(x)$

Note that $(f \circ g)(x) \neq (g \circ f)(x)$.

In Section P.1, an *x*-intercept of a graph was defined to be a point $(a, 0)$ at which the graph crosses the *x*-axis. If the graph represents a function f, then the number a is a *zero* of *f*. In other words, *the zeros of a function f are the solutions of the equation* $f(x) = 0$. For example, the function

$$f(x) = x - 4$$

has a zero at $x = 4$ because $f(4) = 0$.

In Section P.1, you also studied different types of symmetry. In the terminology of functions, a function $y = f(x)$ is **even** when its graph is symmetric with respect to the *y*-axis, and is **odd** when its graph is symmetric with respect to the origin. The symmetry tests in Section P.1 yield the following test for even and odd functions.

Test for Even and Odd Functions

The function $y = f(x)$ is **even** when $f(-x) = f(x)$.

The function $y = f(x)$ is **odd** when $f(-x) = -f(x)$.

Remark

Some functions, such as $f(x) = x^2 + x + 1$, are neither even nor odd.

EXAMPLE 4 Even and Odd Functions and Zeros of Functions

Determine whether each function is even, odd, or neither. Then find the zeros of the function.

a. $f(x) = x^3 - x$ **b.** $g(x) = \dfrac{x^2 - 4}{x^2 + 3}$

Algebraic Solution

a. This function is odd because

$$f(-x) = (-x)^3 - (-x)$$
$$= -x^3 + x$$
$$= -(x^3 - x)$$
$$= -f(x).$$

The zeros of f are

$x^3 - x = 0$	Let $f(x) = 0$.
$x(x^2 - 1) = 0$	Factor.
$x(x - 1)(x + 1) = 0$	Factor.
$x = 0, 1, -1.$	Zeros of f

b. This function is even because

$$g(-x) = \frac{(-x)^2 - 4}{(-x)^2 + 3}$$
$$= \frac{x^2 - 4}{x^2 + 3}$$
$$= g(x).$$

The zeros of g are the zeros of its numerator. (Recall that a fraction is 0 if and only if its numerator is 0.)

$x^2 - 4 = 0$	Set numerator equal to 0.
$(x - 2)(x + 2) = 0$	Factor.
$x = 2, -2$	Zeros of g

Graphical Solution

a. The graph is symmetric with respect to the origin. So, this function is odd. The graph has *x*-intercepts at $(0, 0)$, $(1, 0)$, and $(-1, 0)$. So, the zeros of f are $x = 0$, $x = 1$, and $x = -1$. Use the *zero* or *root* feature of a graphing utility to verify these zeros.

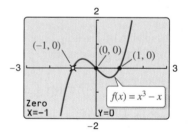

b. The graph is symmetric with respect to the *y*-axis. So, this function is even. The graph has *x*-intercepts at $(2, 0)$ and $(-2, 0)$. So, the zeros of g are $x = 2$ and $x = -2$. Use the *zero* or *root* feature of a graphing utility to verify these zeros.

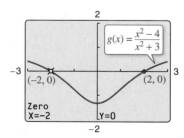

P.3 Exercises

See *CalcChat.com* for tutorial help and worked-out solutions to odd-numbered exercises.

Evaluating a Function In Exercises 1–8, for the function f, evaluate the given expression(s). Simplify the results.

1. $f(x) = 3x - 2$
 (a) $f(0)$ (b) $f(5)$ (c) $f(b)$ (d) $f(x - 1)$

2. $f(x) = x^2(x - 4)$
 (a) $f(4)$ (b) $f\left(\frac{3}{2}\right)$ (c) $f(c)$ (d) $f(t + 4)$

3. $f(x) = \sin 2x$
 (a) $f(0)$ (b) $f\left(-\frac{\pi}{4}\right)$ (c) $f\left(\frac{\pi}{3}\right)$ (d) $f(\pi)$

4. $f(x) = \cos x$
 (a) $f(\pi)$ (b) $f\left(\frac{5\pi}{4}\right)$ (c) $f\left(\frac{2\pi}{3}\right)$ (d) $f\left(-\frac{\pi}{6}\right)$

5. $f(x) = x^3$
 $$\frac{f(x + \Delta x) - f(x)}{\Delta x}$$

6. $f(x) = 3x - 1$
 $$\frac{f(x) - f(1)}{x - 1}$$

7. $f(x) = \dfrac{1}{\sqrt{x - 1}}$
 $$\frac{f(x) - f(2)}{x - 2}$$

8. $f(x) = x^3 - x$
 $$\frac{f(x) - f(1)}{x - 1}$$

Finding the Domain and Range of a Function In Exercises 9–24, find the domain and range of the function algebraically. Use a graphing utility to verify your results.

9. $f(x) = 8 - x$ **10.** $g(x) = x^2 - 5$

11. $f(x) = 2x^2$ **12.** $h(x) = 4 - x^2$

13. $f(x) = x^3$ **14.** $f(x) = \frac{1}{4}x^3 + 3$

15. $g(x) = \sqrt{6x}$ **16.** $h(x) = -\sqrt{x + 3}$

17. $f(x) = \sqrt{16 - x^2}$ **18.** $f(x) = |x - 3|$

19. $g(t) = 3 \sin \pi t$ **20.** $h(\theta) = -5 \cos \dfrac{\theta}{2}$

21. $f(t) = \sec \dfrac{\pi t}{4}$ **22.** $h(t) = \cot t$

23. $f(x) = \dfrac{9}{x}$ **24.** $f(x) = \dfrac{x - 4}{x + 2}$

Finding the Domain of a Function In Exercises 25–30, find the domain of the function.

25. $f(x) = \sqrt{x} + \sqrt{1 - x}$ **26.** $f(x) = \sqrt{x^2 - 5x + 6}$

27. $g(x) = \dfrac{2}{1 - \cos x}$ **28.** $h(x) = \dfrac{1}{\sin x - (1/2)}$

29. $f(x) = \dfrac{1}{|x + 3|}$ **30.** $g(x) = \dfrac{1}{|x^2 - 16|}$

Finding the Domain and Range of a Piecewise Function In Exercises 31–34, evaluate the function at the given values of the independent variable. Then find the domain and range.

31. $f(x) = \begin{cases} 3x + 1, & x < 0 \\ 2x + 3, & x \ge 0 \end{cases}$
 (a) $f(-1)$ (b) $f(0)$ (c) $f(2)$ (d) $f(t^2 + 1)$

32. $f(x) = \begin{cases} x^2 + 1, & x \le 1 \\ 2x^2 + 4, & x > 1 \end{cases}$
 (a) $f(-2)$ (b) $f(0)$ (c) $f(1)$ (d) $f(x^2 + 2)$

33. $f(x) = \begin{cases} |x| + 1, & x < 1 \\ -x + 1, & x \ge 1 \end{cases}$
 (a) $f(-3)$ (b) $f(1)$ (c) $f(3)$ (d) $f(b^2 + 1)$

34. $f(x) = \begin{cases} \sqrt{x + 4}, & x \le 5 \\ (x - 5)^2, & x > 5 \end{cases}$
 (a) $f(-3)$ (b) $f(0)$ (c) $f(5)$ (d) $f(10)$

Using the Vertical Line Test In Exercises 35–38, use the Vertical Line Test to determine whether y is a function of x. To print an enlarged copy of the graph, go to *MathGraphs.com*.

35. $x - y^2 = 0$ **36.** $\sqrt{x^2 - 4} - y = 0$

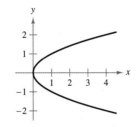 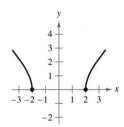

37. $y = \begin{cases} x + 1, & x \le 0 \\ -x + 2, & x > 0 \end{cases}$ **38.** $x^2 + y^2 = 4$

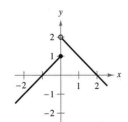 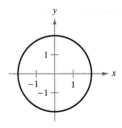

Deciding Whether an Equation Is a Function In Exercises 39–42, determine whether y is a function of x.

39. $x^2 + y^2 = 36$ **40.** $x^2 + y = 9$

41. $y^2 = x^2 - 1$ **42.** $x^2 y - x^2 + 4y = 0$

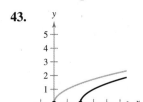 **Transformation of a Function** In Exercises 43–46, the graph shows one of the eight basic functions on page 26 and a transformation of the function. Describe the transformation. Then use your description to write an equation for the transformation.

43.

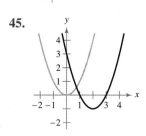

44.

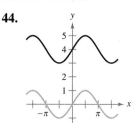

45.

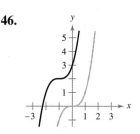

46.

Matching In Exercises 47–52, use the graph of $y = f(x)$ to match the function with its graph.

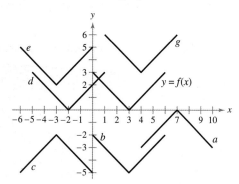

47. $y = f(x + 5)$

48. $y = f(x) - 5$

49. $y = -f(-x) - 2$

50. $y = -f(x - 4)$

51. $y = f(x + 6) + 2$

52. $y = f(x - 1) + 3$

53. Sketching Transformations Use the graph of f shown in the figure to sketch the graph of each function. To print an enlarged copy of the graph, go to *MathGraphs.com*.

(a) $f(x + 3)$ (b) $f(x - 1)$

(c) $f(x) + 2$ (d) $f(x) - 4$

(e) $3f(x)$ (f) $\frac{1}{4}f(x)$

(g) $-f(x)$ (h) $-f(-x)$

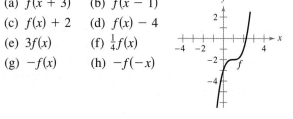

54. Sketching Transformations Use the graph of f shown in the figure to sketch the graph of each function. To print an enlarged copy of the graph, go to *MathGraphs.com*.

(a) $f(x - 4)$ (b) $f(x + 2)$

(c) $f(x) + 4$ (d) $f(x) - 1$

(e) $2f(x)$ (f) $\frac{1}{2}f(x)$

(g) $f(-x)$ (h) $-f(x)$

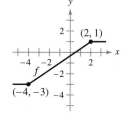

 Combinations of Functions In Exercises 55 and 56, find (a) $f(x) + g(x)$, (b) $f(x) - g(x)$, (c) $f(x) \cdot g(x)$, and (d) $f(x)/g(x)$.

55. $f(x) = 2x - 5$

$g(x) = 4 - 3x$

56. $f(x) = x^2 + 3x + 2$

$g(x) = x + 1$

57. Evaluating Composite Functions Given $f(x) = \sqrt{x}$ and $g(x) = x^2 - 1$, evaluate each expression.

(a) $f(g(1))$ (b) $g(f(1))$ (c) $g(f(0))$

(d) $f(g(-4))$ (e) $f(g(x))$ (f) $g(f(x))$

58. Evaluating Composite Functions Given $f(x) = \sin x$ and $g(x) = \pi x$, evaluate each expression.

(a) $f(g(2))$ (b) $f\left(g\left(\frac{1}{2}\right)\right)$ (c) $g(f(0))$

(d) $g\left(f\left(\frac{\pi}{4}\right)\right)$ (e) $f(g(x))$ (f) $g(f(x))$

 Finding Composite Functions In Exercises 59–62, find the composite functions $f \circ g$ and $g \circ f$. Find the domain of each composite function. Are the composite functions equal?

59. $f(x) = \dfrac{3}{x}$, $g(x) = x^2 - 1$ **60.** $f(x) = x^3$, $g(x) = \sqrt[3]{x}$

61. $f(x) = x^2 - 1$, $g(x) = \cos x$

62. $f(x) = \dfrac{1}{x}$, $g(x) = \sqrt{x + 2}$

63. Evaluating Composite Functions Use the graphs of f and g to evaluate each expression. If the result is undefined, explain why.

(a) $(f \circ g)(3)$ (b) $g(f(2))$

(c) $g(f(5))$ (d) $(f \circ g)(-3)$

(e) $(g \circ f)(-1)$ (f) $f(g(-1))$

64. Ripples You drop a pebble into a calm pond, causing ripples in the form of concentric circles. The radius (in feet) of the outer ripple is given by $r(t) = 0.6t$, where t is the time in seconds after the pebble strikes the water. The area of the circle is given by the function $A(r) = \pi r^2$. Find and interpret $(A \circ r)(t)$.

Implementing Processes   In Exercises 65 and 66, $F(x) = f \circ g \circ h$. **Identify functions for f, g, and h. (There are many correct answers.)**

65. $F(x) = \sqrt{4x - 4}$ **66.** $F(x) = -4 \sin(1 - x)$

Error Analysis   In Exercises 67 and 68, describe and correct the error when evaluating the expression given that $f(x) = x^2 + 3x - 5$ and $g(x) = \sqrt{11 - 4x}$.

67. $f(p - 4) = (p - 4)^2 + 3(p - 4) - 5$
$$= p^2 - 8p - 16 + 3p - 12 - 5$$
$$= p^2 - 5p - 33 \qquad ✗$$

68. $(g \circ f)(-2.5) = g(f(-2.5))$
$$= g(-6.25)$$
$$= 36 \qquad ✗$$

Implementing Processes   In Exercises 69 and 70, find the coordinates of a second point on the graph of a function f when the given point is on the graph and the function is (a) even and (b) odd.

69. $\left(-\frac{3}{2}, 4\right)$ **70.** $(9, 4)$

71. Even and Odd Functions   The graphs of f, g, and h are shown in the figure. Decide whether each function is even, odd, or neither.

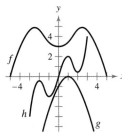

Figure for 71   Figure for 72

72. Even and Odd Functions   The domain of the function f shown in the figure is $-6 \leq x \leq 6$. Complete the graph of f given that f is (a) even and (b) odd.

Even and Odd Functions and Zeros of Functions   In Exercises 73–76, determine whether the function is even, odd, or neither. Then find the zeros of the function. Use a graphing utility to verify your result.

73. $f(x) = x^2(4 - x^2)$ **74.** $f(x) = \sqrt[3]{x}$
75. $f(x) = x \cos x$ **76.** $f(x) = \sin^2 x$

Writing Functions   In Exercises 77–80, write an equation for a function that has the given graph.

77. Line segment connecting $(-2, 4)$ and $(0, -6)$

78. Line segment connecting $(3, 1)$ and $(4, 12)$

79. The bottom half of the parabola $x + y^2 = 0$

80. The bottom half of the circle $x^2 + y^2 = 64$

81. Graphical Reasoning   An electronically controlled thermostat is programmed to lower the temperature during the night automatically (see figure). The temperature T in degrees Celsius is given in terms of t, the time in hours on a 24-hour clock.

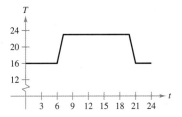

(a) Approximate $T(4)$ and $T(15)$.

(b) The thermostat is reprogrammed to produce a temperature $H(t) = T(t - 1)$. How does this change the temperature? Explain.

(c) The thermostat is reprogrammed to produce a temperature $H(t) = T(t) - 1$. How does this change the temperature? Explain.

82. AUTOMOBILE AERODYNAMICS

The horsepower H required to overcome wind drag on an automobile is approximated by

$$H(x) = 0.0002x^3 - 0.0091x^2 + 0.3161x - 1.2035,$$
$$10 \leq x \leq 100$$

where x is the speed of the automobile in miles per hour.

(a) Use a graphing utility to graph H.

(b) Rewrite H so that x represents the speed in kilometers per hour. [Find $H(x/1.6)$.]

EXPLORING CONCEPTS

83. Connecting Representations   The graph of the distance that a student drives in a 10-minute trip to school is shown in the figure. Give a verbal description of the characteristics of the student's drive to school.

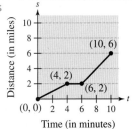

84. Connecting Representations   A student who commutes 27 miles to attend college remembers, after driving a few minutes, that a term paper that is due has been forgotten. Driving faster than usual, the student returns home, picks up the paper, and once again starts toward school. Sketch a possible graph of the student's distance from home as a function of time. Explain how you obtained your graph.

Sketching a Graph In Exercises 85–88, sketch a possible graph of the situation.

85. The speed of an airplane as a function of time during a 5-hour flight

86. The height of a baseball as a function of horizontal distance during a home run

87. The amount of a brand of sneaker sold by a sporting goods store as a function of the price of the sneaker

88. The value of a new car as a function of time over a period of 8 years

89. Domain Find the value of c such that the domain of $f(x) = \sqrt{c - x^2}$ is $[-5, 5]$.

90. Domain Find all values of c such that the domain of
$$f(x) = \frac{x + 3}{x^2 + 3cx + 6}$$
is the set of all real numbers.

91. Modeling Data The table shows the average numbers of acres per farm in the United States for selected years. *(Source: Statista)*

Year	2007	2009	2011	2013	2015	2017
Acreage	418	423	429	435	441	444

(a) Plot the data, where A is the acreage and t is the time in years, with $t = 7$ corresponding to 2007. Sketch a freehand curve that approximates the data.

(b) Use the curve in part (a) to approximate $A(14)$.

92. HOW DO YOU SEE IT? Water runs into a vase of height 30 centimeters at a constant rate. The vase is full after 5 seconds. Use this information and the shape of the vase shown to answer the questions when d is the depth of the water in centimeters and t is the time in seconds (see figure).

(a) Explain why d is a function of t.

(b) Determine the domain and range of the function.

(c) Sketch a possible graph of the function.

(d) Use the graph in part (c) to approximate $d(4)$. What does this represent?

30 cm

93. Connecting Representations Write the function $f(x) = |x| + |x - 2|$ without using absolute value signs. (For a review of absolute value, see Appendix C.1.)

94. Connecting Representations Use a graphing utility to graph the polynomial functions $p_1(x) = x^3 - x + 1$ and $p_2(x) = x^3 - x$. How many zeros does each function have? Is there a cubic polynomial that has no zeros? Explain.

95. Proof Prove that the function is odd.
$$f(x) = a_{2n+1}x^{2n+1} + \cdots + a_3x^3 + a_1x$$

96. Proof Prove that the function is even.
$$f(x) = a_{2n}x^{2n} + a_{2n-2}x^{2n-2} + \cdots + a_2x^2 + a_0$$

97. Proof Prove that the product of two even (or two odd) functions is even.

98. Proof Prove that the product of an odd function and an even function is odd.

99. Length A right triangle is formed in the first quadrant by the x- and y-axes and a line through the point $(3, 2)$ (see figure). Write the length L of the hypotenuse as a function of a.

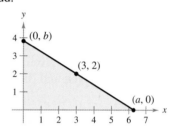

100. Volume An open box of maximum volume is to be made from a square piece of material 24 centimeters on a side by cutting equal squares from the corners and turning up the sides (see figure).

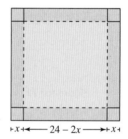
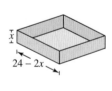

(a) Write the volume V as a function of x, the length of the corner squares. What is the domain of the function?

(b) Use a graphing utility to graph the volume function and approximate the dimensions of the box that yield a maximum volume. Use the *table* feature to verify your answer.

True or False? In Exercises 101–104, determine whether the statement is true or false. If it is false, explain why or give an example that shows it is false.

101. If $f(a) = f(b)$, then $a = b$.

102. If f is a function, then $f(ax) = af(x)$.

103. The graph of a function of x cannot have symmetry with respect to the x-axis.

104. If the domain of a function consists of a single number, then its range must also consist of only one number.

P.4   Inverse Functions

▶ Verify that one function is the inverse function of another function.
▶ Determine whether a function has an inverse function.
▶ Develop properties of the six inverse trigonometric functions.

Inverse Functions

Recall from Section P.3 that a function can be represented by a set of ordered pairs. For instance, the function $f(x) = x + 3$ from $A = \{1, 2, 3, 4\}$ to $B = \{4, 5, 6, 7\}$ can be written as

$$f: \{(1, 4), (2, 5), (3, 6), (4, 7)\}.$$

By interchanging the first and second coordinates of each ordered pair, you can form the **inverse function** of f. This function is denoted by f^{-1}. It is a function from B to A, and can be written as

$$f^{-1}: \{(4, 1), (5, 2), (6, 3), (7, 4)\}.$$

Note that the domain of f is equal to the range of f^{-1}, and vice versa, as shown in Figure P.27. The functions f and f^{-1} have the effect of "undoing" each other. That is, when you form the composition of f with f^{-1} or the composition of f^{-1} with f you obtain the identity function.

$$f(f^{-1}(x)) = x \quad \text{and} \quad f^{-1}(f(x)) = x$$

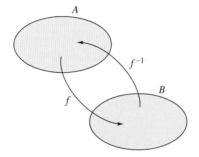

Domain of f = range of f^{-1}
Domain of f^{-1} = range of f
Figure P.27

Communication and Notation

Although the notation used to denote an inverse function resembles *exponential notation*, it is a different use of -1 as a superscript. That is, in general,

$$f^{-1}(x) \neq \frac{1}{f(x)}.$$

Definition of Inverse Function

A function g is the **inverse function** of the function f when

$$f(g(x)) = x \text{ for each } x \text{ in the domain of } g$$

and

$$g(f(x)) = x \text{ for each } x \text{ in the domain of } f.$$

The function g is denoted by f^{-1} (read "f inverse").

Here are some important observations about inverse functions.

1. If g is the inverse function of f, then f is the inverse function of g.
2. The domain of f^{-1} is equal to the range of f, and the range of f^{-1} is equal to the domain of f.
3. A function need not have an inverse function, but when it does, the inverse function is unique. (See Exercise 136.)

You can think of f^{-1} as undoing what has been done by f. For example, subtraction can be used to undo addition, and division can be used to undo multiplication. So,

$$f(x) = x + c \quad \text{and} \quad f^{-1}(x) = x - c \qquad \text{Subtraction can be used to undo addition.}$$

are inverse functions of each other and

$$f(x) = cx \quad \text{and} \quad f^{-1}(x) = \frac{x}{c}, \ c \neq 0 \qquad \text{Division can be used to undo multiplication.}$$

are inverse functions of each other.

Exploration

Finding Inverse Functions   Explain how to "undo" each of the functions below. Then use your explanation to write the inverse function of f.

a. $f(x) = x - 5$

b. $f(x) = 6x$

c. $f(x) = \dfrac{x}{2}$

d. $f(x) = 3x + 2$

e. $f(x) = x^3$

f. $f(x) = 4(x - 2)$

Use a graphing utility to graph each function and its inverse function in the same "square" viewing window. What observation can you make about each pair of graphs?

EXAMPLE 1   Verifying Inverse Functions

Show that the functions are inverse functions of each other.

$$f(x) = 2x^3 - 1 \quad \text{and} \quad g(x) = \sqrt[3]{\frac{x+1}{2}}$$

Solution

Because the domains and ranges of both f and g consist of all real numbers, you can conclude that both composite functions exist for all x. The composition of f with g is

$$f(g(x)) = 2\left(\sqrt[3]{\frac{x+1}{2}}\right)^3 - 1$$

$$= 2\left(\frac{x+1}{2}\right) - 1$$

$$= x + 1 - 1$$

$$= x.$$

The composition of g with f is

$$g(f(x)) = \sqrt[3]{\frac{(2x^3 - 1) + 1}{2}} = \sqrt[3]{\frac{2x^3}{2}} = \sqrt[3]{x^3} = x.$$

Because $f(g(x)) = x$ and $g(f(x)) = x$, you can conclude that f and g are inverse functions of each other (see Figure P.28). To demonstrate this, use a graphing utility with $y_1 = f(x)$, $y_2 = g(x)$, $y_3 = f(g(x))$, and $y_4 = g(f(x))$, as shown in the figure at the left below. Then use the *table* feature to create a table, as shown in the figure at the right below. Note that the entries for x, y_3, and y_4 are the same, which supports the conclusion that f and g are inverse functions of each other.

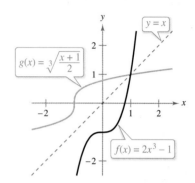

f and g are inverse functions of each other.

Figure P.28

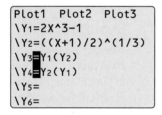

In Example 1, compare the functions f and g verbally to help you recognize the "undoing" pattern. For f: first cube x, then multiply by 2, then subtract 1. For g: first add 1, then divide by 2, then take the cube root.

In Figure P.28, the graphs of f and $g = f^{-1}$ appear to be mirror images of each other with respect to the line $y = x$. The graph of f^{-1} is a **reflection** of the graph of f in the line $y = x$. This idea is generalized in the next definition.

Reflective Property of Inverse Functions

The graph of f contains the point (a, b) if and only if the graph of f^{-1} contains the point (b, a).

To see the validity of the Reflective Property of Inverse Functions, consider the point (a, b) on the graph of f. This implies $f(a) = b$ and you can write

$$f^{-1}(b) = f^{-1}(f(a)) = a.$$

So, (b, a) is on the graph of f^{-1}, as shown in Figure P.29. A similar argument will verify this result in the other direction.

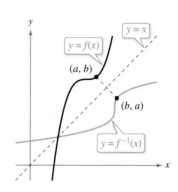

The graph of f^{-1} is a reflection of the graph of f in the line $y = x$.

Figure P.29

Existence of an Inverse Function

Not every function has an inverse function, and the Reflective Property of Inverse Functions suggests a graphical test for those that do—the **Horizontal Line Test** for an inverse function. This test states that a function f has an inverse function if and only if every horizontal line intersects the graph of f at most once. (See Figure P.30.) The next definition formally states why the Horizontal Line Test is valid.

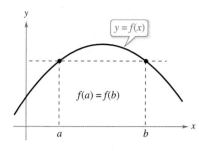

If a horizontal line intersects the graph of f twice, then f is not one-to-one.
Figure P.30

The Existence of an Inverse Function

A function has an inverse function if and only if it is one-to-one.

EXAMPLE 2   The Existence of an Inverse Function

Which of the functions has an inverse function?

a. $f(x) = x^3 - 1$

b. $f(x) = x^3 - x + 1$

Solution

a. From the graph of f shown in Figure P.31(a), it appears that f is one-to-one over its entire domain. To verify this, suppose that there exist x_1 and x_2 such that $f(x_1) = f(x_2)$. By showing that $x_1 = x_2$, it follows that f is one-to-one.

$$f(x_1) = f(x_2)$$
$$x_1^3 - 1 = x_2^3 - 1$$
$$x_1^3 = x_2^3$$
$$\sqrt[3]{x_1^3} = \sqrt[3]{x_2^3}$$
$$x_1 = x_2$$

Because f is one-to-one, you can conclude that f must have an inverse function.

b. From the graph of f shown in Figure P.31(b), you can see that the function does not pass the Horizontal Line Test. In other words, it is not one-to-one. For instance, f has the same value when $x = -1, 0$, and 1.

$$f(-1) = f(1) = f(0) = 1 \qquad \text{Not one-to-one}$$

So, f does not have an inverse function. ■

Often it is easier to prove that a function has an inverse function than to find the inverse function. For instance, by sketching the graph of

$$f(x) = x^3 + x - 1$$

you can see that it is one-to-one. Yet it would be difficult to determine the inverse of this function algebraically.

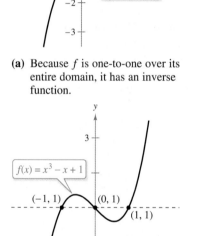

(a) Because f is one-to-one over its entire domain, it has an inverse function.

(b) Because f is not one-to-one, it does not have an inverse function.
Figure P.31

Guidelines for Finding an Inverse Function

1. Determine whether the function given by $y = f(x)$ has an inverse function.

2. Solve for x as a function of y: $x = g(y) = f^{-1}(y)$.

3. Interchange x and y. The resulting equation is $y = f^{-1}(x)$.

4. Define the domain of f^{-1} as the range of f.

5. Verify that $f(f^{-1}(x)) = x$ and $f^{-1}(f(x)) = x$.

EXAMPLE 3 Finding an Inverse Function

Find the inverse function of $f(x) = \sqrt{2x - 3}$.

Solution

The function has an inverse function because it is one-to-one on its entire domain, $\left[\frac{3}{2}, \infty\right)$, as shown in Figure P.32. To find an equation for the inverse function, let $y = f(x)$ and solve for x in terms of y.

$$\sqrt{2x - 3} = y \qquad \text{Let } y = f(x).$$

$$2x - 3 = y^2 \qquad \text{Square each side.}$$

$$x = \frac{y^2 + 3}{2} \qquad \text{Solve for } x.$$

$$y = \frac{x^2 + 3}{2} \qquad \text{Interchange } x \text{ and } y.$$

$$f^{-1}(x) = \frac{x^2 + 3}{2} \qquad \text{Replace } y \text{ by } f^{-1}(x).$$

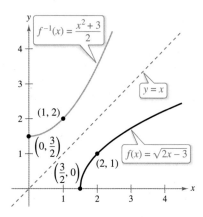

The domain of f^{-1}, $[0, \infty)$, is the range of f.
Figure P.32

The domain of f^{-1} is the range of f, which is $[0, \infty)$. You can verify this result by showing that $f(f^{-1}(x)) = x$ and $f^{-1}(f(x)) = x$.

$$f(f^{-1}(x)) = \sqrt{2\left(\frac{x^2 + 3}{2}\right) - 3} = \sqrt{x^2} = x, \quad x \geq 0$$

$$f^{-1}(f(x)) = \frac{\left(\sqrt{2x - 3}\right)^2 + 3}{2} = \frac{2x - 3 + 3}{2} = x, \quad x \geq \frac{3}{2}$$

Consider a function that is *not* one-to-one on its entire domain. By restricting the domain to an interval on which the function is one-to-one, you can conclude that the new function has an inverse function on the restricted domain.

EXAMPLE 4 Testing Whether a Function Is One-to-One

See LarsonCalculusforAP.com for an interactive version of this type of example.

Show that the sine function $f(x) = \sin x$ is not one-to-one on the entire real number line. Then show that f is one-to-one on the closed interval $[-\pi/2, \pi/2]$.

Solution

It is clear that f is not one-to-one, because many different x-values yield the same y-value. For instance,

$$\sin 0 = 0 = \sin \pi.$$

Moreover, from the graph of $f(x) = \sin x$ in Figure P.33, you can see that when f is restricted to the interval $[-\pi/2, \pi/2]$, the restricted function is one-to-one.

> **Justification**
>
> Producing examples and counterexamples can be helpful when investigating whether a statement is true or false.

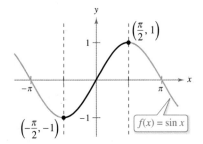

f is one-to-one on the interval $[-\pi/2, \pi/2]$.
Figure P.33

Inverse Trigonometric Functions

From the graphs of the six basic trigonometric functions, you can see that they do not have inverse functions. (The graphs of the six basic trigonometric functions are shown in Appendix C.3.) The functions that are called "inverse trigonometric functions" are actually inverses of trigonometric functions whose domains have been restricted.

For instance, in Example 4, you saw that the sine function is one-to-one on the interval

$$\left[-\frac{\pi}{2}, \frac{\pi}{2}\right]. \qquad \text{See Figure P.34(a).}$$

On this interval, you can define the inverse of the *restricted* sine function as

$$y = \arcsin x \qquad \text{if and only if} \qquad \sin y = x$$

where

$$-1 \le x \le 1 \qquad \text{and} \qquad -\frac{\pi}{2} \le \arcsin x \le \frac{\pi}{2}.$$

From Figures P.34(a) and P.34(b), you can see that you can obtain the graph of $y = \arcsin x$ by reflecting the graph of $y = \sin x$ in the line $y = x$ on the interval

$$\left[-\frac{\pi}{2}, \frac{\pi}{2}\right].$$

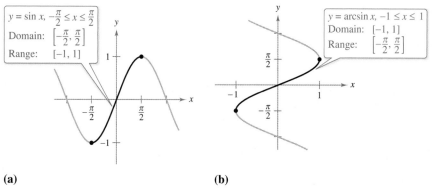

(a) **(b)**

Figure P.34

Under suitable restrictions, each of the six trigonometric functions is one-to-one and so has an inverse function, as indicated in the next definition. (The term "iff" is used to represent the phrase "if and only if.")

Definitions of Inverse Trigonometric Functions

Function	Domain	Range
$y = \arcsin x$ iff $\sin y = x$	$-1 \le x \le 1$	$-\dfrac{\pi}{2} \le y \le \dfrac{\pi}{2}$
$y = \arccos x$ iff $\cos y = x$	$-1 \le x \le 1$	$0 \le y \le \pi$
$y = \arctan x$ iff $\tan y = x$	$-\infty < x < \infty$	$-\dfrac{\pi}{2} < y < \dfrac{\pi}{2}$
$y = \operatorname{arccot} x$ iff $\cot y = x$	$-\infty < x < \infty$	$0 < y < \pi$
$y = \operatorname{arcsec} x$ iff $\sec y = x$	$\lvert x \rvert \ge 1$	$0 \le y \le \pi, \quad y \ne \dfrac{\pi}{2}$
$y = \operatorname{arccsc} x$ iff $\csc y = x$	$\lvert x \rvert \ge 1$	$-\dfrac{\pi}{2} \le y \le \dfrac{\pi}{2}, \quad y \ne 0$

The graphs of the six inverse trigonometric functions are shown in Figure P.35.

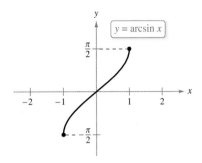

Domain: $[-1, 1]$
Range: $[-\pi/2, \pi/2]$

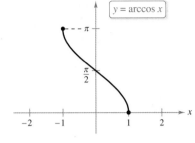

Domain: $[-1, 1]$
Range: $[0, \pi]$

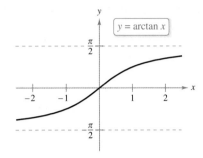

Domain: $(-\infty, \infty)$
Range: $(-\pi/2, \pi/2)$

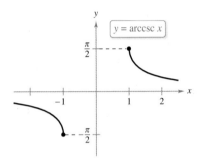

Domain: $(-\infty, -1] \cup [1, \infty)$
Range: $[-\pi/2, 0) \cup (0, \pi/2]$
Figure P.35

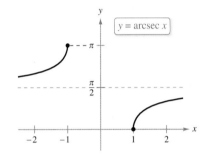

Domain: $(-\infty, -1] \cup [1, \infty)$
Range: $[0, \pi/2) \cup (\pi/2, \pi]$

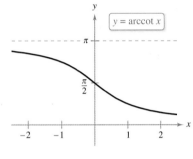

Domain: $(-\infty, \infty)$
Range: $(0, \pi)$

When evaluating inverse trigonometric functions, remember that they denote angles in *radian measure*. (For a review of radian measure, see Appendix C.3.)

EXAMPLE 5   Evaluating Inverse Trigonometric Functions

Evaluate each expression.

a. $\arcsin\left(-\dfrac{1}{2}\right)$ **b.** $\arccos 0$ **c.** $\arctan \sqrt{3}$ **d.** $\arcsin(0.3)$

Solution

a. By definition, $y = \arcsin\left(-\frac{1}{2}\right)$ implies that $\sin y = -\frac{1}{2}$. In the interval $[-\pi/2, \pi/2]$, the correct value of y is $-\pi/6$.

$$\arcsin\left(-\frac{1}{2}\right) = -\frac{\pi}{6}$$

b. By definition, $y = \arccos 0$ implies that $\cos y = 0$. In the interval $[0, \pi]$, you have $y = \pi/2$.

$$\arccos 0 = \frac{\pi}{2}$$

c. By definition, $y = \arctan \sqrt{3}$ implies that $\tan y = \sqrt{3}$. In the interval $(-\pi/2, \pi/2)$, you have $y = \pi/3$.

$$\arctan \sqrt{3} = \frac{\pi}{3}$$

d. Using a calculator set in *radian* mode produces

$$\arcsin(0.3) \approx 0.3047. \text{ (See Figure P.36.)}$$

```
sin⁻¹(0.3)
            .304692654
```

Figure P.36

Inverse functions have the properties $f(f^{-1}(x)) = x$ and $f^{-1}(f(x)) = x$. When applying these properties to inverse trigonometric functions, remember that the trigonometric functions have inverse functions only in restricted domains. For x-values outside these domains, these two properties do not hold. For example, $\arcsin(\sin \pi)$ is equal to 0, not π.

Properties of Inverse Trigonometric Functions

1. If $-1 \le x \le 1$ and $-\pi/2 \le y \le \pi/2$, then

$$\sin(\arcsin x) = x \quad \text{and} \quad \arcsin(\sin y) = y.$$

2. If $-\pi/2 < y < \pi/2$, then

$$\tan(\arctan x) = x \quad \text{and} \quad \arctan(\tan y) = y.$$

3. If $|x| \ge 1$ and $0 \le y < \pi/2$ or $\pi/2 < y \le \pi$, then

$$\sec(\text{arcsec } x) = x \quad \text{and} \quad \text{arcsec}(\sec y) = y.$$

Similar properties hold for the other inverse trigonometric functions.

EXAMPLE 6   Solving an Equation

Solve $\arctan(2x - 3) = \dfrac{\pi}{4}$ for x.

Algebraic Solution

$$\arctan(2x - 3) = \frac{\pi}{4} \qquad \text{Write original equation.}$$

$$\tan[\arctan(2x - 3)] = \tan \frac{\pi}{4} \qquad \text{Take tangent of each side.}$$

$$2x - 3 = 1 \qquad \tan(\arctan x) = x$$

$$x = 2 \qquad \text{Solve for } x.$$

Graphical Solution

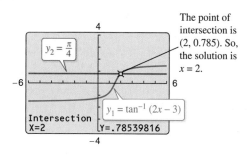

The point of intersection is $(2, 0.785)$. So, the solution is $x = 2$.

$y_2 = \frac{\pi}{4}$

$y_1 = \tan^{-1}(2x - 3)$

Intersection
X=2   Y=.78539816

Some problems in calculus require that you evaluate expressions such as $\cos(\arcsin x)$, as shown in Example 7.

EXAMPLE 7   Using Right Triangles

a. Given $y = \arcsin x$, where $0 < y < \pi/2$, find $\cos y$.

b. Given $y = \text{arcsec}(\sqrt{5}/2)$, find $\tan y$.

Solution

a. Because $y = \arcsin x$, you know that $\sin y = x$. This relationship between x and y can be represented by a right triangle, as shown in Figure P.37(a).

$$\cos y = \cos(\arcsin x) = \frac{\text{adj.}}{\text{hyp.}} = \sqrt{1 - x^2}$$

(This result is also valid for $-\pi/2 < y < 0$.)

b. Use the right triangle shown in Figure P.37(b).

$$\tan y = \tan\left(\text{arcsec } \frac{\sqrt{5}}{2}\right) = \frac{\text{opp.}}{\text{adj.}} = \frac{1}{2}$$

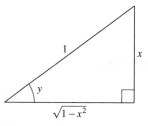

(a) $y = \arcsin x$

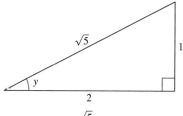

(b) $y = \text{arcsec } \dfrac{\sqrt{5}}{2}$

Figure P.37

P.4   Exercises

See *CalcChat.com* for tutorial help and worked-out solutions to odd-numbered exercises.

Verifying Inverse Functions In Exercises 1–8, show that f and g are inverse functions (a) analytically, (b) numerically, and (c) graphically.

1. $f(x) = 5x + 1$,　　　$g(x) = \dfrac{x-1}{5}$

2. $f(x) = 3 - 4x$,　　　$g(x) = \dfrac{3-x}{4}$

3. $f(x) = x^3$,　　　　　$g(x) = \sqrt[3]{x}$

4. $f(x) = 1 - x^3$,　　　$g(x) = \sqrt[3]{1-x}$

5. $f(x) = \sqrt{x-4}$,　　　$g(x) = x^2 + 4$,　$x \geq 0$

6. $f(x) = 16 - x^2$,　$x \geq 0$,　$g(x) = \sqrt{16-x}$

7. $f(x) = \dfrac{1}{x}$,　　　　$g(x) = \dfrac{1}{x}$

8. $f(x) = \dfrac{1}{1+x}$,　$x \geq 0$,　$g(x) = \dfrac{1-x}{x}$,　$0 < x \leq 1$

Matching In Exercises 9–12, match the graph of the function with the graph of its inverse function. [The graphs of the inverse functions are labeled (a), (b), (c), and (d).]

(a)
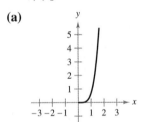

(b)
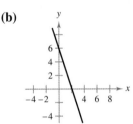

(c)
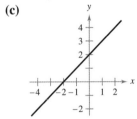

(d)
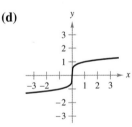

9.
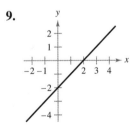

10.
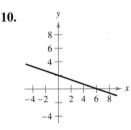

11.
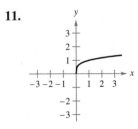

12.
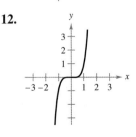

Using a Table to Find an Inverse Function In Exercises 13 and 14, use the table of values for $y = f(x)$ to complete a table for $y = f^{-1}(x)$.

13.

x	-1	0	1	2	3	4
$f(x)$	3	5	7	9	11	13

14.

x	-3	-2	-1	0	1	2
$f(x)$	10	5	0	-5	-10	-15

Using the Horizontal Line Test In Exercises 15–18, sketch the graph of the function by hand. Then use the Horizontal Line Test to determine whether the function is one-to-one on its entire domain and therefore has an inverse function.

15. $f(x) = \frac{3}{4}x + 6$　　　**16.** $f(x) = 5x - 3$

17. $f(\theta) = \sin \theta$　　　**18.** $f(x) = \dfrac{x^2}{x^2 + 4}$

 The Existence of an Inverse Function In Exercises 19–24, use a graphing utility to graph the function. Determine whether the function is one-to-one on its entire domain and therefore has an inverse function.

19. $h(s) = \dfrac{1}{s-2} - 3$　　**20.** $f(x) = \dfrac{6x}{x^2 + 4}$

21. $g(t) = \dfrac{1}{\sqrt{t^2 + 1}}$　　**22.** $f(x) = 5x\sqrt{x-1}$

23. $g(x) = (x + 5)^3$　　**24.** $h(x) = |x + 4| - |x - 4|$

 The Existence of an Inverse Function In Exercises 25–30, determine whether the function is one-to-one on its entire domain and therefore has an inverse function.

25. $f(x) = 2 - x - x^3$　　**26.** $f(x) = \frac{1}{4}x^4 - 2x^2$

27. $f(x) = \dfrac{2}{2x + 1}$　　**28.** $f(x) = \sqrt[3]{x + 1}$

29. $f(x) = \tan \pi x$　　**30.** $f(x) = \sin \frac{3}{2}x$

Finding an Inverse Function In Exercises 31–38, (a) find the inverse function of f, (b) graph f and f^{-1} on the same set of coordinate axes, (c) describe the relationship between the graphs, and (d) state the domains and ranges of f and f^{-1}.

31. $f(x) = 2x - 3$　　**32.** $f(x) = 8 - 5x$

33. $f(x) = x^5$　　　**34.** $f(x) = x^3 - 1$

35. $f(x) = \sqrt{x}$　　**36.** $f(x) = x^2$,　$x \geq 0$

37. $f(x) = \sqrt{4 - x^2}$,　$0 \leq x \leq 2$

38. $f(x) = \sqrt{x^2 - 4}$,　$x \geq 2$

Finding an Inverse Function In Exercises 39–46, (a) find the inverse function of f, (b) use a graphing utility to graph f and f^{-1} in the same viewing window, (c) describe the relationship between the graphs, and (d) state the domains and ranges of f and f^{-1}.

39. $f(x) = \sqrt[3]{x - 1}$ **40.** $f(x) = 3\sqrt[5]{2x - 1}$

41. $f(x) = x^{2/3}, \quad x \geq 0$ **42.** $f(x) = x^{3/5}$

43. $f(x) = \dfrac{x}{x + 2}$ **44.** $f(x) = \dfrac{x + 1}{x - 2}$

45. $f(x) = \dfrac{\sqrt{x} + 2}{\sqrt{x}}$ **46.** $f(x) = \dfrac{x}{\sqrt{x^2 + 7}}$

Error Analysis In Exercises 47 and 48, describe and correct the error in finding the inverse of the function.

47.
$$f(x) = \sqrt[3]{5 - x}$$
$$\sqrt[3]{5 - x} = y$$
$$5 - x = y^3$$
$$-x = y^3 - 5$$
$$x = y^3 + 5$$
$$y = x^3 + 5$$
$$f^{-1}(x) = x^3 + 5 \quad ✗$$

48.
$$g(x) = \dfrac{4 - x}{x}$$
$$\dfrac{4 - x}{x} = y, \quad x \neq 0$$
$$4 - x = yx$$
$$4 = x(y - 1)$$
$$\dfrac{4}{y - 1} = x$$
$$\dfrac{4}{x - 1} = y$$
$$\dfrac{4}{x - 1} = g^{-1}(x) \quad ✗$$

Finding an Inverse Function In Exercises 49 and 50, use the graph of the function f to make a table of values for the given points. Then make a second table that can be used to find f^{-1}, and sketch the graph of f^{-1}. To print an enlarged copy of the graph, go to *MathGraphs.com*.

49.
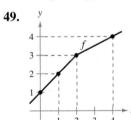

50.
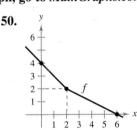

51. Cost You need a total of 50 pounds of two commodities costing $1.25 and $1.60 per pound.

  (a) Write the total cost function y in terms of the number of pounds of the each commodity. Let x be the number of pounds of the less expensive commodity.

  (b) Find the inverse function of the cost function. What does each variable represent in the inverse function?

  (c) What is the domain of the inverse function? Validate or explain your answer using the context of the problem.

  (d) Determine the number of pounds of the less expensive commodity purchased when the total cost is $73.

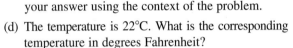

52. TEMPERATURE

The formula $C = \frac{5}{9}(F - 32)$, where $F \geq -459.7$, represents the Celsius temperature C as a function of the Fahrenheit temperature F.

  (a) Find the inverse function of C.

  (b) What does the inverse function represent?

  (c) What is the domain of the inverse function? Validate or explain your answer using the context of the problem.

  (d) The temperature is 22°C. What is the corresponding temperature in degrees Fahrenheit?

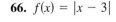 **Testing Whether a Function Is One-to-One** In Exercises 53–58, determine whether the function is one-to-one. If it is, find its inverse function.

53. $f(x) = \sqrt{x - 2}$ **54.** $f(x) = \sqrt{16 - x^2}$

55. $f(x) = -10$ **56.** $f(x) = |x - 2|, \quad x \leq 2$

57. $f(x) = ax + b, \quad a \neq 0$ **58.** $f(x) = (x + a)^3 + b$

Showing a Function Is One-to-One In Exercises 59–64, show that f is one-to-one on the given interval and therefore has an inverse function on that interval.

59. $f(x) = (x - 2)^2, \quad [2, \infty)$

60. $f(x) = |x + 4|, \quad [-4, \infty)$

61. $f(x) = \dfrac{5}{x^2}, \quad (0, \infty)$

62. $f(x) = \cot x, \quad (0, \pi)$

63. $f(x) = \cos x, \quad [0, \pi]$

64. $f(x) = \sec x, \quad \left[0, \dfrac{\pi}{2}\right)$

Making a Function One-to-One In Exercises 65 and 66, the function is not one-to-one. Delete part of the domain so that the function that remains is one-to-one. Find the inverse function of the remaining function and give the domain of the inverse function. (*Note:* There is more than one correct answer.)

65. $f(x) = (x - 3)^2$ **66.** $f(x) = |x - 3|$

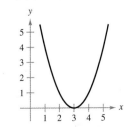   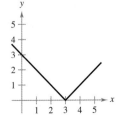

Finding an Inverse Function In Exercises 67–72, (a) sketch a graph of the function f, (b) determine an interval on which f is one-to-one, (c) find the inverse function of f on the interval found in part (b), and (d) give the domain of the inverse function. (*Note:* There is more than one correct answer.)

67. $f(x) = (x + 2)^2$

68. $f(x) = (12 - x)^2$

69. $f(x) = \sqrt{x^2 - 4x}$

70. $f(x) = -\sqrt{25 - x^2}$

71. $f(x) = 3 \cos x$

72. $f(x) = 2 \sin x$

Finding Values In Exercises 73–78, find $f^{-1}(a)$ for the function f and real number a.

Function	Real Number
73. $f(x) = x^3 + 2x - 1$	$a = 2$
74. $f(x) = 2x^5 + x^3 + 1$	$a = -2$
75. $f(x) = \sin x, \quad -\dfrac{\pi}{2} \le x \le \dfrac{\pi}{2}$	$a = \dfrac{1}{2}$
76. $f(x) = \cos 2x, \quad 0 \le x \le \dfrac{\pi}{2}$	$a = 1$
77. $f(x) = x^3 - \dfrac{4}{x}, \quad x > 0$	$a = 6$
78. $f(x) = \sqrt{x - 4}$	$a = 2$

Using Composite and Inverse Functions In Exercises 79–82, use the functions $f(x) = x + 4$ and $g(x) = 2x - 5$ to find the indicated function.

79. $g^{-1} \circ f^{-1}$

80. $f^{-1} \circ g^{-1}$

81. $(f \circ g)^{-1}$

82. $(g \circ f)^{-1}$

Using Composite and Inverse Functions In Exercises 83–86, use the functions $f(x) = \frac{1}{8}x - 3$ and $g(x) = x^3$ to find the indicated value.

83. $(f^{-1} \circ g^{-1})(1)$

84. $(g^{-1} \circ f^{-1})(-2)$

85. $(f^{-1} \circ f^{-1})(3)$

86. $(g^{-1} \circ g^{-1})(-5)$

Graphical Reasoning In Exercises 87 and 88, use the graph of the function f to sketch the graph of f^{-1}. To print an enlarged copy of the graph, go to *MathGraphs.com*.

87.

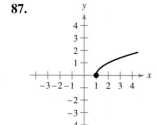

88.

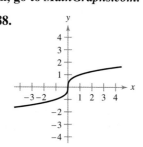

Graphical Reasoning In Exercises 89 and 90, (a) use the graph of the function f to determine whether f is one-to-one, (b) state the domain of f^{-1}, and (c) estimate the value of $f^{-1}(2)$.

89.

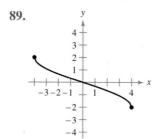

90.

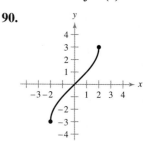

Numerical and Graphical Analysis In Exercises 91 and 92, (a) use a graphing utility to complete the table, (b) plot the points in the table and graph the function by hand, (c) use a graphing utility to graph the function and compare the result with your hand-drawn graph in part (b), and (d) determine any intercepts and symmetry of the graph.

x	-1	-0.8	-0.6	-0.4	-0.2	0	0.2	0.4	0.6	0.8	1
y											

91. $y = \arcsin x$

92. $y = \arccos x$

93. **Missing Coordinates** Determine the missing coordinates of the points on the graph of the function.

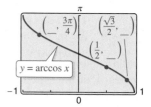

94. **HOW DO YOU SEE IT?** You use a graphing utility to graph $f(x) = \sin x$ and then use the *draw inverse* function to graph g (see figure). Is g the inverse function of f? Why or why not?

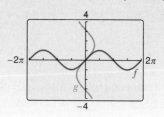

Evaluating an Inverse Trigonometric Function In Exercises 95–102, evaluate the expression without using a calculator.

95. $\arcsin \frac{1}{2}$

96. $\arcsin 0$

97. $\arccos 1$

98. $\arccos \frac{1}{2}$

99. $\arctan \dfrac{\sqrt{3}}{3}$

100. $\operatorname{arccot}(-\sqrt{3})$

101. $\operatorname{arccsc}(-\sqrt{2})$

102. $\operatorname{arcsec}(-\sqrt{2})$

Approximating an Inverse Trigonometric Function In Exercises 103–106, use a calculator to approximate the value. Round your answer to two decimal places.

103. $\arccos(-0.6)$ **104.** $\arcsin(-0.28)$

105. $\text{arcsec } 1.437$ **106.** $\arctan(-4)$

Using Properties In Exercises 107 and 108, use the properties of inverse trigonometric functions to evaluate the expression.

107. $\cos[\arccos(-0.4)]$

108. $\arcsin(\sin 5\pi)$

 Using a Right Triangle In Exercises 109–114, use the figure to write the expression in algebraic form given $y = \arccos x$, where $0 < y < \pi/2$.

109. $\cos y$

110. $\sin y$

111. $\tan y$

112. $\cot y$

113. $\sec y$

114. $\csc y$

 Simplifying an Expression In Exercises 115–118, write the expression in algebraic form. [*Hint:* Sketch a right triangle, as demonstrated in Example 7.]

115. $\cos(\arcsin 2x)$ **116.** $\csc(\arctan 6x)$

117. $\sin(\text{arcsec } x)$ **118.** $\sec[\arcsin(x - 1)]$

 Evaluating Expressions In Exercises 119–122, evaluate each expression without using a calculator. [*Hint:* Sketch a right triangle, as demonstrated in Example 7.]

119. (a) $\sin\left(\arctan \dfrac{3}{4}\right)$ **120.** (a) $\tan\left(\arccos \dfrac{\sqrt{2}}{2}\right)$

  (b) $\sec\left(\arcsin \dfrac{4}{5}\right)$ (b) $\cos\left(\arcsin \dfrac{5}{13}\right)$

121. (a) $\cot\left[\arcsin\left(-\dfrac{1}{2}\right)\right]$ **122.** (a) $\sec\left[\arctan\left(-\dfrac{3}{5}\right)\right]$

  (b) $\csc\left[\arctan\left(-\dfrac{5}{12}\right)\right]$ (b) $\tan\left[\arcsin\left(-\dfrac{5}{6}\right)\right]$

Solving an Equation In Exercises 123–126, solve the equation for x algebraically. Use a graphing utility to verify your results.

123. $\arcsin(4x - \pi) = \dfrac{1}{2}$

124. $\arctan(2x - 3) = -1$

125. $\arcsin \sqrt{2x} = \arccos \sqrt{x}$

126. $\arctan x = \text{arccot } x$

EXPLORING CONCEPTS

127. Justifying Explain why $\tan \pi = 0$ does not imply that $\arctan 0 = \pi$.

128. Implementing Processes Explain how to graph $y = \text{arccot } x$ on a graphing utility that does not have the arccotangent function.

Sketching a Graph In Exercises 129–132, sketch the graph of the function. Use a graphing utility to verify your graph.

129. $f(x) = \arcsin(x - 1)$

130. $f(x) = \text{arcsec } 2x$

131. $f(x) = \arctan x + \dfrac{\pi}{2}$

132. $f(x) = \arccos \dfrac{x}{4}$

133. Proof Prove that if f and g are one-to-one functions, then $(f \circ g)^{-1}(x) = (g^{-1} \circ f^{-1})(x)$.

134. Proof Prove that if f has an inverse function, then $(f^{-1})^{-1} = f$.

135. Proof Prove that $\cos(\sin^{-1} x) = \sqrt{1 - x^2}$.

136. Proof Prove that if a function has an inverse function, then the inverse function is unique.

True or False? In Exercises 137 and 138, determine whether the statement is true or false. If it is false, explain why or give an example that shows it is false.

137. If $f(x) = x^n$ where n is odd, then f^{-1} exists.

138. There exists no function f such that $f = f^{-1}$.

139. Verifying an Identity Verify each identity.

(a) $\text{arccot } x = \begin{cases} \pi + \arctan(1/x), & x < 0 \\ \pi/2, & x = 0 \\ \arctan(1/x), & x > 0 \end{cases}$

(b) $\text{arcsec } x = \arccos(1/x), \quad |x| \geq 1$

(c) $\text{arccsc } x = \arcsin(1/x), \quad |x| \geq 1$

140. Using an Identity Use the results of Exercise 139 and a graphing utility to evaluate each expression.

(a) $\text{arccot } 0.25$ (b) $\text{arcsec } 1.8$

(c) $\text{arccsc}(-4.1)$ (d) $\text{arccot}(-2.3)$

141. Verifying an Identity Verify each identity.

(a) $\arctan x + \arctan \dfrac{1}{x} = \dfrac{\pi}{2}, \quad x > 0$

(b) $\arcsin(-x) = -\arcsin x, \quad |x| \leq 1$

(c) $\arccos(-x) = \pi - \arccos x, \quad |x| \leq 1$

142. Determining Conditions Let $f(x) = ax^2 + bx + c$, where $a > 0$ and the domain is all real numbers such that $x \leq -b/(2a)$. Find f^{-1}.

P.5   Exponential and Logarithmic Functions

▶ Develop and use properties of exponential functions.
▶ Understand the definition of the number e.
▶ Understand the definition of the natural logarithmic function, and develop and use properties of the natural logarithmic function.

Exponential Functions

An **exponential function** involves a constant raised to a power, such as $f(x) = 2^x$. You already know how to evaluate 2^x for *rational* values of x. For instance,

$$2^0 = 1, \quad 2^2 = 4, \quad 2^{-1} = \frac{1}{2}, \quad \text{and} \quad 2^{1/2} = \sqrt{2} \approx 1.4142136.$$

For *irrational* values of x, you can define 2^x by considering a sequence of rational numbers that approach x. A full discussion of this process would not be appropriate now, but here is the general idea. To define the number $2^{\sqrt{2}}$, note that

$$\sqrt{2} = 1.414213 \ldots$$

and consider the numbers below (which are of the form 2^r, where r is rational).

$$2^1 = 2 < 2^{\sqrt{2}} < 4 = 2^2$$
$$2^{1.4} = 2.639015 \ldots < 2^{\sqrt{2}} < 2.828427 \ldots = 2^{1.5}$$
$$2^{1.41} = 2.657371 \ldots < 2^{\sqrt{2}} < 2.675855 \ldots = 2^{1.42}$$
$$2^{1.414} = 2.664749 \ldots < 2^{\sqrt{2}} < 2.666597 \ldots = 2^{1.415}$$
$$2^{1.4142} = 2.665119 \ldots < 2^{\sqrt{2}} < 2.665303 \ldots = 2^{1.4143}$$
$$2^{1.41421} = 2.665137 \ldots < 2^{\sqrt{2}} < 2.665156 \ldots = 2^{1.41422}$$
$$2^{1.414213} = 2.665143 \ldots < 2^{\sqrt{2}} < 2.665144 \ldots = 2^{1.414214}$$

From these calculations, it seems reasonable to conclude that

$$2^{\sqrt{2}} \approx 2.66514.$$

In practice, you can use a calculator to approximate numbers such as $2^{\sqrt{2}}$, as shown in Figure P.38.

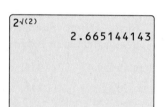

Figure P.38

In general, you can use any positive base a, $a \neq 1$, to define an exponential function. So, the exponential function with base a is written as $f(x) = a^x$. Exponential functions, even those with irrational values of x, obey the familiar properties of exponents.

Properties of Exponents

Let a and b be positive real numbers, and let x and y be any real numbers.

1. $a^0 = 1$ 2. $a^x a^y = a^{x+y}$ 3. $(a^x)^y = a^{xy}$ 4. $(ab)^x = a^x b^x$

5. $\dfrac{a^x}{a^y} = a^{x-y}$ 6. $\left(\dfrac{a}{b}\right)^x = \dfrac{a^x}{b^x}$ 7. $a^{-x} = \dfrac{1}{a^x}$

Justification

Note that base $a = 1$ is excluded because it yields $f(x) = 1^x = 1$. This is a *constant* function, not an *exponential* function.

EXAMPLE 1   Using Properties of Exponents

a. $(2^2)(2^3) = 2^{2+3} = 2^5$ **b.** $\dfrac{2^2}{2^3} = 2^{2-3} = 2^{-1} = \dfrac{1}{2}$

c. $(3^x)^3 = 3^{3x}$ **d.** $\left(\dfrac{1}{3}\right)^{-x} = (3^{-1})^{-x} = 3^x$ ■

EXAMPLE 2   Sketching Graphs of Exponential Functions

See LarsonCalculusforAP.com for an interactive version of this type of example.

Sketch the graphs of the functions

$$f(x) = 2^x, \quad g(x) = \left(\frac{1}{2}\right)^x = 2^{-x}, \quad \text{and} \quad h(x) = 3^x.$$

Solution

To sketch the graphs of these functions by hand, you can complete a table of values, plot the corresponding points, and connect the points with smooth curves.

x	-3	-2	-1	0	1	2	3	4
2^x	$\frac{1}{8}$	$\frac{1}{4}$	$\frac{1}{2}$	1	2	4	8	16
2^{-x}	8	4	2	1	$\frac{1}{2}$	$\frac{1}{4}$	$\frac{1}{8}$	$\frac{1}{16}$
3^x	$\frac{1}{27}$	$\frac{1}{9}$	$\frac{1}{3}$	1	3	9	27	81

Another way to graph these functions is to use a graphing utility. In either case, you should obtain graphs similar to those shown in Figure P.39. Note that the graphs of f and h are increasing, and the graph of g is decreasing. Also, the graph of h is increasing more rapidly than the graph of f.

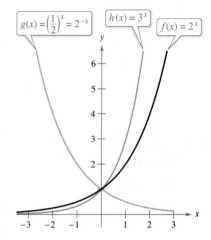

Figure P.39

The shapes of the graphs in Figure P.39 are typical of the exponential functions $f(x) = a^x$ and $g(x) = a^{-x}$ where $a > 1$, as shown in Figure P.40.

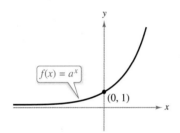
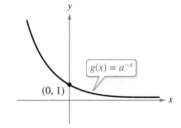

Figure P.40

Properties of Exponential Functions

Let a be a real number that is greater than 1.

1. The domain of $f(x) = a^x$ and $g(x) = a^{-x}$ is $(-\infty, \infty)$.
2. The range of $f(x) = a^x$ and $g(x) = a^{-x}$ is $(0, \infty)$.
3. The y-intercept of $f(x) = a^x$ and $g(x) = a^{-x}$ is $(0, 1)$.
4. The functions $f(x) = a^x$ and $g(x) = a^{-x}$ are one-to-one.

Technology

Functions of the form $h(x) = b^{cx}$ have the same types of properties and graphs as functions of the form $f(x) = a^x$ and $g(x) = a^{-x}$. To see why this is true, notice that $b^{cx} = (b^c)^x$. For instance, $f(x) = 2^{3x}$ can be written as $f(x) = (2^3)^x$ or $f(x) = 8^x$. Try confirming this by graphing $f(x) = 2^{3x}$ and $g(x) = 8^x$ in the same viewing window.

The Number e

In calculus, the natural (or convenient) choice for a base of an exponential number is the irrational number e, whose decimal approximation is $e \approx 2.71828182846$. This choice may seem anything but natural. The convenience of this particular base, however, will become apparent as you continue in this course.

EXAMPLE 3 Investigating the Number e

Describe the behavior of $f(x) = (1 + x)^{1/x}$ at x-values close to 0.

Numerical Solution

Use the *table* feature of a graphing utility to examine $f(x)$ at x-values close to 0.

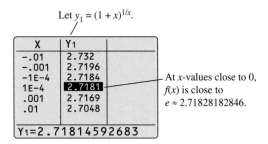

Let $y_1 = (1 + x)^{1/x}$.

At x-values close to 0, $f(x)$ is close to $e \approx 2.71828182846$.

Graphical Solution

Use the *zoom* and *trace* features of a graphing utility to examine $f(x)$ at x-values close to 0.

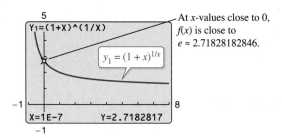

At x-values close to 0, $f(x)$ is close to $e \approx 2.71828182846$.

Although the function f in Example 3 is not defined when $x = 0$, you were still able to examine its behavior near $x = 0$. When you study limits in Chapter 1, you will learn that you can describe this behavior in symbols as

$$\lim_{x \to 0} (1 + x)^{1/x} = e$$

which is read as "the limit of $(1 + x)^{1/x}$ as x approaches 0 is e."

EXAMPLE 4 The Graph of the Natural Exponential Function

Sketch the graph of $f(x) = e^x$.

Solution

To sketch the graph of f by hand, complete a table of values, plot the corresponding points, and connect the points with a smooth curve (see figure).

x	-2	-1	0	1	2
e^x	$\frac{1}{e^2} \approx 0.135$	$\frac{1}{e} \approx 0.368$	1	$e \approx 2.718$	$e^2 \approx 7.389$

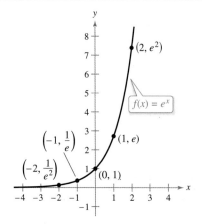

The Natural Logarithmic Function

Because the natural exponential function

$$f(x) = e^x$$

is one-to-one, it must have an inverse function. This inverse function is called the **natural logarithmic function.** The domain of the natural logarithmic function is the set of positive real numbers.

> ### Definition of the Natural Logarithmic Function
>
> Let x be a positive real number. The **natural logarithmic function,** denoted by $\ln x$, is defined as
>
> $$\ln x = b \quad \text{if and only if} \quad e^b = x.$$

The definition of the natural logarithmic function tells you that a logarithmic equation can be written in an equivalent exponential form, and vice versa. Here are some examples.

Logarithmic Form	*Exponential Form*
$\ln 1 = 0$	$e^0 = 1$
$\ln e = 1$	$e^1 = e$
$\ln e^{-1} = -1$	$e^{-1} = \dfrac{1}{e}$

Because the function $g(x) = \ln x$ is defined to be the inverse function of $f(x) = e^x$, it follows that the graph of the natural logarithmic function is a reflection of the graph of the natural exponential function in the line $y = x$, as shown in Figure P.41. Several other properties of the natural logarithmic function also follow directly from its definition as the inverse of the natural exponential function.

> ### Properties of the Natural Logarithmic Function
>
> 1. The domain of $g(x) = \ln x$ is $(0, \infty)$.
> 2. The range of $g(x) = \ln x$ is $(-\infty, \infty)$.
> 3. The x-intercept of $g(x) = \ln x$ is $(1, 0)$.
> 4. The function $g(x) = \ln x$ is one-to-one.

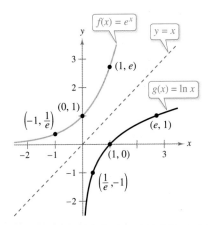

Figure P.41

Because $f(x) = e^x$ and $g(x) = \ln x$ are inverse functions of each other, you can conclude that

$$\ln e^x = x \quad \text{and} \quad e^{\ln x} = x.$$

One of the properties of exponents states that when you multiply two exponential functions (having the same base), you add their exponents. For instance,

$$e^x e^y = e^{x+y}.$$

The logarithmic version of this property states that the natural logarithm of the product of two numbers is equal to the sum of the natural logs of the numbers. That is,

$$\ln xy = \ln x + \ln y.$$

This property and the properties dealing with the natural log of a quotient and the natural log of a power are listed on the next page.

Properties of Logarithms

Let x, y, and z be real numbers such that $x > 0$ and $y > 0$.

1. $\ln xy = \ln x + \ln y$

2. $\ln \dfrac{x}{y} = \ln x - \ln y$

3. $\ln x^z = z \ln x$

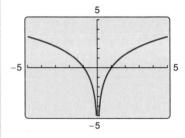
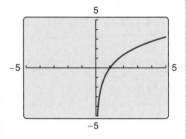

EXAMPLE 5   Expanding Logarithmic Expressions

a. $\ln \dfrac{10}{9} = \ln 10 - \ln 9$ Property 2

b. $\ln \sqrt{3x + 2} = \ln(3x + 2)^{1/2}$ Rewrite with rational exponent.

$\qquad\qquad = \dfrac{1}{2} \ln(3x + 2)$ Property 3

c. $\ln \dfrac{6x}{5} = \ln(6x) - \ln 5$ Property 2

$\qquad\quad = \ln 6 + \ln x - \ln 5$ Property 1

d. $\ln \dfrac{(x^2 + 3)^2}{x\sqrt[3]{x^2 + 1}} = \ln(x^2 + 3)^2 - \ln\!\left(x\sqrt[3]{x^2 + 1}\right)$

$\qquad\qquad = 2 \ln(x^2 + 3) - \left[\ln x + \ln(x^2 + 1)^{1/3}\right]$

$\qquad\qquad = 2 \ln(x^2 + 3) - \ln x - \ln(x^2 + 1)^{1/3}$

$\qquad\qquad = 2 \ln(x^2 + 3) - \ln x - \dfrac{1}{3} \ln(x^2 + 1)$ ■

When using the properties of logarithms to rewrite logarithmic functions, you must check to see whether the domain of the rewritten function is the same as the domain of the original function. For instance, the domain of $f(x) = \ln x^2$ is all real numbers except $x = 0$, and the domain of $g(x) = 2 \ln x$ is all positive real numbers.

EXAMPLE 6   Solving Exponential and Logarithmic Equations

Solve for x.

a. $7 = e^{x+1}$ **b.** $\ln(2x - 3) = 5$

Solution

a. $7 = e^{x+1}$ Write original equation.

$\qquad \ln 7 = \ln(e^{x+1})$ Take natural log of each side.

$\qquad \ln 7 = x + 1$ Apply inverse property.

$\qquad -1 + \ln 7 = x$ Solve for x.

$\qquad 0.946 \approx x$ Use a calculator.

b. $\ln(2x - 3) = 5$ Write original equation.

$\qquad e^{\ln(2x-3)} = e^5$ Exponentiate each side.

$\qquad 2x - 3 = e^5$ Apply inverse property.

$\qquad x = \dfrac{1}{2}(e^5 + 3)$ Solve for x.

$\qquad x \approx 75.707$ Use a calculator.   ■

You can check the solutions in Example 6 by substituting the values of x into the original equations, then using a calculator to evaluate.

Evaluating an Expression In Exercises 1 and 2, evaluate the expressions.

1. (a) $25^{3/2}$ (b) $81^{1/2}$ (c) 3^{-2} (d) $27^{-1/3}$

2. (a) $64^{1/3}$ (b) 5^{-4} (c) $\left(\frac{1}{8}\right)^{1/3}$ (d) $\left(\frac{1}{4}\right)^{3}$

 Using Properties of Exponents In Exercises 3–6, use the properties of exponents to simplify the expressions.

3. (a) $(5^2)(5^3)$ (b) $(5^2)(5^{-3})$ (c) $\dfrac{5^{3x}}{25^{2x}}$ (d) $\left(\dfrac{1}{4}\right)^{2x}(2^{6x})$

4. (a) $(2^2)^3$ (b) $(5^4)^{1/2}$
   (c) $[(27^{-1})(27^{2/3})]^{3x}$ (d) $(25^{3/2})(5^{2x})$

5. (a) $e^3(e^4)$ (b) $(e^3)^4$ (c) $(e^3)^{-2}$ (d) e^0

6. (a) $\left(\dfrac{1}{e}\right)^{-2}$ (b) $\left(\dfrac{e^5}{e^2}\right)^{-1}$ (c) $\dfrac{e^{-1/2}}{e^4}$ (d) $\dfrac{1}{e^{-3}}$

 Solving an Equation In Exercises 7–22, solve for x.

7. $3^x = 81$

8. $4^x = 256$

9. $6^{x-2} = 36$

10. $5^{x+1} = 125$

11. $\left(\frac{1}{2}\right)^x = 32$

12. $\left(\frac{1}{4}\right)^x = 16$

13. $\left(\frac{1}{3}\right)^{x-1} = 27$

14. $\left(\frac{1}{5}\right)^{2x} = 625$

15. $4^3 = (x+2)^3$

16. $18^2 = (5x-7)^2$

17. $x^{3/4} = 8$

18. $(x+3)^{3/2} = 64$

19. $4e^x = (2e)^2$

20. $e^x = 1$

21. $e^{-2x} = e^5$

22. $e^{4x} = e^{-3}$

Using the Definition of e In Exercises 23 and 24, use a calculator to determine whether the expression is greater than, less than, or equal to e.

23. $\left(1 + \dfrac{1}{1{,}000{,}000}\right)^{1{,}000{,}000}$

24. $1 + 1 + \frac{1}{2} + \frac{1}{6} + \frac{1}{24} + \frac{1}{120} + \frac{1}{720} + \frac{1}{5040}$

 Sketching the Graph of an Exponential Function In Exercises 25–38, sketch the graph of the function.

25. $y = 6^x$

26. $y = 3^{x-1}$

27. $y = \left(\frac{1}{3}\right)^x$

28. $y = 2^{-x^2}$

29. $f(x) = 4^{-x^2}$

30. $f(x) = 3^{|x|}$

31. $y = e^{-x}$

32. $y = \frac{1}{2}e^x$

33. $y = e^x + 3$

34. $y = e^{x-1}$

35. $h(x) = e^{x-5}$

36. $g(x) = -e^{x/2}$

37. $y = e^{-x^2}$

38. $y = e^{-x/3}$

 Finding the Domain In Exercises 39–44, find the domain of the function.

39. $f(x) = \dfrac{1}{3 + e^x}$

40. $f(x) = \dfrac{1}{5 - e^x}$

41. $f(x) = \sqrt{1 - 4^x}$

42. $f(x) = \sqrt{1 + 3^{-x}}$

43. $f(x) = \sin e^{-x}$

44. $f(x) = \cos e^{-x}$

45. **Identifying a Relationship** Use a graphing utility to graph $f(x) = e^x$ and the given function in the same viewing window. How are the two graphs related?
   (a) $g(x) = e^{x-2}$ (b) $h(x) = -\frac{1}{2}e^x$ (c) $q(x) = e^{-x} + 3$

46. **Describing the Shape of a Graph** Use a graphing utility to graph the function. Describe the behavior of the graph as x increases without bound and as x decreases without bound.
   (a) $f(x) = \dfrac{8}{1 + e^{-0.5x}}$ (b) $g(x) = \dfrac{8}{1 + e^{-0.5/x}}$

Matching In Exercises 47–50, match the equation with the correct graph. Assume that a and C are positive real numbers. [The graphs are labeled (a), (b), (c), and (d).]

(a)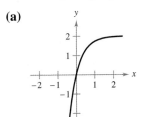

(b)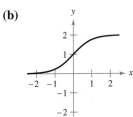

(c)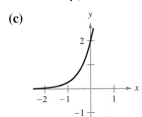

(d)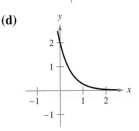

47. $y = Ce^{ax}$

48. $y = Ce^{-ax}$

49. $y = C(1 - e^{-ax})$

50. $y = \dfrac{C}{1 + e^{-ax}}$

Finding an Exponential Function In Exercises 51 and 52, find the exponential function $y = Ca^x$ that fits the graph.

51.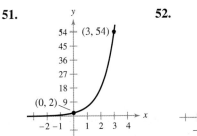

52.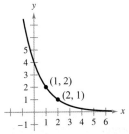

Writing Exponential or Logarithmic Equations In Exercises 53–56, write the exponential equation as a logarithmic equation, or vice versa.

53. $e^0 = 1$ **54.** $e^{-2} = 0.1353 \ldots$

55. $\ln 5 = 1.6094 \ldots$ **56.** $\ln 0.5 = -0.6931 \ldots$

 Sketching the Graph of a Logarithmic Function In Exercises 57–64, sketch the graph of the function and state its domain.

57. $f(x) = 2 \ln x$ **58.** $f(x) = -3 \ln x$

59. $f(x) = \ln 2x$ **60.** $f(x) = \ln|x|$

61. $f(x) = \ln(x - 1)$ **62.** $f(x) = \ln x - 4$

63. $f(x) = \ln(x + 2)$ **64.** $f(x) = \ln(x - 2) + 1$

 Writing an Equation In Exercises 65–68, write an equation for the function having the given characteristics.

65. The shape of $f(x) = e^x$, but shifted eight units upward and reflected in the x-axis

66. The shape of $f(x) = e^x$, but shifted six units to the left and two units downward

67. The shape of $f(x) = \ln x$, but shifted five units to the right and one unit downward

68. The shape of $f(x) = \ln x$, but shifted three units upward and reflected in the y-axis

 Inverse Functions In Exercises 69–72, illustrate that the functions f and g are inverse functions of each other by using a graphing utility to graph them in the same viewing window.

69. $f(x) = e^{2x}$, $g(x) = \ln \sqrt{x}$

70. $f(x) = e^{x/3}$, $g(x) = \ln x^3$

71. $f(x) = e^x - 1$, $g(x) = \ln(x + 1)$

72. $f(x) = e^{x-1}$, $g(x) = 1 + \ln x$

 Finding Inverse Functions In Exercises 73–76, (a) find the inverse function of f, (b) use a graphing utility to graph f and f^{-1} in the same viewing window, and (c) verify that $f^{-1}(f(x)) = x$ and $f(f^{-1}(x)) = x$.

73. $f(x) = e^{4x-1}$ **74.** $f(x) = 3e^{-x}$

75. $f(x) = 2 \ln(x - 1)$ **76.** $f(x) = 2 + \ln 3x$

 Applying Inverse Properties In Exercises 77–82, apply the inverse properties of $\ln x$ and e^x to simplify the given expression.

77. $\ln e^{x^2}$ **78.** $\ln e^{2x-1}$

79. $e^{\ln(5x+2)}$ **80.** $e^{\ln \sqrt{x}}$

81. $-1 + \ln e^{2x}$ **82.** $-9 + e^{\ln x^4}$

 Using Properties of Logarithms In Exercises 83 and 84, use the properties of logarithms to approximate the indicated logarithms, given that $\ln 2 \approx 0.6931$ and $\ln 3 \approx 1.0986$.

83. (a) $\ln 6$ (b) $\ln \frac{2}{3}$ (c) $\ln 81$ (d) $\ln \sqrt{3}$

84. (a) $\ln 0.125$ (b) $\ln 72$ (c) $\ln \sqrt[3]{18}$ (d) $\ln \frac{1}{54}$

 Expanding a Logarithmic Expression In Exercises 85–94, use the properties of logarithms to expand the logarithmic expression.

85. $\ln \dfrac{x}{5}$ **86.** $\ln \sqrt{x^3}$

87. $\ln \dfrac{xy}{z}$ **88.** $\ln xyz$

89. $\ln\left(x\sqrt{x^2 + 16}\right)$ **90.** $\ln \sqrt[3]{z + 1}$

91. $\ln \sqrt{\dfrac{x - 1}{x}}$ **92.** $\ln z(z - 1)^2$

93. $\ln 3e^2$ **94.** $\ln \dfrac{1}{e}$

 Condensing a Logarithmic Expression In Exercises 95–102, write the expression as the logarithm of a single quantity.

95. $\ln x + \ln 7$

96. $\ln y + \ln x^2$

97. $\ln(x - 2) - \ln(x + 2)$

98. $3 \ln x + 2 \ln y - 4 \ln z$

99. $\frac{1}{3}[2 \ln(x + 3) + \ln x - \ln(x^2 - 1)]$

100. $2[\ln x - \ln(x + 1) - \ln(x - 1)]$

101. $2 \ln 3 - \frac{1}{2} \ln(x^2 + 1)$

102. $\frac{3}{2}[\ln(x^2 + 1) - \ln(x + 1) - \ln(x - 1)]$

Error Analysis In Exercises 103 and 104, describe and correct the error.

103. $\left(\dfrac{e^4}{e^6}\right)^{-3} = (e^{-2})^{-3} = \left(\dfrac{1}{e^2}\right)^{-3} = \dfrac{-1}{e^{-6}} = -e^6$

104. $\ln\left[\dfrac{4(x - 3)^3}{x^3(x - 1)^2}\right]$

$= \ln[4(x - 3)^3] - \ln[x^3(x - 1)^2]$

$= \ln 4 + \ln(x - 3)^3 - \ln x^3 + \ln(x - 1)^2$

$= \ln 4 + 3 \ln(x - 3) - 3 \ln x + 2 \ln(x - 1)$

 Solving an Exponential or Logarithmic Equation In Exercises 105–108, solve for x accurate to three decimal places.

105. (a) $e^{\ln x} = 4$ **106.** (a) $e^{\ln 2x} = 16$

     (b) $\ln(3x - 2) = 3$ (b) $\ln(x/2) = 0$

107. (a) $\ln x = 2$ **108.** (a) $\ln(x^2 - 4) = 8$

     (b) $e^{x+2} = 8$ (b) $e^{-2x} = 5$

Solving an Inequality In Exercises 109–112, solve the inequality for *x*.

109. $e^x > 6$

110. $e^{1-x} < 7$

111. $-2 < \ln x < 0$

112. $1 < \ln x < 100$

 Verifying Properties of Logarithms In Exercises 113 and 114, (a) verify that $f = g$ by using a graphing utility to graph f and g in the same viewing window and (b) verify that $f = g$ algebraically.

113. $f(x) = \ln \dfrac{x^2}{4}$

  $g(x) = 2 \ln x - \ln 4$

114. $f(x) = \ln \sqrt{x(x^2 + 1)}$

  $g(x) = \frac{1}{2}[\ln x + \ln(x^2 + 1)]$

EXPLORING CONCEPTS

115. Justifying Explain why $\ln e^x = x$.

116. Connecting Representation Describe the relationship between the graphs of $f(x) = \ln x$ and $g(x) = e^x$.

117. Connecting Representations The table of values below was obtained by evaluating a function. Determine which of the statements may be true and which must be false. Explain your reasoning.

(a) *y* is an exponential function of *x*.

(b) *x* is an exponential function of *y*.

(c) *y* is a logarithmic function of *x*.

(d) *y* is a linear function of *x*.

x	1	2	8
y	0	1	3

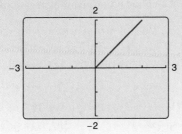

118. HOW DO YOU SEE IT? The figure below shows the graph of $y_1 = \ln e^x$ or $y_2 = e^{\ln x}$. Which graph is it? What are the domains of y_1 and y_2? Does $\ln e^x = e^{\ln x}$ for all real values of *x*? Explain.

Sound Intensity In Exercises 119 and 120, use the following information. The relationship between the number of decibels β and the intensity I of a sound in watts per square centimeter is

$$\beta = \frac{10}{\ln 10} \ln\!\left(\frac{I}{10^{-16}}\right).$$

119. Use the properties of logarithms to write the formula in simpler form.

120. Determine the number of decibels of a sound with an intensity of 10^{-5} watt per square centimeter.

True or False? In Exercises 121 and 122, determine whether the statement is true or false. If it is false, explain why or give an example that shows it is false.

121. $\ln(x + 25) = \ln x + \ln 25$ **122.** $\ln xy = \ln x \ln y$

 123. Comparing Functions Use a graphing utility to graph the functions $f(x) = 6^x$ and $g(x) = x^6$ in the same viewing window. Where do these graphs intersect? As *x* increases, which function grows more rapidly?

 124. Comparing Functions Use a graphing utility to graph the functions $f(x) = \ln x$ and $g(x) = x^{1/4}$ in the same viewing window. Where do these graphs intersect? As *x* increases, which function grows more rapidly?

 Finding a Model In Exercises 125 and 126, use the *regression* feature of a graphing utility to find an exponential or a logarithmic model to fit the data.

125.

x	1	2	3	4	5
y	0	0.1732	0.2747	0.3466	0.4024

126.

x	-2	-1	0	1	2
y	0.1026	0.7579	5.6000	41.3787	305.7496

Stirling's Formula For large values of *n*,

$$n! = 1 \cdot 2 \cdot 3 \cdot 4 \cdots (n-1) \cdot n$$

can be approximated by Stirling's Formula,

$$n! \approx \left(\frac{n}{e}\right)^n \sqrt{2\pi n}.$$

In Exercises 127 and 128, find the exact value of *n*!, and then approximate *n*! using Stirling's Formula.

127. $n = 10$ **128.** $n = 16$

129. Proof Prove that $\ln(x/y) = \ln x - \ln y$, $x > 0$, $y > 0$.

130. Proof Prove that $\ln x^y = y \ln x$.

 131. Analyzing a Function Let $f(x) = \ln\!\left(x + \sqrt{x^2 + 1}\right)$.

(a) Use a graphing utility to graph f and determine its domain.

(b) Show that f is an odd function.

(c) Find the inverse function of f.

Finding Intercepts In Exercises 1–4, find any intercepts algebraically. Use a graphing utility to verify your results.

1. $y = 5x - 8$

2. $y = x^2 - 8x + 12$

3. $y = \dfrac{x - 3}{x - 4}$

4. $y = (x - 3)\sqrt{x + 4}$

Testing for Symmetry In Exercises 5–8, test for symmetry with respect to each axis and to the origin.

5. $y = x^2 + 4x$

6. $y = x^4 - x^2 + 3$

7. $y^2 = x^2 - 5$

8. $xy = -2$

Using Intercepts and Symmetry to Sketch a Graph In Exercises 9–14, find any intercepts and test for symmetry. Then sketch the graph of the equation.

9. $y = -\frac{1}{2}x + 3$

10. $y = -x^2 + 4$

11. $y = x^3 - 4x$

12. $y^2 = 9 - x$

13. $y = 2\sqrt{4 - x}$

14. $y = |x - 4| - 4$

Finding Points of Intersection In Exercises 15 and 16, find the points of intersection of the graphs of the equations. Use a graphing utility to verify your results.

15. $x - y = -5$
     $x^2 - y = 1$

16. $x^2 + y^2 = 1$
     $-x + y = 1$

17. Stress Test A machine part was tested by bending it x centimeters 10 times per minute until the time y (in hours) of failure. The results are recorded in the table.

x	3	6	9	12	15	18	21	24	27	30
y	61	56	53	55	48	35	36	33	28	23

(a) Use the regressions capabilities of a graphing utility to find a linear model for the data.

(b) Use a graphing utility to plot the data and graph the model. How well does the model fit the data? Explain.

18. Median Income The data in the table show the median incomes y (in thousands of dollars) for samples of householders of various ages x in the United States in 2017. (*Adapted from U.S. Census Bureau*)

x	20	30	40	50	60	70
y	40.1	62.3	78.4	80.7	68.6	41.1

(a) Use the regression capabilities of a graphing utility to find a quadratic model for the data.

(b) Use a graphing utility to plot the data and graph the model.

(c) Use the model to approximate the median incomes for a sample of 27-year-old householders and a sample of 56-year-old householders.

Finding the Slope of a Line In Exercises 19 and 20, plot the pair of points and find the slope of the line passing through them.

19. $\left(\frac{3}{2}, 1\right), \left(5, \frac{5}{2}\right)$

20. $(-7, 8), (-1, 8)$

Finding an Equation of a Line In Exercises 21–24, find an equation of the line that passes through the point and has the indicated slope. Then sketch the line.

21. $(3, -5), m = \frac{7}{4}$

22. $(-8, 1), m$ is undefined.

23. $(-3, 0), m = -\frac{2}{3}$

24. $(5, 4), m = 0$

Sketching a Line in the Plane In Exercises 25–28, sketch the graph of the equation.

25. $y = 6$

26. $x = -3$

27. $y = 4x - 2$

28. $3x + 2y = 12$

Finding an Equation of a Line In Exercises 29 and 30, find an equation of the line that passes through the points. Then sketch the line.

29. $(0, 0), (8, 2)$

30. $(-5, 5), (10, -1)$

31. Finding Parallel and Perpendicular Lines Find equations of the lines passing through $(-3, 5)$ and having the following characteristics.

(a) Parallel to the line $5x - 3y = 3$

(b) Perpendicular to the line $3x + 4y = 8$

(c) Parallel to the y-axis

32. Break-Even Analysis A contractor purchases a piece of equipment for \$36,500 that costs an average of \$9.25 per hour for fuel and maintenance. The equipment operator is paid \$13.50 per hour, and customers are charged \$30 per hour.

(a) Write an equation for the cost C of operating this equipment for t hours.

(b) Write an equation for the revenue R derived from t hours of use.

(c) Find the break-even point for this equipment by finding the time at which $R = C$.

Evaluating a Function In Exercises 33–36, for the function f, evaluate the given expression(s). Simplify the results.

33. $f(x) = 5x + 4$
  (a) $f(0)$ (b) $f(5)$ (c) $f(-3)$ (d) $f(t + 1)$

34. $f(x) = x^3 - 2x$
  (a) $f(-3)$ (b) $f(2)$ (c) $f(-1)$ (d) $f(c - 1)$

35. $f(x) = 4x^2$
  $\dfrac{f(x + \Delta x) - f(x)}{\Delta x}$

36. $f(x) = 2x - 6$
  $\dfrac{f(x) - f(1)}{x - 1}$

Finding the Domain and Range of a Function In Exercises 37–40, find the domain and range of the function algebraically. Use a graphing utility to verify your results.

37. $f(x) = x^2 + 3$

38. $g(x) = \sqrt{6 - x}$

39. $f(x) = -|x + 1|$

40. $h(x) = 2/(x + 1)$

Finding the Domain and Range of a Piecewise Function In Exercises 41 and 42, evaluate the function at the given values of the independent variable. Then find the domain and range.

41. $f(x) = \begin{cases} x + 2, & x \le 0 \\ x^2, & x > 0 \end{cases}$
(a) $f(-1)$ (b) $f(0)$
(c) $f(1)$ (d) $f(x^2 + 1)$

42. $f(x) = \begin{cases} 1/x, & x < \pi \\ \cos x, & x \ge \pi \end{cases}$
(a) $f(-\pi/2)$ (b) $f(\pi/2)$
(c) $f(\pi)$ (d) $f(3\pi/2)$

Using the Vertical Line Test In Exercises 43–46, sketch the graph of the equation and use the Vertical Line Test to determine whether y is a function of x.

43. $x - y^2 = 6$

44. $x^2 - y = 0$

45. $y = \dfrac{|x - 2|}{x - 2}$

46. $x = 9 - y^2$

Transformations of a Function In Exercises 47 and 48, the graph of g is a transformation of the graph of $f(x) = x^3 - 3x^2$. Use the graph to write an equation for g.

47.
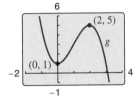

48.
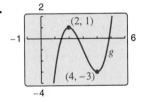

Combinations of Functions In Exercises 49 and 50, find (a) $f(x) + g(x)$, (b) $f(x) - g(x)$, (c) $f(x) \cdot g(x)$, and (d) $f(x)/g(x)$.

49. $f(x) = x + 5$
    $g(x) = 1 - 12x$

50. $f(x) = x^2 + 2x$
    $g(x) = 4 - x^2$

Finding Composite Functions In Exercises 51 and 52, find the composite functions $f \circ g$ and $g \circ f$. Find the domain of each composite function. Are the composite functions equal?

51. $f(x) = x^3 + 1$, $g(x) = \sqrt[3]{x^3 - 1}$

52. $f(x) = \dfrac{1}{x + 2}$, $g(x) = \dfrac{1 - 2x}{x}$

Even and Odd Functions and Zeros of Functions In Exercises 53–56, determine whether the function is even, odd, or neither. Then find the zeros of the function. Use a graphing utility to verify your result.

53. $f(x) = x^3 - 5x^2$

54. $f(x) = x^6 + 6x^2$

55. $f(x) = \cos^2 x$

56. $f(x) = x^2 \sin x$

Finding an Inverse Function In Exercises 57–64, (a) find the inverse function of f, (b) use a graphing utility to graph f and f^{-1} in the same viewing window, (c) verify that $f^{-1}(f(x)) = x$ and $f(f^{-1}(x)) = x$, and (d) state the domains and ranges of f and f^{-1}.

57. $f(x) = \frac{1}{2}x - 3$

58. $f(x) = 5x - 7$

59. $f(x) = \sqrt{x + 1}$

60. $f(x) = x^3 + 2$

61. $f(x) = \sqrt[3]{x + 1}$

62. $f(x) = x^2 - 5$, $x \ge 0$

63. $f(x) = \ln \sqrt{x}$

64. $f(x) = e^{1-x}$

Testing Whether a Function Is One-to One In Exercises 65–68, determine whether the function is one-to-one. If it is, find its inverse function.

65. $f(x) = |x|$, $-2 \le x \le 2$

66. $f(x) = \dfrac{x + 5}{x - 5}$

67. $f(x) = \sqrt[3]{x^3 - 3}$

68. $f(x) = \sqrt{x^2 + 1}$

Evaluating an Expression In Exercises 69 and 70, evaluate the expression without using a calculator. (*Hint:* Make a sketch of a right triangle.)

69. $\cos\left(\arcsin \frac{1}{2}\right)$

70. $\tan(\text{arccot } 2)$

Solving an Equation In Exercises 71–74, solve the equation for x algebraically. Use a graphing utility to verify your results.

71. $\arccos(3x - 2) = 2$

72. $\arctan(4x - 5) = 0$

73. $\arcsin \sqrt{1 - x} = \arccos \sqrt{1 - x}$

74. $\arccos x = \arctan x$

Sketching a Graph In Exercises 75–82, sketch the graph of the function and state its domain. Use a graphing utility to verify your results.

75. $f(x) = 2 \arctan(x + 3)$

76. $h(x) = -3 \arcsin 2x$

77. $f(x) = e^x - 4$

78. $f(x) = e^{x+5}$

79. $y = e^{-x/2}$

80. $y = 4e^{-x^2}$

81. $f(x) = \ln x + 3$

82. $f(x) = -\ln(x + 1) + 1$

83. Expanding a Logarithmic Expression Use the properties of logarithms to expand the expression

$$\ln \sqrt[5]{\frac{4x^2 - 1}{4x^2 + 1}}.$$

84. Condensing a Logarithmic Expression Write the expression $3[\ln x - 2 \ln(x^2 + 1)] + 2 \ln 5$ as the logarithm of a single quantity.

Solving an Exponential or Logarithmic Equation In Exercises 85–88, solve for x accurate to three decimal places.

85. $e^{\ln 6x} = 19$

86. $e^{-3x+2} = 8$

87. $\ln \sqrt{x + 1} = 2$

88. $\ln(x - 3) = 10$

P   Performance Task

Height of a Ferris Wheel Car

The Ferris wheel was designed by U.S. engineer George Ferris (1859–1896). The first Ferris wheel (shown at the right) was built for the 1893 World's Columbian Exposition in Chicago and later used at the 1904 Louisiana Purchase Exposition in St. Louis. This wheel had a diameter of 250 feet, and each of its 36 cars could hold 60 passengers.

Exercises

In Exercises 1–3, use the following information. A Ferris wheel with a diameter of 100 feet rotates at a constant rate of 4 revolutions per minute. Let the center of the Ferris wheel be at the origin.

1. **Writing and Using an Equation** Each car on the Ferris wheel travels around a circle.

   (a) Write an equation of the circle, where x and y are measured in feet. (For a review of writing equations of circles, see Appendix C.2.)

   (b) Sketch a graph of the equation you wrote in part (a).

   (c) Use the Vertical Line Test to determine whether y is a function of x.

   (d) What does your answer to part (c) mean in the context of the problem?

2. **Writing and Using an Equation** The height h (in feet) from the bottom of a Ferris wheel car located at the point (x, y) to the ground is given by $h = 50 + y$, where y is related to the angle θ (in radians) by the equation $y = 50 \sin \theta$, as shown in the figure.

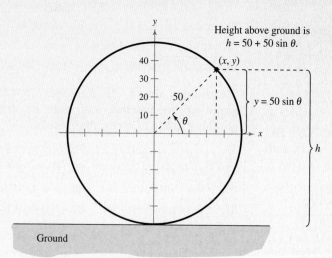

   (a) Write an equation of the height h in terms of time t (in minutes). (*Hint:* One revolution is 2π radians.) Assume that the clearance between the bottom of each car and the ground is negligible when the car is at its minimum height.

   (b) Sketch a graph of the equation you wrote in part (a).

   (c) Use the Vertical Line Test to determine whether h is a function of t.

   (d) What does your answer to part (c) mean in the context of the problem?

3. **Transforming an Equation** The equation you wrote in Exercise 2(a) yields a height of 50 feet when $t = 0$. Alter the equation so that the height of the car is 0 feet when $t = 0$. Justify your answer.

1 Limits and Their Properties

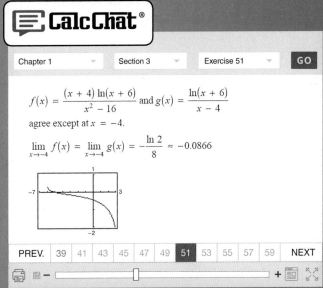

1.3 Free-Falling Object *(Exercises 109 and 110, p. 86)*

1.5 Average Speed *(Exercise 76, p. 107)*

57

1.1   A Preview of Calculus

▶ Understand what calculus is and how it compares with precalculus.
▶ Understand that the tangent line problem is basic to calculus.
▶ Understand that the area problem is also basic to calculus.

What Is Calculus?

Calculus is the mathematics of change. For instance, calculus is the mathematics of velocities, accelerations, tangent lines, slopes, areas, volumes, arc lengths, centroids, curvatures, and a variety of other concepts that have enabled scientists, engineers, and economists to model real-life situations.

Although precalculus mathematics also deals with velocities, accelerations, tangent lines, slopes, and so on, there is a fundamental difference between precalculus mathematics and calculus. Precalculus mathematics is more static, whereas calculus is more dynamic. Here are some examples.

- An object traveling at a constant velocity can be analyzed with precalculus mathematics. To analyze the velocity of an accelerating object, you need calculus.
- The slope of a line can be analyzed with precalculus mathematics. To analyze the slope of a curve, you need calculus.
- The curvature of a circle is constant and can be analyzed with precalculus mathematics. To analyze the variable curvature of a general curve, you need calculus.
- The area of a rectangle can be analyzed with precalculus mathematics. To analyze the area under a general curve, you need calculus.

Each of these situations involves the same general strategy—the reformulation of precalculus mathematics through the use of a limit process. So, one way to answer the question "What is calculus?" is to say that calculus is a "limit machine" that involves three stages. The first stage is precalculus mathematics, such as the slope of a line or the area of a rectangle. The second stage is the limit process, and the third stage is a new calculus formulation, such as a derivative or integral.

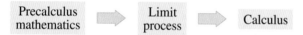

Some students try to learn calculus as if it were simply a collection of new formulas. This is unfortunate. If you reduce calculus to the memorization of differentiation and integration formulas, you will miss a great deal of understanding, self-confidence, and satisfaction.

On the next two pages are listed some familiar precalculus concepts coupled with their calculus counterparts. Throughout the text, your goal should be to learn how precalculus formulas and techniques are used as building blocks to produce the more general calculus formulas and techniques.

As you proceed through this text, come back to this discussion repeatedly. Try to keep track of where you are relative to the three stages involved in the study of calculus. For instance, note how these chapters relate to the three stages.

Chapter P: Preparation for Calculus   Precalculus

Chapter 1: Limits and Their Properties   Limit process

Chapter 2: Differentiation   Calculus

This cycle is repeated many times on a smaller scale throughout the text.

Remark

As you progress through this course, remember that learning calculus is just one of your goals. Your most important goal is to learn how to use calculus to model and solve real-life problems. Here are a few problem-solving strategies that may help you.

- Be sure you understand the question. What is given? What are you asked to find?
- Outline a plan. There are many approaches you could use: look for a pattern, solve a simpler problem, work backwards, draw a diagram, use technology, or any of many other approaches.
- Complete your plan. Be sure to answer the question Verbalize your answer. For example, rather than writing the answer as $x = 4.6$, it would be better to write the answer as, "The area of the region is 4.6 square meters."
- Look back at your work. Does your answer make sense? Is there a way you can check the reasonableness of your answer?

Without Calculus	With Differential Calculus
Value of $f(x)$ when $x = c$	Limit of $f(x)$ as x approaches c
Slope of a line	Slope of a curve
Secant line to a curve	Tangent line to a curve
Average rate of change between $t = a$ and $t = b$	Instantaneous rate of change at $t = c$
Curvature of a circle	Curvature of a curve
Height of a curve when $x = c$	Maximum height of a curve on an interval
Tangent plane to a sphere	Tangent plane to a surface
Direction of motion along a line	Direction of motion along a curve

Without Calculus		With Integral Calculus	
Area of a rectangle		Area under a curve	
Work done by a constant force		Work done by a variable force	
Center of a rectangle		Centroid of a region	
Length of a line segment		Length of an arc	
Surface area of a cylinder		Surface area of a solid of revolution	
Mass of a solid of constant density		Mass of a solid of variable density	
Volume of a rectangular solid		Volume of a region under a surface	
Sum of a finite number of terms	$a_1 + a_2 + \cdots + a_n = S$	Sum of an infinite number of terms	$a_1 + a_2 + a_3 + \cdots = S$

The Tangent Line Problem

The notion of a limit is fundamental to the study of calculus. The following brief descriptions of two classic problems in calculus—*the tangent line problem* and *the area problem*—should give you some idea of the way limits are used in calculus.

In the tangent line problem, you are given a function f and a point P on its graph and are asked to find an equation of the tangent line to the graph at point P, as shown in Figure 1.1.

Except for cases involving a vertical tangent line, the problem of finding the **tangent line** at a point P is equivalent to finding the *slope* of the tangent line at P. You can approximate this slope by using a line through the point of tangency and a second point on the curve, as shown in Figure 1.2(a). Such a line is called a **secant line.** If $P(c, f(c))$ is the point of tangency and

$$Q(c + \Delta x, f(c + \Delta x))$$

is a second point on the graph of f, then the slope of the secant line through these two points can be found using precalculus and is

$$m_{\text{sec}} = \frac{f(c + \Delta x) - f(c)}{c + \Delta x - c} = \frac{f(c + \Delta x) - f(c)}{\Delta x}.$$

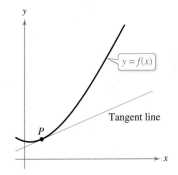

The tangent line to the graph of f at P

Figure 1.1

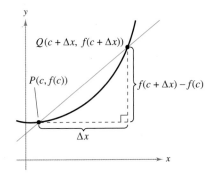

(a) The secant line through $(c, f(c))$ and $(c + \Delta x, f(c + \Delta x))$

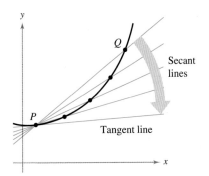

(b) As Q approaches P, the secant lines approach the tangent line.

Figure 1.2

As point Q approaches point P, the slopes of the secant lines approach the slope of the tangent line, as shown in Figure 1.2(b). When such a "limiting position" exists, the slope of the tangent line is said to be the **limit** of the slopes of the secant lines. (Much more will be said about this important calculus concept in Chapter 2.)

Exploration

The following points lie on the graph of $f(x) = x^2$.

$$Q_1(1.5, f(1.5)), \quad Q_2(1.1, f(1.1)), \quad Q_3(1.01, f(1.01)),$$

$$Q_4(1.001, f(1.001)), \quad Q_5(1.0001, f(1.0001))$$

Each successive point gets closer to the point $P(1, 1)$. Find the slopes of the secant lines through Q_1 and P, Q_2 and P, and so on. Graph these secant lines on a graphing utility. Then use your results to estimate the slope of the tangent line to the graph of f at the point P.

The Area Problem

In the tangent line problem, you saw how the limit process can be applied to the slope of a line to find the slope of a general curve. A second classic problem in calculus is finding the area of a plane region that is bounded by the graphs of functions. This problem can also be solved with a limit process. In this case, the limit process is applied to the area of a rectangle to find the area of a general region.

As a simple example, consider the region bounded by the graph of the function $y = f(x)$, the x-axis, and the vertical lines $x = a$ and $x = b$, as shown in Figure 1.3. You can approximate the area of the region with several rectangular regions, as shown in Figure 1.4. As you increase the number of rectangles, the approximation tends to become better and better because the amount of area missed by the rectangles decreases. Your goal is to determine the limit of the sum of the areas of the rectangles as the number of rectangles increases without bound.

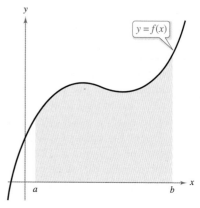

Area under a curve

Figure 1.3

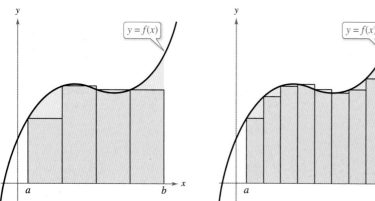

Approximation using four rectangles

Figure 1.4

Approximation using eight rectangles

The tangent line problem and the area problem are closely related. You will learn about the relationship between these two problems when you study the Fundamental Theorem of Calculus in Chapter 4.

Exploration

Consider the region bounded by the graphs of $f(x) = x^2$, $y = 0$, and $x = 1$, as shown in part (a) of the figure. The area of the region can be approximated by two sets of rectangles—one set inscribed within the region and the other set circumscribed over the region, as shown in parts (b) and (c). Find the sum of the areas of each set of rectangles. Then use your results to approximate the area of the region.

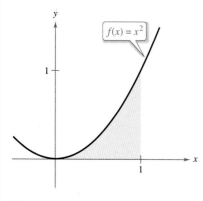

(a) Bounded region

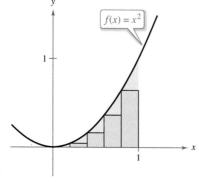

(b) Inscribed rectangles

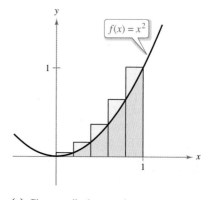

(c) Circumscribed rectangles

Precalculus or Calculus In Exercises 1–4, decide whether you can solve the problem using precalculus. If you can, solve it. If the problem seems to require calculus, explain your reasoning and use a graphical or numerical approach to estimate the solution.

1. Find the distance traveled in 15 seconds by an object traveling at a constant velocity of 20 feet per second.

2. Find the distance traveled in 15 seconds by an object moving with a velocity of $v(t) = 20 + 7 \cos t$ feet per second.

3. RATE OF CHANGE

A bicyclist is riding on a path modeled by the function $f(x) = 0.04(8x - x^2)$, where x and $f(x)$ are measured in miles (see figure). Find the rate of change of elevation at $x = 2$.

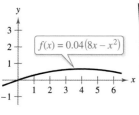

4. A particle moves along a path modeled by the function $f(x) = 0.45x$, where x and $f(x)$ are measured in inches (see figure). Find the rate of change of $f(x)$ at $x = 3$.

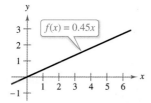

Precalculus or Calculus In Exercises 5–10, determine whether you can find the area of the region using precalculus. If you can, find it. If the problem seems to require calculus, explain your reasoning and use a graphical or numerical approach to estimate the solution.

5.
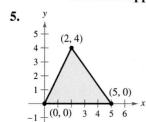

6.
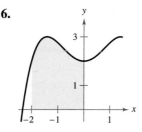

7.
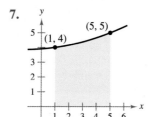

8.
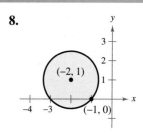

9.
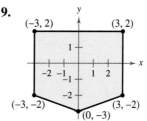

10.
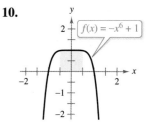

 Finding Volume In Exercises 11 and 12, find the volume of the solid shown.

11.
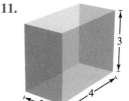

12.
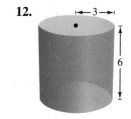

13. **Secant Lines** Consider the function $f(x) = \sqrt{x}$ and the point $P(4, 2)$ on the graph of f.

   (a) Graph f and the secant lines passing through $P(4, 2)$ and $Q(x, f(x))$ for x-values of 1, 3, and 5.

   (b) Find the slope of each secant line.

   (c) Use the results of part (b) to estimate the slope of the tangent line to the graph of f at $P(4, 2)$. Describe how to improve your approximation of the slope.

14. **Secant Lines** Consider the function

   $$f(x) = 6x - x^2$$

   and the point $P(2, 8)$ on the graph of f.

   (a) Graph f and the secant lines passing through $P(2, 8)$ and $Q(x, f(x))$ for x-values of 3, 2.5, and 1.5.

   (b) Find the slope of each secant line.

   (c) Use the results of part (b) to estimate the slope of the tangent line to the graph of f at $P(2, 8)$. Describe how to improve your approximation of the slope.

15. **Connecting Representations** Describe a classic problem in calculus equivalent to finding the slope of a curve at a point.

The symbol ▨ and a red exercise number indicates that a video solution can be seen at *CalcView.com*.

Erik Isakson/Tetra images/Getty Images

16. **HOW DO YOU SEE IT?** How would you describe the instantaneous rate of change of an automobile's position on a highway?

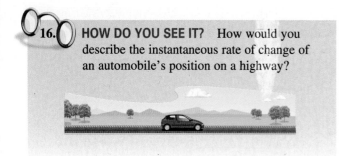

17. Approximating Area Use the rectangles in each graph to approximate the area of the region bounded by $y = 5/x$, $y = 0$, $x = 1$, and $x = 5$. Describe how you could continue this process to obtain a more accurate approximation of the area.

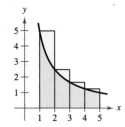 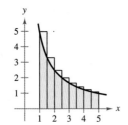

18. Approximating Area Use the rectangles in each graph to approximate the area of the region bounded by $y = \sin x$, $y = 0$, $x = 0$, and $x = \pi$. Describe how you could continue this process to obtain a more accurate approximation of the area.

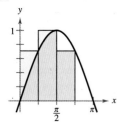 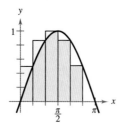

EXPLORING CONCEPTS

19. Approximating the Length of a Curve Consider the length of the graph of $f(x) = 5/x$ from $(1, 5)$ to $(5, 1)$.

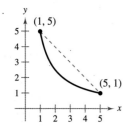 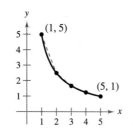

(a) Approximate the length of the curve by finding the distance between its two endpoints, as shown in the first figure.

(b) Approximate the length of the curve by finding the sum of the lengths of four line segments, as shown in the second figure.

(c) Which approximation is more accurate? Explain.

EXPLORING CONCEPTS (continued)

20. Approximating the Length of a Curve Describe how to continue the process in Exercise 19 to obtain more accurate approximations of the length of the curve.

21. Finding Area Describe the process of approximating the area of a region bounded by the graph of a function $y = f(x)$, the x-axis, and two vertical lines.

22. Think About It How do you think the slope of the tangent line to the graph of f at $(1, 2)$ compares to the slope of the tangent line at $(2, 4)$? Explain your reasoning.

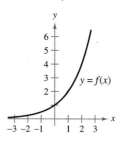

Calculus AP® – Exam Preparation Questions

23. Multiple Choice The table gives the slope of the secant line through the points $P(1, -3)$ and $Q(x, y)$ on the graph of $f(x) = x^2 - 4$.

$Q(x, y)$	Slope
$(1.01, -2.98)$	2.0
$(1.1, -2.79)$	2.1
$(1.5, -1.75)$	2.5
$(2, 0)$	3.0

Which is the best estimate of the slope of the tangent line to the graph of f at the point $(1, -3)$?

(A) 1   (B) 2

(C) 5   (D) undefined

24. Multiple Choice Which value best approximates the area of the region shown in the graph?

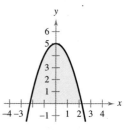

(A) 10   (B) 14

(C) 18   (D) 20

1.2   Finding Limits Graphically and Numerically

▶ Estimate a limit using a numerical or graphical approach.
▶ Learn different ways that a limit can fail to exist.
▶ Study and use a formal definition of limit.

An Introduction to Limits

To sketch the graph of the function

$$f(x) = \frac{x^3 - 1}{x - 1}$$

for values other than $x = 1$, you can use standard curve-sketching techniques. At $x = 1$, however, it is not clear what to expect. To get an idea of the behavior of the graph of f near $x = 1$, you can use two sets of x-values—one set that approaches 1 from the left and one set that approaches 1 from the right, as shown in the table.

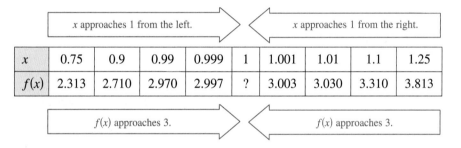

	x approaches 1 from the left.					x approaches 1 from the right.			
x	0.75	0.9	0.99	0.999	1	1.001	1.01	1.1	1.25
$f(x)$	2.313	2.710	2.970	2.997	?	3.003	3.030	3.310	3.813

	$f(x)$ approaches 3.		$f(x)$ approaches 3.	

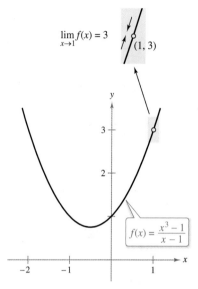

$$\lim_{x \to 1} f(x) = 3$$
$(1, 3)$

$$f(x) = \frac{x^3 - 1}{x - 1}$$

The limit of $f(x)$ as x approaches 1 is 3.
Figure 1.5

The graph of f is a parabola that has a hole at the point $(1, 3)$, as shown in Figure 1.5. Although x cannot equal 1, you can move arbitrarily close to 1, and as a result $f(x)$ moves arbitrarily close to 3. Using limit notation, you can write

$$\lim_{x \to 1} f(x) = 3. \qquad \text{This is read as "the limit of } f(x) \text{ as } x \text{ approaches 1 is 3."}$$

This discussion leads to an informal definition of limit. If $f(x)$ becomes arbitrarily close to a single number L as x approaches c from either side, then the **limit** of $f(x)$ as x approaches c is L. This limit is written as

$$\lim_{x \to c} f(x) = L.$$

Exploration

The discussion above gives an example of how you can estimate a limit *numerically* by constructing a table and *graphically* by drawing a graph. Estimate the following limit numerically by completing the table.

$$\lim_{x \to 2} \frac{x^2 - 3x + 2}{x - 2}$$

x	1.75	1.9	1.99	1.999	2	2.001	2.01	2.1	2.25
$f(x)$	?	?	?	?	?	?	?	?	?

Then use a graphing utility to estimate the limit graphically.

Connecting Representations

Notice when you substitute $x = 2$ into

$$f(x) = \frac{x^2 - 3x + 2}{x - 2}$$

it produces the fractional form $\frac{0}{0}$, which is called an *indeterminate form.* You will learn more about this form in Section 1.3.

EXAMPLE 1 Estimating a Limit

Evaluate the function $f(x) = x/\left(\sqrt{x+1} - 1\right)$ at several x-values near 0 and use the results to estimate the limit

$$\lim_{x \to 0} \frac{x}{\sqrt{x+1} - 1}.$$

Numerical Solution

Create a table that shows $f(x)$ for several x-values near 0.

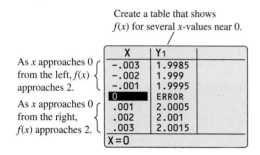

As x approaches 0 from the left, $f(x)$ approaches 2.

As x approaches 0 from the right, $f(x)$ approaches 2.

X	Y₁
−.003	1.9985
−.002	1.999
−.001	1.9995
0	ERROR
.001	2.0005
.002	2.001
.003	2.0015

X=0

From the results shown in the table, you can estimate the limit to be 2.

Graphical Solution

Use a graphing utility to graph $y_1 = \dfrac{x}{\sqrt{x+1} - 1}$.

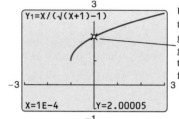

Y₁=X/(√(X+1)−1)

X=1E−4   Y=2.00005

Use the *trace* feature to determine that as x gets closer to 0, $f(x)$ gets closer and closer to 2 from the left and from the right.

From the graph, you can estimate the limit to be 2.

In Example 1, note that the function is undefined at $x = 0$, and yet $f(x)$ appears to be approaching a limit as x approaches 0. This often happens, and it is important to realize that *the existence or nonexistence of $f(x)$ at $x = c$ has no bearing on the existence of the limit of $f(x)$ as x approaches c.*

EXAMPLE 2 Finding a Limit

Find the limit of $f(x)$ as x approaches 2, where

$$f(x) = \begin{cases} 1, & x \neq 2 \\ 0, & x = 2 \end{cases}.$$

Solution

Because $f(x) = 1$ for all x other than $x = 2$, you can estimate that the limit is 1, as shown in Figure 1.6. So, you can write

$$\lim_{x \to 2} f(x) = 1.$$

The fact that $f(2) = 0$ has no bearing on the existence or value of the limit as x approaches 2. For instance, as x approaches 2, the function

$$g(x) = \begin{cases} 1, & x \neq 2 \\ 2, & x = 2 \end{cases}$$

has the same limit as f.

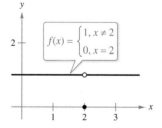

The limit of $f(x)$ as x approaches 2 is 1.
Figure 1.6

So far in this section, you have been estimating limits numerically and graphically. Each of these approaches produces an estimate of the limit. In Section 1.3, you will study analytic techniques for evaluating limits. Throughout the course, try to develop a habit of using this four-pronged approach to problem solving.

1. Numerical approach — Construct a table of values.

2. Graphical approach — Draw a graph by hand or using technology.

3. Analytic approach — Use algebra or calculus.

4. Verbal approach — Communicate the result verbally or in writing.

Limits That Fail to Exist

In the next three examples, you will examine some limits that fail to exist.

EXAMPLE 3   Different Right and Left Behavior

Show that the limit $\lim\limits_{x \to 0} \dfrac{|x|}{x}$ does not exist.

Solution

Consider the graph of the function

$$f(x) = \frac{|x|}{x}.$$

In Figure 1.7 and from the definition of absolute value,

$$|x| = \begin{cases} x, & x \geq 0 \\ -x, & x < 0 \end{cases} \qquad \text{Definition of absolute value}$$

you can see that

$$\frac{|x|}{x} = \begin{cases} 1, & x > 0 \\ -1, & x < 0 \end{cases}.$$

So, no matter how close x gets to 0, there will be both positive and negative x-values that yield $f(x) = 1$ or $f(x) = -1$. Specifically, if δ (the lowercase Greek letter delta) is a positive number, then for x-values satisfying the inequality $0 < |x| < \delta$, you can classify the values of $|x|/x$ as -1 or 1 on the intervals

$$(-\delta, 0) \qquad \text{or} \qquad (0, \delta).$$

| Negative x-values yield $|x|/x = -1$. | Positive x-values yield $|x|/x = 1$. |

Because $|x|/x$ approaches a different number from the right side of 0 than it approaches from the left side, the limit $\lim\limits_{x \to 0} \left(|x|/x\right)$ does not exist.

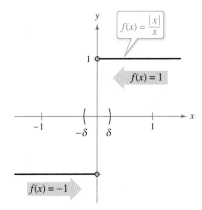

$\lim\limits_{x \to 0} f(x)$ does not exist.

Figure 1.7

─── **Insight** ───

On the AP® Exam, a limit that does not exist may be referred to as "nonexistent."

EXAMPLE 4   Unbounded Behavior

Discuss the existence of the limit $\lim\limits_{x \to 0} \dfrac{1}{x^2}$.

Solution

Consider the graph of the function $f(x) = 1/x^2$. In Figure 1.8, you can see that as x approaches 0 from either the right or the left, $f(x)$ increases without bound. This means that by choosing x close enough to 0, you can force $f(x)$ to be as large as you want. For instance, $f(x)$ will be greater than 100 when you choose x within $\frac{1}{10}$ of 0. That is,

$$0 < |x| < \frac{1}{10} \implies f(x) = \frac{1}{x^2} > 100.$$

Similarly, you can force $f(x)$ to be greater than 1,000,000, as shown.

$$0 < |x| < \frac{1}{1000} \implies f(x) = \frac{1}{x^2} > 1,000,000$$

Because $f(x)$ does not become arbitrarily close to a single number L as x approaches 0, you can conclude that the limit does not exist.

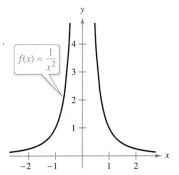

$\lim\limits_{x \to 0} f(x)$ does not exist.

Figure 1.8

EXAMPLE 5 Oscillating Behavior

See LarsonCalculusforAP.com for an interactive version of this type of example.

Discuss the existence of the limit $\lim\limits_{x \to 0} \sin (1/x)$.

Solution

Let $f(x) = \sin(1/x)$. In Figure 1.9, you can see that as x approaches 0, $f(x)$ oscillates between -1 and 1. So, the limit does not exist because no matter how small you choose δ, it is possible to choose x_1 and x_2 within δ units of 0 such that $\sin(1/x_1) = 1$ and $\sin(1/x_2) = -1$, as shown in the table.

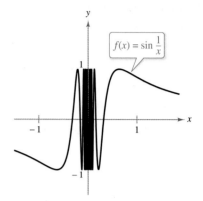

$\lim\limits_{x \to 0} f(x)$ does not exist.
Figure 1.9

x	$\dfrac{2}{\pi}$	$\dfrac{2}{3\pi}$	$\dfrac{2}{5\pi}$	$\dfrac{2}{7\pi}$	$\dfrac{2}{9\pi}$	$\dfrac{2}{11\pi}$	$x \to 0$
$\sin \dfrac{1}{x}$	1	-1	1	-1	1	-1	Limit does not exist.

Common Types of Behavior Associated with Nonexistence of a Limit

1. $f(x)$ approaches a different number from the right side of c than it approaches from the left side.
2. $f(x)$ increases or decreases without bound as x approaches c.
3. $f(x)$ oscillates between two fixed values as x approaches c.

In addition to $f(x) = \sin(1/x)$, there are many other interesting functions that have unusual limit behavior. An often cited one is the *Dirichlet function*

$$f(x) = \begin{cases} 0, & \text{if } x \text{ is rational} \\ 1, & \text{if } x \text{ is irrational} \end{cases}.$$

Because this function has *no limit* at any real number c, it is *not continuous* at any real number c. You will study continuity more closely in Section 1.4.

Technology Pitfall

When you use a graphing utility to investigate the behavior of a function near the x-value at which you are trying to evaluate a limit, remember that you cannot always trust the graphs that graphing utilities draw. When you use a graphing utility to graph the function in Example 5 over an interval containing 0, you will most likely obtain an incorrect graph such as the one shown in Figure 1.10. The reason that a graphing utility cannot show the correct graph is that the graph has infinitely many oscillations over any interval that contains 0.

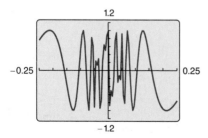

Incorrect graph of $f(x) = \sin(1/x)$
Figure 1.10

A Formal Definition of Limit

Consider again the informal definition of limit. If $f(x)$ becomes arbitrarily close to a single number L as x approaches c from either side, then the limit of $f(x)$ as x approaches c is L, written as

$$\lim_{x \to c} f(x) = L.$$

At first glance, this definition looks fairly technical. Even so, it is informal because exact meanings have not yet been given to the two phrases

"$f(x)$ becomes arbitrarily close to L"

and

"x approaches c."

The first person to assign mathematically rigorous meanings to these two phrases was Augustin-Louis Cauchy. His **ε-δ definition of limit** is the standard used today.

In Figure 1.11, let ε (the lowercase Greek letter epsilon) represent a (small) positive number. Then the phrase "$f(x)$ becomes arbitrarily close to L" means that $f(x)$ lies in the interval $(L - \varepsilon, L + \varepsilon)$. Using absolute value, you can write this as

$$|f(x) - L| < \varepsilon.$$

Similarly, the phrase "x approaches c" means that there exists a positive number δ such that x lies in either the interval $(c - \delta, c)$ or the interval $(c, c + \delta)$. This fact can be concisely expressed by the double inequality

$$0 < |x - c| < \delta.$$

The first inequality

$$0 < |x - c| \qquad \text{The distance between } x \text{ and } c \text{ is more than 0.}$$

expresses the fact that $x \neq c$. The second inequality

$$|x - c| < \delta \qquad x \text{ is within } \delta \text{ units of } c.$$

says that x is within a distance δ of c.

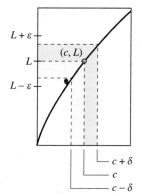

The ε-δ definition of the limit of $f(x)$ as x approaches c.

Figure 1.11

Definition of Limit

Let f be a function defined on an open interval containing c (except possibly at c), and let L be a real number. The statement

$$\lim_{x \to c} f(x) = L$$

means that for each $\varepsilon > 0$ there exists a $\delta > 0$ such that if

$$0 < |x - c| < \delta$$

then

$$|f(x) - L| < \varepsilon.$$

Connecting Representations

Throughout this text, the expression

$$\lim_{x \to c} f(x) = L$$

implies two statements—the limit exists *and* the limit is L.

Some functions do not have limits as x approaches c, but those that do cannot have two different limits as x approaches c. That is, *if the limit of a function exists, then the limit is unique.* (See Exercise 73.)

The next three examples should help you develop a better understanding of the ε-δ definition of limit.

EXAMPLE 6   Finding a δ for a Given ε

Given the limit

$$\lim_{x \to 3} (2x - 5) = 1$$

find δ such that

$$|(2x - 5) - 1| < 0.01$$

whenever

$$0 < |x - 3| < \delta.$$

Solution

In this problem, you are working with a given value of ε—namely, $\varepsilon = 0.01$. To find an appropriate δ, try to establish a connection between the absolute values

$$|(2x - 5) - 1| \quad \text{and} \quad |x - 3|.$$

Notice that

$$|(2x - 5) - 1| = |2x - 6| = 2|x - 3|.$$

Because the inequality $|(2x - 5) - 1| < 0.01$ is equivalent to $2|x - 3| < 0.01$, you can choose

$$\delta = \tfrac{1}{2}(0.01) = 0.005.$$

This choice works because

$$0 < |x - 3| < 0.005$$

implies that

$$|(2x - 5) - 1| = 2|x - 3| < 2(0.005) = 0.01.$$

As you can see in Figure 1.12, for x-values within 0.005 of 3 ($x \ne 3$), the values of $f(x)$ are within 0.01 of 1.

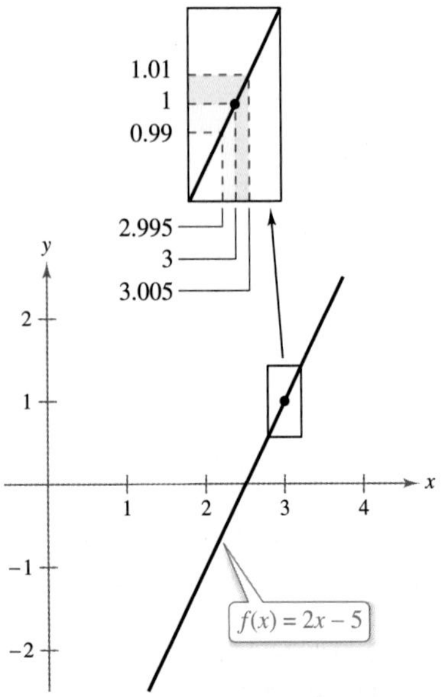

> **Communication and Notation**
>
> When encountering new notations in mathematics, be sure you know how the notations are read. For instance, the limit in Example 6 is read as "the limit of $2x$ minus 5 as x approaches 3 is 1."

> **Justification**
>
> In Example 6, note that 0.005 is the *largest* value of δ that will guarantee
>
> $$|(2x - 5) - 1| < 0.01$$
>
> whenever
>
> $$0 < |x - 3| < \delta.$$
>
> Any *smaller* positive value of δ would also work.

The limit of $f(x)$ as x approaches 3 is 1.
Figure 1.12

In Example 6, you found a δ-value for a *given* ε. This does not prove the existence of the limit. To do that, you must prove that you can find a δ for *any* ε, as shown in the next example.

EXAMPLE 7   Using the ε-δ Definition of Limit

Use the ε-δ definition of limit to prove that $\lim\limits_{x \to 2} (3x - 2) = 4$.

Solution

You must show that for each $\varepsilon > 0$, there exists a $\delta > 0$ such that

$$|(3x - 2) - 4| < \varepsilon$$

whenever

$$0 < |x - 2| < \delta.$$

Because your choice of δ depends on ε, you need to establish a connection between the absolute values $|(3x - 2) - 4|$ and $|x - 2|$.

$$|(3x - 2) - 4| = |3x - 6| = 3|x - 2|$$

So, for a given $\varepsilon > 0$, you can choose $\delta = \varepsilon/3$. This choice works because

$$0 < |x - 2| < \delta = \frac{\varepsilon}{3}$$

implies that

$$|(3x - 2) - 4| = 3|x - 2| < 3\left(\frac{\varepsilon}{3}\right) = \varepsilon.$$

As you can see in Figure 1.13, for x-values within δ of 2 ($x \neq 2$), the values of $f(x)$ are within ε of 4.

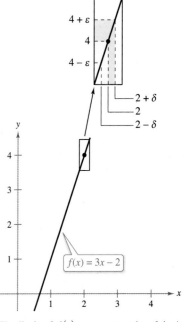

The limit of $f(x)$ as x approaches 2 is 4.
Figure 1.13

EXAMPLE 8   Using the ε-δ Definition of Limit

Use the ε-δ definition of limit to prove that $\lim\limits_{x \to 2} x^2 = 4$.

Solution

You must show that for each $\varepsilon > 0$, there exists a $\delta > 0$ such that

$$|x^2 - 4| < \varepsilon$$

whenever

$$0 < |x - 2| < \delta.$$

To find an appropriate δ, begin by writing $|x^2 - 4| = |x - 2||x + 2|$. You are interested in values of x close to 2, so choose x in the interval $(1, 3)$. To satisfy this restriction, let $\delta < 1$. Furthermore, for all x in the interval $(1, 3)$, $x + 2 < 5$ and thus $|x + 2| < 5$. So, letting δ be the minimum of $\varepsilon/5$ and 1, it follows that, whenever $0 < |x - 2| < \delta$, you have

$$|x^2 - 4| = |x - 2||x + 2| < \left(\frac{\varepsilon}{5}\right)(5) = \varepsilon.$$

As you can see in Figure 1.14, for x-values within δ of 2 ($x \neq 2$), the values of $f(x)$ are within ε of 4.

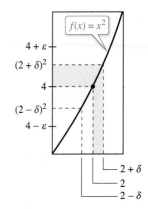

The limit of $f(x)$ as x approaches 2 is 4.
Figure 1.14

Throughout this chapter, you will use the ε-δ definition of limit primarily to prove theorems about limits and to establish the existence or nonexistence of particular types of limits. For *finding* limits, you will learn techniques that are easier to use than the ε-δ definition of limit.

1.2 Exercises

See *CalcChat.com* for tutorial help and worked-out solutions to odd-numbered exercises.

Estimating a Limit Numerically In Exercises 1–6, complete the table and use the result to estimate the limit. Use a graphing utility to graph the function to confirm your result.

1. $\lim\limits_{x \to 4} \dfrac{x - 4}{x^2 - 5x + 4}$

x	3.9	3.99	3.999	4	4.001	4.01	4.1
$f(x)$				?			

2. $\lim\limits_{x \to 0} \dfrac{\sqrt{x + 1} - 1}{x}$

x	-0.1	-0.01	-0.001	0	0.001	0.01	0.1
$f(x)$				?			

3. $\lim\limits_{x \to 0} \dfrac{\sin x}{x}$

x	-0.1	-0.01	-0.001	0	0.001	0.01	0.1
$f(x)$				?			

4. $\lim\limits_{x \to 0} \dfrac{\cos x - 1}{x}$

x	-0.1	-0.01	-0.001	0	0.001	0.01	0.1
$f(x)$				?			

5. $\lim\limits_{x \to 0} \dfrac{e^x - 1}{x}$

x	-0.1	-0.01	-0.001	0	0.001	0.01	0.1
$f(x)$				?			

6. $\lim\limits_{x \to 0} \dfrac{\ln(x + 1)}{x}$

x	-0.1	-0.01	-0.001	0	0.001	0.01	0.1
$f(x)$				?			

Estimating a Limit Numerically In Exercises 7–16, create a table of values for the function and use the result to estimate the limit (if it exists). If the limit does not exist, explain why. Use a graphing utility to graph the function to confirm your result.

7. $\lim\limits_{x \to 1} \dfrac{x - 2}{x^2 + x - 6}$

8. $\lim\limits_{x \to 1} \dfrac{x^4 - 1}{x^6 - 1}$

9. $\lim\limits_{x \to 0} \dfrac{\sin 2x}{x}$

10. $\lim\limits_{x \to 0} \dfrac{\tan x}{\tan 2x}$

11. $\lim\limits_{x \to -6} \dfrac{\sqrt{10 - x} - 4}{x + 6}$

12. $\lim\limits_{x \to 2} \dfrac{[x/(x + 1)] - (2/3)}{x - 2}$

13. $\lim\limits_{x \to 0} \dfrac{2}{x^3}$

14. $\lim\limits_{x \to 0} \dfrac{3|x|}{x^2}$

15. $\lim\limits_{x \to 0} \dfrac{4}{1 + e^{1/x}}$

16. $\lim\limits_{x \to 3} \dfrac{\ln x}{x - 3}$

Finding a Limit Graphically In Exercises 17–24, use the graph to find the limit (if it exists). If the limit does not exist, explain why.

17. $\lim\limits_{x \to 3} (4 - x)$

18. $\lim\limits_{x \to 0} \sec x$

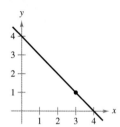

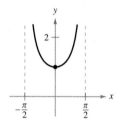

19. $\lim\limits_{x \to 2} f(x)$

$f(x) = \begin{cases} 4 - x, & x \neq 2 \\ 0, & x = 2 \end{cases}$

20. $\lim\limits_{x \to 1} f(x)$

$f(x) = \begin{cases} x^2 + 3, & x \neq 1 \\ 2, & x = 1 \end{cases}$

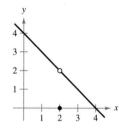

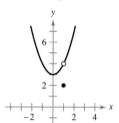

21. $\lim\limits_{x \to 2} \dfrac{|x - 2|}{x - 2}$

22. $\lim\limits_{x \to 0} \dfrac{4}{2 + e^{1/x}}$

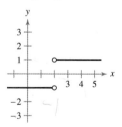

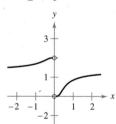

23. $\lim\limits_{x \to \pi/2} \tan x$

24. $\lim\limits_{x \to 0} \cos \dfrac{1}{x}$

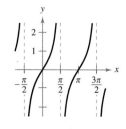

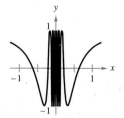

Graphical Reasoning   **In Exercises 25 and 26, use the graph of the function f to decide whether the value of the given quantity exists. If it does, find it. If not, explain why.**

25. (a) $f(0)$

    (b) $\lim_{x \to 0} f(x)$

    (c) $f(1)$

    (d) $\lim_{x \to 1} f(x)$

    (e) $f(4)$

    (f) $\lim_{x \to 4} f(x)$

26. (a) $f(-2)$

    (b) $\lim_{x \to -2} f(x)$

    (c) $f(0)$

    (d) $\lim_{x \to 0} f(x)$

    (e) $f(2)$

    (f) $\lim_{x \to 2} f(x)$

    (g) $f(4)$

    (h) $\lim_{x \to 4} f(x)$

   Limits of a Piecewise Function   In Exercises 27 and 28, sketch the graph of f. Then identify the values of c for which $\lim_{x \to c} f(x)$ exists.

27. $f(x) = \begin{cases} x^2, & x \le 2 \\ 8 - 2x, & 2 < x < 4 \\ 4, & x \ge 4 \end{cases}$

28. $f(x) = \begin{cases} \sin x, & x < 0 \\ 1 - \cos x, & 0 \le x \le \pi \\ \cos x, & x > \pi \end{cases}$

Sketching a Graph   In Exercises 29 and 30, sketch a graph of a function f that satisfies the given values. (There are many correct answers.)

29. $f(0)$ is undefined.

    $\lim_{x \to 0} f(x) = 4$

    $f(2) = 6$

    $\lim_{x \to 2} f(x) = 3$

30. $f(-2) = 0$

    $f(2) = 0$

    $\lim_{x \to -2} f(x) = 0$

    $\lim_{x \to 2} f(x)$ does not exist.

31. **Finding a δ for a Given ε**   The graph of $f(x) = x + 1$ is shown in the figure. Find δ such that if $0 < |x - 2| < \delta$, then $|f(x) - 3| < 0.4$.

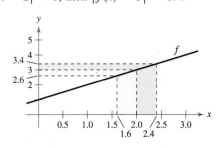

32. **Finding a δ for a Given ε**   The graph of

    $$f(x) = \frac{1}{x - 1}$$

    is shown in the figure. Find δ such that if $0 < |x - 2| < \delta$, then $|f(x) - 1| < 0.01$.

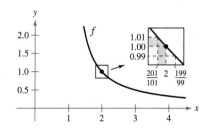

33. **Finding a δ for a Given ε**   The graph of

    $$f(x) = 2 - \frac{1}{x}$$

    is shown in the figure. Find δ such that if $0 < |x - 1| < \delta$, then $|f(x) - 1| < 0.1$.

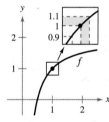

Figure for 33   Figure for 34

34. **Finding a δ for a Given ε**   The graph of $f(x) = x^2 - 1$ is shown in the figure. Find δ such that if $0 < |x - 2| < \delta$, then $|f(x) - 3| < 0.2$.

   Finding a δ for a Given ε In Exercises 35–38, find the limit L. Then find $\delta > 0$ such that $|f(x) - L| < 0.01$ whenever $0 < |x - c| < \delta$.

35. $\lim_{x \to 2} (3x + 2)$

36. $\lim_{x \to 6} \left(6 - \frac{x}{3} \right)$

37. $\lim_{x \to 2} (x^2 - 3)$

38. $\lim_{x \to 4} (x^2 + 6)$

   Using the ε-δ Definition of Limit   In Exercises 39–50, find the limit L. Then use the ε-δ definition to prove that the limit is L.

39. $\lim_{x \to 4} (x + 2)$

40. $\lim_{x \to -2} (4x + 5)$

41. $\lim_{x \to -4} \left(\frac{1}{2}x - 1 \right)$

42. $\lim_{x \to 3} \left(\frac{3}{4}x + 1 \right)$

43. $\lim_{x \to 6} 3$

44. $\lim_{x \to 2} (-1)$

45. $\lim_{x \to 0} \sqrt[3]{x}$

46. $\lim_{x \to 4} \sqrt{x}$

47. $\lim_{x \to -5} |x - 5|$

48. $\lim_{x \to 3} |x - 3|$

49. $\lim_{x \to 1} (x^2 + 1)$

50. $\lim_{x \to -4} (x^2 + 4x)$

Communicating   In Exercises 51 and 52, use a graphing utility to graph the function and estimate the limit (if it exists). **What is the domain of the function? Can you determine the exact domain solely by analyzing the graph? Explain. Then describe how to use a combined graphical and analytical approach to find the exact domain.**

51. $f(x) = \dfrac{\sqrt{x + 5} - 3}{x - 4}$

$\lim\limits_{x \to 4} f(x)$

52. $f(x) = \dfrac{x - 3}{x^2 - 4x + 3}$

$\lim\limits_{x \to 3} f(x)$

53. MODELING DATA

A resort rents stand up paddle boards at a rate of $25 for the first hour and $15 for each additional hour or fraction thereof. A formula for the cost C is given by

$C(t) = 25 - 15[\![1 - t]\!]$

where t is the time in hours.

(*Note:* $[\![x]\!]$ = greatest integer n such that $n \le x$. For example, $[\![3.2]\!] = 3$ and $[\![-1.6]\!] = -2$.)

(a) Use a graphing utility to graph the cost function for $0 < t \le 6$.

(b) Use the graph to complete the table and observe the behavior of the function as t approaches 3.5. Use the graph and the table to find $\lim\limits_{t \to 3.5} C(t)$.

t	3	3.3	3.4	3.5	3.6	3.7	4
C				?			

(c) Use the graph to complete the table and observe the behavior of the function as t approaches 3.

t	2	2.5	2.9	3	3.1	3.5	4
C				?			

Does the limit of $C(t)$ as t approaches 3 exist? Explain.

54. Modeling Data   Repeat Exercise 53 for

$C(t) = 30 - 18.50[\![1 - t]\!]$.

EXPLORING CONCEPTS

55. Communication and Notation   Write a brief description of the graphical meaning of the notation $\lim\limits_{x \to 8} f(x) = 25$.

56. Using the Definition of Limit   The definition of limit on page 69 requires that f is a function defined on an open interval containing c, except possibly at c. Why is this requirement necessary?

57. Connecting Representations   Describe three types of behavior associated with the nonexistence of a limit. Illustrate each type with a graph of a function.

58. Connecting Representations   Given the limit

$\lim\limits_{x \to 2} (2x + 1) = 5$

use a sketch to show the meaning of the phrase "$0 < |x - 2| < 0.25$ implies $|(2x + 1) - 5| < 0.5$."

59. Jewelry   A gem store makes souvenir rings. The intended inner circumference of a large ring is 6 centimeters.

(a) What is the intended radius of a large ring?

(b) The actual inner circumferences of large rings at the store vary from 5.9 centimeters to 6.1 centimeters. How do the radii vary?

(c) Use the ε-δ definition of limit to describe this situation, where ε is the variation of the circumference.

60. Sports   An official table tennis ball has a volume of 2.04 inches.

(a) What is the radius of an official table tennis ball?

(b) A batch of 100 table tennis balls vary in volume from 2.00 cubic inches to 2.08 cubic inches. How does the radii vary?

(c) Use the ε-δ definition of limit to describe this situation, where ε is the variation of the volume.

61. Estimating a Limit   Estimate

$\lim\limits_{x \to 0} (1 + x)^{1/x}$

by evaluating

$f(x) = (1 + x)^{1/x}$

at x-values near 0. Sketch the graph of f.

62. Estimating a Limit   Estimate

$\lim\limits_{x \to 0} \dfrac{|x + 1| - |x - 1|}{x}$

by evaluating

$f(x) = \dfrac{|x + 1| - |x - 1|}{x}$

at x-values near 0. Sketch the graph of f.

The symbol **⚡** indicates an exercise in which you are instructed to use a graphing utility. The solutions of other exercises may also be facilitated by the use of appropriate technology.

63. Graphical Analysis The statement

$$\lim_{x \to 2} \frac{x^2 - 4}{x - 2} = 4$$

means that for each $\varepsilon > 0$ there corresponds a $\delta > 0$ such that if $0 < |x - 2| < \delta$, then

$$\left| \frac{x^2 - 4}{x - 2} - 4 \right| < \varepsilon.$$

If $\varepsilon = 0.001$, then

$$\left| \frac{x^2 - 4}{x - 2} - 4 \right| < 0.001.$$

Use a graphing utility to graph each side of this inequality. Use the *zoom* feature to find an interval $(2 - \delta, 2 + \delta)$ such that the graph of the left side is below the graph of the right side of the inequality.

64. HOW DO YOU SEE IT? Use the graph of f to identify the values of c for which $\lim_{x \to c} f(x)$ exists.

(a)   (b)

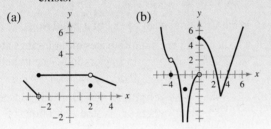

True or False? In Exercises 65–68, determine whether the statement is true or false. If it is false, explain why or give an example that shows it is false.

65. If f is undefined at $x = c$, then the limit of $f(x)$ as x approaches c does not exist.

66. If the limit of $f(x)$ as x approaches c is 0, then there must exist a number k such that $f(k) < 0.001$.

67. If $f(c) = L$, then $\lim_{x \to c} f(x) = L$.

68. If $\lim_{x \to c} f(x) = L$, then $f(c) = L$.

Determining a Limit In Exercises 69 and 70, consider the function $f(x) = \sqrt{x}$.

69. Is $\lim_{x \to 0.25} f(x) = 0.5$ a true statement? Explain.

70. Is $\lim_{x \to 0} f(x) = 0$ a true statement? Explain.

 71. Evaluating Limits Use a graphing utility to evaluate

$$\lim_{x \to 0} \frac{\sin nx}{x}$$

for several values of n. What do you notice?

 72. Evaluating Limits Use a graphing utility to evaluate

$$\lim_{x \to 0} \frac{\tan nx}{x}$$

for several values of n. What do you notice?

73. Proof Prove that if the limit of $f(x)$ as x approaches c exists, then the limit must be unique. [*Hint:* Let $\lim_{x \to c} f(x) = L_1$ and $\lim_{x \to c} f(x) = L_2$ and prove that $L_1 = L_2$.]

74. Proof Consider the line $f(x) = mx + b$, where $m \neq 0$. Use the ε-δ definition of limit to prove that $\lim_{x \to c} f(x) = mc + b$.

75. Proof Prove that $\lim_{x \to c} f(x) = L$ is equivalent to $\lim_{x \to c} [f(x) - L] = 0$.

76. Proof

(a) Given that $\lim_{x \to 0} (3x + 1)(3x - 1)x^2 + 0.01 = 0.01$, prove that there exists an open interval (a, b) containing 0 such that

$$(3x + 1)(3x - 1)x^2 + 0.01 > 0$$

for all $x \neq 0$ in (a, b).

(b) Given that $\lim_{x \to c} g(x) = L$, where $L > 0$, prove that there exists an open interval (a, b) containing c such that $g(x) > 0$ for all $x \neq c$ in (a, b).

Calculus AP® – Exam Preparation Questions

77. Multiple Choice What is the limit of $h(x) = \sin x$ as x approaches π?

(A) -1 (B) 0   (C) π (D) nonexistent

78. Multiple Choice The function $f(x) = 10/x^4$ is shown in the figure. What is $\lim_{x \to 0} f(x)$?

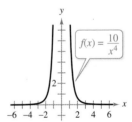

(A) 0   (B) 1   (C) 10   (D) nonexistent

79. Multiple Choice What is the limit of $f(x)$ as x approaches 0, where $f(x) = (e^{3x} - e^x)/x$?

(A) 0   (B) 2   (C) 4   (D) nonexistent

80. Multiple Choice Consider the function

$$f(x) = \begin{cases} \sqrt{x - 3}, & x > 3 \\ 6 - 2x, & x \leq 3 \end{cases}.$$

Which of the following statements is true?

  I. $\lim_{x \to 3} \sqrt{x - 3} = 0$ II. $\lim_{x \to 3} (6 - 2x) = 0$

  III. $\lim_{x \to 3} f(x) = 0$

(A) II only   (B) III only

(C) II and III only   (D) I and III only

1.3 Evaluating Limits Analytically

▶ Evaluate a limit using properties of limits.
▶ Develop and use a strategy for finding limits.
▶ Evaluate a limit using the dividing out technique.
▶ Evaluate a limit using the rationalizing technique.
▶ Evaluate a limit using the Squeeze Theorem.

Properties of Limits

In Section 1.2, you learned that the limit of $f(x)$ as x approaches c does not depend on the value of f at $x = c$. It may happen, however, that the limit is precisely $f(c)$. In such cases, you can evaluate the limit by **direct substitution.** That is,

$$\lim_{x \to c} f(x) = f(c). \qquad \text{Substitute } c \text{ for } x.$$

Such *well-behaved* functions are **continuous at c.** You will examine this concept more closely in Section 1.4.

Theorem 1.1 Some Basic Limits

Let b and c be real numbers, and let n be a positive integer.

1. $\displaystyle\lim_{x \to c} b = b$ 2. $\displaystyle\lim_{x \to c} x = c$ 3. $\displaystyle\lim_{x \to c} x^n = c^n$

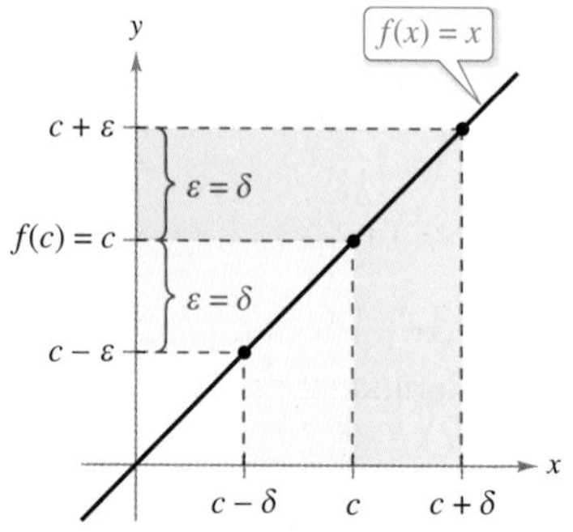

Proof

The proofs of Properties 1 and 3 of Theorem 1.1 are left as exercises (see Exercises 115 and 116). To prove Property 2, you need to show that for each $\varepsilon > 0$ there exists a $\delta > 0$ such that $|x - c| < \varepsilon$ whenever $0 < |x - c| < \delta$. To do this, choose $\delta = \varepsilon$. The second inequality then implies the first, as shown in Figure 1.15.

Figure 1.15

EXAMPLE 1 Evaluating Basic Limits

a. $\displaystyle\lim_{x \to 2} 3 = 3$ **b.** $\displaystyle\lim_{x \to -4} x = -4$ **c.** $\displaystyle\lim_{x \to 2} x^2 = 2^2 = 4$

Theorem 1.2 Properties of Limits

Let b and c be real numbers, let n be a positive integer, and let f and g be functions with the limits $\displaystyle\lim_{x \to c} f(x) = L$ and $\displaystyle\lim_{x \to c} g(x) = K$.

1. Scalar multiple: $\displaystyle\lim_{x \to c} [bf(x)] = bL$

2. Sum or difference: $\displaystyle\lim_{x \to c} [f(x) \pm g(x)] = L \pm K$

3. Product: $\displaystyle\lim_{x \to c} [f(x)g(x)] = LK$

4. Quotient: $\displaystyle\lim_{x \to c} \frac{f(x)}{g(x)} = \frac{L}{K}, \quad K \neq 0$

5. Power: $\displaystyle\lim_{x \to c} [f(x)]^n = L^n$

The proof of Property 1 of this theorem is left as an exercise (see Exercise 117). The proofs of the other four properties are given in Appendix A.

> ### Connecting Representations
>
> To become skilled at evaluating limits, you should memorize each property in words. For example, in words, Property 3 of Theorem 1.2 says that the limit of the product of two functions equals the product of their limits.

The symbol ▨ indicates a video of this proof is available at *LarsonCalculusforAP.com.*

EXAMPLE 2   The Limit of a Polynomial

Find the limit: $\lim\limits_{x \to 2} (4x^2 + 3)$.

Solution

$$\begin{aligned}
\lim_{x \to 2} (4x^2 + 3) &= \lim_{x \to 2} 4x^2 + \lim_{x \to 2} 3 && \text{Property 2, Theorem 1.2}\\
&= 4\left(\lim_{x \to 2} x^2\right) + \lim_{x \to 2} 3 && \text{Property 1, Theorem 1.2}\\
&= 4(2^2) + 3 && \text{Properties 1 and 3, Theorem 1.1}\\
&= 19 && \text{Simplify.}
\end{aligned}$$

Use the *trace* feature of a graphing utility to check this answer (see Figure 1.16).

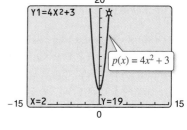

The limit of $p(x)$ as x approaches 2 is 19.
Figure 1.16

In Example 2, note that the limit (as x approaches 2) of the *polynomial function* $p(x) = 4x^2 + 3$ is simply the value of p at $x = 2$.

$$\lim_{x \to 2} p(x) = p(2) = 4(2^2) + 3 = 19$$

This *direct substitution* property is valid for all polynomial functions. Direct substitution can also be used to find the limit of a rational function (unless the substitution results in a zero denominator).

Theorem 1.3   Limits of Polynomial and Rational Functions

If p is a polynomial function and c is a real number, then

$$\lim_{x \to c} p(x) = p(c).$$

If r is a rational function given by $r(x) = p(x)/q(x)$ and c is a real number such that $q(c) \neq 0$, then

$$\lim_{x \to c} r(x) = r(c) = \frac{p(c)}{q(c)}.$$

EXAMPLE 3   The Limit of a Rational Function

Find the limit: $\lim\limits_{x \to 1} \dfrac{x^2 + x + 2}{x + 1}$.

Solution

The denominator is not 0 when $x = 1$, so apply Theorem 1.3 to obtain

$$\lim_{x \to 1} \frac{x^2 + x + 2}{x + 1} = \frac{1^2 + 1 + 2}{1 + 1} = \frac{4}{2} = 2.$$

Use the *trace* feature of a graphing utility to check this answer (see Figure 1.17).

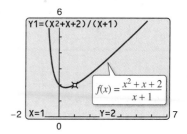

The limit of $f(x)$ as x approaches 1 is 2.
Figure 1.17

Polynomial functions and rational functions are two of the three basic types of algebraic functions. The next theorem deals with the limit of the third type of algebraic function—one that involves a radical.

Theorem 1.4   The Limit of a Function Involving a Radical

Let n be a positive integer. The limit below is valid for all c when n is odd, and is valid for $c > 0$ when n is even.

$$\lim_{x \to c} \sqrt[n]{x} = \sqrt[n]{c}$$

A proof of this theorem is given in Appendix A.

The next theorem greatly expands your ability to evaluate limits because it shows how to analyze the limit of a composite function.

> **Theorem 1.5 The Limit of a Composite Function**
>
> If f and g are functions such that
>
> $$\lim_{x \to c} g(x) = L \quad \text{and} \quad \lim_{x \to L} f(x) = f(L)$$
>
> then
>
> $$\lim_{x \to c} f(g(x)) = f\left(\lim_{x \to c} g(x)\right) = f(L).$$
>
> A proof of this theorem is given in Appendix A.

EXAMPLE 4 Limits of Composite Functions

See LarsonCalculusforAP.com for an interactive version of this type of example.

a. Because

$$\lim_{x \to 0} (x^2 + 4) = 0^2 + 4 = 4 \quad \text{and} \quad \lim_{x \to 4} \sqrt{x} = \sqrt{4} = 2$$

you can conclude that

$$\lim_{x \to 0} \sqrt{x^2 + 4} = \sqrt{4} = 2.$$

b. Because

$$\lim_{x \to 3} (2x^2 - 10) = 2(3^2) - 10 = 8 \quad \text{and} \quad \lim_{x \to 8} \sqrt[3]{x} = \sqrt[3]{8} = 2$$

you can conclude that

$$\lim_{x \to 3} \sqrt[3]{2x^2 - 10} = \sqrt[3]{8} = 2.$$

You have seen that the limits of many algebraic functions can be evaluated by direct substitution. The basic transcendental functions (trigonometric, exponential, and logarithmic) also possess this desirable quality, as shown in the next theorem (presented without proof).

> **Theorem 1.6 Limits of Transcendental Functions**
>
> Let c be a real number in the domain of the given transcendental function.
>
> **1.** $\lim_{x \to c} \sin x = \sin c$ **2.** $\lim_{x \to c} \cos x = \cos c$
>
> **3.** $\lim_{x \to c} \tan x = \tan c$ **4.** $\lim_{x \to c} \cot x = \cot c$
>
> **5.** $\lim_{x \to c} \sec x = \sec c$ **6.** $\lim_{x \to c} \csc x = \csc c$
>
> **7.** $\lim_{x \to c} a^x = a^c, a > 0$ **8.** $\lim_{x \to c} \ln x = \ln c$

EXAMPLE 5 Limits Involving Transcendental Functions

a. $\lim_{x \to 0} \tan x = \tan(0) = 0$

b. $\lim_{x \to 0} \sin^2 x = \lim_{x \to 0} (\sin x)^2 = 0^2 = 0$

c. $\lim_{x \to -1} xe^x = \left(\lim_{x \to -1} x\right)\left(\lim_{x \to -1} e^x\right) = (-1)(e^{-1}) = -e^{-1}$

d. $\lim_{x \to e} \ln x^3 = \lim_{x \to e} 3 \ln x = 3 \ln e = 3(1) = 3$

A Strategy for Finding Limits

On the preceding three pages, you studied several types of functions whose limits can be evaluated by direct substitution. This knowledge, together with the next theorem, can be used to develop a strategy for finding limits.

Theorem 1.7   Functions That Agree at All but One Point

Let c be a real number, and let $f(x) = g(x)$ for all $x \neq c$ in an open interval containing c. If the limit of $g(x)$ as x approaches c exists, then the limit of $f(x)$ also exists and

$$\lim_{x \to c} f(x) = \lim_{x \to c} g(x).$$

A proof of this theorem is given in Appendix A.

EXAMPLE 6   **Finding the Limit of a Function**

Find $\lim_{x \to 1} f(x)$, where

$$f(x) = \begin{cases} x^2 + x + 1, & x \neq 1 \\ 1, & x = 1 \end{cases}.$$

Solution

Note that f is defined at $x = 1$ and $f(1) = 1$. The limit as x approaches 1, however, does not depend on the value of the function at 1. A function that agrees with f for all x-values other than $x = 1$ is

$$g(x) = x^2 + x + 1. \qquad \text{\small g agrees with f for all x-values except $x = 1$.}$$

(See Figure 1.18.) The limit of $g(x)$ as x approaches 1 exists, so you can apply Theorem 1.7 to conclude that f and g have the same limit as x approaches 1.

$$\begin{aligned}
\lim_{x \to 1} f(x) &= \lim_{x \to 1} g(x) && \text{\small Apply Theorem 1.7.} \\
&= \lim_{x \to 1} (x^2 + x + 1) && \text{\small Substitute for $g(x)$.} \\
&= 1^2 + 1 + 1 && \text{\small Use direct substitution.} \\
&= 3 && \text{\small Simplify.}
\end{aligned}$$

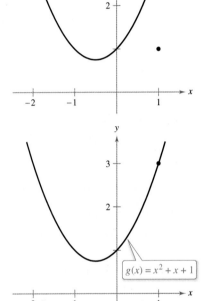

f and g agree at all but one point.
Figure 1.18

A Strategy for Finding Limits

1. Learn to recognize which limits can be evaluated by direct substitution. (These limits are listed in Theorems 1.1 through 1.6.)

2. When the limit of $f(x)$ as x approaches c *cannot* be evaluated by direct substitution, try to find a function g that agrees with f for all x other than $x = c$. [Choose g such that the limit of $g(x)$ *can* be evaluated by direct substitution.] Then apply Theorem 1.7 to conclude *analytically* that

$$\lim_{x \to c} f(x) = \lim_{x \to c} g(x) = g(c).$$

3. Use a *graph* or *table* to reinforce your conclusion.

When applying the above strategy for finding a limit, recall that some functions do not have a limit (as x approaches c). For example, the limit below does not exist.

$$\lim_{x \to 1} \frac{x^3 + 1}{x - 1}$$

Dividing Out Technique

Another procedure for finding a limit analytically is the **dividing out technique.** This technique involves dividing out common factors, as shown in Example 7.

Algebra Review

For a review of factoring expressions, see the *Chapter 1 Algebra Review* on page A36.

EXAMPLE 7   Dividing Out Technique

See LarsonCalculusforAP.com for an interactive version of this type of example.

Find the limit: $\lim\limits_{x \to -3} \dfrac{x^2 + x - 6}{x + 3}$.

Solution

Although you are taking the limit of a rational function, you *cannot* apply Theorem 1.3 because the limit of the denominator is 0.

$$\lim_{x \to -3} \frac{x^2 + x - 6}{x + 3} \Bigg\langle \begin{array}{l} \lim\limits_{x \to -3} (x^2 + x - 6) = 0 \\[2mm] \qquad\qquad \text{Direct substitution fails.} \\[2mm] \lim\limits_{x \to -3} (x + 3) = 0 \end{array}$$

Because the limit of the numerator is also 0, the numerator and denominator have a *common factor* of $(x + 3)$. So, for all $x \neq -3$, you can divide out this factor to obtain

$$f(x) = \frac{x^2 + x - 6}{x + 3} = \frac{(x + 3)(x - 2)}{x + 3} = x - 2 = g(x), \quad x \neq -3.$$

Using Theorem 1.7 and direct substitution, it follows that

$$\lim_{x \to -3} \frac{x^2 + x - 6}{x + 3} = \lim_{x \to -3} (x - 2) = -5.$$

This result is shown graphically in Figure 1.19. Note that the graph of the function f coincides with the graph of the function $g(x) = x - 2$, except that the graph of f has a hole at the point $(-3, -5)$.

In Example 7, direct substitution produced the meaningless fractional form 0/0. An expression such as 0/0 is called an **indeterminate form** because you cannot (from the form alone) determine the limit. When you try to evaluate a limit and encounter this form, remember that you must rewrite the fraction so that the new denominator does not have 0 as its limit. One way to do this is to *divide out common factors*. Another way is to use the *rationalizing technique* shown on the next page.

Justification

In the solution to Example 7, be sure you see the usefulness of the Factor Theorem of Algebra. This theorem states that if c is a zero of a polynomial function, then $(x - c)$ is a factor of the polynomial. So, when you apply direct substitution to a rational function and obtain

$$r(c) = \frac{p(c)}{q(c)} = \frac{0}{0}$$

you can conclude that $(x - c)$ must be a common factor of both $p(x)$ and $q(x)$.

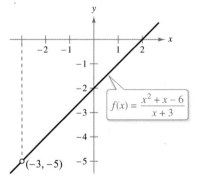

f is undefined when $x = -3$. The limit of $f(x)$ as x approaches -3 is -5.
Figure 1.19

Technology Pitfall

Remember that a graphing utility can give misleading information about the graph of a function. Graph the function from Example 7

$$f(x) = \frac{x^2 + x - 6}{x + 3}$$

on a graphing utility (see figure). On some graphing utilities, the graph may appear to be defined at every real number. However, because f is undefined when $x = -3$, you know that the graph of f has a hole at $x = -3$. You can verify this on a graphing utility using the *trace* or *table* feature.

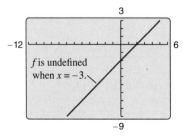

f is undefined when $x = -3$.

Misleading graph of f

Rationalizing Technique

Another way to find a limit analytically is the **rationalizing technique,** which involves rationalizing either the numerator or denominator of a fractional expression. Recall that rationalizing the numerator (denominator) means multiplying the numerator and denominator by the conjugate of the numerator (denominator). For instance, to rationalize the numerator of

$$\frac{\sqrt{x} + 4}{x}$$

multiply the numerator and denominator by the conjugate of $\sqrt{x} + 4$, which is $\sqrt{x} - 4$.

> ### Algebra Review
>
> For a review of rationalizing techniques, see the *Chapter 1 Algebra Review* on page A37.

EXAMPLE 8 **Rationalizing Technique**

Find the limit: $\displaystyle\lim_{x \to 0} \frac{\sqrt{x + 1} - 1}{x}$.

Solution By direct substitution, you obtain the indeterminate form $0/0$.

$$\lim_{x \to 0} \frac{\sqrt{x + 1} - 1}{x}$$

$$\lim_{x \to 0}\left(\sqrt{x + 1} - 1\right) = 0$$

Direct substitution fails.

$$\lim_{x \to 0} x = 0$$

In this case, you can rewrite the fraction by rationalizing the numerator.

$$\frac{\sqrt{x + 1} - 1}{x} = \left(\frac{\sqrt{x + 1} - 1}{x}\right)\left(\frac{\sqrt{x + 1} + 1}{\sqrt{x + 1} + 1}\right)$$

$$= \frac{(x + 1) - 1}{x\left(\sqrt{x + 1} + 1\right)}$$

$$= \frac{x}{x\left(\sqrt{x + 1} + 1\right)}$$

$$= \frac{1}{\sqrt{x + 1} + 1}, \quad x \neq 0$$

Now, using Theorem 1.7, you can evaluate the limit as shown.

$$\lim_{x \to 0} \frac{\sqrt{x + 1} - 1}{x} = \lim_{x \to 0} \frac{1}{\sqrt{x + 1} + 1}$$

$$= \frac{1}{1 + 1}$$

$$= \frac{1}{2}$$

> ### Implementing Processes
>
> The rationalizing technique for evaluating limits is based on multiplication by a convenient form of 1. In Example 8, the convenient form is
>
> $$1 = \frac{\sqrt{x + 1} + 1}{\sqrt{x + 1} + 1}.$$

A table or a graph can reinforce your conclusion that the limit is $\frac{1}{2}$. (See Figure 1.20.)

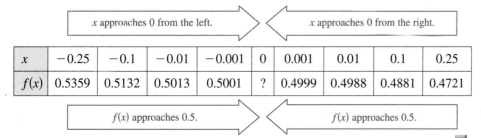

x approaches 0 from the left.					x approaches 0 from the right.			
x	-0.25	-0.1	-0.01	-0.001	0	0.001	0.01	0.1	0.25
$f(x)$	0.5359	0.5132	0.5013	0.5001	?	0.4999	0.4988	0.4881	0.4721

$f(x)$ approaches 0.5. $f(x)$ approaches 0.5.

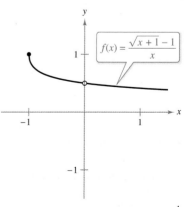

The limit of $f(x)$ as x approaches 0 is $\frac{1}{2}$.
Figure 1.20

The Squeeze Theorem

The next theorem concerns the limit of a function that is squeezed between two other functions, each of which has the same limit at a given x-value, as shown in Figure 1.21.

Theorem 1.8   The Squeeze Theorem

If $h(x) \leq f(x) \leq g(x)$ for all x in an open interval containing c, except possibly at c itself, and if

$$\lim_{x \to c} h(x) = L = \lim_{x \to c} g(x)$$

then $\lim_{x \to c} f(x)$ exists and is equal to L.

A proof of this theorem is given in Appendix A.

$h(x) \leq f(x) \leq g(x)$

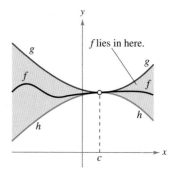

f lies in here.

The Squeeze Theorem
Figure 1.21

You can see the usefulness of the Squeeze Theorem (also called the Sandwich Theorem or the Pinching Theorem) in the proof of Theorem 1.9.

Theorem 1.9   Three Special Limits

1. $\lim\limits_{x \to 0} \dfrac{\sin x}{x} = 1$ **2.** $\lim\limits_{x \to 0} \dfrac{1 - \cos x}{x} = 0$ **3.** $\lim\limits_{x \to 0} (1 + x)^{1/x} = e$

Justification

The third limit of Theorem 1.9 will be used in Section 2.2 in the development of the formula for the derivative of the exponential function $f(x) = e^x$.

Proof

The proof of the second limit is left as an exercise. (See Exercise 121.) Recall from Section P.5 that the third limit is actually the definition of the number e. To avoid the confusion of two different uses of x, the proof of the first limit is presented using the variable θ, where θ is an acute positive angle *measured in radians*. Figure 1.22 shows a circular sector that is squeezed between two triangles.

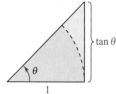   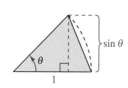

Area of triangle	$\geq$	Area of sector	$\geq$	Area of triangle
$\dfrac{\tan \theta}{2}$	$\geq$	$\dfrac{\theta}{2}$	$\geq$	$\dfrac{\sin \theta}{2}$

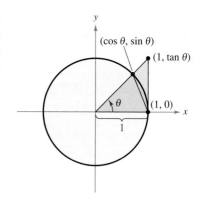

A circular sector is used to prove Theorem 1.9.

Figure 1.22

Multiplying each expression by $2/\sin \theta$ produces

$$\frac{1}{\cos \theta} \geq \frac{\theta}{\sin \theta} \geq 1$$

and taking reciprocals and reversing the inequalities yields

$$\cos \theta \leq \frac{\sin \theta}{\theta} \leq 1.$$

Because $\cos \theta = \cos(-\theta)$ and $(\sin \theta)/\theta = [\sin(-\theta)]/(-\theta)$, you can conclude that this inequality is valid for *all* nonzero θ in the open interval $(-\pi/2, \pi/2)$. Finally, because $\lim\limits_{\theta \to 0} \cos \theta = 1$ and $\lim\limits_{\theta \to 0} 1 = 1$, you can apply the Squeeze Theorem to conclude that

$$\lim_{\theta \to 0} \frac{\sin \theta}{\theta} = 1.$$

EXAMPLE 9   A Limit Involving a Trigonometric Function

Find the limit: $\lim\limits_{x \to 0} \dfrac{\tan x}{x}$.

Algebraic Solution

Direct substitution yields the indeterminate form $0/0$. To solve this problem, you can write $\tan x$ as $(\sin x)/(\cos x)$ and obtain

$$\lim_{x \to 0} \frac{\tan x}{x} = \lim_{x \to 0} \left(\frac{\sin x}{x} \right) \left(\frac{1}{\cos x} \right).$$

Now, because

$$\lim_{x \to 0} \frac{\sin x}{x} = 1 \quad \text{and} \quad \lim_{x \to 0} \frac{1}{\cos x} = 1$$

you can obtain

$$\lim_{x \to 0} \frac{\tan x}{x} = \left(\lim_{x \to 0} \frac{\sin x}{x} \right) \left(\lim_{x \to 0} \frac{1}{\cos x} \right)$$
$$= (1)(1)$$
$$= 1.$$

Numerical Solution

Use the *table* feature of a graphing utility to show values of $y_1 = (\tan x)/x$ for several x-values near 0. From the table, you can estimate the limit to be 1.

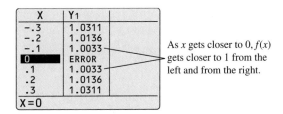

As x gets closer to 0, $f(x)$ gets closer to 1 from the left and from the right.

EXAMPLE 10   A Limit Involving a Trigonometric Function

Find the limit: $\lim\limits_{x \to 0} \dfrac{\sin 4x}{x}$.

Solution

Direct substitution yields the indeterminate form $0/0$. You can rewrite the limit as

$$\lim_{x \to 0} \frac{\sin 4x}{x} = 4 \left(\lim_{x \to 0} \frac{\sin 4x}{4x} \right). \qquad \text{Multiply and divide by 4.}$$

Now, by letting $y = 4x$ and observing that x approaches 0 if and only if y approaches 0, you can write

$$\lim_{x \to 0} \frac{\sin 4x}{x} = 4 \left(\lim_{x \to 0} \frac{\sin 4x}{4x} \right)$$
$$= 4 \left(\lim_{y \to 0} \frac{\sin y}{y} \right) \qquad \text{Let } y = 4x.$$
$$= 4(1) \qquad \text{Apply Theorem 1.9(1).}$$
$$= 4. \qquad \text{See Figure 1.23.}$$

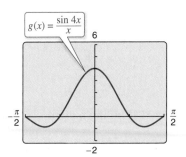

The limit of $g(x)$ as x approaches 0 is 4.
Figure 1.23

Technology

Use a graphing utility to confirm the limits in the examples and in the exercise set. For instance, Figure 1.23 shows the graph of

$$g(x) = \frac{\sin 4x}{x}.$$

The graph appears to contain the point $(0, 4)$, which supports the conclusion obtained in Example 10.

1.3 Exercises

See *CalcChat.com* for tutorial help and worked-out solutions to odd-numbered exercises.

Evaluating a Basic Limit In Exercises 1–6, find the limit.

1. $\lim\limits_{x \to 3} 6$

2. $\lim\limits_{x \to -2} 4$

3. $\lim\limits_{x \to 4} x$

4. $\lim\limits_{x \to -6} x$

5. $\lim\limits_{x \to 7} x^2$

6. $\lim\limits_{x \to -2} x^4$

 Evaluating Limits In Exercises 7–10, use the given information to evaluate each limit.

7.
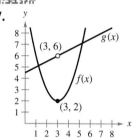

(3, 6)
g(x)
f(x)
(3, 2)

(a) $\lim\limits_{x \to 3} [3f(x)]$

(b) $\lim\limits_{x \to 3} [f(x) + g(x)]$

(c) $\lim\limits_{x \to 3} [f(x)g(x)]$

(d) $\lim\limits_{x \to 3} \dfrac{g(x)}{f(x)}$

8.

f(x)
(1, 2)
(1, −1)
g(x)

(a) $\lim\limits_{x \to 1} [5g(x)]$

(b) $\lim\limits_{x \to 1} [g(x) - f(x)]$

(c) $\lim\limits_{x \to 1} [g(x)f(x)]$

(d) $\lim\limits_{x \to 1} \dfrac{f(x)}{g(x)}$

9. $\lim\limits_{x \to c} f(x) = 16$

(a) $\lim\limits_{x \to c} [f(x)]^2$

(b) $\lim\limits_{x \to c} \sqrt{f(x)}$

(c) $\lim\limits_{x \to c} [3f(x)]$

(d) $\lim\limits_{x \to c} [f(x)]^{3/2}$

10. $\lim\limits_{x \to c} f(x) = 27$

(a) $\lim\limits_{x \to c} \sqrt[3]{f(x)}$

(b) $\lim\limits_{x \to c} \dfrac{f(x)}{18}$

(c) $\lim\limits_{x \to c} [f(x)]^2$

(d) $\lim\limits_{x \to c} [f(x)]^{2/3}$

 Finding a Limit In Exercises 11–26, find the limit. Use a graphing utility to verify your result.

11. $\lim\limits_{x \to -3} (2x + 5)$

12. $\lim\limits_{x \to 0} (3x - 1)$

13. $\lim\limits_{x \to -3} (x^2 + 3x)$

14. $\lim\limits_{x \to 2} (-x^3 + 1)$

15. $\lim\limits_{x \to -3} (2x^2 + 4x + 1)$

16. $\lim\limits_{x \to 1} (2x^3 - 6x + 5)$

17. $\lim\limits_{x \to 13} \sqrt{x + 1}$

18. $\lim\limits_{x \to 2} \sqrt[3]{12x + 3}$

19. $\lim\limits_{x \to -4} (1 - x)^3$

20. $\lim\limits_{x \to 0} (3x - 2)^4$

21. $\lim\limits_{x \to 2} \dfrac{3}{2x + 1}$

22. $\lim\limits_{x \to -5} \dfrac{5}{x + 3}$

23. $\lim\limits_{x \to 1} \dfrac{x}{x^2 + 4}$

24. $\lim\limits_{x \to 1} \dfrac{3x + 5}{x + 1}$

25. $\lim\limits_{x \to 7} \dfrac{3x}{\sqrt{x + 2}}$

26. $\lim\limits_{x \to 2} \dfrac{\sqrt{x + 7}}{x + 2}$

 Finding Limits In Exercises 27–30, find the limits.

27. $f(x) = 5 - x$, $g(x) = x^3$

(a) $\lim\limits_{x \to 1} f(x)$ (b) $\lim\limits_{x \to 4} g(x)$ (c) $\lim\limits_{x \to 1} g(f(x))$

28. $f(x) = x + 7$, $g(x) = x^2$

(a) $\lim\limits_{x \to -3} f(x)$ (b) $\lim\limits_{x \to 4} g(x)$ (c) $\lim\limits_{x \to -3} g(f(x))$

29. $f(x) = 4 - x^2$, $g(x) = \sqrt{x + 1}$

(a) $\lim\limits_{x \to 1} f(x)$ (b) $\lim\limits_{x \to 3} g(x)$ (c) $\lim\limits_{x \to 1} g(f(x))$

30. $f(x) = 2x^2 - 3x + 1$, $g(x) = \sqrt[3]{x + 6}$

(a) $\lim\limits_{x \to 4} f(x)$ (b) $\lim\limits_{x \to 21} g(x)$ (c) $\lim\limits_{x \to 4} g(f(x))$

Error Analysis In Exercises 31 and 32, describe and correct the error in finding the limit, where $f(x) = 2x - 5$ and $g(x) = x + 1$.

31. $\lim\limits_{x \to 4} g(x)f(x) = \lim\limits_{x \to 4} g(3) = 4$

32. $\lim\limits_{x \to 4} g(f(x)) = g(4) = 5$

 Finding a Limit of a Transcendental Function In Exercises 33–46, find the limit.

33. $\lim\limits_{x \to \pi/2} \sin x$

34. $\lim\limits_{x \to \pi} \tan x$

35. $\lim\limits_{x \to 1} \cos \dfrac{\pi x}{3}$

36. $\lim\limits_{x \to 2} \sin \dfrac{\pi x}{4}$

37. $\lim\limits_{x \to 0} \sec 2x$

38. $\lim\limits_{x \to \pi} \cos 3x$

39. $\lim\limits_{x \to 5\pi/6} \sin x$

40. $\lim\limits_{x \to 5\pi/3} \cos x$

41. $\lim\limits_{x \to 3} \tan \dfrac{\pi x}{4}$

42. $\lim\limits_{x \to 7} \sec \dfrac{\pi x}{6}$

43. $\lim\limits_{x \to 0} e^x \cos 2x$

44. $\lim\limits_{x \to 0} e^{-x} \sin \pi x$

45. $\lim\limits_{x \to 1} (\ln 3x + e^x)$

46. $\lim\limits_{x \to 1} \ln \dfrac{x}{e^x}$

Finding a Limit In Exercises 47–52, write a simpler function that agrees with the given function at all but one point. Then find the limit of the function. Use a graphing utility to confirm your result.

47. $\lim\limits_{x \to -2} f(x)$, where $f(x) = \begin{cases} -x^3 - 4, & x \neq -2 \\ -2, & x = -2 \end{cases}$

48. $\lim\limits_{x \to 3} g(x)$, where $g(x) = \begin{cases} 3x^2 - x + 1, & x \neq 3 \\ 3, & x = 3 \end{cases}$

49. $\lim\limits_{x \to -1} \dfrac{x^2 - 1}{x + 1}$

50. $\lim\limits_{x \to 2} \dfrac{x^3 - 8}{x - 2}$

51. $\lim\limits_{x \to -4} \dfrac{(x + 4)\ln(x + 6)}{x^2 - 16}$

52. $\lim\limits_{x \to 0} \dfrac{e^{2x} - 1}{e^x - 1}$

Finding a Limit   **In Exercises 53–68, find the limit.**

53. $\lim\limits_{x \to 0} \dfrac{x}{x^2 - x}$

54. $\lim\limits_{x \to 0} \dfrac{x^3 + 9x}{3x}$

55. $\lim\limits_{x \to -3} \dfrac{x^2 - 9}{x + 3}$

56. $\lim\limits_{x \to 5} \dfrac{5 - x}{x^2 - 25}$

57. $\lim\limits_{x \to -3} \dfrac{x^2 + x - 6}{x^2 - 9}$

58. $\lim\limits_{x \to 2} \dfrac{x^2 + 2x - 8}{x^2 - x - 2}$

59. $\lim\limits_{x \to 4} \dfrac{\sqrt{x + 5} - 3}{x - 4}$

60. $\lim\limits_{x \to 3} \dfrac{\sqrt{x + 1} - 2}{x - 3}$

61. $\lim\limits_{x \to 0} \dfrac{\sqrt{x + 5} - \sqrt{5}}{x}$

62. $\lim\limits_{x \to 0} \dfrac{\sqrt{2 + x} - \sqrt{2}}{x}$

63. $\lim\limits_{x \to 0} \dfrac{[1/(3 + x)] - (1/3)}{x}$

64. $\lim\limits_{x \to 0} \dfrac{[1/(x + 4)] - (1/4)}{x}$

65. $\lim\limits_{\Delta t \to 0} \dfrac{2(x + \Delta x) - 2x}{\Delta x}$

66. $\lim\limits_{\Delta x \to 0} \dfrac{(x + \Delta x)^2 - x^2}{\Delta x}$

67. $\lim\limits_{\Delta x \to 0} \dfrac{(x + \Delta x)^2 - 2(x + \Delta x) + 1 - (x^2 - 2x + 1)}{\Delta x}$

68. $\lim\limits_{\Delta x \to 0} \dfrac{(x + \Delta x)^3 - x^3}{\Delta x}$

Finding a Limit   **In Exercises 69–72, find**

$$\lim_{\Delta x \to 0} \frac{f(x + \Delta x) - f(x)}{\Delta x}.$$

69. $f(x) = 3x - 2$

70. $f(x) = x^2 - 4x$

71. $f(x) = \dfrac{1}{x + 3}$

72. $f(x) = \dfrac{1}{x^2}$

Finding a Limit of a Transcendental Function
In Exercises 73–86, find the limit of the transcendental function.

73. $\lim\limits_{x \to 0} \dfrac{\sin x}{5x}$

74. $\lim\limits_{x \to 0} \dfrac{3(1 - \cos x)}{x}$

75. $\lim\limits_{x \to 0} \dfrac{(\sin x)(1 - \cos x)}{x^2}$

76. $\lim\limits_{\theta \to 0} \dfrac{\cos \theta \tan \theta}{\theta}$

77. $\lim\limits_{x \to 0} \dfrac{\sin^2 x}{x}$

78. $\lim\limits_{x \to 0} \dfrac{\tan^2 x}{x}$

79. $\lim\limits_{h \to 0} \dfrac{(1 - \cos h)^2}{h}$

80. $\lim\limits_{\phi \to \pi} \phi \sec \phi$

81. $\lim\limits_{x \to 0} \dfrac{6 - 6 \cos x}{3x}$

82. $\lim\limits_{x \to 0} \dfrac{\cos x - \sin x - 1}{2x}$

83. $\lim\limits_{x \to 0} \dfrac{1 - e^{-x}}{e^x - 1}$

84. $\lim\limits_{x \to 0} \dfrac{4(e^{2x} - 1)}{e^x - 1}$

85. $\lim\limits_{t \to 0} \dfrac{\sin 3t}{2t}$

86. $\lim\limits_{x \to 0} \dfrac{\sin 2x}{\sin 3x}$ $\left[\text{Hint: Find } \lim\limits_{x \to 0} \left(\dfrac{2 \sin 2x}{2x} \right)\left(\dfrac{3x}{3 \sin 3x} \right). \right]$

Connecting Representations   **In Exercises 87–94, use a graphing utility to graph the function and estimate the limit. Use a table to reinforce your conclusion. Then find the limit by analytic methods.**

87. $\lim\limits_{x \to 0} \dfrac{\sqrt{x + 2} - \sqrt{2}}{x}$

88. $\lim\limits_{x \to 16} \dfrac{4 - \sqrt{x}}{x - 16}$

89. $\lim\limits_{x \to 0} \dfrac{[1/(2 + x)] - (1/2)}{x}$

90. $\lim\limits_{x \to 2} \dfrac{x^5 - 32}{x - 2}$

91. $\lim\limits_{t \to 0} \dfrac{\sin 3t}{t}$

92. $\lim\limits_{x \to 0} \dfrac{\cos x - 1}{2x^2}$

93. $\lim\limits_{x \to 1} \dfrac{\ln x}{x - 1}$

94. $\lim\limits_{x \to \ln 2} \dfrac{e^{3x} - 8}{e^{2x} - 4}$

Using the Squeeze Theorem   **In Exercises 95 and 96, use the Squeeze Theorem to find** $\lim\limits_{x \to c} f(x)$.

95. $c = 0; \; 4 - x^2 \le f(x) \le 4 + x^2$

96. $c = a; \; b - |x - a| \le f(x) \le b + |x - a|$

Using the Squeeze Theorem   **In Exercises 97–100, use a graphing utility to graph the given function and the equations** $y = |x|$ **and** $y = -|x|$ **in the same viewing window. Using the graphs to observe the Squeeze Theorem visually, find** $\lim\limits_{x \to 0} f(x)$.

97. $f(x) = |x| \sin x$

98. $f(x) = |x| \cos x$

99. $f(x) = x \sin \dfrac{1}{x}$

100. $h(x) = x \cos \dfrac{1}{x}$

True or False?   **In Exercises 101–104, determine whether the statement is true or false. If it is false, explain why or give an example that shows it is false.**

101. $\lim\limits_{x \to 0} \dfrac{|x|}{x} = 1$

102. $\lim\limits_{x \to \pi} \dfrac{\sin x}{x} = 1$

103. If $f(x) = g(x)$ for all real numbers other than $x = 0$ and $\lim\limits_{x \to 0} f(x) = L$, then $\lim\limits_{x \to 0} g(x) = L$.

104. If $f(x) < g(x)$ for all $x \ne a$, then $\lim\limits_{x \to a} f(x) < \lim\limits_{x \to a} g(x)$.

EXPLORING CONCEPTS

105. Communicating

(a) In the context of finding limits, discuss what is meant by two functions that agree at all but one point.

(b) Give an example of two functions that agree at all but one point.

106. Graphical Reasoning   Use a graphing utility to graph $f(x) = x$, $g(x) = \sin x$, and $h(x) = (\sin x)/x$ in the same viewing window. Compare the magnitudes of $f(x)$ and $g(x)$ when x is close to 0. Use the comparison to write a short paragraph explaining why $\lim\limits_{x \to 0} h(x) = 1$.

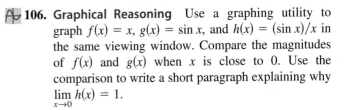

107. Graphical Reasoning Use a graphing utility to graph $f(x) = x$, $g(x) = \sin^2 x$, and $h(x) = (\sin^2 x)/x$ in the same viewing window. Compare the magnitudes of $f(x)$ and $g(x)$ when x is close to 0. Use the comparison to write a short paragraph explaining why $\lim\limits_{x \to 0} h(x) = 0$.

108. HOW DO YOU SEE IT? Would you use the dividing out technique or the rationalizing technique to find the limit of the function? Explain your reasoning.

(a) $\lim\limits_{x \to -2} \dfrac{x^2 + x - 2}{x + 2}$ (b) $\lim\limits_{x \to 0} \dfrac{\sqrt{x + 4} - 2}{x}$

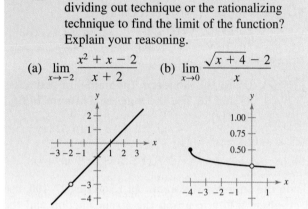

FREE-FALLING OBJECT

In Exercises 109 and 110, use the position function $s(t) = -16t^2 + 500$, which gives the height (in feet) of a paint can that has fallen for t seconds when dropped from a height of 500 feet. The velocity at time $t = a$ seconds is given by

$$\lim\limits_{t \to a} \dfrac{s(a) - s(t)}{a - t}.$$

109. How fast will the paint can be falling after 2 seconds?

110. When will the paint can hit the ground? At what velocity will the paint can impact the ground?

Free-Falling Object In Exercises 111 and 112, use the position function $s(t) = -4.9t^2 + 200$, which gives the height (in meters) of an object that has fallen for t seconds from a height of 200 meters. The velocity at time $t = a$ seconds is given by

$$\lim\limits_{t \to a} \dfrac{s(a) - s(t)}{a - t}.$$

111. Find the velocity of the object when $t = 3$.

112. At what velocity will the object impact the ground?

113. Finding Functions Find two functions f and g such that $\lim\limits_{x \to 0} f(x)$ and $\lim\limits_{x \to 0} g(x)$ do not exist, but $\lim\limits_{x \to 0} [f(x) + g(x)]$ does exist.

114. Proof Prove that if $\lim\limits_{x \to c} f(x)$ exists and $\lim\limits_{x \to c} [f(x) + g(x)]$ does not exist, then $\lim\limits_{x \to c} g(x)$ does not exist.

115. Proof Prove Property 1 of Theorem 1.1.

116. Proof Prove Property 3 of Theorem 1.1. (You may use Property 3 of Theorem 1.2.)

117. Proof Prove Property 1 of Theorem 1.2.

118. Proof Prove that if $\lim\limits_{x \to c} f(x) = 0$, then $\lim\limits_{x \to c} |f(x)| = 0$.

119. Proof

(a) Prove that if $\lim\limits_{x \to c} |f(x)| = 0$, then $\lim\limits_{x \to c} f(x) = 0$. (*Note:* This is the converse of Exercise 118.)

(b) Prove that if $\lim\limits_{x \to c} f(x) = L$, then $\lim\limits_{x \to c} |f(x)| = |L|$. [*Hint:* Use the inequality
$$\big||f(x)| - |L|\big| \le |f(x) - L|.]$$

120. Justifying Find a function f to show that the converse of Exercise 119(b) is not true. [*Hint:* Find a function f such that $\lim\limits_{x \to c} |f(x)| = |L|$ but $\lim\limits_{x \to c} f(x)$ does not exist.]

121. Proof Prove the second part of Theorem 1.9.

122. Piecewise Functions Find (if possible) $\lim\limits_{x \to 0} f(x)$ and $\lim\limits_{x \to 0} g(x)$.

$$f(x) = \begin{cases} 0, & \text{if } x \text{ is rational} \\ 1, & \text{if } x \text{ is irrational} \end{cases}$$

$$g(x) = \begin{cases} 0, & \text{if } x \text{ is rational} \\ x, & \text{if } x \text{ is irrational} \end{cases}$$

Calculus AP® – Exam Preparation Questions

123. Multiple Choice $\lim\limits_{x \to 2} \dfrac{\sqrt{x + 7} - 3}{x - 2}$ is

(A) 0. (B) $\frac{1}{6}$. (C) $\frac{1}{3}$. (D) nonexistent.

124. Multiple Choice Which of the following limits do not exist?

I. $\lim\limits_{x \to 1} \dfrac{x^3 + 1}{x - 1}$ II. $\lim\limits_{x \to 0} \dfrac{|x|}{x}$

III. $\lim\limits_{x \to 2} f(x)$, where $f(x) = \begin{cases} 3, & x \le 2 \\ 0, & x > 2 \end{cases}$

(A) None (B) I and II only

(C) III only (D) I, II, and III

125. Multiple Choice $\lim\limits_{x \to 3} \dfrac{x^4 - 81}{x - 3}$ is

(A) 0. (B) 81.

(C) 108. (D) nonexistent.

1.4   Continuity and One-Sided Limits

▶ Determine continuity at a point and continuity on an open interval.
▶ Determine one-sided limits and continuity on a closed interval.
▶ Use properties of continuity.
▶ Understand and use the Intermediate Value Theorem.

Continuity at a Point and on an Open Interval

In mathematics, the term *continuous* has much the same meaning as it has in everyday usage. Informally, to say that a function f is continuous at $x = c$ means that there is no interruption in the graph of f at c. That is, its graph is unbroken at c, and there are no holes, jumps, or gaps. Figure 1.24 identifies three values of x at which the graph of f is *not* continuous. At all other points in the interval (a, b), the graph of f is uninterrupted and **continuous.**

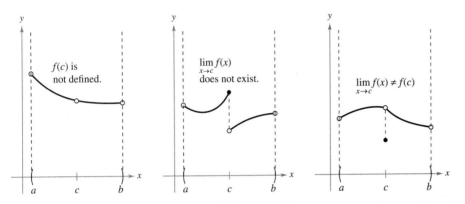

Three conditions exist for which the graph of f is not continuous at $x = c$.
Figure 1.24

In Figure 1.24, it appears that continuity at $x = c$ can be destroyed by any one of three conditions.

1. The function is not defined at $x = c$.
2. The limit of $f(x)$ does not exist at $x = c$.
3. The limit of $f(x)$ exists at $x = c$, but it is not equal to $f(c)$.

If *none* of the three conditions is true, then the function f is called **continuous at c,** as indicated in the important definition below.

> #### Definition of Continuity
>
> *Continuity at a Point*
> A function f is **continuous at c** when these three conditions are met.
>
> 1. $f(c)$ is defined.
> 2. $\lim\limits_{x \to c} f(x)$ exists.
> 3. $\lim\limits_{x \to c} f(x) = f(c)$
>
> *Continuity on an Open Interval*
> A function is **continuous on an open interval (a, b)** when the function is continuous at each point in the interval. A function that is continuous on the entire real number line $(-\infty, \infty)$ is **everywhere continuous.**

Exploration

Informally, you might say that a function is *continuous* on an open interval when its graph can be drawn with a pencil without lifting the pencil from the paper. Use a graphing utility to graph each function on the given interval. From the graphs, which functions would you say are continuous on the interval? Do you think you can trust the results you obtained graphically? Explain your reasoning.

Function	Interval
a. $y = x^2 + 1$	$(-3, 3)$
b. $y = \dfrac{1}{x - 2}$	$(-3, 3)$
c. $y = \dfrac{\sin x}{x}$	$(-\pi, \pi)$
d. $y = \dfrac{x^2 - 4}{x + 2}$	$(-3, 3)$

Insight

You must know the definition of continuity for the AP® Exam and, when applicable, be able to explain why a function is not continuous.

Consider an open interval I that contains a real number c. If a function f is defined on I (except possibly at c), and f is not continuous at c, then f is said to have a **discontinuity** at c. Discontinuities fall into two categories: **removable** and **nonremovable.** A discontinuity at c is called removable when f can be made continuous by appropriately defining (or redefining) $f(c)$. For instance, the functions shown in Figures 1.25(a) and (c) have removable discontinuities at c and the function shown in Figure 1.25(b) has a nonremovable discontinuity at c. The discontinuity at c in Figure 1.25(b) is sometimes called a *jump discontinuity.*

EXAMPLE 1 Continuity of a Function

Discuss the continuity of each function.

a. $f(x) = \dfrac{1}{x}$ **b.** $g(x) = \dfrac{x^2 - 1}{x - 1}$ **c.** $h(x) = \begin{cases} x + 1, & x \le 0 \\ e^x, & x > 0 \end{cases}$ **d.** $y = \sin x$

Solution

a. The domain of f is all nonzero real numbers. From Theorem 1.3, you can conclude that f is continuous at every x-value in its domain. At $x = 0$, f has a nonremovable discontinuity, as shown in Figure 1.26(a). In other words, there is no way to define $f(0)$ so as to make the function continuous at $x = 0$.

b. The domain of g is all real numbers except $x = 1$. From Theorem 1.3, you can conclude that g is continuous at every x-value in its domain. At $x = 1$, the function has a removable discontinuity, as shown in Figure 1.26(b). By defining $g(1)$ as 2, the "redefined" function is continuous for all real numbers.

c. The domain of h is all real numbers. The function h is continuous on $(-\infty, 0)$ and $(0, \infty)$ and, because $\lim\limits_{x \to 0} h(x) = 1$, h is continuous on the entire real number line, as shown in Figure 1.26(c).

d. The domain of y is all real numbers. From Theorem 1.6, you can conclude that the function is continuous on its entire domain, $(-\infty, \infty)$, as shown in Figure 1.26(d).

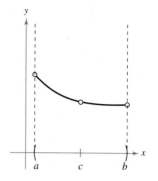

(a) Removable discontinuity

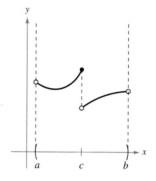

(b) Nonremovable discontinuity

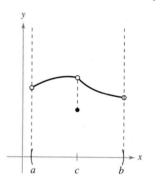

(c) Removable discontinuity
Figure 1.25

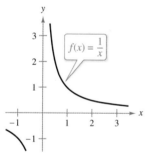

(a) Nonremovable discontinuity at $x = 0$

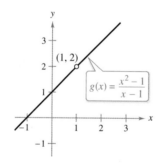

(b) Removable discontinuity at $x = 1$

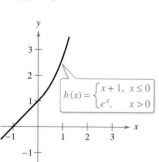

(c) Everywhere continuous

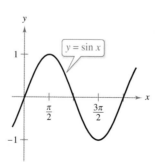

(d) Everywhere continuous
Figure 1.26

Communication and Notation

You may want to refer to the function in Example 1(a) as "discontinuous," but this terminology may be confusing. Rather than saying the function is discontinuous, it is more precise to say that the function has a discontinuity at $x = 0$.

One-Sided Limits and Continuity on a Closed Interval

To understand continuity on a closed interval, you first need to look at a different type of limit called a **one-sided limit.** For instance, the **limit from the right** (or right-hand limit) means that x approaches c from values greater than c. [See Figure 1.27(a).] This limit is denoted as

$$\lim_{x \to c^+} f(x) = L. \qquad \text{Limit from the right}$$

Similarly, the **limit from the left** (or left-hand limit) means that x approaches c from values less than c. [See Figure 1.27(b).] This limit is denoted as

$$\lim_{x \to c^-} f(x) = L. \qquad \text{Limit from the left}$$

One-sided limits are useful in taking limits of functions involving radicals. For instance, if n is an even integer, then

$$\lim_{x \to 0^+} \sqrt[n]{x} = 0.$$

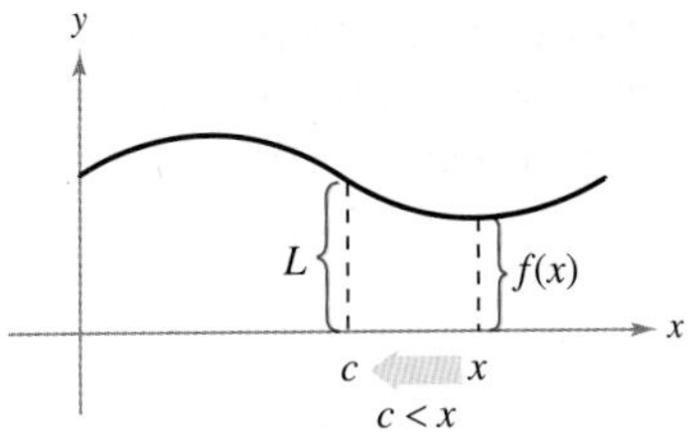

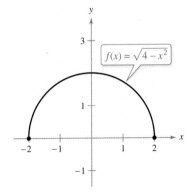

(a) Limit as x approaches c from the right.

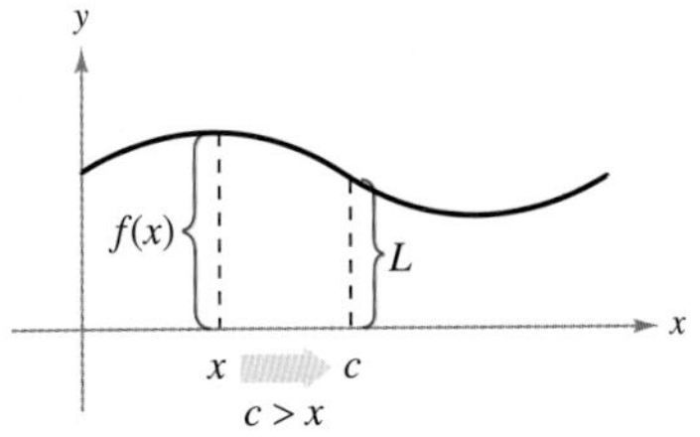

(b) Limit as x approaches c from the left.
Figure 1.27

 EXAMPLE 2   **A One-Sided Limit**

Find the limit of

$$f(x) = \sqrt{4 - x^2}$$

as x approaches -2 from the right.

Solution

As shown in Figure 1.28, the limit as x approaches -2 from the right is

$$\lim_{x \to -2^+} \sqrt{4 - x^2} = 0.$$

One-sided limits can be used to investigate the behavior of **step functions.** One common type of step function is the **greatest integer function** $[\![x]\!]$, defined as

$$[\![x]\!] = \text{greatest integer } n \text{ such that } n \le x. \qquad \text{Greatest integer function}$$

For instance, $[\![2.5]\!] = 2$ and $[\![-2.5]\!] = -3$.

The limit of $f(x)$ as x approaches -2 from the right is 0.
Figure 1.28

EXAMPLE 3   **The Greatest Integer Function**

Find the limit of the greatest integer function

$$f(x) = [\![x]\!]$$

as x approaches 0 from the left and from the right.

Solution

As shown in Figure 1.29, the limit as x approaches 0 *from the left* is

$$\lim_{x \to 0^-} [\![x]\!] = -1$$

and the limit as x approaches 0 *from the right* is

$$\lim_{x \to 0^+} [\![x]\!] = 0.$$

The greatest integer function has a discontinuity at zero because the left- and right-hand limits at zero are different. By similar reasoning, you can see that the greatest integer function has a discontinuity at any integer n.

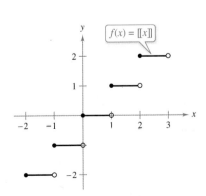

Greatest integer function
Figure 1.29

When the limit from the left is not equal to the limit from the right, the (two-sided) limit *does not exist*. The next theorem makes this more explicit. The proof of this theorem follows directly from the definition of a one-sided limit.

Theorem 1.10   The Existence of Limit

Let f be a function, and let c and L be real numbers. The limit of $f(x)$ as x approaches c is L if and only if

$$\lim_{x \to c^-} f(x) = L \quad \text{and} \quad \lim_{x \to c^+} f(x) = L.$$

The concept of a one-sided limit allows you to extend the definition of continuity to closed intervals. Basically, a function is continuous on a closed interval when it is continuous in the interior of the interval and exhibits one-sided continuity at the endpoints. The definition below formally states this.

Definition of Continuity on a Closed Interval

A function f is **continuous on the closed interval** $[a, b]$ when f is continuous on the open interval (a, b) and

$$\lim_{x \to a^+} f(x) = f(a)$$

and

$$\lim_{x \to b^-} f(x) = f(b).$$

The function f is **continuous from the right** at a and **continuous from the left** at b. (See Figure 1.30.)

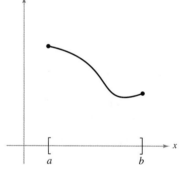

Continuous function on a closed interval

Figure 1.30

Similar definitions can be made to cover continuity on intervals of the form $(a, b]$ and $[a, b)$ that are neither open nor closed, or on infinite intervals. For example,

$$f(x) = \sqrt{x}$$

is continuous on the infinite interval $[0, \infty)$, and the function

$$g(x) = \sqrt{2 - x}$$

is continuous on the infinite interval $(-\infty, 2]$.

EXAMPLE 4   Continuity on a Closed Interval

Discuss the continuity of

$$f(x) = \sqrt{1 - x^2}.$$

Solution

The domain of f is the closed interval $[-1, 1]$. At all points in the open interval $(-1, 1)$, the continuity of f follows from Theorems 1.4 and 1.5. Moreover, because

$$\lim_{x \to -1^+} \sqrt{1 - x^2} = 0 = f(-1) \qquad \text{Continuous from the right}$$

and

$$\lim_{x \to 1^-} \sqrt{1 - x^2} = 0 = f(1) \qquad \text{Continuous from the left}$$

you can conclude that f is continuous on the closed interval $[-1, 1]$, as shown in Figure 1.31.

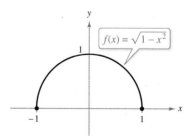

f is continuous on $[-1, 1]$.

Figure 1.31

The next example shows how you can use a one-sided limit to investigate the "lower limit" of the temperature of matter.

EXAMPLE 5   Charles's Law and Absolute Zero

On the Kelvin scale, *absolute zero* is the temperature 0 K. Although temperatures very close to 0 K have been produced in laboratories, absolute zero has never been attained. In fact, evidence suggests that absolute zero *cannot* be attained. How did scientists determine that 0 K is the "lower limit" of the temperature of matter? What is absolute zero on the Celsius scale?

Solution

The determination of absolute zero stems from the work of the French physicist Jacques Charles (1746–1823). Charles discovered that the volume of gas at a constant pressure increases linearly with the temperature of the gas. The table illustrates this relationship between volume and temperature. To generate the values in the table, one mole of hydrogen is held at a constant pressure of one atmosphere. The volume V is approximated and is measured in liters, and the temperature T is measured in degrees Celsius.

T	-40	-20	0	20	40	60	80
V	19.1482	20.7908	22.4334	24.0760	25.7186	27.3612	29.0038

> **Remark**
>
> Charles's Law for gases (assuming constant pressure) can be stated as
>
> $$V = kT$$
>
> where V is volume, k is a constant, and T is temperature.

The points represented by the table are shown in the figure at the right. Moreover, by using the points in the table, you can determine that T and V are related by the linear equation

$$V = 0.08213T + 22.4334.$$

Solving for T, you get an equation for the temperature of the gas.

$$T = \frac{V - 22.4334}{0.08213}$$

By reasoning that the volume of the gas can approach 0 (but can never equal or go below 0), you can determine that the "least possible temperature" is

$$\lim_{V \to 0^+} T = \lim_{V \to 0^+} \frac{V - 22.4334}{0.08213}$$

$$= \frac{0 - 22.4334}{0.08213} \qquad \text{Use direct substitution.}$$

$$\approx -273.15.$$

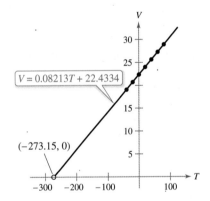

The volume of hydrogen gas depends on its temperature.

So, absolute zero on the Kelvin scale (0 K) is approximately $-273.15°$ on the Celsius scale. ■

The table below shows the temperatures in Example 5 converted to the Fahrenheit scale. Try repeating the solution shown in Example 5 using these temperatures and volumes. Use the result to find the value of absolute zero on the Fahrenheit scale.

T	-40	-4	32	68	104	140	176
V	19.1482	20.7908	22.4334	24.0760	25.7186	27.3612	29.0038

Properties of Continuity

In Section 1.3, you studied several properties of limits. Each of those properties yields a corresponding property pertaining to the continuity of a function. For instance, Theorem 1.11 follows directly from Theorem 1.2.

Theorem 1.11 Properties of Continuity

If b is a real number and f and g are continuous at $x = c$, then the functions listed below are also continuous at c.

1. Scalar multiple: bf **2.** Sum or difference: $f \pm g$

3. Product: fg **4.** Quotient: $\dfrac{f}{g}, \quad g(c) \neq 0$

A proof of this theorem is given in Appendix A.

The list below summarizes the functions you have studied so far that are continuous at every point in their domains.

1. Polynomial: $p(x) = a_n x^n + a_{n-1} x^{n-1} + \cdots + a_1 x + a_0$

2. Rational: $r(x) = \dfrac{p(x)}{q(x)}, \quad q(x) \neq 0$

3. Radical: $f(x) = \sqrt[n]{x}$

4. Trigonometric: $\sin x$, $\cos x$, $\tan x$, $\cot x$, $\sec x$, $\csc x$

5. Exponential and logarithmic: $f(x) = a^x$, $f(x) = e^x$, $f(x) = \ln x$

By combining Theorem 1.11 with this list, you can conclude that a wide variety of elementary functions are continuous at every point in their domains.

EXAMPLE 6   Applying Properties of Continuity

See LarsonCalculusforAP.com for an interactive version of this type of example.

By Theorem 1.11, it follows that each function below is continuous at every point in its domain.

$$f(x) = x + e^x, \quad f(x) = 3 \tan x, \quad f(x) = \frac{x^2 + 1}{\cos x}$$

The next theorem, which is a consequence of Theorem 1.5, allows you to determine the continuity of *composite* functions such as

$$f(x) = \ln 3x, \quad f(x) = \sqrt{x^2 + 1}, \quad \text{and} \quad f(x) = \tan \frac{1}{x}.$$

Theorem 1.12 Continuity of a Composite Function

If g is continuous at c and f is continuous at $g(c)$, then the composite function given by $(f \circ g)(x) = f(g(x))$ is continuous at c.

Proof

By the definition of continuity, $\lim\limits_{x \to c} g(x) = g(c)$ and $\lim\limits_{x \to g(c)} f(x) = f(g(c))$. Apply Theorem 1.5 with $L = g(c)$ to obtain $\lim\limits_{x \to c} f(g(x)) = f\left(\lim\limits_{x \to c} g(x)\right) = f(g(c))$. So, $(f \circ g)(x) = f(g(x))$ is continuous at c.

Justification

One consequence of Theorem 1.12 is that when f and g satisfy the given conditions, you can determine the limit of $f(g(x))$ as x approaches c to be

$$\lim_{x \to c} f(g(x)) = f(g(c)).$$

EXAMPLE 7   Testing for Continuity

Describe the interval(s) on which each function is continuous.

a. $f(x) = \tan x$ **b.** $g(x) = \begin{cases} \sin \dfrac{1}{x}, & x \neq 0 \\ 0, & x = 0 \end{cases}$ **c.** $h(x) = \begin{cases} x \sin \dfrac{1}{x}, & x \neq 0 \\ 0, & x = 0 \end{cases}$

Solution

a. The tangent function $f(x) = \tan x$ is undefined at

$$x = \frac{\pi}{2} + n\pi, \quad n \text{ is an integer.}$$

At all other points, f is continuous. So, $f(x) = \tan x$ is continuous on the open intervals

$$\ldots, \left(-\frac{3\pi}{2}, -\frac{\pi}{2}\right), \left(-\frac{\pi}{2}, \frac{\pi}{2}\right), \left(\frac{\pi}{2}, \frac{3\pi}{2}\right), \ldots$$

as shown in Figure 1.32(a).

b. Because $y = 1/x$ is continuous except at $x = 0$ and the sine function is continuous for all real values of x, it follows from Theorem 1.12 that

$$y = \sin \frac{1}{x}$$

is continuous at all real values except $x = 0$. At $x = 0$, the limit of $g(x)$ does not exist (see Example 5, Section 1.2). So, g is continuous on the intervals $(-\infty, 0)$ and $(0, \infty)$, as shown in Figure 1.32(b).

c. This function is similar to the function in part (b) except that the oscillations are damped by the factor x. Using the Squeeze Theorem, you obtain

$$-|x| \leq x \sin \frac{1}{x} \leq |x|, \quad x \neq 0$$

and you can conclude that

$$\lim_{x \to 0} h(x) = 0.$$

So, h is continuous on the entire real number line, as shown in Figure 1.32(c).

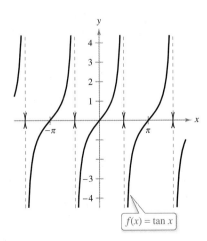

(a) f is continuous on each open interval in its domain.

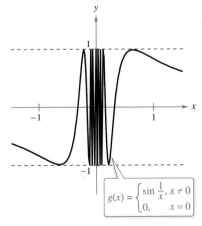

(b) g is continuous on $(-\infty, 0)$ and $(0, \infty)$.

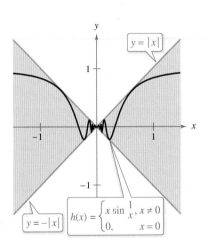

(c) h is everywhere continuous.

Figure 1.32

The Intermediate Value Theorem

Theorem 1.13 is an important theorem concerning the behavior of functions that are continuous on a closed interval.

> **Theorem 1.13   Intermediate Value Theorem**
>
> If f is continuous on the closed interval $[a, b]$, $f(a) \neq f(b)$, and k is any number between $f(a)$ and $f(b)$, then there is at least one number c in $[a, b]$ such that
>
> $$f(c) = k.$$

> ▶ **Remark**   The Intermediate Value Theorem tells you that at least one number c exists, but it does not provide a method for finding c. Such theorems are called **existence theorems.** By referring to a text on advanced calculus, you will find that a proof of this theorem is based on a property of real numbers called *completeness.* The Intermediate Value Theorem states that for a continuous function f, if x takes on all values between a and b, then $f(x)$ must take on all values between $f(a)$ and $f(b)$.

Insight

Be sure you understand the Intermediate Value Theorem for the AP® Exam. Make sure you know the conditions of the theorem and what conclusion can be reached by applying the theorem.

As an example of the application of the Intermediate Value Theorem, consider a person's height. A boy is 5 feet tall on his thirteenth birthday and 5 feet 2 inches tall on his fourteenth birthday. Then, for any height h between 5 feet and 5 feet 2 inches, there must have been a time t when his height was exactly h. This seems reasonable because human growth is continuous and a person's height does not abruptly change from one value to another.

The Intermediate Value Theorem guarantees the existence of *at least one* number c in the closed interval $[a, b]$. There may, of course, be more than one number c such that

$$f(c) = k$$

as shown in Figure 1.33. A function that is not continuous does not necessarily exhibit the intermediate value property. For example, the graph of the function shown in Figure 1.34 jumps over the horizontal line

$$y = k$$

and for this function there is no value of c in $[a, b]$ such that $f(c) = k$.

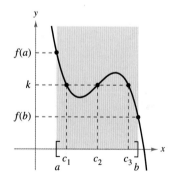

f is continuous on $[a, b]$.
[There exist three c's such that $f(c) = k$.]
Figure 1.33

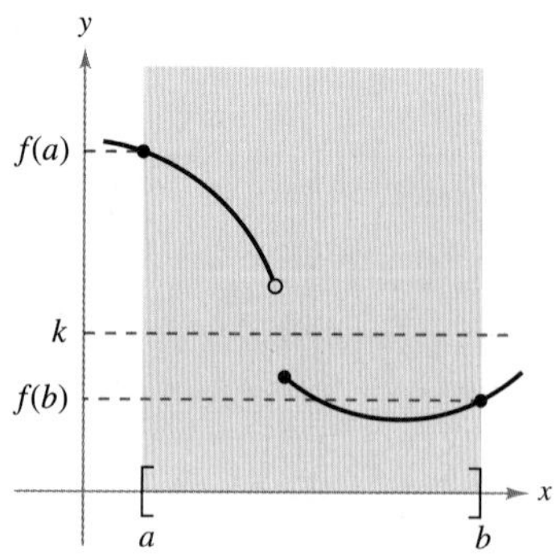

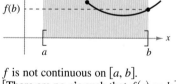

f is not continuous on $[a, b]$.
[There are no c's such that $f(c) = k$.]
Figure 1.34

You can often use the Intermediate Value Theorem to locate the zeros of a function that is continuous on a closed interval. Specifically, if f is continuous on $[a, b]$ and $f(a)$ and $f(b)$ differ in sign, then the Intermediate Value Theorem guarantees the existence of at least one zero of f in the closed interval $[a, b]$.

EXAMPLE 8   An Application of the Intermediate Value Theorem

Use the Intermediate Value Theorem to show that the polynomial function

$$f(x) = x^3 + 2x - 1$$

has a zero in the interval $[0, 1]$.

Algebraic Solution

Note that f is continuous on the closed interval $[0, 1]$. Because

$$f(0) = 0^3 + 2(0) - 1 = -1 \quad \text{and} \quad f(1) = 1^3 + 2(1) - 1 = 2$$

it follows that $f(0) < 0$ and $f(1) > 0$. You can therefore apply the Intermediate Value Theorem to conclude that there must be some c in $[0, 1]$ such that

$$f(c) = 0 \qquad \text{f has a zero in the closed interval $[0, 1]$.}$$

as shown in the figure below.

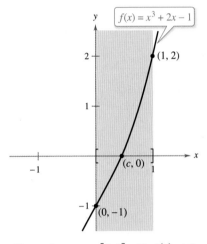

f is continuous on $[0, 1]$ with $f(0) < 0$ and $f(1) > 0$.

Numerical Solution

Note that f is continuous on the closed interval $[0, 1]$. From the table, you can see that $f(0)$ and $f(1)$ differ in sign. So, you can conclude from the Intermediate Value Theorem that the function has a zero in the interval $[0, 1]$.

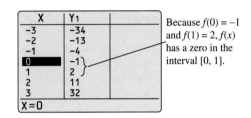

Because $f(0) = -1$ and $f(1) = 2$, $f(x)$ has a zero in the interval $[0, 1]$.

The **bisection method** for approximating the real zeros of a continuous function is similar to the method used in Example 8. If you know that a zero exists in the closed interval $[a, b]$, then the zero must lie in the interval $[a, (a + b)/2]$ or $[(a + b)/2, b]$. From the sign of $f([a + b]/2)$, you can determine which interval contains the zero. By repeatedly bisecting the interval, you can "close in" on the zero of the function.

Technology

You can use the *root* or *zero* feature of a graphing utility to approximate the real zeros of a continuous function. Using this feature, the zero of the function in Example 8, $f(x) = x^3 + 2x - 1$, is approximately 0.453, as shown in the figure.

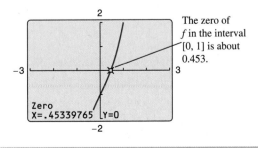

The zero of f in the interval $[0, 1]$ is about 0.453.

1.4   Exercises

See *CalcChat.com* for tutorial help and worked-out solutions to odd-numbered exercises.

Limits and Continuity   In Exercises 1–6, use the graph to determine the limit, and discuss the continuity of the function.

(a) $\lim_{x \to c^+} f(x)$ (b) $\lim_{x \to c^-} f(x)$ (c) $\lim_{x \to c} f(x)$

1.
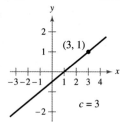

2.
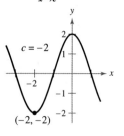

3.
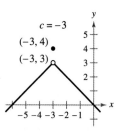

4.
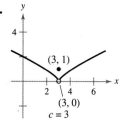

5.
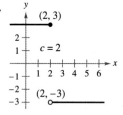

6.
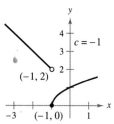

Finding a Limit   In Exercises 7–28, find the limit (if it exists). If it does not exist, explain why.

7. $\lim_{x \to 8^+} \dfrac{1}{x + 8}$

8. $\lim_{x \to 3^-} \dfrac{3}{x + 3}$

9. $\lim_{x \to 4^+} \dfrac{x - 4}{x^2 - 16}$

10. $\lim_{x \to 5^+} \dfrac{5 - x}{x^2 - 25}$

11. $\lim_{x \to -7^-} \dfrac{x}{\sqrt{x^2 - 49}}$

12. $\lim_{x \to 4^-} \dfrac{\sqrt{x} - 2}{x - 4}$

13. $\lim_{x \to 0^-} \dfrac{|x|}{x}$

14. $\lim_{x \to 12^+} \dfrac{|x - 12|}{x - 12}$

15. $\lim_{\Delta x \to 0^-} \dfrac{\dfrac{1}{x + \Delta x} - \dfrac{1}{x}}{\Delta x}$

16. $\lim_{\Delta x \to 0^+} \dfrac{(x + \Delta x)^2 + x + \Delta x - (x^2 + x)}{\Delta x}$

17. $\lim_{x \to 3^-} f(x)$, where $f(x) = \begin{cases} \dfrac{x + 2}{2}, & x \le 3 \\ \dfrac{12 - 2x}{3}, & x > 3 \end{cases}$

18. $\lim_{x \to 3} f(x)$, where $f(x) = \begin{cases} x^2 - 4x + 6, & x < 3 \\ -x^2 + 4x - 2, & x \ge 3 \end{cases}$

19. $\lim_{x \to \pi} \cot x$

20. $\lim_{x \to \pi/2} \sec x$

21. $\lim_{x \to 4^-} (7[\![x]\!] - 5)$

22. $\lim_{x \to 2^+} (4x - [\![x]\!])$

23. $\lim_{x \to 2} (3 - [\![-x]\!])$

24. $\lim_{x \to 1} \left(1 - \left[\!\left[-\dfrac{x}{2} \right]\!\right] \right)$

25. $\lim_{x \to 4^+} \ln(x - 4)$

26. $\lim_{x \to 5^-} \ln(5 - x)$

27. $\lim_{x \to 2^-} \ln[x^2(4 - x)]$

28. $\lim_{x \to 10^+} \ln \dfrac{x}{\sqrt{x - 9}}$

Continuity of a Function   In Exercises 29–32, discuss the continuity of each function.

29. $f(x) = \dfrac{1}{x^2 - .4}$

30. $f(x) = \dfrac{x^2 - 1}{x + 1}$

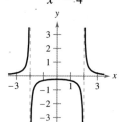

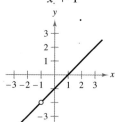

31. $f(x) = \begin{cases} x, & x < 1 \\ 2, & x = 1 \\ 2x - 1, & x > 1 \end{cases}$

32. $f(x) = \frac{1}{2}[\![x]\!] + x$

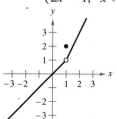

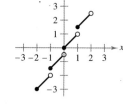

Continuity on a Closed Interval   In Exercises 33–36, discuss the continuity of the function on the closed interval.

Function	Interval
33. $g(x) = \sqrt{49 - x^2}$	$[-7, 7]$
34. $f(t) = 3 - \sqrt{9 - t^2}$	$[-3, 3]$
35. $f(x) = \begin{cases} 3 - x, & x \le 0 \\ 3 + \frac{1}{2}x, & x > 0 \end{cases}$	$[-1, 4]$
36. $g(x) = \dfrac{1}{x^2 - 9}$	$[-1, 3]$

Error Analysis   In Exercises 37 and 38, describe and correct the error.

37. $\lim_{x \to -1^-} \dfrac{1}{x^2 - 1} = 0$

38. $g(x) = \dfrac{1}{\sqrt{2 - x}}$ is continuous on $(-\infty, 2]$.   ✗

Removable and Nonremovable Discontinuities
In Exercises 39–62, find the x-values (if any) at which f is not continuous. Which of the discontinuities are removable?

39. $f(x) = \dfrac{4}{x}$

40. $f(x) = \dfrac{6}{x - 4}$

41. $f(x) = 3x - \cos x$

42. $f(x) = x^2 - 4x + 4$

43. $f(x) = \dfrac{1}{4 - x^2}$

44. $f(x) = \dfrac{x}{x^2 - x}$

45. $f(x) = \dfrac{x}{x^2 + 1}$

46. $f(x) = \dfrac{x - 5}{x^2 - 25}$

47. $f(x) = \dfrac{x + 2}{x^2 - 3x - 10}$

48. $f(x) = \dfrac{x + 2}{x^2 - x - 6}$

49. $f(x) = \dfrac{|x + 9|}{x + 9}$

50. $f(x) = \dfrac{|x - 5|}{x - 5}$

51. $f(x) = \begin{cases} x, & x \le 1 \\ x^2, & x > 1 \end{cases}$

52. $f(x) = \begin{cases} -2x + 3, & x < 1 \\ x^2, & x \ge 1 \end{cases}$

53. $f(x) = \begin{cases} \frac{1}{2}x + 1, & x \le 2 \\ 3 - x, & x > 2 \end{cases}$

54. $f(x) = \begin{cases} -2x, & x \le 2 \\ x^2 + 1, & x > 2 \end{cases}$

55. $f(x) = \begin{cases} \tan \dfrac{\pi x}{4}, & |x| < 1 \\ x, & |x| \ge 1 \end{cases}$

56. $f(x) = \begin{cases} \csc \dfrac{\pi x}{6}, & |x - 3| \le 2 \\ 2, & |x - 3| > 2 \end{cases}$

57. $f(x) = \begin{cases} \ln(x + 1), & x \ge 0 \\ 1 - x^2, & x < 0 \end{cases}$

58. $f(x) = \begin{cases} 10 - 3e^{5-x}, & x > 5 \\ 10 - \frac{3}{5}x, & x \le 5 \end{cases}$

59. $f(x) = \csc x$

60. $f(x) = \tan \dfrac{\pi x}{2}$

61. $f(x) = [\![x - 5]\!]$

62. $f(x) = 8 - [\![x]\!]$

Making a Function Continuous In Exercises 63–68, find the constant(s) such that the function is continuous on the entire real number line.

63. $f(x) = \begin{cases} x^3, & x \le 2 \\ ax^2, & x > 2 \end{cases}$

64. $g(x) = \begin{cases} \dfrac{4 \sin x}{x}, & x < 0 \\ a - 2x, & x \ge 0 \end{cases}$

65. $f(x) = \begin{cases} 2, & x \le -1 \\ ax + b, & -1 < x < 3 \\ -2, & x \ge 3 \end{cases}$

66. $g(x) = \begin{cases} \dfrac{x^2 - a^2}{x - a}, & x \ne a \\ 8, & x = a \end{cases}$

67. $f(x) = \begin{cases} ae^{x-1} + 3, & x < 1 \\ \arctan(x - 1) + 2, & x \ge 1 \end{cases}$

68. $f(x) = \begin{cases} 2e^{ax} - 2, & x \le 4 \\ \ln(x - 3) + x^2, & x > 4 \end{cases}$

Continuity of a Composite Function In Exercises 69–72, discuss the continuity of the composite function $h(x) = f(g(x))$.

69. $f(x) = x^2$
$g(x) = x - 1$

70. $f(x) = \dfrac{1}{\sqrt{x}}$
$g(x) = x - 1$

71. $f(x) = \dfrac{1}{x - 6}$
$g(x) = x^2 + 5$

72. $f(x) = \sin x$
$g(x) = x^2$

Finding Discontinuities In Exercises 73–76, use a graphing utility to graph the function. Determine any x-values at which the function is not continuous.

73. $f(x) = [\![x]\!] - x$

74. $h(x) = \dfrac{1}{x^2 + 2x - 15}$

75. $g(x) = \begin{cases} x^2 - 3x, & x > 4 \\ 2x - 5, & x \le 4 \end{cases}$

76. $f(x) = \begin{cases} \dfrac{\cos x - 1}{x}, & x < 0 \\ 5x, & x \ge 0 \end{cases}$

Testing for Continuity In Exercises 77–84, describe the interval(s) on which the function is continuous.

77. $f(x) = \dfrac{x^2 - 16}{x - 4}$

78. $f(x) = \dfrac{x + 1}{\sqrt{x}}$

79. $f(x) = 3 - \sqrt{x}$

80. $f(x) = x\sqrt{x + 3}$

81. $f(x) = \sec \dfrac{\pi x}{4}$

82. $f(x) = \cos \dfrac{1}{x}$

83. $f(x) = \begin{cases} \dfrac{x^2 - 1}{x - 1}, & x \ne 1 \\ 2, & x = 1 \end{cases}$

84. $f(x) = \begin{cases} 2x - 4, & x \ne 3 \\ 1, & x = 3 \end{cases}$

Communicating In Exercises 85–88, use a graphing utility to graph the function on the interval $[-4, 4]$. Does the graph of the function appear to be continuous on this interval? Is the function continuous on $[-4, 4]$? Write a short paragraph about the importance of examining a function analytically as well as graphically.

85. $f(x) = \dfrac{\sin x}{x}$

86. $f(x) = \dfrac{x^3 - 8}{x - 2}$

87. $f(x) = \dfrac{\ln(x^2 + 1)}{x}$

88. $f(x) = \dfrac{e^{-x} + 1}{e^x - 1}$

Existence of a Zero In Exercises 89–92, explain why the function has at least one zero in the given interval.

89. $f(x) = \frac{1}{12}x^4 - x^3 + 4, \ [1, 2]$

90. $f(x) = -\dfrac{5}{x} + \tan \dfrac{\pi x}{10}, \ [1, 4]$

91. $h(x) = -2e^{-x/2} \cos 2x, \ \left[0, \dfrac{\pi}{2}\right]$

92. $g(t) = (t^3 + 2t - 2) \ln(t^2 + 4), \ [0, 1]$

Using the Intermediate Value Theorem In Exercises 93–98, use the Intermediate Value Theorem and a graphing utility to approximate the zero of the function in the interval $[0, 1]$. Repeatedly "zoom in" on the graph of the function to approximate the zero accurate to two decimal places. Use the *zero* or *root* feature of the graphing utility to approximate the zero accurate to four decimal places.

93. $f(x) = x^3 + x - 1$
94. $f(x) = x^4 - x^2 + 3x - 1$
95. $g(t) = 2 \cos t - 3t$
96. $h(\theta) = \tan \theta + 3\theta - 4$
97. $f(x) = x + e^x - 3$
98. $g(x) = 5 \ln(x + 1) - 2$

 Using the Intermediate Value Theorem In Exercises 99–102, verify that the Intermediate Value Theorem applies to the indicated interval and find the value of c guaranteed by the theorem.

99. $f(x) = x^2 + x - 1$, $[0, 5]$, $f(c) = 11$

100. $f(x) = x^2 - 6x + 8$, $[0, 3]$, $f(c) = 0$

101. $f(x) = x^3 - x^2 + x - 2$, $[0, 3]$, $f(c) = 4$

102. $f(x) = \dfrac{x^2 + x}{x - 1}$, $\left[\dfrac{5}{2}, 4\right]$, $f(c) = 6$

103. INVENTORY MANAGEMENT

The number of units in inventory in a small company is given by

$$N(t) = 25\left(2\left[\!\left[\tfrac{1}{2}t + 1\right]\!\right] - t\right)$$

where t is the time in months. Sketch the graph of this function and discuss its continuity. How often must this company replenish its inventory?

104. **HOW DO YOU SEE IT?** Every day you dissolve 28 ounces of chlorine in a swimming pool. The graph shows the amount of chlorine $f(t)$ in the pool after t days. Estimate and interpret $\lim\limits_{x\to 4^-} f(t)$ and $\lim\limits_{t\to 4^+} f(t)$.

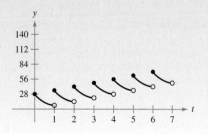

EXPLORING CONCEPTS

105. Communicating Describe how continuity is destroyed at $x = c$ for each of the following graphs.

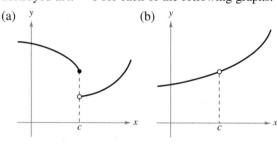

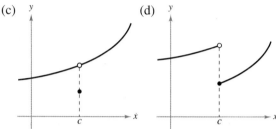

106. Justifying Sketch the graph of any function f such that

$$\lim_{x\to 3^+} f(x) = 1 \quad \text{and} \quad \lim_{x\to 3^-} f(x) = 0.$$

Is the function continuous at $x = 3$? Explain.

107. Connecting Representations If the functions f and g are continuous for all real x, is $f + g$ always continuous for all real x? Is f/g always continuous for all real x? If either is not continuous, give an example to verify your conclusion.

108. Communicating Describe the difference between a discontinuity that is removable and a discontinuity that is nonremovable. Then give an example of a function that satisfies each description: (a) a function with a nonremovable discontinuity at $x = 4$, (b) a function with a removable discontinuity at $x = -4$, and (c) a function that has both of the characteristics described in parts (a) and (b).

True or False? In Exercises 109–112, determine whether the statement is true or false. If it is false, explain why or give an example that shows it is false.

109. If $\lim\limits_{x\to c} f(x) = L$ and $f(c) = L$, then f is continuous at c.

110. If $f(x) = g(x)$ for $x \neq c$ and $f(c) \neq g(c)$, then either f or g is not continuous at c.

111. The limit of the greatest integer function as x approaches 0 from the left is -1.

112. The function

$$f(x) = \frac{|x - 1|}{x - 1}$$

is continuous on $(-\infty, \infty)$.

113. **Déjà Vu** At 8:00 A.M. on Saturday, a person begins running up the side of a mountain to a weekend campsite. On Sunday morning at 8:00 A.M., the person runs back down the mountain. It takes 20 minutes to run up, but only 10 minutes to run down. Prove that at some point on the way down, the person passes the same place at exactly the same time on both days. [*Hint:* Let $s(t)$ and $r(t)$ be the position functions for the runs up and down, and apply the Intermediate Value Theorem to the function $f(t) = s(t) - r(t)$.]

114. **Volume** Use the Intermediate Value Theorem to show that for all spheres with radii in the interval $[5, 8]$, there is one with a volume of 1500 cubic centimeters.

115. **Dirichlet Function** Show that the Dirichlet function

$$f(x) = \begin{cases} 0, & \text{if } x \text{ is rational} \\ 1, & \text{if } x \text{ is irrational} \end{cases}$$

is not continuous at any real number.

116. **Continuity of a Function** Show that the function

$$f(x) = \begin{cases} 0, & \text{if } x \text{ is rational} \\ kx, & \text{if } x \text{ is irrational} \end{cases}$$

is continuous only at $x = 0$. (Assume that k is any nonzero real number.)

117. **Making a Function Continuous** Find all values of c such that f is continuous on $(-\infty, \infty)$.

$$f(x) = \begin{cases} 1 - x^2, & x \le c \\ x, & x > c \end{cases}$$

118. **Making a Function Continuous** Let

$$f(x) = \frac{\sqrt{x + c^2} - c}{x}, \quad c > 0.$$

What is the domain of f? How can you define f at $x = 0$ in order for f to be continuous there?

119. **Modeling Data** The table lists the frequency F (in Hertz) of a musical note at various times t (in seconds).

t	0	1	2	3	4	5
F	436	444	434	446	433	444

(a) Plot the data and connect the points with a curve.

(b) Does there appear to be a limiting frequency of the note? Explain.

120. **Signum Function** The **signum function** is defined by

$$\text{sgn}(x) = \begin{cases} -1, & x < 0 \\ 0, & x = 0 \\ 1, & x > 0 \end{cases}.$$

Sketch a graph of $\text{sgn}(x)$ and find the following (if possible).

(a) $\lim\limits_{x \to 0^-} \text{sgn}(x)$ (b) $\lim\limits_{x \to 0^+} \text{sgn}(x)$ (c) $\lim\limits_{x \to 0} \text{sgn}(x)$

121. **Think About It** Describe how the functions $f(x) = 3 + [\![x]\!]$ and $g(x) = 3 - [\![-x]\!]$ differ.

122. **Continuity of a Function** Discuss the continuity of the function $h(x) = x[\![x]\!]$.

123. **Proof** Prove that if $\lim\limits_{\Delta x \to 0} f(c + \Delta x) = f(c)$, then f is continuous at c.

124. **Proof** Prove that if f is continuous and has no zeros on $[a, b]$, then either $f(x) > 0$ for all x in $[a, b]$ or $f(x) < 0$ for all x in $[a, b]$.

125. **Proof** Prove that for any real number y there exists x in $(-\pi/2, \pi/2)$ such that $\tan x = y$.

126. **Proof**

(a) Let $f_1(x)$ and $f_2(x)$ be continuous on the closed interval $[a, b]$. If $f_1(a) < f_2(a)$ and $f_1(b) > f_2(b)$, prove that there exists c between a and b such that $f_1(c) = f_2(c)$.

(b) Show that there exists c in $[0, \pi/2]$ such that $\cos x = x$. Use a graphing utility to approximate c to three decimal places.

Calculus AP® – Exam Preparation Questions

127. **Multiple Choice** On which interval is the graph of $f(x) = 3/\sqrt{x^2 - 1}$ continuous?

(A) $(-\infty, -1)$ (B) $(-1, 1)$
(C) $[1, \infty)$ (D) $[-1, 1]$

128. **Multiple Choice** Given

$$f(x) = \begin{cases} \dfrac{x^3 + x - 2}{x - 1}, & x \ne 1 \\ c, & x = 1 \end{cases}$$

for what constant c is the graph of f continuous on the entire real number line?

(A) -1 (B) 0 (C) 1 (D) 4

129. **Free Response** The function p is defined as

$$p(x) = \begin{cases} 2, & x \le -1 \\ ax + b, & -1 < x < 3 \\ -2, & x \ge 3 \end{cases}$$

(a) Find the constants a and b such that p is continuous on the entire real number line.

(b) Use a graph to verify your results in part (a).

(c) Find $\lim\limits_{x \to 0} p(x)$.

130. **Free Response** The function f is defined as

$$f(x) = \begin{cases} x^2 + 5, & x \le 2 \\ \dfrac{x^4 - 16}{x^2 - 4}, & x > 2 \end{cases}.$$

Find the value of each limit, or explain why the limit does not exist.

(a) $\lim\limits_{x \to 2^+} f(x)$ (b) $\lim\limits_{x \to 2^-} f(x)$
(c) $\lim\limits_{x \to 2} f(x)$ (d) $\lim\limits_{x \to -2} f(x)$

1.5   Infinite Limits

▶ Determine infinite limits from the left and from the right.
▶ Find and sketch the vertical asymptotes of the graph of a function.

Infinite Limits

Consider the function $f(x) = 3/(x - 2)$. From Figure 1.35 and the table, you can see that $f(x)$ *decreases without bound* as x approaches 2 from the left, and $f(x)$ *increases without bound* as x approaches 2 from the right.

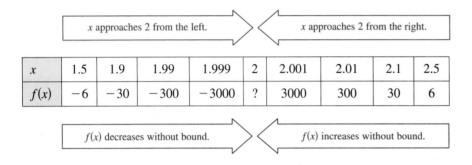

x	1.5	1.9	1.99	1.999	2	2.001	2.01	2.1	2.5
$f(x)$	-6	-30	-300	-3000	?	3000	300	30	6

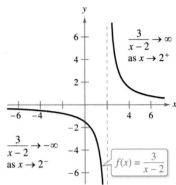

$f(x)$ increases and decreases without bound as x approaches 2.

Figure 1.35

This behavior is denoted as

$$\lim_{x \to 2^-} \frac{3}{x - 2} = -\infty \qquad f(x) \text{ decreases without bound as } x \text{ approaches 2 from the left.}$$

and

$$\lim_{x \to 2^+} \frac{3}{x - 2} = \infty. \qquad f(x) \text{ increases without bound as } x \text{ approaches 2 from the right.}$$

The symbols ∞ and $-\infty$ refer to positive infinity and negative infinity, respectively. These symbols do not represent real numbers. They are convenient symbols used to describe unbounded conditions more concisely. A limit in which $f(x)$ increases or decreases without bound as x approaches c is called an **infinite limit.**

Definition of Infinite Limits

Let f be a function that is defined at every real number in some open interval containing c (except possibly at c itself). The statement

$$\lim_{x \to c} f(x) = \infty$$

means that for each $M > 0$ there exists a $\delta > 0$ such that $f(x) > M$ whenever $0 < |x - c| < \delta$. (See Figure 1.36.) Similarly, the statement

$$\lim_{x \to c} f(x) = -\infty$$

means that for each $N < 0$ there exists a $\delta > 0$ such that $f(x) < N$ whenever

$$0 < |x - c| < \delta.$$

To define the **infinite limit from the left,** replace $0 < |x - c| < \delta$ by $c - \delta < x < c$. To define the **infinite limit from the right,** replace $0 < |x - c| < \delta$ by $c < x < c + \delta$.

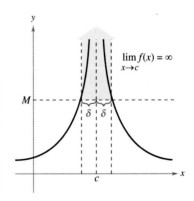

Infinite limits
Figure 1.36

Be sure you see that the equal sign in the statement $\lim f(x) = \infty$ does not mean that the limit exists! On the contrary, it tells you how the limit **fails to exist** by denoting the unbounded behavior of $f(x)$ as x approaches c.

EXAMPLE 1   Determining Infinite Limits from a Graph

Determine the limit of each function shown in Figure 1.37 as x approaches 1 from the left and from the right.

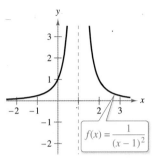

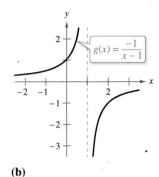

(a)   (b)

Each graph has an asymptote at $x = 1$.

Figure 1.37

Algebraic Solution

a. When x approaches 1 from the left or the right, $(x - 1)^2$ is a small positive number. Thus, the quotient $1/(x - 1)^2$ is a large positive number, and $f(x)$ approaches infinity from each side of $x = 1$. So, you can conclude that

$$\lim_{x \to 1} \frac{1}{(x - 1)^2} = \infty.$$ Limit from each side is infinity.

Figure 1.37(a) supports this conclusion.

b. When x approaches 1 from the left, $x - 1$ is a small negative number. Thus, the quotient $-1/(x - 1)$ is a large positive number, and $f(x)$ approaches infinity from the left of $x = 1$. So, you can conclude that

$$\lim_{x \to 1^-} \frac{-1}{x - 1} = \infty.$$ Limit from the left side is infinity.

When x approaches 1 from the right, $x - 1$ is a small positive number. Thus, the quotient $-1/(x - 1)$ is a large negative number, and $f(x)$ approaches negative infinity from the right of $x = 1$. So, you can conclude that

$$\lim_{x \to 1^+} \frac{-1}{x - 1} = -\infty.$$ Limit from the right side is negative infinity.

Figure 1.37(b) supports this conclusion.

Numerical Solution

Use a graphing utility to create a table of values to analyze the limit of each function as x approaches 1 from the left and from the right.

a. Enter x-values that are closer and closer to 1 using *ask* mode.

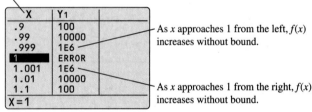

So, it appears that $\displaystyle\lim_{x \to 1} \frac{1}{(x - 1)^2} = \infty.$

b. Enter x-values that are closer and closer to 1 using *ask* mode.

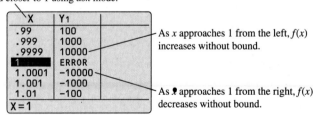

So, it appears that $\displaystyle\lim_{x \to 1^-} \frac{-1}{x - 1} = \infty$ and $\displaystyle\lim_{x \to 1^+} \frac{-1}{x - 1} = -\infty.$

Exploration

Use a graphing utility to graph each function. For each function, analytically find the single real number c that is not in the domain. Then graphically find the limit (if it exists) of $f(x)$ as x approaches c from the left and from the right.

a. $f(x) = \dfrac{3}{x - 4}$ b. $f(x) = \dfrac{1}{2 - x}$ c. $f(x) = \dfrac{2}{(x - 3)^2}$ d. $f(x) = \dfrac{-3}{(x + 2)^2}$

Vertical Asymptotes

If it were possible to extend the graphs in Figure 1.37 toward positive and negative infinity, you would see that each graph becomes arbitrarily close to the vertical line $x = 1$. This line is a **vertical asymptote** of the graph of f. (You will study other types of asymptotes in the next section.)

Definition of Vertical Asymptote

If $f(x)$ approaches infinity (or negative infinity) as x approaches c from the right or the left, then the line $x = c$ is a **vertical asymptote** of the graph of f.

In Example 1, note that each of the functions is a *quotient* and that the vertical asymptote occurs at a number at which the denominator is 0 (and the numerator is not 0). The next theorem generalizes this observation.

Theorem 1.14 Vertical Asymptotes

Let f and g be continuous functions on an open interval containing c. If $f(c) \neq 0$, $g(c) = 0$, and there exists an open interval containing c such that $g(x) \neq 0$ for all $x \neq c$ in the interval, then the graph of the function

$$h(x) = \frac{f(x)}{g(x)}$$

has a vertical asymptote at $x = c$.
A proof of this theorem is given in Appendix A.

EXAMPLE 2 Finding Vertical Asymptotes

See LarsonCalculusforAP.com for an interactive version of this type of example.

a. When $x = -1$, the denominator of

$$h(x) = \frac{1}{2(x + 1)}$$

is 0 and the numerator is not 0. So, by Theorem 1.14, you can conclude that $x = -1$ is a vertical asymptote, as shown in Figure 1.38(a).

b. By factoring the denominator as

$$h(x) = \frac{x^2 + 1}{x^2 - 1} = \frac{x^2 + 1}{(x - 1)(x + 1)}$$

you can see that the denominator is 0 at $x = -1$ and $x = 1$. Also, because the numerator is not 0 at these two points, you can apply Theorem 1.14 to conclude that the graph of h has two vertical asymptotes, as shown in Figure 1.38(b).

c. By writing the cotangent function in the form

$$h(x) = \cot x = \frac{\cos x}{\sin x}$$

you can apply Theorem 1.14 to conclude that vertical asymptotes occur at all values of x such that $\sin x = 0$ and $\cos x \neq 0$, as shown in Figure 1.38(c). So, the graph of this function has infinitely many vertical asymptotes. These asymptotes occur at $x = n\pi$, where n is an integer.

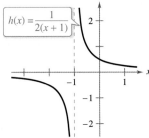

$h(x) = \dfrac{1}{2(x + 1)}$

(a)

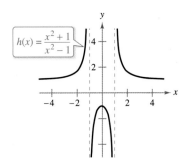

$h(x) = \dfrac{x^2 + 1}{x^2 - 1}$

(b)

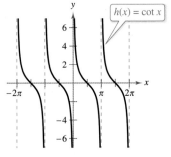

$h(x) = \cot x$

(c)

Functions with vertical asymptotes
Figure 1.38

Theorem 1.14 requires that the value of the numerator at $x = c$ be nonzero. When both the numerator and the denominator are 0 at $x = c$, you obtain the *indeterminate form* $0/0$, and you cannot determine the limit behavior at $x = c$ without further investigation, as illustrated in Example 3.

EXAMPLE 3   A Rational Function with Common Factors

Determine all vertical asymptotes of the graph of $h(x) = \dfrac{x^2 + 2x - 8}{x^2 - 4}$.

Solution

Begin by simplifying the expression, as shown.

$$h(x) = \frac{x^2 + 2x - 8}{x^2 - 4} = \frac{(x + 4)(x - 2)}{(x + 2)(x - 2)} = \frac{x + 4}{x + 2}, \quad x \neq 2$$

At all x-values other than $x = 2$, the graph of h coincides with the graph of $k(x) = (x + 4)/(x + 2)$. So, you can apply Theorem 1.14 to k to conclude that there is a vertical asymptote at $x = -2$, as shown in Figure 1.39. From the graph, you can see that

$$\lim_{x \to -2^-} \frac{x^2 + 2x - 8}{x^2 - 4} = -\infty \quad \text{and} \quad \lim_{x \to -2^+} \frac{x^2 + 2x - 8}{x^2 - 4} = \infty.$$

Note that $x = 2$ is *not* a vertical asymptote.

EXAMPLE 4   Determining Infinite Limits

Find each limit.

$$\lim_{x \to 1^-} \frac{x^2 - 3x}{x - 1} \quad \text{and} \quad \lim_{x \to 1^+} \frac{x^2 - 3x}{x - 1}$$

Solution

Because the denominator is 0 when $x = 1$ (and the numerator is not 0), you know that the graph of

$$h(x) = \frac{x^2 - 3x}{x - 1}$$

has a vertical asymptote at $x = 1$. This means that each of the given limits is either ∞ or $-\infty$. You can determine the result by analyzing h at values of x close to 1, or by using a graphing utility. From the graph of h shown in Figure 1.40, you can see that $h(x)$ approaches ∞ from the left of $x = 1$ and approaches $-\infty$ from the right of $x = 1$. So, you can conclude that

$$\lim_{x \to 1^-} \frac{x^2 - 3x}{x - 1} = \infty \qquad \text{The limit from the left is infinity.}$$

and

$$\lim_{x \to 1^+} \frac{x^2 - 3x}{x - 1} = -\infty. \qquad \text{The limit from the right is negative infinity.}$$

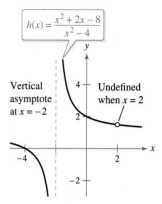

$h(x)$ increases and decreases without bound as x approaches -2.
Figure 1.39

Connecting Representations

In Example 3, note that h has a nonremovable discontinuity at $x = -2$.

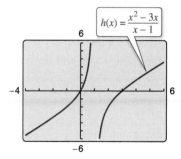

The graph of h has a vertical asymptote at $x = 1$.
Figure 1.40

Technology Pitfall

When using a graphing utility, be careful to interpret correctly the graph of a function with a vertical asymptote—some graphing utilities have difficulty drawing this type of graph.

Theorem 1.15 **Properties of Infinite Limits**

Let c and L be real numbers, and let f and g be functions such that

$$\lim_{x \to c} f(x) = \infty \quad \text{and} \quad \lim_{x \to c} g(x) = L.$$

1. Sum or difference: $\displaystyle\lim_{x \to c} [f(x) \pm g(x)] = \infty$

2. Product: $\displaystyle\lim_{x \to c} [f(x)g(x)] = \infty, \quad L > 0$

$\displaystyle\lim_{x \to c} [f(x)g(x)] = -\infty, \quad L < 0$

3. Quotient: $\displaystyle\lim_{x \to c} \frac{g(x)}{f(x)} = 0$

Similar properties hold for one-sided limits and for functions for which the limit of $f(x)$ as x approaches c is $-\infty$. (See Example 5.)

Remark

Be sure you understand that Property 2 of Theorem 1.15 is not valid when $\displaystyle\lim_{x \to c} g(x) = 0$.

Proof

Here is a proof of the sum property. (The proofs of the remaining properties are left as an exercise [see Exercise 82].) To show that the limit of $f(x) + g(x)$ is infinite, choose $M > 0$. You then need to find $\delta > 0$ such that $[f(x) + g(x)] > M$ whenever $0 < |x - c| < \delta$. For simplicity's sake, you can assume L is positive. Let $M_1 = M + 1$. Because the limit of $f(x)$ is infinite, there exists δ_1 such that $f(x) > M_1$ whenever $0 < |x - c| < \delta_1$. Also, because the limit of $g(x)$ is L, there exists δ_2 such that $|g(x) - L| < 1$ whenever $0 < |x - c| < \delta_2$. By letting δ be the smaller of δ_1 and δ_2, you can conclude that $0 < |x - c| < \delta$ implies $f(x) > M + 1$ and $|g(x) - L| < 1$. The second of these two inequalities implies that $g(x) > L - 1$, and, adding this to the first inequality, you can write

$$f(x) + g(x) > (M + 1) + (L - 1) = M + L > M.$$

So, you can conclude that

$$\lim_{x \to c} [f(x) + g(x)] = \infty.$$

EXAMPLE 5 Determining Limits

a. Because $\displaystyle\lim_{x \to 0} 1 = 1$ and $\displaystyle\lim_{x \to 0} \frac{1}{x^2} = \infty$, you can write

$$\lim_{x \to 0}\left(1 + \frac{1}{x^2}\right) = \infty. \qquad \text{Property 1, Theorem 1.15}$$

b. Because $\displaystyle\lim_{x \to 1^-} (x^2 + 1) = 2$ and $\displaystyle\lim_{x \to 1^-} (\cot \pi x) = -\infty$, you can write

$$\lim_{x \to 1^-} \frac{x^2 + 1}{\cot \pi x} = 0. \qquad \text{Property 3, Theorem 1.15}$$

c. Because $\displaystyle\lim_{x \to 0^+} 3 = 3$ and $\displaystyle\lim_{x \to 0^+} \ln x = -\infty$, you can write

$$\lim_{x \to 0^+} 3 \ln x = -\infty. \qquad \text{Property 2, Theorem 1.15 (See Figure 1.41.)}$$

d. Because $\displaystyle\lim_{x \to 0^-} x^2 = 0$ and $\displaystyle\lim_{x \to 0^-} \frac{1}{x} = -\infty$, you can write

$$\lim_{x \to 0^-} \left(x^2 + \frac{1}{x}\right) = -\infty. \qquad \text{Property 1, Theorem 1.15}$$

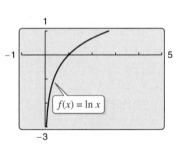

The graph of $f(x) = \ln x$ supports the conclusion that the natural logarithmic function has a vertical asymptote at $x = 0$. This implies that $\displaystyle\lim_{x \to 0^+} \ln x = -\infty$.

Figure 1.41

1.5   Exercises

 Determining Infinite Limits from a Graph **In Exercises 1–4, determine whether** $f(x)$ **approaches** ∞ **or** $-\infty$ **as** x **approaches** -2 **from the left and from the right.**

1. $f(x) = 2\left|\dfrac{x}{x^2 - 4}\right|$

2. $f(x) = \dfrac{1}{x + 2}$

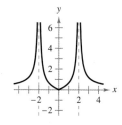

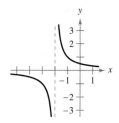

3. $f(x) = \tan\dfrac{\pi x}{4}$

4. $f(x) = \sec\dfrac{\pi x}{4}$

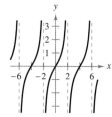

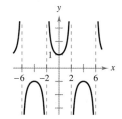

 Determining Infinite Limits **In Exercises 5–8, determine whether** $f(x)$ **approaches** ∞ **or** $-\infty$ **as** x **approaches 4 from the left and from the right.**

5. $f(x) = \dfrac{1}{x - 4}$

6. $f(x) = \dfrac{-1}{x - 4}$

7. $f(x) = \dfrac{1}{(x - 4)^2}$

8. $f(x) = \dfrac{-1}{(x - 4)^2}$

Numerical Reasoning **In Exercises 9–14, determine whether** $f(x)$ **approaches** ∞ **or** $-\infty$ **as** x **approaches** -3 **from the left and from the right by completing the table. Use a graphing utility to graph the function to confirm your answer.**

x	-3.5	-3.1	-3.01	-3.001	-3
$f(x)$					?

x	-2.999	-2.99	-2.9	-2.5
$f(x)$				

9. $f(x) = \dfrac{1}{x^2 - 9}$

10. $f(x) = \dfrac{x}{x^2 - 9}$

11. $f(x) = \dfrac{x^2}{x^2 - 9}$

12. $f(x) = \dfrac{1}{x^3 - 9x}$

13. $f(x) = \sec(\pi x/2)$

14. $f(x) = \cot(\pi x/3)$

 Finding Vertical Asymptotes **In Exercises 15–34, find any vertical asymptotes of the graph of the function.**

15. $f(x) = \dfrac{1}{x^2}$

16. $f(x) = \dfrac{2}{(x - 3)^3}$

17. $f(x) = \dfrac{x^2}{x^2 - 4}$

18. $f(x) = \dfrac{3x}{x^2 + 9}$

19. $f(x) = \dfrac{x - 3}{x^2 + 3x}$

20. $h(s) = \dfrac{3s + 4}{s^2 - 16}$

21. $f(x) = \dfrac{3}{x^2 + x - 2}$

22. $g(x) = \dfrac{x^3 - 8}{x - 2}$

23. $f(x) = \dfrac{x^2 - 2x - 15}{x^3 - 5x^2 + x - 5}$

24. $h(x) = \dfrac{x^2 - 9}{x^3 + 3x^2 - x - 3}$

25. $f(x) = \dfrac{e^{-2x}}{x - 1}$

26. $g(x) = xe^{-2x}$

27. $h(t) = \dfrac{\ln(t^2 + 1)}{t + 2}$

28. $f(z) = \ln(z^2 - 4)$

29. $f(x) = \dfrac{1}{e^x - 1}$

30. $f(x) = \ln(x + 3)$

31. $f(x) = \csc \pi x$

32. $f(x) = \tan \pi x$

33. $s(t) = \dfrac{t}{\sin t}$

34. $g(\theta) = \dfrac{\tan \theta}{\theta}$

 Vertical Asymptote or Removable Discontinuity **In Exercises 35–38, determine whether the graph of the function has a vertical asymptote or a removable discontinuity at** $x = -1$. **Graph the function using a graphing utility to confirm your answer.**

35. $f(x) = \dfrac{x^2 - 1}{x + 1}$

36. $f(x) = \dfrac{x^2 - 2x - 8}{x + 1}$

37. $f(x) = \dfrac{x^2 + 1}{x + 1}$

38. $f(x) = \dfrac{\ln(x^2 + 1)}{x + 1}$

 Finding a One-Sided Limit **In Exercises 39–48, use a graphing utility to find the one-sided limit.**

39. $\displaystyle\lim_{x \to 6^+} \dfrac{1}{(x - 6)^2}$

40. $\displaystyle\lim_{x \to 1^-} \dfrac{x^2 + x + 1}{x^3 - 1}$

41. $\displaystyle\lim_{x \to 5^-} \dfrac{1}{x^2 - 25}$

42. $\displaystyle\lim_{x \to 7^+} \dfrac{-x^3}{x^2 - 49}$

43. $\displaystyle\lim_{x \to (3\pi)^+} \left(-\csc\dfrac{x}{3}\right)$

44. $\displaystyle\lim_{x \to 4^+} \sec\dfrac{\pi x}{8}$

45. $\displaystyle\lim_{x \to 0^-} \dfrac{2e^x}{\sin x}$

46. $\displaystyle\lim_{x \to (\pi/2)^+} \dfrac{-2e^x}{\cos x}$

47. $\displaystyle\lim_{x \to 0^+} \dfrac{e^{-x}}{\ln|\sin x|}$

48. $\displaystyle\lim_{x \to 0^-} \dfrac{-\cos x}{\ln|\cos x|}$

Finding a One-Sided Limit In Exercises 49–66, find the one-sided limit (if it exists).

49. $\lim\limits_{x \to -1^+} 1/(x + 1)$

50. $\lim\limits_{x \to 1^-} -1/(x - 1)^2$

51. $\lim\limits_{x \to 2^+} x/(x - 2)$

52. $\lim\limits_{x \to 2^-} x^2/(2x - x^2)$

53. $\lim\limits_{x \to 2^-} \dfrac{x + 3}{x^2 + x - 6}$

54. $\lim\limits_{x \to (3/2)^+} \dfrac{6x^2 + x - 1}{4x^2 - 4x - 3}$

55. $\lim\limits_{x \to 0^-} \left(1 + \dfrac{1}{x}\right)$

56. $\lim\limits_{x \to 0^+} \left(6 - \dfrac{1}{x^3}\right)$

57. $\lim\limits_{x \to -4^-} \left(x^2 + \dfrac{2}{x + 4}\right)$

58. $\lim\limits_{x \to 2^+} \left(\dfrac{x}{3} + \cot\dfrac{\pi x}{2}\right)$

59. $\lim\limits_{x \to 0^+} \dfrac{3x + 2}{\tan \pi x}$

60. $\lim\limits_{x \to (\pi/2)^+} \dfrac{x^2 - 2}{\sec x}$

61. $\lim\limits_{x \to 8^-} \dfrac{e^x}{(x - 8)^3}$

62. $\lim\limits_{x \to \pi^+} \dfrac{e^{-0.5x}}{\sin(-x)}$

63. $\lim\limits_{x \to 0^+} 16 \ln x$

64. $\lim\limits_{x \to 4^+} \ln(x^2 - 16)$

65. $\lim\limits_{x \to (\pi/2)^-} x \sec x$

66. $\lim\limits_{x \to (1/2)^+} x^2 \tan \pi x$

Error Analysis In Exercises 67 and 68, describe and correct the error.

67. $h(x) = \dfrac{3x + 15}{x^2 - 25} = \dfrac{3x + 15}{(x + 5)(x - 5)}$

So, the graph of h has two vertical asymptotes at $x = 5$ and $x = -5$.

68. Because $\lim\limits_{x \to -1^-} \dfrac{1}{1 + x^2} = \dfrac{1}{2}$ and $\lim\limits_{x \to -1^-} \tan\dfrac{\pi x}{2} = \infty$,

$\lim\limits_{x \to -1^-} \left(\dfrac{1}{1 + x^2} - \tan\dfrac{\pi x}{2}\right) = \infty.$

EXPLORING CONCEPTS

69. Communication and Notation In your own words, describe the meaning of an infinite limit. Is ∞ a real number?

70. Think About It Does the graph of every rational function have a vertical asymptote? Explain.

71. Communication and Notation Consider a rational function $f(x)$ with vertical asymptote $x = a$. Explain how you can find $\lim\limits_{x \to a^+} f(x)$ and $\lim\limits_{x \to a^-} f(x)$.

72. Communication and Notation Explain how you can use the graph of f (see figure) to find $\lim\limits_{x \to 2^-} g(x)$ and $\lim\limits_{x \to 2^+} g(x)$, where $g(x) = 1/f(x)$. To print an enlarged copy of the graph, go to *MathGraphs.com*.

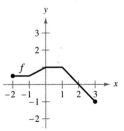

73. Numerical and Graphical Reasoning Use a graphing utility to complete the table for each function and graph each function to estimate the limit. What is the value of the limit when the power of x in the denominator is greater than 3?

x	1	0.5	0.2	0.1	0.01	0.001	0.0001
$f(x)$							

(a) $\lim\limits_{x \to 0^+} \dfrac{x - \sin x}{x}$

(b) $\lim\limits_{x \to 0^+} \dfrac{x - \sin x}{x^2}$

(c) $\lim\limits_{x \to 0^+} \dfrac{x - \sin x}{x^3}$

(d) $\lim\limits_{x \to 0^+} \dfrac{x - \sin x}{x^4}$

(e) $\lim\limits_{x \to 0^+} \dfrac{x - \sin x}{x^5}$

(f) $\lim\limits_{x \to 0^+} \dfrac{x - \sin x}{x^6}$

74. **HOW DO YOU SEE IT?** For a quantity of gas at a constant temperature, the pressure P is inversely proportional to the volume V. What is the limit of P as V approaches 0 from the right? Explain what this means in the context of the problem.

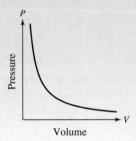

75. Rate of Change A 25-foot ladder is leaning against a house (see figure). If the base of the ladder is pulled away from the house at a rate of 2 feet per second, then the top will move down the wall at a rate of

$r = \dfrac{2x}{\sqrt{625 - x^2}}$ ft/sec

where x is the distance between the base of the ladder and the house, and r is the rate in feet per second.

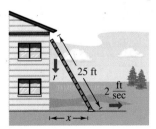

(a) Find the rate r when x is 7 feet.

(b) Find the rate r when x is 15 feet.

(c) Find the limit of r as x approaches 25 from the left. Explain your result in the context of the problem.

76. AVERAGE SPEED

On a trip of d miles to another city, a truck driver's average speed was x miles per hour. On the return trip, the average speed was y miles per hour. The average speed for the round trip was 50 miles per hour.

(a) Write y as a function of x. What is the domain?

(b) Complete the table.

x	30	40	50	60
y				

Are the values of y different than you expected? Explain.

(c) Find the limit of y as x approaches 25 from the right and interpret its meaning.

True or False? In Exercises 77–80, determine whether the statement is true or false. If it is false, explain why or give an example that shows it is false.

77. The graph of a rational function cannot cross a vertical asymptote.

78. The graphs of polynomial functions have no vertical asymptotes.

79. The graphs of trigonometric functions have no vertical asymptotes.

80. If the rational function f has a vertical asymptote at $x = 0$, then f is undefined at $x = 0$.

81. Finding Functions Find functions f and g such that

$$\lim_{x \to c} f(x) = \infty \quad \text{and} \quad \lim_{x \to c} g(x) = \infty$$

but $\lim_{x \to c} [f(x) - g(x)] \neq 0$.

82. Proof Prove the difference, product, and quotient properties in Theorem 1.15.

83. Proof Prove that if $\lim_{x \to c} f(x) = \infty$, then $\lim_{x \to c} \dfrac{1}{f(x)} = 0$.

84. Proof Prove that if

$$\lim_{x \to c} \frac{1}{f(x)} = 0$$

then $\lim_{x \to c} f(x)$ does not exist.

Infinite Limits In Exercises 85 and 86, use the ε–δ definition of infinite limits to prove the statement.

85. $\displaystyle\lim_{x \to 3^+} \frac{1}{x - 3} = \infty$

86. $\displaystyle\lim_{x \to 5^-} \frac{1}{x - 5} = -\infty$

grandriver/E+/Getty Images

Calculus AP® – Exam Preparation Questions

87. Multiple Choice What are the vertical asymptotes of the graph of

$$f(x) = \frac{5(x^2 - 4)}{2x^2 - 5x + 2}?$$

(A) $x = \dfrac{1}{2}$ (B) $x = \dfrac{1}{2}$ and $x = 2$

(C) $x = -\dfrac{1}{2}$ and $x = -2$ (D) $x = -\dfrac{1}{2}$

88. Multiple Choice $\displaystyle\lim_{x \to -1^-} \left(\sec \frac{\pi x}{2} + 2x \right)$ is

(A) $-\infty$.   (B) -1.   (C) -2.   (D) ∞.

89. Multiple Choice The graph of the function f is shown. The line $x = 1$ is a vertical asymptote.

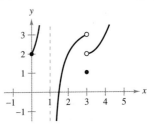

Which of the following statements about f is true?

(A) $\displaystyle\lim_{x \to 1} f(x) = \infty$ (B) $\displaystyle\lim_{x \to 3^-} f(x) < \lim_{x \to 3^+} f(x)$

(C) $\displaystyle\lim_{x \to 3} f(x) = 1$ (D) $\displaystyle\lim_{x \to 0^+} f(x) = \lim_{x \to 3^+} f(x)$

SECTION PROJECT

Graphs and Limits of Trigonometric Functions

Recall from Theorem 1.9 that the limit of $f(x) = (\sin x)/x$ as x approaches 0 is 1.

(a) Use a graphing utility to graph the function f on the interval $-\pi \le x \le \pi$. Explain how the graph helps confirm this theorem.

(b) Explain how you could use a table of values to confirm the value of this limit numerically.

(c) Graph $g(x) = \sin x$ by hand. Sketch a tangent line to g at the point $(0, 0)$ and visually estimate its slope.

(d) Let $(x, \sin x)$ be a point on the graph of g near $(0, 0)$. Write a formula for the slope of the secant line joining $(x, \sin x)$ and $(0, 0)$. Evaluate this formula at $x = 0.1$ and $x = 0.01$. Then find the exact slope of the tangent line to g at the point $(0, 0)$.

(e) Sketch the graph of the cosine function $h(x) = \cos x$. What is the slope of the tangent line to h at the point $(0, 1)$? Use limits to find this slope analytically.

(f) Find the slope of the tangent line to $k(x) = \tan x$ at $(0, 0)$.

1.6 Limits at Infinity

▶ Determine (finite) limits at infinity.
▶ Determine the horizontal asymptotes, if any, of the graph of a function.
▶ Determine infinite limits at infinity.

Limits at Infinity

This section discusses the "end behavior" of a function on an *infinite* interval. Consider the graph of

$$f(x) = \frac{3x^2}{x^2 + 1}$$

as shown in Figure 1.42. Graphically, you can see that $f(x)$ appears to approach 3 as x increases without bound or decreases without bound. You can come to the same conclusions numerically, as shown in the table.

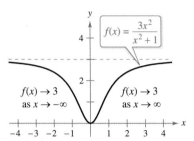

The limit of $f(x)$ as x approaches $-\infty$ or ∞ is 3.

Figure 1.42

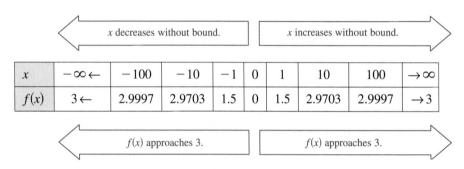

x	$-\infty \leftarrow$	-100	-10	-1	0	1	10	100	$\rightarrow \infty$
$f(x)$	$3 \leftarrow$	2.9997	2.9703	1.5	0	1.5	2.9703	2.9997	$\rightarrow 3$

The table suggests that $f(x)$ approaches 3 as x increases without bound $(x \to \infty)$. Similarly, $f(x)$ approaches 3 as x decreases without bound $(x \to -\infty)$. These **limits at infinity** are denoted by

$$\lim_{x \to -\infty} f(x) = 3 \qquad \text{Limit at negative infinity}$$

and

$$\lim_{x \to \infty} f(x) = 3. \qquad \text{Limit at positive infinity}$$

To say that a statement is true as x increases *without bound* means that for some (large) real number M, the statement is true for *all* x in the interval $\{x: x > M\}$. The next definition uses this concept.

Connecting Representations

The statement $\lim_{x \to -\infty} f(x) = L$ or $\lim_{x \to \infty} f(x) = L$ means that the limit exists *and* the limit is equal to L.

Definition of Limits at Infinity

Let L be a real number.

1. The statement $\lim_{x \to \infty} f(x) = L$ means that for each $\varepsilon > 0$ there exists an $M > 0$ such that $|f(x) - L| < \varepsilon$ whenever $x > M$.
2. The statement $\lim_{x \to -\infty} f(x) = L$ means that for each $\varepsilon > 0$ there exists an $N < 0$ such that $|f(x) - L| < \varepsilon$ whenever $x < N$.

The definition of a limit at infinity is shown in Figure 1.43. In this figure, note that for a given positive number ε, there exists a positive number M such that, for $x > M$, the graph of f will lie between the horizontal lines

$$y = L + \varepsilon \quad \text{and} \quad y = L - \varepsilon.$$

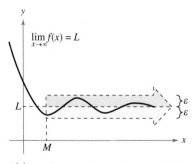

$f(x)$ is within ε units of L as $x \to \infty$.

Figure 1.43

Horizontal Asymptotes

In Figure 1.43, the graph of f approaches the line $y = L$ as x increases without bound. The line $y = L$ is called a **horizontal asymptote** of the graph of f.

Definition of a Horizontal Asymptote

The line $y = L$ is a **horizontal asymptote** of the graph of f when

$$\lim_{x \to -\infty} f(x) = L \quad \text{or} \quad \lim_{x \to \infty} f(x) = L.$$

Exploration

Use a graphing utility to graph

$$f(x) = \frac{2x^2 + 4x - 6}{3x^2 + 2x - 16}.$$

What is the horizontal asymptote of the graph? How far to the right do you have to move on the graph so that the graph is within 0.001 unit of its horizontal asymptote? Explain your reasoning.

Note that from this definition, it follows that the graph of a *function* of x can have at most two horizontal asymptotes—one to the right and one to the left.

Limits at infinity have many of the same properties of limits discussed in Section 1.3. For example, if $\lim\limits_{x \to \infty} f(x)$ and $\lim\limits_{x \to \infty} g(x)$ both exist, then

$$\lim_{x \to \infty} [f(x) + g(x)] = \lim_{x \to \infty} f(x) + \lim_{x \to \infty} g(x)$$

and

$$\lim_{x \to \infty} [f(x)g(x)] = \left[\lim_{x \to \infty} f(x) \right]\left[\lim_{x \to \infty} g(x) \right].$$

Similar properties hold for limits at $-\infty$.

When evaluating limits at infinity, the next theorem is helpful.

Theorem 1.16   Limits at Infinity

1. If r is a positive rational number and c is any real number, then

$$\lim_{x \to \infty} \frac{c}{x^r} = 0 \quad \text{and} \quad \lim_{x \to -\infty} \frac{c}{x^r} = 0.$$

The second limit is valid only if x^r is defined when $x < 0$.

2. $\lim\limits_{x \to -\infty} e^x = 0$ and $\lim\limits_{x \to \infty} e^{-x} = 0$

A proof of the first part of this theorem is given in Appendix A.

> **EXAMPLE 1**   **Finding Limits at Infinity**

Find each limit.

a. $\displaystyle\lim_{x \to \infty} \left(5 - \frac{2}{x^2} \right)$ **b.** $\displaystyle\lim_{x \to \infty} \frac{3}{e^x}$

Solution

a. $\displaystyle\lim_{x \to \infty} \left(5 - \frac{2}{x^2} \right) = \lim_{x \to \infty} 5 - \lim_{x \to \infty} \frac{2}{x^2}$ Property of limits

$\qquad\qquad\qquad = 5 - 0$ Apply Theorem 1.16.

$\qquad\qquad\qquad = 5$

b. $\displaystyle\lim_{x \to \infty} \frac{3}{e^x} = \lim_{x \to \infty} 3e^{-x}$ Rewrite function.

$\qquad\qquad = 3 \lim_{x \to \infty} e^{-x}$ Property of limits

$\qquad\qquad = 3(0)$ Apply Theorem 1.16.

$\qquad\qquad = 0$

EXAMPLE 2 Finding a Limit at Infinity

Find the limit: $\displaystyle\lim_{x\to\infty} \frac{2x-1}{x+1}$.

Algebraic Solution

Note that both the numerator and the denominator approach infinity as x approaches infinity.

$$\lim_{x\to\infty} (2x-1)\to\infty$$

and

$$\lim_{x\to\infty} (x+1)\to\infty.$$

This results in ∞/∞, an *indeterminate form*. To resolve this problem, divide both the numerator and the denominator by x. After dividing, the limit may be found as shown.

$$\lim_{x\to\infty} \frac{2x-1}{x+1} = \lim_{x\to\infty} \frac{\dfrac{2x-1}{x}}{\dfrac{x+1}{x}} \qquad \text{Divide numerator and denominator by } x.$$

$$= \lim_{x\to\infty} \frac{2-\dfrac{1}{x}}{1+\dfrac{1}{x}} \qquad \text{Simplify.}$$

$$= \frac{\lim\limits_{x\to\infty} 2 - \lim\limits_{x\to\infty} \dfrac{1}{x}}{\lim\limits_{x\to\infty} 1 + \lim\limits_{x\to\infty} \dfrac{1}{x}} \qquad \begin{array}{l}\text{Take limits of numerator}\\ \text{and denominator.}\end{array}$$

$$= \frac{2-0}{1+0} \qquad \text{Apply Theorem 1.16.}$$

$$= 2$$

So, the line $y = 2$ is a horizontal asymptote to the right. Note that by taking the limit as $x \to -\infty$, you can see that $y = 2$ is also a horizontal asymptote to the left.

Graphical Solution

Use a graphing utility to graph

$$y = \frac{2x-1}{x+1}.$$

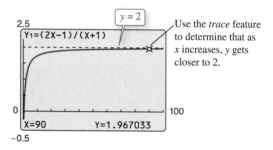

Use the *trace* feature to determine that as x increases, y gets closer to 2.

From the graph, you can estimate the limit to be

$$\lim_{x\to\infty} \frac{2x-1}{x+1} = 2.$$

Also, notice that the line $y = 2$ appears to be a horizontal asymptote to the right.

In the algebraic solution to Example 2, the initial limit resulted in the indeterminate form ∞/∞. This problem was resolved by rewriting the rational function in an equivalent form; specifically, by dividing the numerator and denominator by x. In general, when you encounter an indeterminate form like this one, divide the numerator and denominator by the highest power of x in the *denominator*.

You can use the guidelines below for finding limits at infinity of rational functions.

Guidelines for Finding Limits at $\pm\infty$ of Rational Functions

1. If the degree of the numerator is *less than* the degree of the denominator, then the limit of the rational function is 0.

2. If the degree of the numerator is *equal to* the degree of the denominator, then the limit of the rational function is the ratio of the leading coefficients.

3. If the degree of the numerator is *greater than* the degree of the denominator, then the limit of the rational function does not exist.

EXAMPLE 3   **Finding Limits at Infinity of Rational Functions**

See LarsonCalculusforAP.com for an interactive version of this type of example.

Use the guidelines on the preceding page to find each limit. Then verify the result analytically.

a. $\lim\limits_{x\to\infty} \dfrac{2x + 5}{3x^2 + 1}$ **b.** $\lim\limits_{x\to\infty} \dfrac{2x^2 + 5}{3x^2 + 1}$ **c.** $\lim\limits_{x\to\infty} \dfrac{2x^3 + 5}{3x^2 + 1}$

Solution

a. The degree of the numerator is *less than* the degree of the denominator. So, the limit is 0. You can verify this algebraically by dividing both the numerator and the denominator by x^2.

$$\lim_{x\to\infty} \frac{2x + 5}{3x^2 + 1} = \lim_{x\to\infty} \frac{\dfrac{2}{x} + \dfrac{5}{x^2}}{3 + \dfrac{1}{x^2}} = \frac{0 + 0}{3 + 0} = \frac{0}{3} = 0$$

b. The degree of the numerator is equal to the degree of the denominator. So, the limit is the ratio of the leading coefficients, which is 2/3. You can verify this algebraically by dividing both the numerator and the denominator by x^2.

$$\lim_{x\to\infty} \frac{2x^2 + 5}{3x^2 + 1} = \lim_{x\to\infty} \frac{2 + \dfrac{5}{x^2}}{3 + \dfrac{1}{x^2}} = \frac{2 + 0}{3 + 0} = \frac{2}{3}$$

c. The degree of the numerator is greater than the degree of the denominator. So, the limit does not exist. You can verify this algebraically by dividing both the numerator and the denominator by x^2.

$$\lim_{x\to\infty} \frac{2x^3 + 5}{3x^2 + 1} = \lim_{x\to\infty} \frac{2x + \dfrac{5}{x^2}}{3 + \dfrac{1}{x^2}} = \frac{\infty}{3}$$

The limit *does not exist* because the numerator increases without bound while the denominator approaches 3. ∎

> **Implementing Processes**
>
> Recall from Section P.3 that a rational function is the quotient of two polynomials. Be sure you understand that the guidelines on page 110 *do not* apply to limits at infinity of functions that "look rational," such as
>
> $$\lim_{x\to\infty} \frac{\sin x}{e^x + 1}.$$
>
> To find a limit like this one, compare the behavior of the numerator to that of the denominator.

The guidelines for finding limits at infinity of rational functions seem reasonable when you consider that for large values of *x*, the highest-power term of the rational function is the most "influential" in determining the limit. For instance,

$$\lim_{x\to\infty} \frac{1}{x^2 + 1}$$

is 0 because the denominator overpowers the numerator as *x* increases or decreases without bound, as shown in Figure 1.44.

The function shown in Figure 1.44 is a special case of a type of curve studied by the Italian mathematician Maria Gaetana Agnesi (1718–1799). The general form of this function is

$$f(x) = \frac{8a^3}{x^2 + 4a^2} \qquad \text{Witch of Agnesi}$$

and, through a mistranslation of the Italian word *vertéré*, the curve has come to be known as the Witch of Agnesi. Agnesi's work with this curve first appeared in a comprehensive text on calculus that was published in 1748.

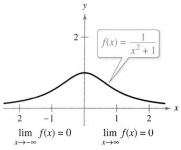

$$\lim_{x\to-\infty} f(x) = 0 \qquad \lim_{x\to\infty} f(x) = 0$$

f has a horizontal asymptote at $y = 0$.
Figure 1.44

In Figure 1.44, you can see that the function

$$f(x) = \frac{1}{x^2 + 1}$$

approaches the same horizontal asymptote to the right and to the left. This is always true of rational functions. Functions that are not rational, however, may approach different horizontal asymptotes to the right and to the left. A common example of such a function is the **logistic function** shown in the next example. (You will learn more about the logistic function in Section 5.4.)

EXAMPLE 4   A Function with Two Horizontal Asymptotes

Show that the *logistic function*

$$f(x) = \frac{1}{1 + e^{-x}}$$

has different horizontal asymptotes to the left and to the right.

Solution

Begin by sketching a graph of the function. From Figure 1.45, it appears that

$$y = 0 \quad \text{and} \quad y = 1$$

are horizontal asymptotes to the left and to the right, respectively. The table shows the same results numerically.

x	-10	-5	-2	-1	1	2	5	10
$f(x)$	0.000	0.007	0.119	0.269	0.731	0.881	0.993	1.000

You can obtain the same results analytically, as follows.

$$\lim_{x \to \infty} \frac{1}{1 + e^{-x}} = \frac{\lim\limits_{x \to \infty} 1}{\lim\limits_{x \to \infty} (1 + e^{-x})}$$

$$= \frac{1}{1 + 0}$$

$$= 1 \qquad \text{\small $y = 1$ is a horizontal asymptote to the right.}$$

For the horizontal asymptote to the left, note that as $x \to -\infty$ the denominator of

$$\frac{1}{1 + e^{-x}}$$

approaches infinity. So, the quotient approaches 0 and thus the limit is 0. You can conclude that $y = 0$ is a horizontal asymptote to the left. ■

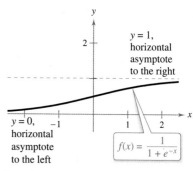

Functions that are not rational may have different right and left horizontal asymptotes.
Figure 1.45

Technology Pitfall

If you use a graphing utility to estimate a limit, be sure that you also confirm the estimate analytically—the graphs shown by a graphing utility can be misleading. For instance, Figure 1.46 shows one view of the graph of

$$y = \frac{2x^3 + 1000x^2 + x}{x^3 + 1000x^2 + x + 1000}.$$

From this view, one could be convinced that the graph has $y = 1$ as a horizontal asymptote. An analytical approach shows that the horizontal asymptote is actually $y = 2$. Confirm this by enlarging the viewing window on the graphing utility.

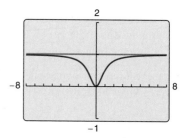

The horizontal asymptote appears to be the line $y = 1$, but it is actually the line $y = 2$.
Figure 1.46

In Section 1.4, Example 7(c), you used the Squeeze Theorem to evaluate a limit involving a trigonometric function. This theorem is also valid for limits at infinity.

EXAMPLE 5   Limits Involving Trigonometric Functions

Find each limit.

a. $\lim\limits_{x \to \infty} \sin x$ **b.** $\lim\limits_{x \to \infty} \dfrac{\sin x}{x}$

Solution

a. As x approaches infinity, the sine function oscillates between 1 and -1. So, this limit does not exist.

b. Because $-1 \le \sin x \le 1$, it follows that for $x > 0$,

$$-\frac{1}{x} \le \frac{\sin x}{x} \le \frac{1}{x}$$

where

$$\lim_{x \to \infty} \left(-\frac{1}{x} \right) = 0 \quad \text{and} \quad \lim_{x \to \infty} \frac{1}{x} = 0.$$

So, by the Squeeze Theorem, you can obtain

$$\lim_{x \to \infty} \frac{\sin x}{x} = 0$$

as shown in Figure 1.47.

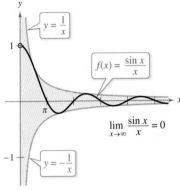

As x increases without bound, $f(x)$ approaches 0.

Figure 1.47

EXAMPLE 6   Oxygen Level in a Pond

Let $f(t)$ measure the level of oxygen in a pond, where $f(t) = 1$ is the normal (unpolluted) level and the time t is measured in weeks. When $t = 0$, organic waste is dumped into the pond, and as the waste material oxidizes, the level of oxygen in the pond is

$$f(t) = \frac{t^2 - t + 1}{t^2 + 1}.$$

What percent of the normal level of oxygen exists in the pond after 1 week? After 2 weeks? After 10 weeks? What is the limit as t approaches infinity?

Solution

When $t = 1, 2,$ and 10, the levels of oxygen are as shown.

$$f(1) = \frac{1^2 - 1 + 1}{1^2 + 1} = \frac{1}{2} = 50\% \qquad \text{1 week}$$

$$f(2) = \frac{2^2 - 2 + 1}{2^2 + 1} = \frac{3}{5} = 60\% \qquad \text{2 weeks}$$

$$f(10) = \frac{10^2 - 10 + 1}{10^2 + 1} = \frac{91}{101} \approx 90.1\% \qquad \text{10 weeks}$$

To find the limit as t approaches infinity, you can use the guidelines on page 110, or you can divide the numerator and the denominator by t^2 to obtain

$$\lim_{t \to \infty} \frac{t^2 - t + 1}{t^2 + 1} = \lim_{t \to \infty} \frac{1 - \dfrac{1}{t} + \dfrac{1}{t^2}}{1 + \dfrac{1}{t^2}} = \frac{1 - 0 + 0}{1 + 0} = 1 = 100\%.$$

(See Figure 1.48.)

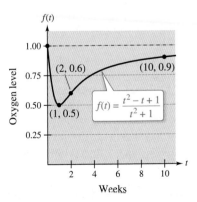

The level of oxygen in a pond approaches the normal level of 1 as t approaches ∞.

Figure 1.48

Infinite Limits at Infinity

Many functions do not approach a finite limit as x increases (or decreases) without bound. For instance, no polynomial function has a finite limit at infinity. You can use the definition below to describe the behavior of polynomial and other functions at infinity.

Definition of Infinite Limits at Infinity

Let f be a function defined on the interval (a, ∞).

1. The statement $\lim\limits_{x \to \infty} f(x) = \infty$ means that for each positive number M, there is a corresponding number $N > 0$ such that $f(x) > M$ whenever $x > N$.

2. The statement $\lim\limits_{x \to \infty} f(x) = -\infty$ means that for each negative number M, there is a corresponding number $N > 0$ such that $f(x) < M$ whenever $x > N$.

Similar definitions can be given for the statements

$$\lim\limits_{x \to -\infty} f(x) = \infty \quad \text{and} \quad \lim\limits_{x \to -\infty} f(x) = -\infty.$$

Connecting Representations

Determining whether a function has an infinite limit at infinity is useful in analyzing the "end behavior" of its graph. You will see examples of this in Section 3.5 on curve sketching.

EXAMPLE 7   Finding Infinite Limits at Infinity

Find each limit.

a. $\lim\limits_{x \to \infty} x^3$ **b.** $\lim\limits_{x \to -\infty} x^3$

Solution

a. As x increases without bound, x^3 also increases without bound. So, you can write

$$\lim\limits_{x \to \infty} x^3 = \infty.$$

b. As x decreases without bound, x^3 also decreases without bound. So, you can write

$$\lim\limits_{x \to -\infty} x^3 = -\infty.$$

The graph of $f(x) = x^3$ in Figure 1.49 illustrates these two results. These results agree with the Leading Coefficient Test for polynomial functions as described in Section P.3.

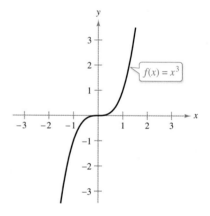

Figure 1.49

EXAMPLE 8   Finding Infinite Limits at Infinity

Find each limit.

a. $\lim\limits_{x \to \infty} \dfrac{2x^2 - 4x}{x + 1}$ **b.** $\lim\limits_{x \to -\infty} \dfrac{2x^2 - 4x}{x + 1}$

Solution

One way to evaluate each of these limits is to use long division to rewrite the improper rational function as the sum of a polynomial and a rational function.

a. $\lim\limits_{x \to \infty} \dfrac{2x^2 - 4x}{x + 1} = \lim\limits_{x \to \infty} \left(2x - 6 + \dfrac{6}{x + 1} \right) = \infty$

b. $\lim\limits_{x \to -\infty} \dfrac{2x^2 - 4x}{x + 1} = \lim\limits_{x \to -\infty} \left(2x - 6 + \dfrac{6}{x + 1} \right) = -\infty$

The statements above can be interpreted as saying that as x approaches $\pm\infty$, the function $f(x) = (2x^2 - 4x)/(x + 1)$ behaves like the function $g(x) = 2x - 6$. In Section 3.5, you will see that this is graphically described by saying that the line $y = 2x - 6$ is a *slant asymptote* of the graph of f, as shown in Figure 1.50.

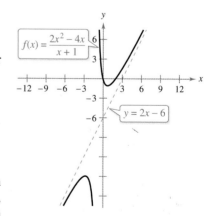

Figure 1.50

1.6   Exercises   See *CalcChat.com* for tutorial help and worked-out solutions to odd-numbered exercises.

Connecting Representations   In Exercises 1–6, match the function with one of the graphs [(a), (b), (c), (d), (e), or (f)] using horizontal asymptotes as an aid.

(a)

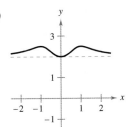

(b)

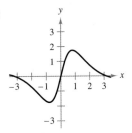

(c)

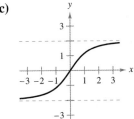

(d)

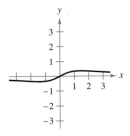

(e)

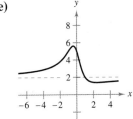

(f)

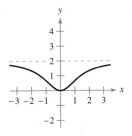

1. $f(x) = \dfrac{2x^2}{x^2 + 2}$

2. $f(x) = \dfrac{2x}{\sqrt{x^2 + 2}}$

3. $f(x) = \dfrac{x}{x^2 + 2}$

4. $f(x) = 2 + \dfrac{x^2}{x^4 + 1}$

5. $f(x) = \dfrac{4 \sin x}{x^2 + 1}$

6. $f(x) = \dfrac{2x^2 - 3x + 5}{x^2 + 1}$

Finding a Limit at Infinity   In Exercises 7–12, find the limit.

7. $\displaystyle\lim_{x \to \infty} \left(12 - \dfrac{3}{x^4}\right)$

8. $\displaystyle\lim_{x \to \infty} \left(\dfrac{100}{x^6} + e\right)$

9. $\displaystyle\lim_{x \to \infty} 15e^{-x}$

10. $\displaystyle\lim_{x \to \infty} 7e^{-x}$

11. $\displaystyle\lim_{x \to -\infty} (x^{-3} - 9e^x)$

12. $\displaystyle\lim_{x \to -\infty} (e^x - 5x^{-2})$

Finding a Limit at Infinity   In Exercises 13–16, find the limit by rewriting the rational function in an equivalent form.

13. $\displaystyle\lim_{x \to \infty} \dfrac{6x - 3}{3x + 2}$

14. $\displaystyle\lim_{x \to \infty} \dfrac{5 - 2x}{x + 6}$

15. $\displaystyle\lim_{x \to -\infty} \dfrac{4x^2 - 3x}{3x^2 + 3}$

16. $\displaystyle\lim_{x \to -\infty} \dfrac{5x^3 + 7}{4x^3 + x}$

Finding Limits at Infinity   In Exercises 17 and 18, find $\displaystyle\lim_{x \to \infty} h(x)$, if it exists.

17. $f(x) = 5x^3 - 3$

(a) $h(x) = \dfrac{f(x)}{x^2}$

(b) $h(x) = \dfrac{f(x)}{x^3}$

(c) $h(x) = \dfrac{f(x)}{x^4}$

18. $f(x) = -4x^2 + 2x - 5$

(a) $h(x) = \dfrac{f(x)}{x}$

(b) $h(x) = \dfrac{f(x)}{x^2}$

(c) $h(x) = \dfrac{f(x)}{x^3}$

Finding Limits at Infinity   In Exercises 19–22, find each limit, if it exists.

19. (a) $\displaystyle\lim_{x \to \infty} \dfrac{x^2 + 2}{x^3 - 1}$

(b) $\displaystyle\lim_{x \to \infty} \dfrac{x^2 + 2}{x^2 - 1}$

(c) $\displaystyle\lim_{x \to \infty} \dfrac{x^2 + 2}{x - 1}$

20. (a) $\displaystyle\lim_{x \to \infty} \dfrac{3 - 2x}{3x^3 - 1}$

(b) $\displaystyle\lim_{x \to \infty} \dfrac{3 - 2x}{3x - 1}$

(c) $\displaystyle\lim_{x \to \infty} \dfrac{3 - 2x^2}{3x - 1}$

21. (a) $\displaystyle\lim_{x \to \infty} \dfrac{5 - 2x^{3/2}}{3x^2 - 4}$

(b) $\displaystyle\lim_{x \to \infty} \dfrac{5 - 2x^{3/2}}{3x^{3/2} - 4}$

(c) $\displaystyle\lim_{x \to \infty} \dfrac{5 - 2x^{3/2}}{3x - 4}$

22. (a) $\displaystyle\lim_{x \to \infty} \dfrac{5x^{3/2}}{4x^2 + 1}$

(b) $\displaystyle\lim_{x \to \infty} \dfrac{5x^{3/2}}{4x^{3/2} + 1}$

(c) $\displaystyle\lim_{x \to \infty} \dfrac{5x^{3/2}}{4\sqrt{x} + 1}$

Finding a Limit   In Exercises 23–46, find the limit, if it exists.

23. $\displaystyle\lim_{x \to \infty} \dfrac{2x - 1}{3x + 2}$

24. $\displaystyle\lim_{x \to -\infty} \dfrac{4x^2 + 5}{x^2 + 3}$

25. $\displaystyle\lim_{x \to \infty} \dfrac{x}{x^2 - 1}$

26. $\displaystyle\lim_{x \to -\infty} \dfrac{5x^3 + 1}{10x^3 - 3x^2 + 7}$

27. $\displaystyle\lim_{x \to -\infty} \dfrac{-4}{3 + 3e^{-2x}}$

28. $\displaystyle\lim_{x \to \infty} \dfrac{6}{5 + 2e^{-4x}}$

29. $\displaystyle\lim_{x \to -\infty} \dfrac{x}{\sqrt{x^2 - x}}$

30. $\displaystyle\lim_{x \to -\infty} \dfrac{x}{\sqrt{x^2 + 1}}$

31. $\displaystyle\lim_{x \to -\infty} \dfrac{2x + 1}{\sqrt{x^2 - x}}$

32. $\displaystyle\lim_{x \to \infty} \dfrac{5x^2 + 2}{\sqrt{x^2 + 3}}$

33. $\displaystyle\lim_{x \to \infty} \dfrac{\sqrt{x^2 - 1}}{2x - 1}$

34. $\displaystyle\lim_{x \to -\infty} \dfrac{\sqrt{x^4 - 1}}{x^3 - 1}$

35. $\displaystyle\lim_{x \to \infty} \dfrac{x + 1}{(x^2 + 1)^{1/3}}$

36. $\displaystyle\lim_{x \to -\infty} \dfrac{2x}{(x^6 - 1)^{1/3}}$

37. $\displaystyle\lim_{x \to \infty} \dfrac{1}{2x + \sin x}$

38. $\displaystyle\lim_{x \to \infty} \cos \dfrac{1}{x}$

39. $\displaystyle\lim_{x \to \infty} \dfrac{\sin 2x}{x}$

40. $\displaystyle\lim_{x \to \infty} \dfrac{x - \cos x}{x}$

41. $\displaystyle\lim_{x \to \infty} (2 - 5e^{-x})$

42. $\displaystyle\lim_{x \to \infty} \dfrac{8}{4 - 10^{-x/2}}$

43. $\lim\limits_{x \to \infty} \log_{10}(1 + 10^{-x})$ **44.** $\lim\limits_{x \to \infty}\left(\dfrac{5}{2} + \ln\dfrac{x^2 + 1}{x^2}\right)$

45. $\lim\limits_{t \to \infty}(8t^{-1} - \arctan t)$ **46.** $\lim\limits_{u \to \infty} \operatorname{arcsec}(u + 1)$

Error Analysis In Exercises 47 and 48, describe and correct the error in finding the limit.

47. $\lim\limits_{x \to -\infty} \dfrac{5x^3}{6x^3 - 5} = \lim\limits_{x \to -\infty} \dfrac{5x^3/x^3}{6x^3/x^3 - 5} = \dfrac{5}{6 - 5} = 5$ ✗

48. $\lim\limits_{x \to -\infty} \dfrac{4x}{\sqrt{x^2 + 8}} = \lim\limits_{x \to -\infty} \dfrac{4x/x}{\sqrt{x^2 + 8}/\sqrt{x^2}}$

$= \lim\limits_{x \to -\infty} \dfrac{4}{\sqrt{1 + 8/x^2}} = 4$ ✗

 Finding Horizontal Asymptotes In Exercises 49–52, use a graphing utility to graph the function and identify any horizontal asymptotes.

49. $f(x) = \dfrac{|x|}{x + 1}$ **50.** $f(x) = \dfrac{|3x + 2|}{x - 2}$

51. $f(x) = \dfrac{3x}{\sqrt{x^2 + 2}}$ **52.** $f(x) = \dfrac{\sqrt{9x^2 - 2}}{2x + 1}$

53. Particle Motion Newton's First Law of Motion and Einstein's Special Theory of Relativity differ concerning the behavior of a particle as its velocity approaches the speed of light c. In the graph, functions N and E represent the velocity v, with respect to time t, of a particle accelerated by a constant force as predicted by Newton and Einstein, respectively. Write limit statements that describe these two theories.

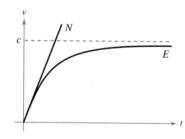

54. Using Symmetry to Find Limits If f is a continuous function such that $\lim\limits_{x \to \infty} f(x) = 5$, find, if possible, $\lim\limits_{x \to -\infty} f(x)$ for each specified condition.

(a) The graph of f is symmetric with respect to the y-axis.

(b) The graph of f is symmetric with respect to the origin.

55. Engine Efficiency The efficiency of an internal combustion engine is

$$\text{Efficiency } (\%) = 100\left[1 - \dfrac{1}{(v_1/v_2)^c}\right]$$

where v_1/v_2 is the ratio of the uncompressed gas to the compressed gas and c is a positive constant dependent on the engine design. Find the limit of the efficiency as the compression ratio approaches infinity.

56. Average Cost A business has a cost of $C = 0.5x + 500$ for producing x units. The average cost per unit is $\overline{C} = C/x$. Find the limit of $\overline{C}$ as x approaches infinity.

 Connecting Representations In Exercises 57 and 58, (a) use a graphing utility to graph f and g in the same viewing window, (b) verify algebraically that f and g represent the same function, and (c) zoom out sufficiently far so that the graph appears as a line. What equation does this line appear to have? (Note that the points at which the function is not continuous are not readily seen when you zoom out.)

57. $f(x) = \dfrac{x^3 - 3x^2 + 2}{x(x - 3)}$ **58.** $f(x) = -\dfrac{x^3 - 2x^2 + 2}{2x^2}$

$g(x) = x + \dfrac{2}{x(x - 3)}$ $g(x) = -\dfrac{1}{2}x + 1 - \dfrac{1}{x^2}$

Finding a Limit In Exercises 59 and 60, find the limit. (*Hint:* Let $x = 1/t$ and find the limit as $t \to 0^+$.)

59. $\lim\limits_{x \to \infty} x \sin(1/x)$ **60.** $\lim\limits_{x \to \infty} x \tan(1/x)$

Finding a Limit In Exercises 61–64, find the limit. (*Hint:* Treat the expression as a fraction whose denominator is 1, and rationalize the numerator.) Use a graphing utility to verify your result.

61. $\lim\limits_{x \to -\infty}\left(x + \sqrt{x^2 + 3}\right)$ **62.** $\lim\limits_{x \to \infty}\left(x - \sqrt{x^2 + x}\right)$

63. $\lim\limits_{x \to -\infty}\left(3x + \sqrt{9x^2 - x}\right)$ **64.** $\lim\limits_{x \to \infty}\left(4x - \sqrt{16x^2 - x}\right)$

Connecting Representations In Exercises 65–68, use a graphing utility to complete the table and estimate the limit as x approaches infinity. Then use a graphing utility to graph the function and estimate the limit. Finally, find the limit analytically and compare your results with the estimates.

x	10^0	10^1	10^2	10^3	10^4	10^5	10^6
$f(x)$							

65. $f(x) = x - \sqrt{x(x - 1)}$ **66.** $f(x) = x^2 - x\sqrt{x(x - 1)}$

67. $f(x) = x \sin\dfrac{1}{2x}$ **68.** $f(x) = \dfrac{x + 1}{x\sqrt{x}}$

EXPLORING CONCEPTS

69. Writing In your own words, describe what is meant by the statements (a) $\lim\limits_{x \to \infty} f(x) = 4$ and (b) $\lim\limits_{x \to -\infty} f(x) = 2$.

70. Writing In your own words, state the guidelines for finding the limit of a rational function. Give examples.

71. Writing Consider the function $f(x) = 2/(1 + e^{1/x})$.

(a) Use a graphing utility to graph f.

(b) Write a short paragraph explaining why the graph has a horizontal asymptote at $y = 1$ and why the function has a nonremovable discontinuity at $x = 0$.

72. **HOW DO YOU SEE IT?**   The graph shows the temperature T, in degrees Fahrenheit, of molten glass t seconds after it is removed from a kiln.

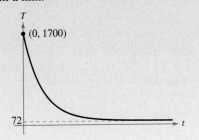

(a) Find $\lim\limits_{t \to 0^+} T$. What does this limit represent?

(b) Find $\lim\limits_{t \to \infty} T$. What does this limit represent?

73. **Using the Definition of Limits at Infinity**   The graph of $f(x) = 2x^2/(x^2 + 2)$ is shown.

(a) Find $L = \lim\limits_{x \to \infty} f(x)$ and $K = \lim\limits_{x \to -\infty} f(x)$.

(b) Determine x_1 and x_2 in terms of ε.

(c) State how x_1 relates to M, where $M > 0$, such that $|f(x) - L| < \varepsilon$ for $x > M$.

(d) State how x_2 relates to N, where $N < 0$, such that $|f(x) - L| < \varepsilon$ for $x < N$.

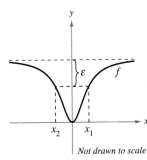

Not drawn to scale

Figure for 73   Figure for 74

74. **Using the Definition of Limits at Infinity**   The graph of $f(x) = 6x/\sqrt{x^2 + 2}$ is shown.

(a) Find $L = \lim\limits_{x \to \infty} f(x)$ and $K = \lim\limits_{x \to -\infty} f(x)$.

(b) Determine x_1 and x_2 in terms of ε.

(c) State how x_1 relates to M, where $M > 0$, such that $|f(x) - L| < \varepsilon$ for $x > M$.

(d) State how x_2 relates to N, where $N < 0$, such that $|f(x) - K| < \varepsilon$ for $x < N$.

75. **Implementing Processes**   Consider

$$\lim_{x \to \infty} \frac{3x}{\sqrt{x^2 + 3}}.$$

(a) Use the definition of limits at infinity to find values of M that correspond to $\varepsilon = 0.5$.

(b) Use the definition of limits at infinity to find values of M that correspond to $\varepsilon = 0.1$.

76. **Reasoning**   Can the graph of a function cross a horizontal asymptote? Explain.

Proof   **In Exercises 77–80, use the definition of limits at infinity to prove the limit.**

77. $\lim\limits_{x \to \infty} \dfrac{1}{x^2} = 0$

78. $\lim\limits_{x \to \infty} \dfrac{2}{\sqrt{x}} = 0$

79. $\lim\limits_{x \to -\infty} \dfrac{1}{x^3} = 0$

80. $\lim\limits_{x \to -\infty} \dfrac{1}{x - 2} = 0$

81. **Distance**   A line with slope m passes through the point $(0, 3)$.

(a) Write the shortest distance d between the line and the point $(3, 0)$ as a function of m.

(b) Use a graphing utility to graph the equation in part (a).

(c) Find $\lim\limits_{m \to \infty} d(m)$ and $\lim\limits_{m \to -\infty} d(m)$. Interpret the results geometrically.

82. **Proof**   Use the definition of infinite limits at infinity to prove that $\lim\limits_{x \to \infty} x^3 = \infty$.

Calculus AP® – Exam Preparation Questions

83. **Multiple Choice**   For $x \geq 0$, the horizontal line $y = 10$ is an asymptote of the graph of the function f. Which of the following statements must be true?

(A) $f(10)$ is undefined.   (B) $\lim\limits_{x \to 10} f(x) = \infty$

(C) $\lim\limits_{x \to \infty} f(x) = 10$ (D) For $x \geq 0$, $f(x) \neq 10$.

84. **Multiple Choice**   What is the horizontal asymptote of the graph of

$$f(x) = \frac{x^3 + x - 5}{4x^2 + 8 - 5x^3}?$$

(A) $y = -1$ (B) $y = -\frac{1}{5}$

(C) $y = \frac{1}{4}$ (D) none

85. **Multiple Choice** $\lim\limits_{x \to \infty} \dfrac{\sqrt{16x^2 - 5}}{6x - 1}$ is

(A) $\frac{2}{3}$.   (B) 3.   (C) 4.   (D) ∞.

86. **Multiple Choice**   The average typing speeds S (in words per minute) of a student after t weeks of typing lessons are shown in the table.

t	5	10	15	20	25	30
S	28	56	79	90	93	94

Which of the following best represents the limit of the student's typing speed?

(A) $\lim\limits_{t \to \infty} \dfrac{65t^2}{100 + t}$ (B) $\lim\limits_{t \to \infty} \dfrac{65t^2}{100 + t^2}$

(C) $\lim\limits_{t \to \infty} \dfrac{100t^2}{65 + t}$ (D) $\lim\limits_{t \to \infty} \dfrac{100t^2}{65 + t^2}$

Precalculus or Calculus In Exercises 1 and 2, decide whether you can solve the problem using precalculus. If you can, solve it. If the problem seems to require calculus, explain your reasoning and use a graphical or numerical approach to estimate the solution.

1. Find the distance between the points $(1, 1)$ and $(3, 9)$ along the curve $y = x^2$.

2. Find the distance between the points $(1, 1)$ and $(3, 9)$ along the line $y = 4x - 3$.

Estimating a Limit Numerically In Exercises 3 and 4, complete the table and use the result to estimate the limit. Use a graphing utility to graph the function to confirm your result.

3. $\lim\limits_{x \to 3} \dfrac{x - 3}{x^2 - 7x + 12}$

x	2.9	2.99	2.999	3	3.001	3.01	3.1
$f(x)$				?			

4. $\lim\limits_{x \to 0} \dfrac{\sqrt{x + 4} - 2}{x}$

x	-0.1	-0.01	-0.001	0	0.001	0.01	0.1
$f(x)$				?			

Finding a Limit Graphically In Exercises 5 and 6, use the graph to find the limit (if it exists). If the limit does not exist, explain why.

5. $h(x) = \dfrac{4x - x^2}{x}$

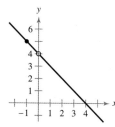

6. $f(t) = \dfrac{\ln(t + 2)}{t}$

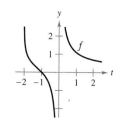

(a) $\lim\limits_{x \to 0} h(x)$

(b) $\lim\limits_{x \to -1} h(x)$

(a) $\lim\limits_{t \to 0} f(t)$

(b) $\lim\limits_{t \to -1} f(t)$

Using the ε–δ Definition of a Limit In Exercises 7–10, find the limit L. Then use the ε–δ definition to prove that the limit is L.

7. $\lim\limits_{x \to 1} (x + 4)$

8. $\lim\limits_{x \to 9} \sqrt{x}$

9. $\lim\limits_{x \to 2} (1 - x^2)$

10. $\lim\limits_{x \to 5} 9$

Finding a Limit In Exercises 11–28, find the limit. Use a graphing utility to verify your result.

11. $\lim\limits_{x \to -6} x^2$

12. $\lim\limits_{x \to 0} (3x - 5)$

13. $\lim\limits_{x \to -5} \sqrt[3]{x - 3}$

14. $\lim\limits_{x \to 6} (x - 2)^2$

15. $\lim\limits_{x \to 3} \dfrac{3}{x - 1}$

16. $\lim\limits_{x \to 2} \dfrac{x}{x^2 + 1}$

17. $\lim\limits_{t \to -2} \dfrac{t + 2}{t^2 - 4}$

18. $\lim\limits_{t \to 4} \dfrac{t^2 - 16}{t - 4}$

19. $\lim\limits_{x \to 5} \dfrac{\sqrt{x - 4} - 1}{x - 5}$

20. $\lim\limits_{x \to 0} \dfrac{\sqrt{1 + x} - 1}{3x}$

21. $\lim\limits_{x \to 0} \dfrac{[1/(x + 1)] - 1}{x}$

22. $\lim\limits_{s \to 0} \dfrac{(1/\sqrt{1 + s}) - 1}{s}$

23. $\lim\limits_{x \to 0} \dfrac{1 - \cos x}{\sin x}$

24. $\lim\limits_{x \to \pi/4} \dfrac{4x}{\tan x}$

25. $\lim\limits_{x \to 1} e^{x-1} \sin \dfrac{\pi x}{2}$

26. $\lim\limits_{x \to 2} \dfrac{\ln(x - 1)^2}{\ln(x - 1)}$

27. $\lim\limits_{\Delta x \to 0} \dfrac{\sin[(\pi/6) + \Delta x] - (1/2)}{\Delta x}$

[*Hint:* $\sin(\theta + \phi) = \sin \theta \cos \phi + \cos \theta \sin \phi$]

28. $\lim\limits_{\Delta x \to 0} \dfrac{\cos(\pi + \Delta x) + 1}{\Delta x}$

[*Hint:* $\cos(\theta + \phi) = \cos \theta \cos \phi - \sin \theta \sin \phi$]

Evaluating a Limit In Exercises 29–32, evaluate the limit given $\lim\limits_{x \to c} f(x) = -6$ and $\lim\limits_{x \to c} g(x) = \frac{1}{2}$.

29. $\lim\limits_{x \to c} [f(x)g(x)]$

30. $\lim\limits_{x \to c} \dfrac{f(x)}{g(x)}$

31. $\lim\limits_{x \to c} [f(x) + 2g(x)]$

32. $\lim\limits_{x \to c} [f(x)]^2$

Connecting Representations In Exercises 33–36, use a graphing utility to graph the function and estimate the limit. Use a table to reinforce your conclusion. Then find the limit by analytic methods.

33. $\lim\limits_{x \to 0} \dfrac{\sqrt{2x + 9} - 3}{x}$

34. $\lim\limits_{x \to 0} \dfrac{[1/(x + 4)] - (1/4)}{x}$

35. $\lim\limits_{x \to 0} \dfrac{20(e^{x/2} - 1)}{x - 1}$

36. $\lim\limits_{x \to 0} \dfrac{\ln(x + 1)}{x + 1}$

Free-Falling Object In Exercises 37 and 38, use the position function $s(t) = -4.9t^2 + 250$, which gives the height (in meters) of an object that has fallen for t seconds from a height of 250 meters. The velocity at time $t = a$ seconds is given by

$$\lim\limits_{t \to a} \dfrac{s(a) - s(t)}{a - t}.$$

37. Find the velocity of the object when $t = 4$.

38. When will the object hit the ground? At what velocity will the object impact the ground?

39. Finding Limits For $f(x) = \sqrt{x(x-1)}$, find (a) the domain of f, (b) $\lim\limits_{x \to 0^-} f(x)$, and (c) $\lim\limits_{x \to 1^+} f(x)$.

40. Finding Limits Let $f(x) = (x^2 - 4)/|x - 2|$. Find each limit (if it exists).

(a) $\lim\limits_{x \to 2^-} f(x)$ (b) $\lim\limits_{x \to 2^+} f(x)$ (c) $\lim\limits_{x \to 2} f(x)$

Finding a Limit In Exercises 41–48, find the limit (if it exists). If it does not exist, explain why.

41. $\lim\limits_{x \to 6^+} \dfrac{1}{x + 6}$

42. $\lim\limits_{x \to 7^-} \dfrac{x - 7}{x^2 - 49}$

43. $\lim\limits_{x \to 9} \dfrac{\sqrt{x} - 3}{x - 9}$

44. $\lim\limits_{x \to -11^-} \dfrac{|x + 11|}{x + 11}$

45. $\lim\limits_{x \to 2^-} (2[\![x]\!] + 1)$

46. $\lim\limits_{x \to 4} [\![x - 1]\!]$

47. $\lim\limits_{x \to 2} f(x)$, where $f(x) = \begin{cases} (x - 2)^2, & x \le 2 \\ 2 - x, & x > 2 \end{cases}$

48. $\lim\limits_{s \to -2} f(s)$, where $f(s) = \begin{cases} -s^2 - 4s - 2, & s \le -2 \\ s^2 + 4s + 6, & s > -2 \end{cases}$

Removable and Nonremovable Discontinuities In Exercises 49–52, find the x-values (if any) at which f is not continuous. Which of the discontinuities are removable?

49. $f(x) = x^2 - 64$

50. $f(x) = \dfrac{1}{x^2 - 9}$

51. $f(x) = \dfrac{x}{x^3 - x}$

52. $f(x) = \dfrac{x + 6}{x^2 - 3x - 54}$

Testing for Continuity In Exercises 53–60, describe the interval(s) on which the function is continuous.

53. $f(x) = -7x^2 + 3$

54. $f(x) = \dfrac{4x^2 + 7x - 2}{x + 2}$

55. $f(x) = \sqrt{x - 4}$

56. $f(x) = [\![x + 3]\!]$

57. $g(x) = 2e^{[\![x]\!]/4}$

58. $h(x) = -5 \ln|2 - x|$

59. $f(x) = \begin{cases} \dfrac{3x^2 - x - 2}{x - 1}, & x \ne 1 \\ 0, & x = 1 \end{cases}$

60. $f(x) = \begin{cases} 5 - x, & x \le 2 \\ 2x - 3, & x > 2 \end{cases}$

Existence of a Zero In Exercises 61 and 62, explain why the function has at least one zero in the given interval.

61. $f(x) = 3x^3 - 2; [0, 1]$

62. $f(x) = 2 \ln(x + 4) - 4; [3, 4]$

Finding Vertical Asymptotes In Exercises 63–68, find any vertical asymptotes of the graph of the function.

63. $f(x) = \dfrac{x^3}{x^2 - 9}$

64. $h(x) = \dfrac{12x}{144 - x^2}$

65. $g(x) = \dfrac{2x + 1}{4x^2 - 1}$

66. $f(x) = \csc \dfrac{\pi x}{3}$

67. $g(x) = \ln(25 - x^2)$

68. $f(x) = 7e^{-3/x}$

Finding a One-Sided Limit In Exercises 69–78, find the one-sided limit (if it exists).

69. $\lim\limits_{x \to 1^-} \dfrac{x^2 + 2x + 1}{x - 1}$

70. $\lim\limits_{x \to (1/2)^+} \dfrac{x}{2x - 1}$

71. $\lim\limits_{x \to -2^+} \dfrac{x + 2}{x^3 + 8}$

72. $\lim\limits_{x \to -1^-} \dfrac{x^2 - 1}{x^4 - 1}$

73. $\lim\limits_{x \to 0^+} \left(x - \dfrac{1}{x^3}\right)$

74. $\lim\limits_{x \to 2^-} \dfrac{1}{\sqrt[3]{x^2 - 4}}$

75. $\lim\limits_{x \to 0^+} \dfrac{\sin 4x}{5x}$

76. $\lim\limits_{x \to 0^+} \dfrac{\sec x}{x}$

77. $\lim\limits_{x \to 0^+} \ln(\sin x)$

78. $\lim\limits_{x \to 0^-} 16e^{-2/x}$

79. Environment A utility company burns coal to generate electricity. The cost C in dollars of removing $p\%$ of the air pollutants in the stack emissions is

$$C = \dfrac{80{,}000p}{100 - p}, \quad 0 \le p < 100.$$

(a) Find the cost of removing 15%, 50%, and 90% of the pollutants.

(b) Find the limit of C as p approaches 100 from the left. Explain your result in the context of the problem.

80. Limits and Continuity The function f is defined as

$$f(x) = \dfrac{\tan 2x}{x}, \quad x \ne 0.$$

(a) Find $\lim\limits_{x \to 0} \dfrac{\tan 2x}{x}$, if it exists.

(b) Can the function f be defined at $x = 0$ such that it is continuous at $x = 0$?

Finding a Limit In Exercises 81–88, find the limit, if it exists.

81. $\lim\limits_{x \to \infty} \left(8 + \dfrac{1}{x}\right)$

82. $\lim\limits_{x \to \infty} \dfrac{1 - 4x}{x + 1}$

83. $\lim\limits_{x \to \infty} \dfrac{3x^2}{5x^2 + 2}$

84. $\lim\limits_{x \to \infty} \dfrac{4x^2}{x^4 + 3}$

85. $\lim\limits_{x \to -\infty} \dfrac{3x^2}{x + 5}$

86. $\lim\limits_{x \to -\infty} \dfrac{\sqrt{x^2 + x}}{-2x}$

87. $\lim\limits_{x \to -\infty} \dfrac{6x}{x + \cos x}$

88. $\lim\limits_{x \to -\infty} \dfrac{x}{2 \sin x}$

Finding Horizontal Asymptotes In Exercises 89–94, use a graphing utility to graph the function and identify any horizontal asymptotes.

89. $f(x) = \dfrac{3}{x} - 2$

90. $g(x) = \dfrac{5x^2}{x^2 + 2}$

91. $h(x) = \dfrac{2x + 3}{x - 4}$

92. $f(x) = \dfrac{3x}{\sqrt{x^2 + 2}}$

93. $f(x) = \dfrac{5}{3 + 2e^{-x}}$

94. $h(x) = 10 \ln \dfrac{x}{x + 1}$

AP® Exam Practice Questions

See *LarsonCalculusforAP.com* for worked-out solutions to these questions.

What You Need to Know

- The AP® Exam, especially the free-response section, stresses the major applications of calculus rather than the foundational limit concept.
- You are not required to use the formal epsilon-delta definition of a limit on the AP® Exam.
- The algebraic methods for evaluating limits (see Section 1.3) are not explicitly tested on the free-response section of the AP® Exam. They are, however, helpful on some multiple-choice questions.
- You should be able to apply the Intermediate Value Theorem, whether the function is presented as an equation or by a table.
- You should be able to find both vertical and horizontal asymptotes given a function or a graph.
- The AP® Exam frequently uses limits at infinity as a way of describing horizontal asymptotes.

Practice Questions

Section 1, Part A, Multiple Choice, No Technology

1. What is the limit of $h(x) = 2$ as x approaches π?

    (A) 0   (B) 2

    (C) π (D) nonexistent

2. What is the limit of

    $$g(x) = \frac{|x + 4|}{x + 4}$$

    as x approaches -4?

    (A) -4 (B) 0

    (C) 1   (D) nonexistent

3. $\lim\limits_{x \to \pi} \dfrac{\sin x}{x}$ is

    (A) 0.   (B) 1.

    (C) π.   (D) nonexistent.

4. $\lim\limits_{x \to -2} \dfrac{3x^2 + 5x + 7}{x - 4}$ is

    (A) $-\dfrac{5}{2}$.   (B) $-\dfrac{3}{2}$.

    (C) -1.   (D) 3.

5. Given $\lim\limits_{x \to 5} f(x) = 10$ and $\lim\limits_{x \to 5} g(x) = 1$, what is the limit of $\lim\limits_{x \to 5} [5f(x) - g(x)]$?

    (A) 9   (B) 15

    (C) 45   (D) 49

6. The line $y = 4$ is a horizontal asymptote to the graph of which function?

    (A) $y = 4x$ (B) $y = \dfrac{1}{x - 4}$

    (C) $y = \dfrac{5x + 16x^2}{4x^2 - 3}$ (D) $y = \dfrac{1 - 4x}{x + 2}$

7. What are the horizontal asymptotes of the graph of

    $$y = \frac{3}{1 - 4^x}?$$

    (A) $y = 0$ only   (B) $y = 3$ only

    (C) $y = 0$ and $y = 3$ (D) $y = 0$ and $y = -3$

8.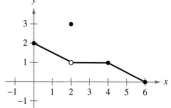

    The graph of the function g is shown above. Which of the following is true?

    I. $\lim\limits_{x \to 2} g(x) = 1$

    II. $\lim\limits_{x \to 2} g(x) = g(2)$

    III. g is continuous at $x = 3$.

    (A) I only   (B) I and III only

    (C) III only   (D) I, II, and III

9. $\lim\limits_{x \to \infty} \dfrac{\sqrt{9x^4 - 5}}{5x - 3x^2}$ is

    (A) $-\infty$.   (B) -3.

    (C) -1.   (D) ∞.

Section 1, Part B, Multiple Choice, Technology Permitted

10. $\lim\limits_{x \to 1} \dfrac{x - 1}{\sqrt{x} - 1}$ is

    (A) 0.   (B) 1.

    (C) 2.   (D) nonexistent.

Section 2, Part A, Free Response, Technology Permitted

11. The position function $s(t) = -4.9t^2 + 398$ gives the height (in meters) of an object that has fallen from a height of 398 meters after t seconds.

    (a) For $1 < t < 2$, explain why there must be a time t at which the height of the object is 382 meters above the ground.

    (b) After how many seconds does the object hit the ground?

    (c) Find

    $$\lim_{t \to 3} \frac{s(t) - s(3)}{t - 3}.$$

    Show the work that leads to your answer. Include units.

Section 2, Part B, Free Response, No Technology

12. The function f is defined as

    $$f(x) = \frac{10}{1 + \frac{1}{4}e^{-x}}.$$

    (a) Find $\lim_{x \to 0} f(x)$.

    (b) Find $\lim_{x \to 0} [f(x) + 4]$.

    (c) State the equation(s) for the horizontal asymptote(s) of the graph of $y = f(x)$. Show the work that leads to your answer.

13. The function f is defined as

    $$f(x) = \frac{x^2 + 5x + 6}{2x^2 + 7x + 3}.$$

    (a) State the value(s) of x for which f is not continuous.

    (b) Evaluate $\lim_{x \to -3} f(x)$. Justify your answer.

    (c) State the equation(s) for the vertical asymptote(s) of the graph of $y = f(x)$.

    (d) State the equation(s) for the horizontal asymptote(s) of the graph of $y = f(x)$. Show the work that leads to your answer.

14. Let f be a function defined by

    $$f(x) = \begin{cases} e^{2x}, & x \le 0 \\ 4 - 3\cos x, & x > 0 \end{cases}.$$

    (a) Find $\lim_{x \to -1} f(x)$.

    (b) Show that f is continuous at $x = 0$.

    (c) Find $\lim_{x \to -\infty} f(x)$.

15.

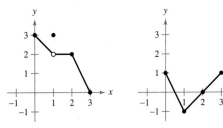

Graph of f Graph of g

The graphs of the functions f and g are shown above. Evaluate each limit using the graphs provided. Show the computations that lead to your answer.

(a) $\lim_{x \to 1} [f(x) + 4]$

(b) $\lim_{x \to 3^-} \dfrac{5}{g(x)}$

(c) $\lim_{x \to 2} [f(x)g(x)]$

(d) $\lim_{x \to 3^-} \dfrac{f(x)}{g(x) - 1}$ (Assume that f and g are linear on the interval $[2, 3]$.)

16. A hot cup of tea is placed on a counter and left to cool. The temperature (in degrees Fahrenheit) of the tea x minutes after the cup is placed on the counter is modeled by a continuous function $T(x)$ for $0 \le x < 10$. The table shows $T(x)$ at various times x.

x	0	3	4	6	8	9
$T(x)$	180	174	172	168	164	162

(a) Find $\lim_{x \to 4} T(x)$. Justify your answer.

(b) Use the data to find the average rate of change in the temperature of the tea for $3 \le x \le 8$. Include units in your final answer.

(c) Use the data to identify the shortest interval during which there must exist a time x for which the temperature of the tea is 166.5°F. Justify your answer.

(d) Use the data to find the best estimate of the slope of the line tangent to the graph of T at $x = 8$.

17. Let a and b represent real numbers. Define

    $$f(x) = \begin{cases} ax^2 + x - b, & x \le 2 \\ ax + b, & 2 < x < 5 \\ 2ax - 7, & x \ge 5 \end{cases}.$$

    (a) Find the values of a and b such that f is continuous on the entire real number line.

    (b) Evaluate $\lim_{x \to 3} f(x)$.

    (c) Let $g(x) = \dfrac{f(x)}{x - 1}$. Evaluate $\lim_{x \to 1} g(x)$.

1 Performance Task

Swimming Speed

A look at records set in various sports over the past century shows that humans continue to run faster, jump higher, and throw farther than ever before. Several factors have allowed this to occur.

One factor is training. Physiologists are working to identify which systems in the human body limit performance, and to create training techniques that develop those systems. Similarly, sports psychologists work with individuals and team members to help them develop the mental "flow" that will allow them to deliver peak performances. Moreover, trainers have developed devices to monitor athletes' bodies and provide them with feedback on their performance. Equipment has also improved vastly over the years. Even sports such as swimming, with no obvious equipment, have benefited from technology. For instance, new styles of swimsuits help reduce drag and improve time even more.

Exercises

In Exercises 1–5, use the scatter plot, which shows the year of a record set in the women's 100-meter freestyle swimming event and the record time. Let x represent the year, where $x = 0$ represents 1900. Let y represent the record time in seconds.

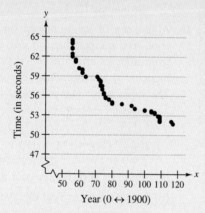

Year (0 ↔ 1900)

1. **Justifying**   Do you think there is a limit to human athletic performance or is there no limit? List several reasons why you think there is a limit or several reasons why you think there is no limit to human athletic performance.

2. **Finding a Limit Graphically**   Use the scatter plot to estimate a reasonable lower limit for the time it takes a woman to swim 100 meters. Predict a reasonable record time for a woman to swim 100 meters in the year 2025. Explain your reasoning.

3. **Finding a Limit Analytically**   A model for the women's 100-meter freestyle record times is given by

$$y = \frac{32.4 - 1.66x}{1 - 0.035x}.$$

   (a) Use a graphing utility to graph the model. Predict a reasonable record time for a woman to swim 100 meters in the year 2025. Explain your reasoning.

   (b) Find the limit of the model as x approaches infinity.

4. **Reasoning**   Do you think the model in Exercise 3 can be used to estimate record times for any year? Explain your reasoning.

5. **Reasoning**   Do you think these results show that there is a limit to how fast a woman can swim 100 meters? Explain your reasoning.

2 Differentiation

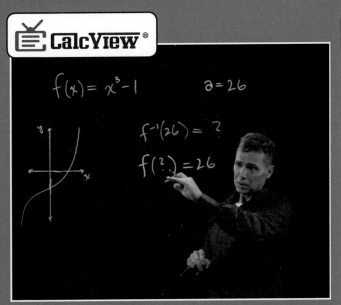

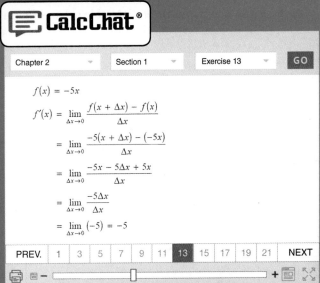

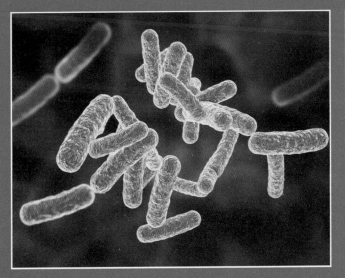

2.4 Bacteria (*Exercise 173, p. 172*)

2.7 Rate of Change (*Example 2, p. 191*)

123

2.1 The Derivative and the Tangent Line Problem

▶ Find the slope of the tangent line to a curve at a point.
▶ Use the limit definition to find the derivative of a function.
▶ Understand the relationship between differentiability and continuity.
▶ Find the derivative of a function given by a table or a graph.

The Tangent Line Problem

Calculus grew out of four major problems that European mathematicians were working on during the seventeenth century.

1. The tangent line problem (Section 1.1 and this section)

2. The velocity and acceleration problem (Sections 2.2 and 2.3)

3. The minimum and maximum problem (Section 3.1)

4. The area problem (Sections 1.1 and 4.2)

Each problem involves the notion of a limit, and calculus can be introduced with any of the four problems.

A brief introduction to the tangent line problem is given in Section 1.1. Although partial solutions to this problem were given by Pierre de Fermat (1601–1665), René Descartes (1596–1650), Christian Huygens (1629–1695), and Isaac Barrow (1630–1677), credit for the first general solution is usually given to Isaac Newton (1642–1727) and Gottfried Leibniz (1646–1716). Newton's work on this problem stemmed from his interest in optics and light refraction.

What does it mean to say that a line is tangent to a curve at a point? For a circle, the tangent line at a point P is the line that is perpendicular to the radial line at point P, as shown in Figure 2.1.

For a general curve, however, the problem is more difficult. For instance, how would you define the tangent lines shown in Figure 2.2? You might say that a line is tangent to a curve at a point P when it touches, but does not cross, the curve at point P. This definition would work for the first curve shown in Figure 2.2, but not for the second. *Or* you might say that a line is tangent to a curve when the line touches or intersects the curve at exactly one point. This definition would work for a circle, but not for more general curves, as the third curve in Figure 2.2 shows.

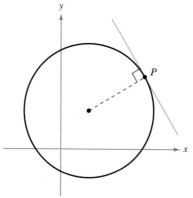

Tangent line to a circle
Figure 2.1

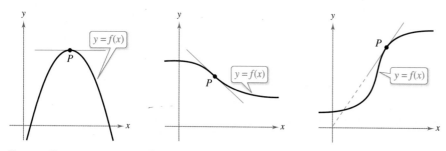

Tangent line to a curve at a point
Figure 2.2

Exploration

Use a graphing utility to graph $f(x) = 2x^3 - 4x^2 + 3x - 5$. On the same screen, graph $y = x - 5$, $y = 2x - 5$, and $y = 3x - 5$. Which of these lines, if any, appears to be tangent to the graph of f at the point $(0, -5)$? Explain your reasoning.

Essentially, the problem of finding the tangent line at a point P boils down to the problem of finding the *slope* of the tangent line at point P. You can approximate this slope using a **secant line*** through the point of tangency and a second point on the curve, as shown in Figure 2.3. If $(c, f(c))$ is the point of tangency and

$$(c + \Delta x, f(c + \Delta x))$$

is a second point on the graph of f, then the slope of the secant line through the two points is given by substitution into the slope formula

$$m = \frac{y_2 - y_1}{x_2 - x_1}$$

$$m_{\text{sec}} = \frac{f(c + \Delta x) - f(c)}{(c + \Delta x) - c} \qquad \begin{array}{l} \text{Change in } y \\ \overline{\text{Change in } x} \end{array}$$

$$m_{\text{sec}} = \frac{f(c + \Delta x) - f(c)}{\Delta x}. \qquad \text{Slope of secant line}$$

The right-hand side of this equation is a **difference quotient.** The denominator Δx is the **change in x,** and the numerator

$$\Delta y = f(c + \Delta x) - f(c)$$

is the **change in y.**

The beauty of this procedure is that you can obtain more and more accurate approximations of the slope of the tangent line by choosing points closer and closer to the point of tangency, as shown in Figure 2.4.

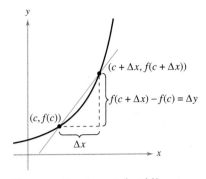

The secant line through $(c, f(c))$ and $(c + \Delta x, f(c + \Delta x))$

Figure 2.3

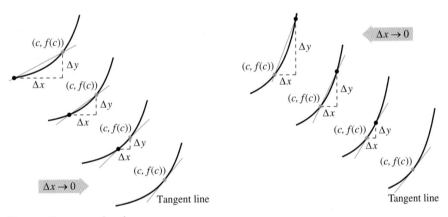

Tangent line approximations

Figure 2.4

Definition of Tangent Line with Slope m

If f is defined on an open interval containing c, and if the limit

$$\lim_{\Delta x \to 0} \frac{\Delta y}{\Delta x} = \lim_{\Delta x \to 0} \frac{f(c + \Delta x) - f(c)}{\Delta x} = m$$

exists, then the line passing through $(c, f(c))$ with slope m is the **tangent line** to the graph of f at the point $(c, f(c))$.

The slope of the tangent line to the graph of f at the point $(c, f(c))$ is also called the **slope of the graph of f at $x = c$.**

---

* This use of the word *secant* comes from the Latin *secare*, meaning to cut, and is not a reference to the trigonometric function of the same name.

EXAMPLE 1   The Slope of the Graph of a Linear Function

To find the slope of the graph of $f(x) = 2x - 3$ when $c = 2$, you can apply the definition of the slope of a tangent line, as shown.

$$\lim_{\Delta x \to 0} \frac{f(2 + \Delta x) - f(2)}{\Delta x} = \lim_{\Delta x \to 0} \frac{[2(2 + \Delta x) - 3] - [2(2) - 3]}{\Delta x}$$

$$= \lim_{\Delta x \to 0} \frac{4 + 2\Delta x - 3 - 4 + 3}{\Delta x}$$

$$= \lim_{\Delta x \to 0} \frac{2\Delta x}{\Delta x}$$

$$= \lim_{\Delta x \to 0} 2$$

$$= 2$$

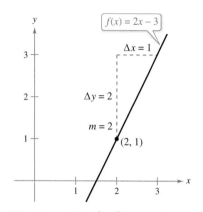

The slope of f at $(2, 1)$ is $m = 2$.
Figure 2.5

The slope of f at $(c, f(c)) = (2, 1)$ is $m = 2$, as shown in Figure 2.5. Notice that the limit definition of the slope of f agrees with the definition of the slope of a line as discussed in Section P.2.

The graph of a linear function has the same slope at any point. This is not true of nonlinear functions, as shown in the next example.

EXAMPLE 2   Tangent Lines to the Graph of a Nonlinear Function

Find the slopes of the tangent lines to the graph of $f(x) = x^2 + 1$ at the points $(0, 1)$ and $(-1, 2)$, as shown in Figure 2.6.

Solution

Let $(c, f(c))$ represent an arbitrary point on the graph of f. Then the slope of the tangent line at $(c, f(c))$ can be found as shown below. [Note in the limit process that c is held constant (as Δx approaches 0).]

$$\lim_{\Delta x \to 0} \frac{f(c + \Delta x) - f(c)}{\Delta x} = \lim_{\Delta x \to 0} \frac{[(c + \Delta x)^2 + 1] - (c^2 + 1)}{\Delta x}$$

$$= \lim_{\Delta x \to 0} \frac{c^2 + 2c(\Delta x) + (\Delta x)^2 + 1 - c^2 - 1}{\Delta x}$$

$$= \lim_{\Delta x \to 0} \frac{2c(\Delta x) + (\Delta x)^2}{\Delta x}$$

$$= \lim_{\Delta x \to 0} (2c + \Delta x)$$

$$= 2c$$

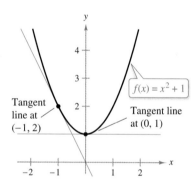

The slope of f at any point $(c, f(c))$ is $m = 2c$.
Figure 2.6

So, the slope at *any* point $(c, f(c))$ on the graph of f is $m = 2c$. At the point $(0, 1)$, the slope is $m = 2(0) = 0$, and at $(-1, 2)$, the slope is $m = 2(-1) = -2$.

The definition of a tangent line to a curve does not cover the possibility of a vertical tangent line. For vertical tangent lines, you can use the following definition. If f is continuous at c and

$$\lim_{\Delta x \to 0} \frac{f(c + \Delta x) - f(c)}{\Delta x} = \infty \quad \text{or} \quad \lim_{\Delta x \to 0} \frac{f(c + \Delta x) - f(c)}{\Delta x} = -\infty$$

then the vertical line $x = c$ passing through $(c, f(c))$ is a **vertical tangent line** to the graph of f. For example, the function shown in Figure 2.7 has a vertical tangent line at $(c, f(c))$. When the domain of f is the closed interval $[a, b]$, you can extend the definition of a vertical tangent line to include the endpoints by considering continuity and limits from the right (for $x = a$) and from the left (for $x = b$).

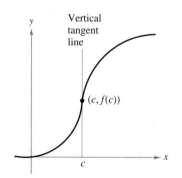

The graph of f has a vertical tangent line at $(c, f(c))$.
Figure 2.7

The Derivative of a Function

You have now arrived at a crucial point in the study of calculus. The limit used to define the slope of a tangent line is also used to define one of the two fundamental operations of calculus—**differentiation.**

Definition of the Derivative of a Function

The **derivative** of f at x is

$$f'(x) = \lim_{\Delta x \to 0} \frac{f(x + \Delta x) - f(x)}{\Delta x}$$

provided the limit exists. For all x for which this limit exists, f' is a function of x.

Communication and Notation

The notation $f'(x)$ is read as "f prime of x."

Be sure you see that the derivative of a function of x is also a function of x. This "new" function gives the slope of the tangent line to the graph of f at the point $(x, f(x))$, provided that the graph has a tangent line at this point. The derivative can also be used to determine the **instantaneous rate of change** (or simply the **rate of change**) of one variable with respect to another.

The process of finding the derivative of a function is called **differentiation.** A function is **differentiable** at x when its derivative exists at x and is **differentiable on an open interval (a, b)** when it is differentiable at every point in the interval.

In addition to $f'(x)$, other notations are used to denote the derivative of $y = f(x)$. The most common are

$$f'(x), \quad \frac{dy}{dx}, \quad y', \quad \frac{d}{dx}[f(x)], \quad D_x[y].$$

Notation for derivatives

The notation dy/dx is read as "the derivative of y *with respect to* x" or simply "dy, dx." Using limit notation, you can write

$$\frac{dy}{dx} = \lim_{\Delta x \to 0} \frac{\Delta y}{\Delta x} = \lim_{\Delta x \to 0} \frac{f(x + \Delta x) - f(x)}{\Delta x} = f'(x).$$

Insight

It is important that you are able to recognize the different notations used to denote the derivative of a function. The AP® Exam may use these notations interchangeably.

EXAMPLE 3   Finding the Derivative by the Limit Process

See LarsonCalculusforAP.com for an interactive version of this type of example.

To find the derivative of $f(x) = x^3 + 2x$, use the definition of the derivative as shown.

$$
\begin{aligned}
f'(x) &= \lim_{\Delta x \to 0} \frac{f(x + \Delta x) - f(x)}{\Delta x} && \text{Definition of derivative}\\[2mm]
&= \lim_{\Delta x \to 0} \frac{(x + \Delta x)^3 + 2(x + \Delta x) - (x^3 + 2x)}{\Delta x}\\[2mm]
&= \lim_{\Delta x \to 0} \frac{x^3 + 3x^2\Delta x + 3x(\Delta x)^2 + (\Delta x)^3 + 2x + 2\Delta x - x^3 - 2x}{\Delta x}\\[2mm]
&= \lim_{\Delta x \to 0} \frac{3x^2\Delta x + 3x(\Delta x)^2 + (\Delta x)^3 + 2\Delta x}{\Delta x}\\[2mm]
&= \lim_{\Delta x \to 0} \frac{\Delta x[3x^2 + 3x\Delta x + (\Delta x)^2 + 2]}{\Delta x}\\[2mm]
&= \lim_{\Delta x \to 0} [3x^2 + 3x\Delta x + (\Delta x)^2 + 2]\\[2mm]
&= 3x^2 + 2
\end{aligned}
$$

Implementing Processes

When using the definition to find a derivative of a function, the key is to rewrite the difference quotient so that Δx does not occur as a factor of the denominator.

EXAMPLE 4   **Using the Derivative to Find the Slope at a Point**

Find $f'(x)$ for $f(x) = \sqrt{x}$. Then find the slopes of the graph of f at the points $(1, 1)$ and $(4, 2)$. Discuss the behavior of f at $(0, 0)$.

Solution

Use the procedure for rationalizing numerators, as discussed in Section 1.3.

$$f'(x) = \lim_{\Delta x \to 0} \frac{f(x + \Delta x) - f(x)}{\Delta x} \qquad \text{Definition of derivative}$$

$$= \lim_{\Delta x \to 0} \frac{\sqrt{x + \Delta x} - \sqrt{x}}{\Delta x}$$

$$= \lim_{\Delta x \to 0} \left(\frac{\sqrt{x + \Delta x} - \sqrt{x}}{\Delta x} \right)\left(\frac{\sqrt{x + \Delta x} + \sqrt{x}}{\sqrt{x + \Delta x} + \sqrt{x}} \right)$$

$$= \lim_{\Delta x \to 0} \frac{(x + \Delta x) - x}{\Delta x \left(\sqrt{x + \Delta x} + \sqrt{x} \right)}$$

$$= \lim_{\Delta x \to 0} \frac{\Delta x}{\Delta x \left(\sqrt{x + \Delta x} + \sqrt{x} \right)}$$

$$= \lim_{\Delta x \to 0} \frac{1}{\sqrt{x + \Delta x} + \sqrt{x}}$$

$$= \frac{1}{2\sqrt{x}}$$

At $(1, 1)$, the slope is $f'(1) = \frac{1}{2}$. At $(4, 2)$, the slope is $f'(4) = \frac{1}{4}$. See Figure 2.8. The domain of f' is all $x > 0$, so the slope of f is undefined at $(0, 0)$, and the graph of f has a vertical tangent line at $(0, 0)$.

> **Connecting Representations**
>
> Remember that the derivative of a function f is itself a function, which can be used to find the slope of the tangent line at the point $(x, f(x))$ on the graph of f.

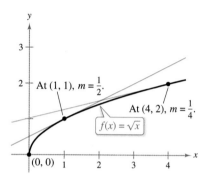

For $x > 0$, the slope of f at $(x, f(x))$ is $m = 1/(2\sqrt{x})$.
Figure 2.8

EXAMPLE 5   **Using the Derivative to Find a Tangent Line**

See LarsonCalculusforAP.com for an interactive version of this type of example.

Find the derivative with respect to t for the function $y = 2/t$. Then find an equation of the tangent line to the graph at $(1, 2)$.

Solution   Considering $y = f(t)$, you obtain

$$\frac{dy}{dt} = \lim_{\Delta t \to 0} \frac{f(t + \Delta t) - f(t)}{\Delta t} \qquad \text{Definition of derivative}$$

$$= \lim_{\Delta t \to 0} \frac{\dfrac{2}{t + \Delta t} - \dfrac{2}{t}}{\Delta t} \qquad f(t + \Delta t) = \frac{2}{t + \Delta t} \text{ and } f(t) = \frac{2}{t}$$

$$= \lim_{\Delta t \to 0} \frac{\dfrac{2t - 2(t + \Delta t)}{t(t + \Delta t)}}{\Delta t} \qquad \text{Combine fractions in numerator.}$$

$$= \lim_{\Delta t \to 0} \frac{-2\Delta t}{\Delta t(t)(t + \Delta t)} \qquad \text{Divide out common factor of } \Delta t.$$

$$= \lim_{\Delta t \to 0} \frac{-2}{t(t + \Delta t)} \qquad \text{Simplify.}$$

$$= -\frac{2}{t^2}. \qquad \text{Evaluate limit as } \Delta t \to 0.$$

Using $dy/dt = -2/t^2$, you know that the slope of the graph of $y = 2/t$ at the point $(1, 2)$ is $m = -2$. Using the point-slope form, you can find that the equation of the tangent line to the graph at $(1, 2)$ is $y - 2 = -2(t - 1)$ or $y = -2t + 4$, as shown in Figure 2.9. Check this equation using the *tangent* feature of a graphing utility. ■

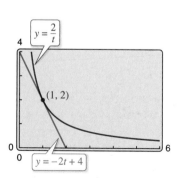

At the point $(1, 2)$, the line $y = -2t + 4$ is tangent to the graph of $y = 2/t$.
Figure 2.9

Differentiability and Continuity

The alternative limit form of the derivative shown below is useful in investigating the relationship between differentiability and continuity. The derivative of f at c is

$$f'(c) = \lim_{x \to c} \frac{f(x) - f(c)}{x - c}$$ Alternative form of derivative

provided this limit exists. (See Figure 2.10.)

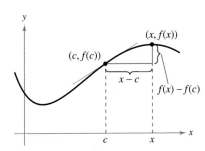

As x approaches c, the secant line approaches the tangent line.
Figure 2.10

Note that the existence of the limit in this alternative form requires that the one-sided limits

$$\lim_{x \to c^-} \frac{f(x) - f(c)}{x - c} \quad \text{and} \quad \lim_{x \to c^+} \frac{f(x) - f(c)}{x - c}$$

exist and are equal. These one-sided limits are called the **derivatives from the left and from the right,** respectively. It follows that f is **differentiable on the closed interval** $[a, b]$ when it is differentiable on (a, b) and when the derivative from the right at a and the derivative from the left at b both exist.

When a function is not continuous at $x = c$, it is also not differentiable at $x = c$. For instance, the greatest integer function $f(x) = [\![x]\!]$ is not continuous at $x = 0$, and so it is not differentiable at $x = 0$. (See Figure 2.11 and Exercise 85.) You can verify this by observing that

$$\lim_{x \to 0^-} \frac{f(x) - f(0)}{x - 0} = \lim_{x \to 0^-} \frac{[\![x]\!] - 0}{x} = \infty$$ Derivative from the left

and

$$\lim_{x \to 0^+} \frac{f(x) - f(0)}{x - 0} = \lim_{x \to 0^+} \frac{[\![x]\!] - 0}{x} = 0.$$ Derivative from the right

Insight

In preparation for the AP® Exam, you should master both the standard and alternative definitions of the derivative and their geometric interpretations.

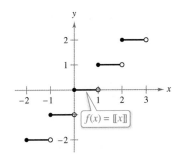

The greatest integer function is not differentiable at $x = 0$ because it is not continuous at $x = 0$.
Figure 2.11

EXAMPLE 6   A Graph with a Sharp Turn

See LarsonCalculusforAP.com for an interactive version of this type of example.

The function $f(x) = |x - 2|$ is continuous at $x = 2$, as shown in Figure 2.12. The one-sided limits, however, are not equal, as shown.

$$\lim_{x \to 2^-} \frac{f(x) - f(2)}{x - 2} = \lim_{x \to 2^-} \frac{|x - 2| - 0}{x - 2} = -1$$ Derivative from the left

$$\lim_{x \to 2^+} \frac{f(x) - f(2)}{x - 2} = \lim_{x \to 2^+} \frac{|x - 2| - 0}{x - 2} = 1$$ Derivative from the right

So, f is not differentiable at $x = 2$ and the graph of f does not have a tangent line at the point $(2, 0)$.

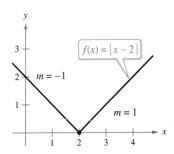

f is not differentiable at $x = 2$ because the derivatives from the left and from the right are not equal.
Figure 2.12

EXAMPLE 7   A Graph with a Vertical Tangent Line

The function $f(x) = x^{1/3}$ is continuous at $x = 0$, as shown in Figure 2.13. However, because the limit

$$\lim_{x \to 0} \frac{f(x) - f(0)}{x - 0} = \lim_{x \to 0} \frac{x^{1/3} - 0}{x} = \lim_{x \to 0} \frac{1}{x^{2/3}} = \infty$$

is infinite, you can conclude that the tangent line is vertical at $x = 0$. So, f is not differentiable at $x = 0$.

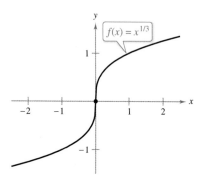

f is not differentiable at $x = 0$ because
f has a vertical tangent line at $x = 0$.
Figure 2.13

From Examples 6 and 7, you can see that a function is not differentiable at a point at which its graph has a sharp turn *or* a vertical tangent line.

Theorem 2.1   Differentiability Implies Continuity

If f is differentiable at $x = c$, then f is continuous at $x = c$.

Proof   You can prove that f is continuous at $x = c$ by showing that $f(x)$ approaches $f(c)$ as $x \to c$. To do this, use the differentiability of f at $x = c$ and consider the following limit.

$$\lim_{x \to c} [f(x) - f(c)] = \lim_{x \to c} \left[(x - c) \left(\frac{f(x) - f(c)}{x - c} \right) \right]$$

$$= \left[\lim_{x \to c} (x - c) \right] \left[\lim_{x \to c} \frac{f(x) - f(c)}{x - c} \right]$$

$$= (0)[f'(c)]$$

$$= 0$$

Because the difference $f(x) - f(c)$ approaches zero as $x \to c$, you can conclude that $\lim_{x \to c} f(x) = f(c)$. So, f is continuous at $x = c$.

The relationship between continuity and differentiability is summarized below.

1. If a function is differentiable at $x = c$, then it is continuous at $x = c$. So, differentiability implies continuity.

2. It is possible for a function to be continuous at $x = c$ and not be differentiable at $x = c$. So, continuity does not imply differentiability. (See Examples 6 and 7.)

Insight

Some questions on the AP® Exam state that a function is differentiable without stating that the function is continuous. You need to recognize that Theorem 2.1 applies in these situations.

Technology

Some graphing utilities, such as *Maple*, *Mathematica*, and the *TI-Nspire*, perform symbolic differentiation. Others perform *numerical differentiation* by finding values of derivatives using the formula

$$f'(x) \approx \frac{f(x + \Delta x) - f(x - \Delta x)}{2 \Delta x}$$

where Δx is a small number such as 0.01. Can you see any problems with this definition? For instance, using this definition, what is the value of the derivative of $f(x) = |x|$ when $x = 0$?

Derivatives of Functions Given by Tables or Graphs

EXAMPLE 8   Derivative of a Function Given by a Table

The table shows $f(x)$ for several values of x, where f is a differentiable function of x on the interval $[0, 6]$. Estimate the instantaneous rate of change of f at $x = 3$.

x	0	2	4	6
$f(x)$	0	10	36	78

Solution

The table does not give $f(x)$ when $x = 3$. So, to estimate the instantaneous rate of change, use a difference quotient with the two values closest to $x = 3$. Because $x = 3$ lies between $x = 2$ and $x = 4$, an estimate for the instantaneous rate of change of f at $x = 3$ is

$$f'(3) \approx \frac{f(4) - f(2)}{4 - 2} = \frac{36 - 10}{2} = 13.$$

EXAMPLE 9   Derivative of a Function Given by a Graph

The graph of f is shown in the figure. Sketch the graph of f'. Explain how you found your answer. [Assume f is a differentiable function of x on the interval $(-\infty, \infty)$.]

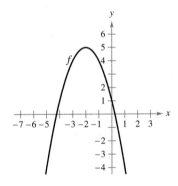

Solution

Moving from left to right, the graph of f rises for $x < -2$. So, in this interval the slopes of the lines tangent to the graph of f are positive (see figure at the left below). Thus, $f'(x) > 0$ for $x < -2$. The slope of the tangent line at $x = 2$ is 0, so $f'(x) = 0$ when $x = -2$. For $x > -2$, the graph of f falls from left to right. So, when $x > -2$, the slopes of the lines tangent to the graph of f are negative. Thus, $f'(x) < 0$ for $x > -2$. Using this information, you can sketch a possible graph of f', as shown in the figure at the right below.

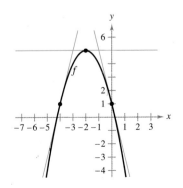
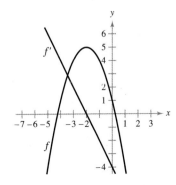

2.1 Exercises

See *CalcChat.com* for tutorial help and worked-out solutions to odd-numbered exercises.

Estimating Slope In Exercises 1 and 2, estimate the slope of the graph at the points (x_1, y_1) and (x_2, y_2).

1.
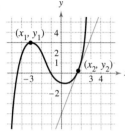

2.
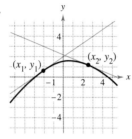

Slopes of Secant Lines In Exercises 3 and 4, use the graph shown in the figure. To print an enlarged copy of the graph, go to *MathGraphs.com*.

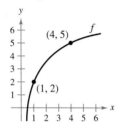

3. Copy the figure and sketch the secant line through the points. Label $f(1)$, $f(4)$, $4 - 1$, $f(4) - f(1)$, and
$$y - 2 = \frac{f(4) - f(1)}{4 - 1}(x - 1).$$

4. Insert the proper inequality symbol ($<$ or $>$) between the given quantities.

   (a) $\dfrac{f(4) - f(1)}{4 - 1}$ ___ $\dfrac{f(4) - f(3)}{4 - 3}$

   (b) $\dfrac{f(4) - f(1)}{4 - 1}$ ___ $f'(1)$

 Finding the Slope of a Tangent Line In Exercises 5–10, find the slope of the tangent line to the graph of the function at the given point.

5. $f(x) = 3 - 5x$, $(-1, 8)$
6. $g(x) = \frac{3}{2}x + 1$, $(-2, -2)$
7. $f(x) = 2x^2 - 3$, $(2, 5)$ **8.** $f(x) = 5 - x^2$, $(3, -4)$
9. $f(t) = 3t - t^2$, $(0, 0)$ **10.** $h(t) = t^2 + 4t$, $(1, 5)$

 Finding the Derivative by the Limit Process In Exercises 11–20, find the derivative of the function by the limit process.

11. $f(x) = 4$ **12.** $g(x) = -8$
13. $f(x) = -5x$ **14.** $f(x) = 6x - 2$
15. $f(x) = x^2 - 3$ **16.** $f(x) = x^2 + x - 5$
17. $f(x) = x^3 - 12x$ **18.** $g(t) = t^3 + 4t$
19. $f(x) = \dfrac{1}{x - 1}$ **20.** $f(x) = \dfrac{1}{x^2}$

 Finding an Equation of a Tangent Line In Exercises 21–28, (a) find an equation of the tangent line to the graph of f at the given point, (b) use a graphing utility to graph the function and its tangent line at the point, and (c) use the *tangent* feature of the graphing utility to confirm your results.

21. $f(x) = x^2 + 3$, $(-1, 4)$
22. $f(x) = x^2 + 2x - 1$, $(1, 2)$
23. $f(x) = x^3$, $(2, 8)$ **24.** $f(x) = x^3 + 1$, $(-1, 0)$
25. $f(x) = 2\sqrt{x}$, $(1, 2)$ **26.** $f(x) = \sqrt{x - 1}$, $(5, 2)$
27. $f(x) = x + \dfrac{4}{x}$, $(-4, -5)$
28. $f(x) = \dfrac{6}{x + 2}$, $(0, 3)$

 Finding an Equation of a Tangent Line In Exercises 29–32, find an equation of any line that is tangent to the graph of f and parallel to the given line.

Function	*Line*
29. $f(x) = -\frac{1}{4}x^2$	$x + y = 0$
30. $f(x) = 2x^2$	$4x + y + 3 = 0$
31. $f(x) = x^3$	$3x - y + 1 = 0$
32. $f(x) = \dfrac{1}{\sqrt{x - 1}}$	$x + 2y + 7 = 0$

The Derivative of a Function Given by a Table In Exercises 33–36, the table shows $f(x)$ for several values of x, where f is a differentiable function of x on the interval $[0, 80]$. Estimate the instantaneous rate of change of f at the given value of x.

x	0	20	40	60	80
$f(x)$	4	32	44	40	20

33. $x = 10$ **34.** $x = 30$
35. $x = 50$ **36.** $x = 40$

Sketching a Derivative In Exercises 37–42, sketch the graph of f'. Explain how you found your answer. To print an enlarged copy of the graph, go to *MathGraphs.com*.

37.
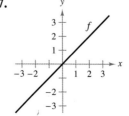

38.
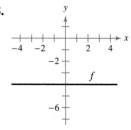

39.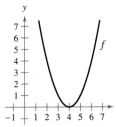

40.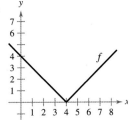

41.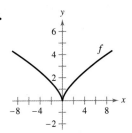

42.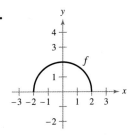

EXPLORING CONCEPTS

43. Sketching a Graph Sketch a graph of a function whose derivative is always negative. Explain how you found the answer.

44. Sketching a Graph Sketch a graph of a function whose derivative is zero at exactly two points. Explain how you found the answer.

45. Using a Tangent Line The tangent line to the graph of $y = g(x)$ at the point $(4, 5)$ passes through the point $(7, 0)$. Find $g(4)$ and $g'(4)$.

46. Using a Tangent Line The tangent line to the graph of $y = h(x)$ at the point $(-1, 4)$ passes through the point $(3, 6)$. Find $h(-1)$ and $h'(-1)$.

 Working Backwards In Exercises 47–50, the limit represents $f'(c)$ for a function f and a number c. Find f and c.

47. $\lim\limits_{\Delta x \to 0} \dfrac{[5 - 3(1 + \Delta x)] - 2}{\Delta x}$

48. $\lim\limits_{\Delta x \to 0} \dfrac{(-2 + \Delta x)^3 + 8}{\Delta x}$

49. $\lim\limits_{x \to 6} \dfrac{-x^2 + 36}{x - 6}$

50. $\lim\limits_{x \to 9} \dfrac{2\sqrt{x} - 6}{x - 9}$

Writing a Function Using Derivatives In Exercises 51 and 52, identify a function f that has the given characteristics. Then sketch the function.

51. $f(0) = 2$

$f'(x) = -3$ for $-\infty < x < \infty$

52. $f(0) = 4$

$f'(0) = 0$

$f'(x) < 0$ for $x < 0$

$f'(x) > 0$ for $x > 0$

Finding an Equation of a Tangent Line In Exercises 53 and 54, find equations of the two tangent lines to the graph of f that pass through the indicated point.

53. $f(x) = 4x - x^2$

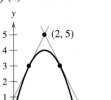

54. $f(x) = x^2$

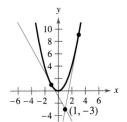

55. Symmetry of a Graph A function f is symmetric with respect to the origin. Is f' necessarily symmetric with respect to the origin? Explain.

56. HOW DO YOU SEE IT? The figure shows the graph of g'.

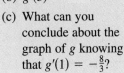

(a) $g'(0) = $ ▢

(b) $g'(3) = $ ▢

(c) What can you conclude about the graph of g knowing that $g'(1) = -\frac{8}{3}$?

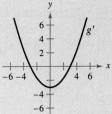

(d) What can you conclude about the graph of g knowing that $g'(-4) = \frac{7}{3}$?

(e) Is $g(6) - g(4)$ positive or negative? Explain.

(f) Is it possible to find $g(2)$ from the graph? Explain.

57. Connecting Representations Consider the function $f(x) = \frac{1}{2}x^2$.

(a) Use a graphing utility to graph the function and estimate the values of $f'(0)$, $f'(\frac{1}{2})$, $f'(1)$, $f'(2)$, and $f'(3)$.

(b) Use your results from part (a) to determine the values of $f'(-\frac{1}{2})$, $f'(-1)$, $f'(-2)$, and $f'(-3)$.

(c) Sketch a possible graph of f'.

(d) Use the definition of derivative to find $f'(x)$.

58. Connecting Representations Consider the function $f(x) = \frac{1}{3}x^3$.

(a) Use a graphing utility to graph the function and estimate the values of $f'(0)$, $f'(\frac{1}{2})$, $f'(1)$, $f'(2)$, and $f'(3)$.

(b) Use your results from part (a) to determine the values of $f'(-\frac{1}{2})$, $f'(-1)$, $f'(-2)$, and $f'(-3)$.

(c) Sketch a possible graph of f'.

(d) Use the definition of derivative to find $f'(x)$.

Implementing Processes In Exercises 59 and 60, evaluate $f(2)$ and $f(2.1)$ and use the results to approximate $f'(2)$.

59. $f(x) = x(4 - x)$ **60.** $f(x) = \frac{1}{4}x^3$

 Using the Alternative Form of the Derivative In Exercises 61–70, use the alternative form of the derivative to find the derivative at $x = c$ (if it exists).

61. $f(x) = x^2 - 5$, $c = 3$ **62.** $g(x) = x^2 - x$, $c = 1$

63. $f(x) = x^3 + 2x^2 + 1$, $c = -2$

64. $f(x) = x^3 + 6x$, $c = 2$

65. $g(x) = \sqrt{|x|}$, $c = 0$ **66.** $f(x) = 3/x$, $c = 4$

67. $f(x) = (x - 6)^{2/3}$, $c = 6$

68. $g(x) = (x + 3)^{1/3}$, $c = -3$

69. $h(x) = |x + 7|$, $c = -7$

70. $f(x) = |x - 6|$, $c = 6$

 Determining Differentiability In Exercises 71–74, describe the x-values at which f is differentiable.

71. $f(x) = \dfrac{x^2}{x^2 - 4}$ **72.** $f(x) = |x^2 - 9|$

73. $f(x) = (x + 4)^{2/3}$ **74.** $f(x) = \begin{cases} x^2 - 4, & x \leq 0 \\ 4 - x^2, & x > 0 \end{cases}$

Graphical Reasoning In Exercises 75–78, use a graphing utility to graph the function and find the x-values at which f is differentiable.

75. $f(x) = |x - 5|$ **76.** $f(x) = \dfrac{4x}{x - 3}$

77. $f(x) = x^{2/5}$

78. $f(x) = \begin{cases} x^3 - 3x^2 + 3x, & x \leq 1 \\ x^2 - 2x, & x > 1 \end{cases}$

 Determining Differentiability In Exercises 79–82, find the derivatives from the left and from the right at $x = 1$ (if they exist). Is the function differentiable at $x = 1$?

79. $f(x) = |x - 1|$ **80.** $f(x) = \sqrt{1 - x^2}$

81. $f(x) = \begin{cases} (x - 1)^3, & x \leq 1 \\ (x - 1)^2, & x > 1 \end{cases}$

82. $f(x) = (1 - x)^{2/3}$

Determining Differentiability In Exercises 83 and 84, determine whether the function is differentiable at $x = 2$.

83. $f(x) = \begin{cases} x^2 + 1, & x \leq 2 \\ 4x - 3, & x > 2 \end{cases}$

84. $f(x) = \begin{cases} \frac{1}{2}x + 2, & x < 2 \\ \sqrt{2x}, & x \geq 2 \end{cases}$

85. Greatest Integer Function and Differentiability Use a graphing utility to graph $g(x) = [\![x]\!]/x$. Then let $f(x) = [\![x]\!]$ and show that

$$\lim_{x \to 0^-} \frac{f(x) - f(0)}{x - 0} = \infty \quad \text{and} \quad \lim_{x \to 0^+} \frac{f(x) - f(0)}{x - 0} = 0.$$

Describe the x-values at which f is differentiable.

86. Differentiability and Continuity Let

$$f(x) = \begin{cases} x \sin \dfrac{1}{x}, & x \neq 0 \\ 0, & x = 0 \end{cases} \quad \text{and} \quad g(x) = \begin{cases} x^2 \sin \dfrac{1}{x}, & x \neq 0 \\ 0, & x = 0 \end{cases}.$$

Show that f is continuous, but not differentiable, at $x = 0$. Show that g is differentiable at 0, and find $g'(0)$.

Calculus AP® – Exam Preparation Questions

87. Multiple Choice $\displaystyle\lim_{x \to 2} \frac{\ln(x + 4) - \ln 6}{x - 2}$ is

(A) 0.

(B) $f'(2)$, where $f(x) = \ln(x + 4)$.

(C) $\dfrac{d}{dx}[\ln(x + 4)]$.

(D) nonexistent.

88. Multiple Choice The graph of a piecewise function g is shown. The graph has a vertical tangent line at $x = -3$. What are the values of x on the interval $(-4, 4)$ at which g is continuous but not differentiable?

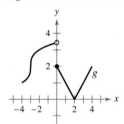

(A) $-3, 0$ (B) $-3, 0, 2$

(C) $-3, 2$ (D) $0, 2$

89. Multiple Choice The graph of f' shows the derivative of which function f?

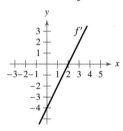

(A) $f(x) = x^2 - 4$

(B) $f(x) = x^3 - 2x + 1$

(C) $f(x) = x^2 + 4x + 1$

(D) $f(x) = x^2 - 4x + 1$

2.2 Basic Differentiation Rules and Rates of Change

▶ Find the derivative of a function using the Constant Rule.
▶ Find the derivative of a function using the Power Rule.
▶ Find the derivative of a function using the Constant Multiple Rule.
▶ Find the derivative of a function using the Sum and Difference Rules.
▶ Find the derivatives of the sine function and of the cosine function.
▶ Find the derivatives of exponential functions.
▶ Use derivatives to find rates of change.

The Constant Rule

In Section 2.1, you used the limit definition to find derivatives. In this and the next two sections, you will be introduced to several "differentiation rules" that allow you to find derivatives without the *direct* use of the limit definition.

Theorem 2.2 The Constant Rule

The derivative of a constant function is 0. That is, if c is a real number, then

$$\frac{d}{dx}[c] = 0. \qquad \text{(See Figure 2.14.)}$$

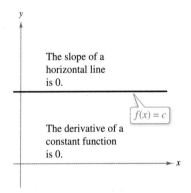

The slope of a horizontal line is 0.

$f(x) = c$

The derivative of a constant function is 0.

Notice that the Constant Rule is equivalent to saying that the slope of a horizontal line is 0. This demonstrates the relationship between slope and derivative.

Figure 2.14

Proof Let $f(x) = c$. Then, by the limit definition of the derivative,

$$\frac{d}{dx}[c] = f'(x)$$

$$= \lim_{\Delta x \to 0} \frac{f(x + \Delta x) - f(x)}{\Delta x}$$

$$= \lim_{\Delta x \to 0} \frac{c - c}{\Delta x}$$

$$= \lim_{\Delta x \to 0} 0$$

$$= 0.$$

EXAMPLE 1 Using the Constant Rule

Function	Derivative
a. $y = 7$	$dy/dx = 0$
b. $f(x) = 0$	$f'(x) = 0$
c. $s(t) = -3$	$s'(t) = 0$
d. $y = k\pi^2$, k is constant	$dy/dx = 0$

Exploration

Writing a Conjecture Use the definition of the derivative given in Section 2.1 to find the derivative of each function. What patterns do you see? Use your results to write a conjecture about the derivative of $f(x) = x^n$.

a. $f(x) = x^1$ **b.** $f(x) = x^2$ **c.** $f(x) = x^3$
d. $f(x) = x^4$ **e.** $f(x) = x^{1/2}$ **f.** $f(x) = x^{-1}$

The Power Rule

Before proving the next rule, it is important to review the procedure for expanding a binomial.

$(x + \Delta x)^2 = x^2 + 2x\Delta x + (\Delta x)^2$

$(x + \Delta x)^3 = x^3 + 3x^2\Delta x + 3x(\Delta x)^2 + (\Delta x)^3$

$(x + \Delta x)^4 = x^4 + 4x^3\Delta x + 6x^2(\Delta x)^2 + 4x(\Delta x)^3 + (\Delta x)^4$

$(x + \Delta x)^5 = x^5 + 5x^4\Delta x + 10x^3(\Delta x)^2 + 10x^2(\Delta x)^3 + 5x(\Delta x)^4 + (\Delta x)^5$

The general binomial expansion for a positive integer n is

$$(x + \Delta x)^n = x^n + nx^{n-1}(\Delta x) + \underbrace{\frac{n(n-1)x^{n-2}}{2}(\Delta x)^2 + \cdots + (\Delta x)^n}_{(\Delta x)^2 \text{ is a factor of these terms.}}.$$

This binomial expansion is used in proving a special case of the Power Rule.

Theorem 2.3   The Power Rule

If n is a rational number, then the function $f(x) = x^n$ is differentiable and

$$\frac{d}{dx}[x^n] = nx^{n-1}.$$

For f to be differentiable at $x = 0$, n must be a number such that x^{n-1} is defined on an interval containing 0.

Proof   If n is a positive integer greater than 1, then the binomial expansion produces

$$\frac{d}{dx}[x^n] = \lim_{\Delta x \to 0} \frac{(x + \Delta x)^n - x^n}{\Delta x}$$

$$= \lim_{\Delta x \to 0} \frac{x^n + nx^{n-1}(\Delta x) + \dfrac{n(n-1)x^{n-2}}{2}(\Delta x)^2 + \cdots + (\Delta x)^n - x^n}{\Delta x}$$

$$= \lim_{\Delta x \to 0} \left[nx^{n-1} + \frac{n(n-1)x^{n-2}}{2}(\Delta x) + \cdots + (\Delta x)^{n-1} \right]$$

$$= nx^{n-1} + 0 + \cdots + 0$$

$$= nx^{n-1}.$$

This proves the case for which n is a positive integer greater than 1. It is left to you to prove the case for $n = 1$. Example 7 in Section 2.3 proves the case for which n is a negative integer. The cases for which n is rational and n is irrational are left as an exercise. (See Section 2.5, Exercise 82.)

When using the Power Rule, the case for which $n = 1$ is best thought of as a separate differentiation rule. That is,

$$\frac{d}{dx}[x] = 1. \qquad \text{Power Rule when } n = 1$$

This rule is consistent with the fact that the slope of the line $y = x$ is 1, as shown in Figure 2.15.

Justification

From Example 7 in Section 2.1, you know that the function $f(x) = x^{1/3}$ is defined at $x = 0$ but is not differentiable at $x = 0$. This is because $x^{-2/3}$ is not defined on an interval containing 0.

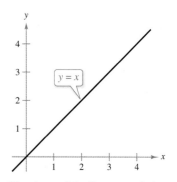

The slope of the line $y = x$ is 1.

Figure 2.15

EXAMPLE 2   Using the Power Rule

Function	Derivative

a. $f(x) = x^3$ $f'(x) = 3x^2$

b. $g(x) = \sqrt[3]{x}$ $g'(x) = \dfrac{d}{dx}[x^{1/3}] = \dfrac{1}{3}x^{-2/3} = \dfrac{1}{3x^{2/3}}$

c. $y = \dfrac{1}{x^2}$ $\dfrac{dy}{dx} = \dfrac{d}{dx}[x^{-2}] = (-2)x^{-3} = -\dfrac{2}{x^3}$

In Example 2(c), note that *before* differentiating, $1/x^2$ was rewritten as x^{-2}. Rewriting is the first step in *many* differentiation problems.

Given:	Rewrite:	Differentiation:	Simplify:
$y = \dfrac{1}{x^2}$	$y = x^{-2}$	$\dfrac{dy}{dx} = (-2)x^{-3}$	$\dfrac{dy}{dx} = -\dfrac{2}{x^3}$

EXAMPLE 3   Finding the Slope of a Graph

See LarsonCalculusforAP.com for an interactive version of this type of example.

Find the slope of the graph of $f(x) = x^4$ for each value of x.

a. $x = -1$ **b.** $x = 0$ **c.** $x = 1$

Solution

The slope of a graph at a point is the value of the derivative at that point. The derivative of f is $f'(x) = 4x^3$.

a. When $x = -1$, the slope is $f'(-1) = 4(-1)^3 = -4$.   Slope is negative.

b. When $x = 0$, the slope is $f'(0) = 4(0)^3 = 0$.   Slope is zero.

c. When $x = 1$, the slope is $f'(1) = 4(1)^3 = 4$.   Slope is positive.

See Figure 2.16.

Note that the slope of the graph is negative at the point $(-1, 1)$, the slope is zero at the point $(0, 0)$, and the slope is positive at the point $(1, 1)$.

Figure 2.16

EXAMPLE 4   Finding an Equation of a Tangent Line

See LarsonCalculusforAP.com for an interactive version of this type of example.

Find an equation of the tangent line to the graph of $f(x) = x^2$ when $x = -2$.

Algebraic Solution

To find the *point* on the graph of f, evaluate the original function at $x = -2$.

$$(-2, f(-2)) = (-2, 4)$$ Point on graph

To find the *slope* of the graph when $x = -2$, evaluate the derivative, $f'(x) = 2x$, at $x = -2$.

$$m = f'(-2) = -4$$ Slope of graph at $(-2, 4)$

Now, using the point-slope form of the equation of a line, you can write

$$y - y_1 = m(x - x_1)$$ Point-slope form

$$y - 4 = -4[x - (-2)]$$ Substitute for y_1, m, and x_1.

$$y = -4x - 4.$$ Simplify.

Graphical Solution

Use a graphing utility to graph $y = x^2$.

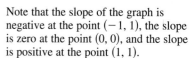

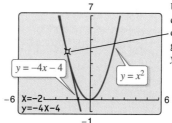

Use the *tangent* feature to determine that the equation of the tangent line to the graph of f when $x = -2$ is $y = -4x - 4$.

The line $y = -4x - 4$ is tangent to the graph of $f(x) = x^2$ at the point $(-2, 4)$.

The Constant Multiple Rule

Theorem 2.4   The Constant Multiple Rule

If f is a differentiable function and c is a real number, then cf is also differentiable and

$$\frac{d}{dx}[cf(x)] = cf'(x).$$

Proof

$$\frac{d}{dx}[cf(x)] = \lim_{\Delta x \to 0} \frac{cf(x + \Delta x) - cf(x)}{\Delta x} \qquad \text{Definition of derivative}$$

$$= \lim_{\Delta x \to 0} c\left[\frac{f(x + \Delta x) - f(x)}{\Delta x}\right]$$

$$= c\left[\lim_{\Delta x \to 0} \frac{f(x + \Delta x) - f(x)}{\Delta x}\right] \qquad \text{Apply Theorem 1.2.}$$

$$= cf'(x)$$

Informally, the Constant Multiple Rule states that constants can be factored out of the differentiation process, even when the constants appear in the denominator.

$$\frac{d}{dx}[cf(x)] = c\frac{d}{dx}[\,f(x)] = cf'(x)$$

$$\frac{d}{dx}\left[\frac{f(x)}{c}\right] = \frac{d}{dx}\left[\left(\frac{1}{c}\right)f(x)\right] = \left(\frac{1}{c}\right)\frac{d}{dx}[\,f(x)] = \left(\frac{1}{c}\right)f'(x)$$

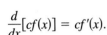 **EXAMPLE 5**   **Using the Constant Multiple Rule**

Function	*Derivative*
a. $y = 5x^3$	$\dfrac{dy}{dx} = \dfrac{d}{dx}[5x^3] = 5\dfrac{d}{dx}[x^3] = 5(3)x^2 = 15x^2$
b. $y = \dfrac{2}{x}$	$\dfrac{dy}{dx} = \dfrac{d}{dx}[2x^{-1}] = 2\dfrac{d}{dx}[x^{-1}] = 2(-1)x^{-2} = -\dfrac{2}{x^2}$
c. $f(t) = \dfrac{4t^2}{5}$	$f'(t) = \dfrac{d}{dt}\left[\dfrac{4}{5}t^2\right] = \dfrac{4}{5}\dfrac{d}{dt}[t^2] = \dfrac{4}{5}(2t) = \dfrac{8}{5}t$
d. $y = 2\sqrt{x}$	$\dfrac{dy}{dx} = \dfrac{d}{dx}[2x^{1/2}] = 2\left(\dfrac{1}{2}x^{-1/2}\right) = x^{-1/2} = \dfrac{1}{\sqrt{x}}$
e. $y = \dfrac{1}{2\sqrt[3]{x^2}}$	$y' = \dfrac{d}{dx}\left[\dfrac{1}{2}x^{-2/3}\right] = \dfrac{1}{2}\left(-\dfrac{2}{3}x^{-5/3}\right) = -\dfrac{1}{3x^{5/3}}$
f. $y = -\dfrac{3x}{2}$	$\dfrac{dy}{dx} = \dfrac{d}{dx}\left[-\dfrac{3}{2}x\right] = -\dfrac{3}{2}(1) = -\dfrac{3}{2}$

> **Implementing Processes**
>
> Before differentiating functions involving radicals, rewrite the function with rational exponents.

The Constant Multiple Rule and the Power Rule can be combined into one rule. The combination rule is

$$\frac{d}{dx}[cx^n] = cnx^{n-1}.$$

EXAMPLE 6 **Using Parentheses When Differentiating**

Original Function	Rewrite	Differentiate	Simplify
a. $y = \dfrac{5}{2x^3}$	$y = \dfrac{5}{2}(x^{-3})$	$y' = \dfrac{5}{2}(-3x^{-4})$	$y' = -\dfrac{15}{2x^4}$
b. $y = \dfrac{5}{(2x)^3}$	$y = \dfrac{5}{8}(x^{-3})$	$y' = \dfrac{5}{8}(-3x^{-4})$	$y' = -\dfrac{15}{8x^4}$
c. $y = \dfrac{7}{3x^{-2}}$	$y = \dfrac{7}{3}(x^2)$	$y' = \dfrac{7}{3}(2x)$	$y' = \dfrac{14x}{3}$
d. $y = \dfrac{7}{(3x)^{-2}}$	$y = 63(x^2)$	$y' = 63(2x)$	$y' = 126x$

The Sum and Difference Rules

Theorem 2.5 The Sum and Difference Rules

The sum (or difference) of two differentiable functions f and g is itself differentiable. Moreover, the derivative of $f + g$ (or $f - g$) is the sum (or difference) of the derivatives of f and g.

$$\frac{d}{dx}[f(x) + g(x)] = f'(x) + g'(x) \qquad \text{Sum Rule}$$

$$\frac{d}{dx}[f(x) - g(x)] = f'(x) - g'(x) \qquad \text{Difference Rule}$$

Proof   A proof of the Sum Rule follows from Theorem 1.2. (The Difference Rule can be proved in a similar way.)

$$\frac{d}{dx}[f(x) + g(x)] = \lim_{\Delta x \to 0} \frac{[f(x + \Delta x) + g(x + \Delta x)] - [f(x) + g(x)]}{\Delta x}$$

$$= \lim_{\Delta x \to 0} \frac{f(x + \Delta x) + g(x + \Delta x) - f(x) - g(x)}{\Delta x}$$

$$= \lim_{\Delta x \to 0} \left[\frac{f(x + \Delta x) - f(x)}{\Delta x} + \frac{g(x + \Delta x) - g(x)}{\Delta x} \right]$$

$$= \lim_{\Delta x \to 0} \frac{f(x + \Delta x) - f(x)}{\Delta x} + \lim_{\Delta x \to 0} \frac{g(x + \Delta x) - g(x)}{\Delta x}$$

$$= f'(x) + g'(x)$$

The Sum and Difference Rules can be extended to any finite number of functions. For instance, if $F(x) = f(x) + g(x) - h(x)$, then $F'(x) = f'(x) + g'(x) - h'(x)$.

EXAMPLE 7 **Using the Sum and Difference Rules**

Function	Derivative
a. $f(x) = x^3 - 4x + 5$	$f'(x) = 3x^2 - 4$
b. $g(x) = -\dfrac{x^4}{2} + 3x^3 - 2x$	$g'(x) = -2x^3 + 9x^2 - 2$
c. $y = \dfrac{3x^2 - x + 1}{x} = 3x - 1 + \dfrac{1}{x}$	$y' = 3 - \dfrac{1}{x^2} = \dfrac{3x^2 - 1}{x^2}$

Implementing Processes

In Example 7(c), note that before differentiating,

$$\frac{3x^2 - x + 1}{x}$$

was rewritten as

$$3x - 1 + \frac{1}{x}.$$

Derivatives of the Sine and Cosine Functions

In Section 1.3, you studied the limits

$$\lim_{\Delta x \to 0} \frac{\sin \Delta x}{\Delta x} = 1 \quad \text{and} \quad \lim_{\Delta x \to 0} \frac{1 - \cos \Delta x}{\Delta x} = 0.$$

These two limits can be used to prove differentiation rules for the sine and cosine functions. (See Section 2.3 for the derivatives of the other trigonometric functions.)

Theorem 2.6 Derivatives of Sine and Cosine Functions

$$\frac{d}{dx}[\sin x] = \cos x \qquad \frac{d}{dx}[\cos x] = -\sin x$$

Proof Here is a proof of the first rule. (The proof of the second rule is left as an exercise. [See Exercise 118.]) In the proof, note the use of the trigonometric identity $\sin(x + \Delta x) = \sin x \cos \Delta x + \cos x \sin \Delta x$.

$$\frac{d}{dx}[\sin x] = \lim_{\Delta x \to 0} \frac{\sin(x + \Delta x) - \sin x}{\Delta x} \qquad \text{Definition of derivative}$$

$$= \lim_{\Delta x \to 0} \frac{\sin x \cos \Delta x + \cos x \sin \Delta x - \sin x}{\Delta x}$$

$$= \lim_{\Delta x \to 0} \frac{\cos x \sin \Delta x - (\sin x)(1 - \cos \Delta x)}{\Delta x}$$

$$= \lim_{\Delta x \to 0} \left[(\cos x)\left(\frac{\sin \Delta x}{\Delta x} \right) - (\sin x)\left(\frac{1 - \cos \Delta x}{\Delta x} \right) \right]$$

$$= (\cos x)\left(\lim_{\Delta x \to 0} \frac{\sin \Delta x}{\Delta x} \right) - (\sin x)\left(\lim_{\Delta x \to 0} \frac{1 - \cos \Delta x}{\Delta x} \right)$$

$$= (\cos x)(1) - (\sin x)(0)$$

$$= \cos x$$

This differentiation rule is shown graphically in Figure 2.17. Note that for each x, the *slope* of the sine curve is equal to the value of the cosine.

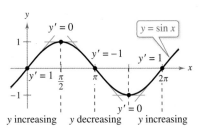

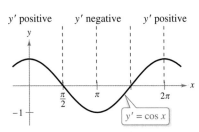

The derivative of the sine function is the cosine function.

Figure 2.17

EXAMPLE 8 Derivatives Involving Sines and Cosines

See LarsonCalculusforAP.com for an interactive version of this type of example.

	Function	*Derivative*
a.	$y = 2 \sin x$	$y' = 2 \cos x$
b.	$y = \dfrac{\sin x}{2} = \dfrac{1}{2} \sin x$	$y' = \dfrac{1}{2} \cos x = \dfrac{\cos x}{2}$
c.	$y = x + \cos x$	$y' = 1 - \sin x$
d.	$y = \cos x - \dfrac{\pi}{3} \sin x$	$y' = -\sin x - \dfrac{\pi}{3} \cos x$

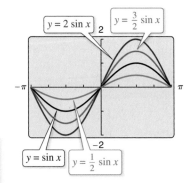

$$\frac{d}{dx}[a \sin x] = a \cos x$$

Figure 2.18

Technology

A graphing utility can provide insight into the interpretation of a derivative. For instance, Figure 2.18 shows the graphs of $y = a \sin x$ for $a = \frac{1}{2}$, 1, $\frac{3}{2}$, and 2. Estimate the slope of each graph at the point $(0, 0)$. Then verify your estimates analytically by evaluating the derivative of each function when $x = 0$.

Derivatives of Exponential Functions

One of the most intriguing (and useful) characteristics of the natural exponential function is that *it is its own derivative*. Consider the following argument.

Let $f(x) = e^x$.

$$f'(x) = \lim_{\Delta x \to 0} \frac{f(x + \Delta x) - f(x)}{\Delta x}$$

$$= \lim_{\Delta x \to 0} \frac{e^{x + \Delta x} - e^x}{\Delta x}$$

$$= \lim_{\Delta x \to 0} \frac{e^x(e^{\Delta x} - 1)}{\Delta x}$$

The definition of e

$$\lim_{\Delta x \to 0} (1 + \Delta x)^{1/\Delta x} = e$$

tells you that for small values of Δx, you have $e \approx (1 + \Delta x)^{1/\Delta x}$, which implies that

$$e^{\Delta x} \approx 1 + \Delta x.$$

Replacing $e^{\Delta x}$ by this approximation produces the following.

$$f'(x) = \lim_{\Delta x \to 0} \frac{e^x[e^{\Delta x} - 1]}{\Delta x}$$

$$= \lim_{\Delta x \to 0} \frac{e^x[(1 + \Delta x) - 1]}{\Delta x}$$

$$= \lim_{\Delta x \to 0} \frac{e^x \Delta x}{\Delta x}$$

$$= e^x$$

This result is stated in the next theorem.

> **Theorem 2.7   Derivative of the Natural Exponential Function**
>
> $$\frac{d}{dx}[e^x] = e^x$$

> **Justification**
>
> The key to the formula for the derivative of $f(x) = e^x$ is the limit
>
> $$\lim_{x \to 0} (1 + x)^{1/x} = e.$$
>
> This important limit was introduced on page 48 and formalized later on page 82. It is used to conclude that for $\Delta x \approx 0$,
>
> $$(1 + \Delta x)^{1/\Delta x} \approx e.$$

You can interpret Theorem 2.7 graphically by saying that the slope of the graph of $f(x) = e^x$ at any point (x, e^x) is equal to the y-coordinate of the point, as shown in Figure 2.19.

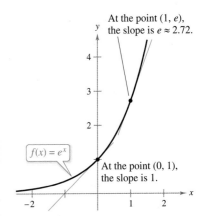

At the point $(1, e)$, the slope is $e \approx 2.72$.

$f(x) = e^x$

At the point $(0, 1)$, the slope is 1.

Figure 2.19

EXAMPLE 9   Derivatives Involving Exponential Functions

Find the derivative of each function.

a. $f(x) = 3e^x$

b. $f(x) = x^2 + e^x$

c. $f(x) = \sin x - e^x$

Solution

a. $f'(x) = 3\frac{d}{dx}[e^x] = 3e^x$

b. $f'(x) = \frac{d}{dx}[x^2] + \frac{d}{dx}[e^x] = 2x + e^x$

c. $f'(x) = \frac{d}{dx}[\sin x] - \frac{d}{dx}[e^x] = \cos x - e^x$

Rates of Change

You have seen how the derivative is used to determine slope. The derivative can also be used to determine the rate of change of one variable with respect to another. Applications involving rates of change, sometimes referred to as instantaneous rates of change, occur in a wide variety of fields. A few examples are population growth rates, production rates, water flow rates, velocity, and acceleration.

A common use for rate of change is to describe the motion of an object moving in a straight line. In such problems, it is customary to use either a horizontal or a vertical line with a designated origin to represent the line of motion. On such lines, movement to the right (or upward) is considered to be in the positive direction, and movement to the left (or downward) is considered to be in the negative direction.

The function s that gives the position (relative to the origin) of an object as a function of time t is called a **position function.** If, over a period of time Δt, the object changes its position by the amount

$$\Delta s = s(t + \Delta t) - s(t)$$

then, by the familiar formula

$$\text{Rate} = \frac{\text{distance}}{\text{time}}$$

the **average velocity** is

$$\underbrace{\frac{\text{Change in distance}}{\text{Change in time}} = \frac{\Delta s}{\Delta t}.}_{}\qquad \text{Average velocity}$$

> ### Connecting Representations
> The change in position Δs is also called the *displacement* of an object over the time interval from t to $t + \Delta t$.

EXAMPLE 10   Finding Average Velocity of a Falling Object

A billiard ball is dropped from a height of 100 feet. The ball's height s at time t is the position function

$$s = -16t^2 + 100 \qquad \text{Position function}$$

where s is measured in feet and t is measured in seconds. Find the average velocity over each time interval.

a. $[1, 2]$ **b.** $[1, 1.5]$ **c.** $[1, 1.1]$

Solution

a. For the interval $[1, 2]$, the object falls from a height of $s(1) = -16(1)^2 + 100 = 84$ feet to a height of $s(2) = -16(2)^2 + 100 = 36$ feet. The average velocity is

$$\frac{\Delta s}{\Delta t} = \frac{36 - 84}{2 - 1} = \frac{-48}{1} = -48 \text{ feet per second.}$$

b. For the interval $[1, 1.5]$, the object falls from a height of 84 feet to a height of $s(1.5) = -16(1.5)^2 + 100 = 64$ feet. The average velocity is

$$\frac{\Delta s}{\Delta t} = \frac{64 - 84}{1.5 - 1} = \frac{-20}{0.5} = -40 \text{ feet per second.}$$

c. For the interval $[1, 1.1]$, the object falls from a height of 84 feet to a height of $s(1.1) = -16(1.1)^2 + 100 = 80.64$ feet. The average velocity is

$$\frac{\Delta s}{\Delta t} = \frac{80.64 - 84}{1.1 - 1} = \frac{-3.36}{0.1} = -33.6 \text{ feet per second.}$$

Note that the average velocities are *negative*, indicating that the object is moving downward. ◼

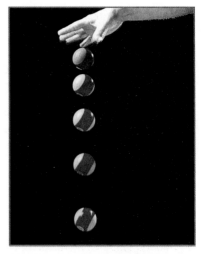

Time-lapse photograph of a free-falling billiard ball

> ### Insight
> On the AP® Exam, be sure to include appropriate units in your solution when applicable. You may not earn a point on a free-response question when you fail to include units with your solution.

Suppose that in Example 10, you wanted to find the *instantaneous* velocity (or simply the velocity) of the object when $t = 1$. Just as you can approximate the slope of the tangent line by calculating the slope of the secant line, you can approximate the velocity at $t = 1$ by calculating the average velocity over a small interval $[1, 1 + \Delta t]$. (See Figure 2.20.) By taking the limit as Δt approaches zero, you obtain the velocity when $t = 1$. Try doing this—you will find that the velocity when $t = 1$ is -32 feet per second.

In general, if $s = s(t)$ is the position function for an object moving along a straight line, then the **velocity** of the object at time t is

$$v(t) = \lim_{\Delta t \to 0} \frac{s(t + \Delta t) - s(t)}{\Delta t} = s'(t).$$ Velocity function

In other words, the velocity function is the derivative of the position function. Velocity can be negative, zero, or positive. The **speed** of an object is the absolute value of its velocity. Speed cannot be negative.

The position of a free-falling object (neglecting air resistance) under the influence of gravity can be represented by the equation

$$s(t) = -\frac{1}{2}gt^2 + v_0 t + s_0$$ Position function

where s_0 is the initial height of the object, v_0 is the initial velocity of the object, and g is the acceleration due to gravity. On Earth, the value of g is approximately 32 feet per second per second or 9.8 meters per second per second.

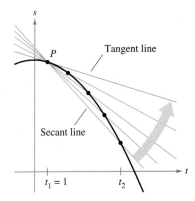

The average velocity between t_1 and t_2 is the slope of the secant line, and the instantaneous velocity at t_1 is the slope of the tangent line.

Figure 2.20

EXAMPLE 11   Using the Derivative to Find Velocity

At time $t = 0$ seconds, a diver jumps from a platform diving board that is 32 feet above the water (see Figure 2.21). The initial velocity of the diver is 16 feet per second. When does the diver hit the water? What is the diver's velocity at impact?

Solution

Begin by writing an equation to represent the position of the diver. Using the position function given above with $g = 32$ feet per second per second, $v_0 = 16$ feet per second, and $s_0 = 32$ feet, you can write

$$s(t) = -\frac{1}{2}(32)t^2 + 16t + 32$$

$$= -16t^2 + 16t + 32.$$ Position function

To find the time t when the diver hits the water, let $s = 0$ and solve for t.

$-16t^2 + 16t + 32 = 0$	Set position function equal to 0.
$-16(t + 1)(t - 2) = 0$	Factor.
$t = -1$ or 2	Solve for t.

Because $t \geq 0$, choose the positive value to conclude that the diver hits the water at $t = 2$ seconds. The velocity at time t is given by the derivative

$$s'(t) = -32t + 16.$$ Velocity function

So, the velocity at time $t = 2$ is

$$s'(2) = -32(2) + 16 = -48 \text{ feet per second.}$$

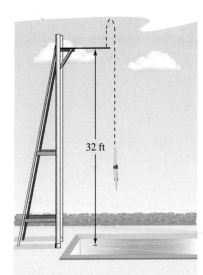

Velocity is positive when an object is rising and is negative when an object is falling. Notice that the diver moves upward for the first half-second because the velocity is positive for $0 < t < \frac{1}{2}$. When the velocity is 0, the diver has reached the maximum height of the dive.

Figure 2.21

In Example 11, notice that the unit for $s'(t)$ is the unit for s (feet) divided by the unit for t (seconds). In general, the unit for $f'(x)$ is the unit for f divided by the unit for x.

2.2 Exercises

See *CalcChat.com* for tutorial help and worked-out solutions to odd-numbered exercises.

Estimating Slope In Exercises 1 and 2, use the graph to estimate the slope of the tangent line to $y = x^n$ at the point $(1, 1)$. **Verify your answer analytically. To print an enlarged copy of the graph, go to *MathGraphs.com*.**

1. (a) $y = x^{1/2}$

(b) $y = x^3$

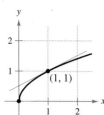

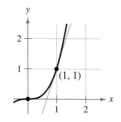

2. (a) $y = x^{-1}$

(b) $y = x^{-1/2}$

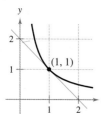

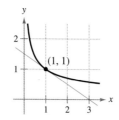

Finding a Derivative In Exercises 3–26, use the rules of differentiation to find the derivative of the function.

3. $y = 12$

4. $f(x) = -9$

5. $y = x^7$

6. $y = x^{12}$

7. $y = \dfrac{1}{x^5}$

8. $y = \dfrac{3}{x^7}$

9. $f(x) = \sqrt[5]{x}$

10. $g(x) = \sqrt[4]{x}$

11. $f(x) = x + 11$

12. $g(x) = 6x + 3$

13. $f(t) = -3t^2 + 2t - 4$

14. $y = t^2 - 3t + 1$

15. $g(x) = x^2 + 4x^3$

16. $y = 4x - 3x^3$

17. $y = 2x^3 + 6x^2 - 1$

18. $s(t) = t^3 + 5t^2 - 3t + 8$

19. $y = \dfrac{\pi}{2} \sin \theta - \cos \theta$

20. $g(t) = \pi \cos t$

21. $y = x^2 - \tfrac{1}{2} \cos x$

22. $y = 7 + \sin x$

23. $y = x^4 - 12e^x$

24. $y = 1/x + e^x - 1$

25. $y = \tfrac{1}{2}e^x - 3 \sin x$

26. $y = \tfrac{3}{4}e^x + 2 \cos x$

Rewriting a Function Before Differentiating In Exercises 27–32, complete the table to find the derivative of the function.

Original Function	Rewrite	Differentiate	Simplify
27. $y = \dfrac{2}{7x^4}$			
28. $y = \dfrac{5}{2x^2}$			

Original Function	Rewrite	Differentiate	Simplify
29. $y = \dfrac{6}{(5x)^3}$			
30. $y = \dfrac{\pi}{(3x)^2}$			
31. $y = \dfrac{\sqrt{x}}{x}$			
32. $y = \dfrac{4x^{-3}}{\sqrt{x}}$			

Finding the Slope of a Graph In Exercises 33–40, find the slope of the graph of the function at the given point. Use the *derivative* feature of a graphing utility to confirm your results.

33. $f(x) = \dfrac{8}{x^2}$, $(2, 2)$

34. $f(t) = 2 - \dfrac{4}{t}$, $(4, 1)$

35. $y = 2x^4 - 3$, $(1, -1)$

36. $f(x) = 2(x - 4)^2$, $(2, 8)$

37. $f(\theta) = 4 \sin \theta - \theta$, $(0, 0)$

38. $g(t) = -2 \cos t + 5$, $(\pi, 7)$

39. $f(t) = \tfrac{3}{4}e^t$, $\left(0, \tfrac{3}{4}\right)$

40. $g(x) = -4e^x$, $(1, -4e)$

Finding a Derivative In Exercises 41–54, find the derivative of the function.

41. $g(t) = t^2 - \dfrac{2}{t^3}$

42. $f(x) = 3x + \dfrac{8}{x^2}$

43. $f(x) = \dfrac{3x^3 + 4x^2}{x}$

44. $f(x) = \dfrac{4x - 2}{\sqrt{x}}$

45. $f(x) = \dfrac{x^3 - 4x^2 + 3}{x^2}$

46. $h(x) = \dfrac{5x^3 + 4x + 2}{x}$

47. $y = x(x^2 + 1)$

48. $y = x^2(3x^2 - 2x)$

49. $f(x) = \sqrt{x} - 4\sqrt[3]{x}$

50. $f(t) = t^{2/3} - t^{1/3} + 6$

51. $f(x) = 5\sqrt{x} + 6 \cos x$

52. $f(x) = \dfrac{3}{\sqrt[3]{x}} + 2 \cos x$

53. $f(x) = x^{-2} - 3e^x$

54. $g(x) = \sqrt{x} - 2e^x$

Error Analysis In Exercises 55 and 56, describe and correct the error when finding the derivatives of the functions

$$y = \dfrac{7}{4\sqrt[4]{x^3}} \quad \text{and} \quad g(x) = \dfrac{6}{x^{-5}} - 2\pi \cos x + \dfrac{3}{4}e^x.$$

55. $\dfrac{dy}{dx} = \dfrac{d}{dx}\left[\dfrac{7}{4}x^{3/4}\right] = \dfrac{7}{4}\left(\dfrac{3}{4}x^{-1/4}\right) = \dfrac{21}{16x^{1/4}}$ ✗

56. $g'(x) = \dfrac{d}{dx}\left[6x^5 - 2\pi \cos x + \dfrac{3}{4}e^x\right]$

$= 30x^4 - 2\pi \sin x + \dfrac{3}{4}e^x$

Finding an Equation of a Tangent Line In Exercises 57–62, (a) find an equation of the tangent line to the graph of f at the given point, (b) use a graphing utility to graph the function and its tangent line at the point, and (c) use the *tangent* feature of a graphing utility to confirm your results.

Function	Point
57. $y = -2x^4 + 5x^2 - 3$	$(1, 0)$
58. $y = x^3 + 2x^2 + 1$	$(-1, 2)$
59. $y = 3\sqrt[3]{x}$	$(-8, -6)$
60. $f(x) = \dfrac{2}{\sqrt[4]{x^3}}$	$(1, 2)$
61. $g(x) = x + e^x$	$(0, 1)$
62. $h(t) = \sin t + \frac{1}{2}e^t$	$(\pi, \frac{1}{2}e^\pi)$

 Horizontal Tangent Line In Exercises 63–70, determine the point(s) (if any) at which the graph of the function has a horizontal tangent line.

63. $y = x^4 - 2x^2 + 3$ 64. $y = x^3 + x$

65. $y = 1/x^2$ 66. $y = x^2 + 9$

67. $y = -4x + e^x$ 68. $y = x + 4e^x$

69. $y = x + \sin x, \quad 0 \le x < 2\pi$

70. $y = \sqrt{3}x + 2\cos x, \quad 0 \le x < 2\pi$

71. **Sketching a Graph** Sketch the graph of a function f such that $f'(x) > 0$ for all x and the rate of change of the function is decreasing.

 72. HOW DO YOU SEE IT? Use the graph of f to answer each question. To print an enlarged copy of the graph, go to *MathGraphs.com*.

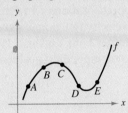

(a) Between which two consecutive points is the average rate of change of the function greatest?

(b) Is the average rate of change of the function between A and B greater than or less than the instantaneous rate of change at B?

(c) Sketch a tangent line to the graph between C and D such that the slope of the tangent line is the same as the average rate of change of the function between C and D.

 Finding a Value In Exercises 73–78, find k such that the line is tangent to the graph of the function.

Function	Line
73. $f(x) = k - x^2$	$y = -6x + 1$
74. $f(x) = kx^2$	$y = -2x + 3$
75. $f(x) = \dfrac{k}{x}$	$y = -\dfrac{3}{4}x + 3$
76. $f(x) = k\sqrt{x}$	$y = x + 4$
77. $f(x) = kx^3$	$y = x + 1$
78. $f(x) = kx^4$	$y = 4x - 1$

EXPLORING CONCEPTS

Connecting Representations In Exercises 79 and 80, the relationship between f and g is given. Explain the relationship between f' and g'.

79. $g(x) = f(x) + 6$ 80. $g(x) = 3f(x) - 1$

Communication and Notation In Exercises 81 and 82, the graphs of a function f and its derivative f' are shown on the same set of coordinate axes. Label the graphs as f or f'. Explain your reasoning. To print an enlarged copy of the graph, go to *MathGraphs.com*.

81. 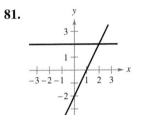   82.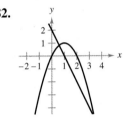

83. **Finding Equations of Tangent Lines** Find equations of the two lines that are tangent to the graphs of both $y = x^2$ and $y = -x^2 + 6x - 5$.

84. **Tangent Lines** Show that the graphs of the two equations $y = x$ and $y = 1/x$ have tangent lines that are perpendicular to each other at their points of intersection.

85. **Tangent Line** Show that the graph of the function $f(x) = 3x + \sin x + 2$ does not have a horizontal tangent line.

86. **Tangent Line** Show that the graph of the function $f(x) = x^5 + 3x^3 + 5x$ does not have a tangent line with a slope of 3.

Finding an Equation of a Tangent Line In Exercises 87 and 88, find an equation of the tangent line to the graph of the function f through the point (x_0, y_0) not on the graph. [*Hint:* To find the point of tangency (x, y), solve the equation $f'(x) = (y_0 - y)/(x_0 - x)$.]

87. $f(x) = \sqrt{x}$ 88. $f(x) = \dfrac{2}{x}$

$(x_0, y_0) = (-4, 0)$ $(x_0, y_0) = (5, 0)$

89. Connecting Representations Use a graphing utility with a square window setting to zoom in on the graph of $f(x) = 4 - \frac{1}{2}x^2$ and approximate $f'(1)$. Then use the derivative to find $f'(1)$ analytically. Compare your results.

90. Connecting Representations Use a graphing utility with a square window setting to zoom in on the graph of $f(x) = 4\sqrt{x} + 1$ and approximate $f'(4)$. Then use the derivative to find $f'(4)$ analytically. Compare your results.

91. Linear Approximation Consider the function $f(x) = x^{3/2}$ with the solution point $(4, 8)$.

(a) Use a graphing utility to graph f. Use the *zoom* feature to obtain successive magnifications of the graph in the neighborhood of the point $(4, 8)$. After zooming in a few times, the graph should appear nearly linear. Use the *trace* feature to determine the coordinates of a point near $(4, 8)$. Find an equation of the secant line $S(x)$ through the two points.

(b) Find the equation of the line $T(x)$ tangent to the graph of f at $(4, 8)$. Why are the linear functions S and T nearly the same?

(c) Use a graphing utility to graph f and T on the same set of coordinate axes. Note that T is a good approximation of f when x is close to 4. What happens to the accuracy of the approximation as you move farther away from the point of tangency?

(d) Demonstrate the conclusion in part (c) by completing the table.

Δx	-3	-2	-1	-0.5	-0.1
$f(4 + \Delta x)$					
$T(4 + \Delta x)$					

Δx	0	0.1	0.5	1	2	3
$f(4 + \Delta x)$						
$T(4 + \Delta x)$						

92. Linear Approximation Repeat Exercise 91 for the function $f(x) = x^3$ and the solution point $(1, 1)$. Explain why the accuracy of the linear approximation decreases more rapidly than in Exercise 91.

Average and Instantaneous Rates of Change In Exercises 93–98, compare the average rate of change of the function over the given interval with the instantaneous rates of change at the endpoints of the interval.

93. $f(t) = 3t + 5$, $[1, 2]$ **94.** $f(t) = t^2 - 3$, $[2, 2.1]$

95. $f(x) = \dfrac{-1}{x}$, $[1, 2]$ **96.** $f(x) = \sin x$, $\left[0, \dfrac{\pi}{6}\right]$

97. $g(x) = x^2 + e^x$, $[0, 1]$ **98.** $h(x) = x^3 - 2e^x$, $[-1, 0]$

Vertical Motion In Exercises 99 and 100, use the position function $s(t) = -16t^2 + v_0t + s_0$ for free-falling objects.

99. A coin drops from the top of a 1362-foot tall building. Find (a) the average velocity on the interval $[1, 2]$, (b) the instantaneous velocities when $t = 1$ and $t = 2$, (c) the time required for the coin to reach ground level, and (d) the velocity of the coin at impact.

100. A ball is thrown straight down from the top of a 220-foot building with an initial velocity of -22 feet per second. Find (a) the average velocity on the interval $[0, 3]$, (b) the instantaneous velocity after 3 seconds, and (c) the velocity after falling 108 feet.

Vertical Motion In Exercises 101 and 102, use the position function $s(t) = -4.9t^2 + v_0t + s_0$ for free-falling objects.

101. A particle moves upward with an initial height of 0 meters and an initial velocity of 120 meters per second. What is its velocity after 5 seconds? after 10 seconds?

102. To estimate the height of a building, a stone is dropped from the top of the building into a pool of water at ground level. The splash is seen 5.6 seconds after the stone is dropped. What is the height of the building?

Connecting Representations In Exercises 103 and 104, the graph of a position function is shown. It represents the distance in miles that a person drives during a 10-minute trip. Make a sketch of the corresponding velocity function.

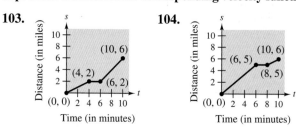

Connecting Representations In Exercises 105 and 106, the graph of a velocity function is shown. It represents the velocity in miles per hour during a 10-minute trip. Make a sketch of the corresponding position function.

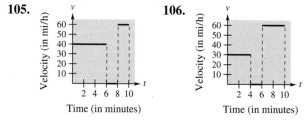

107. Volume The volume of a cube with sides of length s is given by $V = s^3$. Find the rate of change of the volume with respect to s when $s = 6$ centimeters.

108. Area The area of a square with sides of length s is given by $A = s^2$. Find the rate of change of the area with respect to s when $s = 6$ meters.

109. MODELING DATA

The stopping distance of an automobile, on dry, level pavement, traveling at a speed v (in kilometers per hour) is the distance R (in meters) the car travels during the reaction time of the driver plus the distance B (in meters) the car travels after the brakes are applied (see figure). The table shows the results of an experiment.

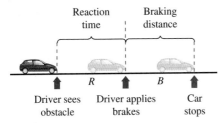

Reaction time		Braking distance		

Driver sees obstacle   Driver applies brakes   Car stops

v	20	40	60	80	100
R	8.3	16.7	25.0	33.3	41.7
B	2.3	9.0	20.2	35.8	55.9

(a) Use the regression capabilities of a graphing utility to find a linear model for reaction time distance R.

(b) Use the regression capabilities of a graphing utility to find a quadratic model for braking time distance B.

(c) Determine the polynomial giving the total stopping distance T.

(d) Use a graphing utility to graph the functions R, B, and T in the same viewing window. Discuss any similarities and differences between the graphs and their respective rates of change.

(e) Find the derivative of T and the rates of change of the total stopping distance for $v = 40$, $v = 80$, and $v = 100$.

(f) Using the results of part (e), what can you say about the total stopping distance and the corresponding rate of change as speed increases?

110. Inventory Management   The annual inventory cost C for a manufacturer is $C = (1{,}200{,}000/Q) + 17.27Q$, where Q is the order size when the inventory is replenished. Find the change in annual cost when Q is increased from 250 to 251, and compare this with the instantaneous rate of change when $Q = 250$.

111. Finding an Equation of a Parabola   Find an equation of the parabola $y = ax^2 + bx + c$ that passes through $(0, 1)$ and is tangent to the line $y = x - 1$ at $(1, 0)$.

112. Proof   Let (a, b) be an arbitrary point on the graph of $y = 1/x$, $x > 0$. Prove that the area of the triangle formed by the tangent line through (a, b) and the coordinate axes is 2.

113. Implementing Processes   Find the equation(s) of the tangent line(s) to the graph of $y = x^3 - 9x$ through the point $(1, -9)$.

114. Implementing Processes   Find the equation(s) of the tangent line(s) to the graph of $y = x^2$ through each point not on the graph. List any restrictions on a.

(a) $(0, a)$ (b) $(a, 0)$

Making a Function Differentiable   **In Exercises 115 and 116, find a and b such that f is differentiable everywhere.**

115. $f(x) = \begin{cases} ax^3, & x \le 2 \\ x^2 + b, & x > 2 \end{cases}$

116. $f(x) = \begin{cases} \cos x, & x < 0 \\ ax + b, & x \ge 0 \end{cases}$

117. Determining Differentiability   Where are the functions $f_1(x) = |\sin x|$ and $f_2(x) = \sin|x|$ differentiable?

118. Proof   Prove that $\dfrac{d}{dx}[\cos x] = -\sin x$.

Calculus AP® – Exam Preparation Questions

119. Multiple Choice   Let $f(x) = \frac{5}{2}\sqrt{x}$. The rate of change of f at $x = c$ is twice its rate of change at $x = 3$. What is the value of c?

(A) $\frac{1}{48}$ (B) $\frac{1}{3}$ (C) $\frac{3}{4}$ (D) 12

120. Multiple Choice   If $y = 6e^x - \dfrac{\pi \sin x}{4}$, $\dfrac{dy}{dx} =$

(A) $6xe^{x-1} - \dfrac{\pi}{4}\cos x$.   (B) $6e^x - \cos x$.

(C) $6e^x + \dfrac{\pi}{4}\cos x$.   (D) $6e^x - \dfrac{\pi}{4}\cos x$.

121. Multiple Choice   The position of a particle is given by $s(t) = 2\cos t + \sin t + t/\pi + 4$, where s is measured in meters and t is measured in seconds. The average velocity, in meters per second, of the particle over $[0, 2\pi]$ is

(A) $-\dfrac{1}{\pi}$.   (B) 0.   (C) $\dfrac{1}{\pi}$.   (D) $\dfrac{7}{\pi}$.

122. Free Response   The number of gallons of water in a swimming pool t minutes after it has started to drain is $f(t) = 20(t^2 - 80t + 1600)$.

(a) How fast is the water draining at the end of 5 minutes? at the end of 10 minutes?

(b) What is the average flow rate during the first 10 minutes?

2.3 Product and Quotient Rules and Higher-Order Derivatives

▶ Find the derivative of a function using the Product Rule.
▶ Find the derivative of a function using the Quotient Rule.
▶ Find the derivative of a trigonometric function.
▶ Find a higher-order derivative of a function.

The Product Rule

In Section 2.2, you learned that the derivative of the sum of two functions is simply the sum of their derivatives. The rules for the derivatives of the product and quotient of two functions are not as simple.

> **Theorem 2.8 The Product Rule**
>
> The product of two differentiable functions f and g is itself differentiable. Moreover, the derivative of fg is the first function times the derivative of the second, plus the second function times the derivative of the first.
>
> $$\frac{d}{dx}[f(x)g(x)] = f(x)g'(x) + g(x)f'(x)$$

Remark

A version of the Product Rule that some people prefer is

$$\frac{d}{dx}[f(x)g(x)]$$

$$= f'(x)g(x) + f(x)g'(x).$$

The advantage of this form is that it generalizes easily to products of three or more factors.

Proof Some mathematical proofs, such as the proof of the Sum Rule, are straightforward. Others involve clever steps that may appear unmotivated to a reader. This proof involves such a step—subtracting and adding the same quantity—which is shown in color.

$$\frac{d}{dx}[f(x)g(x)] = \lim_{\Delta x \to 0} \frac{f(x + \Delta x)g(x + \Delta x) - f(x)g(x)}{\Delta x}$$

$$= \lim_{\Delta x \to 0} \frac{f(x + \Delta x)g(x + \Delta x) - f(x + \Delta x)g(x) + f(x + \Delta x)g(x) - f(x)g(x)}{\Delta x}$$

$$= \lim_{\Delta x \to 0} \left[f(x + \Delta x)\frac{g(x + \Delta x) - g(x)}{\Delta x} + g(x)\frac{f(x + \Delta x) - f(x)}{\Delta x} \right]$$

$$= \lim_{\Delta x \to 0} \left[f(x + \Delta x)\frac{g(x + \Delta x) - g(x)}{\Delta x} \right] + \lim_{\Delta x \to 0} \left[g(x)\frac{f(x + \Delta x) - f(x)}{\Delta x} \right]$$

$$= \lim_{\Delta x \to 0} f(x + \Delta x) \cdot \lim_{\Delta x \to 0} \frac{g(x + \Delta x) - g(x)}{\Delta x} + \lim_{\Delta x \to 0} g(x) \cdot \lim_{\Delta x \to 0} \frac{f(x + \Delta x) - f(x)}{\Delta x}$$

$$= f(x)g'(x) + g(x)f'(x)$$

Note that $\lim_{\Delta x \to 0} f(x + \Delta x) = f(x)$ because f is given to be differentiable and therefore is continuous. ∎

The Product Rule can be extended to cover products involving more than two factors. For example, if f, g, and h are differentiable functions of x, then

$$\frac{d}{dx}[f(x)g(x)h(x)] = f'(x)g(x)h(x) + f(x)g'(x)h(x) + f(x)g(x)h'(x).$$

So, the derivative of $y = x^2 \sin x \cos x$ is

$$\frac{dy}{dx} = 2x \sin x \cos x + x^2 \cos x \cos x + x^2 (\sin x)(-\sin x)$$

$$= 2x \sin x \cos x + x^2(\cos^2 x - \sin^2 x).$$

Justification

The proof of the Product Rule for products of more than two factors is left as an exercise. (See Exercise 141.)

The derivative of a product of two functions is not (in general) given by the product of the derivatives of the two functions. To see this, try comparing the product of the derivatives of

$$f(x) = 3x - 2x^2$$

and

$$g(x) = 5 + 4x$$

with the derivative in Example 1.

EXAMPLE 1 Using the Product Rule

Find the derivative of

$$h(x) = (3x - 2x^2)(5 + 4x).$$

Solution

$$h'(x) = \overbrace{(3x - 2x^2)}^{\text{First}} \overbrace{\frac{d}{dx}[5 + 4x]}^{\substack{\text{Derivative} \\ \text{of second}}} + \overbrace{(5 + 4x)}^{\text{Second}} \overbrace{\frac{d}{dx}[3x - 2x^2]}^{\substack{\text{Derivative} \\ \text{of first}}} \qquad \text{Apply Product Rule.}$$

$$= (3x - 2x^2)(4) + (5 + 4x)(3 - 4x)$$

$$= (12x - 8x^2) + (15 - 8x - 16x^2)$$

$$= -24x^2 + 4x + 15$$

> **Algebra Review**
>
> For a review of simplifying algebraic expressions, see the *Chapter 2 Algebra Review* on pages A38 and A39.

In Example 1, you have the option of finding the derivative with or without the Product Rule. To find the derivative without the Product Rule, you can write

$$D_x[(3x - 2x^2)(5 + 4x)] = D_x[-8x^3 + 2x^2 + 15x]$$

$$= -24x^2 + 4x + 15.$$

In the next example, you must use the Product Rule.

EXAMPLE 2 Using the Product Rule

Find the derivative of

$$y = xe^x.$$

Solution

$$\frac{d}{dx}[xe^x] = x\frac{d}{dx}[e^x] + e^x\frac{d}{dx}[x] \qquad \text{Apply Product Rule.}$$

$$= xe^x + e^x(1)$$

$$= e^x(x + 1)$$

EXAMPLE 3 Using the Product Rule

Find the derivative of $y = 2x \cos x - 2 \sin x$.

Solution

$$\frac{dy}{dx} = \overbrace{(2x)\left(\frac{d}{dx}[\cos x]\right) + (\cos x)\left(\frac{d}{dx}[2x]\right)}^{\text{Product Rule}} - \overbrace{2\frac{d}{dx}[\sin x]}^{\text{Constant Multiple Rule}}$$

$$= (2x)(-\sin x) + (\cos x)(2) - 2(\cos x)$$

$$= -2x \sin x$$

> **Implementing Processes**
>
> In Example 3, notice that you use the Product Rule when both factors of the product are variable, and you use the Constant Multiple Rule when one of the factors is a constant.

The Quotient Rule

> **Theorem 2.9 The Quotient Rule**
>
> The quotient f/g of two differentiable functions f and g is itself differentiable at all values of x for which $g(x) \neq 0$. Moreover, the derivative of f/g is given by the denominator times the derivative of the numerator minus the numerator times the derivative of the denominator, all divided by the square of the denominator.
>
> $$\frac{d}{dx}\left[\frac{f(x)}{g(x)}\right] = \frac{g(x)f'(x) - f(x)g'(x)}{[g(x)]^2}, \quad g(x) \neq 0$$

Remark

From the Quotient Rule, you can see that the derivative of a quotient is not (in general) the quotient of the derivatives.

Proof   As with the proof of Theorem 2.8, the key to this proof is subtracting and adding the same quantity.

$$\frac{d}{dx}\left[\frac{f(x)}{g(x)}\right] = \lim_{\Delta x \to 0} \frac{\dfrac{f(x + \Delta x)}{g(x + \Delta x)} - \dfrac{f(x)}{g(x)}}{\Delta x} \qquad \text{Definition of derivative}$$

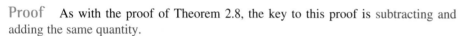

$$= \lim_{\Delta x \to 0} \frac{g(x)f(x + \Delta x) - f(x)g(x + \Delta x)}{\Delta x\, g(x)g(x + \Delta x)}$$

$$= \lim_{\Delta x \to 0} \frac{g(x)f(x + \Delta x) - f(x)g(x) + f(x)g(x) - f(x)g(x + \Delta x)}{\Delta x\, g(x)g(x + \Delta x)}$$

$$= \frac{\displaystyle\lim_{\Delta x \to 0} \frac{g(x)[f(x + \Delta x) - f(x)]}{\Delta x} - \lim_{\Delta x \to 0} \frac{f(x)[g(x + \Delta x) - g(x)]}{\Delta x}}{\displaystyle\lim_{\Delta x \to 0}\, [g(x)g(x + \Delta x)]}$$

$$= \frac{g(x)\left[\displaystyle\lim_{\Delta x \to 0} \frac{f(x + \Delta x) - f(x)}{\Delta x}\right] - f(x)\left[\displaystyle\lim_{\Delta x \to 0} \frac{g(x + \Delta x) - g(x)}{\Delta x}\right]}{\displaystyle\lim_{\Delta x \to 0}\, [g(x)g(x + \Delta x)]}$$

$$= \frac{g(x)f'(x) - f(x)g'(x)}{[g(x)]^2}$$

Note that $\displaystyle\lim_{\Delta x \to 0} g(x + \Delta x) = g(x)$ because g is given to be differentiable and therefore is continuous.

EXAMPLE 4   Using the Quotient Rule

Find the derivative of

$$y = \frac{5x - 2}{x^2 + 1}.$$

Solution

$$\frac{d}{dx}\left[\frac{5x - 2}{x^2 + 1}\right] = \frac{(x^2 + 1)\dfrac{d}{dx}[5x - 2] - (5x - 2)\dfrac{d}{dx}[x^2 + 1]}{(x^2 + 1)^2} \qquad \text{Apply Quotient Rule.}$$

$$= \frac{(x^2 + 1)(5) - (5x - 2)(2x)}{(x^2 + 1)^2}$$

$$= \frac{(5x^2 + 5) - (10x^2 - 4x)}{(x^2 + 1)^2}$$

$$= \frac{-5x^2 + 4x + 5}{(x^2 + 1)^2}$$

Technology

A graphing utility can be used to compare the graph of a function with the graph of its derivative. For instance, in the figure below, the graph of the function in Example 4 appears to have two points that have horizontal tangent lines. What are the values of y' at these two points?

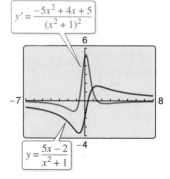

Graphical comparison of a function and its derivative

Note the use of parentheses in Example 4. A liberal use of parentheses is recommended for *all* types of differentiation problems. For instance, with the Quotient Rule, it is a good idea to enclose all factors and derivatives in parentheses, and to pay special attention to the subtraction required in the numerator.

When differentiation rules were introduced in the preceding section, the need for rewriting *before* differentiating was emphasized. The next example illustrates this point with the Quotient Rule.

EXAMPLE 5   Rewriting Before Differentiating

Find an equation of the tangent line to the graph of $f(x) = \dfrac{3 - (1/x)}{x + 5}$ at $(-1, 1)$.

Algebraic Solution

To begin, rewrite the function by multiplying the numerator and denominator by x.

$$f(x) = \frac{3 - (1/x)}{x + 5} = \frac{x\left(3 - \dfrac{1}{x}\right)}{x(x + 5)} = \frac{3x - 1}{x^2 + 5x}$$

Next, apply the Quotient Rule.

$$f'(x) = \frac{(x^2 + 5x)(3) - (3x - 1)(2x + 5)}{(x^2 + 5x)^2} \qquad \text{Quotient Rule}$$

$$= \frac{(3x^2 + 15x) - (6x^2 + 13x - 5)}{(x^2 + 5x)^2} \qquad \text{Simplify.}$$

$$= \frac{-3x^2 + 2x + 5}{(x^2 + 5x)^2}$$

To find the slope at $(-1, 1)$, evaluate $f'(-1)$.

$$f'(-1) = 0 \qquad \begin{array}{l}\text{Slope of graph}\\ \text{at } (-1, 1)\end{array}$$

Then, using the point-slope form of the equation of a line, you can determine that the equation of the tangent line at $(-1, 1)$ is $y = 1$.

Graphical Solution

Use a graphing utility to graph $y = \dfrac{3 - (1/x)}{x + 5}$.

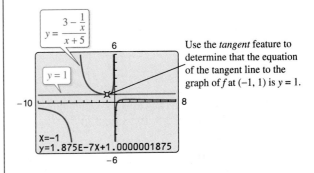

Use the *tangent* feature to determine that the equation of the tangent line to the graph of f at $(-1, 1)$ is $y = 1$.

The line $y = 1$ is tangent to the graph of

$$f(x) = \frac{3 - (1/x)}{x + 5}$$

at the point $(-1, 1)$.

Not every quotient needs to be differentiated by the Quotient Rule. For instance, each quotient in the next example can be considered as the product of a constant times a function of x. In such cases, it is more convenient to use the Constant Multiple Rule.

EXAMPLE 6   Using the Constant Multiple Rule

Original Function	Rewrite	Differentiate	Simplify
a. $y = \dfrac{x^2 + 3x}{6}$	$y = \dfrac{1}{6}(x^2 + 3x)$	$y' = \dfrac{1}{6}(2x + 3)$	$y' = \dfrac{2x + 3}{6}$
b. $y = \dfrac{5x^4}{8}$	$y = \dfrac{5}{8}x^4$	$y' = \dfrac{5}{8}(4x^3)$	$y' = \dfrac{5}{2}x^3$
c. $y = \dfrac{3 - 2x^2}{7x}$	$y = \dfrac{3}{7}x^{-1} - \dfrac{2}{7}x$	$y' = \dfrac{3}{7}(-x^{-2}) - \dfrac{2}{7}$	$y' = -\dfrac{3}{7x^2} - \dfrac{2}{7}$
d. $y = \dfrac{9}{5x^2}$	$y = \dfrac{9}{5}(x^{-2})$	$y' = \dfrac{9}{5}(-2x^{-3})$	$y' = -\dfrac{18}{5x^3}$

> **Insight**
>
> The AP® Exam is timed, so it is important to be efficient. Recognizing ways to rewrite problems before solving, as in Example 6, can accelerate your progression through the exam.

To see the benefit of using the Constant Multiple Rule for some quotients, try using the Quotient Rule to differentiate the functions in Example 6—you should obtain the same results, but with more work.

In Section 2.2, the Power Rule was proved only for the case in which the exponent n is a positive integer greater than 1. The next example extends the proof to include negative integer exponents.

EXAMPLE 7   Power Rule: Negative Integer Exponents

If n is a negative integer, then there exists a positive integer k such that $n = -k$. So, by the Quotient Rule, you can write

$$\frac{d}{dx}[x^n] = \frac{d}{dx}\left[\frac{1}{x^k}\right]$$

$$= \frac{x^k(0) - (1)(kx^{k-1})}{(x^k)^2} \qquad \text{Quotient Rule and Power Rule}$$

$$= \frac{0 - kx^{k-1}}{x^{2k}}$$

$$= -kx^{-k-1}$$

$$= nx^{n-1}. \qquad\qquad n = -k$$

So, the Power Rule

$$\frac{d}{dx}[x^n] = nx^{n-1} \qquad\qquad \text{Power Rule}$$

is valid for any integer n. The cases for which n is rational and n is irrational are left as an exercise. (See Section 2.5, Exercise 82.)

Derivatives of Trigonometric Functions

Knowing the derivatives of the sine and cosine functions, you can use the Quotient Rule to find the derivatives of the four remaining trigonometric functions.

Theorem 2.10   Derivatives of Trigonometric Functions

$$\frac{d}{dx}[\tan x] = \sec^2 x \qquad\qquad \frac{d}{dx}[\cot x] = -\csc^2 x$$

$$\frac{d}{dx}[\sec x] = \sec x \tan x \qquad\qquad \frac{d}{dx}[\csc x] = -\csc x \cot x$$

Proof   Considering $\tan x = (\sin x)/(\cos x)$ and applying the Quotient Rule, you obtain

$$\frac{d}{dx}[\tan x] = \frac{d}{dx}\left[\frac{\sin x}{\cos x}\right]$$

$$= \frac{(\cos x)(\cos x) - (\sin x)(-\sin x)}{\cos^2 x} \qquad \text{Apply Quotient Rule.}$$

$$= \frac{\cos^2 x + \sin^2 x}{\cos^2 x}$$

$$= \frac{1}{\cos^2 x}$$

$$= \sec^2 x.$$

The proofs of the other three parts of the theorem are left as an exercise. (See Exercise 125.)

Remark

In the proof of Theorem 2.10, note the use of the trigonometric identities

$$\sin^2 x + \cos^2 x = 1$$

and

$$\sec x = \frac{1}{\cos x}.$$

These trigonometric identities and others are listed in Appendix C.3 and on the formula pages for this text.

EXAMPLE 8 Differentiating Trigonometric Functions

See LarsonCalculusforAP.com for an interactive version of this type of example.

Function	Derivative
a. $y = x - \tan x$	$\dfrac{dy}{dx} = 1 - \sec^2 x$
b. $y = x \sec x$	$y' = x(\sec x \tan x) + (\sec x)(1)$
	$= (\sec x)(1 + x \tan x)$

EXAMPLE 9 Different Forms of a Derivative

Differentiate both forms of

$$y = \frac{1 - \cos x}{\sin x} = \csc x - \cot x.$$

Solution

First form: $y = \dfrac{1 - \cos x}{\sin x}$

$$y' = \frac{(\sin x)(\sin x) - (1 - \cos x)(\cos x)}{\sin^2 x}$$

$$= \frac{\sin^2 x - \cos x + \cos^2 x}{\sin^2 x}$$

$$= \frac{1 - \cos x}{\sin^2 x} \qquad \sin^2 x + \cos^2 x = 1$$

Second form: $y = \csc x - \cot x$

$$y' = -\csc x \cot x + \csc^2 x$$

To show that the two derivatives are equal, you can write

$$\frac{1 - \cos x}{\sin^2 x} = \frac{1}{\sin^2 x} - \frac{\cos x}{\sin^2 x}$$

$$= \frac{1}{\sin^2 x} - \left(\frac{1}{\sin x}\right)\left(\frac{\cos x}{\sin x}\right)$$

$$= \csc^2 x - \csc x \cot x.$$

> **Connecting Representations**
>
> Because of trigonometric identities, the derivative of a trigonometric function can take many forms. This presents a challenge when you are trying to match your answers to those given in the back of the text.

> **Insight**
>
> When answering free-response questions on the AP® Exam, it is not always necessary to simplify answers completely. However, you must be able to recognize a simplified answer in the choices of a multiple-choice question.

The summary below shows that much of the work in obtaining a simplified form of a derivative occurs *after* differentiating. Note that two characteristics of a simplified form are the absence of negative exponents and the combining of like terms.

	$f'(x)$ After Differentiating	$f'(x)$ After Simplifying
Example 1	$(3x - 2x^2)(4) + (5 + 4x)(3 - 4x)$	$-24x^2 + 4x + 15$
Example 3	$(2x)(-\sin x) + (\cos x)(2) - 2(\cos x)$	$-2x \sin x$
Example 4	$\dfrac{(x^2 + 1)(5) - (5x - 2)(2x)}{(x^2 + 1)^2}$	$\dfrac{-5x^2 + 4x + 5}{(x^2 + 1)^2}$
Example 5	$\dfrac{(x^2 + 5x)(3) - (3x - 1)(2x + 5)}{(x^2 + 5x)^2}$	$\dfrac{-3x^2 + 2x + 5}{(x^2 + 5x)^2}$
Example 9	$\dfrac{(\sin x)(\sin x) - (1 - \cos x)(\cos x)}{\sin^2 x}$	$\dfrac{1 - \cos x}{\sin^2 x}$

Higher-Order Derivatives

Just as you can obtain a velocity function by differentiating a position function, you can obtain an **acceleration** function by differentiating a velocity function. Another way of looking at this is that you can obtain an acceleration function by differentiating a position function *twice*.

$$s(t) \quad \text{Position function}$$
$$v(t) = s'(t) \quad \text{Velocity function}$$
$$a(t) = v'(t) = s''(t) \quad \text{Acceleration function}$$

The function $a(t)$ is the **second derivative** of $s(t)$ and is denoted by $s''(t)$.

The second derivative is an example of a **higher-order derivative.** You can define derivatives of any positive integer order. For instance, the **third derivative** is the derivative of the second derivative. Higher-order derivatives are denoted as shown below.

First derivative: y', $f'(x)$, $\dfrac{dy}{dx}$, $\dfrac{d}{dx}[f(x)]$, $D_x[y]$

Second derivative: y'', $f''(x)$, $\dfrac{d^2y}{dx^2}$, $\dfrac{d^2}{dx^2}[f(x)]$, $D_x^2[y]$

Third derivative: y''', $f'''(x)$, $\dfrac{d^3y}{dx^3}$, $\dfrac{d^3}{dx^3}[f(x)]$, $D_x^3[y]$

Fourth derivative: $y^{(4)}$, $f^{(4)}(x)$, $\dfrac{d^4y}{dx^4}$, $\dfrac{d^4}{dx^4}[f(x)]$, $D_x^4[y]$

$\vdots$

nth derivative: $y^{(n)}$, $f^{(n)}(x)$, $\dfrac{d^ny}{dx^n}$, $\dfrac{d^n}{dx^n}[f(x)]$, $D_x^n[y]$

Communication and Notation

The notations y'' and y''' are read as "y double prime" and "y triple prime," respectively. Notice that the prime notation is only used for the first, second, and third derivatives.

EXAMPLE 10 Particle Motion

The position of a particle as it moves along a line is given by $s(t) = t^2 - 10t + 29$, where s is measured in meters, t is measured in seconds, and $t \geq 0$.

a. Find the displacement of the particle during the first 5 seconds.
b. Find the average velocity of the particle during the first 10 seconds.
c. Find the instantaneous velocity of the particle when $t = 10$.
d. Find the acceleration of the particle when $t = 10$.

Solution

a. The displacement of the particle during the first 5 seconds is

$$s(5) - s(0) = [(5)^2 - 10(5) + 29] - [(0)^2 - 10(0) + 29] = 4 - 29 = -25.$$

So, in the first 5 seconds, the particle moves along the line 25 meters to the left.

b. The average velocity of the particle during the first 10 seconds is

$$\frac{s(10) - s(0)}{10 - 0} = \frac{29 - 29}{10} = 0 \text{ meters per second.}$$

c. The velocity of the particle at any time t is $v(t) = s'(t) = 2t - 10$. So, the instantaneous velocity of the particle when $t = 10$ is

$$v(10) = 2(10) - 10 = 10 \text{ meters per second.}$$

d. The acceleration of the particle at any time t is $a(t) = v'(t) = 2$. So, the acceleration of the particle when $t = 10$ is $a(10) = 2$ meters per second per second.

Exploration

Describe the motion of the particle in Example 10. At what values of t does the particle change direction? Explain your reasoning.

2.3 Exercises

See *CalcChat.com* for tutorial help and worked-out solutions to odd-numbered exercises.

Using the Product Rule In Exercises 1–6, use the Product Rule to find the derivative of the function.

1. $g(x) = (2x - 3)(1 - 5x)$

2. $y = (3x - 4)(x^3 + 5)$

3. $h(t) = \sqrt{t}(1 - t^2)$ 4. $g(s) = \sqrt{s}(s^2 + 8)$

5. $f(x) = e^x \cos x$ 6. $g(x) = \sqrt{x} \sin x$

Using the Quotient Rule In Exercises 7–12, use the Quotient Rule to find the derivative of the function.

7. $f(x) = \dfrac{x}{x - 5}$ 8. $g(t) = \dfrac{3t^2 - 1}{2t + 5}$

9. $h(x) = \dfrac{\sqrt{x}}{x^3 + 1}$ 10. $f(x) = \dfrac{x^2}{2\sqrt{x} + 1}$

11. $g(x) = \dfrac{\sin x}{e^x}$ 12. $f(t) = \dfrac{\cos t}{t^3}$

Finding and Evaluating a Derivative In Exercises 13–20, find $f'(x)$ and $f'(c)$.

13. $f(x) = (x^3 + 4x)(3x^2 + 2x - 5), \quad c = 0$

14. $f(x) = (2x^2 - 3x)(9x + 4), \quad c = -1$

15. $f(x) = \dfrac{x^2 - 4}{x - 3}, \quad c = 1$ 16. $f(x) = \dfrac{x - 4}{x + 4}, \quad c = 3$

17. $f(x) = x \cos x, \quad c = \dfrac{\pi}{4}$ 18. $f(x) = \dfrac{\sin x}{x}, \quad c = \dfrac{\pi}{6}$

19. $f(x) = e^x \sin x, \quad c = 0$ 20. $f(x) = \dfrac{\cos x}{e^x}, \quad c = 0$

Error Analysis In Exercises 21 and 22, describe and correct the error in finding the derivative.

21. $\dfrac{d}{dx}\left[\sqrt{x}(x^2 + 1)\right] = \sqrt{x}(2x) + (2x)\sqrt{x}$

$$= 4x\sqrt{x} \quad ✗$$

22. $\dfrac{d}{dx}\left[\dfrac{3x - 5}{x - 7}\right] = \dfrac{1(3x - 5) - (x - 7)(3)}{(x - 7)^2}$

$$= \dfrac{(3x - 5) - (3x - 21)}{(x - 7)^2}$$

$$= \dfrac{16}{(x - 7)^2} \quad ✗$$

Evaluating a Derivative In Exercises 23–26, $g(3) = -1$, $g'(3) = 2$, $h(3) = -3$, and $h'(3) = 5$. Find $f'(3)$.

23. $f(x) = g(x)h(x)$ 24. $f(x) = [g(x)]^2$

25. $f(x) = \dfrac{g(x)}{h(x)}$ 26. $f(x) = \dfrac{h(x)}{g(x)}$

Implementing Processes In Exercises 27–30, use the Product Rule to find $f'(x)$. Then find $f'(x)$ *without* using the Product Rule, by multiplying first. Which method do you prefer?

27. $f(x) = 3x(2x - 1)$

28. $f(x) = (x + 4)(2x - 3)$

29. $f(x) = (x - 2)(2x^2 + 3x - 5)$

30. $f(x) = (x^2 - 3x + 1)(x^2 + 5x - 3)$

Using the Constant Multiple Rule In Exercises 31–36, complete the table to find the derivative of the function without using the Quotient Rule.

	Function	Rewrite	Differentiate	Simplify
31.	$y = \dfrac{x^3 + 6x}{3}$			
32.	$y = \dfrac{5x^2 - 3}{4}$			
33.	$y = \dfrac{6}{7x^2}$			
34.	$y = \dfrac{10}{3x^3}$			
35.	$y = \dfrac{4x^{3/2}}{x}$			
36.	$y = \dfrac{2x}{x^{1/3}}$			

Finding a Derivative In Exercises 37–52, find the derivative of the algebraic function.

37. $f(x) = \dfrac{4 - 3x - x^2}{x^2 - 1}$ 38. $f(x) = \dfrac{x^2 + 5x + 6}{x^2 - 4}$

39. $f(x) = x\left(1 - \dfrac{4}{x + 3}\right)$ 40. $f(x) = x^4\left(1 - \dfrac{2}{x + 1}\right)$

41. $f(x) = \dfrac{3x - 1}{\sqrt{x}}$ 42. $f(x) = \sqrt[3]{x}(\sqrt{x} + 3)$

43. $h(s) = (s^3 - 2)^2$ 44. $h(x) = (x^2 + 3)^3$

45. $f(x) = \dfrac{2 - \dfrac{1}{x}}{x - 3}$ 46. $h(x) = \dfrac{\dfrac{1}{x^2} + 5x}{x + 1}$

47. $g(s) = s^3\left(5 - \dfrac{s}{s + 2}\right)$ 48. $g(x) = x^2\left(\dfrac{2}{x} - \dfrac{1}{x + 1}\right)$

49. $f(x) = (2x^3 + 5x)(x - 3)(x + 2)$

50. $f(x) = (x^3 - x)(x^2 + 2)(x^2 + x - 1)$

51. $f(x) = \dfrac{x^2 + c^2}{x^2 - c^2}, \quad c$ is a constant.

52. $f(x) = \dfrac{c^2 - x^2}{c^2 + x^2}, \quad c$ is a constant.

Finding a Derivative of a Transcendental Function In Exercises 53–68, find the derivative of the transcendental function.

53. $f(t) = t^2 \sin t$

54. $f(\theta) = (\theta + 1)\cos \theta$

55. $f(t) = \dfrac{\cos t}{t}$

56. $f(x) = \dfrac{\sin x}{x^3}$

57. $f(x) = -e^x + \tan x$

58. $y = e^x - \cot x$

59. $y = \dfrac{3(1 - \sin x)}{2 \cos x}$

60. $y = \dfrac{\sec x}{x}$

61. $y = -\csc x - \sin x$

62. $y = x \sin x + \cos x$

63. $f(x) = x^2 \tan x$

64. $f(x) = \sin x \cos x$

65. $y = 2x \sin x + x^2 e^x$

66. $h(x) = 2e^x \cos x$

67. $y = \dfrac{e^x}{4\sqrt{x}}$

68. $y = \dfrac{2e^x}{x^2 + 1}$

Finding a Derivative Using Technology In Exercises 69–72, use a computer algebra system to find the derivative of the function.

69. $g(x) = \left(\dfrac{x + 1}{x + 2}\right)(2x - 5)$

70. $f(x) = \left(\dfrac{x^2 - x - 3}{x^2 + 1}\right)(x^2 + x + 1)$

71. $g(\theta) = \dfrac{\theta}{1 - \sin \theta}$

72. $f(\theta) = \dfrac{\sin \theta}{1 - \cos \theta}$

Finding the Slope of a Graph In Exercises 73–76, find the slope of the graph of the function at the given point. Use the *derivative* feature of a graphing utility to verify your results.

73. $y = \dfrac{1 + \csc x}{1 - \csc x}$, $\left(\dfrac{\pi}{6}, -3\right)$

74. $f(x) = \tan x \cot x$, $(1, 1)$

75. $h(t) = \dfrac{\sec t}{t}$, $\left(\pi, -\dfrac{1}{\pi}\right)$

76. $f(x) = (\sin x)(\sin x + \cos x)$, $\left(\dfrac{\pi}{4}, 1\right)$

Finding an Equation of a Tangent Line In Exercises 77–84, (a) find an equation of the tangent line to the graph of f at the given point, (b) use a graphing utility to graph the function and its tangent line at the point, and (c) use the *tangent* feature of a graphing utility to confirm your results.

77. $f(x) = (x^3 + 4x - 1)(x - 2)$, $(1, -4)$

78. $f(x) = (x - 2)(x^2 + 4)$, $(1, -5)$

79. $f(x) = \dfrac{x}{x + 4}$, $(-5, 5)$ **80.** $f(x) = \dfrac{x + 3}{x - 3}$, $(4, 7)$

81. $f(x) = \tan x$, $\left(\dfrac{\pi}{4}, 1\right)$ **82.** $f(x) = \sec x$, $\left(\dfrac{\pi}{3}, 2\right)$

83. $f(x) = (x - 1)e^x$, $(1, 0)$

84. $f(x) = \dfrac{e^x}{x + 4}$, $\left(0, \dfrac{1}{4}\right)$

 Horizontal Tangent Line In Exercises 85–88, determine the point(s) at which the graph of the function has a horizontal tangent line.

85. $f(x) = \dfrac{x^2}{x - 1}$

86. $f(x) = \dfrac{x^2}{x^2 + 1}$

87. $g(x) = \dfrac{8(x - 2)}{e^x}$

88. $f(x) = e^x \sin x$, $[0, \pi]$

89. Connecting Representations Find equations of the tangent lines to the graph of $f(x) = (x + 1)/(x - 1)$ that are parallel to the line $2y + x = 6$. Then graph the function and the tangent lines.

90. Connecting Representations Find equations of the tangent lines to the graph of $f(x) = x/(x - 1)$ that pass through the point $(-1, 5)$. Then graph the function and the tangent lines.

Exploring a Relationship In Exercises 91 and 92, verify that $f'(x) = g'(x)$ and explain the relationship between f and g.

91. $f(x) = \dfrac{3x}{x + 2}$, $g(x) = \dfrac{5x + 4}{x + 2}$

92. $f(x) = \dfrac{\sin x - 3x}{x}$, $g(x) = \dfrac{\sin x + 2x}{x}$

 Finding Derivatives In Exercises 93 and 94, use the graphs of f and g. Let $p(x) = f(x)g(x)$ and $q(x) = f(x)/g(x)$.

93. (a) Find $p'(1)$.

    (b) Find $q'(4)$.

94. (a) Find $p'(4)$.

    (b) Find $q'(7)$.

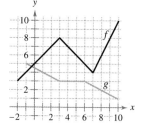 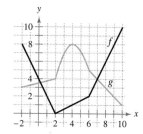

95. Area The length of a rectangle is given by $6t + 5$ and its height is $\sqrt{t}$, where t is time in seconds and the dimensions are in centimeters. Find the rate of change of the area with respect to time.

96. Volume The radius of a right circular cylinder is given by $\sqrt{t + 2}$ and its height is $\frac{1}{2}\sqrt{t}$, where t is time in seconds and the dimensions are in inches. Find the rate of change of the volume with respect to time.

97. Population Growth A population of 500 bacteria is introduced into a culture and grows in number according to the equation

$$P(t) = 500\left(1 + \dfrac{4t}{50 + t^2}\right)$$

where t is measured in hours. Find the rates at which the population is growing when $t = 1, 2,$ and 3.

98. Inventory Replenishment The ordering and transportation cost C for the components used in manufacturing a product is

$$C = 100\left(\frac{200}{x^2} + \frac{x}{x + 30}\right), \quad x \geq 1$$

where C is measured in thousands of dollars and x is the order size in hundreds. Find the rate of change of C with respect to x when (a) $x = 10$, (b) $x = 15$, (c) $x = 20$, and (d) $x = 25$. What do these rates of change imply about increasing order size?

 Finding a Second Derivative   In Exercises 99–108, find the second derivative of the function.

99. $f(x) = x^2 + 7x - 4$

100. $f(x) = 4x^5 - 2x^3 + 5x^2$

101. $f(x) = 4x^{3/2}$ **102.** $f(x) = x^2 + 3x^{-3}$

103. $f(x) = \dfrac{x}{x - 1}$ **104.** $f(x) = \dfrac{x^2 + 3x}{x - 4}$

105. $f(x) = x \sin x$ **106.** $f(x) = \sec x$

107. $g(x) = \dfrac{e^x}{x}$ **108.** $h(t) = e^t \sin t$

 Finding a Higher-Order Derivative   In Exercises 109–112, find the given higher-order derivative.

109. $f'(x) = x^3 - x^{2/5}, \quad f^{(3)}(x)$

110. $f^{(3)}(x) = \sqrt[5]{x^4}, \quad f^{(4)}(x)$

111. $f''(x) = -\sin x, \quad f^{(8)}(x)$

112. $f^{(4)}(t) = t \cos t, \quad f^{(5)}(t)$

EXPLORING CONCEPTS

113. Higher-Order Derivatives Polynomials of what degree satisfy $f^{(n)} = 0$? Explain your reasoning.

114. Sketching a Graph Sketch the graph of a differentiable function f such that $f(0) = 0$, $f'(2) = 0$, and $f''(x)$ is both constant and negative for all real values of x. Explain how you found your answer.

Communicating   In Exercises 115 and 116, the graphs of f, f', and f'' are shown on the same set of coordinate axes. Identify each graph. Explain your reasoning. To print an enlarged copy of the graph, go to *MathGraphs.com.*

115.   **116.**

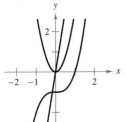   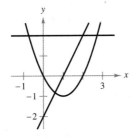

 Sketching Graphs   In Exercises 117–120, the graph of f is shown. Sketch the graphs of f' and f''. To print an enlarged copy of the graph, go to *MathGraphs.com.*

117. 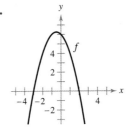   **118.**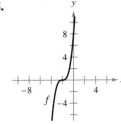

119. 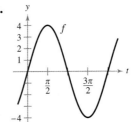   **120.**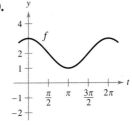

121. Particle Motion In Exercise 119, let f represent the position of a particle as it moves along a line, where f is measured in meters and t is measured in seconds. For $0 \leq t \leq \pi$, describe the motion of the particle. At what values of t does the particle change direction?

122. Particle Motion In Exercise 120, let f represent the position of a particle as it moves along a line, where f is measured in meters and t is measured in seconds. For $0 \leq t \leq 2\pi$, describe the motion of the particle. At what values of t does the particle change direction?

Particle Motion   In Exercises 123 and 124, the position of a particle as it moves along a line is given by $s(t)$, where s is measured in inches, t is measured in seconds, and $t \geq 0$. For the particle, find the (a) displacement during the first 6 seconds, (b) average velocity during the first 6 seconds, (c) instantaneous velocity when $t = 8$, and (d) acceleration when $t = 8$.

123. $s(t) = t^2 - 8t + 18$

124. $s(t) = e^t$

125. Proof Prove each differentiation rule.

(a) $\dfrac{d}{dx}[\cot x] = -\csc^2 x$

(b) $\dfrac{d}{dx}[\sec x] = \sec x \tan x$

(c) $\dfrac{d}{dx}[\csc x] = -\csc x \cot x$

126. Rate of Change Determine any values of x in the interval $[0, 2\pi)$ such that the rate of change of $f(x) = \sec x$ and the rate of change of $g(x) = \csc x$ are equal.

127. Stopping Distance A car is traveling at a rate of 66 feet per second (45 mi/h) when the brakes are applied. The position function for the car is $s(t) = -8.25t^2 + 66t$, where s is measured in feet and t is measured in seconds. Complete the table. Then find the average velocity during the time intervals $[0, 1]$, $[1, 2]$, $[2, 3]$, and $[3, 4]$.

t	0	1	2	3	4
$s(t)$					
$v(t)$					
$a(t)$					

128. HOW DO YOU SEE IT? The figure shows the graphs of the position, velocity, and acceleration functions of a particle.

(a) Copy the graphs of the functions shown. Identify each graph. Explain your reasoning. To print an enlarged copy of the graph, go to *MathGraphs.com*.

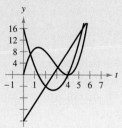

(b) Identify when the particle speeds up and when it slows down. Explain.

Finding a Pattern In Exercises 129 and 130, develop a general rule for $f^{(n)}(x)$ given $f(x)$.

129. $f(x) = x^n$ **130.** $f(x) = 1/x$

131. Finding a Pattern Consider the function $f(x) = g(x)h(x)$.

(a) Use the Product Rule to generate rules for finding $f''(x)$, $f'''(x)$, and $f^{(4)}(x)$.

(b) Use the results of part (a) to write a general rule for $f^{(n)}(x)$.

132. Finding a Pattern Develop a general rule for the nth derivative of $xf(x)$, where f is a differentiable function of x.

Finding a Pattern In Exercises 133 and 134, find the derivatives of the function f for $n = 1, 2, 3,$ and 4. Use the results to write a general rule for $f'(x)$ in terms of n.

133. $f(x) = x^n \sin x$ **134.** $f(x) = (\cos x)/x^n$

True or False? In Exercises 135–138, determine whether the statement is true or false. If it is false, explain why or give an example that shows it is false.

135. If $f'(c)$ and $g'(c)$ are zero and $h(x) = f(x)g(x)$, then $h'(c) = 0$.

136. If $y = (x + 1)(x + 2)(x + 3)(x + 4)$, then $\dfrac{d^4y}{dx^4} = 0$.

137. The second derivative represents the rate of change of the first derivative.

138. If the velocity of an object is constant, then its acceleration is zero.

139. Absolute Value Find the derivative of $f(x) = x|x|$. Does $f''(0)$ exist? (*Hint:* Rewrite the function as a piecewise function and then differentiate each part.)

140. Implementing Processes Let f and g be functions whose first and second derivatives exist on an interval I. Which of the following formulas is (are) true?

(a) $fg'' - f''g = (fg' - f'g)'$

(b) $fg'' + f''g = (fg)''$

141. Proof Use the Product Rule twice to prove that if f, g, and h are differentiable functions of x, then

$$\frac{d}{dx}[f(x)g(x)h(x)] = f'(x)g(x)h(x) + f(x)g'(x)h(x)$$
$$+ f(x)g(x)h'(x).$$

Calculus AP® – Exam Preparation Questions

142. Multiple Choice If f is differentiable at $x = c$, which of the following could be false?

(A) f is continuous at $x = c$.

(B) $\lim_{x \to c} f(x)$ exists.

(C) $f'(c)$ is defined.

(D) $f''(c)$ is defined.

143. Multiple Choice If $y = 4e^x \cot x$, then $\dfrac{dy}{dx} =$

(A) $4xe^{x-1} \cot x - 4e^x \csc^2 x$.

(B) $4e^x(\csc^2 x + \cot x)$.

(C) $4e^x(\cot x - \csc^2 x)$.

(D) $4e^x(\csc^2 x - \cot x)$.

144. Multiple Choice What is the second derivative of

$$h(x) = \frac{x^2 - x}{x + 5}?$$

(A) $h''(x) = \dfrac{60}{(x + 5)^3}$ (B) $h''(x) = \dfrac{60}{x + 5}$

(C) $h''(x) = \dfrac{x^2 + 10x - 5}{(x + 5)^2}$

(D) $h''(x) = \dfrac{x^2 + 10x - 5}{(x + 5)^4}$

145. Multiple Choice Let $f(x) = \sin x - \cos x$ and $f^{(n)}(x)$ represent the nth derivative of $f(x)$. What is the least positive integer n for which $f^{(n)}(x) = f(x)$?

(A) 3   (B) 4   (C) 5   (D) 8

2.4   The Chain Rule

▶ Find the derivative of a composite function using the Chain Rule.
▶ Find the derivative of a function using the General Power Rule.
▶ Simplify the derivative of a function using algebra.
▶ Find the derivative of a transcendental function using the Chain Rule.
▶ Find the derivative of a function involving the natural logarithmic function.
▶ Define and differentiate exponential functions that have bases other than *e*.

The Chain Rule

This text has yet to discuss one of the most powerful differentiation rules—the **Chain Rule.** This rule deals with composite functions and adds a surprising versatility to the rules discussed in the two preceding sections. For example, compare the functions shown below. Those on the left can be differentiated without the Chain Rule, and those on the right are best differentiated with the Chain Rule.

Without the Chain Rule	*With the Chain Rule*
$y = x^2 + 1$	$y = \sqrt{x^2 + 1}$
$y = \sin x$	$y = \sin 6x$
$y = 3x + 2$	$y = (3x + 2)^5$
$y = e^x + \tan x$	$y = e^{5x} + \tan x^2$

Basically, the Chain Rule states that if *y* changes dy/du times as fast as *u*, and *u* changes du/dx times as fast as *x*, then *y* changes $(dy/du)(du/dx)$ times as fast as *x*.

EXAMPLE 1   The Derivative of a Composite Function

A set of gears is constructed so that the second and third gears are on the same axle. (See Figure 2.22.) As the first axle revolves, it drives the second axle, which in turn drives the third axle. Let *y*, *u*, and *x* represent the numbers of revolutions per minute of the first, second, and third axles, respectively. Find dy/du, du/dx, and dy/dx, and show that

$$\frac{dy}{dx} = \frac{dy}{du} \cdot \frac{du}{dx}.$$

Solution

Because the circumference of the second gear is three times that of the first, the first axle must make three revolutions to turn the second axle once. Similarly, the second axle must make two revolutions to turn the third axle once, and you can write $dy/du = 3$ and $du/dx = 2$. Combining these two results, you know that the first axle must make six revolutions to turn the third axle once. So, you can write

$$\frac{dy}{dx} = \boxed{\begin{array}{l}\text{Rate of change of first axle} \\ \text{with respect to second axle}\end{array}} \cdot \boxed{\begin{array}{l}\text{Rate of change of second axle} \\ \text{with respect to third axle}\end{array}}$$

$$= \frac{dy}{du} \cdot \frac{du}{dx}$$

$$= 3 \cdot 2$$

$$= 6$$

$$= \boxed{\begin{array}{l}\text{Rate of change of first axle} \\ \text{with respect to third axle}\end{array}}.$$

In other words, the rate of change of *y* with respect to *x* is the product of the rate of change of *y* with respect to *u* and the rate of change of *u* with respect to *x*. ■

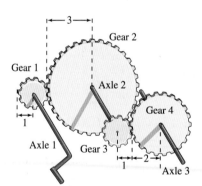

Axle 1: *y* revolutions per minute
Axle 2: *u* revolutions per minute
Axle 3: *x* revolutions per minute
Figure 2.22

Example 1 illustrates a simple case of the Chain Rule. The general rule is stated in the next theorem.

Theorem 2.11   The Chain Rule

If $y = f(u)$ is a differentiable function of u and $u = g(x)$ is a differentiable function of x, then $y = f(g(x))$ is a differentiable function of x and

$$\frac{dy}{dx} = \frac{dy}{du} \cdot \frac{du}{dx}$$

or, equivalently,

$$\frac{d}{dx}[f(g(x))] = f'(g(x))g'(x).$$

Proof   Let $h(x) = f(g(x))$. Then, using the alternative form of the derivative, you need to show that, for $x = c$,

$$h'(c) = f'(g(c))g'(c).$$

An important consideration in this proof is the behavior of g as x approaches c. A problem occurs when there are values of x, other than c, such that

$$g(x) = g(c).$$

Appendix A shows how to use the differentiability of f and g to overcome this problem. For now, assume that $g(x) \neq g(c)$ for values of x other than c. In the proofs of the Product Rule and the Quotient Rule, the same quantity was added and subtracted to obtain the desired form. This proof uses a similar technique—multiplying and dividing by the same (nonzero) quantity. Note that because g is differentiable, it is also continuous, and it follows that $g(x)$ approaches $g(c)$ as x approaches c.

$$h'(c) = \lim_{x \to c} \frac{f(g(x)) - f(g(c))}{x - c} \qquad \text{Alternative form of derivative}$$

$$= \lim_{x \to c} \left[\frac{f(g(x)) - f(g(c))}{x - c} \cdot \frac{g(x) - g(c)}{g(x) - g(c)} \right], \qquad g(x) \neq g(c)$$

$$= \lim_{x \to c} \left[\frac{f(g(x)) - f(g(c))}{g(x) - g(c)} \cdot \frac{g(x) - g(c)}{x - c} \right]$$

$$= \left[\lim_{x \to c} \frac{f(g(x)) - f(g(c))}{g(x) - g(c)} \right]\left[\lim_{x \to c} \frac{g(x) - g(c)}{x - c} \right]$$

$$= f'(g(c))g'(c)$$

> **Remark**
>
> The alternative limit form of the derivative was given at the end of Section 2.1.

When applying the Chain Rule, it is helpful to think of the composite function $f \circ g$ as having two parts—an inner part and an outer part.

Outer function

$$y = f(g(x)) = f(u)$$

Inner function

The derivative of $y = f(u)$ is the derivative of the outer function (at the inner function u) *times* the derivative of the inner function.

$$y' = f'(u) \cdot u'$$

> **Exploration**
>
> ***Using the Chain Rule***   Each of the following functions can be differentiated using rules that you studied in Sections 2.2 and 2.3. For each function, find the derivative using those rules. Then find the derivative using the Chain Rule. Compare your results. Which method is simpler?
>
> **a.** $\dfrac{2}{3x + 1}$
>
> **b.** $(x + 2)^3$
>
> **c.** $\sin 2x$

EXAMPLE 2 **Decomposition of a Composite Function**

$y = f(g(x))$	$u = g(x)$	$y = f(u)$
a. $y = \dfrac{1}{x + 1}$	$u = x + 1$	$y = \dfrac{1}{u}$
b. $y = \sin 2x$	$u = 2x$	$y = \sin u$
c. $y = \sqrt{3x^2 - x + 1}$	$u = 3x^2 - x + 1$	$y = \sqrt{u}$
d. $y = \tan^2 x$	$u = \tan x$	$y = u^2$

EXAMPLE 3 **Using the Chain Rule**

Find dy/dx for $y = (x^2 + 1)^3$.

Solution

For this function, you can consider the inside function to be $u = x^2 + 1$ and the outer function to be $y = u^3$. By the Chain Rule, you obtain

$$\frac{dy}{dx} = \underbrace{3(x^2 + 1)^2}_{\frac{dy}{du}}\underbrace{(2x)}_{\frac{du}{dx}} = 6x(x^2 + 1)^2.$$

The General Power Rule

The function in Example 3 is an example of one of the most common types of composite functions, $y = [u(x)]^n$. The rule for differentiating such functions is called the **General Power Rule,** and it is a special case of the Chain Rule.

Theorem 2.12   The General Power Rule

If $y = [u(x)]^n$, where u is a differentiable function of x and n is a rational number, then

$$\frac{dy}{dx} = n[u(x)]^{n-1}\frac{du}{dx}$$

or, equivalently,

$$\frac{d}{dx}[u^n] = nu^{n-1}u'.$$

Proof   Because $y = [u(x)]^n = u^n$, you apply the Chain Rule to obtain

$$\frac{dy}{dx} = \left(\frac{dy}{du}\right)\left(\frac{du}{dx}\right)$$

$$= \frac{d}{du}[u^n]\frac{du}{dx}.$$

By the (Simple) Power Rule in Section 2.2, you have

$$D_u[u^n] = nu^{n-1}$$

and it follows that

$$\frac{dy}{dx} = nu^{n-1}\frac{du}{dx}.$$

Implementing Processes

You could also solve the problem in Example 3 without using the Chain Rule by observing that

$$y = x^6 + 3x^4 + 3x^2 + 1$$

and

$$y' = 6x^5 + 12x^3 + 6x.$$

Verify that this is the same as the derivative in Example 3. Which method would you use to find

$$\frac{d}{dx}[(x^2 + 1)^{50}]?$$

EXAMPLE 4 Applying the General Power Rule

Find the derivative of $f(x) = (3x - 2x^2)^3$.

Solution

Let $u = 3x - 2x^2$. Then

$$f(x) = (3x - 2x^2)^3 = u^3$$

and, by the General Power Rule, the derivative is

$$\overset{\overset{\displaystyle n}{|}}{f'(x) = 3}\overset{\overset{\displaystyle u^{n-1}}{\overbrace{\quad\quad\quad}}}{(3x - 2x^2)^2}\overset{\overset{\displaystyle u'}{\overbrace{\quad\quad}}}{\frac{d}{dx}[3x - 2x^2]}$$ Apply General Power Rule.

$$= 3(3x - 2x^2)^2(3 - 4x).$$ Differentiate $3x - 2x^2$.

EXAMPLE 5 Differentiating Functions Involving Radicals

Find all points on the graph of

$$f(x) = \sqrt[3]{(x^2 - 1)^2}$$

for which $f'(x) = 0$ and those for which $f'(x)$ does not exist.

Solution

Begin by rewriting the function as

$$f(x) = (x^2 - 1)^{2/3}.$$

Then, applying the General Power Rule (with $u = x^2 - 1$) produces

$$\overset{\overset{\displaystyle n}{|}}{f'(x) = \frac{2}{3}}\overset{\overset{\displaystyle u^{n-1}}{\overbrace{\quad\quad\quad}}}{(x^2 - 1)^{-1/3}}\overset{\overset{\displaystyle u'}{\overbrace{\quad}}}{(2x)}$$ Apply General Power Rule.

$$= \frac{4x}{3\sqrt[3]{x^2 - 1}}.$$ Write in radical form.

So, $f'(x) = 0$ when $x = 0$, and $f'(x)$ does not exist when $x = \pm 1$, as shown in Figure 2.23.

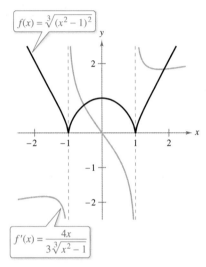

$f(x) = \sqrt[3]{(x^2 - 1)^2}$

$f'(x) = \dfrac{4x}{3\sqrt[3]{x^2 - 1}}$

The derivative of f is 0 at $x = 0$ and is undefined at $x = \pm 1$.
Figure 2.23

EXAMPLE 6 Differentiating Quotients: Constant Numerators

Differentiate the function

$$g(t) = \frac{-7}{(2t - 3)^2}.$$

Solution

Begin by rewriting the function as

$$g(t) = -7(2t - 3)^{-2}.$$

Then, applying the General Power Rule (with $u = 2t - 3$) produces

$$\overset{\overset{\displaystyle n}{\overbrace{\quad}}}{g'(t) = (-7)}\overset{}{\underset{\underset{\substack{\text{Constant}\\\text{Multiple Rule}}}{\smile}}{(-2)}}\overset{\overset{\displaystyle u^{n-1}}{\overbrace{\quad\quad\quad}}}{(2t - 3)^{-3}}\overset{\overset{\displaystyle u'}{\overbrace{\quad}}}{(2)}$$ Apply General Power Rule.

$$= 28(2t - 3)^{-3}$$ Simplify.

$$= \frac{28}{(2t - 3)^3}.$$ Write with positive exponent.

> ## Implementing Processes
>
> Try differentiating the function in Example 6 using the Quotient Rule. You should obtain the same result, but using the Quotient Rule is less efficient than using the General Power Rule.

Simplifying Derivatives

The next three examples demonstrate techniques for simplifying the "raw derivatives" of functions involving products, quotients, and composites.

EXAMPLE 7   Simplifying by Factoring Out the Least Powers

Find the derivative of $f(x) = x^2\sqrt{1 - x^2}$.

Solution

$$f(x) = x^2\sqrt{1 - x^2} \qquad \text{Write original function.}$$

$$= x^2(1 - x^2)^{1/2} \qquad \text{Rewrite.}$$

$$f'(x) = x^2\frac{d}{dx}[(1 - x^2)^{1/2}] + (1 - x^2)^{1/2}\frac{d}{dx}[x^2] \qquad \text{Product Rule}$$

$$= x^2\left[\frac{1}{2}(1 - x^2)^{-1/2}(-2x)\right] + (1 - x^2)^{1/2}(2x) \qquad \text{General Power Rule}$$

$$= -x^3(1 - x^2)^{-1/2} + 2x(1 - x^2)^{1/2} \qquad \text{Simplify.}$$

$$= x(1 - x^2)^{-1/2}[-x^2(1) + 2(1 - x^2)] \qquad \text{Factor.}$$

$$= \frac{x(2 - 3x^2)}{\sqrt{1 - x^2}} \qquad \text{Simplify.}$$

EXAMPLE 8   Simplifying the Derivative of a Quotient

$$f(x) = \frac{x}{\sqrt[3]{x^2 + 4}} \qquad \text{Original function}$$

$$= \frac{x}{(x^2 + 4)^{1/3}} \qquad \text{Rewrite.}$$

$$f'(x) = \frac{(x^2 + 4)^{1/3}(1) - x(1/3)(x^2 + 4)^{-2/3}(2x)}{(x^2 + 4)^{2/3}} \qquad \text{Quotient Rule}$$

$$= \frac{1}{3}(x^2 + 4)^{-2/3}\left[\frac{3(x^2 + 4) - (2x^2)(1)}{(x^2 + 4)^{2/3}}\right] \qquad \text{Factor.}$$

$$= \frac{x^2 + 12}{3(x^2 + 4)^{4/3}} \qquad \text{Simplify.}$$

EXAMPLE 9   Simplifying the Derivative of a Power

See LarsonCalculusforAP.com for an interactive version of this type of example.

$$y = \left(\frac{3x - 1}{x^2 + 3}\right)^2 \qquad \text{Original function}$$

$$y' = 2\left(\frac{3x - 1}{x^2 + 3}\right)\frac{d}{dx}\left[\frac{3x - 1}{x^2 + 3}\right] \qquad \text{General Power Rule}$$

$$= \left[\frac{2(3x - 1)}{x^2 + 3}\right]\left[\frac{(x^2 + 3)(3) - (3x - 1)(2x)}{(x^2 + 3)^2}\right] \qquad \text{Quotient Rule}$$

$$= \frac{2(3x - 1)(3x^2 + 9 - 6x^2 + 2x)}{(x^2 + 3)^3} \qquad \text{Multiply.}$$

$$= \frac{2(3x - 1)(-3x^2 + 2x + 9)}{(x^2 + 3)^3} \qquad \text{Simplify.}$$

Technology

Symbolic differentiation utilities are capable of differentiating very complicated functions. Often, however, the result is given in unsimplified form. If you have access to such a utility, use it to find the derivatives of the functions given in Examples 7, 8, and 9. Then compare the results with those given in these examples.

Transcendental Functions and the Chain Rule

The "Chain Rule versions" of the derivatives of the six trigonometric functions and the natural exponential function are shown below.

$$\frac{d}{dx}[\sin u] = (\cos u)u' \qquad \frac{d}{dx}[\cos u] = -(\sin u)u'$$

$$\frac{d}{dx}[\tan u] = (\sec^2 u)u' \qquad \frac{d}{dx}[\cot u] = -(\csc^2 u)u'$$

$$\frac{d}{dx}[\sec u] = (\sec u \tan u)u' \qquad \frac{d}{dx}[\csc u] = -(\csc u \cot u)u'$$

$$\frac{d}{dx}[e^u] = e^u u'$$

EXAMPLE 10   The Chain Rule and Transcendental Functions

a. $y = \sin 2x$
$\qquad y' = \overset{\cos u}{\cos 2x} \overset{u'}{\frac{d}{dx}[2x]} = (\cos 2x)(2) = 2 \cos 2x$

b. $y = \cos(x - 1)$
$\qquad y' = \overset{-(\sin u)}{-\sin(x - 1)} \overset{u'}{\frac{d}{dx}[x - 1]} = -\sin(x - 1)$

c. $y = e^{3x}$
$\qquad y' = \overset{e^u}{e^{3x}} \overset{u'}{\frac{d}{dx}[3x]} = 3e^{3x}$

> **Communication and Notation**
>
> Be sure you understand the mathematical conventions regarding parentheses and trigonometric functions. For instance, in Example 10(a), $\sin 2x$ means $\sin(2x)$.

EXAMPLE 11   Parentheses and Trigonometric Functions

a. $y = \cos 3x^2 = \cos(3x^2)$ $\qquad y' = (-\sin 3x^2)(6x) = -6x \sin 3x^2$

b. $y = (\cos 3)x^2$ $\qquad y' = (\cos 3)(2x) = 2x \cos 3$

c. $y = \cos(3x)^2 = \cos(9x^2)$ $\qquad y' = (-\sin 9x^2)(18x) = -18x \sin 9x^2$

d. $y = \cos^2 x = (\cos x)^2$ $\qquad y' = 2(\cos x)(-\sin x) = -2 \cos x \sin x$

e. $y = \sqrt{\cos x} = (\cos x)^{1/2}$ $\qquad y' = \frac{1}{2}(\cos x)^{-1/2}(-\sin x) = -\frac{\sin x}{2\sqrt{\cos x}}$

To find the derivative of a function of the form $k(x) = f(g(h(x)))$, you need to apply the Chain Rule twice, as shown in Example 12.

EXAMPLE 12   Repeated Application of the Chain Rule

$$f(t) = \sin^3 4t \qquad \text{Original function}$$
$$= (\sin 4t)^3 \qquad \text{Rewrite.}$$

$$f'(t) = 3(\sin 4t)^2 \frac{d}{dt}[\sin 4t] \qquad \text{Apply Chain Rule once.}$$

$$= 3(\sin 4t)^2(\cos 4t)\frac{d}{dt}[4t] \qquad \text{Apply Chain Rule a second time.}$$

$$= 3(\sin 4t)^2(\cos 4t)(4)$$
$$= 12 \sin^2 4t \cos 4t \qquad \text{Simplify.}$$

The Derivative of the Natural Logarithmic Function

Up to this point in the text, derivatives of algebraic functions have been algebraic and derivatives of transcendental functions have been transcendental. The next theorem looks at an unusual situation in which the derivative of a transcendental function is algebraic. Specifically, the derivative of the natural logarithmic function is the algebraic function $1/x$.

Theorem 2.13   Derivative of the Natural Logarithmic Function

Let u be a differentiable function of x.

1. $\dfrac{d}{dx}[\ln x] = \dfrac{1}{x}, \quad x > 0$

2. $\dfrac{d}{dx}[\ln u] = \dfrac{1}{u}\dfrac{du}{dx} = \dfrac{u'}{u}, \quad u > 0$

Insight

The derivative of the natural logarithmic function is frequently tested on the AP® Exam.

Proof   To prove the first part, let $y = \ln x$, which implies that $e^y = x$. Differentiating both sides of this equation produces the following.

$$y = \ln x$$
$$e^y = x$$
$$\frac{d}{dx}[e^y] = \frac{d}{dx}[x]$$
$$e^y \frac{dy}{dx} = 1 \qquad\qquad \text{Chain Rule}$$
$$\frac{dy}{dx} = \frac{1}{e^y}$$
$$\frac{dy}{dx} = \frac{1}{x}$$

The second part of the theorem can be obtained by applying the Chain Rule to the first part. ∎

EXAMPLE 13   Differentiation of Logarithmic Functions

See LarsonCalculusforAP.com for an interactive version of this type of example.

a. $\dfrac{d}{dx}[\ln 2x] = \dfrac{u'}{u} = \dfrac{2}{2x} = \dfrac{1}{x}$ $u = 2x$

b. $\dfrac{d}{dx}[\ln(x^2 + 1)] = \dfrac{u'}{u} = \dfrac{2x}{x^2 + 1}$ $u = x^2 + 1$

c. $\dfrac{d}{dx}[x \ln x] = x\left(\dfrac{d}{dx}[\ln x]\right) + (\ln x)\left(\dfrac{d}{dx}[x]\right)$ Product Rule

$$= x\left(\frac{1}{x}\right) + (\ln x)(1)$$
$$= 1 + \ln x$$

d. $\dfrac{d}{dx}[(\ln x)^3] = 3(\ln x)^2 \dfrac{d}{dx}[\ln x]$ Chain Rule

$$= 3(\ln x)^2 \frac{1}{x}$$

Scottish mathematician John Napier (1550–1617) used logarithmic properties to simplify *calculations* involving products, quotients, and powers. Of course, given the availability of calculators, there is now little need for this particular application of logarithms. However, there is great value in using logarithmic properties (see Section P.5) to simplify *differentiation* involving products, quotients, and powers.

EXAMPLE 14 Logarithmic Properties as Aids to Differentiation

Differentiate $f(x) = \ln\sqrt{x + 1}$.

Solution Because $\ln x^z = z \ln x$, you can rewrite the function as

$$f(x) = \ln\sqrt{x + 1} = \ln(x + 1)^{1/2} = \frac{1}{2}\ln(x + 1). \qquad \text{Rewrite before differentiating.}$$

So, the first derivative is

$$f'(x) = \frac{1}{2}\left(\frac{1}{x + 1}\right) = \frac{1}{2(x + 1)}. \qquad \text{Differentiate.}$$

EXAMPLE 15 Logarithmic Properties as Aids to Differentiation

Differentiate $f(x) = \ln\dfrac{x(x^2 + 1)^2}{\sqrt{2x^3 - 1}}$.

Solution

Notice how the logarithmic properties

$$\ln xy = \ln x + \ln y, \quad \ln\frac{x}{y} = \ln x - \ln y, \quad \text{and} \quad \ln x^z = z \ln x$$

are used to rewrite the function before differentiating.

$$f(x) = \ln\frac{x(x^2 + 1)^2}{\sqrt{2x^3 - 1}} \qquad \text{Write original function.}$$

$$= \ln x + 2\ln(x^2 + 1) - \frac{1}{2}\ln(2x^3 - 1) \qquad \text{Rewrite before differentiating.}$$

$$f'(x) = \frac{1}{x} + 2\left(\frac{2x}{x^2 + 1}\right) - \frac{1}{2}\left(\frac{6x^2}{2x^3 - 1}\right) \qquad \text{Differentiate.}$$

$$= \frac{1}{x} + \frac{4x}{x^2 + 1} - \frac{3x^2}{2x^3 - 1} \qquad \text{Simplify.} \qquad ■$$

> **Implementing Processes**
>
> In Examples 14 and 15, be sure that you see the benefit of applying logarithmic properties *before* differentiation. Consider, for instance, the difficulty of direct differentiation of the function given in Example 15.

Because the natural logarithm is undefined for negative numbers, you will often encounter expressions of the form $\ln|u|$. Theorem 2.14 states that you can differentiate functions of the form $y = \ln|u|$ as though the absolute value notation was not present.

Theorem 2.14 Derivative Involving Absolute Value

If u is a differentiable function of x such that $u \neq 0$, then

$$\frac{d}{dx}[\ln|u|] = \frac{u'}{u}.$$

Proof If $u > 0$, then $|u| = u$, and the result follows from Theorem 2.13. If $u < 0$, then $|u| = -u$, and you have

$$\frac{d}{dx}[\ln|u|] = \frac{d}{dx}[\ln(-u)] = \frac{-u'}{-u} = \frac{u'}{u}. \qquad ■$$

Bases Other than e

The **base** of the natural exponential function is e. This "natural" base can be used to assign a meaning to a general base a.

> ### Definition of Exponential Function to Base a
>
> If a is a positive real number $(a \neq 1)$ and x is any real number, then the **exponential function to the base a** is denoted by a^x and is defined by
>
> $$a^x = e^{(\ln a)x}.$$
>
> If $a = 1$, then $y = 1^x = 1$ is a constant function.

Logarithmic functions to bases other than e can be defined in much the same way as exponential functions to other bases are defined.

> ### Definition of Logarithmic Function to Base a
>
> If a is a positive real number $(a \neq 1)$ and x is any positive real number, then the **logarithmic function to the base a** is denoted by $\log_a x$ and is defined as
>
> $$\log_a x = \frac{1}{\ln a} \ln x.$$

To differentiate exponential and logarithmic functions to other bases, you have two options: (1) use the definitions of a^x and $\log_a x$ and differentiate using the rules for the natural exponential and logarithmic functions, or (2) use the differentiation rules for bases other than e given in the next theorem.

> **Insight**
>
> Differentiation with bases other than e are rarely tested on the AP® Exam.

> ### Theorem 2.15   Derivatives for Bases Other than e
>
> Let a be a positive real number $(a \neq 1)$ and let u be a differentiable function of x.
>
> **1.** $\dfrac{d}{dx}[a^x] = (\ln a)a^x$ $\qquad$ **2.** $\dfrac{d}{dx}[a^u] = (\ln a)a^u \dfrac{du}{dx}$
>
> **3.** $\dfrac{d}{dx}[\log_a x] = \dfrac{1}{(\ln a)x}$ $\qquad$ **4.** $\dfrac{d}{dx}[\log_a u] = \dfrac{1}{(\ln a)u}\dfrac{du}{dx}$

> **Remark**
>
> These differentiation rules are similar to those for the natural exponential function and the natural logarithmic function. In fact, they differ only by the constant factors $\ln a$ and $1/\ln a$. This points out one reason why, for calculus, e is the most convenient base.

Proof   By definition

$$a^x = e^{(\ln a)x}.$$

Therefore, you can prove the first rule by letting

$$u = (\ln a)x$$

and differentiating with base e to obtain

$$\frac{d}{dx}[a^x] = \frac{d}{dx}[e^{(\ln a)x}] = e^u \frac{du}{dx} = e^{(\ln a)x}(\ln a) = (\ln a)a^x.$$

To prove the third rule, you can write

$$\frac{d}{dx}[\log_a x] = \frac{d}{dx}\left[\frac{1}{\ln a}\ln x\right] = \frac{1}{\ln a}\left(\frac{1}{x}\right) = \frac{1}{(\ln a)x}.$$

The second and fourth rules are simply the Chain Rule versions of the first and third rules.

Differentiating Functions to Other Bases

a. $y' = \dfrac{d}{dx}[2^x] = (\ln 2)2^x$

b. $y' = \dfrac{d}{dx}[2^{3x}] = (\ln 2)2^{3x}(3) = (3 \ln 2)2^{3x}$

c. $y' = \dfrac{d}{dx}[\log_{10} \cos x] = \dfrac{-\sin x}{(\ln 10)\cos x} = -\dfrac{1}{\ln 10} \tan x$

d. After rewriting the function below using logarithmic properties

$$y = \log_3 \frac{\sqrt{x}}{x + 5} = \frac{1}{2} \log_3 x - \log_3(x + 5)$$

you can apply Theorem 2.15 to find the derivative of the function.

$$y' = \frac{d}{dx}\left[\frac{1}{2} \log_3 x - \log_3(x + 5)\right] = \frac{1}{2(\ln 3)x} - \frac{1}{(\ln 3)(x + 5)} = \frac{5 - x}{2(\ln 3)x(x + 5)}$$

> ◄
> **Remark**
> Try writing 2^{3x} as 8^x and differentiating to see that you obtain the same results.

This section concludes with a summary of the differentiation rules studied so far. To become skilled at differentiation, you should memorize each rule in words, not symbols. As an aid to memorization, note that the cofunctions (cosine, cotangent, and cosecant) require a negative sign as part of their derivatives.

Summary of Differentiation Rules

General Differentiation Rules   Let u and v be differentiable functions of x.

Constant Rule:

$$\frac{d}{dx}[c] = 0, c \text{ is a real number.}$$

Constant Multiple Rule:

$$\frac{d}{dx}[cu] = cu', c \text{ is a real number.}$$

Product Rule:

$$\frac{d}{dx}[uv] = uv' + vu'$$

Chain Rule:

$$\frac{d}{dx}[f(u)] = f'(u)u'$$

(Simple) Power Rule:

$$\frac{d}{dx}[x^n] = nx^{n-1}, \frac{d}{dx}[x] = 1, n \text{ is a rational number.}$$

Sum or Difference Rule:

$$\frac{d}{dx}[u \pm v] = u' \pm v'$$

Quotient Rule:

$$\frac{d}{dx}\left[\frac{u}{v}\right] = \frac{vu' - uv'}{v^2}$$

General Power Rule:

$$\frac{d}{dx}[u^n] = nu^{n-1}u', n \text{ is a rational number.}$$

Derivatives of Trigonometric Functions

$$\frac{d}{dx}[\sin x] = \cos x$$

$$\frac{d}{dx}[\sec x] = \sec x \tan x$$

$$\frac{d}{dx}[\cot x] = -\csc^2 x$$

$$\frac{d}{dx}[\tan x] = \sec^2 x$$

$$\frac{d}{dx}[\cos x] = -\sin x$$

$$\frac{d}{dx}[\csc x] = -\csc x \cot x$$

Derivatives of Exponential and Logarithmic Functions

$$\frac{d}{dx}[e^x] = e^x$$

$$\frac{d}{dx}[a^x] = (\ln a)a^x,$$

a is a positive real number ($a \neq 1$).

$$\frac{d}{dx}[\ln x] = \frac{1}{x}, \quad x > 0$$

$$\frac{d}{dx}[\log_a x] = \frac{1}{(\ln a)x},$$

a is a positive real number ($a \neq 1$).

2.4 Exercises

See *CalcChat.com* for tutorial help and worked-out solutions to odd-numbered exercises.

Decomposition of a Composite Function
In Exercises 1–6, complete the table by writing
$u = g(x)$ **and** $y = f(u)$ **such that** $y = f(g(x))$.

$y = f(g(x))$	$u = g(x)$	$y = f(u)$
1. $y = (6x - 5)^4$		
2. $y = \dfrac{1}{\sqrt{x + 1}}$		
3. $y = \csc^3 x$		
4. $y = 3 \tan \pi x^2$		
5. $y = e^{-2x}$		
6. $y = (\ln x)^5$		

Finding a Derivative   In Exercises 7–34, find the derivative of the function.

7. $y = (2x - 7)^3$

8. $y = 5(2 - x^3)^4$

9. $g(x) = 3(9x^2 + 4)^4$

10. $f(t) = (9t + 2)^{2/3}$

11. $f(t) = \sqrt{5 - t}$

12. $g(x) = \sqrt{4 - 3x^2}$

13. $y = \sqrt[3]{6x^2 + 1}$

14. $f(x) = \sqrt{x^2 - 4x + 2}$

15. $y = 2\sqrt[4]{(9 - x^2)^3}$

16. $f(x) = \sqrt[3]{(12x - 5)^4}$

17. $y = \dfrac{1}{x - 2}$

18. $s(t) = \dfrac{1}{4 - 5t - t^2}$

19. $f(t) = \left(\dfrac{1}{2t - 3}\right)^2$

20. $y = -\dfrac{3}{(3t - 2)^4}$

21. $y = \dfrac{1}{\sqrt{3x + 5}}$

22. $g(t) = \dfrac{1}{\sqrt{t^2 - 2}}$

23. $f(x) = x^2(x^2 - 2)^4$

24. $f(x) = x(2x - 5)^3$

25. $y = x\sqrt{1 - x^2}$

26. $y = \frac{1}{2}x^2\sqrt{16 - x^2}$

27. $y = \dfrac{x}{\sqrt{x^2 + 1}}$

28. $y = \dfrac{x}{\sqrt[3]{x^4 + 16}}$

29. $g(x) = \left(\dfrac{x + 5}{x^2 + 2}\right)^2$

30. $h(t) = \left(\dfrac{t^2}{t^3 + 2}\right)^2$

31. $f(v) = \left(\dfrac{1 - 2v}{1 + v}\right)^3$

32. $g(x) = \dfrac{(3x^2 - 2)^2}{(2x + 3)^3}$

33. $f(x) = [(x^2 + 3)^5 + x]^2$ **34.** $g(x) = [2 + (x^2 + 1)^4]^3$

Finding a Derivative Using Technology In Exercises 35–40, use a computer algebra system to find the derivative of the function. Then use the utility to graph the function and its derivative on the same set of coordinate axes. Describe the behavior of the function that corresponds to any zeros of the graph of the derivative.

35. $y = \dfrac{\sqrt{x + 1}}{x^2 + 1}$

36. $y = \sqrt{\dfrac{2x}{x + 1}}$

37. $y = \sqrt{\dfrac{x + 1}{x}}$

38. $g(x) = \sqrt{x - 1} + \sqrt{x}$

39. $y = \dfrac{\cos \pi x + 1}{x}$

40. $y = x^2 \tan \dfrac{1}{x}$

Finding a Derivative   In Exercises 41–98, find the derivative of the function.

41. $g(x) = 5 \tan 3x$

42. $h(x) = \sec x^2$

43. $y = \cos(4 - x)$

44. $y = \sin(x - \pi)$

45. $f(x) = e^{2x}$

46. $y = e^{-x^2}$

47. $y = e^{\sqrt{x}}$

48. $g(t) = e^{-3/t^2}$

49. $y = (\sin 2)x^2$

50. $y = \cos(\pi x)^2$

51. $y = 4 \sec^2 x$

52. $g(t) = 5 \cos^2 \pi t$

53. $f(\theta) = \tan^2 5\theta$

54. $g(\theta) = \cos^2 8\theta$

55. $f(\theta) = \frac{1}{4} \sin^2 2\theta$

56. $h(t) = 2 \cot^2(\pi t + 2)$

57. $f(t) = 3 \sec^2(\pi t - 1)$

58. $y = 3x - 5 \cos(\pi x)^2$

59. $y = \sqrt{x} + \frac{1}{4} \sin(2x)^2$

60. $y = \sin \sqrt[3]{x} + \sqrt[3]{\sin x}$

61. $y = \sin(\tan 2x)$

62. $y = \cos\sqrt{\sin(\tan \pi x)}$

63. $h(x) = \sin 2x \cos 2x$

64. $g(\theta) = \sec(\theta/2)\tan(\theta/2)$

65. $f(x) = \dfrac{\cot x}{\sin x}$

66. $g(v) = \dfrac{\cos v}{\csc v}$

67. $g(t) = (e^{-t} + e^t)^3$

68. $y = x^2 e^{-x}$

69. $y = \ln(e^{x^2})$

70. $y = \ln\left(\dfrac{1 + e^x}{1 - e^x}\right)$

71. $y = \dfrac{2}{e^x + e^{-x}}$

72. $y = \dfrac{e^x - e^{-x}}{2}$

73. $y = x^2 e^x - 2xe^x + 2e^x$ **74.** $y = xe^x - e^x$

75. $f(x) = e^{-x} \ln x$

76. $f(x) = e^3 \ln x$

77. $y = e^x(\sin x + \cos x)$

78. $y = \ln e^x$

79. $g(x) = \ln x^2$

80. $h(x) = \ln(2x^2 + 3)$

81. $y = x^2 \ln x$

82. $y = (\ln x)^4$

83. $y = \ln(x\sqrt{x^2 - 1})$

84. $y = \ln\sqrt{x^2 - 9}$

85. $f(x) = \ln\left(\dfrac{x}{x^2 + 1}\right)$

86. $f(x) = \ln\left(\dfrac{2x}{x + 3}\right)$

87. $g(t) = (\ln t)/t^2$

88. $h(t) = (\ln t)/t$

89. $y = \ln\sqrt{\dfrac{x + 1}{x - 1}}$

90. $y = \ln\sqrt[3]{\dfrac{x - 2}{x + 2}}$

91. $y = \ln|\sin x|$

92. $y = \ln|\csc x|$

93. $y = \ln\left|\dfrac{\cos x}{\cos x - 1}\right|$

94. $y = \ln|\sec x + \tan x|$

95. $y = \ln\left|\dfrac{-1 + \sin x}{2 + \sin x}\right|$ **96.** $y = \ln\sqrt{1 + \sin^2 x}$

97. $y = \dfrac{-\sqrt{x^2 + 1}}{x} + \ln(x + \sqrt{x^2 + 1})$

98. $y = \dfrac{-\sqrt{x^2 + 4}}{2x^2} - \frac{1}{4}\ln\left(\dfrac{2 + \sqrt{x^2 + 4}}{x}\right)$

Error Analysis In Exercises 99–102, describe and correct the error when finding the derivative of the function.

99. If $y = (1 - x)^{1/2}$, then $y' = \frac{1}{2}(1 - x)^{-1/2}$. ✗

100. If $f(x) = \sin^2 2x$, then $f'(x) = 2(\sin 2x)(\cos 2x)$. ✗

101. $\dfrac{d}{dx}\left[\dfrac{e^{3x}}{x}\right] = \dfrac{3xe^{2x} - e^{3x}}{x^2} = e^{2x}\left(\dfrac{3x - e^x}{x^2}\right)$ ✗

102. $\dfrac{d}{dx}[x^4 e^{-2x}] = x^4 e^{-2x} + e^{-2x}(4x^3) = x^3 e^{-2x}(x + 4)$ ✗

Slope of a Tangent Line In Exercises 103 and 104, find the slope of the tangent line to the sine function at the origin. Compare this value with the number of complete cycles in the interval $[0, 2\pi]$.

103. (a) 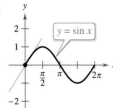 (b)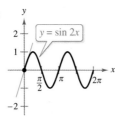

104. (a) 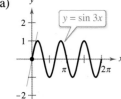 (b)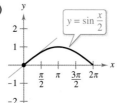

 Slope of a Tangent Line In Exercises 105–108, find the slope of the tangent line to the graph of the function at the given point.

105. $y = e^{4x}$, $(0, 1)$ **106.** $y = e^{-3x}$, $(0, 1)$

107. $y = \ln x^3$, $(1, 0)$ **108.** $y = \ln x^{3/2}$, $(1, 0)$

 Evaluating a Derivative In Exercises 109–116, find and evaluate the derivative of the function at the given point. Use a graphing utility to verify your result.

109. $y = \sqrt{x^2 + 8x}$, $(1, 3)$

110. $y = \sqrt[5]{4x^3}$, $(2, 2)$

111. $f(x) = \dfrac{7}{x^3 - 6}$, $\left(-2, -\dfrac{1}{2}\right)$

112. $f(x) = \dfrac{1}{(x^2 - 3x)^2}$, $\left(4, \dfrac{1}{16}\right)$

113. $f(t) = \dfrac{12t + 5}{t - 1}$, $(0, -5)$

114. $f(x) = \dfrac{x + 5}{2(x - 2)}$, $(9, 1)$

115. $y = 13 - \sec^3 3x$, $(0, 12)$

116. $y = \dfrac{1}{x} + \sqrt{\cos x}$, $\left(\dfrac{\pi}{2}, \dfrac{2}{\pi}\right)$

 Finding an Equation of a Tangent Line In Exercises 117–124, (a) find an equation of the tangent line to the graph of the function at the given point, (b) use a graphing utility to graph the function and its tangent line at the point, and (c) use the *tangent* feature of the graphing utility to confirm your results.

117. $f(x) = \sqrt{7x^2 + 9}$, $(4, 11)$

118. $f(x) = (9 - x^2)^{2/3}$, $(1, 4)$

119. $f(x) = \sin 8x$, $(\pi, 0)$

120. $y = \cos 3x$, $\left(\dfrac{\pi}{4}, -\dfrac{\sqrt{2}}{2}\right)$

121. $f(x) = \tan^2 x$, $\left(\dfrac{\pi}{4}, 1\right)$

122. $y = 2\tan^3 x$, $\left(\dfrac{\pi}{4}, 2\right)$

123. $y = 4 - x^2 - \ln\left(\dfrac{1}{2}x + 1\right)$, $(0, 4)$

124. $y = 2e^{1 - x^2}$, $(1, 2)$

Famous Curves In Exercises 125 and 126, find an equation of the tangent line to the graph at the labeled point. Then use a graphing utility to graph the function and its tangent line at the point in the same viewing window.

125. Semicircle **126.** Bullet-nose curve

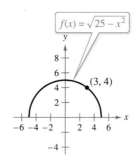 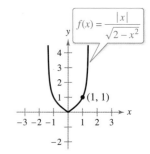

Horizontal Tangent Line In Exercises 127 and 128, determine the point(s) at which the graph of the function has a horizontal tangent line.

127. $f(x) = 2\cos x + \sin 2x$, $0 < x < 2\pi$

128. $f(x) = \dfrac{x}{\sqrt{2x - 1}}$

 **Finding a Second Derivative** In Exercises 129–136, find the second derivative of the function.

129. $f(x) = 5(2 - 7x)^4$ **130.** $f(x) = 4(x^3 + 6)^3$

131. $f(x) = \dfrac{1}{5x - 12}$ **132.** $f(x) = \dfrac{2}{(3x - 8)^2}$

133. $f(x) = \sin x^2$ **134.** $f(x) = \sec^2 \pi x$

135. $f(x) = (2 + 3x)e^{-2x}$ **136.** $g(x) = \sqrt{x} + e^x \ln x$

Evaluating a Second Derivative In Exercises 137–140, evaluate the second derivative of the function at the given point. Use a computer algebra system to verify your result.

137. $h(x) = \frac{1}{4}(2x + 1)^3$, $\left(1, \frac{27}{4}\right)$

138. $f(x) = \frac{1}{\sqrt{x + 9}}$, $\left(0, \frac{1}{3}\right)$

139. $f(x) = \cos x^2$, $(0, 1)$

140. $g(t) = \tan 2t$, $\left(\frac{\pi}{6}, \sqrt{3}\right)$

 Finding a Derivative In Exercises 141–154, find the derivative of the function.

141. $f(x) = 5^x$

142. $g(x) = 2^{8x}$

143. $y = 4^{2x-3}$

144. $y = x(2^{-6x})$

145. $g(t) = t^2 2^t$

146. $f(t) = \frac{2^{3t}}{t}$

147. $h(\theta) = 2^{-\theta} \cos \pi\theta$

148. $g(\alpha) = 2^{-\alpha/2} \sin 4\alpha$

149. $y = \log_5 \tan x$

150. $h(x) = \log_3 \frac{x\sqrt{x - 1}}{2}$

151. $y = \log_{10} \frac{x^2}{\sqrt{x + 1}}$

152. $y = \log_{10} \frac{x^2 - 1}{x}$

153. $g(t) = \frac{8 \log_5 t}{t}$

154. $f(t) = t^{3/2} \log_2 \sqrt{t + 1}$

EXPLORING CONCEPTS

Communication and Notation In Exercises 155 and 156, the graphs of a function f and its derivative f' are shown. Label the graphs as f or f'. Explain your reasoning. To print an enlarged copy of the graph, go to *MathGraphs.com*.

155.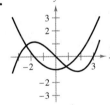

156.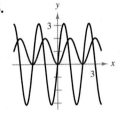

Connecting Representations In Exercises 157 and 158, the relationship between f and g is given. Explain the relationship between f' and g'.

157. $g(x) = f(3x)$

158. $g(x) = f(x^2)$

 Evaluating a Derivative In Exercises 159–162, given that $g(5) = -3$, $g'(5) = 6$, $h(5) = 3$, and $h'(5) = -2$, find $f'(5)$, if possible. If it is not possible, state what additional information is required.

159. $f(x) = g(x)h(x)$

160. $f(x) = g(h(x))$

161. $f(x) = \frac{g(x)}{h(x)}$

162. $f(x) = [g(x)]^3$

 Finding Derivatives In Exercises 163 and 164, the graphs of f and g are shown. Let $h(x) = f(g(x))$ and $s(x) = g(f(x))$. Find each derivative, if it exists. If the derivative does not exist, explain why.

163. (a) Find $h'(1)$.

(b) Find $s'(5)$.

164. (a) Find $h'(3)$.

(b) Find $s'(9)$.

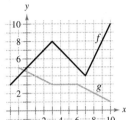
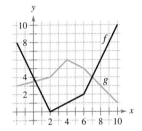

165. Doppler Effect The frequency F of a fire truck siren heard by a stationary observer is given by

$$F = \frac{132,400}{331 \pm v}$$

where $\pm v$ represents the velocity of the accelerating fire truck in meters per second (see figure). Find the rate of change of F with respect to v when

(a) the fire truck is approaching at a velocity of 30 meters per second.

(b) the fire truck is moving away at a velocity of 30 meters per second.

$$F = \frac{132,400}{331 + v} \qquad F = \frac{132,400}{331 - v}$$

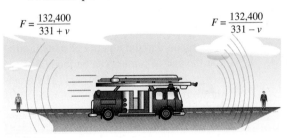

166. Pendulum A 15-centimeter pendulum moves according to the equation $\theta = 0.2 \cos 8t$, where θ is the angular displacement from the vertical in radians and t is the time in seconds. Determine the maximum angular displacement and the rate of change of θ when $t = 3$ seconds.

167. Harmonic Motion The displacement from equilibrium of an object in harmonic motion on the end of a spring is given by

$$y = \frac{1}{3} \cos 12t - \frac{1}{4} \sin 12t$$

where y is measured in feet and t is the time in seconds. Determine the position and velocity of the object when $t = \pi/8$.

168. Wave Motion A buoy oscillates in simple harmonic motion $y = A \cos \omega t$ as waves move past it. The buoy moves a total of 3.5 feet (vertically) from its low point to its high point. It returns to its high point every 10 seconds.

(a) Write an equation describing the motion of the buoy if it is at its high point at $t = 0$.

(b) Determine the velocity of the buoy as a function of t.

169. Modeling Data The table shows the temperatures T (in degrees Fahrenheit) at which water boils at selected pressures p (in pounds per square inch). *(Source: Standard Handbook for Mechanical Engineers)*

p	5	10	14.696 (1 atmosphere)	20
T	162.21	193.19	212.00	227.96

p	30	40	60	80	100
T	250.34	267.26	292.73	312.07	327.86

(a) Use the information in the table to estimate $T'(35)$ and $T'(70)$. Interpret your results.

(b) A model that approximates the data is $T = 87.92 + 34.97 \ln p + 7.92\sqrt{p}$. Use the model to find the rates of change of T with respect to p when $p = 35$ and $p = 70$. Compare the rates of change with the approximations in part (a).

170. HOW DO YOU SEE IT? The cost C (in dollars) of producing x units of a product is $C = 60x + 1350$. For one week, management determined that the number of units produced x at the end of t hours can be modeled by $x = -1.6t^3 + 19t^2 - 0.5t - 1$. The graph shows the cost C in terms of the time t.

Cost of Producing a Product

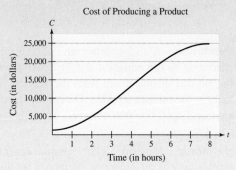

(a) Using the graph, which is greater, the rate of change of the cost after 1 hour or the rate of change of the cost after 4 hours?

(b) Explain why the cost function is not increasing at a constant rate during the 8-hour shift.

171. Depreciation The value V of a machine t years after it is purchased is inversely proportional to the square root of $t + 1$. The initial value of the machine is $10,000.

(a) Write V as a function of t.

(b) Find the rate of depreciation when $t = 1$.

(c) Find the rate of depreciation when $t = 3$.

172. Inflation When the annual rate of inflation averages 5% over 10 consecutive years, the approximate cost c of goods or services during any year in that decade is $C(t) = P(1.05)^t$, where t is the time in years and P is the initial cost.

(a) The price of an oil change for your car is $29.95. Estimate the price after 10 years.

(b) Find the rates of change of C with respect to t when $t = 1$ and $t = 8$.

(c) Is the rate of change of C proportional to C? Justify your answer. If so, what is the constant of proportionality?

173. BIOLOGY

The number N of bacteria in a culture after t days is modeled by

$$N = 400\left[1 - \frac{3}{(t^2 + 2)^2}\right].$$

Find the rate of change of N with respect to t when (a) $t = 0$, (b) $t = 1$, (c) $t = 2$, (d) $t = 3$, and (e) $t = 4$. (f) What can you conclude?

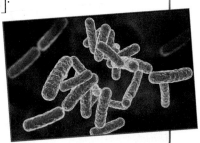

174. Connecting Representations The table shows some values of the derivative of an unknown function f. Find the derivative of each transformation of f and complete the table, if possible. If not possible, explain why.

(a) $g(x) = f(x) - 2$

(b) $h(x) = 2f(x)$

(c) $r(x) = f(-3x)$

(d) $s(x) = f(x + 2)$

x	-2	-1	0	1	2	3
$f'(x)$	4	$\frac{2}{3}$	$-\frac{1}{3}$	-1	-2	-4
$g'(x)$						
$h'(x)$						
$r'(x)$						
$s'(x)$						

175. Finding a Pattern Consider the function $f(x) = \sin \beta x$, where β is a constant.

(a) Find $f'(x)$, $f''(x)$, $f'''(x)$, and $f^{(4)}(x)$.

(b) Verify that the function and its second derivative satisfy the equation $f''(x) + \beta^2 f(x) = 0$.

(c) Use the results of part (a) to write general rules for the even- and odd-order derivatives $f^{(2k)}(x)$ and $f^{(2k-1)}(x)$. [*Hint:* $(-1)^k$ is positive if k is even and negative if k is odd.]

176. Justifying Let f be a differentiable function with period p.

(a) Is the function f' periodic? Verify your answer.

(b) Consider the function $g(x) = f(2x)$. Is the function g' periodic? Verify your answer.

177. Connecting Representations Let $r(x) = f(g(x))$ and $s(x) = g(f(x))$, where f and g are shown in the figure. Find (a) $r'(1)$ and (b) $s'(4)$.

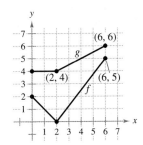

178. Derivatives Involving Trigonometric Functions

(a) Find the derivative of the function $g(x) = \sin^2 x + \cos^2 x$ in two ways.

(b) For $f(x) = \sec^2 x$ and $g(x) = \tan^2 x$, show that $f'(x) = g'(x)$.

179. Derivatives Involving Even and Odd Functions

(a) Show that the derivative of an odd function is even. That is, if $f(-x) = -f(x)$, then $f'(-x) = f'(x)$.

(b) Show that the derivative of an even function is odd. That is, if $f(-x) = f(x)$, then $f'(-x) = -f'(x)$.

180. Proof Let u be a differentiable function of x. Use the fact that $|u| = \sqrt{u^2}$ to prove that

$$\frac{d}{dx}\big[|u|\big] = u'\frac{u}{|u|}, \quad u \neq 0.$$

Derivatives Involving Absolute Value In Exercises 181–184, use the result of Exercise 180 to find the derivative of the function.

181. $g(x) = |5x - 3|$

182. $f(x) = |x^2 - 4|$

183. $h(x) = |x| \cos x$

184. $f(x) - |\sin x|$

True or False? In Exercises 185–188, determine whether the statement is true or false. If it is false, explain why or give an example that shows it is false.

185. The slope of the function $f(x) = \sin ax$ at the origin is a.

186. The slope of the function $f(x) = \cos bx$ at the origin is $-b$.

187. If $f(x) = \ln 2x$ and $g(x) = \ln 3x$, then $f'(x) = g'(x)$.

188. If y is a differentiable function of u, u is a differentiable function of v, and v is a differentiable function of x, then

$$\frac{dy}{dx} = \frac{dy}{du} \cdot \frac{du}{dv} \cdot \frac{dv}{dx}.$$

Linear and Quadratic Approximations The linear and quadratic approximations of a function f at $x = a$ are

$$P_1(x) = f'(a)(x - a) + f(a) \quad \text{and}$$
$$P_2(x) = \tfrac{1}{2}f''(a)(x - a)^2 + f'(a)(x - a) + f(a).$$

In Exercises 189–192, (a) find the specified linear and quadratic approximations of f, (b) use a graphing utility to graph f and the approximations, (c) determine whether P_1 or P_2 is the better approximation, and (d) state how the accuracy changes as you move farther from $x = a$.

189. $f(x) = \tan x$; $\quad a = \dfrac{\pi}{4}$

190. $f(x) = \sec x$; $\quad a = \dfrac{\pi}{6}$

191. $f(x) = e^x$; $\quad a = 0$

192. $f(x) = \ln x$; $\quad a = 1$

Calculus AP® – Exam Preparation Questions

193. Multiple Choice The table shows selected function and derivative values for the differentiable functions $f(x)$ and $g(x)$.

x	$f(x)$	$f'(x)$	$g(x)$	$g'(x)$
1	2	6	-3	-2
2	8	5	-3	3
3	10	-2	5	14
4	2	-15	27	31

If $h(x) = xf(x) + g(3x + 1)$, then $h'(1) =$

(A) 39. (B) 89. (C) 99. (D) 101.

194. Multiple Choice If $h(\theta) = \cos^3 7\theta$, then $h'(\theta) =$

(A) $-21 \cos^2 7\theta$.

(B) $-3 \cos^2 7\theta \sin 7\theta$.

(C) $-21 \cos^2 7\theta \sin 7\theta$.

(D) $21 \cos^2 7\theta \sin 7\theta$.

195. Free Response The function g is defined as $g(x) = (2x^2 + 1)^3$.

(a) Find the slope of the tangent line to the graph of g at $x = 1$.

(b) Find the equation of the tangent line to the graph of g at $x = 1$.

(c) Determine the point(s), if any, at which the graph of g has a horizontal tangent.

(d) Find $g''(x)$.

2.5 Implicit Differentiation

▶ Distinguish between functions written in implicit form and explicit form.
▶ Use implicit differentiation to find the derivative of a function.
▶ Find derivatives of functions using logarithmic differentiation.

Implicit and Explicit Functions

Up to this point in the text, most functions have been expressed in **explicit form.** For example, in the equation $y = 3x^2 - 5$, the variable y is explicitly written as a function of x. Some functions, however, are only implied by an equation. For instance, the function $y = 1/x$ is defined **implicitly** by the equation

$$xy = 1. \qquad \text{Implicit form}$$

To find dy/dx for this equation, you can write y explicitly as a function of x and then differentiate.

Implicit Form	*Explicit Form*	*Derivative*
$xy = 1$	$y = \dfrac{1}{x} = x^{-1}$	$\dfrac{dy}{dx} = -x^{-2} = -\dfrac{1}{x^2}$

This strategy works whenever you can solve for the function explicitly. You cannot, however, use this procedure when you are unable to solve for y as a function of x. For instance, how would you find dy/dx for the equation

$$x^2 - 2y^3 + 4y = 2?$$

For this equation, it is difficult to express y as a function of x explicitly. To find dy/dx, you can use **implicit differentiation.**

To understand how to find dy/dx implicitly, you must realize that the differentiation is taking place *with respect to x*. This means that when you differentiate terms involving x alone, you can differentiate as usual. However, when you differentiate terms involving y, you must apply the Chain Rule, because you are assuming that y is defined implicitly as a differentiable function of x.

EXAMPLE 1 Differentiation with Respect to x

a. $\dfrac{d}{dx}[x^3] = 3x^2$ 　　　　Variables agree: use Simple Power Rule.

　　Variables agree

　　　$\overbrace{u^n} \quad \overbrace{nu^{n-1}} \, \overbrace{u'}$

b. $\dfrac{d}{dx}[y^3] = 3y^2\dfrac{dy}{dx}$ 　　　　Variables disagree: use Chain Rule.

　　Variables disagree

c. $\dfrac{d}{dx}[x + 3y] = 1 + 3\dfrac{dy}{dx}$ 　　　Chain Rule: $\dfrac{d}{dx}[3y] = 3y'$

d. $\dfrac{d}{dx}[xy^2] = x\dfrac{d}{dx}[y^2] + y^2\dfrac{d}{dx}[x]$ 　　Product Rule

　　　　$= x\left(2y\dfrac{dy}{dx}\right) + y^2(1)$ 　　Chain Rule

　　　　$= 2xy\dfrac{dy}{dx} + y^2$ 　　　Simplify.

Implicit Differentiation

> ## Guidelines for Implicit Differentiation
>
> **1.** Differentiate both sides of the equation *with respect to x*.
> **2.** Collect all terms involving dy/dx on one side of the equation and move all other terms to the other side of the equation.
> **3.** Factor out dy/dx.
> **4.** Solve for dy/dx.

In Example 2, note that implicit differentiation can produce an expression for dy/dx that contains both x and y.

EXAMPLE 2   Implicit Differentiation

Find dy/dx given that $y^3 + y^2 - 5y - x^2 = -4$.

Solution

1. Differentiate both sides of the equation with respect to x.

$$\frac{d}{dx}[y^3 + y^2 - 5y - x^2] = \frac{d}{dx}[-4]$$

$$\frac{d}{dx}[y^3] + \frac{d}{dx}[y^2] - \frac{d}{dx}[5y] - \frac{d}{dx}[x^2] = \frac{d}{dx}[-4]$$

$$3y^2 \frac{dy}{dx} + 2y \frac{dy}{dx} - 5 \frac{dy}{dx} - 2x = 0$$

2. Collect the dy/dx terms on one side of the equation and move all other terms to the other side of the equation.

$$3y^2 \frac{dy}{dx} + 2y \frac{dy}{dx} - 5 \frac{dy}{dx} = 2x$$

3. Factor dy/dx out of the left side of the equation.

$$\frac{dy}{dx}(3y^2 + 2y - 5) = 2x$$

4. Solve for dy/dx by dividing by $(3y^2 + 2y - 5)$.

$$\frac{dy}{dx} = \frac{2x}{3y^2 + 2y - 5}$$

To see how you can use an *implicit derivative,* consider the graph shown in Figure 2.24. From the graph, you can see that y is not a function of x. Even so, the derivative found in Example 2 gives a formula for the slope of the tangent line at a point on this graph. The slopes at several points on the graph are shown below the graph.

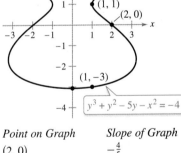

Point on Graph	Slope of Graph
$(2, 0)$	$-\frac{4}{5}$
$(1, -3)$	$\frac{1}{8}$
$x = 0$	0
$(1, 1)$	Undefined

Figure 2.24

Technology

With most graphing utilities, it is easy to graph an equation that explicitly represents y as a function of x. Graphing other equations, however, can require some ingenuity. For instance, to graph the equation given in Example 2, use a graphing utility, set in *parametric* mode, to graph the parametric representations $x = \sqrt{t^3 + t^2 - 5t + 4}$, $y = t$, and $x = -\sqrt{t^3 + t^2 - 5t + 4}$, $y = t$, for $-5 \le t \le 5$. How does the result compare with the graph shown in Figure 2.24?

It is meaningless to solve for dy/dx in an equation that has no solution points. (For example, $x^2 + y^2 = -4$ has no solution points.) If, however, a segment of a graph can be represented by a differentiable function, then dy/dx will have meaning as the slope at each point on the segment. Recall that a function is not differentiable at (a) points with vertical tangents and (b) points at which the function is not continuous.

EXAMPLE 3   Graphs and Differentiable Functions

If possible, represent y as a differentiable function of x.

a. $x^2 + y^2 = 0$

b. $x^2 + y^2 = 1$

c. $x + y^2 = 1$

Solution

a. The graph of this equation is a single point. So, it does not define y as a differentiable function of x. See Figure 2.25(a).

b. The graph of this equation is the unit circle centered at $(0, 0)$. The upper semicircle is given by the differentiable function

$$y = \sqrt{1 - x^2}, \quad -1 < x < 1$$

and the lower semicircle is given by the differentiable function

$$y = -\sqrt{1 - x^2}, \quad -1 < x < 1.$$

At the points $(-1, 0)$ and $(1, 0)$, the slope of the graph is undefined. See Figure 2.25(b).

c. The upper half of this parabola is given by the differentiable function

$$y = \sqrt{1 - x}, \quad x < 1$$

and the lower half of this parabola is given by the differentiable function

$$y = -\sqrt{1 - x}, \quad x < 1.$$

At the point $(1, 0)$, the slope of the graph is undefined. See Figure 2.25(c).

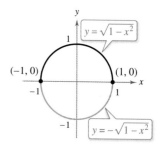

(a)

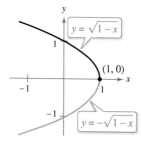

(b)

(c)

Some graph segments can be represented by differentiable functions.
Figure 2.25

EXAMPLE 4   Finding the Slope of a Graph Implicitly

See LarsonCalculusforAP.com for an interactive version of this type of example.

Determine the slope of the tangent line to the graph of $x^2 + 4y^2 = 4$ at the point $\left(\sqrt{2}, -1/\sqrt{2}\right)$.

Algebraic Solution

$$x^2 + 4y^2 = 4 \qquad \text{Write original equation.}$$

$$2x + 8y\frac{dy}{dx} = 0 \qquad \text{Differentiate with respect to } x.$$

$$\frac{dy}{dx} = \frac{-2x}{8y} \qquad \text{Solve for } \frac{dy}{dx}.$$

$$= \frac{-x}{4y} \qquad \text{Simplify.}$$

So, at $\left(\sqrt{2}, -1/\sqrt{2}\right)$, the slope is

$$\frac{dy}{dx} = \frac{-\sqrt{2}}{-4/\sqrt{2}} = \frac{1}{2}. \qquad \begin{array}{l} \text{Evaluate } \frac{dy}{dx} \text{ when } x = \sqrt{2} \\ \text{and } y = -\frac{1}{\sqrt{2}}. \end{array}$$

Graphical Solution

Using a graphing utility to graph $y_1 = \sqrt{(4 - x^2)/4}$ and $y_2 = -\sqrt{(4 - x^2)/4}$.

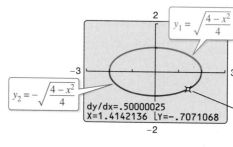

Use the *derivative* feature to determine that the slope of the tangent line to the graph of $x^2 + 4y^2 = 4$ at $\left(\sqrt{2}, -\frac{1}{\sqrt{2}}\right)$ is $\frac{1}{2}$.

To see the benefit of implicit differentiation, try doing Example 4 using the explicit function $y = -\frac{1}{2}\sqrt{4 - x^2}$.

EXAMPLE 5   Finding the Slope of a Graph Implicitly

Determine the slope of the graph of

$$3(x^2 + y^2)^2 = 100xy$$

at the point $(3, 1)$.

Solution

$$\frac{d}{dx}[3(x^2 + y^2)^2] = \frac{d}{dx}[100xy]$$

$$3(2)(x^2 + y^2)\left(2x + 2y\frac{dy}{dx}\right) = 100\left[x\frac{dy}{dx} + y(1)\right]$$

$$12y(x^2 + y^2)\frac{dy}{dx} - 100x\frac{dy}{dx} = 100y - 12x(x^2 + y^2)$$

$$[12y(x^2 + y^2) - 100x]\frac{dy}{dx} = 100y - 12x(x^2 + y^2)$$

$$\frac{dy}{dx} = \frac{100y - 12x(x^2 + y^2)}{-100x + 12y(x^2 + y^2)}$$

$$= \frac{25y - 3x(x^2 + y^2)}{-25x + 3y(x^2 + y^2)}$$

At the point $(3, 1)$, the slope of the graph is

$$\frac{dy}{dx} = \frac{25(1) - 3(3)(3^2 + 1^2)}{-25(3) + 3(1)(3^2 + 1^2)} = \frac{25 - 90}{-75 + 30} = \frac{-65}{-45} = \frac{13}{9}$$

as shown in Figure 2.26. This graph is called a **lemniscate.**

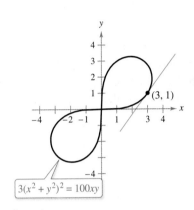

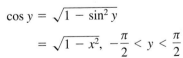

Lemniscate
Figure 2.26

EXAMPLE 6   Determining a Differentiable Function

Find dy/dx implicitly for the equation $\sin y = x$. Then find the largest interval of the form $-a < y < a$ on which y is a differentiable function of x. (See Figure 2.27.)

Solution

$$\frac{d}{dx}[\sin y] = \frac{d}{dx}[x]$$

$$(\cos y)\frac{dy}{dx} = 1$$

$$\frac{dy}{dx} = \frac{1}{\cos y}$$

The largest interval about the origin for which y is a differentiable function of x is $-\pi/2 < y < \pi/2$. To see this, note that $\cos y$ is positive for all y in this interval and is 0 at the endpoints. When you restrict y to the interval $-\pi/2 < y < \pi/2$, you should be able to write dy/dx explicitly as a function of x. To do this, you can use

$$\cos y = \sqrt{1 - \sin^2 y}$$

$$= \sqrt{1 - x^2}, \quad -\frac{\pi}{2} < y < \frac{\pi}{2}$$

and conclude that

$$\frac{dy}{dx} = \frac{1}{\sqrt{1 - x^2}}.$$

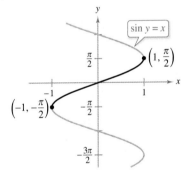

The derivative is $\dfrac{dy}{dx} = \dfrac{1}{\sqrt{1 - x^2}}$.

Figure 2.27

You will study this example further when derivatives of inverse trigonometric functions are defined in Section 2.6.

With implicit differentiation, the form of the derivative often can be simplified (as in Example 6) by an appropriate use of the *original* equation. A similar technique can be used to find and simplify higher-order derivatives obtained implicitly.

EXAMPLE 7   Finding the Second Derivative Implicitly

Given $x^2 + y^2 = 25$, find $\dfrac{d^2y}{dx^2}$.

Solution

Differentiating each term with respect to x produces

$$2x + 2y\frac{dy}{dx} = 0$$

$$2y\frac{dy}{dx} = -2x$$

$$\frac{dy}{dx} = \frac{-2x}{2y}$$

$$= -\frac{x}{y}.$$

Differentiating a second time with respect to x yields

$$\frac{d^2y}{dx^2} = -\frac{(y)(1) - (x)(dy/dx)}{y^2} \qquad \text{Quotient Rule}$$

$$= -\frac{y - (x)(-x/y)}{y^2} \qquad \text{Substitute } -\frac{x}{y} \text{ for } \frac{dy}{dx}.$$

$$= -\frac{y^2 + x^2}{y^3} \qquad \text{Simplify.}$$

$$= -\frac{25}{y^3}. \qquad \text{Substitute 25 for } x^2 + y^2.$$

EXAMPLE 8   Finding a Tangent Line to a Graph

Find the tangent line to the graph of $x^2(x^2 + y^2) = y^2$ at the point $\left(\sqrt{2}/2, \sqrt{2}/2\right)$, as shown in Figure 2.28.

Solution

By rewriting and differentiating implicitly, you obtain

$$x^4 + x^2y^2 - y^2 = 0$$

$$4x^3 + x^2\left(2y\frac{dy}{dx}\right) + 2xy^2 - 2y\frac{dy}{dx} = 0$$

$$2y(x^2 - 1)\frac{dy}{dx} = -2x(2x^2 + y^2)$$

$$\frac{dy}{dx} = \frac{x(2x^2 + y^2)}{y(1 - x^2)}.$$

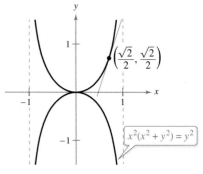

The kappa curve
Figure 2.28

At the point $\left(\sqrt{2}/2, \sqrt{2}/2\right)$, the slope is

$$\frac{dy}{dx} = \frac{\left(\sqrt{2}/2\right)[2(1/2) + (1/2)]}{\left(\sqrt{2}/2\right)[1 - (1/2)]} = \frac{3/2}{1/2} = 3$$

and the equation of the tangent line at this point is

$$y - \frac{\sqrt{2}}{2} = 3\left(x - \frac{\sqrt{2}}{2}\right)$$

$$y = 3x - \sqrt{2}.$$

Logarithmic Differentiation

On occasion, it is convenient to use logarithms as aids in differentiating nonlogarithmic functions. This procedure is called **logarithmic differentiation.**

EXAMPLE 9   Logarithmic Differentiation

Find the derivative of

$$y = \frac{(x - 2)^2}{\sqrt{x^2 + 1}}, \quad x \neq 2.$$

Solution

Note that $y > 0$ for all $x \neq 2$. So, $\ln y$ is defined. Begin by taking the natural logarithm of each side of the equation. Then apply logarithmic properties and differentiate implicitly. Finally, solve for y'.

$$y = \frac{(x - 2)^2}{\sqrt{x^2 + 1}}, \quad x \neq 2 \qquad \text{Write original equation.}$$

$$\ln y = \ln \frac{(x - 2)^2}{\sqrt{x^2 + 1}} \qquad \text{Take natural log of each side.}$$

$$\ln y = 2\ln(x - 2) - \frac{1}{2}\ln(x^2 + 1) \qquad \text{Logarithmic properties}$$

$$\frac{y'}{y} = 2\left(\frac{1}{x - 2}\right) - \frac{1}{2}\left(\frac{2x}{x^2 + 1}\right) \qquad \text{Differentiate.}$$

$$\frac{y'}{y} = \frac{x^2 + 2x + 2}{(x - 2)(x^2 + 1)} \qquad \text{Simplify.}$$

$$y' = y\left[\frac{x^2 + 2x + 2}{(x - 2)(x^2 + 1)}\right] \qquad \text{Solve for } y'.$$

$$y' = \frac{(x - 2)^2}{\sqrt{x^2 + 1}}\left[\frac{x^2 + 2x + 2}{(x - 2)(x^2 + 1)}\right] \qquad \text{Substitute for } y.$$

$$y' = \frac{(x - 2)(x^2 + 2x + 2)}{(x^2 + 1)^{3/2}} \qquad \text{Simplify.}$$

> **Implementing Processes**
>
> You could also solve the problem in Example 9 without using logarithmic differentiation by using the Power and Quotient Rules. Use these rules to find the derivative and show that the result is equivalent to the one in Example 9. Which method do you prefer?

EXAMPLE 10   Logarithmic Differentiation

Find the derivative of $y = x^{2x}$, $x > 0$.

Solution

Note that $y > 0$ for all $x > 0$. So, $\ln y$ is defined.

$$y = x^{2x} \qquad \text{Write original equation.}$$

$$\ln y = \ln(x^{2x}) \qquad \text{Take natural log of each side.}$$

$$\ln y = (2x)(\ln x) \qquad \text{Logarithmic property}$$

$$\frac{y'}{y} = 2x\left(\frac{1}{x}\right) + 2\ln x \qquad \text{Differentiate.}$$

$$\frac{y'}{y} = 2(1 + \ln x) \qquad \text{Simplify.}$$

$$y' = 2y(1 + \ln x) \qquad \text{Solve for } y'.$$

$$y' = 2x^{2x}(1 + \ln x) \qquad \text{Substitute for } y.$$

Here are some guidelines for using logarithmic differentiation. In general, use logarithmic differentiation when differentiating (1) a function involving many factors or (2) a function having both a variable base and a variable exponent.

2.5 Exercises

See *CalcChat.com* for tutorial help and worked-out solutions to odd-numbered exercises.

Finding a Derivative In Exercises 1–20, find dy/dx by implicit differentiation.

1. $x^2 + y^2 = 9$
2. $x^2 - y^2 = 25$
3. $x^{1/2} + y^{1/2} = 16$
4. $x^{1/3} + y^{1/3} = 8$
5. $x^3 - xy + y^2 = 7$
6. $x^2y + y^2x = -2$
7. $\sqrt{3xy} = x + y$
8. $\sqrt{xy} = x^2y + 1$
9. $xe^y - 10x + 3y = 0$
10. $e^{xy} + x^2 - y^2 = 10$
11. $\sin x + 2\cos 2y = 1$
12. $(\sin \pi x + \cos \pi y)^2 = 2$
13. $\csc x = x(1 + \tan y)$
14. $\cot y = x - y$
15. $y = \sin xy$
16. $x = \sec \dfrac{1}{y}$
17. $x^2 - 3\ln y + y^2 = 10$
18. $\ln xy + 5x = 30$
19. $4x^3 + \ln y^2 + 2y = 2x$
20. $4xy + \ln x^2y = 7$

21. Error Analysis Given $4x^2 + 7x - 5y^2 = -7$, describe and correct the error in finding dy/dx.

$$\frac{d}{dx}[4x^2 + 7x - 5y^2] = \frac{d}{dx}[-7]$$

$$8x + 7 - 5y^2\frac{dy}{dx} = 0$$

$$-5y^2\frac{dy}{dx} = -8x - 7$$

$$\frac{dy}{dx} = \frac{8x + 7}{5y^2} \quad \large\pmb{\times}$$

22. Error Analysis Given $e^y + xy = 4$, describe and correct the error in finding dy/dx.

$$\frac{d}{dx}[e^y + xy] = \frac{d}{dx}[4]$$

$$e^y + x\frac{dy}{dx} + y = 0$$

$$x\frac{dy}{dx} = -e^y - y$$

$$\frac{dy}{dx} = \frac{-e^y - y}{x} \quad \large\pmb{\times}$$

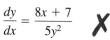

Connecting Representations In Exercises 23–26, (a) find two explicit functions by solving the equation for y in terms of x, (b) sketch the graph of the equation and label the parts given by the corresponding explicit functions, (c) differentiate the explicit functions, and (d) find dy/dx implicitly and verify that the result is equivalent to that of part (c).

23. $x^2 + y^2 = 64$
24. $25x^2 + 36y^2 = 300$
25. $16y^2 - x^2 = 16$
26. $x^2 + y^2 - 4x + 6y = -9$

Finding the Slope of a Graph In Exercises 27–34, find dy/dx by implicit differentiation. Then find the slope of the graph at the given point.

27. $xy = 6$, $(-6, -1)$
28. $3x^3y = 6$, $(1, 2)$
29. $y^2 = \dfrac{x^2 - 49}{x^2 + 49}$, $(7, 0)$
30. $4y^3 = \dfrac{x^2 - 36}{x^3 + 36}$, $(6, 0)$
31. $x\cos y = 1$, $\left(2, \dfrac{\pi}{3}\right)$
32. $\tan(x + y) = x$, $(0, 0)$
33. $3e^{xy} - x = 0$, $(3, 0)$
34. $y^2 = \ln x$, $(e, 1)$

Famous Curves In Exercises 35 and 36, find the slope of the tangent line to the graph at the given point.

35. Witch of Agnesi:
$(x^2 + 4)y = 8$
Point: $(2, 1)$

36. Folium of Descartes:
$x^3 + y^3 - 6xy = 0$
Point: $\left(\frac{4}{3}, \frac{8}{3}\right)$

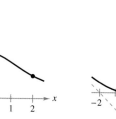

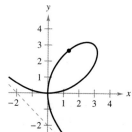

Famous Curves In Exercises 37–40, find an equation of the tangent line to the graph at the given point. To print an enlarged copy of the graph, go to *MathGraphs.com*.

37. Parabola

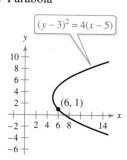

$(y - 3)^2 = 4(x - 5)$

$(6, 1)$

38. Bifolium

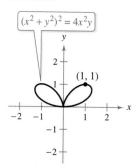

$(x^2 + y^2)^2 = 4x^2y$

$(1, 1)$

39. Cruciform

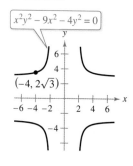

$x^2y^2 - 9x^2 - 4y^2 = 0$

$(-4, 2\sqrt{3})$

40. Kappa curve

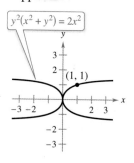

$y^2(x^2 + y^2) = 2x^2$

$(1, 1)$

Finding an Equation of a Tangent Line In Exercises 41–44, use implicit differentiation to find an equation of the tangent line to the graph at the given point.

41. $4xy = 9$, $\left(2, \frac{9}{8}\right)$ **42.** $x^2 + xy + y^2 = 4$, $(0, 2)$

43. $x + y - 1 = \ln(x^2 + y^2)$, $(1, 0)$

44. $y^2 + \ln xy = 2$, $(e, 1)$

45. Ellipse

(a) Use implicit differentiation to find an equation of the tangent line to the ellipse $\dfrac{x^2}{2} + \dfrac{y^2}{8} = 1$ at $(1, 2)$.

(b) Show that the equation of the tangent line to the ellipse $\dfrac{x^2}{a^2} + \dfrac{y^2}{b^2}$ at (x_0, y_0) is $\dfrac{x_0 x}{a^2} + \dfrac{y_0 y}{b^2} = 1$.

46. Hyperbola

(a) Use implicit differentiation to find an equation of the tangent line to the hyperbola $\dfrac{x^2}{6} - \dfrac{y^2}{8} = 1$ at $(3, -2)$.

(b) Show that the equation of the tangent line to the hyperbola $\dfrac{x^2}{a^2} - \dfrac{y^2}{b^2}$ at (x_0, y_0) is $\dfrac{x_0 x}{a^2} - \dfrac{y_0 y}{b^2} = 1$.

 Determining a Differentiable Function In Exercises 47 and 48, find dy/dx implicitly and find the largest interval of the form $-a < y < a$ or $0 < y < a$ such that y is a differentiable function of x. Write dy/dx as a function of x.

47. $\tan y = x$ **48.** $\cos y = x$

 Finding a Second Derivative In Exercises 49–54, find d^2y/dx^2 implicitly in terms of x and y.

49. $x^2 + y^2 = 4$ **50.** $x^2y - 4x = 5$

51. $x^2y - 2 = 5x + y$ **52.** $xy - 1 = 2x + y^2$

53. $7xy + \sin x = 2$ **54.** $3xy - 4\cos x = -6$

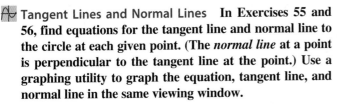 **Tangent Lines and Normal Lines In Exercises 55 and 56, find equations for the tangent line and normal line to the circle at each given point. (The *normal line* at a point is perpendicular to the tangent line at the point.) Use a graphing utility to graph the equation, tangent line, and normal line in the same viewing window.**

55. $x^2 + y^2 = 25$ **56.** $x^2 + y^2 = 36$

$(4, 3), (-3, 4)$ $(6, 0), \left(5, \sqrt{11}\right)$

57. Normal Lines Show that the normal line at any point on the circle $x^2 + y^2 = r^2$ passes through the origin.

58. Circles Two circles of radius 4 are tangent to the graph of $y^2 = 4x$ at the point $(1, 2)$. Find equations of these two circles.

Vertical and Horizontal Tangent Lines In Exercises 59 and 60, find the points at which the graph of the equation has a vertical or horizontal tangent line.

59. $25x^2 + 16y^2 + 200x - 160y + 400 = 0$

60. $4x^2 + y^2 - 8x + 4y + 4 = 0$

 Logarithmic Differentiation In Exercises 61–72, find dy/dx using logarithmic differentiation.

61. $y = x\sqrt{x^2 + 1}$, $x > 0$

62. $y = \sqrt{x^2(x + 1)(x + 2)}$, $x > 0$

63. $y = \dfrac{x^2\sqrt{3x - 2}}{(x + 1)^2}$, $x > \dfrac{2}{3}$ **64.** $y = \sqrt{\dfrac{x^2 - 1}{x^2 + 1}}$, $x > 1$

65. $y = \dfrac{x(x - 1)^{3/2}}{\sqrt{x + 1}}$, $x > 1$

66. $y = \dfrac{(x + 1)(x - 2)}{(x - 1)(x + 2)}$, $x > 2$

67. $y = x^{5/x}$, $x > 0$ **68.** $y = x^{x-1}$, $x > 0$

69. $y = (x - 2)^{x+1}$, $x > 2$ **70.** $y = (1 + x)^{1/x}$, $x > 0$

71. $y = x^{\ln x}$, $x > 0$ **72.** $y = (\ln x)^{\ln x}$, $x > 1$

Orthogonal Trajectories In Exercises 73 and 74, use a graphing utility to graph the equations and show that they are orthogonal. [Two graphs are *orthogonal* if at their point(s) of intersection, their tangent lines are perpendicular to each other.]

73. $x + y = 0$ **74.** $x^3 = 3(y - 1)$

$\quad\ \ x = \sin y$ $\quad\ \ x(3y - 29) = 3$

Orthogonal Trajectories In Exercises 75 and 76, verify that the two families of curves are orthogonal, where C and K are real numbers. Use a graphing utility to graph the two families for two values of C and two values of K.

75. $xy = C$, $x^2 - y^2 = K$ **76.** $x^2 + y^2 = C^2$, $y = Kx$

EXPLORING CONCEPTS ———————————

77. Implicit and Explicit Forms Write two different equations in implicit form that you can write in explicit form. Then write two different equations in implicit form that you cannot write in explicit form.

78. Reasoning Consider the equation $y^2 - a = -x^2$. For what values of a does dy/dx have meaning? Explain.

———————————————————————

79. True or False? Determine whether each statement is true or false. If it is false, explain why and correct it. Assume y is a function of x.

(a) $\dfrac{d}{dx}[\cos x^2] = -2x \sin x^2$

(b) $\dfrac{d}{dy}[\cos y^2] = 2y \sin y^2$

(c) $\dfrac{d}{dx}[\tan y^2] = 2y \sec(y^2)\dfrac{dy}{dx}$

80. **HOW DO YOU SEE IT?**   Use the graph and the implicit derivative of the equation to answer the questions.

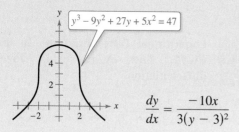

$$y^3 - 9y^2 + 27y + 5x^2 = 47$$

$$\frac{dy}{dx} = \frac{-10x}{3(y-3)^2}$$

(a) Which is greater, the value of dy/dx at $x = -3$ or the value of dy/dx at $x = -1$? Explain your reasoning.

(b) Estimate the points where the graph has a vertical tangent line. Explain how you found each coordinate.

81. Slope   Find all points on the circle $x^2 + y^2 = 100$ where the slope is $\frac{3}{4}$.

82. Proof

(a) Prove (Theorem 2.3) that $d/dx\,[x^n] = nx^{n-1}$ for the case in which n is a rational number. (*Hint:* Write $y = x^{p/q}$ in the form $y^q = x^p$ and differentiate implicitly. Assume that p and q are integers, where $q > 0$.)

(b) Prove part (a) for the case in which n is an irrational number. (*Hint:* Let $y = x^r$, where r is a real number, and use logarithmic differentiation.)

83. Tangent Lines   Find equations of both tangent lines to the graph of the ellipse $(x^2/9) + (y^2/4) = 1$ that pass through the point $(4, 0)$ not on the graph.

Calculus AP® – Exam Preparation Questions

84. Multiple Choice   If $x \ln y = 2$, then $\dfrac{dy}{dx} =$

(A) $-\dfrac{y}{x} - \ln y$. (B) $-\dfrac{y \ln y}{x}$.

(C) $\dfrac{y \ln y}{x}$. (D) $-\dfrac{x \ln y}{y}$.

85. Multiple Choice   What is the slope of the tangent line to the graph of $x^4 - x^2y + y^4 = 1$ at $(1, 1)$?

(A) -1 (B) $-\frac{2}{3}$

(C) $-\frac{2}{5}$ (D) $\frac{2}{5}$

86. Multiple Choice   If $x^2 + y^2 = 100$, what is the value of d^2y/dx^2 at the point $(6, 8)$?

(A) $-\frac{25}{128}$ (B) $-\frac{9}{128}$

(C) $\frac{9}{128}$ (D) $\frac{25}{128}$

87. Free Response   Consider the equation

$$x^2 + 4y^2 + 6x - 8y + 9 = 0.$$

(a) Find $\dfrac{dy}{dx}$.

(b) At what points does the graph of the equation have a vertical tangent line?

(c) At what points does the graph of the equation have a horizontal tangent line?

SECTION PROJECT

Optical Illusions

In each graph below, an optical illusion is created by having lines intersect a family of curves. In each case, the lines appear to be curved. Find the value of dy/dx for the given values of x and y.

(a) Circles: $x^2 + y^2 = C^2$
$x = 3, y = 4, C = 5$

(b) Hyperbolas: $xy = C$
$x = 1, y = 4, C = 4$

(c) Lines: $ax = by$
$x = \sqrt{3}, y = 3,$
$a = \sqrt{3}, b = 1$

(d) Cosine curves:
$y = C \cos x$
$x = \dfrac{\pi}{3}, y = \dfrac{1}{3}, C = \dfrac{2}{3}$

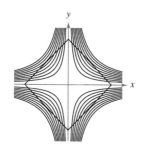

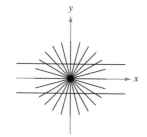

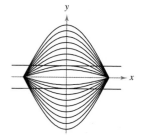

2.6   Derivatives of Inverse Functions

▶ Find the derivative of an inverse function.
▶ Differentiate an inverse trigonometric function.

Derivative of an Inverse Function

The next two theorems discuss the derivative of an inverse function. The reasonableness of Theorem 2.16 follows from the reflective property of inverse functions, as shown in Figure 2.29.

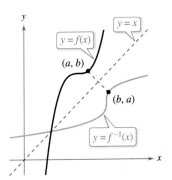

The graph of f^{-1} is a reflection of the graph of f in the line $y = x$.
Figure 2.29

Theorem 2.16   Continuity and Differentiability of Inverse Functions

Let f be a function whose domain is an interval I. If f has an inverse function, then the following statements are true.

1. If f is continuous on its domain, then f^{-1} is continuous on its domain.
2. If f is differentiable on an interval containing c and $f'(c) \neq 0$, then f^{-1} is differentiable at $f(c)$.

A proof of this theorem is given in Appendix A.

Theorem 2.17   The Derivative of an Inverse Function

Let f be a function that is differentiable on an interval I. If f has an inverse function g, then g is differentiable at any x for which $f'(g(x)) \neq 0$. Moreover,

$$g'(x) = \frac{1}{f'(g(x))}, \quad f'(g(x)) \neq 0.$$

A proof of this theorem is given in Appendix A.

EXAMPLE 1   Evaluating the Derivative of an Inverse Function

Let $f(x) = \frac{1}{4}x^3 + x - 1$.

a. What is the value of $f^{-1}(x)$ when $x = 3$?
b. What is the value of $(f^{-1})'(x)$ when $x = 3$?

Solution

Notice that f is one-to-one and therefore has an inverse function.

a. Because $f(2) = 3$, you know that

$$f^{-1}(3) = 2.$$

b. Because the function f is differentiable and has an inverse function, you can apply Theorem 2.17 (with $g = f^{-1}$) to write

$$(f^{-1})'(3) = \frac{1}{f'(f^{-1}(3))} = \frac{1}{f'(2)}.$$

Moreover, using $f'(x) = \frac{3}{4}x^2 + 1$, you can conclude that

$$(f^{-1})'(3) = \frac{1}{f'(2)} = \frac{1}{\frac{3}{4}(2^2) + 1} = \frac{1}{4}.$$

(See Figure 2.30.)

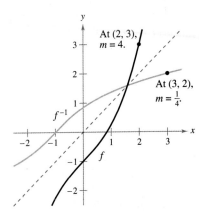

The graphs of the inverse functions f and f^{-1} have reciprocal slopes at points (a, b) and (b, a).
Figure 2.30

In Example 1, note that at the point $(2, 3)$ the slope of the graph of f is 4 and at the point $(3, 2)$ the slope of the graph of f^{-1} is $\frac{1}{4}$. (See Figure 2.30.) This reciprocal relationship (which follows from Theorem 2.17) is sometimes written as

$$\frac{dy}{dx} = \frac{1}{dx/dy}.$$

EXAMPLE 2   Graphs of Inverse Functions Have Reciprocal Slopes

See LarsonCalculusforAP.com for an interactive version of this type of example.

Let $f(x) = x^2$ (for $x \geq 0$) and let $f^{-1}(x) = \sqrt{x}$. Show that the slopes of the graphs of f and f^{-1} are reciprocals at each of the following points.

a. $(2, 4)$ and $(4, 2)$ **b.** $(3, 9)$ and $(9, 3)$

Solution

The derivatives of f and f^{-1} are $f'(x) = 2x$ and $(f^{-1})'(x) = \dfrac{1}{2\sqrt{x}}$.

a. At $(2, 4)$, the slope of the graph of f is $f'(2) = 2(2) = 4$. At $(4, 2)$, the slope of the graph of f^{-1} is

$$(f^{-1})'(4) = \frac{1}{2\sqrt{4}} = \frac{1}{2(2)} = \frac{1}{4}.$$

b. At $(3, 9)$, the slope of the graph of f is $f'(3) = 2(3) = 6$. At $(9, 3)$, the slope of the graph of f^{-1} is

$$(f^{-1})'(9) = \frac{1}{2\sqrt{9}} = \frac{1}{2(3)} = \frac{1}{6}.$$

So, in both cases, the slopes are reciprocals, as shown in Figure 2.31.

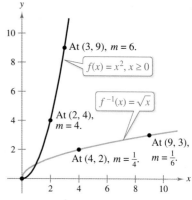

At $(0, 0)$, the derivative of f is 0 and the derivative of f^{-1} does not exist.

Figure 2.31

When determining the derivative of an inverse function, you have two options: (1) you can apply Theorem 2.17, or (2) you can use implicit differentiation. The first approach is illustrated in Example 3, and the second in the proof of Theorem 2.18.

EXAMPLE 3   Finding the Derivative of an Inverse Function

Find the derivative of the inverse tangent function.

Solution

Let $f(x) = \tan x$, $-\pi/2 < x < \pi/2$. Then let $g(x) = \arctan x$ be the inverse tangent function. To find the derivative of $g(x)$, use the fact that $f'(x) = \sec^2 x = \tan^2 x + 1$, and apply Theorem 2.17 as follows.

$$g'(x) = \frac{1}{f'(g(x))} = \frac{1}{f'(\arctan x)} = \frac{1}{[\tan(\arctan x)]^2 + 1} = \frac{1}{x^2 + 1}$$

Derivatives of Inverse Trigonometric Functions

In Section 2.4, you saw that the derivative of the *transcendental* function $f(x) = \ln x$ is the *algebraic* function $f'(x) = 1/x$. You will now see that the derivatives of the inverse trigonometric functions also are algebraic (even though the inverse trigonometric functions are themselves transcendental).

The next theorem lists the derivatives of the six inverse trigonometric functions. Note that the derivatives of arccos u, arccot u, and arccsc u are the *negatives* of the derivatives of arcsin u, arctan u, and arcsec u, respectively.

Theorem 2.18   **Derivatives of Inverse Trigonometric Functions**

Let u be a differentiable function of x.

$$\frac{d}{dx}[\arcsin u] = \frac{u'}{\sqrt{1-u^2}} \qquad \frac{d}{dx}[\arccos u] = \frac{-u'}{\sqrt{1-u^2}}$$

$$\frac{d}{dx}[\arctan u] = \frac{u'}{1+u^2} \qquad \frac{d}{dx}[\text{arccot } u] = \frac{-u'}{1+u^2}$$

$$\frac{d}{dx}[\text{arcsec } u] = \frac{u'}{|u|\sqrt{u^2-1}} \qquad \frac{d}{dx}[\text{arccsc } u] = \frac{-u'}{|u|\sqrt{u^2-1}}$$

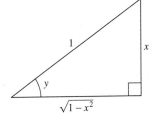

Insight

Differentiation of inverse trigonometric functions is sometimes tested on the AP® Exam. The inverse sine and inverse tangent functions are the most likely topics.

Proof   Let $y = \arcsin x$, $-\pi/2 \le y \le \pi/2$. (See Figure 2.32.) So, $\sin y = x$, and you can use implicit differentiation as follows.

$$y = \arcsin x$$
$$\sin y = x$$
$$(\cos y)\left(\frac{dy}{dx}\right) = 1$$
$$\frac{dy}{dx} = \frac{1}{\cos y}$$
$$\frac{dy}{dx} = \frac{1}{\sqrt{1 - \sin^2 y}}$$
$$\frac{dy}{dx} = \frac{1}{\sqrt{1 - x^2}}$$

$y = \arcsin x$

Figure 2.32

Because u is a differentiable function of x, you can use the Chain Rule to write

$$\frac{d}{dx}[\arcsin u] = \frac{u'}{\sqrt{1-u^2}}, \quad \text{where} \quad u' = \frac{du}{dx}.$$

Proofs of the other differentiation rules are left as an exercise. (See Exercise 77.) ◼

There is no common agreement on the definition of arcsec x (or arccsc x) for negative values of x. For this text, the range of arcsecant was defined to preserve the reciprocal identity arcsec $x = \arccos(1/x)$. For example, to evaluate arcsec(-2), you can write

$$\text{arcsec}(-2) = \arccos(-0.5) \approx 2.09.$$

One of the consequences of the definition of the inverse secant function given in this text is that its graph has a positive slope at every x-value in its domain. This accounts for the absolute value sign in the formula for the derivative of arcsec x.

EXAMPLE 4   **Differentiating Inverse Trigonometric Functions**

a. $\dfrac{d}{dx}[\arcsin 2x] = \dfrac{2}{\sqrt{1-(2x)^2}} = \dfrac{2}{\sqrt{1-4x^2}}$

b. $\dfrac{d}{dx}[\arctan 3x] = \dfrac{3}{1+(3x)^2} = \dfrac{3}{1+9x^2}$

c. $\dfrac{d}{dx}[\arcsin \sqrt{x}] = \dfrac{(1/2)x^{-1/2}}{\sqrt{1-x}} = \dfrac{1}{2\sqrt{x}\sqrt{1-x}} = \dfrac{1}{2\sqrt{x-x^2}}$

d. $\dfrac{d}{dx}[\text{arcsec } e^{2x}] = \dfrac{2e^{2x}}{e^{2x}\sqrt{(e^{2x})^2-1}} = \dfrac{2e^{2x}}{e^{2x}\sqrt{e^{4x}-1}} = \dfrac{2}{\sqrt{e^{4x}-1}}$

The absolute value sign is not necessary because $e^{2x} > 0$. ◼

EXAMPLE 5   A Derivative That Can Be Simplified

$$y = \arcsin x + x\sqrt{1 - x^2}$$

$$y' = \frac{1}{\sqrt{1 - x^2}} + x\left(\frac{1}{2}\right)(-2x)(1 - x^2)^{-1/2} + \sqrt{1 - x^2}$$

$$= \frac{1}{\sqrt{1 - x^2}} - \frac{x^2}{\sqrt{1 - x^2}} + \sqrt{1 - x^2}$$

$$= \sqrt{1 - x^2} + \sqrt{1 - x^2}$$

$$= 2\sqrt{1 - x^2}$$

In the 1600s, Europe was ushered into the scientific age by such great thinkers as Descartes, Galileo, Huygens, Newton, and Kepler. These men believed that nature is governed by basic laws—laws that can, for the most part, be written in terms of mathematical equations. One of the most influential publications of this period— *Dialogue on the Great World Systems* by Galileo Galilei—has become a classic description of modern scientific thought.

As mathematics has developed during the past few hundred years, a small number of elementary functions has proven sufficient for modeling most* phenomena in physics, chemistry, biology, engineering, economics, and a variety of other fields. An **elementary function** is a function from the following list or one that can be formed as the sum, product, quotient, or composition of functions in the list.

Algebraic Functions	*Transcendental Functions*
Polynomial functions	Logarithmic functions
Rational functions	Exponential functions
Functions involving radicals	Trigonometric functions
	Inverse trigonometric functions

With the differentiation rules introduced so far in the text, you can differentiate *any* elementary function. For convenience, these differentiation rules are summarized below.

Basic Differentiation Rules for Elementary Functions

1. $\frac{d}{dx}[cu] = cu'$

2. $\frac{d}{dx}[u \pm v] = u' \pm v'$

3. $\frac{d}{dx}[uv] = uv' + vu'$

4. $\frac{d}{dx}\left[\frac{u}{v}\right] = \frac{vu' - uv'}{v^2}$

5. $\frac{d}{dx}[c] = 0$

6. $\frac{d}{dx}[u^n] = nu^{n-1}u'$

7. $\frac{d}{dx}[x] = 1$

8. $\frac{d}{dx}[|u|] = \frac{u}{|u|}(u'), \quad u \neq 0$

9. $\frac{d}{dx}[\ln u] = \frac{u'}{u}$

10. $\frac{d}{dx}[e^u] = e^u u'$

11. $\frac{d}{dx}[\log_a u] = \frac{u'}{(\ln a)u}$

12. $\frac{d}{dx}[a^u] = (\ln a)a^u u'$

13. $\frac{d}{dx}[\sin u] = (\cos u)u'$

14. $\frac{d}{dx}[\cos u] = -(\sin u)u'$

15. $\frac{d}{dx}[\tan u] = (\sec^2 u)u'$

16. $\frac{d}{dx}[\cot u] = -(\csc^2 u)u'$

17. $\frac{d}{dx}[\sec u] = (\sec u \tan u)u'$

18. $\frac{d}{dx}[\csc u] = -(\csc u \cot u)u'$

19. $\frac{d}{dx}[\arcsin u] = \frac{u'}{\sqrt{1 - u^2}}$

20. $\frac{d}{dx}[\arccos u] = \frac{-u'}{\sqrt{1 - u^2}}$

21. $\frac{d}{dx}[\arctan u] = \frac{u'}{1 + u^2}$

22. $\frac{d}{dx}[\text{arccot } u] = \frac{-u'}{1 + u^2}$

23. $\frac{d}{dx}[\text{arcsec } u] = \frac{u'}{|u|\sqrt{u^2 - 1}}$

24. $\frac{d}{dx}[\text{arccsc } u] = \frac{-u'}{|u|\sqrt{u^2 - 1}}$

*Some important functions used in engineering and science (such as Bessel functions and gamma functions) are not elementary functions.

2.6 Exercises

See *CalcChat.com* for tutorial help and worked-out solutions to odd-numbered exercises.

Evaluating the Derivative of an Inverse Function In Exercises 1–10, verify that f has an inverse function. Then use the function f and the given real number a to find $(f^{-1})'(a)$.

Function	Real Number
1. $f(x) = x^3 - 1$	$a = 26$
2. $f(x) = 3 - 4x^3$	$a = -1$
3. $f(x) = x^3 + 2x - 1$	$a = 2$
4. $f(x) = \frac{1}{27}(x^5 + 2x^3)$	$a = -11$
5. $f(x) = \sin x, \ -\frac{\pi}{2} \le x \le \frac{\pi}{2}$	$a = \frac{1}{2}$
6. $f(x) = \cos 2x, \ 0 \le x \le \frac{\pi}{2}$	$a = 0$
7. $f(x) = \frac{x+6}{x-2}, \ x > 2$	$a = 3$
8. $f(x) = \frac{x+3}{x+1}, \ x > -1$	$a = 2$
9. $f(x) = x^3 - \frac{4}{x}, \ x > 0$	$a = 6$
10. $f(x) = \sqrt{x-4}$	$a = 2$

Graphs of Inverse Functions Have Reciprocal Slopes In Exercises 11–14, show that the slopes of the graphs of f and f^{-1} are reciprocals at the given points.

Function	Point
11. $f(x) = 5 - 2x$	$(4, -3)$
$f^{-1}(x) = \frac{5-x}{2}$	$(-3, 4)$
12. $f(x) = x^3$	$\left(\frac{1}{2}, \frac{1}{8}\right)$
$f^{-1}(x) = \sqrt[3]{x}$	$\left(\frac{1}{8}, \frac{1}{2}\right)$
13. $f(x) = \sqrt{x-4}$	$(5, 1)$
$f^{-1}(x) = x^2 + 4, \ x \ge 0$	$(1, 5)$
14. $f(x) = \frac{4}{1+x^2}, \ x \ge 0$	$(1, 2)$
$f^{-1}(x) = \sqrt{\frac{4-x}{x}}$	$(2, 1)$

Finding a Derivative In Exercises 15–40, find the derivative of the function.

15. $f(x) = \arcsin(x + 1)$ **16.** $f(t) = \arcsin t^2$

17. $g(x) = 3 \arccos \frac{x}{2}$ **18.** $f(x) = \operatorname{arcsec} 8x$

19. $f(x) = \arctan e^x$ **20.** $f(x) = \arctan \sqrt{x}$

21. $g(x) = \dfrac{\arcsin 4x}{x}$ **22.** $g(x) = \dfrac{\arccos x}{x+1}$

23. $g(x) = e^{5x} \arcsin x$ **24.** $h(x) = x^2 \arctan 3x$

25. $h(x) = \operatorname{arccot} 3x$

26. $f(x) = \operatorname{arccsc} 6x$

27. $h(t) = \sin(\arccos t)$

28. $g(t) = \tan(\arcsin t)$

29. $f(x) = \arcsin x + \arccos x$

30. $f(x) = \operatorname{arcsec} x + \operatorname{arccsc} x$

31. $y = 2x \arccos x - 2\sqrt{1 - x^2}$

32. $y = \ln(t^2 + 4) - \frac{1}{2} \arctan \frac{t}{2}$

33. $y = \frac{1}{2}\left(\frac{1}{2} \ln \frac{x+1}{x-1} + \arctan x\right)$

34. $y = \frac{1}{2}\left(x\sqrt{4 - x^2} + 4 \arcsin \frac{x}{2}\right)$

35. $y = x \arcsin x + \sqrt{1 - x^2}$

36. $y = x \arctan 2x - \frac{1}{4} \ln(1 + 4x^2)$

37. $y = 8 \arcsin \frac{x}{4} - \frac{x\sqrt{16 - x^2}}{2}$

38. $y = 25 \arcsin \frac{x}{5} - x\sqrt{25 - x^2}$

39. $y = \arctan x + \frac{x}{1 + x^2}$

40. $y = \arctan \frac{x}{2} - \frac{1}{2(x^2 + 4)}$

Error Analysis In Exercises 41 and 42, describe and correct the error when finding the derivative.

41. $\dfrac{d}{dx}[\arcsin e^{4x}] = \dfrac{e^{4x}}{\sqrt{1 - (e^{4x})^2}} = \dfrac{e^{4x}}{\sqrt{1 - e^{8x}}}$ ✗

42. $\dfrac{d}{dx}[\operatorname{arcsec} x^2] = \dfrac{2x}{x^2\sqrt{x^2 - 1}} = \dfrac{2}{x\sqrt{x^2 - 1}}$ ✗

Finding an Equation of a Tangent Line In Exercises 43–46, find an equation of the tangent line to the graph of f at the given point. Use the *tangent* feature of a graphing utility to verify your result.

43. $f(x) = \arctan x, \ \left(-1, -\frac{\pi}{4}\right)$

44. $f(x) = \arccos x^2, \ \left(0, \frac{\pi}{2}\right)$

45. $f(x) = \arcsin 3x, \ \left(\frac{\sqrt{2}}{6}, \frac{\pi}{4}\right)$

46. $f(x) = \operatorname{arcsec} x, \ \left(\sqrt{2}, \frac{\pi}{4}\right)$

Finding an Equation of a Tangent Line In Exercises 47–52, find an equation of the tangent line to the graph of the function at the given point.

47. $y = 2 \arcsin x, \quad \left(\frac{1}{2}, \frac{\pi}{3}\right)$

48. $y = \arctan \frac{x}{4}, \quad \left(4, \frac{\pi}{4}\right)$

49. $y = \operatorname{arcsec} 2x, \quad \left(\frac{\sqrt{2}}{2}, \frac{\pi}{4}\right)$

50. $y = \frac{1}{2} \arccos x, \quad \left(-\frac{\sqrt{2}}{2}, \frac{3\pi}{8}\right)$

51. $y = 4x \arccos(x - 1), \quad (1, 2\pi)$

52. $y = 3x \arcsin x, \quad \left(\frac{1}{2}, \frac{\pi}{4}\right)$

Tangent Lines In Exercises 53 and 54, find equations of all tangent lines to the graph of f with slope m.

53. $f(x) = \arccos x, \quad m = -2$

54. $f(x) = \arctan x, \quad m = \frac{1}{4}$

Linear and Quadratic Approximations In Exercises 55–58, use a computer algebra system to find the linear approximation

$$P_1(x) = f'(a)(x - a) + f(a)$$

and the quadratic approximation

$$P_2(x) = \frac{1}{2}f''(a)(x - a)^2 + f'(a)(x - a) + f(a)$$

to the function f at $x = a$. Sketch the graph of the function and its linear and quadratic approximations.

55. $f(x) = \arctan x, \ a = 0$ **56.** $f(x) = \arccos x, \ a = 0$

57. $f(x) = \arcsin x, \ a = \frac{1}{2}$ **58.** $f(x) = \arctan x, \ a = 1$

Finding dy/dx at a Point In Exercises 59–62, find dy/dx at the given point for the equation.

59. $x = y^3 - 7y^2 + 2, \ (-4, 1)$

60. $x = 3 \ln(y^2 - 8), \ (0, 3)$

61. $x \arctan x = e^y, \ \left(1, \ln \frac{\pi}{4}\right)$

62. $\arcsin xy = \frac{2}{3} \arctan 2x, \ \left(\frac{1}{2}, 1\right)$

Finding an Equation of a Tangent Line In Exercises 63–66, find an equation of the tangent line to the graph of the equation at the given point.

63. $x^2 + x \arctan y = y - 1, \ \left(-\frac{\pi}{4}, 1\right)$

64. $\arctan xy = \arcsin(x + y), \ (0, 0)$

65. $\arcsin x + \arcsin y = \frac{\pi}{2}, \ \left(\frac{\sqrt{2}}{2}, \frac{\sqrt{2}}{2}\right)$

66. $\arctan(x + y) = y^2 + \pi/4, \ (1, 0)$

EXPLORING CONCEPTS

67. Inverse Secant Function Some calculus textbooks define the inverse secant function using the range $[0, \pi/2) \cup [\pi, 3\pi/2)$.

(a) Sketch the graph of $y = \operatorname{arcsec} x$ using this range.

(b) Show that $y' = \dfrac{1}{x\sqrt{x^2 - 1}}$.

68. Implementing Processes Determine whether the derivative of each trigonometric function is odd or even.

69. Justifying Consider the tangent line j to the graph of f at any point (a, b) and the tangent line k to the graph of f^{-1} at the point (b, a). Identify the line where j and k intersect. Explain your reasoning.

70. **HOW DO YOU SEE IT?** Use the information in the graph of f below.

(a) What is the slope of the tangent line to the graph of f^{-1} at the point $\left(-\frac{1}{2}, -1\right)$? Explain.

(b) What is the slope of the tangent line to the graph of f^{-1} at the point $(1, 2)$? Explain.

At $(2, 1)$, $m = 2$.

At $\left(-1, -\frac{1}{2}\right)$, $m = \frac{1}{2}$.

71. Angular Rate of Change An airplane flies at an altitude of 5 miles toward a point directly over an observer. Consider θ and x as shown in the figure.

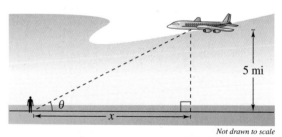

5 mi

Not drawn to scale

(a) Write θ as a function of x.

(b) The speed of the plane is 400 miles per hour. Find $d\theta/dt$ when $x = 10$ miles and $x = 3$ miles.

72. Angular Rate of Change Repeat Exercise 71 for an altitude of 3 miles and describe how the altitude affects the rate of change of θ.

73. Angular Rate of Change In a free-fall experiment, an object is dropped from a height of 256 feet. A camera on the ground 500 feet from the point of impact records the fall of the object (see figure).

(a) Find the position function giving the height of the object at time t, assuming the object is released at time $t = 0$. At what time will the object reach ground level?

(b) Find the rates of change of the angle of elevation of the camera when $t = 1$ and $t = 2$.

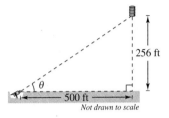

Figure for 73   Figure for 74

74. Angular Rate of Change A television camera at ground level is filming the lift-off of a rocket at a point 800 meters from the launch pad. Let θ be the angle of elevation of the rocket and let s be the distance between the camera and the rocket (see figure). Write θ as a function of s for the period of time when the rocket is moving vertically. Differentiate the result to find $d\theta/dt$ in terms of s and ds/dt.

75. Angular Rate of Change An observer is standing 300 feet from the point at which a balloon is released. The balloon rises at a rate of 5 feet per second. How fast is the angle of elevation of the observer's line of sight increasing when the balloon is 100 feet high?

76. Angular Speed A patrol car is parked 50 feet from a long warehouse (see figure). The revolving light on top of the car turns at a rate of 30 revolutions per minute. Write θ as a function of x. How fast is the light beam moving along the wall when the beam makes an angle of $\theta = 45°$ with the line perpendicular from the light to the wall?

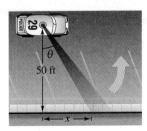

77. Proof Prove the remaining differentiation formulas listed in Theorem 2.18. (The derivative of arcsin u has already been proven.)

78. Proof Show that the function

$$f(x) = \arcsin\frac{x-2}{2} - 2\arcsin\frac{\sqrt{x}}{2}$$

is constant for $0 \le x \le 4$.

True or False? **In Exercises 79–82, determine whether the statement is true or false. If it is false, explain why or give an example that shows it is false.**

79. The derivative of arccsc x is the negative of the derivative of arcsec x.

80. The slope of the graph of the inverse tangent function is positive for all x.

81. For all x in the domain, $\dfrac{d}{dx}[\arctan(\tan x)] = 1$.

82. If $y = \arcsin x$, then $\dfrac{dy}{dx} = \dfrac{1}{dx/dy}$ for all x in $[-1, 1]$.

83. Proof Prove that

$$\arcsin x = \arctan\left(\frac{x}{\sqrt{1-x^2}}\right), \quad |x| < 1.$$

84. Proof Prove that

$$\arccos x = \frac{\pi}{2} - \arctan\left(\frac{x}{\sqrt{1-x^2}}\right), \quad |x| < 1.$$

Calculus AP® – Exam Preparation Questions

85. Multiple Choice If $f(x) = 2x\sqrt{x-6}$, what is the value of $(f^{-1})'(40)$?

(A) $\dfrac{1}{10}$ (B) $\dfrac{1}{9}$ (C) 10   (D) $80\sqrt{34}$

86. Multiple Choice What is the derivative of $f(x) = \dfrac{1}{3}\arctan\dfrac{x}{3}$?

(A) $-\dfrac{1}{9+x^2}$ (B) $\dfrac{1}{9+x^2}$

(C) $\dfrac{3}{9+x^2}$ (D) $\dfrac{1}{1+x^2}$

87. Multiple Choice What is the slope of the tangent line to the graph of $f(x) = \ln(x^3 + 1) + \arctan 4x$ when $x = 1$?

(A) $\dfrac{7}{19}$ (B) $\dfrac{21}{17}$ (C) $\dfrac{59}{34}$ (D) $\dfrac{23}{10}$

88. Free Response The table shows selected values corresponding to the differentiable and invertible function $f(x)$.

x	$f(x)$	$f'(x)$	$f^{-1}(x)$	$(f^{-1})'(x)$	$f'(f^{-1}(x))$
0	5/2	−17/4			−1/17
5	0	−1/17	−5/16	−17/256	

(a) Complete the table.

(b) Find an equation of the tangent line to the graph of f^{-1} at the point $(0, f^{-1}(0))$.

2.7   Related Rates

▶ Find a related rate.
▶ Use related rates to solve real-life problems.

Finding Related Rates

You have seen how the Chain Rule can be used to find dy/dx implicitly. Another important use of the Chain Rule is to find the rates of change of two or more related variables that are changing with respect to *time*.

For example, when water is drained out of a conical tank (see Figure 2.33), the volume V, the radius r, and the height h of the water level are all functions of time t. Knowing that these variables are related by the equation

$$V = \frac{\pi}{3}r^2 h \qquad \text{Original equation}$$

you can differentiate implicitly with respect to t to obtain the **related-rate** equation

$$\frac{d}{dt}[V] = \frac{d}{dt}\left[\frac{\pi}{3}r^2 h\right]$$

$$\frac{dV}{dt} = \frac{\pi}{3}\left[r^2\frac{dh}{dt} + h\left(2r\frac{dr}{dt}\right)\right] \qquad \text{Differentiate with respect to } t.$$

$$= \frac{\pi}{3}\left(r^2\frac{dh}{dt} + 2rh\frac{dr}{dt}\right).$$

From this equation, you can see that the rate of change of V is related to the rates of change of both h and r.

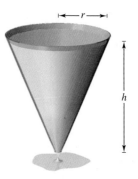
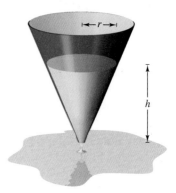
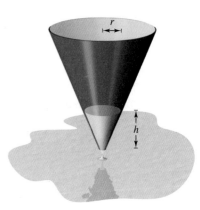

Volume is related to radius and height.
Figure 2.33

Exploration

Finding a Related Rate   In the conical tank shown in Figure 2.33, the height of the water level is changing at a rate of -0.2 foot per minute and the radius is changing at a rate of -0.1 foot per minute. What is the rate of change in the volume when the radius is $r = 1$ foot and the height is $h = 2$ feet? Does the rate of change in the volume depend on the values of r and h? Explain.

 EXAMPLE 1   Two Rates That Are Related

The variables x and y are both differentiable functions of t and are related by the equation $y = x^2 + 3$. Find dy/dt when $x = 1$, given that $dx/dt = 2$ when $x = 1$.

Solution

Using the Chain Rule, you can differentiate both sides of the equation *with respect to t*.

$$y = x^2 + 3 \qquad \text{Write original equation.}$$

$$\frac{d}{dt}[y] = \frac{d}{dt}[x^2 + 3] \qquad \text{Differentiate with respect to } t.$$

$$\frac{dy}{dt} = 2x\frac{dx}{dt} \qquad \text{Chain Rule}$$

When $x = 1$ and $dx/dt = 2$, you have

$$\frac{dy}{dt} = 2(1)(2) = 4. \qquad \blacksquare$$

Problem Solving with Related Rates

In Example 1, you were *given* an equation that related the variables x and y and were asked to find the rate of change of y when $x = 1$.

Equation: $y = x^2 + 3$

Given rate: $\dfrac{dx}{dt} = 2$ when $x = 1$

Find: $\dfrac{dy}{dt}$ when $x = 1$

In each of the remaining examples in this section, you must *create* a mathematical model from a verbal description.

EXAMPLE 2 Ripples in a Pond

A pebble is dropped into a calm pond, causing ripples in the form of concentric circles, as shown in Figure 2.34. The radius r of the outer ripple is increasing at a constant rate of 1 foot per second. When the radius is 4 feet, at what rate is the total area A of the disturbed water changing?

Solution

The variables r and A are related by $A = \pi r^2$. The rate of change of the radius r is $dr/dt = 1$.

Equation: $A = \pi r^2$

Given rate: $\dfrac{dr}{dt} = 1$ foot per second

Find: $\dfrac{dA}{dt}$ when $r = 4$ feet

Total area increases as the outer radius increases.

Figure 2.34

With this information, you can proceed as in Example 1.

$\dfrac{d}{dt}[A] = \dfrac{d}{dt}[\pi r^2]$ Differentiate with respect to t.

$\dfrac{dA}{dt} = 2\pi r \dfrac{dr}{dt}$ Chain Rule

$= 2\pi(4)(1)$ Substitute 4 for r and 1 for $\dfrac{dr}{dt}$.

$= 8\pi$ square feet per second   Simplify.

When the radius is 4 feet, the area is changing at a rate of 8π square feet per second. ∎

Guidelines for Solving Related-Rate Problems

1. Identify all *given* quantities and quantities *to be determined*. Make a sketch and label the quantities.
2. Write an equation involving the variables whose rates of change either are given or are to be determined.
3. Using the Chain Rule, implicitly differentiate both sides of the equation *with respect to time t*.
4. *After* completing Step 3, substitute into the resulting equation all known values for the variables and their rates of change. Then solve for the required rate of change.

Implementing Processes

When using these guidelines, be sure you perform Step 3 before Step 4. Substituting the known values of the variables before differentiating will produce an inappropriate derivative.

The table below lists examples of mathematical models involving rates of change. For instance, the rate of change in the first example is the velocity of a car.

Verbal Statement	Mathematical Model
The velocity of a car after traveling for 1 hour is 50 miles per hour.	x = distance traveled $\dfrac{dx}{dt} = 50$ mi/h when $t = 1$
Water is being pumped into a swimming pool at a rate of 10 cubic meters per hour.	V = volume of water in pool $\dfrac{dV}{dt} = 10$ m³/h
A gear is revolving at a rate of 25 revolutions per minute (1 revolution = 2π rad).	θ = angle of revolution $\dfrac{d\theta}{dt} = 25(2\pi)$ rad/min
A population of bacteria is increasing at a rate of 2000 per hour.	x = number in population $\dfrac{dx}{dt} = 2000$ bacteria per hour

EXAMPLE 3 An Inflating Balloon

Air is being pumped into a spherical balloon at a rate of 4.5 cubic feet per minute. Find the rate of change of the radius when the radius is 1 foot.

Solution

Let V be the volume of the balloon, and let r be its radius. Because the volume is increasing at a rate of 4.5 cubic feet per minute, you know that at time t the rate of change of the volume is $dV/dt = \frac{9}{2}$. So, the problem can be stated as shown.

Given rate: $\quad \dfrac{dV}{dt} = \dfrac{9}{2}$ cubic feet per minute $\quad$ (constant rate)

Find: $\quad \dfrac{dr}{dt} \quad$ when $\quad r = 1$ foot

To find the rate of change of the radius, you must find an equation that relates the radius r to the volume V.

Equation: $\quad V = \dfrac{4}{3}\pi r^3 \qquad$ Volume of a sphere

Differentiating both sides of the equation with respect to t produces

$\dfrac{dV}{dt} = 4\pi r^2 \dfrac{dr}{dt} \qquad$ Differentiate with respect to t.

$\dfrac{dr}{dt} = \dfrac{1}{4\pi r^2}\left(\dfrac{dV}{dt}\right). \qquad$ Solve for $\frac{dr}{dt}$.

Finally, when $r = 1$, the rate of change of the radius is

$\dfrac{dr}{dt} = \dfrac{1}{4\pi(1)^2}\left(\dfrac{9}{2}\right) \approx 0.358$ foot per minute. ∎

In Example 3, note that the volume is increasing at a *constant* rate, but the radius is increasing at a *variable* rate. Just because two rates are related does not mean that they are proportional. In this particular case, the radius is growing more and more slowly as t increases. Do you see why?

> **Remark**
>
> The formula for the volume of a sphere and several other formulas from geometry are listed on the inside back cover of this text.

> **Insight**
>
> On the AP® Exam, a decimal answer must be correct to three decimal places unless otherwise indicated.

EXAMPLE 4   The Speed of an Airplane Tracked by Radar

See LarsonCalculusforAP.com for an interactive version of this type of example.

An airplane is flying on a flight path that will take it directly over a radar tracking station, as shown in Figure 2.35. The distance s is decreasing at a rate of 400 miles per hour when $s = 10$ miles. What is the speed of the plane?

Solution

Let x be the horizontal distance from the station, as shown in Figure 2.35. Notice that when $s = 10$, $x = \sqrt{10^2 - 6^2} = 8$.

Given rate: $ds/dt = -400$ miles per hour   when $s = 10$ miles

Find: dx/dt when $s = 10$ miles   and $x = 8$ miles

You can find the velocity of the plane as shown.

Equation: $x^2 + 6^2 = s^2$ Pythagorean Theorem

$$2x \frac{dx}{dt} = 2s \frac{ds}{dt} \qquad \text{Differentiate with respect to } t.$$

$$\frac{dx}{dt} = \frac{s}{x}\left(\frac{ds}{dt}\right) \qquad \text{Solve for } \frac{dx}{dt}.$$

$$= \frac{10}{8}(-400) \qquad \text{Substitute for } s, x, \text{ and } \frac{ds}{dt}.$$

$$= -500 \text{ miles per hour} \qquad \text{Simplify.}$$

Because the velocity is -500 miles per hour, the *speed* is 500 miles per hour.

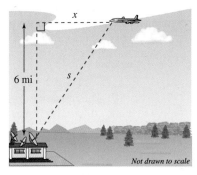

An airplane is flying at an altitude of 6 miles, s miles from the station.
Figure 2.35

EXAMPLE 5   A Changing Angle of Elevation

Find the rate of change in the angle of elevation of the camera shown in Figure 2.36 at 10 seconds after lift-off.

Solution

Let θ be the angle of elevation, as shown in Figure 2.36. When $t = 10$, the height s of the rocket is $s = 50t^2 = 50(10)^2 = 5000$ feet.

Given rate: $ds/dt = 100t = $ velocity of rocket (in feet per second)

Find: $d\theta/dt$ when $t = 10$ seconds   and $s = 5000$ feet

Using Figure 2.36, you can relate s and θ by the equation $\tan \theta = s/2000$.

Equation: $\tan \theta = \dfrac{s}{2000}$ See Figure 2.36.

$$(\sec^2 \theta)\frac{d\theta}{dt} = \frac{1}{2000}\left(\frac{ds}{dt}\right) \qquad \text{Differentiate with respect to } t.$$

$$\frac{d\theta}{dt} = (\cos^2 \theta)\frac{100t}{2000} \qquad \text{Substitute } 100t \text{ for } \frac{ds}{dt}.$$

$$= \left(\frac{2000}{\sqrt{s^2 + 2000^2}}\right)^2 \frac{100t}{2000} \qquad \cos \theta = \frac{2000}{\sqrt{s^2 + 2000^2}}$$

When $t = 10$ and $s = 5000$, you have

$$\frac{d\theta}{dt} = \frac{2000(100)(10)}{5000^2 + 2000^2} = \frac{2}{29} \text{ radian per second.}$$

So, when $t = 10$, θ is changing at a rate of $\frac{2}{29}$ radian per second.

> ### Communication and Notation
>
> The velocity in Example 4 is negative because x represents a distance that is decreasing. In general, quantities that are decreasing in magnitude are represented by a negative rate.

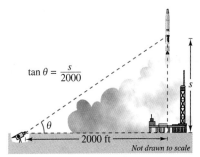

$\tan \theta = \dfrac{s}{2000}$

A television camera at ground level is filming the lift-off of a rocket that is rising vertically according to the position equation $s = 50t^2$, where s is measured in feet and t is measured in seconds. The camera is 2000 feet from the launch pad.
Figure 2.36

EXAMPLE 6 The Velocity of a Piston

In the engine shown in Figure 2.37, a 7-inch connecting rod is fastened to a crank of radius 3 inches. The crankshaft rotates counterclockwise at a constant rate of 200 revolutions per minute. Find the velocity of the piston when $\theta = \pi/3$.

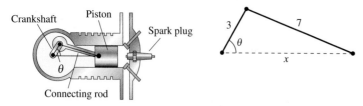

The velocity of a piston is related to the angle of the crankshaft.
Figure 2.37

Solution

Label the distances as shown in Figure 2.37. Because a complete revolution corresponds to 2π radians, it follows that

$$\frac{d\theta}{dt} = 200(2\pi) = 400\pi \text{ radians per minute.}$$

Given rate: $\dfrac{d\theta}{dt} = 400\pi$ radians per minute   (constant rate)

Find: $\dfrac{dx}{dt}$ when $\theta = \dfrac{\pi}{3}$ radians

You can use the Law of Cosines (see Figure 2.38) to find an equation that relates x and θ.

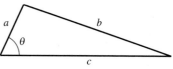

Law of Cosines:
$b^2 = a^2 + c^2 - 2ac \cos \theta$

Figure 2.38

Equation:

$$7^2 = 3^2 + x^2 - 2(3)(x) \cos \theta$$

$$0 = 2x\frac{dx}{dt} - 6\left[-x(\sin \theta)\frac{d\theta}{dt} + (\cos \theta)\frac{dx}{dt}\right]$$

$$(6 \cos \theta - 2x)\frac{dx}{dt} = 6x(\sin \theta)\frac{d\theta}{dt}$$

$$\frac{dx}{dt} = \frac{6x \sin \theta}{6 \cos \theta - 2x}\left(\frac{d\theta}{dt}\right)$$

When $\theta = \pi/3$, you can solve for x, as shown.

$$7^2 = 3^2 + x^2 - 2(3)(x)\cos \frac{\pi}{3}$$

$$49 = 9 + x^2 - 6x\left(\frac{1}{2}\right)$$

$$0 = x^2 - 3x - 40$$

$$0 = (x - 8)(x + 5)$$

$$x = 8 \text{ inches} \qquad \text{Choose positive solution.}$$

So, when $x = 8$ and $\theta = \pi/3$, the velocity of the piston is

$$\frac{dx}{dt} = \frac{6(8)\left(\sqrt{3}/2\right)}{6(1/2) - 16}(400\pi)$$

$$= \frac{9600\pi\sqrt{3}}{-13}$$

$$\approx -4018 \text{ inches per minute.}$$

2.7 Exercises

See *CalcChat.com* for tutorial help and worked-out solutions to odd-numbered exercises.

Using Related Rates In Exercises 1–4, assume that x and y are both differentiable functions of t and find the required values of dy/dt and dx/dt.

Equation	Find	Given
1. $y = \sqrt{x}$	(a) $\dfrac{dy}{dt}$ when $x = 4$	$\dfrac{dx}{dt} = 3$
	(b) $\dfrac{dx}{dt}$ when $x = 25$	$\dfrac{dy}{dt} = 2$
2. $y = 5x^2 - 4x$	(a) $\dfrac{dy}{dt}$ when $x = 2$	$\dfrac{dx}{dt} = 3$
	(b) $\dfrac{dx}{dt}$ when $x = 4$	$\dfrac{dy}{dt} = 9$
3. $xy = 12$	(a) $\dfrac{dy}{dt}$ when $x = 3$	$\dfrac{dx}{dt} = 9$
	(b) $\dfrac{dx}{dt}$ when $x = 6$	$\dfrac{dy}{dt} = \dfrac{5}{6}$
4. $x^2 + y^2 = 25$	(a) $\dfrac{dy}{dt}$ when $x = 3$, $y = 4$	$\dfrac{dx}{dt} = 8$
	(b) $\dfrac{dx}{dt}$ when $x = 4$, $y = 3$	$\dfrac{dy}{dt} = -2$

Particle Motion In Exercises 5–8, a particle is moving along a path modeled by the given function at the rate dx/dt. Find dy/dt for the given values of x.

5. $y = 2x^2 + 1;\ \dfrac{dx}{dt} = 2$ centimeters per second

(a) $x = -1$ (b) $x = 0$ (c) $x = 1$

6. $y = \dfrac{1}{1 + x^2};\ \dfrac{dx}{dt} = 6$ inches per second

(a) $x = -2$ (b) $x = 0$ (c) $x = 2$

7. $y = \tan x;\ \dfrac{dx}{dt} = 3$ feet per second

(a) $x = -\dfrac{\pi}{3}$ (b) $x = -\dfrac{\pi}{4}$ (c) $x = 0$

8. $y = \cos x;\ \dfrac{dx}{dt} = 4$ centimeters per second

(a) $x = \dfrac{\pi}{6}$ (b) $x = \dfrac{\pi}{4}$ (c) $x = \dfrac{\pi}{3}$

EXPLORING CONCEPTS

9. Communicating For $y = ax + b$, when x changes at a constant rate, does y also change at a constant rate? If so, does y change at the same rate as x? Explain.

10. Communicating Let V be the volume of a cube of side length s that is changing with respect to time. If ds/dt is constant, is dV/dt constant? Explain.

11. Error Analysis Describe and correct the error in finding dx/dt for $y = \frac{1}{2}x^2 - x$ when $x = 5$, given that $dy/dt = 3$.

$$\frac{dx}{dt} = (x - 1)\frac{dy}{dt} = (5 - 1)(3) = 12 \quad \textbf{✗}$$

12. Error Analysis Describe and correct the error in finding dy/dt for $y = 4x^2$ when $x = 3$, given that $dx/dt = 4$.

$$\frac{dy}{dt} = 8x = 8(3) = 24 \quad \textbf{✗}$$

13. Area The radius r of a circle is increasing at a rate of 4 centimeters per minute. Find the rate of change of the area when $r = 10$ centimeters.

14. Radius The area A of a circle is decreasing at a rate of 2 square feet per minute. Find the rate of change of the radius when $A = 24$ square feet.

15. Volume The radius r of a sphere is increasing at a rate of 3 inches per minute.

(a) Find the rates of change of the volume when $r = 9$ inches and $r = 36$ inches.

(b) Explain why the rate of change of the volume of the sphere is not constant even though dr/dt is constant.

16. Radius A spherical balloon is inflated with gas at the rate of 800 cubic centimeters per minute.

(a) Find the rates of change of the radius when $r = 30$ centimeters and $r = 85$ centimeters.

(b) Explain why the rate of change of the radius of the sphere is not constant even through dV/dt is constant.

17. Volume All edges of a cube are expanding at a rate of 6 centimeters per second. How fast is the volume changing when each edge is (a) 2 centimeters and (b) 10 centimeters?

18. Surface Area All edges of a cube are expanding at a rate of 6 centimeters per second. How fast is the surface area changing when each edge is (a) 2 centimeters and (b) 10 centimeters?

19. Height Sand streams off a conveyor and onto a conical pile at a rate of 10 cubic feet per minute. The diameter of the base of the cone is approximately three times the height. At what rate is the height of the pile changing when the pile is 15 feet high? $\left(\text{Hint: The formula for the volume of a cone is } V = \frac{1}{3}\pi r^2 h.\right)$

20. Depth A conical tank (with vertex down) is 10 feet across the top and 12 feet deep. Water is flowing into the tank at a rate of 10 cubic feet per minute. Find the rate of change of the depth of the water when the water is 8 feet deep.

21. Depth A swimming pool is 12 meters long, 6 meters wide, 1 meter deep at the shallow end, and 3 meters deep at the deep end (see figure). Water is being pumped into the pool at $\frac{1}{4}$ cubic meter per minute, and there is 1 meter of water at the deep end.

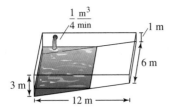

(a) What percent of the pool is filled?

(b) At what rate is the water level rising?

22. Depth A trough is 12 feet long and 3 feet across the top (see figure). Its ends are isosceles triangles with altitudes of 3 feet.

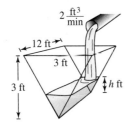

(a) Water is being pumped into the trough at 2 cubic feet per minute. How fast is the water level rising when the depth h is 1 foot?

(b) The water is rising at a rate of $\frac{3}{8}$ inch per minute when $h = 2$ feet. Determine the rate at which water is being pumped into the trough.

23. Moving Ladder A ladder 25 feet long is leaning against the wall of a house (see figure). The base of the ladder is pulled away from the wall at a rate of 2 feet per second.

(a) How fast is the top of the ladder moving down the wall when its base is 7 feet, 15 feet, and 24 feet from the wall?

(b) Consider the triangle formed by the side of the house, the ladder, and the ground. Find the rate at which the area of the triangle is changing when the base of the ladder is 7 feet from the wall.

(c) Find the rate at which the angle between the ladder and the wall of the house is changing when the base of the ladder is 7 feet from the wall.

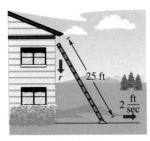
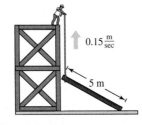

Figure for 23   Figure for 24

24. Construction A construction worker pulls a 5-meter plank up the side of a building under construction by means of a rope tied to one end of the plank (see figure). Assume the opposite end of the plank follows a path perpendicular to the wall of the building and the worker pulls the rope at a rate of 0.15 meter per second. How fast is the end of the plank sliding along the ground when it is 2.5 meters from the wall of the building?

25. Construction A winch at the top of a 12-meter building pulls a pipe of the same length to a vertical position, as shown in the figure. The winch pulls in rope at a rate of -0.2 meter per second. Find the rate of vertical change and the rate of horizontal change at the end of the pipe when $y = 6$ meters.

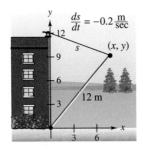

Figure for 25   Figure for 26

26. Boating A boat is pulled into a dock by means of a winch 12 feet above the deck of the boat (see figure).

(a) The winch pulls in rope at a rate of 4 feet per second. Determine the speed of the boat when there is 13 feet of rope out. What happens to the speed of the boat as it gets closer to the dock?

(b) Suppose the boat is moving at a constant rate of 4 feet per second. Determine the speed at which the winch pulls in rope when there is a total of 13 feet of rope out. What happens to the speed at which the winch pulls in rope as the boat gets closer to the dock?

27. Air Traffic Control An air traffic controller spots two planes at the same altitude converging on a point as they fly at right angles to each other (see figure). One plane is 225 miles from the point moving at 450 miles per hour. The other plane is 300 miles from the point moving at 600 miles per hour.

(a) At what rate is the distance s between the planes decreasing?

(b) How much time does the air traffic controller have to get one of the planes on a different flight path?

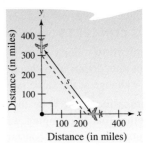

28. Air Traffic Control   An airplane is flying at an altitude of 5 miles and passes directly over a radar antenna (see figure). When the plane is 10 miles away ($s = 10$), the radar detects that the distance s is changing at a rate of 240 miles per hour. What is the speed of the plane?

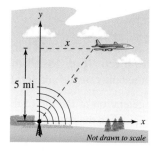

Not drawn to scale

29. Sports   A baseball diamond has the shape of a square with sides 90 feet long (see figure). A player running from second base to third base at a speed of 25 feet per second is 20 feet from third base. At what rate is the player's distance s from home plate changing?

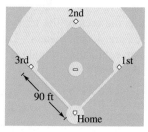

Figure for 29 and 30   Figure for 31

30. Sports   For the baseball diamond in Exercise 29, suppose the player is running from first base to second base at a speed of 25 feet per second. Find the rate at which the distance from home plate is changing when the player is 20 feet from second base.

31. Shadow Length   A man 6 feet tall walks at a rate of 5 feet per second away from a light that is 15 feet above the ground (see figure).

(a) When he is 10 feet from the base of the light, at what rate is the tip of his shadow moving?

(b) When he is 10 feet from the base of the light, at what rate is the length of his shadow changing?

32. Shadow Length   Repeat Exercise 31 for a man 6 feet tall walking at a rate of 5 feet per second *toward* a light that is 20 feet above the ground (see figure).

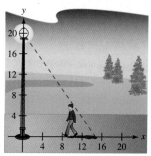
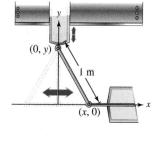

Figure for 32   Figure for 33

33. Machine Design   The endpoints of a movable rod of length 1 meter have coordinates $(x, 0)$ and $(0, y)$ (see figure). The position of the end on the x-axis is $x(t) = (1/2)\sin(\pi t/6)$, where t is the time in seconds.

(a) Find the time of one complete cycle of the rod.

(b) What is the lowest point reached by the end of the rod on the y-axis?

(c) Find the speed of the y-axis endpoint when the x-axis endpoint is $\left(\frac{1}{4}, 0\right)$.

34. Evaporation   As a spherical raindrop falls, it reaches a layer of dry air and begins to evaporate at a rate that is proportional to its surface area ($S = 4\pi r^2$). Show that the radius of the raindrop decreases at a constant rate.

35. Angle of Elevation   A balloon rises at a rate of 4 meters per second from a point on the ground 50 meters from an observer. Find the rate of change of the angle of elevation of the balloon from the observer when the balloon is 50 meters above the ground.

36. Angle of Elevation   An airplane flies at an altitude of 5 miles toward a point directly over an observer (see figure). The speed of the plane is 600 miles per hour. Find the rates at which the angle of elevation θ is changing when the angle is (a) $\theta = 30°$, (b) $\theta = 60°$, and (c) $\theta = 75°$.

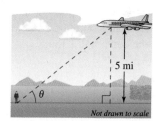

Not drawn to scale

37. Modeling Data   The table shows the numbers (in millions) of students receiving free lunches f and reduced price lunches r through the National School Lunch Program for the years 2009 through 2018. (*Source: U.S. Department of Agriculture*)

Year	2009	2010	2011	2012	2013
f	16.3	17.6	18.4	18.7	18.9
r	3.2	3.0	2.7	2.7	2.6

Year	2014	2015	2016	2017	2018
f	19.2	19.8	20.1	20.0	20.2
r	2.5	2.2	2.0	2.0	1.8

(a) Use a graphing utility to find a model of the form $r(f) = af^3 + bf^2 + cf + d$ for the data, where t is the time in years, with $t = 9$ corresponding to 2009.

(b) Find dr/dt for $t = 13$, when the number of participants in the free lunch program was increasing at a rate of about 0.28 million per year.

38. Linear vs. Angular Speed A patrol car is parked 50 feet from a long warehouse (see figure). The revolving light on top of the car turns at a rate of 30 revolutions per minute. How fast is the light beam moving along the wall when the beam makes angles of (a) $\theta = 30°$, (b) $\theta = 60°$, and (c) $\theta = 70°$ with the perpendicular line from the light to the wall?

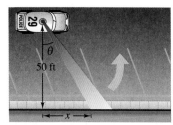

Figure for 38   Figure for 39

39. Linear vs. Angular Speed A wheel of radius 30 centimeters revolves at a rate of 10 revolutions per second. A dot is painted at a point P on the rim of the wheel (see figure).

(a) Find dx/dt as a function of θ.

(b) Use a graphing utility to graph the function in part (a).

(c) When is the absolute value of the rate of change of x greatest? When is it least?

(d) Find dx/dt when $\theta = 30°$ and $\theta = 60°$.

40. **HOW DO YOU SEE IT?** Using the graphs of f, (a) determine whether dy/dt is positive or negative given that dx/dt is negative, and (b) determine whether dx/dt is positive or negative given that dy/dt is positive.

(i) 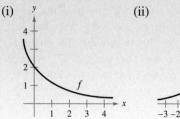   (ii)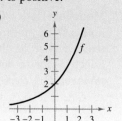

41. Area The included angle of the two sides of constant equal length s of an isosceles triangle is θ.

(a) Show that the area of the triangle is given by

$$A = \frac{1}{2}s^2 \sin \theta.$$

(b) The angle θ is increasing at the rate of $\frac{1}{2}$ radian per minute. Find the rates of change of the area when

$$\theta = \frac{\pi}{6} \quad \text{and} \quad \pi = \frac{\pi}{3}.$$

42. Communication and Notation Describe the relationship between the rate of change of y and the rate of change of x in each expression. Assume all variables and derivatives are positive.

(a) $\dfrac{dy}{dt} = 3\dfrac{dx}{dt}$ (b) $\dfrac{dy}{dt} = x(L - x)\dfrac{dx}{dt}, \quad 0 \le x \le L$

Acceleration In Exercises 43 and 44, find the acceleration of the specified object. (*Hint:* Recall that if a variable is changing at a constant rate, its acceleration is zero.)

43. Find the acceleration of the top of the ladder described in Exercise 23 when the base of the ladder is 7 feet from the wall.

44. Find the acceleration of the boat in Exercise 26(a) when there is a total of 13 feet of rope out.

Calculus AP® – Exam Preparation Questions

45. Multiple Choice The sides of an equilateral triangle are increasing at a rate of $\frac{5}{8}$ centimeters per second. At what rate is the area of the triangle increasing when the sides are 4 centimeters? The formula for the area A of an equilateral triangle is

$$A = \frac{\sqrt{3}s^2}{4}.$$

(A) $\sqrt{3}$ square centimeters per second

(B) $\dfrac{5\sqrt{3}}{4}$ square centimeters per second

(C) $2\sqrt{3}$ square centimeters per second

(D) $5\sqrt{3}$ square centimeters per second

46. Multiple Choice A conical tank (with vertex down) is 12 feet across the top and 6 feet tall. Water is pumped from the tank at the rate of π cubic feet per minute. Find the rate of change of the height of the water level when the water level is 3 feet high.

(A) $-\frac{1}{9}$ foot per minute

(B) $\frac{1}{9}$ foot per minute

(C) $-\frac{1}{3}$ foot per minute

(D) $\frac{1}{3}$ foot per minute

47. Free Response A spherical piece of ice maintains the shape of a sphere as it melts. The volume of the piece of ice is decreasing at a constant rate of $3\pi/2$ cubic feet per hour. The formulas for the volume V and surface area S of a sphere are $V = \frac{4}{3}\pi r^3$ and $S = 4\pi r^2$, where r is the radius of the sphere.

(a) What is the rate of change of the surface area of the piece of ice when the radius is 10 feet?

(b) What is the rate of change of the surface area of the piece of ice when the radius is 5 feet?

2.8   Newton's Method

▶ Approximate a zero of a function using Newton's Method.

Newton's Method

In this section, you will study a technique for approximating the real zeros of a function. The technique is called **Newton's Method,** and it uses tangent lines to approximate the graph of the function near its x-intercepts.

To see how Newton's Method works, consider a function f that is continuous on the interval $[a, b]$ and differentiable on the interval (a, b). If $f(a)$ and $f(b)$ differ in sign, then, by the Intermediate Value Theorem, f must have at least one zero in the interval (a, b). To estimate this zero, you choose

$$x = x_1 \qquad \text{First estimate}$$

as shown in Figure 2.39(a). Newton's Method is based on the assumption that the graph of f and the tangent line at $(x_1, f(x_1))$ both cross the x-axis at *about* the same point. Because you can easily calculate the x-intercept for this tangent line, you can use it as a second (and, usually, better) estimate of the zero of f. The tangent line passes through the point $(x_1, f(x_1))$ with a slope of $f'(x_1)$. In point-slope form, the equation of the tangent line is

$$y - f(x_1) = f'(x_1)(x - x_1)$$
$$y = f'(x_1)(x - x_1) + f(x_1).$$

Letting $y = 0$ and solving for x produces

$$x = x_1 - \frac{f(x_1)}{f'(x_1)}.$$

So, from the initial estimate x_1, you obtain a new estimate

$$x_2 = x_1 - \frac{f(x_1)}{f'(x_1)}. \qquad \text{Second estimate [See Figure 2.39(b).]}$$

You can improve on x_2 and calculate yet a third estimate

$$x_3 = x_2 - \frac{f(x_2)}{f'(x_2)}. \qquad \text{Third estimate}$$

Repeated application of this process is called Newton's Method.

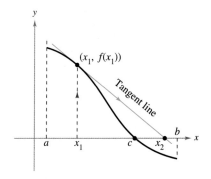

(a)

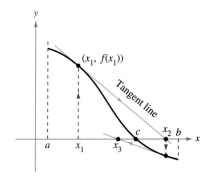

(b)
The x-intercept of the tangent line approximates the zero of f.
Figure 2.39

Newton's Method for Approximating the Zeros of a Function

Let $f(c) = 0$, where f is differentiable on an open interval containing c. Then, to approximate c, use these steps.

1. Make an initial estimate x_1 that is close to c. (A graph is helpful.)
2. Determine a new approximation

$$x_{n+1} = x_n - \frac{f(x_n)}{f'(x_n)}.$$

3. When $|x_n - x_{n+1}|$ is within the desired accuracy, let x_{n+1} serve as the final approximation. Otherwise, return to Step 2 and calculate a new approximation.

Each successive application of this procedure is called an **iteration.**

Insight

Newton's Method is not tested on the AP® Exam.

EXAMPLE 1 Using Newton's Method

Calculate three iterations of Newton's Method to approximate a zero of $f(x) = x^2 - 2$. Use $x_1 = 1$ as the initial guess.

Solution

Because $f(x) = x^2 - 2$, you have $f'(x) = 2x$, and the iterative formula is

$$x_{n+1} = x_n - \frac{f(x_n)}{f'(x_n)} = x_n - \frac{x_n^2 - 2}{2x_n}.$$

The calculations for three iterations are shown in the table.

n	x_n	$f(x_n)$	$f'(x_n)$	$\dfrac{f(x_n)}{f'(x_n)}$	$x_n - \dfrac{f(x_n)}{f'(x_n)}$
1	1.000000	−1.000000	2.000000	−0.500000	1.500000
2	1.500000	0.250000	3.000000	0.083333	1.416667
3	1.416667	0.006945	2.833334	0.002451	1.414216
4	1.414216				

Of course, in this case you know that the two zeros of the function are $\pm\sqrt{2}$. To six decimal places, $\sqrt{2} = 1.414214$. So, after only three iterations of Newton's Method, you have obtained an approximation that is within 0.000002 of an actual root. The first iteration of this process is shown in Figure 2.40.

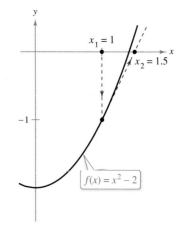

The first iteration of Newton's Method
Figure 2.40

EXAMPLE 2 Using Newton's Method

See LarsonCalculusforAP.com for an interactive version of this type of example.

Use Newton's Method to approximate the zero(s) of

$$f(x) = e^x + x.$$

Continue the iterations until two successive approximations differ by less than 0.0001.

Solution

Begin by sketching a graph of f, as shown in Figure 2.41. From the graph, you can observe that the function has only one zero, which occurs near $x = -0.6$. Next, differentiate f and form the iterative formula

$$x_{n+1} = x_n - \frac{f(x_n)}{f'(x_n)} = x_n - \frac{e^{x_n} + x_n}{e^{x_n} + 1}.$$

The calculations are shown in the table.

n	x_n	$f(x_n)$	$f'(x_n)$	$\dfrac{f(x_n)}{f'(x_n)}$	$x_n - \dfrac{f(x_n)}{f'(x_n)}$
1	−0.60000	−0.05119	1.54881	−0.03305	−0.56695
2	−0.56695	0.00030	1.56725	0.00019	−0.56714
3	−0.56714	0.00000	1.56714	0.00000	−0.56714
4	−0.56714				

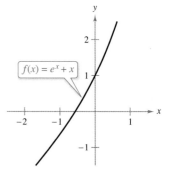

After three iterations of Newton's Method, the zero of f is approximated to the desired accuracy.
Figure 2.41

Because two successive approximations differ by less than the required 0.0001, you can estimate the zero of f to be −0.56714.

When, as in Examples 1 and 2, the approximations approach a limit, the sequence $x_1, x_2, x_3, \ldots, x_n, \ldots$ is said to **converge.** Moreover, when the limit is c, it can be shown that c must be a zero of f.

Newton's Method does not always yield a convergent sequence. One way it can fail is shown in Figure 2.42. Because Newton's Method involves division by $f'(x_n)$, it is clear that the method will fail when the derivative is zero for any x_n in the sequence. When you encounter this problem, you can usually overcome it by choosing a different value for x_1. Another way Newton's Method can fail is shown in Example 3.

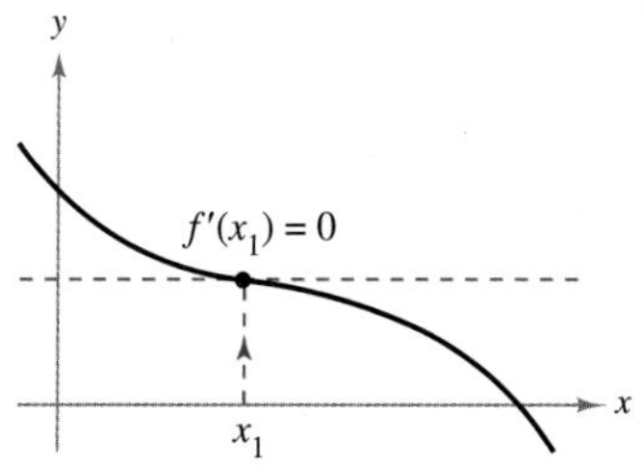

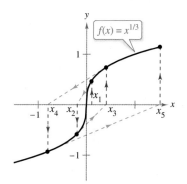

Newton's Method fails to converge when $f'(x_n) = 0$.

Figure 2.42

EXAMPLE 3   An Example in Which Newton's Method Fails

The function $f(x) = x^{1/3}$ is not differentiable at $x = 0$. Show that Newton's Method fails to converge using $x_1 = 0.1$.

Solution

Because $f'(x) = \frac{1}{3}x^{-2/3}$, the iterative formula is

$$x_{n+1} = x_n - \frac{f(x_n)}{f'(x_n)} = x_n - \frac{x_n^{1/3}}{\frac{1}{3}x_n^{-2/3}} = x_n - 3x_n = -2x_n.$$

The calculations are shown in the table. This table and Figure 2.43 indicate that x_n continues to increase in magnitude as $n \to \infty$, and so the limit of the sequence does not exist.

n	x_n	$f(x_n)$	$f'(x_n)$	$\dfrac{f(x_n)}{f'(x_n)}$	$x_n - \dfrac{f(x_n)}{f'(x_n)}$
1	0.10000	0.46416	1.54720	0.30000	−0.20000
2	−0.20000	−0.58480	0.97467	−0.60000	0.40000
3	0.40000	0.73681	0.61401	1.20000	−0.80000
4	−0.80000	−0.92832	0.38680	−2.40000	1.60000

Newton's Method fails to converge for every x-value other than the actual zero of f.

Figure 2.43

It can be shown that a condition sufficient to produce convergence of Newton's Method to a zero of f is that

$$\left| \frac{f(x)f''(x)}{[f'(x)]^2} \right| < 1 \qquad \text{Condition for convergence}$$

on an open interval containing the zero. For instance, in Example 1, this test would yield $f(x) = x^2 - 2$, $f'(x) = 2x$, $f''(x) = 2$, and

$$\left| \frac{f(x)f''(x)}{[f'(x)]^2} \right| = \left| \frac{(x^2 - 2)(2)}{4x^2} \right| = \left| \frac{1}{2} - \frac{1}{x^2} \right|. \qquad \text{Example 1}$$

On the interval $(1, 3)$, this quantity is less than 1 and therefore the convergence of Newton's Method is guaranteed. On the other hand, in Example 3, you have $f(x) = x^{1/3}$, $f'(x) = \frac{1}{3}x^{-2/3}$, $f''(x) = -\frac{2}{9}x^{-5/3}$, and

$$\left| \frac{f(x)f''(x)}{[f'(x)]^2} \right| = \left| \frac{x^{1/3}(-2/9)(x^{-5/3})}{(1/9)(x^{-4/3})} \right| = 2 \qquad \text{Example 3}$$

which is not less than 1 for any value of x, so you cannot conclude that Newton's Method will converge.

2.8 Exercises

 Using Newton's Method In Exercises 1–4, complete two iterations of Newton's Method to approximate a zero of the function using the given initial guess.

1. $f(x) = x^2 - 5$, $x_1 = 2$ **2.** $f(x) = x^3 - 3$, $x_1 = 1.4$
3. $f(x) = \cos x$, $x_1 = 1.6$ **4.** $f(x) = \tan x$, $x_1 = 0.1$

 Using Newton's Method In Exercises 5–16, use Newton's Method to approximate the zero(s) of the function. Continue the iterations until two successive approximations differ by less than 0.001. Then find the zero(s) using a graphing utility to verify your results.

5. $f(x) = x^3 + 2$ **6.** $f(x) = 4 - x^3$
7. $f(x) = x^3 + x - 1$ **8.** $f(x) = x^5 + x - 6$
9. $f(x) = 5\sqrt{x - 1} - 2x$ **10.** $f(x) = x - 2\sqrt{x + 1}$
11. $f(x) = x - e^{-x}$ **12.** $f(x) = x - 3 + \ln x$
13. $f(x) = 1 - x + \sin x$ **14.** $f(x) = x^3 - \cos x$
15. $f(x) = x^3 - 3.9x^2 + 4.79x - 1.881$
16. $f(x) = -x^3 + 2.7x^2 + 3.55x - 2.422$

Error Analysis In Exercises 17 and 18, describe and correct the error when using Newton's Method to find the zeros of the function.

17. $f(x) = x^3 + 5x + 1$; $x_{n+1} = x_n - \dfrac{3x_n^2 + 5}{x_n^3 + 5x_n + 1}$

18. $f(x) = x + e^x + \sin x$

n	x_n	$f(x_n)$	$f'(x_n)$	$x_n - \dfrac{f(x_n)}{f'(x_n)}$
1	-0.300	0.145	0.785	-0.485
2	-0.485	-0.335	0.731	-0.026
3	-0.026	0.922	0.975	-0.972
4	-0.972	-1.420	0.815	0.771

19. Using Newton's Method Consider the function $f(x) = x^3 - 3x^2 + 3$.

(a) Use a graphing utility to graph f.

(b) Use Newton's Method to approximate a zero with $x_1 = 1$ as an initial guess.

(c) Repeat part (b) using $x_1 = \frac{1}{4}$ as an initial guess and observe that the result is different.

(d) To understand why the results in parts (b) and (c) are different, sketch the tangent lines to the graph of f at the points $(1, f(1))$ and $\left(\frac{1}{4}, f\left(\frac{1}{4}\right)\right)$. Explain why it is important to select the initial guess carefully.

20. Using Newton's Method Repeat Exercise 19 for $f(x) = \sin x$ with initial guesses of $x_1 = 1.8$ and $x_1 = 3$.

Points of Intersection In Exercises 21–24, apply Newton's Method to approximate the x-value(s) of the indicated point(s) of intersection of the two graphs. Continue the iterations until two successive approximations differ by less than 0.001. [*Hint:* Let $h(x) = f(x) - g(x)$.]

21. $f(x) = 2x + 1$ **22.** $f(x) = 2 - x^2$
$\quad g(x) = \sqrt{x + 4}$ $\quad g(x) = e^{x/2}$

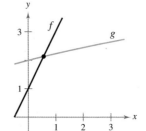   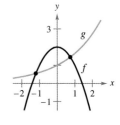

23. $f(x) = x$ **24.** $f(x) = \arccos x$
$\quad g(x) = \tan x$ $\quad g(x) = \arctan x$

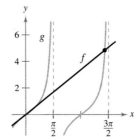   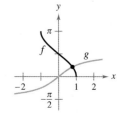

 Failure of Newton's Method In Exercises 25 and 26, apply Newton's Method using the given initial guess, and explain why the method fails.

25. $y = 2x^3 - 6x^2 + 6x - 1$, $x_1 = 1$

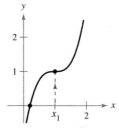   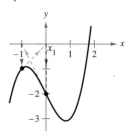

Figure for 25   Figure for 26

26. $y = x^3 - 2x - 2$, $x_1 = 0$

Fixed Point In Exercises 27–30, approximate the fixed point of the function to two decimal places. [A *fixed point* of a function f is a real number c such that $f(c) = c$.]

27. $f(x) = \cos x$ **28.** $f(x) = \cot x$, $0 < x < \pi$
29. $f(x) = e^{x/10}$ **30.** $f(x) = -\ln x$

EXPLORING CONCEPTS

31. Justifying When using Newton's Method, what will the values of subsequent guesses for x be when your initial guess is a zero of f? Explain.

32. Justifying Explain graphically why Newton's Method fails when $f'(x_n) = 0$.

33. Justifying When using Newton's Method to approximate a zero of a polynomial function that has all positive coefficients, your initial guess should not be a positive number. Explain why.

34. HOW DO YOU SEE IT? For what value(s) will Newton's Method fail to converge for the function shown in the graph? Explain your reasoning.

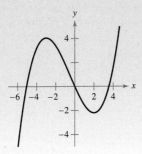

35. Advertising Costs A company that produces electronic devices estimates that the profit for selling one of its models is

$$P = -76x^3 + 4830x^2 - 320,000, \quad 0 \le x \le 60$$

where P is the profit in dollars and x is the advertising expense in tens of thousands of dollars. Use Newton's Method to approximate the smaller of two advertising amounts that yield a profit of $2,500,000.

36. Engine Power The torque produced by a compact automobile engine is approximated by the model

$$T = 0.808x^3 - 17.974x^2 + 71.248x + 110.843, \quad 1 \le x \le 5$$

where T is the torque in foot-pounds and x is the engine speed in thousands of revolutions per minute. Use Newton's Method to approximate the two engine speeds that yield a torque of 170 foot-pounds.

37. Approximating Reciprocals Use Newton's Method to show that the equation $x_{n+1} = x_n(2 - ax_n)$ can be used to approximate $1/a$ when x_1 is an initial guess of the reciprocal of a. Note that this method of approximating reciprocals uses only the operations of multiplication and subtraction. [*Hint:* Consider $f(x) = (1/x) - a$.]

38. Approximating Reciprocals Use the result of Exercise 37 to approximate (a) $\frac{1}{3}$ and (b) $\frac{1}{11}$ to three decimal places.

39. Mechanic's Rule The Mechanic's Rule for approximating $\sqrt{a}$, $a > 0$, is

$$x_{n+1} = \frac{1}{2}\left(x_n + \frac{a}{x_n}\right), \quad n = 1, 2, 3 \ldots$$

where x_1 is an approximation of $\sqrt{a}$.

(a) Use Newton's Method and the function $f(x) = x^2 - a$ to derive the Mechanic's Rule.

(b) Use the Mechanic's Rule to approximate $\sqrt{5}$ and $\sqrt{7}$ to three decimal places.

40. Approximating Radicals

(a) Use Newton's Method and the function $f(x) = x^n - a$ to obtain a general rule for approximating $x = \sqrt[n]{a}$.

(b) Use the general rule found in part (a) to approximate $\sqrt[4]{6}$ and $\sqrt[3]{15}$ to three decimal places.

True or False? In Exercises 41 and 42, determine whether the statement is true or false. If it is false, explain why or give an example that shows it is false.

41. If $f(x)$ is a cubic polynomial such that $f'(x)$ is never zero, then any initial guess will force Newton's Method to converge to the zero of f.

42. The roots of $\sqrt{f(x)} = 0$ coincide with the roots of $f(x) = 0$.

43. Tangent Lines The graph of $f(x) = -\sin x$ has infinitely many tangent lines that pass through the origin. Use Newton's Method to approximate to three decimal places the slope of the tangent line having the greatest slope.

44. Point of Tangency The graph of $f(x) = \cos x$ and a tangent line to f through the origin are shown. Find the coordinates of the point of tangency to three decimal places.

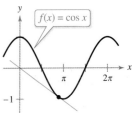

Calculus AP® – Exam Preparation Questions

45. Multiple Choice $\displaystyle\lim_{h \to 0} \frac{\sin(\pi + h) - \sin \pi}{h}$ is

(A) -1.   (B) 0.   (C) 1.   (D) nonexistent.

46. Multiple Choice If $y = -5\sqrt[3]{15x^2 - 1}$, then $y' =$

(A) $\dfrac{10x}{(15x^2 - 1)^{2/3}}$.   (B) $-\dfrac{5}{3(15x^2 - 1)^{2/3}}$.

(C) $-\dfrac{50x}{\sqrt[3]{15x^2 - 1}}$.   (D) $-\dfrac{50x}{(15x^2 - 1)^{2/3}}$.

2   Review Exercises

See *CalcChat.com* for tutorial help and worked-out solutions to odd-numbered exercises.

Finding the Derivative by the Limit Process   **In Exercises 1–4, find the derivative of the function by the limit process.**

1. $f(x) = 12$

2. $f(x) = 5x - 4$

3. $f(x) = x^2 - 4x + 5$

4. $f(x) = \dfrac{6}{x}$

Using the Alternative Form of the Derivative   **In Exercises 5 and 6, use the alternative form of the derivative to find the derivative at $x = c$ (if it exists).**

5. $g(x) = 2x^2 - 3x, \quad c = 2$

6. $f(x) = \dfrac{1}{x + 4}, \quad c = 3$

Determining Differentiability   **In Exercises 7–10, describe the x-values at which f is differentiable.**

7. $f(x) = \dfrac{2}{x - 3}$

8. $f(x) = \dfrac{3x}{x + 1}$

9. $f(x) = \sqrt{x - 1}$

10. $f(x) = (x - 3)^{2/5}$

Finding a Derivative   **In Exercises 11–22, use the rules of differentiation to find the derivative of the function.**

11. $y = 14$

12. $f(t) = 6t^4$

13. $f(x) = x^3 - 15x^2$

14. $g(s) = 2s^5 - 3s^4$

15. $h(x) = 4\sqrt{x} + 6\sqrt[3]{x}$

16. $f(x) = x^{1/2} - x^{-1/2}$

17. $g(t) = \dfrac{3}{2t^2}$

18. $h(x) = \dfrac{9}{10x^4}$

19. $f(\theta) = 4\theta - 5\sin\theta$

20. $g(\alpha) = 4\cos\alpha + 6$

21. $f(t) = 3\cos t - 4e^t$

22. $g(s) = \frac{5}{3}\sin s - 2e^s$

Finding the Slope of a Graph   **In Exercises 23–26, find the slope of the graph of the function at the given point.**

23. $f(x) = \dfrac{27}{x^3}, \quad (3, 1)$

24. $f(x) = 3x^2 - 4x, \quad (1, -1)$

25. $f(x) = 4x^5 + 3x - \sin x, \quad (0, 0)$

26. $f(\theta) = 3\cos\theta - 2\theta, \quad (0, 3)$

27. Vibrating String   A guitar string vibrates with a frequency of $F = 200\sqrt{T}$, where F is measured in vibrations per second and the tension T is measured in pounds. Find the rates of change of the frequency when (a) $T = 4$ pounds and (b) $T = 9$ pounds.

28. Surface Area   The surface area of a cube with sides of length x is given by $S = 6x^2$. Find the rates of change of the surface area with respect to x when (a) $x = 3$ inches and (b) $x = 5$ inches.

Vertical Motion   **In Exercises 29 and 30, use the position function $s(t) = -16t^2 + v_0 t + s_0$ for free-falling objects.**

29. A ball is thrown straight down from the top of a 600-foot building with an initial velocity of -30 feet per second.

(a) Determine the position and velocity functions for the ball.

(b) Determine the average velocity on the interval $[1, 3]$.

(c) Find the instantaneous velocities when $t = 1$ and $t = 3$.

(d) Find the time required for the ball to reach ground level.

(e) Find the velocity of the ball at impact.

30. To estimate the height of a building, a weight is dropped from the top of the building into a pool at ground level. The splash is seen 9.2 seconds after the weight is dropped. What is the height (in feet) of the building?

Finding a Derivative   **In Exercises 31–44, find the derivative of the function.**

31. $h(x) = \sqrt{x}\cos x$

32. $f(t) = 2t^5\sin t$

33. $f(x) = \dfrac{x^2 + x - 1}{x^2 - 1}$

34. $f(x) = \dfrac{2x + 7}{x^2 + 4}$

35. $y = \dfrac{x^4}{\cos x}$

36. $y = \dfrac{\sin x}{x^4}$

37. $y = 3x^2\sec x$

38. $y = 2x - x^2\tan x$

39. $y = 4xe^x - \cot x$

40. $y = x^2(x + \cos x)$

41. $f(x) = (5x^2 + 8)(x^2 - 4x - 6)$

42. $g(x) = (2x^3 + 5x)(3x - 4)$

43. $g(x) = 3x\sin x + x^2\cos x$

44. $f(x) = (2e^x + \tan x)(x^2 + 3x + \sin x)$

Finding an Equation of a Tangent Line   **In Exercises 45–50, find an equation of the tangent line to the graph of f at the given point. Use the *tangent* feature of a graphing utility to confirm your results.**

45.

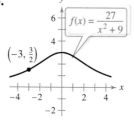

$f(x) = \dfrac{27}{x^2 + 9}$, $\left(-3, \frac{3}{2}\right)$

46.

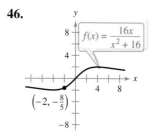

$f(x) = \dfrac{16x}{x^2 + 16}$, $\left(-2, -\frac{8}{5}\right)$

47. $f(x) = (x + 2)(x^2 + 5), \quad (-1, 6)$

48. $f(x) = (x - 4)(x^2 + 6x - 1), \quad (0, 4)$

49. $f(x) = \dfrac{x + 1}{x - 1}, \quad \left(\frac{1}{2}, -3\right)$

50. $f(x) = \dfrac{1 + \cos x}{1 - \cos x}, \quad \left(\frac{\pi}{2}, 1\right)$

Finding a Second Derivative In Exercises 51–56, find the second derivative of the function.

51. $g(t) = -8t^3 - 5t + 12$ **52.** $h(x) = 6x^{-2} + 7x^2$

53. $f(x) = 15x^{5/2}$ **54.** $f(x) = 20\sqrt[5]{x}$

55. $f(\theta) = 3 \tan \theta$ **56.** $h(t) = 10 \cos t - 15 \sin t$

57. Satellites When satellites observe Earth, they can scan only part of Earth's surface. Some satellites have sensors that can measure the angle θ shown in the figure. Let h represent the satellite's distance from Earth's surface, and let r represent Earth's radius.

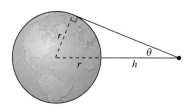

(a) Write h in terms of r and θ.

(b) Find the rate at which h is changing with respect to θ when $\theta = \pi/6$. (Assume $r = 3960$ miles.)

58. Particle Motion The position of a particle as it moves along a line is given by $s(t) = t^2 - 12t + 16$, where s is measured in meters, t is measured in seconds, and $t \geq 0$. Find (a) the displacement during the first 4 seconds, (b) the average velocity during the first 6 seconds, (c) the instantaneous velocity when $t = 6$, and (d) the acceleration when $t = 6$.

Finding a Derivative In Exercises 59–84, find the derivative of the function.

59. $y = (7x + 3)^4$ **60.** $y = (x^2 - 6)^3$

61. $y = \dfrac{1}{x^2 + 4}$ **62.** $f(x) = \dfrac{1}{(5x + 1)^2}$

63. $y = 5 \cos(9x + 1)$ **64.** $y = \cos 4x + 2 \cos^4 x$

65. $y = \dfrac{x}{2} - \dfrac{\sin 2x}{4}$ **66.** $y = \dfrac{\sec^7 x}{7} - \dfrac{\sec^5 x}{5}$

67. $y = x(6x + 1)^5$ **68.** $y = (s^2 - 1)^{5/2}(s^3 + 5)$

69. $f(x) = \dfrac{3x}{\sqrt{x^2 + 1}}$ **70.** $h(x) = \left(\dfrac{x + 5}{x^2 + 3}\right)^2$

71. $g(t) = t^2 e^{1/4}$ **72.** $h(z) = e^{-z^2/2}$

73. $y = \sqrt{e^{2x} + e^{-2x}}$ **74.** $y = 3e^{-3/t}$

75. $g(x) = \dfrac{x^2}{e^x}$ **76.** $f(\theta) = \dfrac{1}{2}e^{\sin 2\theta}$

77. $g(x) = \ln \sqrt{x}$ **78.** $h(x) = \ln \dfrac{x(x - 1)}{x - 2}$

79. $f(x) = x\sqrt{\ln x}$ **80.** $f(x) = \ln[x(x^2 - 2)^{2/3}]$

81. $y = \dfrac{1}{b^2}\left[\ln(a + bx) + \dfrac{a}{a + bx}\right]$

82. $y = \dfrac{1}{b^2}[a + bx - a \ln(a + bx)]$

83. $y = -\dfrac{1}{a} \ln \dfrac{a + bx}{x}$

84. $y = -\dfrac{1}{ax} + \dfrac{b}{a^2} \ln \dfrac{a + bx}{x}$

Finding an Equation of a Tangent Line In Exercises 85–90, find an equation of the tangent line to the graph of the function at the given point. Use the *tangent* feature of a graphing utility to confirm your results.

85. $f(x) = \sqrt{1 + x^3}$, $(2, 3)$

86. $f(x) = \sqrt[3]{1 - x^2}$, $(3, -2)$

87. $f(x) = \dfrac{6}{x^2 + 1}$, $(0, 6)$

88. $f(x) = \left(\dfrac{2x + 1}{2x - 3}\right)^2$, $(2, 25)$

89. $y = \dfrac{5}{2} \csc 3x$, $\left(\dfrac{\pi}{6}, \dfrac{5}{2}\right)$

90. $y = \csc 2x + \cot 2x$, $\left(\dfrac{\pi}{4}, 1\right)$

Finding a Second Derivative In Exercises 91–96, find the second derivative of the function.

91. $y = (8x + 5)^3$ **92.** $y = \dfrac{1}{5x + 1}$

93. $f(x) = \left(\dfrac{x - 1}{x + 1}\right)^2$ **94.** $f(x) = \dfrac{\sqrt{x}}{e^x}$

95. $f(x) = \cot x$ **96.** $y = \sin^2 x$

97. Refrigeration The temperature T (in degrees Fahrenheit) of food in a freezer is given by

$$T = \dfrac{700}{t^2 + 4t + 10}$$

where t is the time in hours. Find the rate of change of T with respect to t at each of the following times. Interpret the results in the context of the problem.

(a) $t = 1$ (b) $t = 3$ (c) $t = 5$ (d) $t = 10$

98. Harmonic Motion The displacement from equilibrium of an object in harmonic motion is given by

$$y = \dfrac{1}{4} \cos 8t - \dfrac{1}{4} \sin 8t$$

where y is measured in feet and t is the time in seconds. Determine the position and velocity of the object when $t = \pi/4$.

99. Circulatory System The speed S of blood that is r centimeters from the center of an artery is given by $S = C(R^2 - r^2)$, where C is a constant, R is the radius of the artery, and S is measured in centimeters per second. After a drug is administered, the artery begins to dilate at a rate of dR/dt. At a constant distance r, find the rate at which S changes with respect to t for $C = 1.76 \times 10^5$, $R = 1.2 \times 10^{-2}$, and $dR/dt = 10^{-5}$.

100. Tractrix A person walking along a dock drags a boat with a 10-meter rope. The person starts at the origin and walks in the positive y-direction, while the boat travels along a path called a *tractrix* (see figure). The equation of this path is

$$y = 10 \ln\left(\frac{10 + \sqrt{100 - x^2}}{x}\right) - \sqrt{100 - x^2}.$$

(a) Use a graphing utility to graph the function.

(b) Determine dy/dx algebraically.

(c) Use the result of part (b) to determine the slopes of the path when $x = 5$ and $x = 9$. Use the *derivative* feature of the graphing utility to check your answers.

(d) What does the slope of the path approach as x approaches 10 from the left? Interpret this limit in the context of the problem.

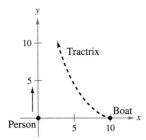

101. Modeling Data The normal daily maximum temperatures T (in degrees Fahrenheit) for Chicago, Illinois, are shown in the table. (*Source: National Oceanic and Atmospheric Administration*)

Month	Jan	Feb	Mar	Apr
Temperature	31.0	35.3	46.6	59.0

Month	May	Jun	Jul	Aug
Temperature	70.0	79.7	84.1	81.9

Month	Sep	Oct	Nov	Dec
Temperature	74.8	62.3	48.2	34.8

(a) Use a graphing utility to plot the data and find a model of the form $T(t) = a + b \sin(ct - d)$, where T is the temperature and t is the time in months, with $t = 1$ corresponding to January.

(b) Use the graphing utility to graph the model from part (a). How well does the model fit the data?

(c) Find T' algebraically and use the graphing utility to graph the derivative.

(d) Based on the graph of the derivative, during what times does the temperature change most rapidly? most slowly? Do your answers agree with your observations of the temperature changes? Explain.

102. Modeling Data The atmospheric pressure decreases with increasing altitude. At sea level, the average air pressure is one atmosphere (1.033227 kilograms per square centimeter). The table gives the pressures p (in atmospheres) at various altitudes h (in kilometers).

h	0	5	10	15	20	25
p	1	0.55	0.25	0.12	0.06	0.02

(a) Use a graphing utility to plot the data and find a model of the form $p = ae^{bh}$, where p is the air pressure and h is the altitude.

(b) Use the graphing utility to graph the model from part (a). How well does the model fit the data?

(c) Find dp/dh algebraically.

(d) Use the result of part (c) to find the rates of change of the air pressure when $h = 5$ and $h = 20$. Use the *derivative* feature of the graphing utility to check your answers.

(e) Interpret the results of part (d) in the context of the problem.

Finding a Derivative In Exercises 103–108, find dy/dx by implicit differentiation.

103. $x^2 - y^2 = 144$

104. $x^2 + 4xy - y^3 = 6$

105. $x^3y - xy^3 = 4$

106. $\sqrt{xy} = x - 4y$

107. $x \sin y = y \cos x$

108. $\cos(x + y) = x$

Famous Curves In Exercises 109–112, find an equation of the tangent line to the graph at the given point. To print an enlarged copy of the graph, go to *MathGraphs.com*.

109. Circle

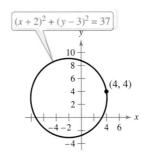

110. Rotated hyperbola

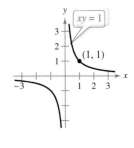

111. Astroid

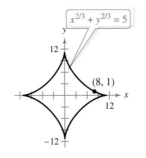

112. Lemniscate

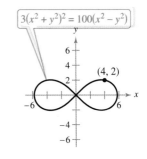

Tangent Lines and Normal Lines   In Exercises 113–116, find equations for the tangent line and the normal line to the graph of the equation at the given point. (The *normal line* at a point is perpendicular to the tangent line at the point.) Use a graphing utility to graph the equation, the tangent line, and the normal line in the same viewing window.

113. $x^2 + y^2 = 10$, $(3, 1)$ **114.** $x^2 - y^2 = 20$, $(6, 4)$

115. $y \ln x + y^2 = 0$, $(e, -1)$

116. $\ln(x + y) = x$, $(0, 1)$

Logarithmic Differentiation   In Exercises 117 and 118, find dy/dx using logarithmic differentiation.

117. $y = \dfrac{x\sqrt{x^2 + 4}}{x + 1}$, $x > 0$ **118.** $y = \dfrac{(x^2 - 9)^x}{x + 3}$, $x > 3$

Evaluating the Derivative of an Inverse Function   In Exercises 119–122, verify that f has an inverse function. Then use the function f and the given real number a to find $(f^{-1})'(a)$.

Function	Real Number
119. $f(x) = x^3 + 2$	$a = -1$
120. $f(x) = x\sqrt{x - 3}$	$a = 4$
121. $f(x) = \tan x, -\dfrac{\pi}{4} \le x \le \dfrac{\pi}{4}$	$a = \dfrac{\sqrt{3}}{3}$
122. $f(x) = \cos x, 0 \le x \le \pi$	$a = 0$

Finding a Derivative   In Exercises 123–126, find dy/dx.

123. $y = \sin(\arctan x)$ **124.** $y = \arctan(2x^2 - 3)$

125. $y = x \operatorname{arcsec} x$ **126.** $y = \frac{1}{2} \arctan e^{2x}$

127. Rate of Change   A point moves along the curve $y = \sqrt{x}$ in such a way that the y-component of the position of the point is increasing at a rate of 2 units per second. At what rate is the x-component changing when (a) $x = \frac{1}{2}$, (b) $x = 1$, and (c) $x = 4$?

128. Surface Area   All edges of a cube are expanding at a rate of 8 centimeters per second. How fast is the surface area changing when each edge is 6.5 centimeters?

129. Linear vs. Angular Speed   A rotating beacon is located 1 kilometer off a straight shoreline (see figure). The beacon rotates at a rate of 3 revolutions per minute. How fast (in kilometers per hour) does the beam of light appear to be moving to a viewer who is $\frac{1}{2}$ kilometer down the shoreline?

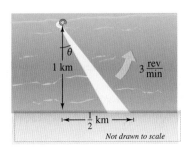

130. Security Camera   A security camera with a variable rate of rotation is centered 50 feet above a 100-foot hallway (see figure). Find a model for the rate of rotation when $|dx/dt| = 2$ feet per second.

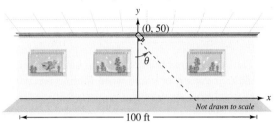

131. Flight Control   An airplane is flying in still air with an airspeed of 275 miles per hour. The plane is climbing at an angle of 18°. Find the rate at which it is gaining altitude.

132. Moving Shadow   A sandbag is dropped from a balloon at a height of 60 meters when the angle of elevation to the sun is 30° (see figure). The position of the sandbag is $s(t) = 60 - 4.9t^2$. Find the rate at which the shadow of the sandbag is traveling along the ground when the sandbag is at a height of 35 meters.

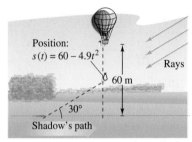

Using Newton's Method   In Exercises 133–136, use Newton's Method to approximate the zero(s) of the function. Continue the iterations until two successive approximations differ by less than 0.001. Then find the zero(s) using a graphing utility to verify your results.

133. $f(x) = x^3 - 3x - 1$ **134.** $f(x) = x^3 + 2x + 1$

135. $g(x) = xe^x - 4$ **136.** $f(x) = 3 - x \ln x$

Points of Intersection   In Exercises 137 and 138, apply Newton's Method to approximate the x-value(s) of the point(s) of intersection of the two graphs. Continue the iterations until two successive approximations differ by less than 0.001. [*Hint:* Let $h(x) = f(x) - g(x)$.]

137. $f(x) = 1 - x$ **138.** $f(x) = \sin x$

$\quad\quad g(x) = x^5 + 2$ $\quad\quad g(x) = x^2 - 2x + 1$

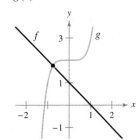

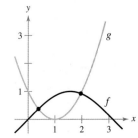

What You Need to Know

- The definition of the derivative is primarily tested on the multiple-choice section of the AP® Exam.

- The AP® Exam requires that you have proficiency with using a function's equation, table of values, or graph when finding the average velocity or average rate of change.

- Questions on the AP® Exam that require the use of the Product, Quotient, or Chain Rule do not typically involve complicated computations. However, be sure you do the more difficult exercises in this chapter because they will help you master and remember these rules.

- Although you should know the derivatives of the six trigonometric functions, the derivatives of the sine, cosine, and tangent functions are the most commonly tested on the AP® Exam.

- Related rate problems make frequent appearances on the AP® Exam because they represent a powerful application of implicit derivatives.

Practice Questions

Section 1, Part A, Multiple Choice, No Technology

1. What is an equation of the tangent line to the graph of $f(x) = 4e^x - x + 6$ at $(0, 10)$?

(A) $y = 4x + 10$

(B) $y = 4x - 10$

(C) $y = 10x - 4$

(D) $y = 3x + 10$

2. Which graph shows a function whose derivative is always negative?

(A)
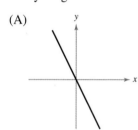

(B)
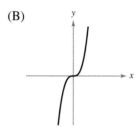

(C)
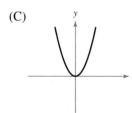

(D)
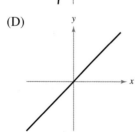

3. If $y = \dfrac{6x^4 - 3x^5 + 5x^3}{x^3}$, then $\dfrac{d^2y}{dx^2} =$

(A) $6 - 6x$.

(B) 6.

(C) $6x$.

(D) -6.

4. If $h(x) = |2x - 5|$, which of the following is true?

(A) h is continuous but is not differentiable at $x = \dfrac{5}{2}$.

(B) h is not continuous but is differentiable at $x = \dfrac{5}{2}$.

(C) h is continuous and differentiable at $x = \dfrac{5}{2}$.

(D) h is neither continuous nor differentiable at $x = \dfrac{5}{2}$.

5. If $f(x) = \dfrac{\sin x}{x^2}$, then $f'(x) =$

(A) $\dfrac{\cos x}{2x}$.

(B) $\dfrac{x \cos x - 2 \sin x}{x^2}$.

(C) $\dfrac{x \cos x - 2 \sin x}{x^3}$.

(D) $\dfrac{\cos x - 2 \sin x}{x^2}$.

6. If $y = \sqrt[4]{8x + 3}$, then $y' =$

(A) $\dfrac{2}{(8x + 3)^{3/4}}$.

(B) $\dfrac{1}{4(8x + 3)^{3/4}}$.

(C) $\dfrac{1}{4}(8x + 3)^{3/4}$.

(D) $\dfrac{8}{(8x + 3)^{3/4}}$.

7. If $y = 6 \cos 2x$, then $y^{(6)} =$

(A) $384 \cos 2x$.

(B) $-384 \cos 2x$.

(C) $384 \sin 2x$.

(D) $-384 \sin 2x$.

8. The table shows the position $s(t)$ of a particle that moves along a straight line at several times t, where t is measured in seconds and s is measured in meters.

t	2.0	2.7	3.2	3.8
$s(t)$	5.2	7.8	10.6	12.2

Which of the following best estimates the velocity of the particle at $t = 3$?

(A) 3.7 m/sec   (B) 3.9 m/sec

(C) 5.6 m/sec   (D) 7.8 m/sec

9. If $2y^3 - 3xy + x^2 = 4$, then $\dfrac{dy}{dx} =$

(A) $-\dfrac{2x}{6y^2 - 3}$.   (B) $\dfrac{2x - 3y}{3x - 6y^2}$.

(C) $\dfrac{2x - 3}{6y^2}$.   (D) $-\dfrac{2x}{6y^2 - 3x}$.

10. The volume of a cylinder with radius r and height h is given by $V = \pi r^2 h$. The radius of the cylinder is increasing at a rate of $\frac{1}{3}$ centimeter per second and the height of the cylinder is increasing at a rate of $\frac{1}{2}$ centimeter per second. At what rate, in cubic centimeters per second, is the volume of the cylinder increasing when its height is 9 centimeters and the radius is 4 centimeters?

(A) $\dfrac{4\pi}{3}$ (B) $\dfrac{8\pi}{3}$ (C) 6π (D) 32π

11. $\displaystyle\lim_{h \to 0} \dfrac{\sqrt{16 + h} - 4}{h}$ is

(A) 0.   (B) $\dfrac{1}{16}$.   (C) $\dfrac{1}{8}$.   (D) $\dfrac{1}{4}$.

Section 1, Part B, Multiple Choice, Technology Permitted

12. Two roads intersect at right angles. You are standing 25 meters north of the intersection on one of the roads. You are watching a car traveling west at 30 meters per second. At how many meters per second is the car traveling away from you 3 seconds after it passes through the intersection?

(A) 23.047   (B) 28.906

(C) 29.032   (D) 30

13. The position $s(t)$ of a particle moving along the x-axis at time t is given by $s(t) = -t^3 + 2t^2 + \frac{3}{2}$, where s is measured in meters and t is measured in seconds. When is the instantaneous velocity of the particle equal to its average velocity on the interval $[0, 4]$?

(A) 1.097 seconds   (B) 2 seconds

(C) 2.333 seconds   (D) 2.431 seconds

Section 2, Part A, Free Response, Technology Permitted

14. A particle moves along the x-axis so that at any time $t \geq 0$, its velocity is given by

$$v(t) = 2 + 3.5 \cos(0.7t).$$

(a) Find $v'(t)$. What does $v'(t)$ represent?

(b) If $v(t) = f'(t)$, what does $f(t)$ represent?

(c) What is the acceleration of the particle at time $t = 5$?

(d) Does the particle ever have a velocity of 0? Explain.

Section 2, Part B, Free Response, No Technology

15. Given:

x	$f(x)$	$f'(x)$	$g(x)$	$g'(x)$
2	-3	1	5	-2
5	4	7	-1	2

(a) If $h(x) = \dfrac{f(x)}{g(x)}$, find $h'(2)$.

(b) If $j(x) = f(g(x))$, find $j'(2)$.

(c) If $k(x) = \sqrt{f(x)}$, find $k'(5)$.

16. The figure shows the graph of the velocity, in feet per second, for a particle moving along the line $x = 4$.

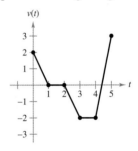

(a) Find all open intervals where the particle is (i) moving upward, (ii) moving downward, and (iii) at rest. Explain your reasoning.

(b) What is the acceleration of the particle at (i) $t = 0.75$ and (ii) $t = 4.2$? Be sure to include units.

17. Consider $g(x) = f(x)\tan x + kx$, where k is a real number, f is differentiable for all x, $f(\pi/4) = 4$, and $f'(\pi/4) = -2$.

(a) For what values of x, if any, in the interval $0 < x < 2\pi$ will the derivative of g fail to exist? Justify your answer.

(b) Given $g'(\pi/4) - 6$, find the value of k.

2   Performance Task

Falling Objects

The position of a free-falling object (neglecting air resistance) under the influence of gravity is given by $s(t) = -\frac{1}{2}gt^2 + v_0 t + s_0$, where s_0 is the initial height of the object, v_0 is the initial velocity of the object, and g is the acceleration due to gravity.

Exercises

In Exercises 1–3, use the table, which shows the data collected from a free-falling object during an experiment.

Time (seconds)	Height (meters)	Velocity (meters/second)
0.00	0.290864	−0.16405
0.02	0.284279	−0.32857
0.04	0.274400	−0.49403
0.06	0.260131	−0.71322
0.08	0.241472	−0.93309
0.10	0.219520	−1.09409
0.12	0.189885	−1.47655
0.14	0.160250	−1.47891
0.16	0.126224	−1.69994
0.18	0.086711	−1.96997
0.20	0.045002	−2.07747
0.22	0.000000	−2.25010

1. **Finding the Position Function**   Use a graphing utility to find the position function for the object. Use the position function to find the initial height, initial velocity, velocity function, and acceleration function.

2. **Analyzing the Velocity Function**   Use a graphing utility to determine whether the velocity function you found in Exercise 1 is a good fit for the data given in the table. Explain your reasoning.

3. **Finding Velocity and Acceleration Functions**   A model for the velocity function is of the form $v(t) = -gt + v_0$. Use a graphing utility and the data from the table to find the velocity function for the object. Compare this velocity function with the one you found in Exercise 1. Then use the new velocity function to determine the acceleration function. Which acceleration function is closer to the acceleration due to gravity on Earth, this one or the one you found in Exercise 1?

4. **Analyzing Another Velocity Function**   A pebble is flicked upward from a height of 0.81 meter. The position function $s(t) = -4.7561t^2 + 2.59t + 0.81$ gives the height (in meters) of the pebble after t seconds.

   (a) Find $s'(t)$.

   (b) Explain how you can use $s'(t)$ to determine the maximum height of the pebble. What is the velocity of the pebble when it reaches its maximum height?

   (c) For which values of t is s' positive? For which values of t is s' negative? What does the graph of s' tell you about the graph of s?

3 Applications of Differentiation

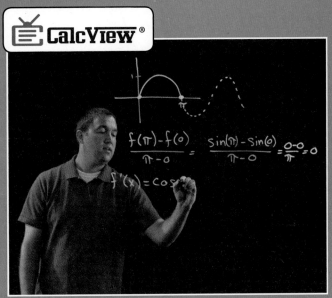

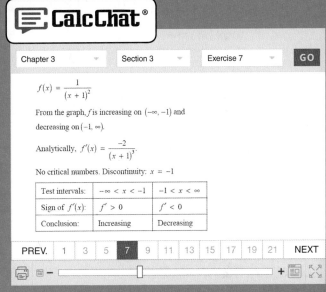

3.3 Path of a Projectile (*Example 5, p. 232*)

3.6 Offshore Oil Well (*Exercise 41, p. 264*)

211

3.1   Extrema on an Interval

▶ Understand the definition of extrema of a function on an interval.
▶ Understand the definition of relative extrema of a function on an open interval.
▶ Find extrema on a closed interval.

Extrema of a Function

In calculus, much effort is devoted to determining the behavior of a function f on an interval I. Does f have a maximum value on I? Does it have a minimum value? Where is the function increasing? Where is it decreasing? In this chapter, you will learn how derivatives can be used to answer these questions. You will also see why these questions are important in real-life applications.

Definition of Extrema

Let f be defined on an interval I containing c.

1. $f(c)$ is the **minimum of f on I** when $f(c) \le f(x)$ for all x in I.
2. $f(c)$ is the **maximum of f on I** when $f(c) \ge f(x)$ for all x in I.

The minimum and maximum of a function on an interval are the **extreme values,** or extrema (the singular form of extrema is extremum), of the function on the interval. The minimum and maximum of a function on an interval are also called the **absolute minimum** and **absolute maximum,** or the **global minimum** and **global maximum,** on the interval. Extrema can occur at interior points or endpoints of an interval. (See Figure 3.1.) Extrema that occur at the endpoints are called **endpoint extrema.**

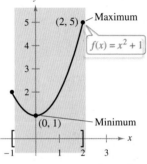

(a) f is continuous, $[-1, 2]$ is closed.

A function need not have a minimum or a maximum on an interval. For instance, in Figures 3.1(a) and 3.1(b), you can see that the function $f(x) = x^2 + 1$ has both a minimum and a maximum on the closed interval $[-1, 2]$ but does not have a maximum on the open interval $(-1, 2)$. Moreover, in Figure 3.1(c), you can see that continuity (or the lack of it) can affect the existence of an extremum on the interval. This suggests the theorem below. (Although the Extreme Value Theorem is intuitively plausible, a proof of this theorem is not within the scope of this text.)

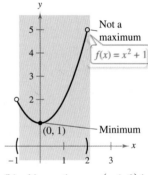

(b) f is continuous, $(-1, 2)$ is open.

Theorem 3.1   The Extreme Value Theorem

If f is continuous on a closed interval $[a, b]$, then f has both a minimum and a maximum on the interval.

Exploration

Finding Minimum and Maximum Values   The Extreme Value Theorem (like the Intermediate Value Theorem) is an *existence theorem* because it tells of the existence of minimum and maximum values but does not show how to find these values. Use the *minimum* and *maximum* features of a graphing utility to find the extrema of each function. In each case, do you think the x-values are exact or approximate? Explain your reasoning.

a. $f(x) = x^2 - 4x + 5$ on the closed interval $[-1, 3]$
b. $f(x) = x^3 - 2x^2 - 3x - 2$ on the closed interval $[-1, 3]$

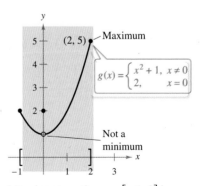

(c) g is not continuous, $[-1, 2]$ is closed.

Figure 3.1

Relative Extrema and Critical Numbers

In Figure 3.2, the graph of $f(x) = x^3 - 3x^2$ has a **relative maximum** at the point $(0, 0)$ and a **relative minimum** at the point $(2, -4)$. Informally, for a continuous function, you can think of a relative maximum as occurring on a "hill" on the graph, and a relative minimum as occurring in a "valley" on the graph. Such a hill and valley can occur in two ways. When the hill (or valley) is smooth and rounded, the graph has a horizontal tangent line at the high point (or low point). When the hill (or valley) is sharp and peaked, the graph represents a function that is not differentiable at the high point (or low point).

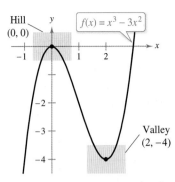

f has a relative maximum at $(0, 0)$ and a relative minimum at $(2, -4)$.

Figure 3.2

Definition of Relative Extrema

1. If there is an open interval containing c on which $f(c)$ is a maximum, then $f(c)$ is called a **relative maximum** of f, or you can say that f has a **relative maximum at $(c, f(c))$**.

2. If there is an open interval containing c on which $f(c)$ is a minimum, then $f(c)$ is called a **relative minimum** of f, or you can say that f has a **relative minimum at $(c, f(c))$**.

The plural of relative maximum is relative maxima, and the plural of relative minimum is relative minima. A relative maximum is sometimes called a **local maximum,** and a relative minimum is sometimes called a **local minimum.**

Example 1 examines the derivatives of functions at *given* relative extrema. (Much more is said about *finding* the relative extrema of a function in Section 3.3.)

EXAMPLE 1   The Value of the Derivative at Relative Extrema

Find the value of the derivative at each relative extremum shown in Figure 3.3.

Solution

a. The derivative of $f(x) = \dfrac{9(x^2 - 3)}{x^3}$ is

$$f'(x) = \frac{x^3(18x) - (9)(x^2 - 3)(3x^2)}{(x^3)^2} \qquad \text{Differentiate using Quotient Rule.}$$

$$= \frac{9(9 - x^2)}{x^4}. \qquad \text{Simplify.}$$

At the point $(3, 2)$, the value of the derivative is $f'(3) = 0$. [See Figure 3.3(a).]

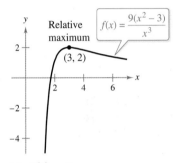

(a) $f'(3) = 0$

b. At $x = 0$, the derivative of $f(x) = |x|$ *does not exist* because the following one-sided limits differ. [See Figure 3.3(b).]

$$\lim_{x \to 0^-} \frac{f(x) - f(0)}{x - 0} = \lim_{x \to 0^-} \frac{|x|}{x} = -1 \qquad \text{Limit from the left}$$

$$\lim_{x \to 0^+} \frac{f(x) - f(0)}{x - 0} = \lim_{x \to 0^+} \frac{|x|}{x} = 1 \qquad \text{Limit from the right}$$

c. The derivative of $f(x) = \sin x$ is

$$f'(x) = \cos x.$$

At the point $(\pi/2, 1)$, the value of the derivative is $f'(\pi/2) = \cos(\pi/2) - 0$. At the point $(3\pi/2, -1)$, the value of the derivative is $f'(3\pi/2) = \cos(3\pi/2) = 0$. [See Figure 3.3(c).]

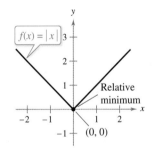

(b) $f'(0)$ does not exist.

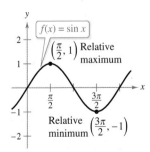

(c) $f'\left(\dfrac{\pi}{2}\right) = 0$; $f'\left(\dfrac{3\pi}{2}\right) = 0$

Figure 3.3

Note in Example 1 that at each relative extremum, the derivative either is zero or does not exist. The x-values at these special points are called **critical numbers.** Figure 3.4 illustrates the two types of critical numbers. Notice in the definition that the critical number c has to be in the domain of f, but c does not have to be in the domain of f'.

Definition of a Critical Number

Let f be defined at c. If $f'(c) = 0$ or if f is not differentiable at c, then c is a **critical number** of f.

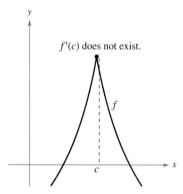

c is a critical number of f.

Figure 3.4

Theorem 3.2 **Relative Extrema Occur Only at Critical Numbers**

If f has a relative minimum or relative maximum at $x = c$, then c is a critical number of f.

Proof

Case 1: If f is *not* differentiable at $x = c$, then, by definition, c is a critical number of f and the theorem is valid.

Case 2: If f is differentiable at $x = c$, then $f'(c)$ must be positive, negative, or 0. Suppose $f'(c)$ is positive. Then

$$f'(c) = \lim_{x \to c} \frac{f(x) - f(c)}{x - c} > 0$$

which implies that there exists an interval (a, b) containing c such that

$$\frac{f(x) - f(c)}{x - c} > 0, \text{ for all } x \neq c \text{ in } (a, b). \qquad \text{See Exercise 76(b), Section 1.2.}$$

Because this quotient is positive, the signs of the denominator and numerator must agree. This produces the following inequalities for x-values in the interval (a, b).

Left of c: $\quad x < c$ and $f(x) < f(c)$ ⟹ $f(c)$ is not a relative minimum.

Right of c: $x > c$ and $f(x) > f(c)$ ⟹ $f(c)$ is not a relative maximum.

So, the assumption that $f'(c) > 0$ contradicts the hypothesis that $f(c)$ is a relative extremum. Assuming that $f'(c) < 0$ produces a similar contradiction, you are left with only one possibility—namely, $f'(c) = 0$. So, by definition, c is a critical number of f and the theorem is valid.

Finding Extrema on a Closed Interval

Theorem 3.2 states that the relative extrema of a function can occur *only* at the critical numbers of the function. Knowing this, you can use the following guidelines to find extrema on a closed interval.

Guidelines for Finding Extrema on a Closed Interval

To find the extrema of a continuous function f on a closed interval $[a, b]$, use these steps.

1. Find the critical numbers of f in (a, b).
2. Evaluate f at each critical number in (a, b).
3. Evaluate f at each endpoint of $[a, b]$.
4. The least of these values is the minimum. The greatest is the maximum.

Algebra Review

For help on the algebra in Example 2, see Example 1(a) in the *Chapter 3 Algebra Review* on page A40.

The next three examples show how to apply these guidelines. Be sure you see that finding the critical numbers of the function is only part of the procedure. Evaluating the function at the critical numbers *and* the endpoints is the other part.

EXAMPLE 2   Finding Extrema on a Closed Interval

Find the extrema of $f(x) = 3x^4 - 4x^3$ on the interval $[-1, 2]$.

Algebraic Solution

Begin by differentiating the function.

$$f(x) = 3x^4 - 4x^3 \qquad \text{Write original function.}$$

$$f'(x) = 12x^3 - 12x^2 \qquad \text{Differentiate.}$$

To find the critical numbers of f in the interval $(-1, 2)$, you must find all x-values for which $f'(x) = 0$ and all x-values for which $f'(x)$ does not exist.

$$12x^3 - 12x^2 = 0 \qquad \text{Set } f'(x) \text{ equal to 0.}$$

$$12x^2(x - 1) = 0 \qquad \text{Factor.}$$

$$x = 0, 1 \qquad \text{Critical numbers}$$

Because f' is defined for all x, you can conclude that these are the only critical numbers of f. By evaluating f at these two critical numbers and at the endpoints of $[-1, 2]$, you can determine that the maximum is $f(2) = 16$ and the minimum is $f(1) = -1$, as shown in the table.

Left Endpoint	Critical Number	Critical Number	Right Endpoint
$f(-1) = 7$	$f(0) = 0$	$f(1) = -1$ Minimum	$f(2) = 16$ Maximum

Graphical Solution

By using the *minimum* and *maximum* features of a graphing utility, you can estimate that the minimum is $f(1) = -1$ and the maximum is $f(2) = 16$. (See Figures 3.5 and 3.6, respectively.)

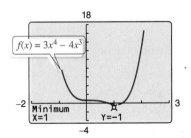

Figure 3.5

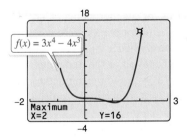

Figure 3.6

In Example 2, note that the critical number $x = 0$ does not yield a relative minimum (see Figure 3.5) or a relative maximum (see Figure 3.6). This tells you that the converse of Theorem 3.2 is not true. In other words, the *critical numbers of a function need not produce relative extrema.*

EXAMPLE 3   Finding Extrema on a Closed Interval

Find the extrema of $f(x) = 2x - 3x^{2/3}$ on the interval $[-1, 3]$.

Solution

Begin by differentiating the function.

$$f(x) = 2x - 3x^{2/3} \qquad \text{Write original function.}$$

$$f'(x) = 2 - \frac{2}{x^{1/3}} \qquad \text{Differentiate.}$$

$$= 2\left(\frac{x^{1/3} - 1}{x^{1/3}}\right) \qquad \text{Simplify.}$$

From this derivative, you can see that the function has two critical numbers in the interval $(-1, 3)$. The number 1 is a critical number because $f'(1) = 0$, and the number 0 is a critical number because $f'(0)$ does not exist. By evaluating f at these two numbers and at the endpoints of the interval, you can conclude that the minimum is $f(-1) = -5$ and the maximum is $f(0) = 0$, as shown in the table. The graph of f is shown in Figure 3.7.

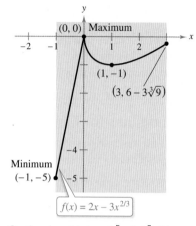

On the closed interval $[-1, 3]$, f has a minimum at $(-1, -5)$ and a maximum at $(0, 0)$.

Figure 3.7

Left Endpoint	Critical Number	Critical Number	Right Endpoint
$f(-1) = -5$ Minimum	$f(0) = 0$ Maximum	$f(1) = -1$	$f(3) = 6 - 3\sqrt[3]{9} \approx -0.24$

> **Algebra Review**
>
> For help on the algebra in Example 3, see Example 2(a) in the *Chapter 3 Algebra Review* on page A41.

EXAMPLE 4   Finding Extrema on a Closed Interval

See LarsonCalculusforAP.com for an interactive version of this type of example.

Find the extrema of $f(x) = 2 \sin x - \cos 2x$ on the interval $[0, 2\pi]$.

Solution

Begin by differentiating the function.

$$f(x) = 2 \sin x - \cos 2x \qquad \text{Write original function.}$$

$$f'(x) = 2 \cos x + 2 \sin 2x \qquad \text{Differentiate.}$$

$$= 2 \cos x + 4 \cos x \sin x \qquad \sin 2x = 2 \cos x \sin x$$

$$= 2(\cos x)(1 + 2 \sin x) \qquad \text{Factor.}$$

Because f is differentiable for all real x, you can find all critical numbers of f by finding the zeros of its derivative. Considering $2(\cos x)(1 + 2 \sin x) = 0$ in the interval $(0, 2\pi)$, the factor $\cos x$ is zero when $x = \pi/2$ and when $x = 3\pi/2$. The factor $(1 + 2 \sin x)$ is zero when $x = 7\pi/6$ and when $x = 11\pi/6$. By evaluating f at these four critical numbers and at the endpoints of the interval, you can conclude that the maximum is $f(\pi/2) = 3$ and the minimum occurs at *two* points, $f(7\pi/6) = -3/2$ and $f(11\pi/6) = -3/2$, as shown in the table. The graph is shown in Figure 3.8.

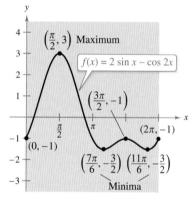

On the closed interval $[0, 2\pi]$, f has two minima at $(7\pi/6, -3/2)$ and $(11\pi/6, -3/2)$ and a maximum at $(\pi/2, 3)$.

Figure 3.8

Left Endpoint	Critical Number	Critical Number	Critical Number	Critical Number	Right Endpoint
$f(0) = -1$	$f\left(\dfrac{\pi}{2}\right) = 3$ Maximum	$f\left(\dfrac{7\pi}{6}\right) = -\dfrac{3}{2}$ Minimum	$f\left(\dfrac{3\pi}{2}\right) = -1$	$f\left(\dfrac{11\pi}{6}\right) = -\dfrac{3}{2}$ Minimum	$f(2\pi) = -1$

3.1 Exercises

See *CalcChat.com* for tutorial help and worked-out solutions to odd-numbered exercises.

Finding the Value of the Derivative at Relative Extrema In Exercises 1–6, find the value of the derivative (if it exists) at each indicated relative extremum.

1. $f(x) = \dfrac{x^2}{x^2 + 4}$

2. $f(x) = \cos \dfrac{\pi x}{2}$

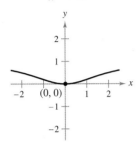

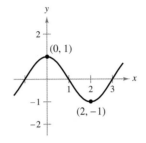

3. $g(x) = x + \dfrac{4}{x^2}$

4. $f(x) = -3x\sqrt{x + 1}$

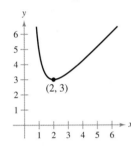

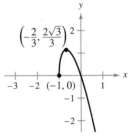

5. $f(x) = (x + 2)^{2/3}$

6. $f(x) = 4 - |x|$

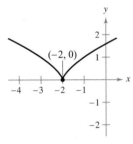

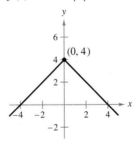

Approximating Critical Numbers In Exercises 7–10, approximate the critical numbers of the function on the open interval shown in the graph. Determine whether the function has a relative maximum, a relative minimum, an absolute maximum, an absolute minimum, or none of these at each critical number.

7.

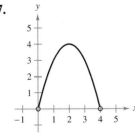

8.

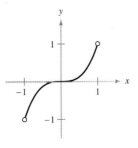

9.

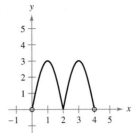

10.

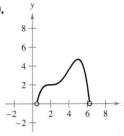

Finding Critical Numbers In Exercises 11–20, find the critical numbers of the function.

11. $f(x) = 4x^2 - 6x$

12. $g(x) = x^4 - 18x^2$

13. $g(t) = t\sqrt{4 - t}, \ t < 3$

14. $f(x) = \dfrac{4x}{x^2 + 1}$

15. $h(x) = \sin^2 x + \cos x$
$\quad 0 < x < 2\pi$

16. $f(\theta) = 2 \sec \theta + \tan \theta$
$\quad 0 < \theta < 2\pi$

17. $f(t) = te^{-5t}$

18. $g(x) = 3x^2(2^x)$

19. $f(x) = x^2 \log_2(x^2 + 1)$

20. $g(t) = 5t \ln t$

Finding Extrema on a Closed Interval In Exercises 21–44, find the absolute extrema of the function on the closed interval. Use a graphing utility to verify your results.

21. $f(x) = -2 + x, \ [-1, 2]$

22. $f(x) = 5 - \frac{3}{4}x, \ [0, 4]$

23. $h(x) = 5 - 2x^2, \ [-3, 1]$

24. $f(x) = 7x^2 + 1, \ [-1, 2]$

25. $f(x) = x^3 - \frac{3}{2}x^2, \ [-1, 2]$

26. $f(x) = 2x^3 - 6x, \ [0, 3]$

27. $y = 3x^{2/3} - 2x, \ [-1, 1]$

28. $g(x) = \sqrt[3]{x}, \ [-8, 8]$

29. $g(x) = \dfrac{6x^2}{x - 2}, \ [-2, 1]$

30. $h(t) = \dfrac{t}{t + 3}, \ [-1, 6]$

31. $y = 3 - |t - 3|, \ [-1, 5]$

32. $g(x) = |x + 4|, \ [-7, 1]$

33. $f(x) = [\![x]\!], \ [-1, 3]$

34. $h(x) = [\![2 - x]\!], \ [-3, 1]$

35. $f(x) = \sin x, \ \left[\dfrac{5\pi}{6}, \dfrac{11\pi}{6}\right]$

36. $g(x) = \sec x, \ \left[-\dfrac{\pi}{6}, \dfrac{\pi}{3}\right]$

37. $y = 3 \cos x, \ [0, 2\pi]$

38. $y = \tan \dfrac{\pi x}{8}, \ [0, 2]$

39. $f(x) = \arctan x^2, \ [-2, 1]$

40. $g(x) = \dfrac{\ln x}{x}, \ [1, 4]$

41. $h(x) = 5e^x - e^{2x}, \ [-1, 2]$

42. $y = x^2 - 8 \ln x, \ [1, 5]$

43. $y = e^x \sin x, \ [0, \pi]$

44. $y = x \ln(x + 3), \ [0, 3]$

45. Error Analysis Describe and correct the error in determining the extrema of $f(x) = -x^4 - 2x^3$ on the interval $[-2, 3]$.

$f'(x) = -4x^3 - 6x^2$ and $-4x^3 - 6x^2 = 0$
when $x = -\frac{3}{2}$ and $x = 0$. So, f has extrema
at $x = -\frac{3}{2}$ and at $x = 0$.

46. Error Analysis Describe and correct the error in determining the extrema of $g(x) = 3x^2 - 4 \ln x$ on the interval $[0.5, 5]$.

$g'(x) = 6x - \dfrac{4}{x}$ and $6x - \dfrac{4}{x} = 0$ when $x = \pm\dfrac{\sqrt{6}}{3}$.

So, g has extrema at $x = \pm\dfrac{\sqrt{6}}{3}$. ✗

 Finding Extrema on an Interval In Exercises 47 and 48, find the absolute extrema of the function (if any exist) on each interval.

47. $f(x) = 2x - 3$

(a) $[0, 2]$ (b) $[0, 2)$

(c) $(0, 2]$ (d) $(0, 2)$

48. $f(x) = \sqrt{9 - x^2}$

(a) $[-3, 3]$ (b) $[-3, 0)$

(c) $(-3, 3)$ (d) $[1, 3)$

Finding Extrema Using Technology In Exercises 49–52, use a graphing utility to graph the function and find the absolute extrema of the function on the given interval.

49. $f(x) = \dfrac{3}{x - 1}$, $(1, 4]$ **50.** $f(x) = \dfrac{2}{2 - x}$, $[0, 2)$

51. $f(x) = \sqrt{x + 4}e^{x^2/10}$, $[-2, 2]$

52. $f(x) = \sqrt{x} + \cos\dfrac{x}{2}$, $[0, 2\pi]$

Finding Absolute Extrema In Exercises 53–56, (a) use a graphing utility to graph the function and approximate any absolute extrema on the given interval. (b) Find the derivative of the function. (c) Use the derivative to find any critical numbers, and use them to find any absolute extrema not located at the endpoints. Compare the results with those in part (a).

53. $f(x) = \frac{4}{3}x\sqrt{3 - x}$, $[0, 3]$

54. $f(x) = 3.2x^5 + 5x^3 - 3.5x$, $[0, 1]$

55. $f(x) = (x^2 - 2x)\ln(x + 3)$, $[0, 3]$

56. $f(x) = (x - 4)\arcsin\dfrac{x}{4}$, $[-2, 4]$

Finding Maximum Values Using Technology In Exercises 57–60, use a computer algebra system to find the maximum value of $|f''(x)|$ on the closed interval. (This value is used in the error estimate for the Trapezoidal Rule, as discussed in Section 4.3.)

57. $f(x) = \sqrt{1 + x^3}$, $[0, 2]$

58. $f(x) = \dfrac{1}{x^2 + 1}$, $\left[\frac{1}{2}, 3\right]$

59. $f(x) = e^{-x^2/2}$, $[0, 1]$

60. $f(x) = x\ln(x + 1)$, $[0, 2]$

61. Think About It Explain why the function $f(x) = \tan x$ has a maximum on $[0, \pi/4]$ but not on $[0, \pi]$.

62. HOW DO YOU SEE IT? Determine whether each labeled point is an absolute maximum or minimum, a relative maximum or minimum, or none of these.

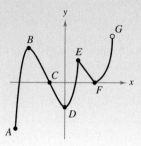

EXPLORING CONCEPTS

Justifying In Exercises 63 and 64, determine from the graph whether f has a minimum in the open interval (a, b). Explain your reasoning.

63. (a)   (b)

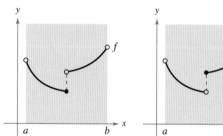

64. (a)   (b)

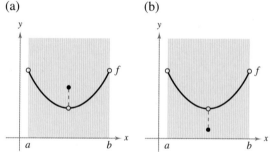

65. Critical Numbers Consider the function

$$f(x) = \dfrac{x - 4}{x + 2}.$$

Is $x = -2$ a critical number of f? Why or why not?

66. Creating the Graph of a Function Graph a function on the interval $[-2, 5]$ having the given characteristics.

Relative minimum at $x = -1$
Critical number (but no extremum) at $x = 0$
Absolute maximum at $x = 2$
Absolute minimum at $x = 5$

67. Power   The formula for the power output P of a battery is $P = VI - RI^2$, where V is the electromotive force in volts, R is the resistance in ohms, and I is the current in amperes. Find the current that corresponds to a maximum value of P in a battery for which $V = 12$ volts and $R = 0.5$ ohm. Assume that a 15-ampere fuse bounds the output in the interval $0 \le I \le 15$. Could the power output be increased by replacing the 15-ampere fuse with a 20-ampere fuse? Explain.

68. Lawn Sprinkler   A lawn sprinkler is constructed in such a way that $d\theta/dt$ is constant, where θ ranges between $45°$ and $135°$ (see figure). The distance the water travels horizontally is

$$x = \frac{v^2 \sin 2\theta}{32}, \quad 45° \le \theta \le 135°$$

where v is the speed of the water. Find dx/dt and explain why this lawn sprinkler does not water evenly. What part of the lawn receives the most water?

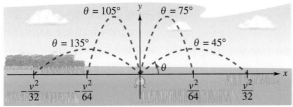

Water sprinkler: $45° \le \theta \le 135°$

69. Honeycomb   The surface area of a cell in a honeycomb is

$$S = 6hs + \frac{3s^2}{2}\left(\frac{\sqrt{3} - \cos\theta}{\sin\theta}\right)$$

where h and s are positive constants and θ is the angle at which the upper faces meet the altitude of the cell (see figure). Find the angle θ ($\pi/6 \le \theta \le \pi/2$) that minimizes the surface area S.

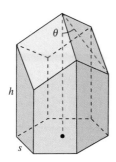

70. Critical Numbers   Consider the cubic function

$$f(x) = ax^3 + bx^2 + cx + d$$

where $a \ne 0$. Show that f can have zero, one, or two critical numbers and give an example of each case.

71. Functions   Let the function f be differentiable on an interval I containing c. If f has a maximum value at $x = c$, show that $-f$ has a minimum value at $x = c$.

True or False?   **In Exercises 72–74, determine whether the statement is true or false. If it is false, explain why or give an example that shows it is false.**

72. If $x = c$ is a critical number of the function f, then it is also a critical number of the function $g(x) = f(x) + k$, where k is a constant.

73. If $f(a)$ is a relative minimum of an even function f, then $f(-a)$ is a relative maximum of f.

74. If there is a relative extremum at the only critical number of a function f in an interval over which f is differentiable, then the relative extremum is an absolute extremum of f in the interval.

Calculus AP® – Exam Preparation Questions

75. Multiple Choice   The critical numbers for $f(x) = x^2(3x - 1)^3$ are

(A) $x = 0$ and $x = \frac{1}{3}$.

(B) $x = 0$ and $x = \frac{2}{15}$.

(C) $x = \frac{2}{15}$ and $x = \frac{1}{3}$.

(D) $x = 0$, $x = \frac{2}{15}$, and $x = \frac{1}{3}$.

76. Multiple Choice   The graph of h' is shown, where the function h is defined on $-1 \le x \le 5$. Which statement is true about the graph of h?

(A) h has a relative minimum at $x = 0$.

(B) h has a relative maximum at $x = 2$.

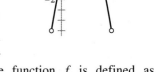

(C) h has a minimum at $x = -1$.

(D) h has no extrema.

77. Free Response   The function f is defined as $f(x) = (4 \ln x)/x^3$ for all $x > 0$.

(a) Find $f'(x)$.

(b) Find an equation of the tangent line to the graph of f at $x = e$.

(c) Find the critical number(s) of f. Does the function have a relative maximum, a relative minimum, or neither at each critical number?

(d) Find $\lim_{x \to 0^+} f(x)$.

78. Free Response   Consider the function $g(x) = \sin x \cos x$.

(a) Find an equation of the tangent line to the graph of g at $(\pi/3, \sqrt{3}/4)$.

(b) Find the critical number(s) of g on the interval $[0, 2\pi]$. Does the function have a relative maximum, a relative minimum, or neither at each critical number?

3.2 Rolle's Theorem and the Mean Value Theorem

▶ Understand and use Rolle's Theorem.
▶ Understand and use the Mean Value Theorem.

Rolle's Theorem

The Extreme Value Theorem (see Section 3.1) states that a continuous function on a closed interval $[a, b]$ must have both a minimum and a maximum on the interval. Both of these values, however, can occur at the endpoints. **Rolle's Theorem,** named after the French mathematician Michel Rolle (1652–1719), gives conditions that guarantee the existence of an extreme value in the *interior* of a closed interval.

Theorem 3.3 Rolle's Theorem

Let f be continuous on the closed interval $[a, b]$ and differentiable on the open interval (a, b). If $f(a) = f(b)$, then there is at least one number c in (a, b) such that $f'(c) = 0$.

Proof Let $f(a) = d = f(b)$.

Case 1: If $f(x) = d$ for all x in $[a, b]$, then f is constant on the interval and, by Theorem 2.2, $f'(x) = 0$ for all x in (a, b).

Case 2: Consider $f(x) > d$ for some x in (a, b). By the Extreme Value Theorem, you know that f has a maximum at some c in the interval. Moreover, because $f(c) > d$, this maximum does not occur at either endpoint. So, f has a maximum in the *open* interval (a, b). This implies that $f(c)$ is a *relative* maximum and, by Theorem 3.2, c is a critical number of f. Finally, because f is differentiable at c, you can conclude that $f'(c) = 0$.

Case 3: When $f(x) < d$ for some x in (a, b), you can use an argument similar to that in Case 2 but involving the minimum instead of the maximum. ■

From Rolle's Theorem, you can see that if a function f is continuous on $[a, b]$ and differentiable on (a, b), and if $f(a) = f(b)$, then there must be at least one x-value between a and b at which the graph of f has a horizontal tangent. [See Figure 3.9(a).] When the differentiability requirement is dropped from Rolle's Theorem, f will still have a critical number in (a, b), but it may not yield a horizontal tangent. Such a case is shown in Figure 3.9(b).

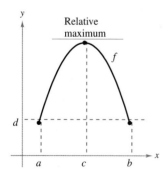

(a) f is continuous on $[a, b]$ and differentiable on (a, b).

(b) f is continuous on $[a, b]$ but *not* differentiable on (a, b).

Figure 3.9

Exploration

Extreme Values in a Closed Interval Sketch a rectangular coordinate plane on a piece of paper. Label the points $(1, 3)$ and $(5, 3)$. Using a pencil or pen, draw the graph of a differentiable function f that starts at $(1, 3)$ and ends at $(5, 3)$. Is there at least one point on the graph for which the derivative is zero? Would it be possible to draw the graph so that there is *not* a point for which the derivative is zero? Explain your reasoning.

EXAMPLE 1   Illustrating Rolle's Theorem

Find the two x-intercepts of $f(x) = x^2 - 3x + 2$ and show that $f'(x) = 0$ at some point between the two x-intercepts.

Solution

Note that f is differentiable on the entire real number line. Setting $f(x)$ equal to 0 produces

$$x^2 - 3x + 2 = 0 \qquad \text{Set } f(x) \text{ equal to 0.}$$
$$(x - 1)(x - 2) = 0 \qquad \text{Factor.}$$
$$x = 1, 2. \qquad \text{Solve for } x.$$

So, $f(1) = f(2) = 0$, and from Rolle's Theorem you know that there *exists* at least one c in the interval $(1, 2)$ such that $f'(c) = 0$. To *find* such a c, differentiate f to obtain

$$f'(x) = 2x - 3 \qquad \text{Differentiate.}$$

and then determine that $f'(x) = 0$ when $x = \frac{3}{2}$. Note that this x-value lies in the open interval $(1, 2)$, as shown in Figure 3.10.

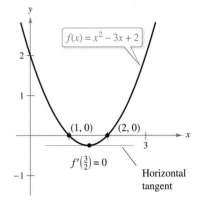

The x-value for which $f'(x) = 0$ is between the two x-intercepts.

Figure 3.10

Rolle's Theorem states that when f satisfies the conditions of the theorem, there must be *at least* one point between a and b at which the derivative is 0. There may, of course, be more than one such point, as shown in the next example.

EXAMPLE 2   Illustrating Rolle's Theorem

Let $f(x) = x^4 - 2x^2$. Find all values of c in the interval $(-2, 2)$ such that $f'(c) = 0$.

Solution

To begin, note that the function satisfies the conditions of Rolle's Theorem. That is, f is continuous on the interval $[-2, 2]$ and differentiable on the interval $(-2, 2)$. Moreover, because $f(-2) = f(2) = 8$, you can conclude that there exists at least one c in $(-2, 2)$ such that $f'(c) = 0$. Because $f'(x) = 4x^3 - 4x$, setting the derivative equal to 0 produces

$$4x^3 - 4x = 0 \qquad \text{Set } f'(x) \text{ equal to 0.}$$
$$4x(x - 1)(x + 1) = 0 \qquad \text{Factor.}$$
$$x = 0, 1, -1. \qquad x\text{-values for which } f'(x) = 0$$

So, in the interval $(-2, 2)$, the derivative is zero at three different values of x, as shown in Figure 3.11.

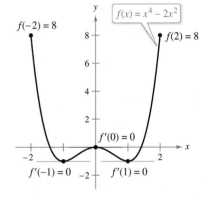

$f'(x) = 0$ for more than one x-value in the interval $(-2, 2)$.

Figure 3.11

Technology Pitfall

A graphing utility can be used to indicate whether the points on the graphs in Examples 1 and 2 are relative minima or relative maxima of the functions. When using a graphing utility, however, you should keep in mind that it can give misleading graphs. For example, use a graphing utility to graph

$$f(x) = 1 - (x - 1)^2 - \frac{1}{1000(x - 1)^{1/7} + 1}.$$

With most viewing windows, it appears that the function has a maximum of 1 when $x = 1$. (See Figure 3.12.) By evaluating the function at $x = 1$, however, you can see that $f(1) = 0$. To determine the behavior of this function near $x = 1$, you need to examine the graph analytically to get the complete picture.

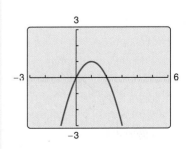

Figure 3.12

The Mean Value Theorem

Rolle's Theorem can be used to prove another theorem—the **Mean Value Theorem.**

Theorem 3.4 **The Mean Value Theorem**

If f is continuous on the closed interval $[a, b]$ and differentiable on the open interval (a, b), then there exists a number c in (a, b) such that

$$f'(c) = \frac{f(b) - f(a)}{b - a}.$$

Remark

The "mean" in the Mean Value Theorem refers to the mean (or average) rate of change of f on the interval $[a, b]$.

Proof Refer to Figure 3.13. The equation of the secant line that passes through the points $(a, f(a))$ and $(b, f(b))$ is

$$y = \left[\frac{f(b) - f(a)}{b - a} \right](x - a) + f(a).$$

Let $g(x)$ be the difference between $f(x)$ and y. Then

$$g(x) = f(x) - y$$
$$= f(x) - \left[\frac{f(b) - f(a)}{b - a} \right](x - a) - f(a).$$

By evaluating g at a and b, you can see that

$$g(a) = 0 = g(b).$$

Because f is continuous on $[a, b]$, it follows that g is also continuous on $[a, b]$. Furthermore, because f is differentiable, g is also differentiable, and you can apply Rolle's Theorem to the function g. So, there exists a number c in (a, b) such that $g'(c) = 0$, which implies that

$$g'(c) = 0$$
$$f'(c) - \frac{f(b) - f(a)}{b - a} = 0.$$

So, there exists a number c in (a, b) such that

$$f'(c) = \frac{f(b) - f(a)}{b - a}.$$

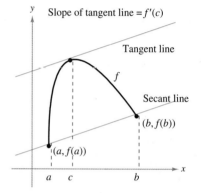

Figure 3.13

Although the Mean Value Theorem can be used directly in problem solving, it is used more often to prove other theorems. In fact, some people consider this to be the most important theorem in calculus—it is closely related to the Fundamental Theorem of Calculus discussed in Section 4.4. For now, you can get an idea of the versatility of the Mean Value Theorem by looking at the results stated in Exercises 78 and 79 in this section.

The Mean Value Theorem has implications for both basic interpretations of the derivative.

- Geometrically, the theorem guarantees the existence of a tangent line that is parallel to the secant line through the points $(a, f(a))$ and $(b, f(b))$, as shown in Figure 3.13. Example 3 illustrates this geometric interpretation of the Mean Value Theorem.

- In terms of rates of change, the Mean Value Theorem implies that there must be a point in the open interval (a, b) at which the instantaneous rate of change is equal to the average rate of change over the interval $[a, b]$. This is illustrated in Example 4.

EXAMPLE 3   Finding a Tangent Line

See LarsonCalculusforAP.com for an interactive version of this type of example.

For $f(x) = 5 - (4/x)$, find all values of c in the open interval $(1, 4)$ such that

$$f'(c) = \frac{f(4) - f(1)}{4 - 1}.$$

Solution

The slope of the secant line through $(1, f(1))$ and $(4, f(4))$ is

$$\frac{f(4) - f(1)}{4 - 1} = \frac{4 - 1}{4 - 1} = 1. \qquad \text{Slope of secant line}$$

Note that the function satisfies the conditions of the Mean Value Theorem. That is, f is continuous on the interval $[1, 4]$ and differentiable on the interval $(1, 4)$. So, there exists at least one number c in $(1, 4)$ such that $f'(c) = 1$. Solving the equation $f'(x) = 1$ yields

$$\frac{4}{x^2} = 1 \qquad \text{Set } f'(x) \text{ equal to 1.}$$

which implies that $x = \pm 2$. So, in the interval $(1, 4)$, you can conclude that $c = 2$, as shown in Figure 3.14.

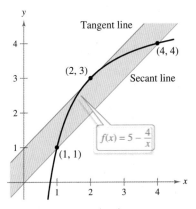

The tangent line at $(2, 3)$ is parallel to the secant line through $(1, 1)$ and $(4, 4)$.

Figure 3.14

Algebra Review

For help on the algebra in Example 3, see Example 2(b) in the *Chapter 3 Algebra Review* on page A41.

EXAMPLE 4   Finding an Instantaneous Rate of Change

Two stationary patrol cars equipped with radar are 5 miles apart on a highway, as shown in Figure 3.15. As a truck passes the first patrol car, its speed is clocked at 55 miles per hour. Four minutes later, when the truck passes the second patrol car, its speed is clocked at 50 miles per hour. Prove that the truck must have exceeded the speed limit (of 55 miles per hour) at some time during the 4 minutes.

Solution

Let $t = 0$ be the time (in hours) when the truck passes the first patrol car. The time when the truck passes the second patrol car is

$$t = \frac{4}{60} = \frac{1}{15} \text{ hour.}$$

By letting $s(t)$ represent the distance (in miles) traveled by the truck, you have $s(0) = 0$ and $s(1/15) = 5$. So, the average velocity of the truck over the five-mile stretch of highway is

$$\text{Average velocity } = \frac{s(1/15) - s(0)}{(1/15) - 0} = \frac{5}{1/15} = 75 \text{ miles per hour.}$$

Assuming that the position function is differentiable, you can apply the Mean Value Theorem to conclude that the truck must have been traveling at a rate of 75 miles per hour sometime during the 4 minutes.

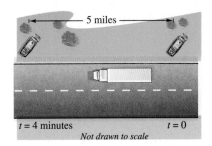

At some time t, the instantaneous velocity is equal to the average velocity over 4 minutes.

Figure 3.15

A useful alternative form of the Mean Value Theorem is: If f is continuous on $[a, b]$ and differentiable on (a, b), then there exists a number c in (a, b) such that

$$f(b) = f(a) + (b - a)f'(c). \qquad \text{Alternative form of Mean Value Theorem}$$

When doing the exercises for this section, keep in mind that polynomial functions, rational functions, and transcendental functions are differentiable at all points in their domains.

3.2 Exercises

See *CalcChat.com* for tutorial help and worked-out solutions to odd-numbered exercises.

Writing In Exercises 1–4, explain why Rolle's Theorem does not apply to the function even though there exist a and b such that $f(a) = f(b)$.

1. $f(x) = \left| \dfrac{1}{x} \right|$, $[-1, 1]$ **2.** $f(x) = \cot \dfrac{x}{2}$, $[\pi, 3\pi]$

3. $f(x) = 1 - |x - 1|$, $[0, 2]$

4. $f(x) = \sqrt{(2 - x^{2/3})^3}$, $[-1, 1]$

Illustrating Rolle's Theorem In Exercises 5–8, find the two x-intercepts of the function f and show that $f'(x) = 0$ at some point between the two x-intercepts.

5. $f(x) = x^2 - x - 2$ **6.** $f(x) = x^2 + 6x$

7. $f(x) = x\sqrt{x + 4}$ **8.** $f(x) = -3x\sqrt{x + 1}$

Illustrating Rolle's Theorem In Exercises 9–22, determine whether Rolle's Theorem can be applied to f on the closed interval $[a, b]$. If Rolle's Theorem can be applied, find all values of c in the open interval (a, b) such that $f'(c) = 0$. If Rolle's Theorem cannot be applied, explain why not.

9. $f(x) = -x^2 + 3x$, $[0, 3]$

10. $f(x) = x^2 - 8x + 5$, $[2, 6]$

11. $f(x) = (x - 1)(x - 2)(x - 3)$, $[1, 3]$

12. $f(x) = (x - 4)(x + 2)^2$, $[-2, 4]$

13. $f(x) = x^{2/3} - 1$, $[-8, 8]$

14. $f(x) = 3 - |x - 3|$, $[0, 6]$

15. $f(x) = \dfrac{x^2 - 2x - 3}{x + 2}$, $[-1, 3]$

16. $f(x) = \dfrac{x^2 - 4}{x - 1}$, $[-2, 2]$

17. $f(x) = \sin x$, $[0, 2\pi]$ **18.** $f(x) = \cos 2x$, $[-\pi, \pi]$

19. $f(x) = \tan x$, $[0, \pi]$ **20.** $f(x) = \sec x$, $[\pi, 2\pi]$

21. $f(x) = (x^2 - 2x)e^x$, $[0, 2]$

22. $f(x) = x - 2 \ln x$, $[1, 3]$

Using Rolle's Theorem In Exercises 23–28, use a graphing utility to graph the function on the closed interval $[a, b]$. Determine whether Rolle's Theorem can be applied to f on the interval and, if so, find all values of c in the open interval (a, b) such that $f'(c) = 0$.

23. $f(x) = x - x^{1/3}$, $[0, 1]$ **24.** $f(x) = |x| - 1$, $[-1, 1]$

25. $f(x) = x - \tan \pi x$, $\left[-\dfrac{1}{4}, \dfrac{1}{4}\right]$

26. $f(x) = \dfrac{x}{2} - \sin \dfrac{\pi x}{6}$, $[-1, 0]$

27. $f(x) = 2 + \arcsin(x^2 - 1)$, $[-1, 1]$

28. $f(x) = 2 + (x^2 - 4x)(2^{-x/4})$, $[0, 4]$

29. Vertical Motion The height of a ball t seconds after it is thrown upward from a height of 6 feet and with an initial velocity of 48 feet per second is $f(t) = -16t^2 + 48t + 6$.

(a) Verify that $f(1) = f(2)$.

(b) According to Rolle's Theorem, what must the velocity be at some time in the interval $(1, 2)$? Find that time.

30. Material Cost The ordering and transportation cost C for components used in a manufacturing process is approximated by

$$C(x) = 10\left(\dfrac{1}{x} + \dfrac{x}{x + 3}\right)$$

where C is measured in thousands of dollars and x is the order size in hundreds.

(a) Verify that $C(3) = C(6)$.

(b) According to Rolle's Theorem, what must the rate of change of the cost be for some order size in the interval $(3, 6)$? Find that order size.

Mean Value Theorem In Exercises 31 and 32, copy the graph and sketch the secant line to the graph through the points $(a, f(a))$ and $(b, f(b))$. Then sketch any tangent lines to the graph for each value of c guaranteed by the Mean Value Theorem. To print an enlarged copy of the graph, go to *MathGraphs.com*.

31. 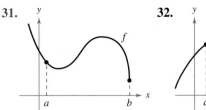 **32.**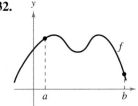

Writing In Exercises 33 and 34, explain why the Mean Value Theorem does not apply to the function f on the interval $[0, 6]$.

33. $f(x) = \dfrac{1}{x - 3}$ **34.** $f(x) = |x - 3|$

35. Mean Value Theorem Consider the graph of the function $f(x) = -x^2 + 5$ (see figure on next page).

(a) Find the equation of the secant line joining the points $(-1, 4)$ and $(2, 1)$.

(b) The tangent line to the graph of f at some point $(c, f(c))$ in the interval $(-1, 2)$ must have what slope?

(c) Find the point $(c, f(c))$ and the equation of the tangent line through this point.

(d) Use a graphing utility to graph f, the secant line, and the tangent line.

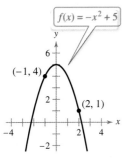

Figure for 35   Figure for 36

36. Mean Value Theorem Consider the graph of the function $f(x) = x^2 - x - 12$ (see figure).

(a) Find the equation of the secant line joining the points $(-2, -6)$ and $(4, 0)$.

(b) The tangent line to the graph of f at some point $(c, f(c))$ in the interval $(-2, 4)$ must have what slope?

(c) Find the point $(c, f(c))$ and the equation of the tangent line through this point.

(d) Use a graphing utility to graph f, the secant line, and the tangent line.

 Using the Mean Value Theorem In Exercises **37–50, determine whether the Mean Value Theorem can be applied to f on the closed interval $[a, b]$. If so, find all values of c in the open interval (a, b) such that**

$$f'(c) = \frac{f(b) - f(a)}{b - a}.$$

If the Mean Value Theorem cannot be applied, explain why not.

37. $f(x) = 6x^3$, $[1, 2]$ **38.** $f(x) = x^6$, $[-1, 1]$

39. $f(x) = x^3 + 2x$, $[-1, 1]$ **40.** $f(x) = x^4 - 8x$, $[0, 2]$

41. $f(x) = \dfrac{x + 2}{x - 1}$, $[-3, 3]$ **42.** $f(x) = \dfrac{x}{x - 5}$, $[1, 4]$

43. $f(x) = |2x + 1|$, $[-1, 3]$

44. $f(x) = \sqrt{2 - x}$, $[-7, 2]$

45. $f(x) = \sin x$, $[0, \pi]$ **46.** $f(x) = e^{-3x}$, $[0, 2]$

47. $f(x) = \cos x + \tan x$, $[0, \pi]$

48. $f(x) = (x + 3) \ln(x + 3)$, $[-2, -1]$

49. $f(x) = x \log_2 x$, $[1, 2]$

50. $f(x) = \arctan(1 - x)$, $[0, 1]$

Using the Mean Value Theorem In Exercises **51–56, use a graphing utility to (a) graph the function f on the given interval, (b) find and graph the secant line through points on the graph of f at the endpoints of the given interval, and (c) find and graph any tangent lines to the graph of f that are parallel to the secant line.**

51. $f(x) = \dfrac{x}{x + 1}$, $\left[-\dfrac{1}{2}, 2\right]$ **52.** $f(x) = \sqrt{x}$, $[1, 9]$

53. $f(x) = x - 2 \sin x$, $[-\pi, \pi]$

54. $f(x) = x^4 - 2x^3 + x^2$, $[0, 6]$

55. $f(x) = 2e^{x/4} \cos \dfrac{\pi x}{4}$, $[0, 2]$

56. $f(x) = \ln|\sec \pi x|$, $\left[0, \frac{1}{4}\right]$

57. Vertical Motion The height of an object t seconds after it is projected upward with an initial velocity of 32 meters per second is given by $s(t) = -4.9t^2 + 32t$.

(a) Find the average velocity of the object during the first 4 seconds.

(b) Use the Mean Value Theorem to verify that at some time during the first 4 seconds of fall, the instantaneous velocity equals the average velocity. Find that time.

58. Sales A company introduces a new product for which the number of units sold S is

$$S(t) = 200\left(5 - \frac{9}{2 + t}\right)$$

where t is the time in months.

(a) Find the average rate of change of $S(t)$ during the first year.

(b) During what month of the first year does $S'(t)$ equal the average rate of change?

EXPLORING CONCEPTS

59. Converse of Rolle's Theorem Let f be continuous on $[a, b]$ and differentiable on (a, b). If there exists c in (a, b) such that $f'(c) = 0$, does it follow that $f(a) = f(b)$? Explain.

60. Rolle's Theorem Let f be continuous on $[a, b]$ and differentiable on (a, b). Also, $f(a) = f(b)$ and c is a real number in the interval such that $f'(c) = 0$. Find an interval for the function g over which Rolle's Theorem can be applied, and find the corresponding critical number of g, where k is a constant.

(a) $g(x) = f(x) + k$

(b) $g(x) = f(x - k)$

(c) $g(x) = f(kx)$

61. Justifying The function

$$f(x) = \begin{cases} 0, & x = 0 \\ 1 - x, & 0 < x \le 1 \end{cases}$$

is differentiable on $(0, 1)$ and satisfies $f(0) = f(1)$. However, its derivative is never zero on $(0, 1)$. Does this contradict Rolle's Theorem? Explain.

62. Mean Value Theorem Can you find a function f such that $f(-2) = -2$, $f(2) = 6$, and $f'(x) < 1$ for all x? Why or why not?

63. Temperature When an object is removed from a furnace and placed in an environment with a constant temperature of 90°F, its core temperature is 1500°F. Five hours later, the core temperature is 390°F. Explain why there must exist a time in the interval when the temperature is decreasing at a rate of 222°F per hour.

64. SPEED

A plane begins its takeoff at 2:00 P.M. on a 2500-mile flight. After 5.5 hours, the plane arrives at its destination. Explain why there are at least two times during the flight when the speed of the plane is 400 miles per hour.

65. Acceleration At 9:13 A.M., a sports car is traveling 35 miles per hour. Two minutes later, the car is traveling 85 miles per hour. Prove that at some time during this two-minute interval, the car's acceleration is exactly 1500 miles per hour squared.

66. HOW DO YOU SEE IT? The figure shows two parts of the graph of a continuous differentiable function f on $[-10, 4]$. The derivative f' is also continuous. To print an enlarged copy of the graph, go to *MathGraphs.com*.

(a) Explain why f must have at least one zero in $[-10, 4]$.

(b) Explain why f' must also have at least one zero in the interval $[-10, 4]$. What are these zeros called?

(c) Make a possible sketch of the function with one zero of f' on the interval $[-10, 4]$.

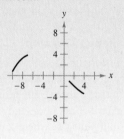

Graphical Reasoning In Exercises 67 and 68, sketch a graph of a function with the given property, for which the conclusion of the Mean Value Theorem is not true.

67. Continuous on $[-5, 5]$ **68.** Not continuous on $[-5, 5]$

Justifying In Exercises 69–72, use the Intermediate Value Theorem and Rolle's Theorem to prove that the equation has exactly one real solution.

69. $x^5 + x^3 + x + 1 = 0$ **70.** $2x^5 + 7x - 1 = 0$

71. $3x + 1 - \sin x = 0$ **72.** $2x - 2 - \cos x = 0$

Reasoning In Exercises 73–76, find a function f that has the derivative $f'(x)$ and whose graph passes through the given point. Explain your reasoning.

73. $f'(x) = 0$, $(3, 4)$ **74.** $f'(x) = 7$, $(0, 1)$

75. $f'(x) = 2x$, $(-1, 3)$ **76.** $f'(x) = 8x - 3$, $(4, -3)$

77. Proof Prove that if $a > 0$ and n is any positive integer, then the polynomial function $p(x) = x^{2n+1} + ax + b$ cannot have two real roots.

78. Proof Prove that if $f'(x) = 0$ for all x in an interval (a, b), then f is constant on (a, b).

79. Proof Let $p(x) = Ax^2 + Bx + C$. Prove that for any interval $[a, b]$, the value c guaranteed by the Mean Value Theorem is the midpoint of the interval.

80. Justifying

(a) Let $f(x) = x^2$ and $g(x) = -x^3 + x^2 + 3x + 2$. Then $f(-1) = g(-1)$ and $f(2) = g(2)$. Show that there is at least one value c in the interval $(-1, 2)$ where the tangent line to f at $(c, f(c))$ is parallel to the tangent line to g at $(c, g(c))$. Identify c.

(b) Let f and g be differentiable functions on $[a, b]$ where $f(a) = g(a)$ and $f(b) = g(b)$. Show that there is at least one value c in the interval (a, b) where the tangent line to f at $(c, f(c))$ is parallel to the tangent line to g at $(c, g(c))$.

Calculus AP® – Exam Preparation Questions

81. Multiple Choice The function f is differentiable with $f(1) = 0$ and $f(5) = 4$. The graph of f' is shown. Which of the following statements is the result of applying the Mean Value Theorem on the interval $[1, 5]$?

(A) $f'(2) = 1.5$
(B) $f'(3) = 1$
(C) $f(1) = 2$
(D) $f(2.5) = 2$

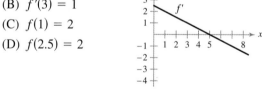

82. Multiple Choice If the Mean Value Theorem is applied to the function $f(x) = x^3 - 4x$ on the interval $[0, 2]$, then the number c that must exist in the interval $(0, 2)$ is

(A) 0.   (B) $\dfrac{1}{2}$.   (C) $\dfrac{\sqrt{3}}{3}$.   (D) $\dfrac{2\sqrt{3}}{3}$.

83. Multiple Choice Which of the following functions do not satisfy the conditions of the Mean Value Theorem on the interval $[-1, 1]$?

(A) $f(x) = \sqrt[5]{x}$ (B) $g(x) = 2x \arccos x$

(C) $h(x) = \dfrac{x}{x - 3}$ (D) $p(x) = \sqrt{x + 1}$

3.3   Increasing and Decreasing Functions and the First Derivative Test

▶ Determine intervals on which a function is increasing or decreasing.
▶ Apply the First Derivative Test to find relative extrema of a function.

Increasing and Decreasing Functions

In this section, you will learn how derivatives can be used to *classify* relative extrema as either relative minima or relative maxima. First, it is important to define increasing and decreasing functions.

Definitions of Increasing and Decreasing Functions

A function f is **increasing** on an interval when, for any two numbers x_1 and x_2 in the interval, $x_1 < x_2$ implies $f(x_1) < f(x_2)$.

A function f is **decreasing** on an interval when, for any two numbers x_1 and x_2 in the interval, $x_1 < x_2$ implies $f(x_1) > f(x_2)$.

A function is increasing when, *as x moves to the right,* its graph moves up, and is decreasing when its graph moves down. For example, the function in Figure 3.16 is decreasing on the interval $(-\infty, a)$, is constant on the interval (a, b), and is increasing on the interval (b, ∞). As shown in Theorem 3.5 below, a positive derivative implies that the function is increasing, a negative derivative implies that the function is decreasing, and a zero derivative on an entire interval implies that the function is constant on that interval.

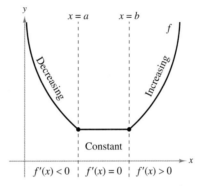

The derivative is related to the slope of a function.

Figure 3.16

Communication and Notation

When discussing the behavior of a function, remember to examine the graph of the function from left to right.

Theorem 3.5   Test for Increasing and Decreasing Functions

Let f be a function that is continuous on the closed interval $[a, b]$ and differentiable on the open interval (a, b).

1. If $f'(x) > 0$ for all x in (a, b), then f is increasing on $[a, b]$.
2. If $f'(x) < 0$ for all x in (a, b), then f is decreasing on $[a, b]$.
3. If $f'(x) = 0$ for all x in (a, b), then f is constant on $[a, b]$.

Justification

The conclusions in the first two cases of Theorem 3.5 are valid even when $f'(x) = 0$ at a finite number of x-values in (a, b).

Proof   To prove the first case, assume that $f'(x) > 0$ for all x in the interval (a, b) and let $x_1 < x_2$ be any two points in the interval. By the Mean Value Theorem, you know that there exists a number c such that $x_1 < c < x_2$, and

$$f'(c) = \frac{f(x_2) - f(x_1)}{x_2 - x_1}.$$

Because $f'(c) > 0$ and $x_2 - x_1 > 0$, you know that $f(x_2) - f(x_1) > 0$, which implies that $f(x_1) < f(x_2)$. So, f is increasing on the interval. The second case has a similar proof (see Exercise 109), and the third case is a consequence of Exercise 78 in Section 3.2.

EXAMPLE 1 Intervals on Which f Is Increasing or Decreasing

Find the open intervals on which $f(x) = x^3 - \frac{3}{2}x^2$ is increasing or decreasing.

Solution

Note that f is differentiable on the entire real number line and the derivative of f is

$$f(x) = x^3 - \frac{3}{2}x^2 \qquad \text{Write original function.}$$
$$f'(x) = 3x^2 - 3x. \qquad \text{Differentiate.}$$

To determine the critical numbers of f, set $f'(x)$ equal to zero.

$$3x^2 - 3x = 0 \qquad \text{Set } f'(x) \text{ equal to 0.}$$
$$3(x)(x - 1) = 0 \qquad \text{Factor.}$$
$$x = 0, 1 \qquad \text{Critical numbers}$$

Because there are no points for which f' does not exist, you can conclude that $x = 0$ and $x = 1$ are the only critical numbers. The table summarizes the testing of the three intervals determined by these two critical numbers.

Interval	$-\infty < x < 0$	$0 < x < 1$	$1 < x < \infty$
Test Value	$x = -1$	$x = \frac{1}{2}$	$x = 2$
Sign of $f'(x)$	$f'(-1) = 6 > 0$	$f'(\frac{1}{2}) = -\frac{3}{4} < 0$	$f'(2) = 6 > 0$
Conclusion	Increasing	Decreasing	Increasing

By Theorem 3.5, f is increasing on the intervals $(-\infty, 0)$ and $(1, \infty)$ and decreasing on the interval $(0, 1)$, as shown in Figure 3.17.

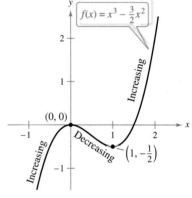

Figure 3.17

Example 1 gives you one instance of how to find intervals on which a function is increasing or decreasing. The guidelines below summarize the steps followed in that example.

> **Guidelines for Finding Intervals on Which a Function Is Increasing or Decreasing**
>
> Let f be continuous on the interval (a, b). To find the open intervals on which f is increasing or decreasing, use the following steps.
>
> 1. Locate the critical numbers of f in (a, b), and use these numbers to determine test intervals.
> 2. Determine the sign of $f'(x)$ at one test value in each of the intervals.
> 3. Use Theorem 3.5 to determine whether f is increasing or decreasing on each interval.
>
> These guidelines are also valid when the interval (a, b) is replaced by an interval of the form $(-\infty, b)$, (a, ∞), or $(-\infty, \infty)$.

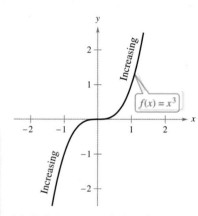

(a) Strictly monotonic function

A function is **strictly monotonic** on an interval when it is either increasing on the entire interval or decreasing on the entire interval. For instance, the function $f(x) = x^3$ is strictly monotonic on the entire real number line because it is increasing on the entire real number line, as shown in Figure 3.18(a). The function shown in Figure 3.18(b) is not strictly monotonic on the entire real number line because it is constant on the interval $[0, 1]$.

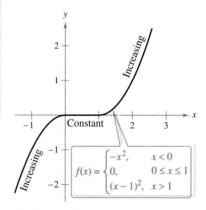

(b) Not strictly monotonic
Figure 3.18

The First Derivative Test

After you have determined the intervals on which a function is increasing or decreasing, it is not difficult to locate the relative extrema of the function. For instance, in Figure 3.19 (from Example 1), the function

$$f(x) = x^3 - \frac{3}{2}x^2$$

has a relative maximum at the point $(0, 0)$ because f is increasing immediately to the left of $x = 0$ and decreasing immediately to the right of $x = 0$. Similarly, f has a relative minimum at the point $\left(1, -\frac{1}{2}\right)$ because f is decreasing immediately to the left of $x = 1$ and increasing immediately to the right of $x = 1$. The next theorem makes this more explicit.

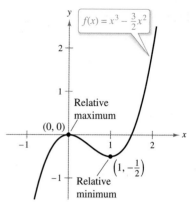

Relative extrema of f
Figure 3.19

Theorem 3.6   The First Derivative Test

Let c be a critical number of a function f that is continuous on an open interval I containing c. If f is differentiable on the interval, except possibly at c, then $f(c)$ can be classified as follows.

1. If $f'(x)$ changes from negative to positive at c, then f has a *relative minimum* at $(c, f(c))$.

2. If $f'(x)$ changes from positive to negative at c, then f has a *relative maximum* at $(c, f(c))$.

3. If $f'(x)$ is positive on both sides of c or negative on both sides of c, then $f(c)$ is neither a relative minimum nor a relative maximum.

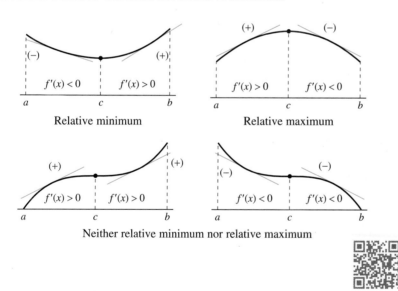

Proof   Assume that $f'(x)$ changes from negative to positive at c. Then there exist a and b in I such that

$$f'(x) < 0 \text{ for all } x \text{ in } (a, c) \quad \text{and} \quad f'(x) > 0 \text{ for all } x \text{ in } (c, b).$$

By Theorem 3.5, f is decreasing on $[a, c]$ and increasing on $[c, b]$. So, $f(c)$ is a minimum of f on the open interval (a, b) and, consequently, a relative minimum of f. This proves the first case of the theorem. The second case can be proved in a similar way. (See Exercise 110.)

Applying the First Derivative Test

Find the relative extrema of $f(x) = \frac{1}{2}x - \sin x$ in the interval $(0, 2\pi)$.

Solution

Note that f is continuous on the interval $(0, 2\pi)$. The derivative of f is $f'(x) = \frac{1}{2} - \cos x$. To determine the critical numbers of f in this interval, set $f'(x)$ equal to 0.

$$\frac{1}{2} - \cos x = 0 \qquad \text{Set } f'(x) \text{ equal to 0.}$$

$$\cos x = \frac{1}{2}$$

$$x = \frac{\pi}{3}, \frac{5\pi}{3} \qquad \text{Critical numbers}$$

Because there are no points for which f' does not exist, you can conclude that $x = \pi/3$ and $x = 5\pi/3$ are the only critical numbers. The table summarizes the testing of the three intervals determined by these two critical numbers. By applying the First Derivative Test, you can conclude that f has a relative minimum at the point where $x = \pi/3$ and a relative maximum at the point where $x = 5\pi/3$, as shown in Figure 3.20.

Interval	$0 < x < \dfrac{\pi}{3}$	$\dfrac{\pi}{3} < x < \dfrac{5\pi}{3}$	$\dfrac{5\pi}{3} < x < 2\pi$
Test Value	$x = \dfrac{\pi}{4}$	$x = \pi$	$x = \dfrac{7\pi}{4}$
Sign of $f'(x)$	$f'\left(\dfrac{\pi}{4}\right) < 0$	$f'(\pi) > 0$	$f'\left(\dfrac{7\pi}{4}\right) < 0$
Conclusion	Decreasing	Increasing	Decreasing

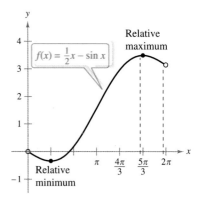

A relative minimum occurs where f changes from decreasing to increasing, and a relative maximum occurs where f changes from increasing to decreasing.

Figure 3.20

Applying the First Derivative Test

Find the relative extrema of $f(x) = (x^2 - 4)^{2/3}$.

Solution

Begin by noting that f is continuous on the entire real number line. The derivative of f

$$f'(x) = \frac{2}{3}(x^2 - 4)^{-1/3}(2x) \qquad \text{General Power Rule}$$

$$= \frac{4x}{3(x^2 - 4)^{1/3}} \qquad \text{Simplify.}$$

is 0 when $x = 0$ and does not exist when $x = \pm 2$. So, the critical numbers are $x = -2$, $x = 0$, and $x = 2$. The table summarizes the testing of the four intervals determined by these three critical numbers. By applying the First Derivative Test, you can conclude that f has a relative minimum at the point $(-2, 0)$, a relative maximum at the point $\left(0, \sqrt[3]{16}\right)$, and another relative minimum at the point $(2, 0)$, as shown in Figure 3.21.

Interval	$-\infty < x < -2$	$-2 < x < 0$	$0 < x < 2$	$2 < x < \infty$
Test Value	$x = -3$	$x = -1$	$x = 1$	$x = 3$
Sign of $f'(x)$	$f'(-3) < 0$	$f'(-1) > 0$	$f'(1) < 0$	$f'(3) > 0$
Conclusion	Decreasing	Increasing	Decreasing	Increasing

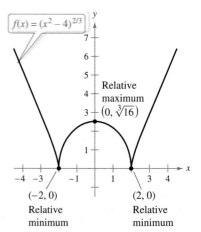

Figure 3.21

Note that in Examples 1 and 2, the given functions are differentiable on the entire real number line. For such functions, the only critical numbers are those for which $f'(x) = 0$. Example 3 concerns a function that has two types of critical numbers—those for which $f'(x) = 0$ and those for which f is not differentiable.

When using the First Derivative Test, be sure to consider the domain of the function. For instance, the function in the next example is not defined when $x = 0$. This x-value must be used with the critical numbers to determine the test intervals.

EXAMPLE 4   Applying the First Derivative Test

See LarsonCalculusforAP.com for an interactive version of this type of example.

Find the relative extrema of $f(x) = \dfrac{x^4 + 1}{x^2}$.

Solution

Note that f is not defined when $x = 0$.

$$f(x) = x^2 + x^{-2} \qquad \text{Rewrite original function.}$$

$$f'(x) = 2x - 2x^{-3} \qquad \text{Differentiate.}$$

$$= 2x - \frac{2}{x^3} \qquad \text{Rewrite with positive exponent.}$$

$$= \frac{2(x^4 - 1)}{x^3} \qquad \text{Simplify.}$$

$$= \frac{2(x^2 + 1)(x - 1)(x + 1)}{x^3} \qquad \text{Factor.}$$

So, $f'(x)$ is zero at $x = \pm 1$. Moreover, because $x = 0$ is not in the domain of f, you should use this x-value along with the critical numbers to determine the test intervals.

$$x = \pm 1 \qquad \text{Critical numbers, } f'(\pm 1) = 0$$

$$x = 0 \qquad \text{0 is not in the domain of } f.$$

The table summarizes the testing of the four intervals determined by these three x-values. By applying the First Derivative Test, you can conclude that f has one relative minimum at the point $(-1, 2)$ and another at the point $(1, 2)$, as shown in Figure 3.22.

Interval	$-\infty < x < -1$	$-1 < x < 0$	$0 < x < 1$	$1 < x < \infty$
Test Value	$x = -2$	$x = -\frac{1}{2}$	$x = \frac{1}{2}$	$x = 2$
Sign of $f'(x)$	$f'(-2) < 0$	$f'(-\frac{1}{2}) > 0$	$f'(\frac{1}{2}) < 0$	$f'(2) > 0$
Conclusion	Decreasing	Increasing	Decreasing	Increasing

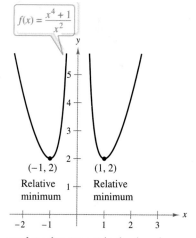

x-values that are not in the domain of f, as well as critical numbers, determine test intervals for f'.

Figure 3.22

Technology

The most difficult step in applying the First Derivative Test is finding the values for which the derivative is equal to 0. For instance, the values of x for which the derivative of

$$f(x) = \frac{x^4 + 1}{x^2 + 1}$$

is equal to zero are $x = 0$ and $x = \pm\sqrt{\sqrt{2} - 1}$. If you have access to technology that can perform symbolic differentiation and solve equations, use it to apply the First Derivative Test to this function.

EXAMPLE 5 The Path of a Projectile

Neglecting air resistance, the path of a projectile that is propelled at an angle θ is

$$y = -\frac{g \sec^2 \theta}{2v_0^2}x^2 + (\tan \theta)x + h, \quad 0 \le \theta \le \frac{\pi}{2}$$

where y is the height, x is the horizontal distance, g is the acceleration due to gravity, v_0 is the initial velocity, and h is the initial height. Let $g = 32$ feet per second per second, $v_0 = 24$ feet per second, and $h = 9$ feet. What value of θ will produce a maximum horizontal distance?

Solution

To find the distance the projectile travels, let $y = 0$, $g = 32$, $v_0 = 24$, and $h = 9$. Then substitute these values in the given equation as shown.

$$-\frac{g \sec^2 \theta}{2v_0^2}x^2 + (\tan \theta)x + h = y$$

$$-\frac{32 \sec^2 \theta}{2(24^2)}x^2 + (\tan \theta)x + 9 = 0$$

$$-\frac{\sec^2 \theta}{36}x^2 + (\tan \theta)x + 9 = 0$$

Next, solve for x using the Quadratic Formula with $a = (-\sec^2 \theta)/36$, $b = \tan \theta$, and $c = 9$.

$$x = \frac{-b \pm \sqrt{b^2 - 4ac}}{2a}$$

$$x = \frac{-\tan \theta \pm \sqrt{(\tan \theta)^2 - 4[(-\sec^2 \theta)/36](9)}}{2[(-\sec^2 \theta)/36]}$$

$$x = \frac{-\tan \theta \pm \sqrt{\tan^2 \theta + \sec^2 \theta}}{(-\sec^2 \theta)/18}$$

$$x = 18(\cos \theta)\left(\sin \theta + \sqrt{\sin^2 \theta + 1}\right), \quad x \ge 0$$

At this point, you need to find the value of θ that produces a maximum value of x. Applying the First Derivative Test by hand would be very tedious. Using technology to solve the equation $dx/d\theta = 0$, however, eliminates most of the messy computations. The result is that the maximum value of x occurs when

$$\theta \approx 0.61548 \text{ radian}, \quad \text{or} \quad 35.3°.$$

This conclusion is reinforced by sketching the path of the projectile for different values of θ, as shown in Figure 3.23. Of the three paths shown, note that the distance traveled is greatest for $\theta = 35°$.

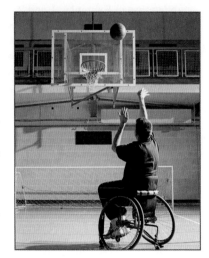

When a projectile is propelled from ground level and air resistance is neglected, the object will travel farthest with an initial angle of 45°. When, however, the projectile is propelled from a point above ground level, the angle that yields a maximum horizontal distance is not 45°. (See Example 5.)

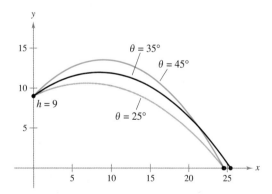

The path of a projectile with initial angle θ
Figure 3.23

3.3   Exercises

Using a Graph   In Exercises 1 and 2, use the graph of f to find (a) the largest open interval on which f is increasing and (b) the largest open interval on which f is decreasing.

1.
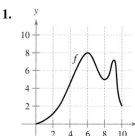

2.
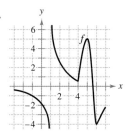

Using a Graph   In Exercises 3–8, use the graph to estimate the open intervals on which the function is increasing or decreasing. Then find the open intervals analytically.

3. $f(x) = -(x + 1)^2$

4. $y = \dfrac{x^3}{4} - 3x$

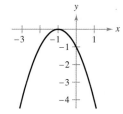
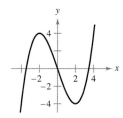

5. $f(x) = x^4 - 2x^2$

6. $g(x) = -3x^5 + 5x^3 + 2$

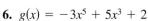

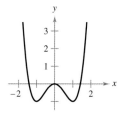
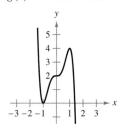

7. $f(x) = \dfrac{1}{(x + 1)^2}$

8. $y = \dfrac{x^2}{2x - 1}$

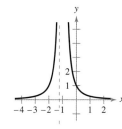
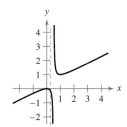

Intervals on Which a Function Is Increasing or Decreasing   In Exercises 9–20, find the open intervals on which the function is increasing or decreasing.

9. $h(x) = 18x - 3x^2$

10. $g(x) = x^3 + 12x^2 - 20$

11. $y = \dfrac{1}{4 - x}$

12. $y = x + \dfrac{9}{x}$

13. $f(x) = \sin x - 1, \quad 0 < x < 2\pi$

14. $h(x) = \cos \dfrac{x}{2}, \quad 0 < x < 2\pi$

15. $y = x\sqrt{16 - x^2}$

16. $g(x) = \dfrac{x - 1}{\sqrt{x^2 + 4}}$

17. $g(x) = e^{-x} + e^{3x}$

18. $h(x) = \sqrt{x}e^{-x}$

19. $f(x) = x^2 \ln \dfrac{x}{2}$

20. $f(x) = \dfrac{\ln x}{\sqrt{x}}$

Applying the First Derivative Test   In Exercises 21–56, (a) find the critical numbers of f (if any), (b) find the open interval(s) on which the function is increasing or decreasing, and (c) apply the First Derivative Test to find all relative extrema. Use a graphing utility to confirm your results.

21. $f(x) = x^2 - 25$

22. $f(x) = \frac{1}{2}x^2 + 7x - 6$

23. $f(x) = -2x^2 + 4x + 3$

24. $f(x) = 8 - x - 5x^2$

25. $f(x) = 2x^3 + 3x^2 - 12x$

26. $f(x) = x^3 - 6x^2 + 15$

27. $f(x) = (x - 1)^2(-3 - x)$

28. $f(x) = (x + 2)^2(x - 1)$

29. $f(x) = (x^5 - 5x)/5$

30. $f(x) = -2x^4 + 64x - 7$

31. $f(x) = x^{1/3} + 1$

32. $f(x) = x^{2/3} - 4$

33. $f(x) = (x + 2)^{2/3}$

34. $f(x) = (x - 3)^{1/3}$

35. $f(x) = 5 - |x - 5|$

36. $f(x) = |x + 3| - 1$

37. $f(x) = 2x + \dfrac{1}{x}$

38. $f(x) = \dfrac{x}{x - 5}$

39. $f(x) = \dfrac{x^2}{x^2 - 9}$

40. $f(x) = \dfrac{x^2 - 2x + 1}{x + 1}$

41. $f(x) = \begin{cases} 4 - x^2, & x \le 0 \\ -2x, & x > 0 \end{cases}$

42. $f(x) = \begin{cases} 2x + 1, & x \le -1 \\ x^2 - 2, & x > -1 \end{cases}$

43. $f(x) = \begin{cases} 6 - x^2, & x \le 1 \\ 6x - x^2, & x > 1 \end{cases}$

44. $f(x) = \begin{cases} -x^3 + 1, & x \le 0 \\ -x^2 + 2x, & x > 0 \end{cases}$

45. $f(x) = (3 - x)e^{x-3}$

46. $f(x) = (x - 1)e^x$

47. $f(x) = 4(x - \arcsin x)$

48. $f(x) = x^2 + \arctan 2x$

49. $f(x) = (x)3^{-x}$

50. $f(x) = 2^{x^2 - 3}$

51. $f(x) = x \ \log_4 x$

52. $f(x) = \dfrac{x^3}{3} - \ln x$

53. $f(x) = \dfrac{e^{2x}}{e^{2x} + 1}$

54. $f(x) = \ln(2 - \ln x)$

55. $f(x) = e^{-1/(x-2)}$

56. $f(x) = e^{1/(x^2 - 1)}$

Error Analysis A function f is differentiable on the interval $[2, 6]$, and has a critical number at $x = 4$. In Exercises 57 and 58, use the given characteristics of f' to describe and correct the error.

57. $f'(x) > 0$ for $2 < x < 4$, $f'(x) > 0$ for $4 < x < 6$ ✗
    $(4, f(4))$ is a relative minimum of f.

58. $f'(x) < 0$ for $2 < x < 4$, $f'(x) > 0$ for $4 < x < 6$ ✗
    $(4, f(4))$ is a relative maximum of f.

 Applying the First Derivative Test In Exercises 59–66, consider the function on the interval $(0, 2\pi)$. (a) Find the open interval(s) on which the function is increasing or decreasing, and (b) apply the First Derivative Test to find all relative extrema. Use a graphing utility to confirm your results.

59. $f(x) = x - 2 \sin x$ 60. $f(x) = \dfrac{x}{2} + \cos x$

61. $f(x) = \sin x + \cos x$

62. $f(x) = \sin x \quad \sqrt{3} \cos x$

63. $f(x) = \sin^2 x + \sin x$

64. $f(x) = \sin x \cos x + 5$

65. $f(x) = \cos^2 2x$ 66. $f(x) = \dfrac{\sin x}{1 + \cos^2 x}$

Finding and Analyzing Derivatives Using Technology In Exercises 67–72, (a) use a computer algebra system to differentiate the function, (b) use a graphing utility to graph f and f' in the same window over the given interval, (c) find the critical numbers of f in the open interval, and (d) find the interval(s) on which f' is positive and the interval(s) on which it is negative. Compare the behavior of f and the sign of f'.

67. $f(x) = 2x\sqrt{9 - x^2}, \quad [-3, 3]$

68. $f(x) = 10(5 - \sqrt{x^2 - 3x + 16}), \quad [0, 5]$

69. $f(t) = t^2 \sin t, \quad [0, 2\pi]$

70. $f(t) = \dfrac{t^3}{\cos t}, \quad [0, \pi]$

71. $f(x) = e^x \sin 2x, \quad [0, \pi]$

72. $f(x) = 2 \sin 3x + 4 \cos 3x, \quad [0, \pi]$

 Think About It In Exercises 73–78, sketch a graph of the derivative of f. To print an enlarged copy of the graph, go to *MathGraphs.com.*

73. 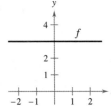   74.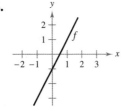

75. 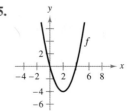   76.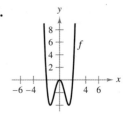

77. 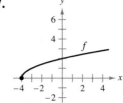   78.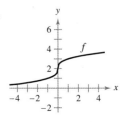

Think About It In Exercises 79 and 80, use the graph of f' to sketch a possible graph of f. (There are many correct answers.)

79. 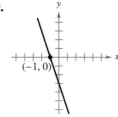   80.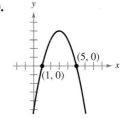

EXPLORING CONCEPTS

Transformations of Functions In Exercises 81–86, assume that f is differentiable for all x, where $f'(x) > 0$ on $(-\infty, -4)$, $f'(x) < 0$ on $(-4, 6)$, and $f'(x) > 0$ on $(6, \infty)$. Give the appropriate inequality symbol for the given value of c. Explain your reasoning.

Function	Sign of $g'(c)$
81. $g(x) = f(x) + 5$	$g'(0) \quad\square\quad 0$
82. $g(x) = 3f(x) - 3$	$g'(-5) \quad\square\quad 0$
83. $g(x) = -f(x)$	$g'(-6) \quad\square\quad 0$
84. $g(x) = -f(x)$	$g'(0) \quad\square\quad 0$
85. $g(x) = f(x - 10)$	$g'(0) \quad\square\quad 0$
86. $g(x) = f(x - 10)$	$g'(8) \quad\square\quad 0$

87. **Think About It** A function f is differentiable on an open interval I that contains c and $f'(c) = 0$. Must f have a relative extremum at $x = c$? Why or why not?

88. **Applying a Theorem** Summarize the information that the First Derivative Test tells you about the graph of f, given its derivative f'. What is something it does *not* tell you about the graph of f?

89. **Sketching a Graph** Sketch the graph of an arbitrary function f such that

$$f'(x) = \begin{cases} > 0, & x < 4 \\ \text{undefined}, & x = 4 \\ < 0, & x > 4 \end{cases}.$$

90. HOW DO YOU SEE IT?   Use the graph of f' to (a) identify the critical numbers of f, (b) identify the open interval(s) on which f is increasing or decreasing, and (c) determine whether f has a relative maximum, a relative minimum, or neither at each critical number.

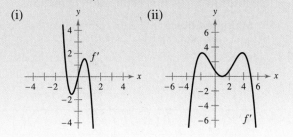

(i)   (ii)

Think About It   **In Exercises 91 and 92, the function f is differentiable on the indicated interval. The table shows $f'(x)$ for selected values of x. (a) Sketch the graph of f, (b) approximate the critical numbers, and (c) find the relative extrema.**

91. f is differentiable on $[-1, 1]$.

x	-1	-0.75	-0.50	-0.25	0
$f'(x)$	-10	-3.2	-0.5	0.8	5.6

x	0.25	0.50	0.75	1
$f'(x)$	3.6	-0.2	-6.7	-20.1

92. f is differentiable on $[0, \pi]$.

x	0	$\pi/6$	$\pi/4$	$\pi/3$	$\pi/2$
$f'(x)$	3.14	-0.23	-2.45	-3.11	0.69

x	$2\pi/3$	$3\pi/4$	$5\pi/6$	π
$f'(x)$	3.00	1.37	-1.14	-2.84

93. Connecting Representations   The concentration C of a chemical in the bloodstream t hours after injection into muscle tissue is

$$C(t) = \frac{3t}{27 + t^3}, \quad t \geq 0.$$

(a) Complete the table and use it to approximate the time when the concentration is greatest.

t	0	0.5	1	1.5	2	2.5	3
$C(t)$							

(b) Use a graphing utility to graph the concentration function and use the graph to approximate the time when the concentration is greatest.

(c) Use calculus to determine analytically the time when the concentration is greatest.

94. Connecting Representations   Consider the functions $f(x) = x$ and $g(x) = \sin x$ on the interval $(0, \pi)$.

(a) Complete the table and make a conjecture about which is the greater function on the interval $(0, \pi)$.

x	0.5	1	1.5	2	2.5	3
$f(x)$						
$g(x)$						

(b) Use a graphing utility to graph the functions and use the graphs to make a conjecture about which is the greater function on the interval $(0, \pi)$.

(c) Prove that $f(x) > g(x)$ on the interval $(0, \pi)$. [*Hint:* Show that $h'(x) > 0$, where $h = f - g$.]

95. Trachea Contraction   Coughing forces the trachea (windpipe) to contract, which affects the velocity v of the air passing through the trachea. The velocity of the air during coughing is

$$v = k(R - r)r^2, \quad 0 \leq r < R$$

where k is a constant, R is the normal radius of the trachea, and r is the radius during coughing. What radius will produce the maximum air velocity?

96. Electrical Resistance   The resistance R of a certain type of resistor is

$$R = \sqrt{0.001T^4 - 4T + 100}$$

where R is measured in ohms and the temperature T is measured in degrees Celsius.

(a) Use a computer algebra system to find dR/dT and the critical number of the function. Determine the minimum resistance for this type of resistor.

(b) Use a graphing utility to graph the function R and use the graph to approximate the minimum resistance for this type of resistor.

Particle Motion Along a Line   **In Exercises 97–100, the function $s(t)$ describes the motion of a particle along a line. (a) Find the velocity function of the particle at any time $t \geq 0$, (b) identify the time interval(s) in which the particle is moving in a positive direction or a negative direction, and (c) identify the time(s) at which the particle changes direction.**

97. $s(t) = 2t^2 - 8t$

98. $s(t) = -t^3 + 10t^2 - 12t + 1$

99. $s(t) = e^{(t-1)^2}$ **100.** $s(t) = 4\ln(t + 1) - t$

Particle Motion Along a Line In Exercises 101 and 102, the graph shows the position of a particle moving along a line. Describe how the particle's position changes with respect to time.

101.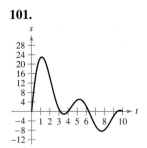

102.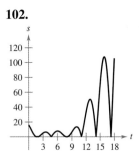

True or False? In Exercises 103–108, determine whether the statement is true or false. If it is false, explain why or give an example that shows it is false.

103. The sum of two increasing functions is increasing.

104. The product of two increasing functions is increasing.

105. Every nth-degree polynomial has $(n - 1)$ critical numbers.

106. An nth-degree polynomial has at most $(n - 1)$ critical numbers.

107. There is no function with an infinite number of critical points.

108. When the relative maxima of the function f are $f(1) = 4$ and $f(3) = 10$, f must have at least one minimum for some x in the interval $(1, 3)$.

109. Proof Prove the second case of Theorem 3.5.

110. Proof Prove the second case of Theorem 3.6.

111. Proof Let $x > 0$ and $n > 1$ be real numbers. Prove that $(1 + x)^n > 1 + nx$.

112. Proof Use the definitions of increasing and decreasing functions to prove that $f(x) = x^3$ is increasing on $(-\infty, \infty)$.

113. Proof Use the definitions of increasing and decreasing functions to prove that $f(x) = 1/x$ is decreasing on $(0, \infty)$.

114. Finding Values Consider $f(x) = axe^{bx^2}$. Find a and b such that the relative maximum of f is $f(4) = 2$.

Calculus AP® – Exam Preparation Questions

115. Multiple Choice The derivative h' of a function h is continuous and has exactly two zeros. Selected values of h' are shown in the table. If the domain of h is the set of all real numbers, then h is decreasing on which of the following intervals?

x	-3	-2	-1	0	1	2	3
$h'(x)$	12	5	0	-3	-4	-3	0

(A) $x < -1$ or $x > 3$

(B) $x < 0$ or $x > 2$

(C) $x > -1$ (D) $-1 < x < 3$

116. Multiple Choice The derivative of the function f is $f'(x) = x - 3 \sin x^2$. Which interval contains the greatest number of relative minimums of f?

(A) $(-2, 2)$

(B) $(-3, 1)$

(C) $(-4, 0)$

(D) $(-1, 3)$

117. Free Response The function f is defined as $f(x) = (x^2 - 1)e^x$.

(a) Find $\lim\limits_{x \to -\infty} f(x)$ and $\lim\limits_{x \to \infty} f(x)$.

(b) Find the critical numbers of f.

(c) Find the open intervals on which f is increasing or decreasing.

(d) Find the relative extrema of f.

SECTION PROJECT

Areas of Triangles

The line joining P and Q crosses two parallel lines b units apart, as shown in the figure. The point R is d units from P.

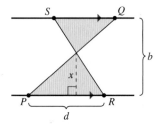

(a) Write an expression $A(x)$ for the sum of the areas of the two shaded triangles, where x is the distance between the lower line and the point where the triangles meet.

(b) From observation alone, do you think that A has a minimum value? a maximum value? Explain. Use the First Derivative Test to check.

(c) If possible, find the minimum and maximum values of A. How far from Q should the point S be positioned to achieve these extrema?

3.4   Concavity and the Second Derivative Test

▶ Determine intervals on which a function is concave upward or concave downward.
▶ Find any points of inflection of the graph of a function.
▶ Apply the Second Derivative Test to find relative extrema of a function.

Concavity

You have already seen that locating the intervals on which a function f increases or decreases helps to describe its graph. In this section, you will see how locating the intervals on which f' increases or decreases can be used to determine where the graph of f is *curving upward* or *curving downward*.

Definition of Concavity

Let f be differentiable on an open interval I. The graph of f is **concave upward** on I when f' is increasing on the interval and **concave downward** on I when f' is decreasing on the interval.

The following graphical interpretation of concavity is useful. (See Appendix A for a proof of these results.)

1. Let f be differentiable on an open interval I. If the graph of f is concave *upward* on I, then the graph of f lies *above* all of its tangent lines on I.
   [See Figure 3.24(a).]

2. Let f be differentiable on an open interval I. If the graph of f is concave *downward* on I, then the graph of f lies *below* all of its tangent lines on I.
   [See Figure 3.24(b).]

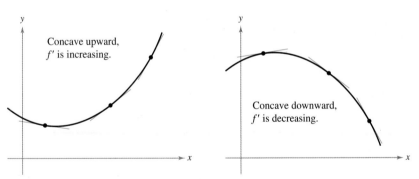

(a) The graph of f lies above its tangent lines.   **(b)** The graph of f lies below its tangent lines.
Figure 3.24

To find the open intervals on which the graph of a function f is concave upward or concave downward, you need to find the intervals on which f' is increasing or decreasing. For instance, the graph of

$$f(x) = \frac{1}{3}x^3 - x$$

is concave downward on the open interval $(-\infty, 0)$ because

$$f'(x) = x^2 - 1$$

is decreasing there. (See Figure 3.25.) Similarly, the graph of f is concave upward on the interval $(0, \infty)$ because f' is increasing on $(0, \infty)$.

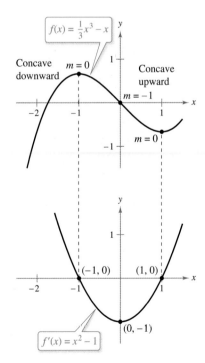

f' is decreasing. f' is increasing.

The concavity of f is related to the slope of the derivative.
Figure 3.25

The next theorem shows how to use the *second* derivative of a function f to determine intervals on which the graph of f is concave upward or concave downward. A proof of this theorem follows directly from Theorem 3.5 and the definition of concavity.

Theorem 3.7 Test for Concavity

Let f be a function whose second derivative exists on an open interval I.

1. If $f''(x) > 0$ for all x in I, then the graph of f is concave upward on I.
2. If $f''(x) < 0$ for all x in I, then the graph of f is concave downward on I.

A proof of this theorem is given in Appendix A.

Justification

A third case of Theorem 3.7 could be that if $f''(x) = 0$ for all x in I, then f is linear. Note, however, that concavity is not defined for a line. In other words, a straight line is neither concave upward nor concave downward.

To apply Theorem 3.7, locate the x-values at which $f''(x) = 0$ or $f''(x)$ does not exist. Use these x-values to determine test intervals. Finally, test the sign of $f''(x)$ in each of the test intervals.

EXAMPLE 1 Determining Concavity

Determine the open intervals on which the graph of

$$f(x) = e^{-x^2/2}$$

is concave upward or concave downward.

Solution

Begin by observing that f is continuous on the entire real number line. Next, find the second derivative of f.

$$f'(x) = -xe^{-x^2/2} \qquad \text{First derivative}$$
$$f''(x) = (-x)(-x)e^{-x^2/2} + e^{-x^2/2}(-1) \qquad \text{Differentiate.}$$
$$= e^{-x^2/2}(x^2 - 1) \qquad \text{Second derivative}$$

Because $f''(x) = 0$ when $x = \pm 1$ and f'' is defined on the entire real number line, you should test f'' in the intervals $(-\infty, -1)$, $(-1, 1)$, and $(1, \infty)$. The results are shown in the table and in Figure 3.26.

Interval	$-\infty < x < -1$	$-1 < x < 1$	$1 < x < \infty$
Test Value	$x = -2$	$x = 0$	$x = 2$
Sign of $f''(x)$	$f''(-2) > 0$	$f''(0) < 0$	$f''(2) > 0$
Conclusion	Concave upward	Concave downward	Concave upward

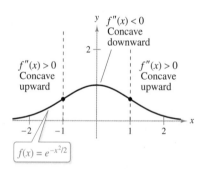

From the sign of $f''(x)$, you can determine the concavity of the graph of f.

Figure 3.26

Note that the function in Example 1 is similar to the **normal probability density function** with a mean of 0, whose general form is

$$f(x) = \frac{2}{\sigma\sqrt{2\pi}} e^{-x^2/(2\sigma^2)} \qquad \text{Normal probability density function}$$

where σ is the **standard deviation** (σ is the lowercase Greek letter sigma). This "bell-shaped" curve is concave downward on the interval $(-\sigma, \sigma)$.

The function given in Example 1 is continuous on the entire real number line. When there are x-values at which a function is not continuous, these values should be used, along with the points at which $f''(x) = 0$ or $f''(x)$ does not exist, to form the test intervals.

EXAMPLE 2   **Determining Concavity**

Determine the open intervals on which the graph of

$$f(x) = \frac{x^2 + 1}{x^2 - 4}$$

is concave upward or concave downward.

Solution

Differentiating twice produces the following.

$$f(x) = \frac{x^2 + 1}{x^2 - 4} \qquad \text{Write original function.}$$

$$f'(x) = \frac{(x^2 - 4)(2x) - (x^2 + 1)(2x)}{(x^2 - 4)^2} \qquad \text{Differentiate.}$$

$$= \frac{-10x}{(x^2 - 4)^2} \qquad \text{First derivative}$$

$$f''(x) = \frac{(x^2 - 4)^2(-10) - (-10x)(2)(x^2 - 4)(2x)}{(x^2 - 4)^4} \qquad \text{Differentiate.}$$

$$= \frac{10(3x^2 + 4)}{(x^2 - 4)^3} \qquad \text{Second derivative}$$

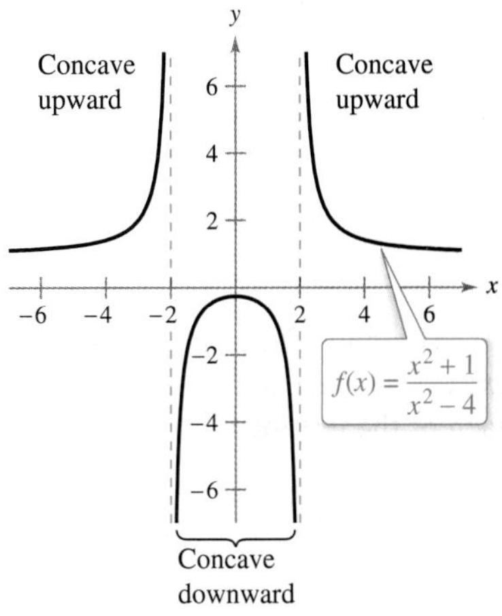

There are no points at which $f''(x) = 0$, but at $x = \pm 2$, the function f is not continuous. So, test for concavity in the intervals $(-\infty, -2)$, $(-2, 2)$, and $(2, \infty)$, as shown in the table. The graph of f is shown in Figure 3.27.

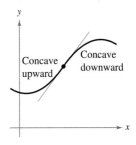

Interval	$-\infty < x < -2$	$-2 < x < 2$	$2 < x < \infty$
Test Value	$x = -3$	$x = 0$	$x = 3$
Sign of $f''(x)$	$f''(-3) > 0$	$f''(0) < 0$	$f''(3) > 0$
Conclusion	Concave upward	Concave downward	Concave upward

Points of Inflection

The graph in Figure 3.26 has two points at which the concavity changes. If the tangent line to the graph exists at such a point, then that point is a **point of inflection.** Three types of points of inflection are shown in Figure 3.28.

Definition of Point of Inflection

Let f be a function that is continuous on an open interval, and let c be a point in the interval. If the graph of f has a tangent line at the point $(c, f(c))$, then this point is a **point of inflection** of the graph of f when the concavity of f changes from upward to downward (or downward to upward) at the point.

This definition of *point of inflection* requires that the tangent line exists at the point of inflection. Some calculus texts do not require this. For instance, using the definition above, the function

$$f(x) = \begin{cases} x^3, & x < 0 \\ x^2 + 2x, & x \geq 0 \end{cases}$$

does *not* have a point of inflection at the origin, even though the concavity of the graph changes from concave downward to concave upward.

Concave upward

Concave downward

Figure 3.27

Concave upward   Concave downward

Concave upward

Concave downward

Concave downward

Concave upward

The concavity of f changes at a point of inflection. Note that the graph crosses its tangent line at a point of inflection.

Figure 3.28

To locate *possible* points of inflection, you can determine the values of x for which $f''(x) = 0$ or $f''(x)$ does not exist. This is similar to the procedure for locating relative extrema of f.

Theorem 3.8   Points of Inflection

If $(c, f(c))$ is a point of inflection of the graph of f, then either $f''(c) = 0$ or $f''(c)$ does not exist.

EXAMPLE 3   Finding Points of Inflection

Determine the points of inflection and discuss the concavity of the graph of

$$f(x) = x^4 - 4x^3.$$

Solution

Differentiating twice produces the following.

$f(x) = x^4 - 4x^3$ Write original function.

$f'(x) = 4x^3 - 12x^2$ Find first derivative.

$f''(x) = 12x^2 - 24x = 12x(x - 2)$ Find second derivative.

Setting $f''(x) = 0$, you can determine that the possible points of inflection occur at $x = 0$ and $x = 2$. By testing the intervals determined by these x-values, you can conclude that they both yield points of inflection. A summary of this testing is shown in the table, and the graph of f is shown in Figure 3.29.

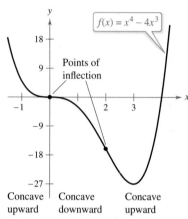

Points of inflection can occur where $f''(x) = 0$ or $f''(x)$ does not exist.
Figure 3.29

Interval	$-\infty < x < 0$	$0 < x < 2$	$2 < x < \infty$
Test Value	$x = -1$	$x = 1$	$x = 3$
Sign of $f''(x)$	$f''(-1) > 0$	$f''(1) < 0$	$f''(3) > 0$
Conclusion	Concave upward	Concave downward	Concave upward

Algebra Review

For help on the algebra in Example 3, see Example 1(c) in the *Chapter 3 Algebra Review* on page A40.

The converse of Theorem 3.8 is not generally true. That is, it is possible for the second derivative to be 0 at a point that is *not* a point of inflection. For instance, the graph of $f(x) = x^4$ is shown in Figure 3.30. The second derivative is 0 when $x = 0$, but the point $(0, 0)$ is not a point of inflection because the graph of f is concave upward on the intervals $-\infty < x < 0$ and $0 < x < \infty$.

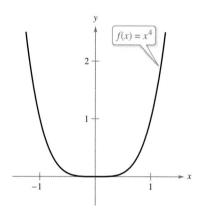

$f''(x) = 0$, but $(0, 0)$ is not a point of inflection.
Figure 3.30

The Second Derivative Test

In addition to testing for concavity, the second derivative can be used to perform a simple test for relative maxima and minima. The test is based on the fact that if the graph of a function f is concave upward on an open interval containing c, and $f'(c) = 0$, then $f(c)$ must be a relative minimum of f. Similarly, if the graph of a function f is concave downward on an open interval containing c, and $f'(c) = 0$, then $f(c)$ must be a relative maximum of f. (See Figure 3.31.)

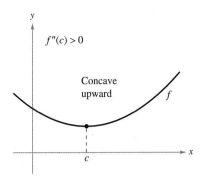

If $f'(c) = 0$ and $f''(c) > 0$, then $f(c)$ is a relative minimum.

Theorem 3.9   Second Derivative Test

Let f be a function such that $f'(c) = 0$ and the second derivative of f exists on an open interval containing c.

1. If $f''(c) > 0$, then f has a relative minimum at $(c, f(c))$.
2. If $f''(c) < 0$, then f has a relative maximum at $(c, f(c))$.

If $f''(c) = 0$, then the test fails. That is, f may have a relative maximum, a relative minimum, or neither. In such cases, you can use the First Derivative Test.

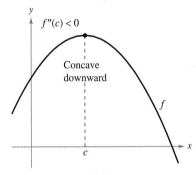

If $f'(c) = 0$ and $f''(c) < 0$, then $f(c)$ is a relative maximum.
Figure 3.31

Proof   If $f'(c) = 0$ and $f''(c) > 0$, then there exists an open interval I containing c for which

$$\frac{f'(x) - f'(c)}{x - c} = \frac{f'(x)}{x - c} > 0$$

for all $x \neq c$ in I. If $x < c$, then $x - c < 0$ and $f'(x) < 0$. Also, if $x > c$, then $x - c > 0$ and $f'(x) > 0$. So, $f'(x)$ changes from negative to positive at c, and the First Derivative Test implies that $f(c)$ is a relative minimum. A proof of the second case is left to you.

EXAMPLE 4   Using the Second Derivative Test

See LarsonCalculusforAP.com for an interactive version of this type of example.

Find the relative extrema of $f(x) = -3x^5 + 5x^3$.

Solution

Begin by finding the first derivative of f.

$$f'(x) = -15x^4 + 15x^2 = 15x^2(1 - x^2)$$

From this derivative, you can see that $x = -1, 0$, and 1 are the only critical numbers of f. By finding the second derivative

$$f''(x) = -60x^3 + 30x = 30x(1 - 2x^2)$$

you can apply the Second Derivative Test as shown below.

> **Algebra Review**
>
> For help on the algebra in Example 4, see Example 1(d) in the *Chapter 3 Algebra Review* on page A40.

$f(x) = -3x^5 + 5x^3$

Point	$(-1, -2)$	$(0, 0)$	$(1, 2)$
Sign of $f''(x)$	$f''(-1) > 0$	$f''(0) = 0$	$f''(1) < 0$
Conclusion	Relative minimum	Test fails	Relative maximum

Because the Second Derivative Test fails at $(0, 0)$, you can use the First Derivative Test and observe that f increases to the left and right of $x = 0$. So, $(0, 0)$ is neither a relative minimum nor a relative maximum (even though the graph has a horizontal tangent line at this point). The graph of f is shown in Figure 3.32.

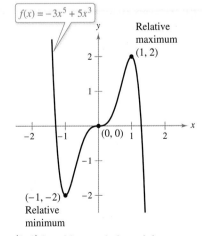

$(0, 0)$ is neither a relative minimum nor a relative maximum.
Figure 3.32

3.4 Exercises

See *CalcChat.com* for tutorial help and worked-out solutions to odd-numbered exercises.

Determining Concavity In Exercises 1–12, determine the open intervals on which the graph of the function is concave upward or concave downward.

1. $y = x^2 - x - 2$

2. $g(x) = 4x - 3x^2$

3. $f(x) = -x^3 + 6x^2 - 9x - 1$

4. $h(x) = x^5 - 5x + 2$

5. $f(x) = \dfrac{24}{x^2 + 12}$

6. $f(x) = \dfrac{2x^2}{3x^2 + 1}$

7. $f(x) = \dfrac{x^2 + 1}{x^2 - 1}$

8. $h(x) = \dfrac{x^2 - 1}{2x - 1}$

9. $g(x) = xe^x$

10. $f(x) = \dfrac{1}{x} \ln x$

11. $y = 2x - \tan x, \quad \left(-\dfrac{\pi}{2}, \dfrac{\pi}{2} \right)$

12. $y = x + \dfrac{2}{\sin x}, \quad (-\pi, \pi)$

Finding Points of Inflection In Exercises 13–34, find any points of inflection and discuss the concavity of the graph of the function.

13. $f(x) = x^3 - 9x^2 + 24x - 18$

14. $f(x) = -x^3 + 6x^2 - 5$

15. $f(x) = \frac{1}{2}x^4 + 2x^3$

16. $f(x) = 4 - x - 3x^4$

17. $f(x) = x\sqrt{x + 3}$

18. $f(x) = x\sqrt{9 - x}$

19. $f(x) = \dfrac{4}{x^2 + 1}$

20. $f(x) = \dfrac{x + 3}{x^2}$

21. $h(x) = \sqrt{16 - x^2}$

22. $g(x) = (x - 1)^{3/2}$

23. $f(x) = \sin \dfrac{x}{2}, \quad [0, 4\pi]$

24. $f(x) = 2 \csc \dfrac{3x}{2}, \quad (0, 2\pi)$

25. $f(x) = 2 \sin x + \sin 2x, \quad [0, 2\pi]$

26. $f(x) = \sin x + \cos x, \quad [0, 2\pi]$

27. $f(x) = \cot\left(\dfrac{\pi}{2} - x \right), \quad [0, 2\pi]$

28. $f(x) = \sec\left(x - \dfrac{\pi}{2} \right), \quad (0, 4\pi)$

29. $y = e^{-3/x}$

30. $y = \frac{1}{2}(e^x - e^{-x})$

31. $y = x - \ln x$

32. $y = \ln\sqrt{x^2 + 9}$

33. $f(x) = \arcsin x^{4/5}$

34. $f(x) = \arctan x^2$

Using the Second Derivative Test In Exercises 35–58, find any relative extrema. Use the Second Derivative Test where applicable.

35. $y = -2x^2 + 10x$

36. $y = x^2 - 4x - 30$

37. $f(x) = x^3 + 5x^2 + 3x$

38. $f(x) = 16x - 1 - 3x^3$

39. $f(x) = x^4 - 4x^3 + 2$

40. $f(x) = -x^4 + 4x^3 + 8x^2$

41. $f(x) = x^{2/3} - 3$

42. $f(x) = \sqrt{x^2 + 1}$

43. $f(x) = x + \dfrac{4}{x}$

44. $f(x) = \dfrac{x}{x - 1}$

45. $f(x) = \cos x - x, \quad [0, 4\pi]$

46. $f(x) = 2 \sin x + \cos 2x, \quad [0, 2\pi]$

47. $f(x) = 8x^2 - \ln x$

48. $y = -x \ln x$

49. $y = \dfrac{x}{\ln x}$

50. $y = x^2 \ln \dfrac{x}{4}$

51. $f(x) = \dfrac{e^x + e^{-x}}{2}$

52. $g(x) = \dfrac{1}{\sqrt{2\pi}} e^{-(x-3)^2/2}$

53. $f(x) = x^2 e^{-x}$

54. $f(x) = xe^{-x}$

55. $f(x) = 8x(4^{-x})$

56. $y = x^2 \log_3 x$

57. $f(x) = \text{arcsec } x - x$

58. $f(x) = \arcsin x - 2x$

EXPLORING CONCEPTS

59. Think About It A function f is continuous on an open interval containing c and $f''(c) = 0$. Must $(c, f(c))$ be an inflection point? Explain why or why not and sketch an example.

60. Think About It S represents weekly sales of a product. What can you say about S' and S'' for each of the following statements?

(a) The rate of change of sales is increasing.

(b) Sales are increasing at a slower and slower rate.

(c) The rate of change of sales is constant.

(d) Sales are constant.

(e) Sales are declining, but at a slower and slower rate.

Sketching a Graph In Exercises 61–68, sketch the graph of a continuous function f that has the following characteristics.

61. When $x > 0$, $f'(x)$ is positive and increasing.

62. When $x > 0$, $f'(x)$ is positive and decreasing.

63. When $x > 0$, $f'(x)$ is negative and $f''(x)$ is positive.

64. When $x > 0$, $f'(x)$ is negative and $f''(x)$ is negative.

65. When $x > 0$, $f'(x) > 0$ and constant.

66. When $x > 0$, $f'(x) < 0$ and $f''(x) = 0$.

67. When $x < 0$, $f'(x) > 0$ and $f''(x) > 0$, and when $x > 0$, $f'(x) > 0$ and $f''(x) < 0$.

68. When $x < 0$, $f'(x) < 0$ and $f''(x) < 0$, and when $x > 0$, $f'(x) > 0$ and $f''(x) < 0$.

69. Sketching Graphs   The graph of f is shown. Graph f, f', and f'' on the same set of coordinate axes. To print an enlarged copy of the graph, go to *MathGraphs.com*.

(a)
(b)

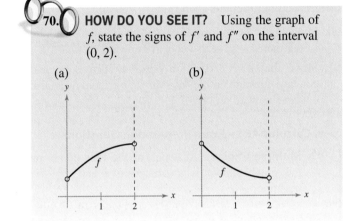

70. 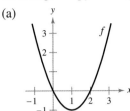 **HOW DO YOU SEE IT?**   Using the graph of f, state the signs of f' and f'' on the interval $(0, 2)$.

(a)
(b)

Think About It   In Exercises 71 and 72, sketch the graph of a function f having the given characteristics.

71. $f(0) = f(2) = 0$
$f'(x) > 0$ for $x < 1$
$f'(1) = 0$
$f'(x) < 0$ for $x > 1$
$f''(x) < 0$

72. $f(2) = f(4) = 0$
$f'(x) < 0$ for $x < 3$
$f'(3)$ does not exist.
$f'(x) > 0$ for $x > 3$
$f''(x) < 0, x \neq 3$

73. Think About It   The figure shows the graph of f''. Sketch a graph of f. (The answer is not unique.) To print an enlarged copy of the graph, go to *MathGraphs.com*.

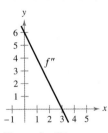

Figure for 73

Figure for 74

74. Think About It   Water is running into the vase shown in the figure at a constant rate.

(a) Graph the depth d of the water as a function of time.

(b) Does the function have any extrema? Explain.

(c) Interpret the inflection points of the graph of d.

75. Conjecture   Consider the function $f(x) = (x - 2)^n$.

(a) Use a graphing utility to graph f for $n = 1, 2, 3$, and 4. Use the graphs to make a conjecture about the relationship between n and any inflection points of the graph of f.

(b) Verify your conjecture in part (a).

76. Inflection Point   Consider the function $f(x) = \sqrt[3]{x}$.

(a) Graph the function and identify the inflection point.

(b) Does $f''(x)$ exist at the inflection point? Explain.

77. Aircraft Glide Path   A small aircraft starts its descent from an altitude of 1 mile, 4 miles west of the runway (see figure).

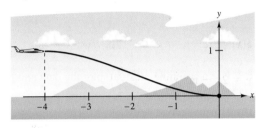

(a) Find the cubic function

$$f(x) = ax^3 + bx^2 + cx + d$$

on the interval $[-4, 0]$ that describes a smooth glide path for the landing.

(b) Use the function in part (a) to determine the distance at which the plane is descending at the greatest rate.

78. Highway Design   A section of highway connecting two hillsides with grades of 6% and 4% is to be built between two points that are separated by a horizontal distance of 2000 feet (see figure). At the point where the two hillsides come together, there is a 50-foot difference in elevation.

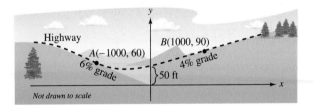

(a) Find the cubic function

$$f(x) = ax^3 + bx^2 + cx + d, \quad -1000 \le x \le 1000$$

that models the section of highway connecting the hillsides. At points A and B, the slope of the model must match the grade of the hillside.

(b) Use a graphing utility to graph the model.

(c) Use a graphing utility to graph the derivative of the model.

(d) Determine the grade at the steepest part of the transitional section of the highway.

79. Average Cost The total cost C of operating a factory is $C = 0.5x^2 + 15x + 5000$, where x is the number of units produced. Use the First and Second Derivative Tests to find the level of production that will minimize the average cost per unit. (The average cost per unit is C/x.) Which method do you prefer? Explain.

80. Modeling Data The average typing speed S (in words per minute) of a typing student after t weeks of lessons is shown in the table.

t	5	10	15	20	25	30
S	38	56	79	90	93	94

A model for the data is

$$S = \frac{100t^2}{65 + t^2}, \quad t > 0.$$

(a) Use a graphing utility to plot the data and graph the model.

(b) Use the second derivative to determine the concavity of S. Compare the result with the graph in part (a).

(c) What is the sign of the first derivative for $t > 0$? By combining this information with the concavity of the model, what inferences can be made about the typing speed as t increases?

Linear and Quadratic Approximations In Exercises 81–84, use a graphing utility to graph the function. Then graph the linear and quadratic approximations $P_1(x) = f(a) + f'(a)(x - a)$ and $P_2(x) = f(a) + f'(a)(x - a) + \frac{1}{2}f''(a)(x - a)^2$ in the same viewing window. Compare the values of f, P_1, and P_2 and their first derivatives at $x = a$. How do the approximations change as you move farther away from $x = a$?

Function	Value of a
81. $f(x) = 2(\sin x + \cos x)$	$a = \frac{\pi}{4}$
82. $f(x) = 2(\sin x + \cos x)$	$a = 0$
83. $f(x) = \arctan x$	$a = -1$
84. $f(x) = \frac{\sqrt{x}}{x - 1}$	$a = 2$

85. Determining Concavity Use a graphing utility to graph $y = x \sin(1/x)$. Show that the graph is concave downward to the right of $x = 1/\pi$.

86. Point of Inflection and Extrema Show that the point of inflection of $f(x) = x(x - a)^2$ lies midway between the relative extrema of f for a real number a.

True or False? In Exercises 87–89, determine whether the statement is true or false. If it is false, explain why or give an example that shows it is false.

87. The graph of every cubic polynomial has precisely one point of inflection.

88. If $f''(2) = 0$, then the graph of f must have a point of inflection at $x = 2$.

89. A polynomial function of degree n can have up to $(n - 1)$ points of inflection.

Proof In Exercises 90 and 91, let f and g represent differentiable functions such that $f'' \neq 0$ and $g'' \neq 0$.

90. Show that if f and g are concave upward on the interval (a, b), then $f + g$ is also concave upward on (a, b).

91. Prove that if f and g are positive, increasing, and concave upward on the interval (a, b), then fg is also concave upward on (a, b).

Calculus AP® – Exam Preparation Questions

92. Multiple Choice At which of the four points on the graph shown is dy/dx positive and d^2y/dx^2 negative?

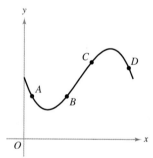

(A) A (B) B

(C) C (D) D

93. Multiple Choice The graph of the function $h(x) = 4xe^{-x}$ is

(A) decreasing and concave upward on $(2, \infty)$.

(B) increasing and concave downward on $(-\infty, 2)$.

(C) increasing and concave upward on $(2, \infty)$.

(D) decreasing and concave upward on $(1, \infty)$.

94. Free Response Consider the function $f(x) = 2 \sin x - x$ on $[0, 2\pi]$.

(a) Find $f'(x)$ and $f''(x)$.

(b) What are the critical numbers of f?

(c) Find all relative extrema of f.

(d) How many point(s) of inflection does the graph of f have? Where do they occur?

3.5   A Summary of Curve Sketching

▶ Analyze and sketch the graph of a function.

Analyzing the Graph of a Function

It would be difficult to overstate the importance of using graphs in mathematics. Descartes's introduction of analytic geometry contributed significantly to the rapid advances in calculus that began during the mid-seventeenth century. In the words of Lagrange, "As long as algebra and geometry traveled separate paths their advance was slow and their applications limited. But when these two sciences joined company, they drew from each other fresh vitality and thenceforth marched on at a rapid pace toward perfection."

So far, you have studied several concepts that are useful in analyzing the graph of a function.

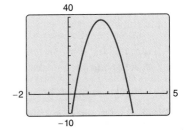

• x-intercepts and y-intercepts	(Section P.1)
• Symmetry	(Section P.1)
• Domain and range	(Section P.3)
• Continuity	(Section 1.4)
• Vertical asymptotes	(Section 1.5)
• Horizontal asymptotes	(Section 1.6)
• Infinite limits at infinity	(Section 1.6)
• Differentiability	(Section 2.1)
• Relative extrema	(Section 3.1)
• Increasing and decreasing functions	(Section 3.3)
• Concavity	(Section 3.4)
• Points of inflection	(Section 3.4)

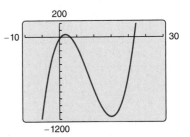

When you are sketching the graph of a function, either by hand or with a graphing utility, remember that normally you cannot show the *entire* graph. The decision as to which part of the graph you choose to show is often crucial. For instance, which of the viewing windows in Figure 3.33 better represents the graph of

$$f(x) = x^3 - 25x^2 + 74x - 20?$$

Different viewing windows for the graph of $f(x) = x^3 - 25x^2 + 74x - 20$
Figure 3.33

By seeing both views, it is clear that the second viewing window gives a more complete representation of the graph. But would a third viewing window reveal other interesting portions of the graph? To answer this, you need to use calculus to interpret the first and second derivatives. To determine a good viewing window for the graph of a function, use the guidelines below.

Guidelines for Analyzing the Graph of a Function

1. Determine the domain and range of the function.
2. Determine the intercepts, asymptotes, and symmetry of the graph.
3. Locate the x-values for which $f'(x)$ and $f''(x)$ either are zero or do not exist. Use the results to determine relative extrema and points of inflection.

In the guidelines above, note the importance of *algebra* (as well as calculus) for solving the equations

$$f(x) = 0, \quad f'(x) = 0, \quad \text{and} \quad f''(x) = 0.$$

EXAMPLE 1   Sketching the Graph of a Rational Function

Analyze and sketch the graph of $f(x) = \dfrac{2(x^2 - 9)}{x^2 - 4}$.

Solution

Domain:	All real numbers except $x = \pm 2$
Range:	$(-\infty, 2) \cup \left[\frac{9}{2}, \infty\right]$
x-intercepts:	$(-3, 0), (3, 0)$
y-intercept:	$\left(0, \frac{9}{2}\right)$
Vertical asymptotes:	$x = -2, x = 2$
Horizontal asymptote:	$y = 2$
Symmetry:	With respect to y-axis
First derivative:	$f'(x) = \dfrac{20x}{(x^2 - 4)^2}$
Second derivative:	$f''(x) = \dfrac{-20(3x^2 + 4)}{(x^2 - 4)^3}$
Critical number:	$x = 0$
Possible points of inflection:	None
Test intervals:	$(-\infty, -2), (-2, 0), (0, 2), (2, \infty)$

The table shows how the test intervals are used to determine several characteristics of the graph. The graph of f is shown in Figure 3.34.

	$f(x)$	$f'(x)$	$f''(x)$	Characteristic of Graph
$-\infty < x < -2$		$-$	$-$	Decreasing, concave downward
$x = -2$	Undef.	Undef.	Undef.	Vertical asymptote
$-2 < x < 0$		$-$	$+$	Decreasing, concave upward
$x = 0$	$\frac{9}{2}$	0	$+$	Relative minimum
$0 < x < 2$		$+$	$+$	Increasing, concave upward
$x = 2$	Undef.	Undef.	Undef.	Vertical asymptote
$2 < x < \infty$		$+$	$-$	Increasing, concave downward

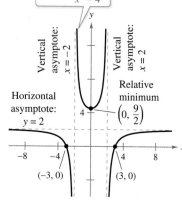

Using calculus, you can be certain that you have determined all characteristics of the graph of f.

Figure 3.34

Be sure you understand all of the implications of creating a table such as that shown in Example 1. By using calculus, you can be *sure* that the graph has no relative extrema or points of inflection other than those shown in Figure 3.34.

Technology Pitfall

Without using the type of analysis outlined in Example 1, it is easy to obtain an incomplete view of the basic characteristics of a graph. For instance, Figure 3.35 shows a view of the graph of

$$g(x) = \frac{2(x^2 - 9)(x - 20)}{(x^2 - 4)(x - 21)}.$$

From this view, it appears that the graph of g is about the same as the graph of f shown in Figure 3.34. The graphs of these two functions, however, differ significantly. Try enlarging the viewing window to see the differences.

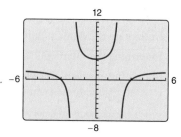

By not using calculus, you may overlook important characteristics of the graph of g.

Figure 3.35

EXAMPLE 2   Sketching the Graph of a Rational Function

Analyze and sketch the graph of $f(x) = \dfrac{x^2 - 2x + 4}{x - 2}$.

Solution

Domain:	All real numbers except $x = 2$
Range:	$(-\infty, -2] \cup [6, \infty)$
x-intercepts:	None
y-intercept:	$(0, -2)$
Vertical asymptote:	$x = 2$
Horizontal asymptotes:	None
Symmetry:	None
End behavior:	$\displaystyle\lim_{x \to -\infty} f(x) = -\infty, \lim_{x \to \infty} f(x) = \infty$
First derivative:	$f'(x) = \dfrac{x(x - 4)}{(x - 2)^2}$
Second derivative:	$f''(x) = \dfrac{8}{(x - 2)^3}$
Critical numbers:	$x = 0, x = 4$
Possible points of inflection:	None
Test intervals:	$(-\infty, 0), (0, 2), (2, 4), (4, \infty)$

The analysis of the graph of f is shown in the table, and the graph is shown in Figure 3.36.

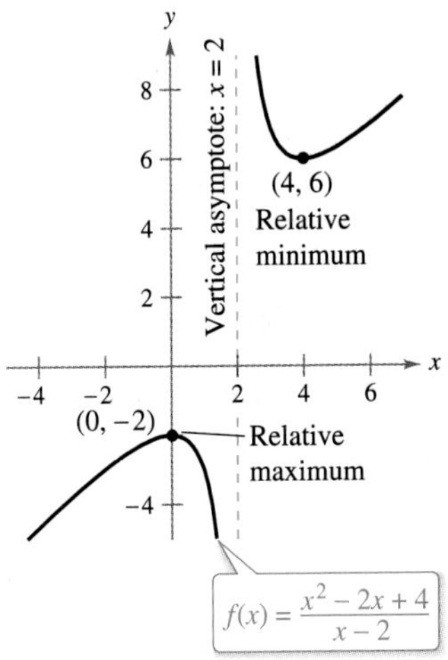

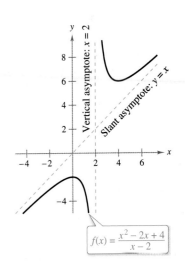

Figure 3.36

	$f(x)$	$f'(x)$	$f''(x)$	Characteristic of Graph
$-\infty < x < 0$		$+$	$-$	Increasing, concave downward
$x = 0$	-2	0	$-$	Relative maximum
$0 < x < 2$		$-$	$-$	Decreasing, concave downward
$x = 2$	Undef.	Undef.	Undef.	Vertical asymptote
$2 < x < 4$		$-$	$+$	Decreasing, concave upward
$x = 4$	6	0	$+$	Relative minimum
$4 < x < \infty$		$+$	$+$	Increasing, concave upward

Although the graph of the function in Example 2 has no horizontal asymptote, it does have a slant asymptote. The graph of a rational function (having no common factors and whose denominator is of degree 1 or greater) has a **slant asymptote** when the degree of the numerator exceeds the degree of the denominator by exactly 1. To find the slant asymptote, use long division to rewrite the rational function as the sum of a first-degree polynomial (the slant asymptote) and another rational function.

$$f(x) = \frac{x^2 - 2x + 4}{x - 2} \qquad \text{Write original equation.}$$

$$= x + \frac{4}{x - 2} \qquad \text{Rewrite using long division.}$$

In Figure 3.37, note that the graph of f approaches the slant asymptote $y = x$ as x approaches $-\infty$ or ∞.

A slant asymptote
Figure 3.37

Sketching the Graph of a Logistic Function

Analyze and sketch the graph of the *logistic function* $f(x) = \dfrac{1}{1 + e^{-x}}$.

Solution

$$f'(x) = \frac{e^{-x}}{(1 + e^{-x})^2}$$ Find first derivative.

$$f''(x) = \frac{e^{-x}(e^{-x} - 1)}{(1 + e^{-x})^3}$$ Find second derivative.

The graph has only one intercept, $\left(0, \frac{1}{2}\right)$. It has no vertical asymptotes, but it has two horizontal asymptotes: $y = 1$ (to the right) and $y = 0$ (to the left). The function has no critical numbers and one possible point of inflection (at $x = 0$). The domain of the function is all real numbers. The analysis of the graph of f is shown in the table, and the graph is shown in Figure 3.38.

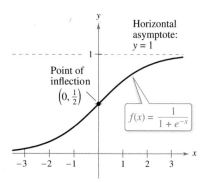

Figure 3.38

	$f(x)$	$f'(x)$	$f''(x)$	Characteristic of Graph
$-\infty < x < 0$		$+$	$+$	Increasing, concave upward
$x = 0$	$\dfrac{1}{2}$	$+$	0	Point of inflection
$0 < x < \infty$		$+$	$-$	Increasing, concave downward

Sketching the Graph of a Radical Function

Analyze and sketch the graph of $f(x) = 2x^{5/3} - 5x^{4/3}$.

Solution

$$f'(x) = \frac{10}{3}x^{1/3}(x^{1/3} - 2)$$ Find first derivative.

$$f''(x) = \frac{20(x^{1/3} - 1)}{9x^{2/3}}$$ Find second derivative.

The graph has two intercepts: $(0, 0)$ and $\left(\frac{125}{8}, 0\right)$. There are no horizontal or vertical asymptotes. The function has two critical numbers ($x = 0$ and $x = 8$) and two possible points of inflection ($x = 0$ and $x = 1$). The domain is all real numbers. The analysis of the graph of f is shown in the table, and the graph is shown in Figure 3.39.

> ## Algebra Review
>
> For help on the algebra in Example 4, see Example 1(b) in the *Chapter 3 Algebra Review* on page A40.

	$f(x)$	$f'(x)$	$f''(x)$	Characteristic of Graph
$-\infty < x < 0$		$+$	$-$	Increasing, concave downward
$x = 0$	0	0	Undef.	Relative maximum
$0 < x < 1$		$-$	$-$	Decreasing, concave downward
$x = 1$	-3	$-$	0	Point of inflection
$1 < x < 8$		$-$	$+$	Decreasing, concave upward
$x = 8$	-16	0	$+$	Relative minimum
$8 < x < \infty$		$+$	$+$	Increasing, concave upward

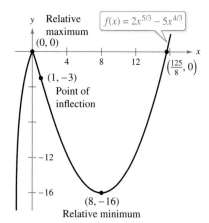

Figure 3.39

EXAMPLE 5   Sketching the Graph of a Polynomial Function

See LarsonCalculusforAP.com for an interactive version of this type of example.

Analyze and sketch the graph of

$$f(x) = x^4 - 12x^3 + 48x^2 - 64x.$$

Solution

Begin by factoring to obtain

$$\begin{aligned} f(x) &= x^4 - 12x^3 + 48x^2 - 64x \\ &= x(x - 4)^3. \end{aligned}$$

Then, using the factored form of $f(x)$, you can perform the following analysis.

Domain:	All real numbers
Range:	$[-27, \infty)$
x-intercepts:	$(0, 0), (4, 0)$
y-intercept:	$(0, 0)$
Vertical asymptotes:	None
Horizontal asymptotes:	None
Symmetry:	None
End behavior:	$\lim\limits_{x \to -\infty} f(x) = \infty, \ \lim\limits_{x \to \infty} f(x) = \infty$
First derivative:	$f'(x) = 4(x - 1)(x - 4)^2$
Second derivative:	$f''(x) = 12(x - 4)(x - 2)$
Critical numbers:	$x = 1, x = 4$
Possible points of inflection:	$x = 2, x = 4$
Test intervals:	$(-\infty, 1), (1, 2), (2, 4), (4, \infty)$

The analysis of the graph of f is shown in the table, and the graph is shown in Figure 3.40(a). Use a graphing utility to check your work, as shown in Figure 3.40(b).

	$f(x)$	$f'(x)$	$f''(x)$	Characteristic of Graph
$-\infty < x < 1$		$-$	$+$	Decreasing, concave upward
$x = 1$	-27	0	$+$	Relative minimum
$1 < x < 2$		$+$	$+$	Increasing, concave upward
$x = 2$	-16	$+$	0	Point of inflection
$2 < x < 4$		$+$	$-$	Increasing, concave downward
$x = 4$	0	0	0	Point of inflection
$4 < x < \infty$		$+$	$+$	Increasing, concave upward

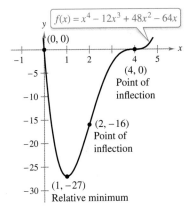

(a) A polynomial function of even degree must have at least one relative extremum.

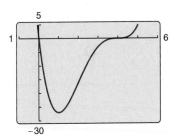

(b) From the result shown by the graphing utility, the sketch in Figure 3.40(a) appears to be correct.

Figure 3.40

The fourth-degree polynomial function in Example 5 has one relative minimum and no relative maxima. In general, a polynomial function of degree n can have *at most* $n - 1$ relative extrema, and *at most* $n - 2$ points of inflection. Moreover, polynomial functions of even degree must have *at least* one relative extremum.

Remember from the Leading Coefficient Test described in Section P.3 that the "end behavior" of the graph of a polynomial function is determined by its leading coefficient and its degree. For instance, because the polynomial in Example 5 has a positive leading coefficient, the graph rises to the right. Moreover, because the degree is even, the graph also rises to the left.

EXAMPLE 6   Sketching the Graph of a Trigonometric Function

Analyze and sketch the graph of $f(x) = (\cos x)/(1 + \sin x)$.

Solution   Because the function has a period of 2π, you can restrict the analysis of the graph to any interval of length 2π. For convenience, choose $[-\pi/2, 3\pi/2]$.

Domain: All real numbers except $x = \dfrac{3 + 4n}{2}\pi$

Range: All real numbers

Period: 2π

x-intercept: $\left(\dfrac{\pi}{2}, 0\right)$

y-intercept: $(0, 1)$

Vertical asymptotes: $x = -\dfrac{\pi}{2}, x = \dfrac{3\pi}{2}$ See Justification below.

Horizontal asymptotes: None

Symmetry: None

First derivative: $f'(x) = -\dfrac{1}{1 + \sin x}$

Second derivative: $f''(x) = \dfrac{\cos x}{(1 + \sin x)^2}$

Critical numbers: None

Possible points of inflection: $x = \dfrac{\pi}{2}$

Test intervals: $\left(-\dfrac{\pi}{2}, \dfrac{\pi}{2}\right), \left(\dfrac{\pi}{2}, \dfrac{3\pi}{2}\right)$

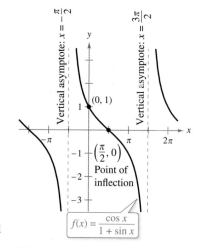

Figure 3.41

The analysis of the graph of f on the interval $[-\pi/2, 3\pi/2]$ is shown in the table, and the graph is shown in Figure 3.41.

	$f(x)$	$f'(x)$	$f''(x)$	Characteristic of Graph
$x = -\dfrac{\pi}{2}$	Undef.	Undef.	Undef.	Vertical asymptote
$-\dfrac{\pi}{2} < x < \dfrac{\pi}{2}$		$-$	$+$	Decreasing, concave upward
$x = \dfrac{\pi}{2}$	0	$-$	0	Point of inflection
$\dfrac{\pi}{2} < x < \dfrac{3\pi}{2}$		$-$	$-$	Decreasing, concave downward
$x = \dfrac{3\pi}{2}$	Undef.	Undef.	Undef.	Vertical asymptote

▶ **Justification**   In Example 6, substituting $-\pi/2$ or $3\pi/2$ into f yields the indeterminate form $0/0$. To determine that f has vertical asymptotes at these two values, rewrite f as

$$f(x) = \frac{\cos x}{1 + \sin x} = \frac{(\cos x)(1 - \sin x)}{(1 + \sin x)(1 - \sin x)} = \frac{(\cos x)(1 - \sin x)}{\cos^2 x} = \frac{1 - \sin x}{\cos x}.$$

Next, use Theorem 1.14 to conclude that the graph of f has vertical asymptotes at $x = -\pi/2$ and $3\pi/2$.

EXAMPLE 7   Analyzing an Inverse Trigonometric Graph

Analyze the graph of $y = (\arctan x)^2$.

Solution

From the derivative

$$y' = 2(\arctan x)\left(\frac{1}{1+x^2}\right) = \frac{2\arctan x}{1+x^2}$$

you can see that the only critical number is $x = 0$. By the First Derivative Test, this value corresponds to a relative minimum at the point $(0, 0)$. Use the first derivative to conclude that the graph is decreasing on the interval $(-\infty, 0)$ and increasing on $(0, \infty)$. From the second derivative

$$y'' = \frac{(1+x^2)\left(\frac{2}{1+x^2}\right) - (2\arctan x)(2x)}{(1+x^2)^2}$$

$$= \frac{2(1 - 2x\arctan x)}{(1+x^2)^2}$$

it follows that points of inflection occur when

$$2x\arctan x = 1.$$

Using Newton's Method, these points occur when $x \approx \pm 0.765$. Finally, because

$$\lim_{x \to \pm\infty} (\arctan x)^2 = \frac{\pi^2}{4}$$

it follows that the graph has a horizontal asymptote at

$$y = \frac{\pi^2}{4}.$$

The graph is shown in Figure 3.42.

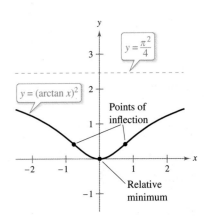

The graph of $y = (\arctan x)^2$ has a horizontal asymptote at $y = \pi^2/4$.
Figure 3.42

EXAMPLE 8   Analyzing a Logarithmic Graph

Analyze the graph of $f(x) = \ln(x^2 + 2x + 3)$.

Solution

Note that the domain of f is all real numbers. The graph of f has no x-intercepts, but it does have a y-intercept at $(0, \ln 3)$. From the derivative

$$f'(x) = \frac{2x+2}{x^2 + 2x + 3}$$

you can see that the only critical number is $x = -1$. By the First Derivative Test, this value corresponds to a relative minimum at $(-1, \ln 2)$. You can use the first derivative to conclude that the graph of f is decreasing on the interval $(-\infty, -1)$ and increasing on $(-1, \infty)$. From the second derivative

$$f''(x) = \frac{(x^2 + 2x + 3)(2) - (2x+2)(2x+2)}{(x^2 + 2x + 3)^2}$$

$$= \frac{-2(x^2 + 2x - 1)}{(x^2 + 2x + 3)^2}$$

it follows that points of inflection occur when $x^2 + 2x - 1 = 0$. Using the Quadratic Formula, these points occur when $x = -1 \pm \sqrt{2}$. Also, the graph of f is concave downward on the intervals $\left(-\infty, -1 - \sqrt{2}\right)$ and $\left(-1 + \sqrt{2}, \infty\right)$, and concave upward on $\left(-1 - \sqrt{2}, -1 + \sqrt{2}\right)$. The graph of f is shown in Figure 3.43.

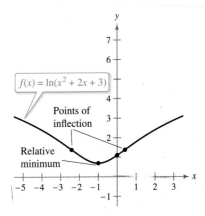

Figure 3.43

EXAMPLE 9   Graphical Reasoning: First Derivative

Let f be a function of x defined on the closed interval $-8 \le x \le 8$. The graph of f', the first derivative of f, is shown in Figure 3.44.

a. Determine the intervals on which f is increasing.

b. Determine the intervals on which the graph of f is concave downward.

c. Find all x-values at which f has a relative extremum.

d. Find all x-values at which the graph of f has a point of inflection.

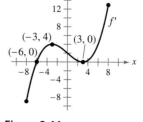

Figure 3.44

Solution

Begin by making a table that shows the signs of $f'(x)$ and where f' is increasing or decreasing.

Interval	$-8 < x < -6$	$-6 < x < -3$	$-3 < x < 3$	$3 < x < 8$
Sign of $f'(x)$	$f'(x) < 0$	$f'(x) > 0$	$f'(x) > 0$	$f'(x) > 0$
Graph of f'	Increasing	Increasing	Decreasing	Increasing

a. Because $f'(x) > 0$ on the intervals $(-6, -3)$, $(-3, 3)$, and $(3, 8)$, f must be increasing on the entire interval $(-6, 8)$.

b. The graph of f is concave downward where f' is decreasing. So, from the table, the graph of f is concave downward on the interval $(-3, 3)$.

c. Because the sign of $f'(x)$ changes from negative to positive at $x = -6$, f has a relative minimum when $x = -6$. Note that there is no relative extremum at $x = 3$ because the sign of $f'(x)$ does not change.

d. Because the graph of f' changes from increasing to decreasing, or vice versa, at $x = -3$ and $x = 3$, the graph of f has points of inflection when $x = -3$ and $x = 3$.

EXAMPLE 10   Graphical Reasoning: Second Derivative

Let f be a function of x defined on the closed interval $-3 \le x \le 3$. The graph of f'', the second derivative of f, is shown in Figure 3.45.

a. Determine the intervals on which the graph of f is concave downward.

b. Determine the intervals on which f' is increasing.

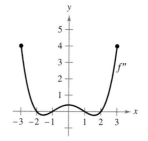

Figure 3.45

Solution

Begin by making a table that shows the signs of $f''(x)$ and where the graph of f is concave upward or concave downward.

Interval	$-3 < x < -2$	$-2 < x < -1$	$-1 < x < 1$	$1 < x < 2$	$2 < x < 3$
Sign of $f''(x)$	$f''(x) > 0$	$f''(x) < 0$	$f''(x) > 0$	$f''(x) < 0$	$f''(x) > 0$
Graph of f	Concave upward	Concave downward	Concave upward	Concave downward	Concave upward

a. From the table, the graph of f is concave downward on the intervals $(-2, -1)$ and $(1, 2)$.

b. Because the graph of f is concave upward on the intervals $(-3, -2)$, $(-1, 1)$, and $(2, 3)$, f' is increasing on the intervals $(-3, -2)$, $(-1, 1)$, and $(2, 3)$.

3.5 Exercises

See *CalcChat.com* for tutorial help and worked-out solutions to odd-numbered exercises.

Graphing a Function In Exercises 1–34, analyze and sketch a graph of the function. Label any intercepts, relative extrema, points of inflection, and asymptotes. Use a graphing utility to verify your results.

1. $y = \dfrac{1}{x - 2} - 3$

2. $y = \dfrac{x}{x^2 + 1}$

3. $y = \dfrac{x}{1 - x}$

4. $y = \dfrac{x - 4}{x - 3}$

5. $y = \dfrac{x}{x^2 - 4}$

6. $y = \dfrac{2x}{9 - x^2}$

7. $y = \dfrac{x^2}{x^2 + 3}$

8. $y = \dfrac{x^2 + 1}{x^2 - 4}$

9. $y = \dfrac{3x}{x^2 - 1}$

10. $f(x) = \dfrac{x - 3}{x}$

11. $y = 3 + \dfrac{2}{x}$

12. $y = \dfrac{4}{x^2} + 1$

13. $f(x) = x + \dfrac{32}{x^2}$

14. $f(x) = \dfrac{x^3}{x^2 - 9}$

15. $y = \dfrac{x^2 - 6x + 12}{x - 4}$

16. $y = \dfrac{-x^2 - 4x - 7}{x + 3}$

17. $g(t) = \dfrac{10}{1 + 4e^{-1}}$

18. $h(x) = \dfrac{8}{2 + 3e^{-x/2}}$

19. $y = \dfrac{x^3}{\sqrt{x^2 - 4}}$

20. $y = \dfrac{x}{\sqrt{x^2 - 4}}$

21. $y = x\sqrt{4 - x}$

22. $g(x) = x\sqrt{9 - x^2}$

23. $y = 3x^{2/3} - 2x$

24. $y = (x + 1)^2 - 3(x + 1)^{2/3}$

25. $y = 2 - x - x^3$

26. $y = -\frac{1}{3}(x^3 - 3x + 2)$

27. $y = 3x^4 + 4x^3$

28. $y = -2x^4 + 3x^2$

29. $y = x^5 - 5x$

30. $y = (x - 1)^5$

31. $y = |2x - 3|$

32. $y = |x^2 - 6x + 5|$

33. $xy = 9$

34. $x^2y = 9$

Error Analysis In Exercises 35 and 36, use the graph to describe and correct the error in each statement.

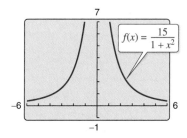

$f(x) = \dfrac{15}{1 + x^2}$

35. The graph of f has a vertical asymptote at $x = 0$ and a horizontal asymptote at $y = 0$.

36. f has no relative extrema.

Analyzing the Graph of a Function Using Technology In Exercises 37–40, use a computer algebra system to analyze and graph the function. Identify any relative extrema, points of inflection, and asymptotes.

37. $f(x) = \dfrac{20x}{x^2 + 1} - \dfrac{1}{x}$

38. $f(x) = x + \dfrac{4}{x^2 + 1}$

39. $f(x) = \dfrac{4x}{\sqrt{x^2 + 15}}$

40. $y = \dfrac{x}{2} + \ln\dfrac{x}{x + 3}$

Graphing a Trigonometric Function In Exercises 41–52, analyze and sketch a graph of the function over the given interval. Label any intercepts, relative extrema, points of inflection, and asymptotes. Use a graphing utility to verify your results.

	Function	*Interval*
41.	$f(x) = (\sin x)/(1 + \cos x)$	$-\pi < x < \pi$
42.	$f(x) = (\sin x)/(1 - \cos x)$	$0 < x < 2\pi$
43.	$f(x) = 2x - 4\sin x$	$0 \le x \le 2\pi$
44.	$f(x) = -x + 2\cos x$	$0 \le x \le 2\pi$
45.	$y = \sin x - \frac{1}{18}\sin 3x$	$0 \le x \le 2\pi$
46.	$y = \cos x - \frac{1}{4}\cos 2x$	$0 \le x \le 2\pi$
47.	$y = 2x - \tan x$	$-\dfrac{\pi}{2} < x < \dfrac{\pi}{2}$
48.	$y = 2(x - 2) + \cot x$	$0 < x < \pi$
49.	$y = 2(\csc x + \sec x)$	$0 < x < \dfrac{\pi}{2}$
50.	$y = \sec^2\dfrac{\pi x}{8} - 2\tan\dfrac{\pi x}{8} - 1$	$-3 < x < 3$
51.	$g(x) = x\tan x$	$-\dfrac{3\pi}{2} < x < \dfrac{3\pi}{2}$
52.	$g(x) = x\cot x$	$-2\pi < x < 2\pi$

Graphing a Transcendental Function In Exercises 53–62, analyze and sketch a graph of the function. Label any intercepts, relative extrema, points of inflection, and asymptotes. Use a graphing utility to verify your results.

53. $f(x) = e^{3x}(2 - x)$

54. $f(x) = 1 + e^{3x}(4 - 2x)$

55. $y = (x - 1)\ln(x - 1)$

56. $y = \frac{1}{24}x^3 - \ln x$

57. $g(x) = 6\arcsin\left(\dfrac{x - 2}{2}\right)^2$

58. $h(x) = 7\arctan(x + 1) - \ln(x^2 + 2x + 2)$

59. $f(x) = \dfrac{x}{3^{x-3}}$

60. $g(t) = (5 - t)5^t$

61. $g(x) = \log_4(x - x^2)$

62. $f(x) = \log_2|x^2 - 4x|$

EXPLORING CONCEPTS

63. Using a Derivative Let $f'(t) < 0$ for all t in the interval $(2, 8)$. Explain why $f(3) > f(5)$.

64. Using a Derivative Let $f(0) = 3$ and $2 \le f'(x) \le 4$ for all x in the interval $[-5, 5]$. Determine the greatest and least possible values of $f(2)$.

Identifying Graphs In Exercises 65 and 66, the graphs of f, f', and f'' are shown on the same set of coordinate axes. Identify each graph. Explain your reasoning. To print an enlarged copy of the graph, go to *MathGraphs.com*.

65.

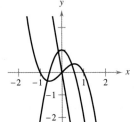

66.

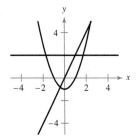

Horizontal and Vertical Asymptotes In Exercises 67–70, use a graphing utility to graph the function. Use the graph to determine whether it is possible for the graph of a function to cross its horizontal asymptote.

67. $f(x) = \dfrac{4(x-1)^2}{x^2 - 4x + 5}$

68. $g(x) = \dfrac{3x^4 - 5x + 3}{x^4 + 1}$

69. $h(x) = \dfrac{\sin 2x}{x}$

70. $f(x) = \dfrac{\cos 3x}{4x}$

Slant Asymptote In Exercises 71–74, use a graphing utility to graph the function and determine the slant asymptote of the graph. Zoom out repeatedly and describe how the graph on the display appears to change. Why does this occur?

71. $f(x) = -\dfrac{x^2 - 3x - 1}{x - 2}$

72. $g(x) = \dfrac{2x^2 - 8x - 15}{x - 5}$

73. $f(x) = \dfrac{2x^3}{x^2 + 1}$

74. $h(x) = \dfrac{-x^3 + x^2 + 4}{x^2}$

Slant Asymptotes In Exercises 75 and 76, the graph of the function has two slant asymptotes. Identify each slant asymptote. Then graph the function and its asymptotes.

75. $y = \sqrt{4 + 16x^2}$

76. $y = \sqrt{x^2 + 6x}$

Think About It In Exercises 77 and 78, create a function whose graph has the given characteristics. (There is more than one correct answer.)

77. Vertical asymptote: $x = 3$

   Horizontal asymptote: $y = 0$

78. Vertical asymptote: $x = 2$

   Slant asymptote: $y = -x$

79. Graphical Reasoning The graph of the first derivative of a function f on the interval $[-7, 5]$ is shown. Use the graph to answer each question.

(a) On what interval(s) is f decreasing?

(b) On what interval(s) is the graph of f concave downward?

(c) At what x-value(s) does f have relative extrema?

(d) At what x-value(s) does the graph of f have a point of inflection?

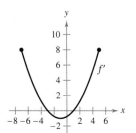

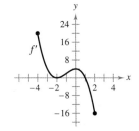

Figure for 79 Figure for 80

80. Graphical Reasoning The graph of the first derivative of a function f on the interval $[-4, 2]$ is shown. Use the graph to answer each question.

(a) On what interval(s) is f increasing?

(b) On what interval(s) is the graph of f concave upward?

(c) At what x-value(s) does f have relative extrema?

(d) At what x-value(s) does the graph of f have a point of inflection?

Graphical Reasoning In Exercises 81–84, the graph of the second derivative of a function f is shown in the figure. Use the graph to find (a) the interval(s) on which the graph of f is concave upward or concave downward, (b) the interval(s) on which f' is increasing or decreasing, and (c) the x-value(s) at which the graph of f has a point of inflection.

81.

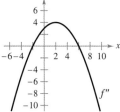

82.

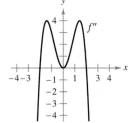

83.

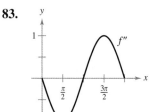

84.

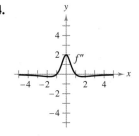

Graphical Reasoning In Exercises 85–88, use the graph of f' to sketch a graph of f and the graph of f''. To print an enlarged copy of the graph, go to *MathGraphs.com.*

85.

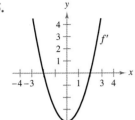

86.

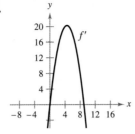

87.

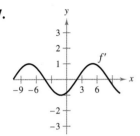

88.

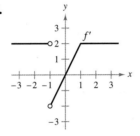

(Submitted by Bill Fox, Moberly Area Community College, Moberly, MO)

89. Graphical Reasoning Consider the function

$$f(x) = \tan(\sin \pi x).$$

(a) Use a graphing utility to graph the function.

(b) Identify any symmetry of the graph.

(c) Is the function periodic? If so, what is the period?

(d) Identify any extrema on $(-1, 1)$.

(e) Use a graphing utility to determine the concavity of the graph on $(0, 1)$.

90. HOW DO YOU SEE IT? The graph of f is shown in the figure.

(a) For which values of x is $f'(x)$ zero? positive? negative? What do these values mean?

(b) For which values of x is $f''(x)$ zero? positive? negative? What do these values mean?

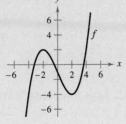

(c) On what open interval is f' an increasing function?

(d) For which value of x is $f'(x)$ minimum? For this value of x, how does the rate of change of f compare with the rates of change of f for other values of x? Explain.

91. Graphical Reasoning Identify the real numbers x_0, x_1, x_2, x_3, and x_4 in the figure that satisfy each statement.

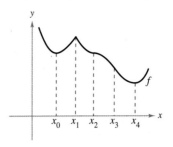

(a) $f'(x) = 0$

(b) $f''(x) = 0$

(c) $f'(x)$ does not exist.

(d) f has a relative maximum.

(e) f has a point of inflection.

92. Justifying Let $P(x_0, y_0)$ be an arbitrary point on the graph of f such that $f'(x_0) \neq 0$, as shown in the figure. Verify each statement.

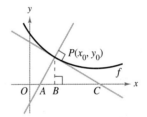

(a) The x-intercept of the tangent line is

$$\left(x_0 - \frac{f(x_0)}{f'(x_0)}, 0\right).$$

(b) The y-intercept of the tangent line is

$$(0, f(x_0) - x_0 f'(x_0)).$$

(c) The x-intercept of the normal line is

$$(x_0 + f(x_0)f'(x_0), 0).$$

(*Hint:* The *normal line* at a point is perpendicular to the tangent line at the point.)

(d) The y-intercept of the normal line is

$$\left(0, y_0 + \frac{x_0}{f'(x_0)}\right).$$

(e) $|BC| = \left|\dfrac{f(x_0)}{f'(x_0)}\right|$

(f) $|PC| = \left|\dfrac{f(x_0)\sqrt{1 + [f'(x_0)]^2}}{f'(x_0)}\right|$

(g) $|AB| = |f(x_0)f'(x_0)|$

(h) $|AP| = |f(x_0)|\sqrt{1 + [f'(x_0)]^2}$

93. Comparing Functions Let f be a function that is positive and differentiable on the entire real number line. Let $g(x) = \ln f(x)$.

(a) If g is increasing, must f be increasing? Explain.

(b) If the graph of f is concave upward, must the graph of g be concave upward? Explain.

94. Connecting Representations Consider the function

$$f(x) = \frac{2x^n}{x^4 + 1}$$

for nonnegative integer values of n.

(a) Discuss the relationship between the value of n and the symmetry of the graph.

(b) For which values of n will the x-axis be the horizontal asymptote?

(c) For which value of n will $y = 2$ be the horizontal asymptote?

(d) What is the asymptote of the graph when $n = 5$?

(e) Use a graphing utility to graph f for the indicated values of n in the table. Use the graph to determine the number of extrema M and the number of inflection points N of the graph.

n	0	1	2	3	4	5
M						
N						

95. Connecting Representations Consider the function

$$f(x) = \frac{ax}{(x - b)^2}.$$

Determine the effect on the graph of f as a and b are changed. Consider cases where a and b are both positive or both negative, and cases where a and b have opposite signs.

96. Connecting Representations Consider the function

$$f(x) = \tfrac{1}{2}(ax)^2 - ax, \quad a \neq 0.$$

(a) Determine the changes (if any) in the intercepts, extrema, and concavity of the graph of f when a is varied.

(b) In the same viewing window, use a graphing utility to graph the function for four different values of a.

Examining a Function In Exercises 97 and 98, use a graphing utility to graph the function. Explain why there is no vertical asymptote when a superficial examination of the function may indicate that there should be one.

97. $h(x) = \dfrac{6 - 2x}{3 - x}$ **98.** $g(x) = \dfrac{x^2 + x - 2}{x - 1}$

Calculus AP® – Exam Preparation Questions

99. Multiple Choice What are the equations of the asymptotes of the function

$$f(x) = \frac{x^3 - 1}{x^2 - x}?$$

(A) $x = 0, x = 1$

(B) $x = 0, x = 1, y = x + 1$

(C) $x = 0, y = x + 1$ (D) $x = 0, x = 1, y = x$

100. Multiple Choice The figure shows the graph of the derivative of a function f. Which of the following statements must be true?

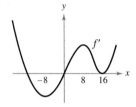

(A) f is concave downward on the interval $[0, 16]$.

(B) f is increasing on the interval $[-8, 8]$.

(C) f has a local minimum at $x = -8$.

(D) f has a point of inflection at $x = 16$.

101. Multiple Choice The figure shows the graph of the second derivative of a function g. Which of the following statements are true?

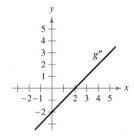

I. The graph of g is concave upward on the interval $(2, \infty)$.

II. g' is decreasing on the interval $(-\infty, 2)$.

III. The graph of g has a point of inflection at $x = 2$.

(A) I and II only   (B) I and III only

(C) III only   (D) I, II, and III

102. Free Response The derivative of a function f is $f'(x) = -12(x - 2)^2(x - 4)$.

(a) Does f have any relative extrema? If so, where do they occur?

(b) On what interval(s) is f decreasing?

(c) On what interval(s) is the graph of f concave downward?

(d) How many point(s) of inflection does the graph of f have? Where do they occur?

3.6   Optimization Problems

▶ Solve applied minimum and maximum problems.

Applied Minimum and Maximum Problems

One of the most common applications of calculus involves the determination of minimum and maximum values. Consider how frequently you hear or read terms such as greatest profit, least cost, least time, greatest voltage, optimum size, least size, greatest strength, and greatest distance. Before outlining a general problem-solving strategy for such problems, consider the next example.

EXAMPLE 1   Finding Maximum Volume

A manufacturer wants to design an open box having a square base and a surface area of 108 square inches, as shown in Figure 3.46. What dimensions will produce a box with maximum volume?

Solution

Because the box has a square base, its volume is

$$V = x^2 h. \qquad \text{Primary equation}$$

This equation is called the **primary equation** because it gives a formula for the quantity to be optimized. The surface area of the box is

$$S = (\text{area of base}) + (\text{area of four sides})$$
$$108 = x^2 + 4xh. \qquad \text{Secondary equation}$$

Because V is to be maximized, you want to write V as a function of just one variable. To do this, you can solve the equation $x^2 + 4xh = 108$ for h in terms of x to obtain $h = (108 - x^2)/(4x)$. Substituting into the primary equation produces

$$V = x^2 h \qquad \text{Function of two variables}$$
$$= x^2 \left(\frac{108 - x^2}{4x} \right) \qquad \text{Substitute for } h.$$
$$= 27x - \frac{x^3}{4}. \qquad \text{Function of one variable}$$

Before finding which x-value will yield a maximum value of V, you should determine the *feasible domain*. That is, what values of x make sense in this problem? You know that $V \geq 0$. You also know that x must be nonnegative and that the area of the base $(A = x^2)$ is at most 108. So, the feasible domain is

$$0 \leq x \leq \sqrt{108}. \qquad \text{Feasible domain}$$

To maximize V, find its critical numbers on the interval $\left(0, \sqrt{108} \right)$.

$$\frac{dV}{dx} = 27 - \frac{3x^2}{4} \qquad \text{Differentiate with respect to } x.$$
$$27 - \frac{3x^2}{4} = 0 \qquad \text{Set derivative equal to 0.}$$
$$3x^2 = 108 \qquad \text{Simplify.}$$
$$x = \pm 6 \qquad \text{Critical numbers}$$

So, the critical numbers are $x = \pm 6$. You do not need to consider $x = -6$ because it is outside the domain. Evaluating V at the critical number $x = 6$ and at the endpoints of the domain produces $V(0) = 0$, $V(6) = 108$, and $V\left(\sqrt{108} \right) = 0$. So, V is maximum when $x = 6$, and the dimensions of the box are 6 inches by 6 inches by 3 inches. ∎

Open box with square base:
$S = x^2 + 4xh = 108$
Figure 3.46

Technology

You can check the answer to Example 1 by using a graphing utility to graph the volume function

$$V = 27x - \frac{x^3}{4}.$$

Use a viewing window in which $0 \leq x \leq \sqrt{108} \approx 10.4$ and $0 \leq y \leq 120$. Then use the *maximum* or *trace* feature to determine the x-value that produces a maximum volume.

In Example 1, you should realize that there are infinitely many open boxes having 108 square inches of surface area. To begin solving the problem, you might ask yourself which basic shape would seem to yield a maximum volume. Should the box be tall, squat, or nearly cubical?

You might even try calculating a few volumes, as shown in Figure 3.47, to see if you can get a better feeling for what the optimum dimensions should be. Remember that you are not ready to begin solving a problem until you have clearly identified what the problem is.

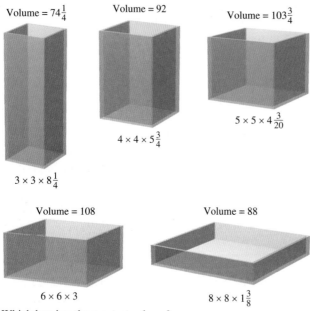

Volume = $74\frac{1}{4}$

$3 \times 3 \times 8\frac{1}{4}$

Volume = 92

$4 \times 4 \times 5\frac{3}{4}$

Volume = $103\frac{3}{4}$

$5 \times 5 \times 4\frac{3}{20}$

Volume = 108

$6 \times 6 \times 3$

Volume = 88

$8 \times 8 \times 1\frac{3}{8}$

Which box has the greatest volume?
Figure 3.47

Example 1 illustrates the following guidelines for solving applied minimum and maximum problems.

Guidelines for Solving Applied Minimum and Maximum Problems

1. Identify all *given* quantities and all quantities *to be determined.* If possible, make a sketch.

2. Write a **primary equation** for the quantity that is to be maximized or minimized. (Several useful formulas from geometry are listed on the inside back cover of this text.)

3. Reduce the primary equation to one having a *single independent variable.* This may involve the use of **secondary equations** relating the independent variables of the primary equation.

4. Determine the feasible domain of the primary equation. That is, determine the values for which the stated problem makes sense.

5. Determine the desired maximum or minimum value by the calculus techniques discussed in Sections 3.1 through 3.4.

▶ **Implementing Processes**   For Step 5, recall that to determine the maximum or minimum value of a continuous function f on a closed interval, you should compare the values of f at its critical numbers with the values of f at the endpoints of the interval.

EXAMPLE 2 **Finding Minimum Distance**

See LarsonCalculusforAP.com for an interactive version of this type of example.

Which points on the graph of $y = 4 - x^2$ are closest to the point $(0, 2)$?

Solution

Figure 3.48 shows that there are two points at a minimum distance from the point $(0, 2)$. The distance between the point $(0, 2)$ and a point (x, y) on the graph of $y = 4 - x^2$ is

$$d = \sqrt{(x - 0)^2 + (y - 2)^2}.$$ Primary equation

Using the secondary equation $y = 4 - x^2$, you can rewrite the primary equation as

$$d = \sqrt{x^2 + (4 - x^2 - 2)^2} = \sqrt{x^4 - 3x^2 + 4}.$$

Because d is smallest when the expression inside the radical is smallest, you need only find the critical numbers of $f(x) = x^4 - 3x^2 + 4$. Note that the domain of f is the entire real number line. So, there are no endpoints of the domain to consider. Moreover, the derivative of f

$$f'(x) = 4x^3 - 6x = 2x(2x^2 - 3)$$

is zero when

$$x = 0, \quad \sqrt{\frac{3}{2}}, \quad -\sqrt{\frac{3}{2}}.$$

Testing these critical numbers using the First Derivative Test verifies that $x = 0$ yields a relative maximum, whereas both $x = \sqrt{3/2}$ and $x = -\sqrt{3/2}$ yield a minimum distance. So, the closest points are $\left(\sqrt{3/2}, 5/2\right)$ and $\left(-\sqrt{3/2}, 5/2\right)$.

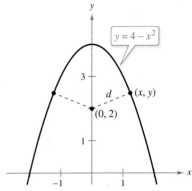

The quantity to be minimized is distance: $d = \sqrt{(x - 0)^2 + (y - 2)^2}$.

Figure 3.48

Algebra Review

For help on the algebra in Example 2, see Example 1(e) in the *Chapter 3 Algebra Review* on page A40.

EXAMPLE 3 **Finding Minimum Area**

A rectangular page is to contain 24 square inches of print. The margins at the top and bottom of the page are to be $1\frac{1}{2}$ inches, and the margins on the left and right are to be 1 inch. (See Figure 3.49.) What should the dimensions of the page be so that the least amount of paper is used?

Solution

Let A be the area to be minimized.

$$A = (x + 3)(y + 2)$$ Primary equation

The printed area inside the margins is

$$24 = xy.$$ Secondary equation

Solving this equation for y produces $y = 24/x$. Substituting into the primary equation produces

$$A = (x + 3)\left(\frac{24}{x} + 2\right) = 30 + 2x + \frac{72}{x}.$$ Function of one variable

Because x must be positive, you are interested only in values of A for $x > 0$. To find the critical numbers, differentiate with respect to x

$$\frac{dA}{dx} = 2 - \frac{72}{x^2}$$

and note that the derivative is zero when $x^2 = 36$, or $x = \pm 6$. So, the critical numbers are $x = \pm 6$. You do not have to consider $x = -6$ because it is outside the domain. The First Derivative Test confirms that A is a minimum when $x = 6$. So, $y = \frac{24}{6} = 4$ and the dimensions of the page should be $x + 3 = 9$ inches by $y + 2 = 6$ inches. ∎

1 in.   1 in.
$1\frac{1}{2}$ in.
x
$1\frac{1}{2}$ in.

The quantity to be minimized is area: $A = (x + 3)(y + 2)$.

Figure 3.49

Algebra Review

For help on the algebra in Example 3, see Example 2(c) in the *Chapter 3 Algebra Review* on page A41.

EXAMPLE 4   Finding Minimum Length

Two posts, one 12 feet high and the other 28 feet high, stand 30 feet apart. They are to be stayed by two wires, attached to a single stake, running from ground level to the top of each post. Where should the stake be placed to use the least amount of wire?

Solution   Let W be the wire length to be minimized. Using the figure at the right, you can write

$W = y + z.$ Primary equation

In this problem, rather than solving for y in terms of z (or vice versa), you can solve for both y and z in terms of a third variable x, as shown in the figure at the right. From the Pythagorean Theorem, you obtain

$$x^2 + 12^2 = y^2$$
$$(30 - x)^2 + 28^2 = z^2$$

which implies that

$$y = \sqrt{x^2 + 144}$$
$$z = \sqrt{x^2 - 60x + 1684}.$$

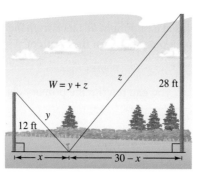

The quantity to be minimized is length. From the diagram, you can see that x varies between 0 and 30.

So, you can rewrite the primary equation as

$$W = y + z = \sqrt{x^2 + 144} + \sqrt{x^2 - 60x + 1684}, \quad 0 \le x \le 30.$$

Differentiating W with respect to x yields

$$\frac{dW}{dx} = \frac{x}{\sqrt{x^2 + 144}} + \frac{x - 30}{\sqrt{x^2 - 60x + 1684}}.$$

By letting $dW/dx = 0$, you obtain

$$\frac{x}{\sqrt{x^2 + 144}} + \frac{x - 30}{\sqrt{x^2 - 60x + 1684}} = 0$$

$$\frac{x}{\sqrt{x^2 + 144}} = \frac{30 - x}{\sqrt{x^2 - 60x + 1684}}$$

$$x\sqrt{x^2 - 60x + 1684} = (30 - x)\sqrt{x^2 + 144}$$

$$x^2(x^2 - 60x + 1684) = (30 - x)^2(x^2 + 144)$$

$$x^4 - 60x^3 + 1684x^2 = x^4 - 60x^3 + 1044x^2 - 8640x + 129{,}600$$

$$640x^2 + 8640x - 129{,}600 = 0$$

$$320(x - 9)(2x + 45) = 0$$

$$x = 9, -22.5.$$

Because $x = -22.5$ is not in the domain and

$$W(0) \approx 53.04, \quad W(9) = 50, \quad \text{and} \quad W(30) \approx 60.31$$

you can conclude that the wires should be staked at 9 feet from the 12-foot pole.

Technology

From Example 4, you can see that applied optimization problems can involve a lot of algebra. If you have access to a graphing utility, you can confirm that $x = 9$ yields a minimum value of W by graphing $W = \sqrt{x^2 + 144} + \sqrt{x^2 - 60x + 1684}$, as shown in Figure 3.50.

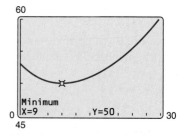

You can confirm the minimum value of W with a graphing utility.

Figure 3.50

In each of the first four examples, the extreme value occurred at a critical number. Although this happens often, remember that an extreme value can also occur at an endpoint of an interval, as shown in Example 5.

EXAMPLE 5   An Endpoint Maximum

Four feet of wire is to be used to form a square and a circle. How much of the wire should be used for the square and how much should be used for the circle to enclose the maximum total area?

Solution

The total area (see Figure 3.51) is

$$A = \text{(area of square)} + \text{(area of circle)}$$
$$A = x^2 + \pi r^2. \qquad \text{Primary equation}$$

Because the total length of wire is 4 feet, you obtain

$$4 = \text{(perimeter of square)} + \text{(circumference of circle)}$$
$$4 = 4x + 2\pi r. \qquad \text{Secondary equation}$$

So, $r = 2(1 - x)/\pi$, and by substituting into the primary equation you have

$$A = x^2 + \pi \left[\frac{2(1 - x)}{\pi} \right]^2 = x^2 + \frac{4(1 - x)^2}{\pi} = \frac{1}{\pi}[(\pi + 4)x^2 - 8x + 4].$$

The feasible domain is $0 \le x \le 1$, restricted by the square's perimeter. Because

$$\frac{dA}{dx} = \frac{2(\pi + 4)x - 8}{\pi}$$

the only critical number in $(0, 1)$ is $x = 4/(\pi + 4) \approx 0.56$. So, using $A(0) \approx 1.273$, $A(0.56) \approx 0.56$, and $A(1) = 1$, you can conclude that the maximum area occurs when $x = 0$. That is, *all* the wire is used for the circle.

EXAMPLE 6   Finding a Maximum Revenue

The demand function for a product is modeled by $p = 56e^{-0.000012x}$, where p is the price per unit (in dollars) and x is the number of units. What price (to the nearest penny) will yield a maximum revenue?

Solution

The revenue function is given by

$$R = xp. \qquad \text{Revenue function}$$

Substituting for p (from the demand function) produces

$$R = 56xe^{-0.000012x}. \qquad \text{Primary equation}$$

The rate of change of revenue R with respect to the number of units sold x is called the *marginal revenue* and is given by

$$\frac{dR}{dx} = 56x(e^{-0.000012x})(-0.000012) + e^{-0.000012x}(56).$$

Setting the marginal revenue equal to zero

$$56x(e^{-0.000012x})(-0.000012) + e^{-0.000012x}(56) = 0$$

you can determine that there is one critical number, $x \approx 83,333$. So, the maximum revenue occurs when the production level is 83,333 units (see Figure 3.52). To the nearest penny, the price that corresponds to this level is $p = 56e^{-0.000012x} = \$20.60$.

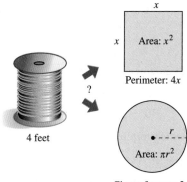

x

x Area: x^2

Perimeter: $4x$

4 feet   ?

r

Area: πr^2

Circumference: $2\pi r$

The quantity to be maximized is area: $A = x^2 + \pi r^2$.

Figure 3.51

Algebra Review

For help on the algebra in Example 5, see Example 2(d) in the *Chapter 3 Algebra Review* on page A41.

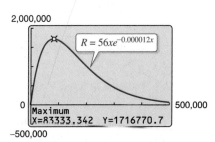

2,000,000

$R = 56xe^{-0.000012x}$

0   500,000

Maximum
X=83333.342 Y=1716770.7

−500,000

The maximum revenue occurs when the production level is 83,333 units.

Figure 3.52

3.6 Exercises

See *CalcChat.com* for tutorial help and worked-out solutions to odd-numbered exercises.

1. Connecting Representations Find two positive numbers whose sum is 110 and whose product is a maximum.

(a) Complete six rows of a table such as the one below. (The first two rows are shown.)

First Number, x	Second Number	Product, P
10	$110 - 10$	$10(110 - 10) = 1000$
20	$110 - 20$	$20(110 - 20) = 1800$

(b) Use a graphing utility to generate additional rows of the table. Use the table to estimate the solution. (*Hint:* Use the *table* feature of the graphing utility.)

(c) Write the product P as a function of x.

(d) Use a graphing utility to graph the function in part (c) and estimate the solution from the graph.

(e) Use calculus to find the critical number of the function in part (c). Then find the two numbers.

2. Connecting Representations An open box of maximum volume is to be made from a square piece of material, 24 inches on a side, by cutting equal squares from the corners and turning up the sides (see figure).

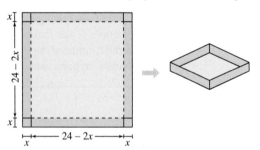

(a) Complete six rows of a table such as the one below. (The first two rows are shown.) Use the table to guess the maximum volume.

Height, x	Length and Width	Volume, V
1	$24 - 2(1)$	$1[24 - 2(1)]^2 = 484$
2	$24 - 2(2)$	$2[24 - 2(2)]^2 = 800$

(b) Write the volume V as a function of x.

(c) Use calculus to find the critical number of the function in part (b) and find the maximum value.

(d) Use a graphing utility to graph the function in part (b) and verify the maximum volume from the graph.

 Finding Numbers In Exercises 3–8, find two positive numbers that satisfy the given requirements.

3. The sum is 28 and the product is a maximum.

4. The product is 185 and the sum is a minimum.

5. The product is 147 and the sum of the first number plus three times the second number is a minimum.

6. The second number is the reciprocal of the first number and the sum is a minimum.

7. The sum of the first number and twice the second number is 108 and the product is a maximum.

8. The sum of the first number squared and the second number is 54 and the product is a maximum.

 Maximum Area In Exercises 9 and 10, find the length and width of a rectangle that has the given perimeter and a maximum area.

9. Perimeter: 80 meters   **10.** Perimeter: P units

 Minimum Perimeter In Exercises 11 and 12, find the length and width of a rectangle that has the given area and a minimum perimeter.

11. Area: 49 square feet   **12.** Area: A square miles

 Minimum Distance In Exercises 13–18, find the point(s) on the graph of f that are closest to the given point. Use a graphing utility to estimate if necessary.

13. $f(x) = x^2$, $\left(2, \frac{1}{2}\right)$ **14.** $f(x) = (x - 1)^2$, $(-5, 3)$

15. $f(x) = \sqrt{x}$, $(4, 0)$ **16.** $f(x) = \sqrt{x - 8}$, $(12, 0)$

17. $f(x) = x^2 + 6x$, $(-3, 1)$ **18.** $f(x) = 2 \sin x$, $\left(\frac{\pi}{2}, 0\right)$

Minimum Area In Exercises 19 and 20, a rectangular page has the given features. Find the dimensions of the page such that the least amount of paper is used.

19. 30 square inches of print, 1-inch margins

20. 36 square inches of print, $1\frac{1}{2}$-inch margins

21. Minimum Length A farmer plans to fence a rectangular pasture adjacent to a river (see figure). The area of the pasture must be at least 245,000 square meters. No fencing is needed along the river. What dimensions will require the least amount of fencing?

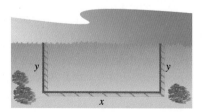

22. Maximum Volume   A rectangular solid (with a square base) has a surface area of 337.5 square centimeters. Find the dimensions that will result in a solid with maximum volume.

23. Maximum Area   A Norman window is constructed by adjoining a semicircle to the top of an ordinary rectangular window (see figure). Find the dimensions of a Norman window of maximum area when the total perimeter is 16 feet.

24. Maximum Area   A rectangle is bounded by the x-axis and the semicircle $y = \sqrt{25 - x^2}$ (see figure). (a) What length and width should the rectangle have so that its area is a maximum? (b) Find the dimensions of the rectangle inscribed in a semicircle of radius r with maximum area.

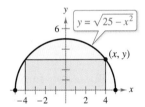

25. Maximum Area   A rectangle is bounded by the x- and y-axes and the graph of $y = c - dx$, where $c, d > 0$. Find the dimensions of the rectangle with maximum area.

26. Maximum Area   Find the area of the largest rectangle that can be inscribed under the curve $y = e^{-x^2}$ in the first and second quadrants.

27. Connecting Representations   An exercise room consists of a rectangle with a semicircle on each end. A 200-meter running track runs around the outside of the room.

(a) Draw a figure to represent the problem. Let x and y represent the length and width of the rectangle.

(b) Complete six rows of a table such as the one below. (The first two rows are shown.) Use the table to guess the maximum area A of the rectangular region.

Length, x	Width, y	Area, xy
10	$\frac{2}{\pi}(100 - 10)$	$(10)\frac{2}{\pi}(100 - 10) \approx 573$
20	$\frac{2}{\pi}(100 - 20)$	$(20)\frac{2}{\pi}(100 - 20) \approx 1019$

(c) Write the area A as a function of x.

(d) Use calculus to find the critical number of the function in part (c) and find the maximum value.

(e) Use a graphing utility to graph the function in part (c) and verify the maximum area from the graph.

28. Connecting Representations   A right circular cylinder is designed to hold 22 cubic inches of a soft drink (approximately 12 fluid ounces).

(a) Complete six rows of a table such as the one below. (The first two rows are shown.)

Radius, r	Height	Surface Area, S
0.2	$\dfrac{22}{\pi(0.2)^2}$	$2\pi(0.2)\left[0.2 + \dfrac{22}{\pi(0.2)^2}\right] \approx 220.3$
0.4	$\dfrac{22}{\pi(0.4)^2}$	$2\pi(0.4)\left[0.4 + \dfrac{22}{\pi(0.4)^2}\right] \approx 111.0$

(b) Use a graphing utility to generate additional rows of the table. Use the table to estimate the minimum surface area. (*Hint:* Use the *table* feature of the graphing utility.)

(c) Write the surface area S as a function of r.

(d) Use a graphing utility to graph the function in part (c) and estimate the minimum surface area from the graph.

(e) Use calculus to find the critical number of the function in part (c) and find dimensions that will yield the minimum surface area.

EXPLORING CONCEPTS ─────────

29. Think About It   Do there exist two positive numbers such that the product is 100 and the sum is a maximum? Explain why or why not.

30. Area and Perimeter   The perimeter of a rectangle is 20 feet. The maximum area occurs when its length and width are both 5 feet. Are there dimensions that yield a minimum area? Explain.

─────────

31. Minimum Surface Area   A solid is formed by adjoining two hemispheres to the ends of a right circular cylinder. The total volume of the solid is 14 cubic centimeters. Find the radius of the cylinder that produces the minimum surface area.

32. Minimum Cost   An industrial tank of the shape described in Exercise 31 must have a volume of 4000 cubic feet. The hemispherical ends cost twice as much per square foot of surface area as the sides. Find the dimensions that will minimize cost.

33. Minimum Area   The sum of the perimeters of an equilateral triangle and a square is 10. Find the dimensions of the triangle and the square that produce a minimum total area.

34. Maximum Area Twenty feet of wire is to be used to form two figures. In each of the following cases, how much wire should be used for each figure so that the total enclosed area is maximum? {*Hint:* The area of a regular polygon with n sides of length x is $A = (n/4)[\cot(\pi/n)]x^2$.}

(a) Equilateral triangle and square

(b) Square and regular pentagon

(c) Regular pentagon and regular hexagon

(d) Regular hexagon and circle

What can you conclude from this pattern?

35. Minimum Length and Minimum Area A right triangle is formed in the first quadrant by the x- and y-axes and a line through the point $(1, 2)$.

(a) Write the length L of the hypotenuse as a function of x.

(b) Use a graphing utility to approximate x graphically such that the length of the hypotenuse is a minimum.

(c) Find the vertices of the triangle such that its area is a minimum.

36. Maximum Area Find the area of the largest isosceles triangle that can be inscribed in a circle of radius 6 (see figure).

(a) Solve by writing the area as a function of x.

(b) Solve by writing the area as a function of α. (*Hint:* First express each side of the right triangle containing α in terms of x.)

(c) Identify the type of triangle of maximum area.

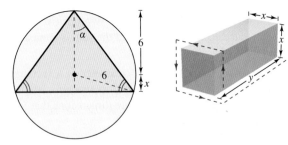

Figure for 36   Figure for 37

37. Maximum Volume A package to be sent by a postal service can have a maximum combined length and girth (perimeter of a cross section) of 108 inches. (a) Find the dimensions of the package of maximum volume that can be sent when the cross section is square (see figure). (b) What are the dimensions of a cylindrical package of maximum volume? (The cross section is circular.)

38. Maximum Profit Assume that the amount of money deposited in a bank is proportional to the square of the interest rate the bank pays on this money. Furthermore, the bank can reinvest this money at 12%. Find the interest rate the bank should pay to maximize profit. (Use the simple interest formula.)

39. Beam Strength A wooden beam has a rectangular cross section of height h and width w (see figure). The strength S of the beam is directly proportional to the width and the square of the height. What are the dimensions of the strongest beam that can be cut from a round log of diameter 20 inches? (*Hint:* $S = kh^2w$, where k is the proportionality constant.)

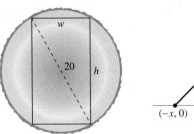

Figure for 39   Figure for 40

40. Minimum Length Two factories are located at the coordinates $(-x, 0)$ and $(x, 0)$ and their power supply is at $(0, h)$ (see figure). Find y such that the total length of power line from the power supply to the factories is a minimum.

41. MINIMUM COST

An offshore oil well is 2 kilometers off the coast. The refinery is 4 kilometers down the coast. Laying pipe in the ocean is twice as expensive as laying it on land. What path should the pipe follow in order to minimize the cost?

42. Illumination A light source is located over the center of a circular table of diameter 4 feet (see figure). Find the height h of the light source such that the illumination I at the perimeter of the table is maximum when

$$I = \frac{k \sin \alpha}{s^2}$$

where s is the slant height, α is the angle at which the light strikes the table, and k is a constant.

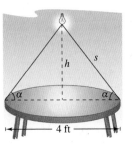

43. Population Growth Fifty elk are introduced into a game preserve. It is estimated that their population will increase according to the model $p(t) = 250/(1 + 4e^{-t/3})$, where t is measured in years. At what rate is the population increasing when $t = 2$? After how many years is the population increasing most rapidly?

44. Pulling an Object The horizontal acceleration of an object pulled by a rope at an angle θ with force F is given by $a = F(\cos\theta + u\sin\theta)/m - ug$, where m is the mass of the object, u is the coefficient of friction, and g is the acceleration due to gravity. Find the angle that maximizes the acceleration a of the object.

45. Maximum Volume A sector with central angle θ is cut from a circle of radius 12 inches (see figure), and the edges of the sector are brought together to form a cone. Find the magnitude of θ such that the volume of the cone is a maximum.

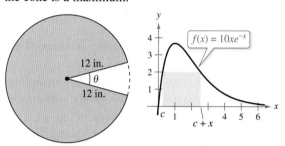

Figure for 45   Figure for 46

46. Area Perform the following steps to find the maximum area of the rectangle shown in the figure.

(a) Solve for c in the equation $f(c) = f(c + x)$.

(b) Use the result in part (a) to write the area A as a function of x. [*Hint: $A = xf(c)$*]

(c) Use a graphing utility to graph A. Use the graph to approximate the dimensions of the rectangle of maximum area. Determine the required area.

(d) Use a graphing utility to graph the expression for c found in part (a). Use the graph to approximate $\lim_{x \to 0^+} c$ and $\lim_{x \to \infty} c$. Use this result to describe the changes in the dimensions and position of the rectangle for $0 < x < \infty$.

47. Minimum Distance Let $f(x) = 2 - 2\sin x$. Sketch the graph of f on the interval $[0, \pi/2]$.

(a) Find the distance from the origin to the y-intercept and the distance from the origin to the x-intercept.

(b) Write the distance d from the origin to a point on the graph of f as a function of x.

(c) Use calculus to find the value of x that minimizes the function d on the interval $[0, \pi/2]$. What is the minimum distance? Use a graphing utility to verify your results.

(Submitted by Tim Chapell, Penn Valley Community College, Kansas City, MO)

48. HOW DO YOU SEE IT? The graph shows the profit P (in thousands of dollars) of a company in terms of its advertising cost x (in thousands of dollars).

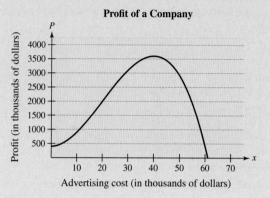

(a) Estimate the interval on which the profit is increasing.

(b) Estimate the interval on which the profit is decreasing.

(c) Estimate the amount of money the company should spend on advertising in order to yield a maximum profit.

(d) The *point of diminishing returns* is the point at which the rate of growth of the profit function begins to decline. Estimate the point of diminishing returns.

49. Maximum Rate Verify that the function

$$y = \frac{L}{1 + ae^{-x/b}}, \qquad a > 0, \; b > 0, \; L > 0$$

increases at the maximum rate when $y = L/2$.

50. Maximum Rate The concentration C of a chemical in the bloodstream t hours after injection into muscle tissue is given by $C = (3t^2 + t)/(50 + t^3)$, $t \geq 0$. When is the concentration increasing at (a) the maximum rate and (b) the minimum rate?

Minimum Distance In Exercises 51–53, consider a fuel distribution center located at the origin of the rectangular coordinate system (units in miles; see figures). The center supplies three factories with coordinates $(4, 1)$, $(5, 6)$, and $(10, 3)$. A trunk line will run from the distribution center along the line $y = mx$, and feeder lines will run to the three factories. The objective is to find m such that the lengths of the feeder lines are minimized.

51. Minimize the sum of the squares of the lengths of the vertical feeder lines (see figure on next page). Find the equation of the trunk line by this method and then determine the sum of the lengths of the feeder lines.

52. Minimize the sum of the absolute values of the lengths of the vertical feeder lines (see figure). Find the equation of the trunk line by this method and then determine the sum of the lengths of the feeder lines. (*Hint:* Use a graphing utility to graph the function representing the sum and approximate the required critical number.)

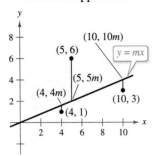 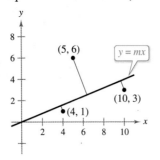

Figure for 51 and 52   Figure for 53

53. Minimize the sum of the perpendicular distances from the trunk line to the factories. A formula for the perpendicular distance between a point (x_1, y_1) and a line $Ax + By + C = 0$ is shown below.

$$\text{Distance} = \frac{|Ax_1 + By_1 + C|}{\sqrt{A^2 + B^2}}$$

Find the equation of the trunk line by this method and then determine the sum of the lengths of the feeder lines. (*Hint:* Use a graphing utility to graph the function representing the sum and approximate the required critical number.)

Calculus AP® – Exam Preparation Questions

54. Multiple Choice What is the maximum area of a right triangle with hypotenuse 12?

(A) 18   (B) 24

(C) 36   (D) 48

55. Free Response A right cone has a slant height of 6, as shown in the figure.

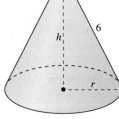

(a) Write the volume V of the cone as a function of one variable, r. The formula for the volume of a cone is

$$V = \frac{1}{3}\pi r^2 h.$$

(b) What are the dimensions that maximize the volume of the cone?

56. Free Response A rectangle is bounded by the x-axis and the graph of $y = 25 - x^2$.

(a) What are the dimensions of the rectangle so that its area is a maximum? Justify your answer.

(b) What are the dimensions of the rectangle so that its perimeter is a maximum? Justify your answer.

SECTION PROJECT

Stopping Distance

The department of transportation must determine the speed limit on a bridge such that the flow rate of cars is maximum per unit time. The greater the speed limit, the farther apart the cars must be in order to keep a safe stopping distance. Experimental data on the stopping distances d (in meters) for various vehicles at different speeds s (in meters per second) are shown in the table.

s	2.8	5.6	8.3
d	0.5	2.8	4.3

s	11.1	13.9	16.7
d	8.9	17.2	20.1

(a) Use the regression feature of a graphing utility to find a function

$$d(s) = as^2 + bs + c$$

that models the data.

(b) Consider two consecutive vehicles of average length 5.5 meters, traveling at a safe speed on the bridge. Let T be the difference between the times (in seconds) when the front bumpers of the vehicles pass a given point on the bridge. Verify that this difference in times is given by

$$T = \frac{d(s)}{s} + \frac{5.5}{s}.$$

(c) Determine the speed that minimizes the time between vehicles T. What is the minimum value of T? Use a graphing utility to verify your answers.

(d) What do you think the speed limit on the bridge should be (in kilometers per hour)? Explain your reasoning

(e) Repeat parts (a) through (d) using a cubic model for the data. Compare the results.

(f) Use the Internet or some other reference source to research the stopping distances of vehicles. Determine whether the stopping distance of a car is better modeled by a quadratic or cubic function of its speed. Explain your reasoning.

3.7 Linear Approximation and Differentials

▶ Understand the concept of a tangent line approximation.
▶ Compare the value of the differential, *dy*, with the actual change in *y*, Δy.
▶ Estimate a propagated error using a differential.
▶ Find the differential of a function using differentiation formulas.

Tangent Line Approximations

Newton's Method (see Section 2.8) is an example of the use of a tangent line to approximate the graph of a function. In this section, you will study other situations in which the graph of a function can be approximated by a straight line.

To begin, consider a function f that is differentiable at c. The equation for the tangent line at the point $(c, f(c))$ is

$$y - f(c) = f'(c)(x - c)$$

$$y = f(c) + f'(c)(x - c)$$

and is called the **tangent line approximation** (or **linear approximation**) **of** f **at** c. Because c is a constant, y is a linear function of x. Moreover, by restricting the values of x to those sufficiently close to c, the values of y can be used as approximations (to any desired degree of accuracy) of the values of the function f. In other words, as x approaches c, the limit of y is $f(c)$.

Exploration

Tangent Line Approximation
Use a graphing utility to graph $f(x) = x^2$. In the same viewing window, graph the tangent line to the graph of f at the point $(1, 1)$. Zoom in twice on the point of tangency. Does your graphing utility distinguish between the two graphs? Use the *trace* feature to compare the two graphs. As the x-values get closer to 1, what can you say about the y-values?

EXAMPLE 1   Using a Tangent Line Approximation

See LarsonCalculusforAP.com for an interactive version of this type of example.

Find the tangent line approximation of $f(x) = 1 + \sin x$ at the point $(0, 1)$. Then use a table to compare the y-values of the linear function with those of $f(x)$ on an open interval containing $x = 0$.

Solution

The derivative of f is $f'(x) = \cos x$. So, the equation of the tangent line to the graph of f at the point $(0, 1)$ is

$$y = f(0) + f'(0)(x - 0)$$

$$y = 1 + (1)(x - 0)$$

$$y = 1 + x. \qquad \text{Tangent line approximation}$$

The table compares the values of y given by this linear approximation with the values of $f(x)$ near $x = 0$. Notice that the closer x is to 0, the better the approximation. This conclusion is reinforced by the graph shown in Figure 3.53.

x	-0.5	-0.1	-0.01	0	0.01	0.1	0.5
$f(x) = 1 + \sin x$	0.521	0.9002	0.9900002	1	1.0099998	1.0998	1.479
$y = 1 + x$	0.5	0.9	0.99	1	1.01	1.1	1.5

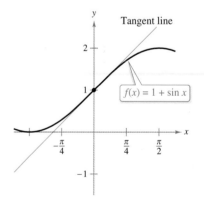

The tangent line approximation of f at the point $(0, 1)$.

Figure 3.53

▶ **Remark**   Be sure you see that this linear approximation of $f(x) = 1 + \sin x$ depends on the point of tangency. At a different point on the graph of f, you would obtain a different tangent line approximation.

Differentials

When the tangent line to the graph of f at the point $(c, f(c))$

$$y = f(c) + f'(c)(x - c)$$ Tangent line at $(c, f(c))$

is used as an approximation of the graph of f, the quantity $x - c$ is called the change in x, and is denoted by Δx, as shown in Figure 3.54. When Δx is small, the change in y (denoted by Δy) can be approximated as shown.

$$\Delta y = f(c + \Delta x) - f(c)$$ Actual change in y

$$\approx f'(c)\Delta x$$ Approximate change in y

For such an approximation, the quantity Δx is traditionally denoted by dx, and is called the **differential of x.** The expression $f'(x)\,dx$ is denoted by dy, and is called the **differential of y.**

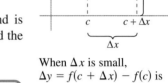

Definition of Differentials

Let $y = f(x)$ represent a function that is differentiable on an open interval containing x. The **differential of x** (denoted by dx) is any nonzero real number. The **differential of y** (denoted by dy) is

$$dy = f'(x)\,dx.$$

When Δx is small, $\Delta y = f(c + \Delta x) - f(c)$ is approximated by $f'(c)\Delta x$.

Figure 3.54

In many types of applications, the differential of y can be used as an approximation of the change in y. That is,

$$\Delta y \approx dy \quad\quad \text{or} \quad\quad \Delta y \approx f'(x)\,dx.$$

EXAMPLE 2   Comparing Δy and dy

Let $y = x^2$. Find dy when $x = 1$ and $dx = 0.01$. Compare this value with Δy for $x = 1$ and $\Delta x = 0.01$.

Solution

Because $y = f(x) = x^2$, you have $f'(x) = 2x$, and the differential dy is

$$dy = f'(x)\,dx = f'(1)(0.01) = 2(0.01) = 0.02.$$ Differential of y

Now, using $\Delta x = 0.01$, the change in y is

$$\Delta y = f(x + \Delta x) - f(x) = f(1.01) - f(1) = (1.01)^2 - 1^2 = 0.0201.$$

Figure 3.55 shows the geometric comparison of dy and Δy. Try comparing other values of dy and Δy. You will see that the values become closer to each other as dx (or Δx) approaches 0.

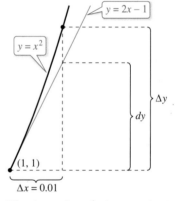

The change in y, Δy is approximated by the differential of y, dy.

Figure 3.55

In Example 2, the tangent line to the graph of $f(x) = x^2$ at $x = 1$ is

$$y = 2x - 1.$$ Tangent line to the graph of f at $x = 1$

For x-values near 1, this line is close to the graph of f, as shown in Figure 3.55 and in the table.

x	0.5	0.9	0.99	1	1.01	1.1	1.5
$f(x) = x^2$	0.25	0.81	0.9801	1	1.0201	1.21	2.25
$y = 2x - 1$	0	0.8	0.98	1	1.02	1.2	2

Error Propagation

Physicists and engineers tend to make liberal use of the approximation of Δy by dy. One way this occurs in practice is in the estimation of errors propagated by physical measuring devices. For example, if you let x represent the measured value of a variable and let $x + \Delta x$ represent the exact value, then Δx is the *error in measurement.* Finally, if the measured value x is used to compute another value $f(x)$, then the difference between $f(x + \Delta x)$ and $f(x)$ is the **propagated error.**

$$\underbrace{f(\overbrace{x + \Delta x}^{\text{Measurement error}})}_{\text{Exact value}} - \underbrace{f(x)}_{\text{Measured value}} = \overbrace{\Delta y}^{\text{Propagated error}}$$

EXAMPLE 3   Estimation of Error

The measured radius of a ball bearing is 0.7 inch, as shown in the figure. The measurement is correct to within 0.01 inch. Estimate the propagated error in the volume V of the ball bearing.

Solution

The formula for the volume of a sphere is

$$V = \frac{4}{3}\pi r^3$$

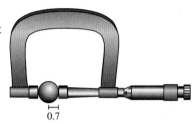

0.7

Ball bearing with measured radius that is correct to within 0.01 inch.

where r is the radius of the sphere. So, you can write

$$r = 0.7 \qquad \text{Measured radius}$$

and

$$-0.01 \le \Delta r \le 0.01. \qquad \text{Possible error}$$

To approximate the propagated error in the volume, differentiate V to obtain $dV/dr = 4\pi r^2$ and write

$$\begin{aligned}
\Delta V &\approx dV && \text{Approximate } \Delta V \text{ by } dV. \\
&= 4\pi r^2 \, dr \\
&\approx 4\pi (0.7)^2 (\pm 0.01) && \text{Substitute for } r \text{ and } dr. \\
&\approx \pm 0.06158 \text{ cubic inch.}
\end{aligned}$$

So, the volume has a propagated error of about 0.06 cubic inch.   ■

Would you say that the propagated error in Example 3 is large or small? The answer is best given in *relative* terms by comparing dV with V. The ratio

$$\begin{aligned}
\frac{dV}{V} &= \frac{4\pi r^2 \, dr}{\frac{4}{3}\pi r^3} && \text{Ratio of } dV \text{ to } V \\
&= \frac{3 \, dr}{r} && \text{Simplify.} \\
&\approx \frac{3(\pm 0.01)}{0.7} && \text{Substitute for } dr \text{ and } r. \\
&\approx \pm 0.0429
\end{aligned}$$

is called the **relative error.** The corresponding **percent error** is approximately 4.29%.

Calculating Differentials

Each of the differentiation rules that you studied in Chapter 2 can be written in **differential form.** For example, let u and v be differentiable functions of x. By the definition of differentials, you have

$$du = u' \, dx$$

and

$$dv = v' \, dx.$$

So, you can write the differential form of the Product Rule as shown below.

$$d[uv] = \frac{d}{dx}[uv] \, dx \qquad \text{Differential of } uv$$

$$= [uv' + vu'] \, dx \qquad \text{Product Rule}$$

$$= uv' \, dx + vu' \, dx$$

$$= u \, dv + v \, du$$

Differential Formulas

Let u and v be differentiable functions of x.

Constant multiple: $d[cu] = c \, du$

Sum or difference: $d[u \pm v] = du \pm dv$

Product: $d[uv] = u \, dv + v \, du$

Quotient: $d\left[\dfrac{u}{v}\right] = \dfrac{v \, du - u \, dv}{v^2}$

EXAMPLE 4   Finding Differentials

Function	Derivative	Differential
a. $y = x^2$	$\dfrac{dy}{dx} = 2x$	$dy = 2x \, dx$
b. $y = \sqrt{x}$	$\dfrac{dy}{dx} = \dfrac{1}{2\sqrt{x}}$	$dy = \dfrac{dx}{2\sqrt{x}}$
c. $y = 2 \sin x$	$\dfrac{dy}{dx} = 2 \cos x$	$dy = 2 \cos x \, dx$
d. $y = xe^x$	$\dfrac{dy}{dx} = e^x(x + 1)$	$dy = e^x(x + 1) \, dx$
e. $y = \dfrac{1}{x}$	$\dfrac{dy}{dx} = -\dfrac{1}{x^2}$	$dy = -\dfrac{dx}{x^2}$

The notation in Example 4 is called the **Leibniz notation** for derivatives and differentials, named after the German mathematician Gottfried Wilhelm Leibniz (1646–1716). The beauty of this notation is that it provides an easy way to remember several important calculus formulas by making it seem as though the formulas were derived from algebraic manipulations of differentials. For instance, in Leibniz notation, the *Chain Rule*

$$\frac{dy}{dx} = \frac{dy}{du} \frac{du}{dx}$$

would appear to be true because the du's divide out. Even though this reasoning is *incorrect,* the notation does help one remember the Chain Rule.

EXAMPLE 5   **Finding the Differential of a Composite Function**

$$y = f(x) = \sin 3x \qquad \text{Original function}$$

$$f'(x) = 3 \cos 3x \qquad \text{Apply Chain Rule.}$$

$$dy = f'(x)\, dx = 3 \cos 3x\, dx \qquad \text{Differential form}$$

EXAMPLE 6   **Finding the Differential of a Composite Function**

$$y = f(x) = (x^2 + 1)^{1/2} \qquad \text{Original function}$$

$$f'(x) = \frac{1}{2}(x^2 + 1)^{-1/2}(2x) = \frac{x}{\sqrt{x^2 + 1}} \qquad \text{Apply Chain Rule.}$$

$$dy = f'(x)\, dx = \frac{x}{\sqrt{x^2 + 1}}\, dx \qquad \text{Differential form}$$

Differentials can be used to approximate function values. To do this for the function given by $y = f(x)$, use the formula

$$f(x + \Delta x) \approx f(x) + dy = f(x) + f'(x)\, dx$$

which is derived from the approximation

$$\Delta y = f(x + \Delta x) - f(x) \approx dy.$$

The key to using this formula is to choose a value for x that makes the calculations easier, as shown in Example 7.

> **Connecting Representations**
>
> This formula is equivalent to the tangent line approximation given earlier in this section.

EXAMPLE 7   **Approximating Function Values**

Use differentials to approximate $\sqrt{16.5}$.

Solution

Using $f(x) = \sqrt{x}$, you can write

$$f(x + \Delta x) \approx f(x) + f'(x)\, dx = \sqrt{x} + \frac{1}{2\sqrt{x}}\, dx.$$

Now, choosing $x = 16$ and $dx = 0.5$, you obtain the following approximation.

$$f(x + \Delta x) = \sqrt{16.5} \approx \sqrt{16} + \frac{1}{2\sqrt{16}}(0.5) = 4 + \left(\frac{1}{8}\right)\left(\frac{1}{2}\right) = 4.0625$$

So, $\sqrt{16.5} \approx 4.0625$.

The tangent line approximation to $f(x) = \sqrt{x}$ at $x = 16$ is the line $g(x) = \frac{1}{8}x + 2$. For x-values near 16, the graphs of f and g are close together, as shown in Figure 3.56. For instance,

$$f(16.5) = \sqrt{16.5} \approx 4.0620$$

and

$$g(16.5) = \frac{1}{8}(16.5) + 2 = 4.0625.$$

In fact, if you use a graphing utility to zoom in near the point of tangency $(16, 4)$, you will see that the two graphs appear to coincide. Notice also that as you move farther away from the point of tangency, the linear approximation becomes less accurate.

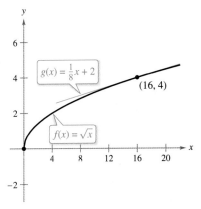

Figure 3.56

3.7 Exercises

See *CalcChat.com* for tutorial help and worked-out solutions to odd-numbered exercises.

Using a Tangent Line Approximation In Exercises 1–8, find the tangent line approximation T to the graph of f at the given point. Use this linear approximation to complete the table.

x	1.9	1.99	2	2.01	2.1
$f(x)$					
$T(x)$					

1. $f(x) = x^2$, $(2, 4)$ **2.** $f(x) = \dfrac{6}{x^2}$, $\left(2, \dfrac{3}{2}\right)$

3. $f(x) = x^5$, $(2, 32)$ **4.** $f(x) = \sqrt{x}$, $(2, \sqrt{2})$

5. $f(x) = \sin x$, $(2, \sin 2)$

6. $f(x) = \csc x$, $(2, \csc 2)$

7. $f(x) = 3^x$, $(2, 9)$ **8.** $f(x) = \log_2 x$, $(2, 1)$

Verifying a Tangent Line Approximation In Exercises 9 and 10, verify the tangent line approximation of the function at the given point. Then use a graphing utility to graph the function and its approximation in the same viewing window.

Function	Approximation	Point
9. $f(x) = \sqrt{x + 4}$	$y = 2 + \dfrac{x}{4}$	$(0, 2)$
10. $f(x) = \tan x$	$y = x$	$(0, 0)$

Comparing Δy and dy In Exercises 11–14, use the information to evaluate and compare Δy and dy.

Function	x-Value	Differential of x
11. $y = 0.5x^3$	$x = 1$	$\Delta x = dx = 0.1$
12. $y = 6 - 2x^2$	$x = -2$	$\Delta x = dx = 0.1$
13. $y = x - 2x^3$	$x = 3$	$\Delta x = dx = 0.001$
14. $y = 7x^2 - 5x$	$x = -4$	$\Delta x = dx = 0.001$

Finding a Differential In Exercises 15–28, find the differential dy of the given function.

15. $y = 3x^2 - 4$ **16.** $y = 3x^{2/3}$

17. $y = x \tan x$ **18.** $y = \csc 2x$

19. $y = \dfrac{x + 1}{2x - 1}$ **20.** $y = \sqrt{x} + \dfrac{1}{\sqrt{x}}$

21. $y = \sqrt{9 - x^2}$ **22.** $y = x\sqrt{1 - x^2}$

23. $y = 3x - \sin^2 x$ **24.** $y = x \cos x$

25. $y = \ln\sqrt{4 - x^2}$ **26.** $y = e^{-0.5x} \cos 4x$

27. $y = x \arcsin x$ **28.** $y = \arctan(x - 2)$

Using Differentials In Exercises 29 and 30, use differentials and the graph of f to approximate (a) $f(1.9)$ and (b) $f(2.04)$. To print an enlarged copy of the graph, go to *MathGraphs.com*.

29.
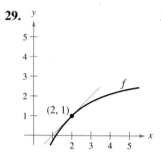

30.
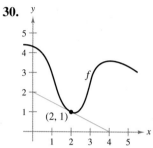

Error Analysis In Exercises 31 and 32, describe and correct the error in finding the differential dy of the given function.

31. $y = \sqrt{x^2 - 4}$

$$dy = \frac{1}{2}(x^2 - 4)^{-1/2}(2x) = \frac{x}{\sqrt{x^2 - 4}} \quad ✗$$

32. $y = 4x^3$

$$dy = (4x^3)(12x^2)dx \quad ✗$$

Using Differentials In Exercises 33 and 34, use differentials and the graph of g' to approximate (a) $g(2.93)$ and (b) $g(3.1)$ given that $g(3) = 8$.

33.
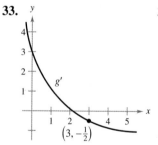

34.
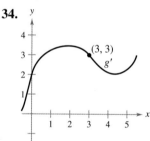

35. Area The measurement of the side of a square floor tile is 10 inches, with a possible error of $\frac{1}{32}$ inch.

(a) Use differentials to approximate the possible propagated error in computing the area of the square.

(b) Approximate the percent error in computing the area of the square.

36. Circumference The measurement of the circumference of a circle is found to be 64 centimeters, with a possible error of 0.9 centimeter.

(a) Approximate the percent error in computing the area of the circle.

(b) Estimate the maximum allowable percent error in measuring the circumference if the error in computing the area cannot exceed 3%.

37. Volume and Surface Area   The measurement of the edge of a cube is found to be 15 inches, with a possible error of 0.03 inch.

(a) Use differentials to approximate the possible propagated error in computing the volume of the cube.

(b) Use differentials to approximate the possible propagated error in computing the surface area of the cube.

(c) Approximate the percent errors in parts (a) and (b).

38. Volume and Surface Area   The radius of a spherical balloon is measured as 8 inches, with a possible error of 0.02 inch.

(a) Approximate the possible propagated error in computing the volume of the sphere.

(b) Approximate the possible propagated error in computing the surface area of the sphere.

(c) Approximate the percent errors in parts (a) and (b).

39. Stopping Distance   The total stopping distance T of a vehicle is $T = 2x + 0.05x^2$, where T is in feet and x is the speed in miles per hour. Approximate the change and percent change in total stopping distance as speed changes from $x = 25$ to $x = 26$ miles per hour.

40.   HOW DO YOU SEE IT?   The graph shows the profit P (in dollars) from selling x units of an item. Use the graph to determine which is greater, the change in profit when the production level changes from 400 to 401 units or the change in profit when the production level changes from 900 to 901 units. Explain your reasoning.

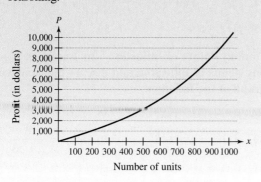

Number of units

41. Relative Humidity   When the dew point is 65° Fahrenheit, the relative humidity H (in percent) is modeled by

$$H = \frac{4347}{400,000,000} e^{369,444/(50t + 19,793)}$$

where t is the air temperature in degrees Fahrenheit. Use differentials to approximate the change in relative humidity at $t = 72$ for a 1-degree change in the air temperature.

42. Surveying   A surveyor standing 50 feet from the base of a large tree measures the angle of elevation to the top of the tree as 71.5°. How accurately must the angle be measured for the percent error in estimating the height of the tree to be less than 6%?

   Approximating Function Values   **In Exercises 43–46, use differentials to approximate the value of the expression. Compare your answer with that of a calculator.**

43. $\sqrt{99.4}$ **44.** $\sqrt[3]{26}$

45. $\sqrt[4]{624}$ **46.** $(3.02)^3$

EXPLORING CONCEPTS

47. Comparing Δy and dy   Describe the change in accuracy of dy as an approximation for Δy when Δx approaches 0. Use a graph to support your answer.

48. Reasoning   For what value(s) of a would you use $y = x$ to approximate $f(x) = \sin x$ near $x = a$?

True or False?   **In Exercises 49–51, determine whether the statement is true or false. If it is false, explain why or give an example that shows it is false.**

49. If $y = ax + b$, then $\Delta y / \Delta x = dy/dx$.

50. If y is differentiable, then $\lim_{\Delta x \to 0} (\Delta y - dy) = 0$.

51. If $y = f(x)$, f is increasing and differentiable, and $\Delta x > 0$, then $\Delta y \geq dy$.

Calculus AP® – Exam Preparation Questions

52. Multiple Choice   If $y = x^2 \ln x$, then $dy =$

(A) $(2x \ln x + x) \, dx$.   (B) $(2x \ln x + 1/x) \, dx$.

(C) $(2x \ln x) \, dx$.   (D) $(2 \ln x + x) \, dx$.

53. Multiple Choice   The function f is twice differentiable with $f(3) = 8$, $f'(3) = 22$, and $f''(3) = 18$. What is the value of the approximation of $f(2.9)$ using the line tangent to the graph of f at $x = 3$?

(A) 5.5   (B) 5.8   (C) 5.9   (D) 6.1

54. Multiple Choice   Using the tangent line approximation of $f(x) = \cos^{-1} x$ at the point $(1/2, \pi/3)$, what is the value of $\cos^{-1}(0.52)$?

(A) 0.501   (B) 1.012   (C) 1.024   (D) 1.029

55. Free Response   The profit P for a company is $P = 100xe^{-x/400}$, where x is the number of units sold.

(a) Find P'.

(b) How many units produce a maximum profit P?

(c) Approximate the change and percent change in profit as sales increase from $x = 120$ to $x = 130$ units.

3   Review Exercises

See *CalcChat.com* for tutorial help and worked-out solutions to odd-numbered exercises.

Finding Extrema on a Closed Interval   In Exercises 1–8, find the absolute extrema of the function on the closed interval. Use a graphing utility to verify your results.

1. $f(x) = x^2 + 5x$, $[-4, 0]$

2. $f(x) = x^3 + 6x^2$, $[-6, 1]$

3. $f(x) = \sqrt{x} - 2$, $[0, 4]$

4. $h(x) = 3x - x^{3/2}$, $[0, 9]$

5. $f(x) = \dfrac{4x}{x^2 + 9}$, $[-4, 4]$

6. $f(x) = \dfrac{x}{\sqrt{x^2 + 1}}$, $[0, 2]$

7. $g(x) = 2x + 5\cos x$, $[0, 2\pi]$

8. $f(x) = \sin 2x$, $[0, 2\pi]$

Illustrating Rolle's Theorem   In Exercises 9–12, determine whether Rolle's Theorem can be applied to f on the closed interval $[a, b]$. If Rolle's Theorem can be applied, find all values of c in the open interval (a, b) such that $f'(c) = 0$. If Rolle's Theorem cannot be applied, explain why not.

9. $f(x) = 2x^2 - 7$, $[0, 4]$

10. $f(x) = (x - 2)(x + 3)^2$, $[-3, 2]$

11. $f(x) = \sin 2x$, $[-\pi, \pi]$

12. $f(x) = \dfrac{x^2}{1 - x^2}$, $[-2, 2]$

Using the Mean Value Theorem   In Exercises 13–18, determine whether the Mean Value Theorem can be applied to f on the closed interval $[a, b]$. If the Mean Value Theorem can be applied, find all values of c in the open interval (a, b) such that

$$f'(c) = \frac{f(b) - f(a)}{b - a}.$$

If the Mean Value Theorem cannot be applied, explain why not.

13. $f(x) = x^{2/3}$, $[1, 8]$ 14. $f(x) = \dfrac{1}{x}$, $[1, 4]$

15. $f(x) = |5 - x|$, $[2, 6]$

16. $f(x) = 2x - 3\sqrt{x}$, $[-1, 1]$

17. $f(x) = x - \cos x$, $\left[-\dfrac{\pi}{2}, \dfrac{\pi}{2}\right]$

18. $f(x) = x\log_2 x$, $[1, 2]$

19. **Mean Value Theorem**   Can the Mean Value Theorem be applied to the function

$$f(x) = \frac{1}{x^2}$$

on the interval $[-2, 1]$? Explain.

20. **Mean Value Theorem**

   (a) For the function $f(x) = Ax^2 + Bx + C$, determine the value of c guaranteed by the Mean Value Theorem on the interval $[x_1, x_2]$.

   (b) Demonstrate the result of part (a) for $f(x) = 2x^2 - 3x + 1$ on the interval $[0, 4]$.

Intervals on Which a Function Is Increasing or Decreasing   In Exercises 21–28, find the open intervals on which the function is increasing or decreasing.

21. $f(x) = x^2 + 3x - 12$ 22. $g(x) = (x + 1)^3$

23. $h(x) = \sqrt{x}(x - 3)$, $x > 0$

24. $h(x) = (x + 2)^{1/3} + 8$

25. $g(x) = \tan^2 x$, $[0, 2\pi]$

26. $f(x) = \sin x + \cos x$, $[0, 2\pi]$

27. $f(t) = (2 - t)2^t$ 28. $g(x) = 2x \ln x$

Applying the First Derivative Test   In Exercises 29–36, (a) find the critical numbers of the function (if any), (b) find the open interval(s) on which the function is increasing or decreasing, and (c) apply the First Derivative Test to find all relative extrema. Use a graphing utility to confirm your results.

29. $f(x) = x^3 - 5x^2$ 30. $f(x) = -x^4 + 2x^3 + 3$

31. $f(x) = \dfrac{x + 4}{x^2}$ 32. $f(x) = \dfrac{x^2 - 3x - 4}{x - 2}$

33. $f(x) = \cos x - \sin x$, $(0, 2\pi)$

34. $g(x) = \dfrac{3}{2}\sin\left(\dfrac{\pi x}{2} - 1\right)$, $[0, 4]$

35. $f(x) = x^2 e^x$ 36. $f(x) = \sqrt{x} - \log_{10} x$

Finding Points of Inflection   In Exercises 37–42, find any points of inflection and discuss the concavity of the graph of the function.

37. $f(x) = x^3 - 9x^2$ 38. $f(x) = 6x^4 - x^2$

39. $g(x) = x\sqrt{x + 5}$ 40. $h(x) = \dfrac{1}{1 + x^3}$

41. $f(x) = x + \cos x$, $[0, 2\pi]$

42. $f(x) = \tan\dfrac{x}{4}$, $(0, 2\pi)$

Using the Second Derivative Test   In Exercises 43–48, find any relative extrema. Use the Second Derivative Test where applicable.

43. $f(x) = (x + 9)^2$ 44. $h(t) = t - 4\sqrt{t + 1}$

45. $f(x) = 2x^3 + 11x^2 - 8x - 12$

46. $f(x) = 2x + \dfrac{18}{x}$ 47. $f(t) = \dfrac{t}{\ln t}$

48. $h(x) = x - 2\cos x$, $[0, 4\pi]$

Think About It In Exercises 49 and 50, sketch the graph of a function f having the given characteristics.

49. $f(0) = f(6) = 0$

$f'(3) = f'(5) = 0$

$f'(x) > 0$ for $x < 3$

$f'(x) > 0$ for $3 < x < 5$

$f'(x) < 0$ for $x > 5$

$f''(x) < 0$ for $x < 3$

or $x > 4$

$f''(x) > 0$ for $3 < x < 4$

50. $f(0) = 4$, $f(6) = 0$

$f'(x) < 0$ for $x < 2$

or $x > 4$

$f'(2)$ does not exist.

$f'(4) = 0$

$f'(x) > 0$ for

$2 < x < 4$

$f''(x) < 0$ for $x \neq 2$

51. Specific Gravity A model for the specific gravity of water S is

$$S = \frac{5.755}{10^8}T^3 - \frac{8.521}{10^6}T^2 + \frac{6.540}{10^5}T + 0.99987,$$

$$0 < T < 25$$

where T is the water temperature in degrees Celsius.

(a) Use the second derivative to determine the concavity of S.

(b) Use a graphing utility to graph the function over the specified domain. (Use a setting in which $0.996 \leq S \leq 1.001$.)

(c) Estimate the maximum value of the function.

52. Graphical Reasoning Use the graph of f' to sketch a graph of f and the graph of f''.

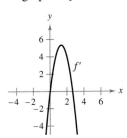

Graphing a Function In Exercises 53–62, analyze and sketch a graph of the function. Label any intercepts, relative extrema, points of inflection, and asymptotes. Use a graphing utility to verify your results.

53. $f(x) = 4x - x^2$

54. $f(x) = 4x^3 - x^4$

55. $f(x) = \dfrac{5 - 3x}{x - 2}$

56. $f(x) = \dfrac{2x}{1 + x^2}$

57. $f(x) = x^3 + x + \dfrac{4}{x}$

58. $f(x) = x^2 + \dfrac{1}{x}$

59. $f(x) = x\sqrt{16 - x^2}$

60. $f(x) = x^{1/3}(x + 3)^{2/3}$

61. $y = \dfrac{4}{1 + 4e^{-x}}$

62. $y = \dfrac{1}{2}x + \sin x$, $[0, 2\pi]$

63. Maximum Area A rancher has 400 feet of fencing with which to enclose two adjacent rectangular corrals (see figure). What dimensions should be used so that the enclosed area will be a maximum?

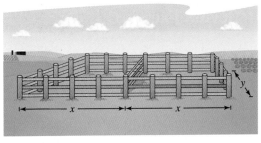

Figure for 63

64. Maximum Area Find the dimensions of the rectangle of maximum area, with sides parallel to the coordinate axes, that can be inscribed in the ellipse given by

$$\frac{x^2}{144} + \frac{y^2}{16} = 1.$$

65. Minimum Length The wall of a building is to be braced by a beam that must pass over a parallel fence 5 feet high and 4 feet from the building. Find the length of the shortest beam that can be used.

66. Maximum Length A hallway of width 6 feet meets a hallway of width 9 feet at right angles. Find the length of the longest pipe that can be carried level around this corner in two ways. (*Hint:* Write a primary function L for the length of a line passing through the inside corner of the hallway from one outer wall to the other, and find the *minimum* of L.)

(a) Minimize $L(x)$, where x is the distance between the outer corner of the hallway and where the pipe touches one wall.

(b) Minimize $L(\theta)$, where θ is the angle between the pipe and the wall of the narrower highway.

67. Maximum Volume Find the volume of the largest right circular cone that can be inscribed in a sphere of radius r.

68. Maximum Volume Find the volume of the largest right circular cylinder that can be inscribed in a sphere of radius r.

Comparing Δy and dy In Exercises 69 and 70, use the information to evaluate and compare Δy and dy.

Function	x-Value	Differential of x
69. $y = 0.5x^2$	$x = 3$	$\Delta x = dx = 0.01$
70. $y = x^3 - 6x$	$x = 2$	$\Delta x = dx = 0.1$

Finding a Differential In Exercises 71 and 72, find the differential dy of the given function.

71. $y = x(1 - \cos x)$

72. $y = \sqrt{x^3 - 1}$

73. Volume and Surface Area The radius of a sphere is measured as 9 centimeters, with a possible error of 0.025 centimeter. Use differentials to approximate the possible propagated error in computing (a) the volume and (b) the surface area of the sphere.

AP® Exam Practice Questions

See *LarsonCalculusforAP.com* for worked-out solutions to these questions.

What You Need to Know

- On some free-response questions, there may be more than one way of applying derivatives and theorems to justify your answer.

- Be prepared to apply the Mean Value Theorem. It may be referred to directly, or it may be necessary to use the theorem to justify your answer.

- Questions that involve position, velocity, and acceleration functions are very common on the AP® Exam.

- Be prepared to apply the Second Derivative Test to justify whether a point is a local maximum or a local minimum. Be prepared also to use the second derivative to identify a point of inflection.

- Tangent line approximations, and whether such an approximation overestimates or underestimates a function value, is commonly tested on the free-response section.

Practice Questions

Section 1, Part A, Multiple Choice, No Technology

1. What are the critical numbers of

    $f(x) = 4x^3 + 6x^2 - 72x - 9$?

    (A) $x = -2$ and $x = 3$

    (B) $x = -3$ and $x = 2$

    (C) $x = -2$

    (D) $x = -3$

2. The graph of the function f is shown. Which of the following is true?

    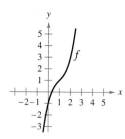

    I. $f'(x) > 0$ on the entire real number line.

    II. $f''(x) < 0$ on the interval $(-\infty, 1)$.

    III. $f''(x) > 0$ on the interval $(1, \infty)$.

    (A) I only   (B) II and III only

    (C) I and III only   (D) I, II, and III

3. The position of an object along a vertical line is given by $s(t) = -t^3 + 3t^2 + 9t + 5$, where s is measured in feet and t is measured in seconds. The maximum velocity of the object in the time interval $[0, 4]$ is

    (A) 9 feet per second.

    (B) 12 feet per second.

    (C) 16 feet per second.

    (D) 32 feet per second.

4. The function g is differentiable on the interval $[2, 6]$. The table shows selected values of g on $[2, 6]$. Which of the following statements must be true?

x	2	3	4	5	6
$g(x)$	7	4	1	4	7

    (A) The minimum value of g on $[2, 6]$ is 1.

    (B) The maximum value of g on $[2, 6]$ is 7.

    (C) There exists a number c, with $2 < c < 6$, for which $g'(c) = 0$.

    (D) $g'(x) < 0$ for $2 < x < 4$.

5. Consider the graph of $y = f(x)$ shown below. If f is a function such that f' and f'' are defined in a region around $x = 2$, then which of the following must be true?

    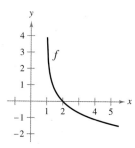

    (A) $f''(2) < f(2)$ (B) $f''(2) < f'(2)$

    (C) $f(2) = f'(2)$ (D) $f''(2) > f(2)$

6. If $y = \arctan 4x$, then $dy =$

    (A) $\dfrac{4}{1 + 16x^2}\, dx.$ (B) $\dfrac{4x}{1 + 16x^2}\, dx.$

    (C) $-\dfrac{4x}{1 + 16x^2}\, dx.$ (D) $-\dfrac{4}{1 + 16x^2}\, dx.$

7. If the Mean Value Theorem is applied to the function $f(x) = \ln(x - 3)$ on the interval $[4, 8]$, then what number c must exist in $(4, 8)$?

(A) 5.485

(B) 5.885

(C) 6

(D) 6.368

Section 2, Part A, Free Response, Technology Permitted

8. Consider the function $f(x) = \frac{1}{2}x^3 - \sin x + 1$.

(a) Approximate the relative extrema of f.

(b) Find the tangent line approximation of f at $x = \pi/2$.

(c) Use your tangent line approximation to approximate the value of $f(1.5)$. Is your approximation an underestimate or an overestimate of the actual value of $f(1.5)$? Justify your answer.

Section 2, Part B, Free Response, No Technology

9. The table shows the behavior of a function f that is continuous on the entire real number line, with $f(2) = 4$ and $\lim_{x \to \infty} f(x) = 0$.

	$x < 4$	$x = 4$	$x > 4$
$f'(x)$	$f'(x) > 0$	Undefined	$f'(x) < 0$
$f''(x)$	$f''(x) < 0$	Undefined	$f''(x) > 0$

(a) For what values of x is f increasing? Justify your answer.

(b) Does f have a relative maximum at $x = 4$? Explain.

(c) If possible, find the x-coordinate of each inflection point of the graph of f. Justify your answer.

(d) Does the Mean Value Theorem apply over the interval $[3, 5]$? Justify your answer.

(e) Sketch a possible graph of f.

10. Consider the function

$$f(x) = 2x + \cos 2x$$

on the interval $[0, \pi]$.

(a) Find the maximum value of f. Justify your answer.

(b) Explain how the conditions of the Mean Value Theorem are satisfied by f for $0 \le x \le \pi$. Find the value of x whose existence is guaranteed by the Mean Value Theorem.

11.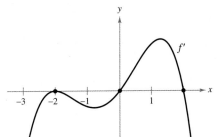

The figure above shows the graph of f', the derivative of f. The function f is a twice differentiable function on the entire real number line, with $f''(-0.8) = 0$ and $f''(1.3) = 0$.

(a) For what values of x is f increasing?

(b) For what values of x is the graph of f concave downward? Justify your answer.

(c) Is

$$\frac{f(-0.5) - f(0)}{-0.5 - 0}$$

positive or negative? Justify your answer.

12. Consider the function

$$f(x) = \frac{1 - 4x^2}{x}.$$

(a) For what values of x is f decreasing?

(b) For what values of x is the graph of f concave downward? Justify your answer.

(c) Does the graph of f have any points of inflection? Justify your answer.

13.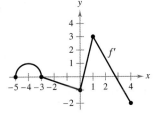

The figure above shows the graph of f', the derivative of f, on the interval $[-5, 4]$. The function f is differentiable on the interval and $f''(-4) = 0$.

(a) Find $f'(-1)$ and $f''(-1)$.

(b) Identify each x-value at which a relative extremum of f occurs in the interval $(-5, 0)$. Justify your answer.

(c) Find the x-coordinate of each inflection point of the graph of f. Justify your answer.

(d) Given $g(x) = f(x) + \sin^2 x$, is g increasing or decreasing at $x = -\pi/4$? Justify your answer.

3 Performance Task

Maximum and Minimum Temperature

In a 24-hour period, a human's body temperature will vary about 3 degrees. When at rest (usually at night), the body conserves heat and the body temperature drops. During activity (usually in the daytime), the body produces heat and the body temperature rises. This situation can be modeled by the periodic function

$$T(x) = 1.8 \sin^3\left(\frac{\pi}{12}x - \frac{\pi}{2}\right) + 98.6$$

where T represents the body's temperature (in degrees Fahrenheit) and x represents the time (in hours), with $x = 0$ corresponding to 12 A.M.

Exercises

1. **Finding the Derivative**   What is the derivative of T? Are T and T' continuous functions?

2. **Applying Rolle's Theorem**   Does Rolle's Theorem apply on the interval $[0, 12]$? Does it apply on the interval $[0, 24]$? Explain your reasoning.

3. **Analyzing the Derivative**   Find all values of c in the interval $(0, 24)$ such that $T'(c) = 0$.

4. **Using the Mean Value Theorem**   Explain why there must exist a time from midnight to noon when the body temperature is increasing at a rate of 0.3°F per hour.

5. **Finding Critical Numbers**   Find the critical numbers of T on the interval $[0, 24]$.

6. **Finding Extrema**   During the course of a 24-hour period, at what time(s) is a human's body temperature the greatest? At what time(s) is a human's body temperature the least?

7. **Finding Points of Inflection**   Use a graphing utility to determine the points of inflection of the graph of T and discuss its concavity. Choose one of the inflection points you found and interpret its meaning in the context of the problem.

In Exercises 8–10, use the graph, which shows the function g that models the body temperature of a person who works third shift, meaning that the person rests during the day and is active at night.

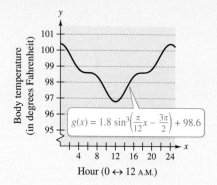

$$g(x) = 1.8 \sin^3\left(\frac{\pi}{12}x - \frac{3\pi}{2}\right) + 98.6$$

Hour (0 ↔ 12 A.M.)

8. **Finding Critical Numbers**   Does g have the same critical numbers as T on the interval $[0, 24]$? Explain.

9. **Finding Extrema**   During the course of a 24-hour period, at what time(s) is this person's body temperature the greatest? At what time(s) is it the least?

10. **Determining Concavity**   Discuss the concavity of the graph of g.

4 Integration

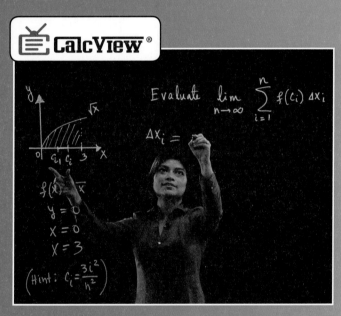

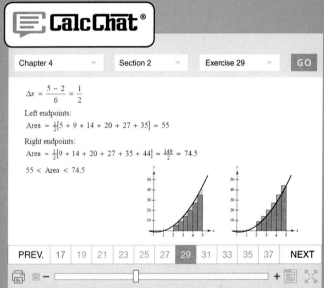

4.1 Grand Canyon *(Exercise 60, p. 288)*

4.4 The Speed of Sound *(Example 5, p. 322)*

4.1   Antiderivatives and Indefinite Integration

▶ Write the general solution of a differential equation and use indefinite integral notation for antiderivatives.
▶ Use basic integration rules to find antiderivatives.
▶ Find a particular solution of a differential equation.

Antiderivatives

To find a function F whose derivative is $f(x) = 3x^2$, you might use your knowledge of derivatives to conclude that

$$F(x) = x^3 \quad \text{because} \quad \frac{d}{dx}[x^3] = 3x^2.$$

The function F is an *antiderivative* of f.

Definition of Antiderivative

A function F is an **antiderivative** of f on an interval I when $F'(x) = f(x)$ for all x in I.

Note that F is called *an* antiderivative of f rather than *the* antiderivative of f. To see why, observe that

$$F_1(x) = x^3, \quad F_2(x) = x^3 - 5, \quad \text{and} \quad F_3(x) = x^3 + 97$$

are all antiderivatives of $f(x) = 3x^2$. In fact, for any constant C, the function $F(x) = x^3 + C$ is an antiderivative of f.

Theorem 4.1   Representation of Antiderivatives

If F is an antiderivative of f on an interval I, then G is an antiderivative of f on the interval I if and only if G is of the form $G(x) = F(x) + C$ for all x in I where C is a constant.

Proof   The proof of Theorem 4.1 in one direction is straightforward. That is, if $G(x) = F(x) + C$, $F'(x) = f(x)$, and C is a constant, then

$$G'(x) = \frac{d}{dx}[F(x) + C]$$

$$= F'(x) + 0$$

$$= f(x).$$

To prove this theorem in the other direction, assume that G is an antiderivative of f. Define a function H such that

$$H(x) = G(x) - F(x).$$

For any two points a and b $(a < b)$ in the interval, H is continuous on $[a, b]$ and differentiable on (a, b). By the Mean Value Theorem,

$$H'(c) = \frac{H(b) - H(a)}{b - a}$$

for some c in (a, b). However, $H'(c) = 0$, so $H(a) = H(b)$. Because a and b are arbitrary points in the interval, you know that H is a constant function C. So, $G(x) - F(x) = C$ and it follows that $G(x) = F(x) + C$. ∎

Using Theorem 4.1, you can represent the entire family of antiderivatives of a function by adding a constant to a *known* antiderivative. For example, knowing that

$$D_x[x^2] = 2x$$

you can represent the family of *all* antiderivatives of $f(x) = 2x$ by

$$G(x) = x^2 + C \qquad \text{Family of all antiderivatives of } f(x) = 2x$$

where C is a constant. The constant C is called the **constant of integration.** The family of functions represented by G is the **general antiderivative** of f, and $G(x) = x^2 + C$ is the **general solution** of the *differential equation*

$$G'(x) = 2x. \qquad \text{Differential equation}$$

A **differential equation** in x and y is an equation that involves x, y, and derivatives of y. For instance,

$$y' = 3x \quad \text{and} \quad y' = x^2 + 1$$

are examples of differential equations.

EXAMPLE 1   Solving a Differential Equation

Find the general solution of the differential equation $dy/dx = 2$.

Solution

To begin, you need to find a function whose derivative is 2. One such function is

$$y = 2x. \qquad 2x \text{ is an antiderivative of 2.}$$

Now, you can use Theorem 4.1 to conclude that the general solution of the differential equation is

$$y = 2x + C. \qquad \text{General solution}$$

The graphs of several functions of the form $y = 2x + C$ are shown in Figure 4.1. ■

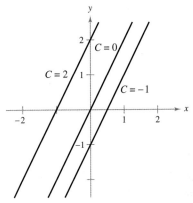

Functions of the form $y = 2x + C$

Figure 4.1

When solving a differential equation of the form

$$\frac{dy}{dx} = f(x)$$

it is convenient to write it in the equivalent differential form

$$dy = f(x)\, dx.$$

The operation of finding all solutions of this equation is called **antidifferentiation** (or **indefinite integration**) and is denoted by an integral sign $\int$. The general solution is denoted by

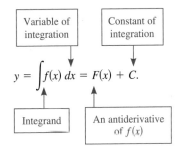

$$y = \int f(x)\, dx = F(x) + C.$$

The expression $\int f(x)\, dx$ is read as the *antiderivative of f with respect to x*. So, the differential dx serves to identify x as the variable of integration. The term **indefinite integral** is a synonym for antiderivative.

Communication and Notation

In this text, the notation $\int f(x)\, dx = F(x) + C$ means that F is an antiderivative of f on an interval.

Basic Integration Rules

The inverse nature of integration and differentiation can be verified by substituting $F'(x)$ for $f(x)$ in the indefinite integration definition to obtain

$$\int F'(x)\, dx = F(x) + C.$$

Integration is the "inverse" of differentiation.

Insight

On the free-response section of the AP® Exam, remember to include the constant of integration C when finding antiderivatives.

Moreover, if $\int f(x)\, dx = F(x) + C$, then

$$\frac{d}{dx}\left[\int f(x)\, dx\right] = f(x).$$

Differentiation is the "inverse" of integration.

Implementing Processes

The Power Rule for Integration has the restriction that $n \neq -1$. To evaluate $\int x^{-1}\, dx$, use the Log Rule for Integration. (See Exercise 70.)

These two equations allow you to obtain integration formulas directly from differentiation formulas, as shown in the following summary.

Basic Integration Rules

Differentiation Formula	*Integration Formula*
$\dfrac{d}{dx}[C] = 0$	$\displaystyle\int 0\, dx = C$
$\dfrac{d}{dx}[kx] = k$	$\displaystyle\int k\, dx = kx + C$
$\dfrac{d}{dx}[kf(x)] = kf'(x)$	$\displaystyle\int kf(x)\, dx = k\int f(x)\, dx$
$\dfrac{d}{dx}[f(x) \pm g(x)] = f'(x) \pm g'(x)$	$\displaystyle\int [f(x) \pm g(x)]\, dx = \int f(x)\, dx \pm \int g(x)\, dx$
$\dfrac{d}{dx}[x^n] = nx^{n-1}$	$\displaystyle\int x^n\, dx = \frac{x^{n+1}}{n+1} + C, \quad n \neq -1$ Power Rule
$\dfrac{d}{dx}[\sin x] = \cos x$	$\displaystyle\int \cos x\, dx = \sin x + C$
$\dfrac{d}{dx}[\cos x] = -\sin x$	$\displaystyle\int \sin x\, dx = -\cos x + C$
$\dfrac{d}{dx}[\tan x] = \sec^2 x$	$\displaystyle\int \sec^2 x\, dx = \tan x + C$
$\dfrac{d}{dx}[\sec x] = \sec x \tan x$	$\displaystyle\int \sec x \tan x\, dx = \sec x + C$
$\dfrac{d}{dx}[\cot x] = -\csc^2 x$	$\displaystyle\int \csc^2 x\, dx = -\cot x + C$
$\dfrac{d}{dx}[\csc x] = -\csc x \cot x$	$\displaystyle\int \csc x \cot x\, dx = -\csc x + C$
$\dfrac{d}{dx}[e^x] = e^x$	$\displaystyle\int e^x\, dx = e^x + C$
$\dfrac{d}{dx}[a^x] = (\ln a)a^x$	$\displaystyle\int a^x\, dx = \left(\frac{1}{\ln a}\right)a^x + C$
$\dfrac{d}{dx}[\ln x] = \dfrac{1}{x},\ x > 0$	$\displaystyle\int \frac{1}{x}\, dx = \ln|x| + C$ Log Rule

EXAMPLE 2 Describing Antiderivatives

$$\int 3x \, dx = 3\int x \, dx \qquad\qquad \text{Constant Multiple Rule}$$

$$= 3\int x^1 \, dx \qquad\qquad \text{Rewrite } x \text{ as } x^1.$$

$$= 3\left(\frac{x^2}{2}\right) + C \qquad \text{Power Rule } (n = 1)$$

$$= \frac{3}{2}x^2 + C \qquad\qquad \text{Simplify.}$$

The antiderivatives of $3x$ are of the form $\frac{3}{2}x^2 + C$, where C is any constant.

When finding indefinite integrals, a strict application of the basic integration rules tends to produce complicated constants of integration. For instance, in Example 2, the solution could have been written as

$$\int 3x \, dx = 3\int x \, dx = 3\left(\frac{x^2}{2} + C\right) = \frac{3}{2}x^2 + 3C.$$

Because C represents *any* constant, it is both cumbersome and unnecessary to write $3C$ as the constant of integration. So, $\frac{3}{2}x^2 + 3C$ is written in the simpler form $\frac{3}{2}x^2 + C$.

> **Implementing Processes**
>
> In Example 2, note that the general pattern of integration is similar to that of differentiation.
>
> Original integral
>
> ↓
>
> Rewrite
>
> ↓
>
> Integrate
>
> ↓
>
> Simplify

EXAMPLE 3 Rewriting Before Integrating

See LarsonCalculusforAP.com for an interactive version of this type of example.

	Original Integral	Rewrite	Integrate	Simplify
a.	$\int \dfrac{1}{x^3} \, dx$	$\int x^{-3} \, dx$	$\dfrac{x^{-2}}{-2} + C$	$-\dfrac{1}{2x^2} + C$
b.	$\int \sqrt{x} \, dx$	$\int x^{1/2} \, dx$	$\dfrac{x^{3/2}}{3/2} + C$	$\dfrac{2}{3}x^{3/2} + C$
c.	$\int 2\sin x \, dx$	$2\int \sin x \, dx$	$2(-\cos x) + C$	$-2\cos x + C$
d.	$\int \dfrac{3}{x} \, dx$	$3\int \dfrac{1}{x} \, dx$	$3(\ln|x|) + C$	$3\ln|x| + C$

> **Justification**
>
> The properties of logarithms presented on page 50 can be used to rewrite antiderivatives in different forms. For instance, the antiderivative in Example 3(d) can be rewritten as
>
> $$3\ln|x| + C = \ln|x|^3 + C.$$

EXAMPLE 4 Integrating Polynomial Functions

a. $\displaystyle\int dx = \int 1 \, dx \qquad\qquad$ Integrand is understood to be 1.

$\qquad = x + C \qquad\qquad\qquad$ Integrate.

b. $\displaystyle\int (x + 2) \, dx = \int x \, dx + \int 2 \, dx$

$\qquad\qquad = \dfrac{x^2}{2} + C_1 + 2x + C_2 \qquad$ Integrate.

$\qquad\qquad - \dfrac{x^2}{2} + 2x + C \qquad\qquad C = C_1 + C_2$

The second line in the solution is usually omitted.

c. $\displaystyle\int (3x^4 - 5x^2 + x) \, dx = 3\left(\dfrac{x^5}{5}\right) - 5\left(\dfrac{x^3}{3}\right) + \dfrac{x^2}{2} + C = \dfrac{3}{5}x^5 - \dfrac{5}{3}x^3 + \dfrac{1}{2}x^2 + C$

> **Remark**
>
> The basic integration rules allow you to integrate any polynomial function.

EXAMPLE 5 Rewriting Before Integrating

$$\int \frac{x+1}{\sqrt{x}}\,dx = \int \left(\frac{x}{\sqrt{x}} + \frac{1}{\sqrt{x}}\right) dx \qquad \text{Rewrite as two fractions.}$$

$$= \int (x^{1/2} + x^{-1/2})\,dx \qquad \text{Rewrite with fractional exponents.}$$

$$= \frac{x^{3/2}}{3/2} + \frac{x^{1/2}}{1/2} + C \qquad \text{Integrate.}$$

$$= \frac{2}{3}x^{3/2} + 2x^{1/2} + C \qquad \text{Simplify.}$$

$$= \frac{2}{3}\sqrt{x}(x+3) + C$$

> **Algebra Review**
>
> For help on the algebra in Example 5, see Example 2(a) in the *Chapter 4 Algebra Review* on page A43.

When integrating quotients, do not integrate the numerator and denominator separately. This is no more valid in integration than it is in differentiation. For instance, in Example 5, be sure you understand that

$$\int \frac{x+1}{\sqrt{x}}\,dx = \frac{2}{3}\sqrt{x}(x+3) + C$$

is not the same as

$$\frac{\int (x+1)\,dx}{\int \sqrt{x}\,dx} = \frac{\frac{1}{2}x^2 + x + C_1}{\frac{2}{3}x\sqrt{x} + C_2}.$$

> **Implementing Processes**
>
> Before you begin the exercise set, be sure you realize that one of the most important steps in integration is *rewriting the integrand* in a form that fits one of the basic integration rules.

EXAMPLE 6 Rewriting Before Integrating

$$\int \frac{\sin x}{\cos^2 x}\,dx = \int \left(\frac{1}{\cos x}\right)\left(\frac{\sin x}{\cos x}\right) dx \qquad \text{Rewrite as a product.}$$

$$= \int \sec x \tan x\,dx \qquad \text{Rewrite using trigonometric identities.}$$

$$= \sec x + C \qquad \text{Integrate.}$$

EXAMPLE 7 Rewriting Before Integrating

	Original Integral	*Rewrite*	*Integrate*	*Simplify*
a.	$\int \dfrac{2}{\sqrt{x}}\,dx$	$2\int x^{-1/2}\,dx$	$2\left(\dfrac{x^{1/2}}{1/2}\right) + C$	$4x^{1/2} + C$
b.	$\int (t^2 + 1)^2\,dt$	$\int (t^4 + 2t^2 + 1)\,dt$	$\dfrac{t^5}{5} + 2\left(\dfrac{t^3}{3}\right) + t + C$	$\dfrac{1}{5}t^5 + \dfrac{2}{3}t^3 + t + C$
c.	$\int \dfrac{x^3 + 3}{x^2}\,dx$	$\int (x + 3x^{-2})\,dx$	$\dfrac{x^2}{2} + 3\left(\dfrac{x^{-1}}{-1}\right) + C$	$\dfrac{1}{2}x^2 - \dfrac{3}{x} + C$
d.	$\int \sqrt[3]{x}(x - 4)\,dx$	$\int (x^{4/3} - 4x^{1/3})\,dx$	$\dfrac{x^{7/3}}{7/3} - 4\left(\dfrac{x^{4/3}}{4/3}\right) + C$	$\dfrac{3}{7}x^{7/3} - 3x^{4/3} + C$

> **Algebra Review**
>
> For help on the algebra in Examples 7(c) and 7(d), see Examples 2(b) and 2(c) in the *Chapter 4 Algebra Review* on page A43.

As you do the exercises, note that you can check your answer to an antidifferentiation problem by differentiating. For instance, in Example 7(a), you can check that $4x^{1/2} + C$ is the correct antiderivative by differentiating the answer to obtain

$$D_x[4x^{1/2} + C] = 4\left(\frac{1}{2}\right)x^{-1/2} = \frac{2}{\sqrt{x}}. \qquad \text{Use differentiation to check antiderivative.}$$

Initial Conditions and Particular Solutions

You have already seen that the equation $y = \int f(x)\,dx$ has many solutions (each differing from the others by a constant). This means that the graphs of any two antiderivatives of f are vertical translations of each other. For example, Figure 4.2 shows the graphs of several antiderivatives of the form

$$y = \int (3x^2 - 1)\,dx = x^3 - x + C \qquad \text{General solution}$$

for various integer values of C. Each of these antiderivatives is a solution of the differential equation

$$\frac{dy}{dx} = 3x^2 - 1.$$

In many applications of integration, you are given enough information to determine a **particular solution.** To do this, you need only know the value of $y = F(x)$ for one value of x. This information is called an **initial condition.** For example, in Figure 4.2, only one curve passes through the point $(2, 4)$. To find this curve, you can use the general solution

$$F(x) = x^3 - x + C \qquad \text{General solution}$$

and the initial condition

$$F(2) = 4. \qquad \text{Initial condition}$$

By using the initial condition in the general solution, you can determine that

$$F(2) = 8 - 2 + C = 4$$

which implies that $C = -2$. So, you obtain

$$F(x) = x^3 - x - 2. \qquad \text{Particular solution}$$

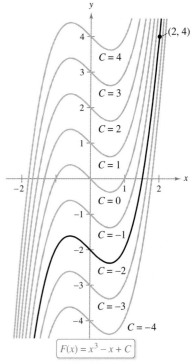

The particular solution that satisfies the initial condition $F(2) = 4$ is $F(x) = x^3 - x - 2$.

Figure 4.2

EXAMPLE 8   Finding a Particular Solution

Find the general solution of

$$F'(x) = e^x \qquad \text{Differential equation}$$

and find the particular solution that satisfies the initial condition

$$F(0) = 3. \qquad \text{Initial condition}$$

Solution

To find the general solution, integrate to obtain

$$F(x) = \int e^x\,dx$$

$$= e^x + C. \qquad \text{General solution}$$

Using the initial condition $F(0) = 3$, you can solve for C as follows.

$$F(0) = e^0 + C$$

$$3 = 1 + C$$

$$2 = C$$

So, the particular solution is

$$F(x) = e^x + 2 \qquad \text{Particular solution}$$

as shown in Figure 4.3. Note that Figure 4.3 also shows the solution curves that correspond to $C = -3, -2, -1, 0, 1,$ and 3. ∎

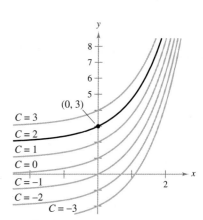

The particular solution that satisfies the initial condition $F(0) = 3$ is $F(x) = e^x + 2$.

Figure 4.3

So far in this section, you have been using x as the variable of integration. In applications, it is often convenient to use a different variable. For instance, in the next example, involving *time*, the variable of integration is t.

EXAMPLE 9 Solving a Vertical Motion Problem

A ball is thrown upward with an initial velocity of 64 feet per second from an initial height of 80 feet. [Assume that the acceleration is $a(t) = -32$ feet per second per second.]

a. Find the position function giving the height s as a function of the time t.

b. When does the ball hit the ground?

Solution

a. Let $t = 0$ represent the initial time. The two given initial conditions can be written as follows.

$$s(0) = 80 \qquad \text{Initial height is 80 feet.}$$
$$s'(0) = 64 \qquad \text{Initial velocity is 64 feet per second.}$$

Recall that $a(t) = s''(t)$. So, you can write

$$s''(t) = -32$$
$$s'(t) = \int s''(t)\, dt = \int -32\, dt = -32t + C_1.$$

Using the initial velocity, you obtain $s'(0) = 64 = -32(0) + C_1$, which implies that $C_1 = 64$. Next, by integrating $s'(t)$, you obtain

$$s(t) = \int s'(t)\, dt = \int (-32t + 64)\, dt = -16t^2 + 64t + C_2.$$

Using the initial height, you obtain

$$s(0) = 80 = -16(0^2) + 64(0) + C_2$$

which implies that $C_2 = 80$. So, the position function is

$$s(t) = -16t^2 + 64t + 80. \qquad \text{See Figure 4.4.}$$

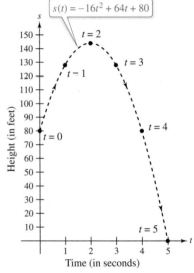

Height of a ball at time t
Figure 4.4

b. Using the position function found in part (a), you can find the time at which the ball hits the ground by solving the equation $s(t) = 0$.

$$-16t^2 + 64t + 80 = 0$$
$$-16(t + 1)(t - 5) = 0$$
$$t = -1, 5$$

Because t must be positive, you can conclude that the ball hits the ground 5 seconds after it is thrown.

In Example 9, note that the position function has the form

$$s(t) = -\frac{1}{2}gt^2 + v_0 t + s_0$$

where g is the acceleration due to gravity, v_0 is the initial velocity, and s_0 is the initial height, as presented in Section 2.2.

Example 9 shows how to use calculus to analyze vertical motion problems in which the acceleration is determined by a gravitational force. You can use a similar strategy to analyze other linear motion problems (vertical or horizontal) in which the acceleration (or deceleration) is the result of some other force, as you will see in Exercises 63–66.

4.1   Exercises

See *CalcChat.com* for tutorial help and worked-out solutions to odd-numbered exercises.

Integration and Differentiation **In Exercises 1 and 2,** verify the statement by showing that the derivative of the right side equals the integrand of the left side.

1. $\int \left(-\dfrac{6}{x^4} \right) dx = \dfrac{2}{x^3} + C$

2. $\int \left(8x^3 + \dfrac{1}{2x^2} \right) dx = 2x^4 - \dfrac{1}{2x} + C$

 Solving a Differential Equation **In Exercises 3–6, find the general solution of the differential equation and check the result by differentiation.**

3. $\dfrac{dy}{dt} = 9t^2$

4. $\dfrac{dy}{dt} = 5$

5. $\dfrac{dy}{dx} = x^{3/2}$

6. $\dfrac{dy}{dx} = 2x^{-3}$

 Rewriting Before Integrating **In Exercises 7–10, complete the table to find the indefinite integral.**

Original Integral	Rewrite	Integrate	Simplify
7. $\int \sqrt[3]{x}\, dx$			
8. $\int \dfrac{1}{4x^2}\, dx$			
9. $\int \dfrac{1}{x\sqrt{x}}\, dx$			
10. $\int \dfrac{1}{(3x)^2}\, dx$			

 Finding an Indefinite Integral **In Exercises 11–34, find the indefinite integral and check the result by differentiation.**

11. $\int (3x^3 - 6x^2 + 2)\, dx$

12. $\int (x^2 + 7)\, dx$

13. $\int (x^{3/2} + 2x + 1)\, dx$

14. $\int \left(\sqrt{x} + 5x^{3/2} \right) dx$

15. $\int \sqrt[3]{x^2}\, dx$

16. $\int \left(\sqrt[4]{x^3} + 1 \right) dx$

17. $\int \dfrac{1}{x^5}\, dx$

18. $\int -\dfrac{3}{x^7}\, dx$

19. $\int \dfrac{x + 6}{\sqrt{x}}\, dx$

20. $\int \dfrac{x^4 - 3x^2 + 5}{x^4}\, dx$

21. $\int (x + 1)(3x - 2)\, dx$

22. $\int (4t^2 + 3)^2\, dt$

23. $\int (5\cos x + 4\sin x)\, dx$

24. $\int (\theta^2 + \sec^2\theta)\, d\theta$

25. $\int (2\sin x - 5e^x)\, dx$

26. $\int (\sec y)(\tan y - \sec y)\, dy$

27. $\int (\tan^2 y + 1)\, dy$

28. $\int 2\sin\left(\dfrac{x}{2} \right)\cos\left(\dfrac{x}{2} \right) dx$

29. $\int (2x - 4^x)\, dx$

30. $\int (\cos x + 3^x)\, dx$

31. $\int -\dfrac{1}{\cos^2\theta}\, d\theta$

32. $\int 3\dfrac{\cos\theta}{\sin^2\theta}\, d\theta$

33. $\int \left(x - \dfrac{5}{x} \right) dx$

34. $\int \left(\dfrac{4}{x} + \sec^2 x \right) dx$

Error Analysis **In Exercises 35 and 36, describe and correct the error in finding the indefinite integral.**

35. $\int \dfrac{3x^3 - 4}{x^2}\, dx = \int (3x - 4x^{-2})\, dx$

$\qquad = \dfrac{3x^2}{2} - \dfrac{4}{x} + C$

36. $\int -\dfrac{15}{x^6}\, dx = \int -15x^{-6}\, dx$

$\qquad = \dfrac{3}{x^5}$

Sketching a Graph **In Exercises 37 and 38, the graph of the derivative of a function is given. Sketch the graphs of *two* functions that have the given derivative. (There is more than one correct answer.) To print an enlarged copy of the graph, go to *MathGraphs.com*.**

37.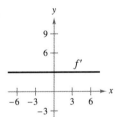

38.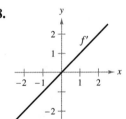

 Finding a Particular Solution **In Exercises 39–48, find the particular solution that satisfies the differential equation and the initial condition.**

39. $f'(x) = 6x,\ f(0) = 8$

40. $f'(s) = -12s^3,\ f(3) = 3$

41. $f'(\theta) = \cos\theta,\ f(\pi) = 1$

42. $f'(t) = e^t,\ f(0) = -6$

43. $f''(x) = 2,\ f'(2) = 5,\ f(2) = 10$

44. $f''(x) = x^2,\ f'(0) = 8,\ f(0) = 4$

45. $f''(x) = x^{-3/2},\ f'(4) = 2,\ f(0) = 0$

46. $f''(x) = \dfrac{2}{x^2},\ f'(1) = 4,\ f(1) = 3$

47. $f''(s) = 2e^s,\ f'(0) = -1,\ f(0) = 5$

48. $f''(x) = \sin x,\ f'(0) = 1,\ f(0) = 6$

EXPLORING CONCEPTS

49. Antiderivatives and Indefinite Integrals What is the difference, if any, between finding the antiderivative of $f(x)$ and finding the integral $\int f(x)\, dx$?

50. Comparing Functions Consider $f(x) = \tan^2 x$ and $g(x) = \sec^2 x$. What do you notice about the derivatives of f and g? What can you conclude about the relationship between f and g?

51. Sketching Graphs The graphs of f and f' each pass through the origin. Use the graph of f'' shown in the figure to sketch the graphs of f and f'. To print an enlarged copy of the graph, go to *MathGraphs.com*.

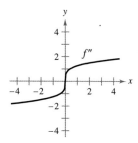

52. HOW DO YOU SEE IT? The graph of f' such that $f(0) = -4$, is shown in the figure.

(a) Approximate the slope of f at $x = 4$. Explain.

(b) Is it possible that $f(2) = -1$? Explain.

(c) Is $f(5) - f(4) > 0$? Explain.

(d) Approximate the value of x where f is maximum. Explain.

(e) Approximate any open intervals on which the graph of f is concave upward and any open intervals on which it is concave downward. Approximate the x-coordinates of any points of inflection.

53. Tree Growth An evergreen nursery sells a type of shrub after 6 years of growth and shaping. The growth rate during those 6 years is approximated by

$$\frac{dh}{dt} = 1.5t + 5$$

where t is the time in years and h is the height in centimeters. The seedlings are 12 centimeters tall when planted ($t = 0$).

(a) Find the height after t years.

(b) How tall are the shrubs when they are sold?

54. Population Growth The rate of growth dP/dt of a population of bacteria is proportional to the square root of t, where P is the population size and t is the time in days ($0 \le t \le 10$). That is, $dP/dt = k\sqrt{t}$. The initial size of the population is 500. After 1 day, the population has grown to 600. Estimate the population after 7 days.

Vertical Motion In Exercises 55–58, assume that the acceleration is $a(t) = -32$ feet per second per second. (Neglect air resistance.)

55. A ball is thrown vertically upward from a height of 6 feet with an initial velocity of 60 feet per second. How high will the ball go?

56. A baseball is thrown upward from a height of 6 feet with an initial velocity of 40 feet per second. Determine its maximum height.

57. A balloon, rising vertically with a velocity of 16 feet per second, releases a sandbag at the instant it is 64 feet above the ground.

(a) How many seconds after its release will the bag strike the ground?

(b) At what velocity will it hit the ground?

58. With what initial velocity must an object be thrown upward (from ground level) to reach the top of the Washington Monument, which has a height of approximately 555 feet?

Vertical Motion In Exercises 59 and 60, assume that the acceleration is $a(t) = -9.8$ meters per second per second. (Neglect air resistance.)

59. With what initial velocity must an object be thrown upward (from a height of 2 meters) to reach a maximum height of 200 meters?

60. GRAND CANYON

The Grand Canyon is 1800 meters deep at its deepest point. A rock is dropped from the rim above this point. Write the height of the rock as a function of the time t in seconds. How long will it take the rock to hit the canyon floor?

61. Lunar Gravity On the moon, the acceleration of a free-falling object is $a(t) = -1.6$ meters per second per second. A stone is dropped from a cliff on the moon and hits the surface of the moon 20 seconds later. How far did it fall? What was its velocity at impact?

62. Escape Velocity   The minimum velocity required for an object to escape Earth's gravitational pull is obtained from the solution of the equation

$$\int v \, dv = -GM \int \frac{1}{y^2} \, dy$$

where v is the velocity of the object projected from Earth, y is the distance from the center of Earth, G is the gravitational constant, and M is the mass of Earth. Show that v and y are related by the equation

$$v^2 = v_0^2 + 2GM\left(\frac{1}{y} - \frac{1}{R}\right)$$

where v_0 is the initial velocity of the object and R is the radius of Earth.

Particle Motion   In Exercises 63–66, consider a particle moving along the x-axis where $x(t)$ is the position of the particle at time t, $x'(t)$ is its velocity, and $x''(t)$ is its acceleration.

63. $x(t) = t^3 - 6t^2 + 9t - 2, \ 0 \le t \le 5$

(a) Find the velocity and acceleration of the particle.

(b) Find the open t-intervals on which the particle is moving to the right.

(c) Find the velocity of the particle when the acceleration is 0.

64. Repeat Exercise 63 for the position function

$$x(t) = (t - 1)(t - 3)^2, \ 0 \le t \le 5.$$

65. A particle moves along the x-axis at a velocity of $v(t) = 1/\sqrt{t}, t > 0$. At time $t = 1$, its position is $x = 4$. Find the acceleration and position functions for the particle.

66. A particle, initially at rest, moves along the x-axis such that its acceleration at time $t > 0$ is given by $a(t) = \cos t$. At the time $t = 0$, its position is $x = 3$.

(a) Find the velocity and position functions for the particle.

(b) Find the values of t for which the particle is at rest.

67. Acceleration   The maker of an automobile advertises that it takes 13 seconds to accelerate from 25 kilometers per hour to 80 kilometers per hour. Assume the acceleration is constant.

(a) Find the acceleration in meters per second per second.

(b) Find the distance the car travels during the 13 seconds.

68. Deceleration   A car traveling at 45 miles per hour is brought to a stop, at constant deceleration, 132 feet from where the brakes are applied.

(a) How far has the car moved when its speed has been reduced to 30 miles per hour? to 15 miles per hour?

(b) Draw the real number line from 0 to 132. Plot the points found in part (a). What can you conclude?

69. Horizontal Tangent   Find a function f such that the graph of f has a horizontal tangent at $(3, 1)$ and $f''(x) = 2x$.

70. Verifying a Rule   Verify the natural log rule

$$\int \frac{1}{x} \, dx = \ln|x| + C$$

by showing that the derivative of $\ln|x| + C$ is $1/x$.

Finding a Function   In Exercises 71 and 72, the graph of f' is shown. Find an equation for f given that f is continuous and $f(0) = 1$. Then sketch the graph of f.

71.   **72.**

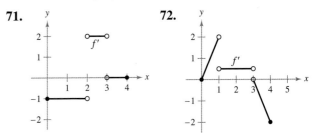

True or False? In Exercises 73 and 74, determine whether the statement is true or false. If it is false, explain why or give an example that shows it is false.

73. If $p(x)$ is a polynomial function, then the graph of exactly one antiderivative of p contains the origin.

74. $\int f(x)g(x) \, dx = \left(\int f(x) \, dx\right)\left(\int g(x) \, dx\right)$

Calculus AP® – Exam Preparation Questions

75. Multiple Choice $\displaystyle\int \sqrt{x}\,(10x - 3) \, dx =$

(A) $\frac{2}{5}x^{5/2} - \frac{2}{3}x^{3/2} + C$ (B) $2x^{5/2} - 2x^{3/2} + C$

(C) $2x^{5/2} - x^{3/2} + C$ (D) $4x^{5/2} - 2x^{3/2} + C$

76. Multiple Choice   The graph of f' is shown. If $f(0) = 3$, what is the value of $f(10)$?

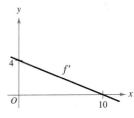

(A) 0   (B) 4   (C) 20   (D) 23

77. Free Response   The rate of growth of a population P is given by $dP/dt = 20t^3 - 35t^{4/3}$, where t is time in years. The initial population is 8000.

(a) Is the population always increasing? Justify your answer.

(b) When is the population at its lowest point? Round your answer to one decimal place.

(c) Find the population function. Estimate the population after 10 years.

4.2   Area

▶ Use sigma notation to write and evaluate a sum.
▶ Understand the concept of area.
▶ Approximate the area of a plane region.
▶ Find the area of a plane region using limits.

Sigma Notation

In the preceding section, you studied antidifferentiation. In this section, you will look further into a problem introduced in Section 1.1—that of finding the area of a region in the plane. At first glance, these two ideas may seem unrelated, but you will discover in Section 4.4 that they are closely related by an extremely important theorem called the Fundamental Theorem of Calculus.

This section begins by introducing a concise notation for sums. This notation is called **sigma notation** because it uses the uppercase Greek letter sigma, written as Σ.

Sigma Notation

The sum of n terms $a_1, a_2, a_3, \ldots, a_n$ is written as

$$\sum_{i=1}^{n} a_i = a_1 + a_2 + a_3 + \cdots + a_n$$

where i is the **index of summation**, a_i is the ***i*th term** of the sum, and the **upper and lower bounds of summation** are n and 1.

▶ **Remark**   The upper and lower bounds must be constant with respect to the index of summation. The lower bound, however, does not have to be 1. Any integer less than or equal to the upper bound is legitimate.

EXAMPLE 1   Using Sigma Notation

a. $\displaystyle\sum_{i=1}^{6} i = 1 + 2 + 3 + 4 + 5 + 6$

b. $\displaystyle\sum_{i=0}^{5} (i + 1) = 1 + 2 + 3 + 4 + 5 + 6$

c. $\displaystyle\sum_{j=3}^{7} j^2 = 3^2 + 4^2 + 5^2 + 6^2 + 7^2$

d. $\displaystyle\sum_{j=1}^{5} \frac{1}{\sqrt{j}} = \frac{1}{\sqrt{1}} + \frac{1}{\sqrt{2}} + \frac{1}{\sqrt{3}} + \frac{1}{\sqrt{4}} + \frac{1}{\sqrt{5}}$

e. $\displaystyle\sum_{k=1}^{n} \frac{1}{n}(k^2 + 1) = \frac{1}{n}(1^2 + 1) + \frac{1}{n}(2^2 + 1) + \cdots + \frac{1}{n}(n^2 + 1)$

f. $\displaystyle\sum_{i=1}^{n} f(x_i)\Delta x = f(x_1)\Delta x + f(x_2)\Delta x + \cdots + f(x_n)\Delta x$

From parts (a) and (b), notice that the same sum can be represented in different ways using sigma notation. ■

Although any variable can be used as the index of summation, i, j, and k are often used. Notice in Example 1 that the index of summation does not appear in the terms of the expanded sum.

The properties of summation shown below can be derived using the Associative and Commutative Properties of Addition and the Distributive Property of Addition over Multiplication. (In the first property, k is a constant.)

1. $\displaystyle\sum_{i=1}^{n} ka_i = k\sum_{i=1}^{n} a_i$

2. $\displaystyle\sum_{i=1}^{n}(a_i \pm b_i) = \sum_{i=1}^{n} a_i \pm \sum_{i=1}^{n} b_i$

The next theorem lists some useful formulas for sums of powers.

Theorem 4.2   Summation Formulas

1. $\displaystyle\sum_{i=1}^{n} c = cn,$ c is a constant

2. $\displaystyle\sum_{i=1}^{n} i = \frac{n(n+1)}{2}$

3. $\displaystyle\sum_{i=1}^{n} i^2 = \frac{n(n+1)(2n+1)}{6}$

4. $\displaystyle\sum_{i=1}^{n} i^3 = \frac{n^2(n+1)^2}{4}$

A proof of this theorem is given in Appendix A.

EXAMPLE 2   Evaluating a Sum

Evaluate $\displaystyle\sum_{i=1}^{n} \frac{i+1}{n^2}$ for $n = 10, 100, 1000,$ and $10,000.$

Solution

$$\sum_{i=1}^{n} \frac{i+1}{n^2} = \frac{1}{n^2}\sum_{i=1}^{n}(i+1)$$ Factor the constant $\frac{1}{n^2}$ out of sum.

$$= \frac{1}{n^2}\left(\sum_{i=1}^{n} i + \sum_{i=1}^{n} 1\right)$$ Write as two sums.

$$= \frac{1}{n^2}\left[\frac{n(n+1)}{2} + n\right]$$ Apply Theorem 4.2.

$$= \frac{1}{n^2}\left[\frac{n^2 + 3n}{2}\right]$$ Simplify.

$$= \frac{n+3}{2n}$$ Simplify.

Now you can evaluate the sum by substituting the appropriate values of n, as shown in the table below.

n	10	100	1000	10,000
$\displaystyle\sum_{i=1}^{n} \frac{i+1}{n^2} = \frac{n+3}{2n}$	0.65000	0.51500	0.50150	0.50015

In the table, note that the sum appears to approach a limit as n increases. Although the discussion of limits at infinity in Section 1.6 applies to a variable x, where x can be any real number, many of the same results hold true for limits involving the variable n, where n is restricted to positive integer values. So, to find the limit of $(n+3)/2n$ as n approaches infinity, you can write

$$\lim_{n\to\infty} \frac{n+3}{2n} = \lim_{n\to\infty}\left(\frac{n}{2n} + \frac{3}{2n}\right) = \lim_{n\to\infty}\left(\frac{1}{2} + \frac{3}{2n}\right) = \frac{1}{2} + 0 = \frac{1}{2}.$$

Area

In Euclidean geometry, the simplest type of plane region is a rectangle. Although people often say that the *formula* for the area of a rectangle is

$$A = bh$$

it is actually more proper to say that this is the *definition* of the **area of a rectangle.**

From this definition, you can develop formulas for the areas of many other plane regions. For example, to determine the area of a triangle, you can form a rectangle whose area is twice that of the triangle, as shown in Figure 4.5. Once you know how to find the area of a triangle, you can determine the area of any polygon by subdividing the polygon into triangular regions, as shown in Figure 4.6.

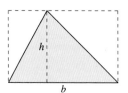

Triangle: $A = \frac{1}{2}bh$
Figure 4.5

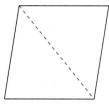
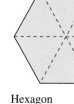
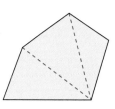

Parallelogram   Hexagon   Polygon
Figure 4.6

Finding the areas of regions other than polygons is more difficult. The ancient Greeks were able to determine formulas for the areas of some general regions (principally those bounded by conics) by the *exhaustion* method. The clearest description of this method was given by Archimedes (287–212 B.C.). Essentially, the method is a limiting process in which the area is squeezed between two polygons—one inscribed in the region and one circumscribed about the region.

For instance, in Figure 4.7, the area of a circular region is approximated by an *n*-sided inscribed polygon and an *n*-sided circumscribed polygon. For each value of *n*, the area of the inscribed polygon is less than the area of the circle, and the area of the circumscribed polygon is greater than the area of the circle. Moreover, as *n* increases, the areas of both polygons become better and better approximations of the area of the circle.

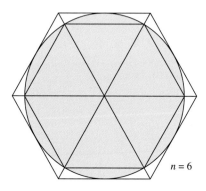
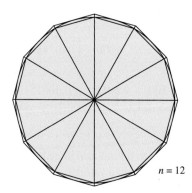

The exhaustion method for finding the area of a circular region
Figure 4.7

A process that is similar to that used by Archimedes to determine the area of a plane region is used in the remaining examples in this section.

The Area of a Plane Region

Recall from Section 1.1 that the origins of calculus are connected to two classic problems: the tangent line problem and the area problem. Example 3 begins the investigation of the area problem.

EXAMPLE 3   **Approximating the Area of a Plane Region**

Use the five rectangles in Figures 4.8(a) and 4.8(b) to find *two* approximations of the area of the region lying between the graph of

$$f(x) = -x^2 + 5$$

and the x-axis between $x = 0$ and $x = 2$.

Solution

a. The right endpoints of the five intervals are

$$\frac{2}{5}i \qquad \text{Right endpoints}$$

where $i = 1, 2, 3, 4, 5$. The width of each rectangle is $\frac{2}{5}$, and the height of each rectangle can be obtained by evaluating f at the right endpoint of each interval.

$$\left[0, \frac{2}{5}\right], \left[\frac{2}{5}, \frac{4}{5}\right], \left[\frac{4}{5}, \frac{6}{5}\right], \left[\frac{6}{5}, \frac{8}{5}\right], \left[\frac{8}{5}, \frac{10}{5}\right]$$

Evaluate f at the right endpoints of these intervals.

The sum of the areas of the five rectangles is

$$\sum_{i=1}^{5} f\left(\overbrace{\frac{2i}{5}}^{\text{Height}}\right)\left(\overbrace{\frac{2}{5}}^{\text{Width}}\right) = \sum_{i=1}^{5}\left[-\left(\frac{2i}{5}\right)^2 + 5\right]\left(\frac{2}{5}\right) = \frac{162}{25} = 6.48.$$

Because each of the five rectangles lies inside the parabolic region, you can conclude that the area of the parabolic region is greater than 6.48.

b. The left endpoints of the five intervals are

$$\frac{2}{5}(i - 1) \qquad \text{Left endpoints}$$

where $i = 1, 2, 3, 4, 5$. The width of each rectangle is $\frac{2}{5}$, and the height of each rectangle can be obtained by evaluating f at the left endpoint of each interval. So, the sum is

$$\sum_{i=1}^{5} f\left(\overbrace{\frac{2i - 2}{5}}^{\text{Height}}\right)\left(\overbrace{\frac{2}{5}}^{\text{Width}}\right) = \sum_{i=1}^{5}\left[-\left(\frac{2i - 2}{5}\right)^2 + 5\right]\left(\frac{2}{5}\right) = \frac{202}{25} = 8.08.$$

Because the parabolic region lies within the union of the five rectangular regions, you can conclude that the area of the parabolic region is less than 8.08.

By combining the results in parts (a) and (b), you can conclude that

$$6.48 < (\text{Area of region}) < 8.08.$$

By increasing the number of rectangles used in Example 3, you can obtain closer and closer approximations of the area of the region. For instance, using 25 rectangles of width $\frac{2}{25}$ each, you can conclude that

$$7.1712 < (\text{Area of region}) < 7.4912.$$

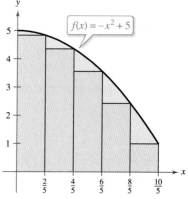

(a) The area of the parabolic region is greater than the area of the rectangles.

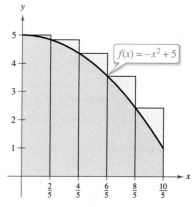

(b) The area of the parabolic region is less than the area of the rectangles.

Figure 4.8

Finding Area by the Limit Definition

The procedure used in Example 3 can be generalized as follows. Consider a plane region bounded above by the graph of a nonnegative, continuous function

$$y = f(x)$$

as shown in Figure 4.9. The region is bounded below by the x-axis, and the left and right boundaries of the region are the vertical lines $x = a$ and $x = b$.

To approximate the area of the region, begin by subdividing the interval $[a, b]$ into n subintervals, each of width

$$\Delta x = \frac{b - a}{n}$$

as shown in Figure 4.10. The endpoints of the intervals are

$$\overbrace{a + 0(\Delta x)}^{a \,=\, x_0} < \overbrace{a + 1(\Delta x)}^{x_1} < \overbrace{a + 2(\Delta x)}^{x_2} < \cdots < \overbrace{a + n(\Delta x)}^{x_n \,=\, b}.$$

Because f is continuous, the Extreme Value Theorem guarantees the existence of a minimum and a maximum of f on *each* subinterval.

$f(m_i)$ = Minimum of f on ith subinterval

$f(M_i)$ = Maximum of f on ith subinterval

Next, define an **inscribed rectangle** lying *inside* the ith subregion and a **circumscribed rectangle** extending *outside* the ith subregion. The height of the ith inscribed rectangle is $f(m_i)$ and the height of the ith circumscribed rectangle is $f(M_i)$. For *each* i, the area of the inscribed rectangle is less than or equal to the area of the circumscribed rectangle.

$$\begin{pmatrix} \text{Area of inscribed} \\ \text{rectangle} \end{pmatrix} = f(m_i)\,\Delta x \le f(M_i)\,\Delta x = \begin{pmatrix} \text{Area of circumscribed} \\ \text{rectangle} \end{pmatrix}$$

The sum of the areas of the inscribed rectangles is called a **lower sum,** and the sum of the areas of the circumscribed rectangles is called an **upper sum.**

$$\text{Lower sum} = s(n) = \sum_{i=1}^{n} f(m_i)\,\Delta x \qquad \text{Area of inscribed rectangles}$$

$$\text{Upper sum} = S(n) = \sum_{i=1}^{n} f(M_i)\,\Delta x \qquad \text{Area of circumscribed rectangles}$$

From Figure 4.11, you can see that the lower sum $s(n)$ is less than or equal to the upper sum $S(n)$. Moreover, the actual area of the region lies between these two sums.

$$s(n) \le (\text{Area of region}) \le S(n)$$

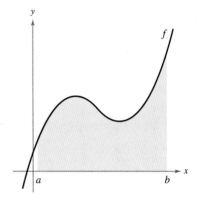

The region under a curve
Figure 4.9

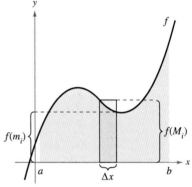

The interval $[a, b]$ is divided into n subintervals of width $\Delta x = \dfrac{b - a}{n}$.

Figure 4.10

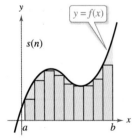

Area of inscribed rectangles is less than area of region.

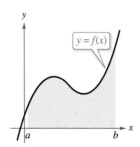

Area of region

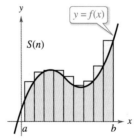

Area of circumscribed rectangles is greater than area of region.

Figure 4.11

EXAMPLE 4   Finding Upper and Lower Sums for a Region

Find the upper and lower sums for the region bounded by the graph of $f(x) = x^2$ and the x-axis between $x = 0$ and $x = 2$.

Solution

To begin, partition the interval $[0, 2]$ into n subintervals, each of width

$$\Delta x = \frac{b - a}{n} = \frac{2 - 0}{n} = \frac{2}{n}.$$

Figure 4.12 shows the endpoints of the subintervals and several inscribed and circumscribed rectangles. Because f is increasing on the interval $[0, 2]$, the minimum value on each subinterval occurs at the left endpoint, and the maximum value occurs at the right endpoint.

Left Endpoints

$$m_i = 0 + (i - 1)\left(\frac{2}{n}\right) = \frac{2(i - 1)}{n}$$

Right Endpoints

$$M_i = 0 + i\left(\frac{2}{n}\right) = \frac{2i}{n}$$

Using the left endpoints, the lower sum is

$$
\begin{aligned}
s(n) &= \sum_{i=1}^{n} f(m_i)\,\Delta x \\
&= \sum_{i=1}^{n} f\left[\frac{2(i - 1)}{n}\right]\left(\frac{2}{n}\right) \\
&= \sum_{i=1}^{n} \left[\frac{2(i - 1)}{n}\right]^2\left(\frac{2}{n}\right) \\
&= \sum_{i=1}^{n} \left(\frac{8}{n^3}\right)(i^2 - 2i + 1) \\
&= \frac{8}{n^3}\left(\sum_{i=1}^{n} i^2 - 2\sum_{i=1}^{n} i + \sum_{i=1}^{n} 1\right) \\
&= \frac{8}{n^3}\left\{\frac{n(n + 1)(2n + 1)}{6} - 2\left[\frac{n(n + 1)}{2}\right] + n\right\} \\
&= \frac{4}{3n^3}(2n^3 - 3n^2 + n) \\
&= \frac{8}{3} - \frac{4}{n} + \frac{4}{3n^2}. \qquad \text{Lower sum}
\end{aligned}
$$

Using the right endpoints, the upper sum is

$$
\begin{aligned}
S(n) &= \sum_{i=1}^{n} f(M_i)\,\Delta x \\
&= \sum_{i=1}^{n} f\left(\frac{2i}{n}\right)\left(\frac{2}{n}\right) \\
&= \sum_{i=1}^{n} \left(\frac{2i}{n}\right)^2\left(\frac{2}{n}\right) \\
&= \sum_{i=1}^{n} \left(\frac{8}{n^3}\right)i^2 \\
&= \frac{8}{n^3}\left[\frac{n(n + 1)(2n + 1)}{6}\right] \\
&= \frac{4}{3n^3}(2n^3 + 3n^2 + n) \\
&= \frac{8}{3} + \frac{4}{n} + \frac{4}{3n^2}. \qquad \text{Upper sum}
\end{aligned}
$$

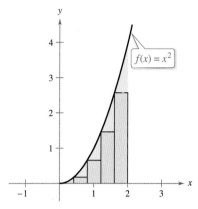

Inscribed rectangles

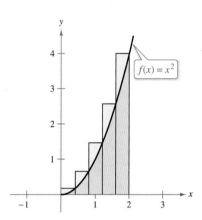

Circumscribed rectangles
Figure 4.12

Algebra Review

For help on the algebra in Example 4, see Example 1(a) in the *Chapter 4 Algebra Review* on page A42.

Example 4 illustrates some important things about lower and upper sums. First, notice that for any value of n, the lower sum is less than (or equal to) the upper sum.

$$s(n) = \frac{8}{3} - \frac{4}{n} + \frac{4}{3n^2} < \frac{8}{3} + \frac{4}{n} + \frac{4}{3n^2} = S(n)$$

Second, the difference between these two sums lessens as n increases. In fact, when you take the limits as $n \to \infty$, both the lower sum and the upper sum approach $\frac{8}{3}$.

$$\lim_{n \to \infty} s(n) = \lim_{n \to \infty} \left(\frac{8}{3} - \frac{4}{n} + \frac{4}{3n^2} \right) = \frac{8}{3} \qquad \text{Lower sum limit}$$

and

$$\lim_{n \to \infty} S(n) = \lim_{n \to \infty} \left(\frac{8}{3} + \frac{4}{n} + \frac{4}{3n^2} \right) = \frac{8}{3} \qquad \text{Upper sum limit}$$

The next theorem shows that the equivalence of the limits (as $n \to \infty$) of the upper and lower sums is not mere coincidence. It is true for all functions that are continuous and nonnegative on the closed interval $[a, b]$. The proof of this theorem is best left to a course in advanced calculus.

Theorem 4.3   Limits of the Lower and Upper Sums

Let f be continuous and nonnegative on the interval $[a, b]$. The limits as $n \to \infty$ of both the lower and upper sums exist and are equal to each other. That is,

$$\lim_{n \to \infty} s(n) = \lim_{n \to \infty} \sum_{i=1}^{n} f(m_i) \Delta x$$

$$= \lim_{n \to \infty} \sum_{i=1}^{n} f(M_i) \Delta x$$

$$= \lim_{n \to \infty} S(n)$$

where $\Delta x = (b - a)/n$ and $f(m_i)$ and $f(M_i)$ are the minimum and maximum values of f on the ith subinterval.

In Theorem 4.3, the same limit is attained for both the minimum value $f(m_i)$ and the maximum value $f(M_i)$. So, it follows from the Squeeze Theorem (Theorem 1.8) that the choice of x in the ith subinterval does not affect the limit. This means that you are free to choose an *arbitrary* x-value in the ith subinterval, as shown in the *definition of the area of a region in the plane*.

Definition of the Area of a Region in the Plane

Let f be continuous and nonnegative on the interval $[a, b]$. (See Figure 4.13.) The area of the region bounded by the graph of f, the x-axis, and the vertical lines $x = a$ and $x = b$ is

$$\text{Area} = \lim_{n \to \infty} \sum_{i=1}^{n} f(c_i) \Delta x$$

where $x_{i-1} \le c_i \le x_i$ and

$$\Delta x = \frac{b - a}{n}.$$

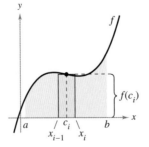

The width of the ith subinterval is $\Delta x = x_i - x_{i-1}$.

Figure 4.13

Exploration

For the region given in Example 4, evaluate the lower sum

$$s(n) = \frac{8}{3} - \frac{4}{n} + \frac{4}{3n^2}$$

and the upper sum

$$S(n) = \frac{8}{3} + \frac{4}{n} + \frac{4}{3n^2}$$

for $n = 10$, 100, and 1000. Use your results to determine the area of the region.

EXAMPLE 5   Finding Area by the Limit Definition

Find the area of the region bounded by the graph of $f(x) = x^3$, the x-axis, and the vertical lines $x = 0$ and $x = 1$, as shown in Figure 4.14.

Solution

Begin by noting that f is continuous and nonnegative on the interval $[0, 1]$. Next, partition the interval $[0, 1]$ into n subintervals, each of width $\Delta x = 1/n$. According to the definition of area, you can choose any x-value in the ith subinterval. For this example, the right endpoints $c_i = i/n$ are convenient.

$$\text{Area} = \lim_{n \to \infty} \sum_{i=1}^{n} f(c_i)\, \Delta x$$

$$= \lim_{n \to \infty} \sum_{i=1}^{n} \left(\frac{i}{n}\right)^3 \left(\frac{1}{n}\right) \qquad \text{Right endpoints: } c_i = \frac{i}{n}$$

$$= \lim_{n \to \infty} \frac{1}{n^4} \sum_{i=1}^{n} i^3$$

$$= \lim_{n \to \infty} \frac{1}{n^4} \left[\frac{n^2(n+1)^2}{4}\right]$$

$$= \lim_{n \to \infty} \left(\frac{1}{4} + \frac{1}{2n} + \frac{1}{4n^2}\right)$$

$$= \frac{1}{4}$$

The area of the region is $\frac{1}{4}$.

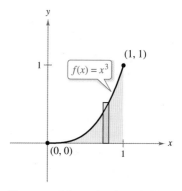

The area of the region bounded by the graph of f, the x-axis, $x = 0$, and $x = 1$ is $\frac{1}{4}$.

Figure 4.14

EXAMPLE 6   Finding Area by the Limit Definition

See LarsonCalculusforAP.com for an interactive version of this type of example.

Find the area of the region bounded by the graph of $f(x) = 4 - x^2$, the x-axis, and the vertical lines $x = 1$ and $x = 2$, as shown in Figure 4.15.

Solution

Note that the function f is continuous and nonnegative on the interval $[1, 2]$. So, begin by partitioning the interval into n subintervals, each of width $\Delta x = 1/n$. Choosing the right endpoint $c_i = a + i\Delta x = 1 + i/n$ of each subinterval, you obtain

$$\text{Area} = \lim_{n \to \infty} \sum_{i=1}^{n} f(c_i)\, \Delta x$$

$$= \lim_{n \to \infty} \sum_{i=1}^{n} \left[4 - \left(1 + \frac{i}{n}\right)^2\right]\left(\frac{1}{n}\right)$$

$$= \lim_{n \to \infty} \sum_{i=1}^{n} \left(3 - \frac{2i}{n} - \frac{i^2}{n^2}\right)\left(\frac{1}{n}\right)$$

$$= \lim_{n \to \infty} \left(\frac{1}{n}\sum_{i=1}^{n} 3 - \frac{2}{n^2}\sum_{i=1}^{n} i - \frac{1}{n^3}\sum_{i=1}^{n} i^2\right)$$

$$= \lim_{n \to \infty} \left[3 - \left(1 + \frac{1}{n}\right) - \left(\frac{1}{3} + \frac{1}{2n} + \frac{1}{6n^2}\right)\right]$$

$$= 3 - 1 - \frac{1}{3}$$

$$= \frac{5}{3}.$$

The area of the region is $\frac{5}{3}$.

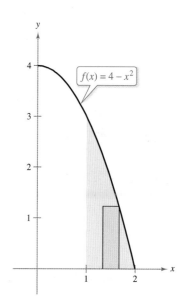

The area of the region bounded by the graph of f, the x-axis, $x = 1$, and $x = 2$ is $\frac{5}{3}$.

Figure 4.15

The next example looks at a region that is bounded by the y-axis (rather than by the x-axis).

EXAMPLE 7 A Region Bounded by the y-axis

Find the area of the region bounded by the graph of $f(y) = y^2$ and the y-axis for $0 \le y \le 1$, as shown in Figure 4.16.

Solution

When f is a continuous, nonnegative function of y, you can still use the same basic procedure shown in Examples 5 and 6. Begin by partitioning the interval $[0, 1]$ into n subintervals, each of width $\Delta y = 1/n$. Then, using the upper endpoints $c_i = i/n$, you obtain

$$
\begin{aligned}
\text{Area} &= \lim_{n \to \infty} \sum_{i=1}^{n} f(c_i) \, \Delta y \\
&= \lim_{n \to \infty} \sum_{i=1}^{n} \left(\frac{i}{n}\right)^2 \left(\frac{1}{n}\right) \qquad \text{Upper endpoints: } c_i = \frac{i}{n} \\
&= \lim_{n \to \infty} \frac{1}{n^3} \sum_{i=1}^{n} i^2 \\
&= \lim_{n \to \infty} \frac{1}{n^3} \left[\frac{n(n+1)(2n+1)}{6} \right] \\
&= \lim_{n \to \infty} \left(\frac{1}{3} + \frac{1}{2n} + \frac{1}{6n^2} \right) \\
&= \frac{1}{3}.
\end{aligned}
$$

The area of the region is $\frac{1}{3}$.

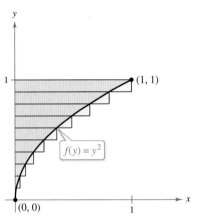

The area of the region bounded by the graph of f and the y-axis for $0 \le y \le 1$ is $\frac{1}{3}$.

Figure 4.16

In Examples 5, 6, and 7, c_i is chosen to be a value that is convenient for calculating the limit. Because each limit gives the exact area for *any* c_i, there is no need to find values that give good approximations when n is small. For an *approximation,* however, you should try to find a value of c_i that gives a good approximation of the area of the ith subregion. In general, a good value to choose is the midpoint of the interval, $c_i = (x_{i-1} + x_i)/2$, and apply the **Midpoint Rule.**

$$
\text{Area} \approx \sum_{i=1}^{n} f\left(\frac{x_{i-1} + x_i}{2} \right) \Delta x \qquad \text{Midpoint Rule}
$$

> **Remark**
>
> You will study other approximation methods in Section 4.3. One of the methods, the Trapezoidal Rule, is similar to the Midpoint Rule.

EXAMPLE 8 Approximating Area with the Midpoint Rule

Use the Midpoint Rule with $n = 4$ to approximate the area of the region bounded by the graph of $f(x) = \sin x$ and the x-axis for $0 \le x \le \pi$, as shown in Figure 4.17.

Solution

For $n = 4$, $\Delta x = \pi/4$. The midpoints of the subregions are shown below.

$$
c_1 = \frac{0 + (\pi/4)}{2} = \frac{\pi}{8} \qquad\qquad c_2 = \frac{(\pi/4) + (\pi/2)}{2} = \frac{3\pi}{8}
$$

$$
c_3 = \frac{(\pi/2) + (3\pi/4)}{2} = \frac{5\pi}{8} \qquad c_4 = \frac{(3\pi/4) + \pi}{2} = \frac{7\pi}{8}
$$

So, the area is approximated by

$$
\text{Area} \approx \sum_{i=1}^{n} f(c_i) \, \Delta x = \sum_{i=1}^{4} (\sin c_i)\left(\frac{\pi}{4}\right) = \frac{\pi}{4}\left(\sin \frac{\pi}{8} + \sin \frac{3\pi}{8} + \sin \frac{5\pi}{8} + \sin \frac{7\pi}{8} \right)
$$

which is about 2.052.

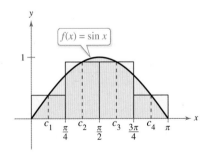

The area of the region bounded by the graph of $f(x) = \sin x$ and the x-axis for $0 \le x \le \pi$ is about 2.052.

Figure 4.17

Finding a Sum In Exercises 1–6, find the sum. Use the summation capabilities of a graphing utility to verify your result.

1. $\sum_{i=1}^{6} (3i + 2)$

2. $\sum_{k=3}^{9} (k^2 + 1)$

3. $\sum_{k=0}^{4} \frac{1}{k^2 + 1}$

4. $\sum_{j=4}^{6} \frac{6}{j}$

5. $\sum_{k=0}^{6} c$

6. $\sum_{i=1}^{4} [(i - 1)^2 + (i + 1)^3]$

Using Sigma Notation In Exercises 7–12, use sigma notation to write the sum.

7. $\frac{1}{5(1)} + \frac{1}{5(2)} + \frac{1}{5(3)} + \cdots + \frac{1}{5(11)}$

8. $\frac{3}{1 + 1} + \frac{3}{1 + 2} + \frac{3}{1 + 3} + \cdots + \frac{3}{1 + 18}$

9. $\left[7\left(\frac{1}{6}\right) + 5\right] + \left[7\left(\frac{2}{6}\right) + 5\right] + \cdots + \left[7\left(\frac{6}{6}\right) + 5\right]$

10. $\left[1 - \left(\frac{1}{4}\right)^2\right] + \left[1 - \left(\frac{2}{4}\right)^2\right] + \cdots + \left[1 - \left(\frac{4}{4}\right)^2\right]$

11. $\left[\left(\frac{2}{n}\right)^3 - \frac{2}{n}\right]\left(\frac{2}{n}\right) + \cdots + \left[\left(\frac{2n}{n}\right)^3 - \frac{2n}{n}\right]\left(\frac{2}{n}\right)$

12. $\left[2\left(1 + \frac{3}{n}\right)^2\right]\left(\frac{3}{n}\right) + \cdots + \left[2\left(1 + \frac{3n}{n}\right)^2\right]\left(\frac{3}{n}\right)$

Evaluating a Sum In Exercises 13–20, use the properties of summation and Theorem 4.2 to evaluate the sum. Use the summation capabilities of a graphing utility to verify your result.

13. $\sum_{i=1}^{12} 7$

14. $\sum_{i=1}^{20} -13$

15. $\sum_{i=1}^{24} 4i$

16. $\sum_{i=1}^{16} (5i - 4)$

17. $\sum_{i=1}^{20} (i - 1)^2$

18. $\sum_{i=1}^{10} (i^2 - 1)$

19. $\sum_{i=1}^{15} i(i - 1)^2$

20. $\sum_{i=1}^{25} (i^3 - 2i)$

Evaluating a Sum In Exercises 21–24, use the summation formulas to rewrite the expression without the summation notation. Use the result to find the sums for $n = 10$, 100, 1000, and 10,000.

21. $\sum_{i=1}^{n} \frac{2i + 1}{n^2}$

22. $\sum_{j=1}^{n} \frac{7j + 4}{n^2}$

23. $\sum_{k=1}^{n} \frac{6k(k - 1)}{n^3}$

24. $\sum_{i=1}^{n} \frac{2i^3 - 3i}{n^4}$

Error Analysis In Exercises 25 and 26, describe and correct the error in finding the sum.

25. $\sum_{i=1}^{n} 4i = 4n\left[\frac{n(n + 1)}{2}\right] = 2n^2(n + 1) = 2n^3 + 2n^2$ ✗

26. $\sum_{i=1}^{n} (n + 2) = \frac{n(n + 1)}{2} + 2n$

$= \frac{n^2 + n}{2} + 2n$

$= \frac{n^2 + 5n}{2}$ ✗

Approximating the Area of a Plane Region In Exercises 27–32, use left and right endpoints and the given number of rectangles to find two approximations of the area of the region between the graph of the function and the x-axis over the given interval.

27. $f(x) = 2x + 5$, $[0, 2]$, 4 rectangles

28. $f(x) = 9 - x$, $[2, 4]$, 6 rectangles

29. $g(x) = 2x^2 - x - 1$, $[2, 5]$, 6 rectangles

30. $g(x) = x^2 + 1$, $[1, 3]$, 8 rectangles

31. $f(x) = \cos x$, $\left[0, \frac{\pi}{2}\right]$, 4 rectangles

32. $g(x) = \sin x$, $[0, \pi]$, 6 rectangles

Finding Upper and Lower Sums for a Region In Exercises 33–36, use upper and lower sums to approximate the area of the region using the given number of subintervals (of equal width).

33. $y = \sqrt{x}$

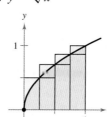

34. $y = 4e^{-x}$

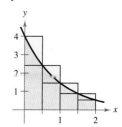

35. $y = \frac{1}{x}$

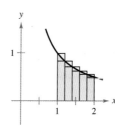

36. $y = \sqrt{1 - x^2}$

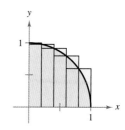

Using Upper and Lower Sums In Exercises 37 and 38, bound the area of the shaded region by approximating the upper and lower sums. Use rectangles of width 1. To print an enlarged copy of the graph, go to *MathGraphs.com.*

37.

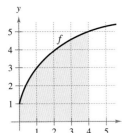

38.

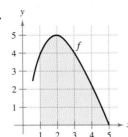

 Finding Upper and Lower Sums for a Region In Exercises 39–42, find the upper and lower sums for the region bounded by the graph of the function and the *x*-axis over the given interval, using *n* subintervals.

39. $f(x) = 3x$, $[0, 4]$ 40. $f(x) = 6 - 2x$, $[1, 2]$
41. $f(x) = 5x^2$, $[0, 1]$ 42. $f(x) = 9 - x^2$, $[0, 2]$

43. **Numerical Reasoning** Consider a triangle bounded by the graphs of $y = x$, $y = 0$, and $x = 2$.

   (a) Sketch the region and find its area.

   (b) Divide the interval $[0, 2]$ into n subintervals of equal width and show that the endpoints are

   $$0 < 1\left(\frac{2}{n}\right) < \cdots < (n - 1)\left(\frac{2}{n}\right) < n\left(\frac{2}{n}\right).$$

   (c) Show that $s(n) = \sum_{i=1}^{n} \left[(i - 1)\left(\frac{2}{n}\right)\right]\left(\frac{2}{n}\right).$

   (d) Show that $S(n) = \sum_{i=1}^{n} \left[i\left(\frac{2}{n}\right)\right]\left(\frac{2}{n}\right).$

   (e) Find $s(n)$ and $S(n)$ for $n = 5, 10, 50,$ and $100.$

   (f) Show that $\lim_{n \to \infty} s(n) = \lim_{n \to \infty} S(n) = 2.$

44. **Numerical Reasoning** Consider a trapezoid bounded by the graphs of $y = x$, $y = 0$, $x = 1$, and $x = 3$.

   (a) Sketch the region and find its area.

   (b) Divide the interval $[1, 3]$ into n subintervals of equal width and show that the endpoints are

   $$1 < 1 + 1\left(\frac{2}{n}\right) < \cdots < 1 + (n - 1)\left(\frac{2}{n}\right) < 1 + n\left(\frac{2}{n}\right).$$

   (c) Show that $s(n) = \sum_{i=1}^{n} \left[1 + (i - 1)\left(\frac{2}{n}\right)\right]\left(\frac{2}{n}\right).$

   (d) Show that $S(n) = \sum_{i=1}^{n} \left[1 + i\left(\frac{2}{n}\right)\right]\left(\frac{2}{n}\right).$

   (e) Find $s(n)$ and $S(n)$ for $n = 5, 10, 50,$ and $100.$

   (f) Show that $\lim_{n \to \infty} s(n) = \lim_{n \to \infty} S(n) = 4.$

 Finding a Limit In Exercises 45–50, find a formula for the sum of *n* terms. Use the formula to find the limit as $n \to \infty$.

45. $\lim_{n \to \infty} \sum_{i=1}^{n} \frac{24i}{n^2}$ 46. $\lim_{n \to \infty} \sum_{i=1}^{n} \left(\frac{3i}{n}\right)\left(\frac{3}{n}\right)$

47. $\lim_{n \to \infty} \sum_{i=1}^{n} \frac{1}{n^3}(i - 1)^2$ 48. $\lim_{n \to \infty} \sum_{i=1}^{n} \left(1 + \frac{2i}{n}\right)^2\left(\frac{2}{n}\right)$

49. $\lim_{n \to \infty} \sum_{i=1}^{n} \left(1 + \frac{i}{n}\right)\left(\frac{2}{n}\right)$ 50. $\lim_{n \to \infty} \sum_{i=1}^{n} \left(2 + \frac{3i}{n}\right)^3\left(\frac{3}{n}\right)$

 Finding Area by the Limit Definition In Exercises 51–60, use the limit process to find the area of the region bounded by the graph of the function and the *x*-axis over the given interval. Sketch the region.

51. $y = -4x + 5$, $[0, 1]$ 52. $y = 3x - 2$, $[2, 5]$
53. $y = x^2 + 2$, $[0, 1]$ 54. $y = \frac{1}{2}x^2 + 3$, $[0, 2]$
55. $y = 25 - x^2$, $[1, 4]$ 56. $y = 4 - x^2$, $[-2, 2]$
57. $y = 27 - x^3$, $[1, 3]$ 58. $y = 2x - x^3$, $[0, 1]$
59. $y = x^2 - x^3$, $[-1, 1]$ 60. $y = 2x^3 - x^2$, $[1, 2]$

 Finding Area by the Limit Definition In Exercises 61–66, use the limit process to find the area of the region bounded by the graph of the function and the *y*-axis over the given *y*-interval. Sketch the region.

61. $f(y) = 4y$, $0 \le y \le 2$
62. $g(y) = \frac{1}{2}y$, $2 \le y \le 4$
63. $f(y) = y^2$, $0 \le y \le 5$
64. $f(y) = 4y - y^2$, $1 \le y \le 2$
65. $g(y) = 4y^2 - y^3$, $1 \le y \le 3$
66. $h(y) = y^3 + 3$, $1 \le y \le 2$

 Approximating Area with the Midpoint Rule In Exercises 67–72, use the Midpoint Rule with $n = 4$ to approximate the area of the region bounded by the graph of the function and the *x*-axis over the given interval.

67. $f(x) = x^2 + 3$, $[0, 2]$ 68. $f(x) = x^2 + 4x$, $[0, 4]$
69. $f(x) = \tan x$, $\left[0, \frac{\pi}{4}\right]$ 70. $f(x) = \cos x$, $\left[0, \frac{\pi}{2}\right]$
71. $f(x) = \ln x$, $[1, 5]$ 72. $f(x) = xe^x$, $[0, 2]$

True or False? In Exercises 73 and 74, determine whether the statement is true or false. If it is false, explain why or give an example that shows it is false.

73. The sum of the first n positive integers is $n(n + 1)/2$.

74. If f is continuous and nonnegative on $[a, b]$, then the limits as $n \to \infty$ of its lower sum $s(n)$ and upper sum $S(n)$ both exist and are equal.

EXPLORING CONCEPTS

75. Implementing Processes   A function is continuous, nonnegative, concave upward, and decreasing on the interval $[0, a]$. Does using the right endpoints of the subintervals produce an overestimate or an underestimate of the area of the region bounded by the function and the x-axis?

76. Connecting Representations   Explain why the Midpoint Rule tends to result in a better area approximation than each endpoint method.

---

77. Graphical Reasoning   A region is bounded by the graphs of $f(x) = 8x/(x + 1)$, $x = 0$, $x = 4$, and $y = 0$.

(a) Sketch the region and the rectangles representing the lower sum when $n = 4$. Find this lower sum.

(b) Sketch the region and the rectangles representing the upper sum when $n = 4$. Find this upper sum.

(c) Sketch the region and the rectangles representing the Midpoint Rule approximation when $n = 4$. Then use the Midpoint Rule to approximate the area.

(d) Verify the following formulas for approximating the area of the region using n subintervals of equal width.

Lower sum: $s(n) = \sum_{i=1}^{n} f\left[(i - 1)\dfrac{4}{n}\right]\left(\dfrac{4}{n}\right)$

Upper sum: $S(n) = \sum_{i=1}^{n} f\left[(i)\dfrac{4}{n}\right]\left(\dfrac{4}{n}\right)$

Midpoint Rule: $M(n) = \sum_{i=1}^{n} f\left[\left(i - \dfrac{1}{2}\right)\dfrac{4}{n}\right]\left(\dfrac{4}{n}\right)$

(e) Use a graphing utility to create a table of values of $s(n)$, $S(n)$, and $M(n)$ for $n = 4, 8, 20, 100$, and 200.

(f) Explain why $s(n)$ increases, whereas $S(n)$ and $M(n)$ decrease for increasing values of n, as shown in the table in part (e).

78. HOW DO YOU SEE IT?   The function shown in the graph below is increasing on the interval $[1, 4]$. The interval will be divided into 12 subintervals.

(a) What are the left endpoints of the first and last subintervals?

(b) What are the right endpoints of the first two subintervals?

(c) When using the right endpoints, do the rectangles lie below or extend above the graph of the function?

79. Justifying   Use the figure to write a short paragraph explaining why the formula

$$1 + 2 + \cdots + n = \tfrac{1}{2}n(n + 1)$$

is valid for all positive integers n.

80. Graphical Reasoning   Consider an n-sided regular polygon inscribed in a circle of radius r. Join the vertices of the polygon to the center of the circle, forming n congruent triangles (see figure).

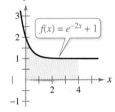

(a) Determine the central angle θ in terms of n.

(b) Show that the area of each triangle is $\tfrac{1}{2}r^2 \sin \theta$.

(c) Let A_n be the sum of the areas of the n triangles. Find $\lim\limits_{n\to\infty} A_n$.

Calculus AP® – Exam Preparation Questions

81. Multiple Choice   Which value best approximates the area of the region bounded by the graph of

$$f(x) = \sin\frac{\pi x}{4}$$

and the x-axis over the interval $[0, 4]$?

(A) 2   (B) 2.5

(C) 3   (D) π

82. Multiple Choice $\lim\limits_{n\to\infty} \sum_{i=1}^{n} \left(\dfrac{1}{n}\right)\left[8\left(\dfrac{i}{n}\right) + 3\right] =$

(A) 3   (D) 4

(C) 7   (D) 8

83. Multiple Choice   Find the Midpoint Rule approximation for the area of the shaded region. Use 8 subintervals of equal width.

(A) 4.425

(B) 4.480

(C) 6.719

(D) 8.959

4.3 Riemann Sums and Definite Integrals

▶ Understand the definition of a Riemann sum.
▶ Evaluate a definite integral using limits and geometric formulas.
▶ Evaluate a definite integral using properties of definite integrals.
▶ Approximate a definite integral using the Trapezoidal Rule.
▶ Analyze the approximate error in the Trapezoidal Rule.

Riemann Sums

In the definition of area given in Section 4.2, the partitions have subintervals of *equal width*. This was done only for computational convenience. The next example shows that it is not necessary to have subintervals of equal width.

EXAMPLE 1   A Partition with Subintervals of Unequal Widths

Consider the region bounded by the graph of $f(x) = \sqrt{x}$ and the x-axis for $0 \le x \le 1$, as shown in Figure 4.18. Evaluate the limit

$$\lim_{n \to \infty} \sum_{i=1}^{n} f(c_i)\,\Delta x_i$$

where c_i is the right endpoint of the partition given by $c_i = i^2/n^2$ and Δx_i is the width of the ith interval.

Solution

The width of the ith interval is

$$\Delta x_i = \frac{i^2}{n^2} - \frac{(i-1)^2}{n^2}$$

$$= \frac{i^2 - i^2 + 2i - 1}{n^2}$$

$$= \frac{2i - 1}{n^2}.$$

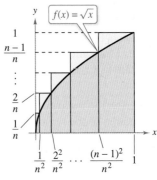

The subintervals do not have equal widths.

Figure 4.18

So, the limit is

$$\lim_{n \to \infty} \sum_{i=1}^{n} f(c_i)\,\Delta x_i = \lim_{n \to \infty} \sum_{i=1}^{n} \sqrt{\frac{i^2}{n^2}} \left(\frac{2i - 1}{n^2}\right)$$

$$= \lim_{n \to \infty} \frac{1}{n^3} \sum_{i=1}^{n} (2i^2 - i)$$

$$= \lim_{n \to \infty} \frac{1}{n^3} \left\{ 2\left[\frac{n(n+1)(2n+1)}{6}\right] - \frac{n(n+1)}{2} \right\}$$

$$= \lim_{n \to \infty} \frac{4n^3 + 3n^2 - n}{6n^3}$$

$$= \frac{2}{3}.$$

> **Algebra Review**
>
> For help on the algebra in Example 1, see Example 1(b) in the *Chapter 4 Algebra Review* on page A42.

From Example 7 in Section 4.2, you know that the region shown in Figure 4.19 has an area of $\frac{1}{3}$. Because the square bounded by $0 \le x \le 1$ and $0 \le y \le 1$ has an area of 1, you can conclude that the area of the region shown in Figure 4.18 has an area of $\frac{2}{3}$. This agrees with the limit found in Example 1, even though that example used a partition having subintervals of unequal widths. The reason this particular partition gave the proper area is that as n increases, the *width of the largest subinterval approaches zero*. This is a key feature of the development of definite integrals.

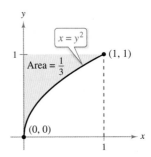

The area of the region bounded by the graph of $x = y^2$ and the y-axis for $0 \le y \le 1$ is $\frac{1}{3}$.

Figure 4.19

In Section 4.2, the limit of a sum was used to define the area of a region in the plane. Finding area by this method is only one of *many* applications involving the limit of a sum. A similar approach can be used to determine quantities as diverse as arc lengths, average values, centroids, volumes, work, and surface areas. The next definition is named after Georg Friedrich Bernhard Riemann (1826–1866). Although the definite integral had been defined and used long before Riemann's time, he generalized the concept to cover a broader category of functions.

In the definition of a Riemann sum below, note that the function f has no restrictions other than being defined on the interval $[a, b]$. (In Section 4.2, the function f was assumed to be continuous and nonnegative because you were finding the area under a curve.)

Definition of Riemann Sum

Let f be defined on the closed interval $[a, b]$, and let Δ be a partition of $[a, b]$ given by

$$a = x_0 < x_1 < x_2 < \cdots < x_{n-1} < x_n = b$$

where Δx_i is the width of the ith subinterval

$$[x_{i-1}, x_i].   \quad \textit{i}\text{th subinterval}$$

If c_i is *any* point in the ith subinterval, then the sum

$$\sum_{i=1}^{n} f(c_i)\, \Delta x_i, \quad x_{i-1} \le c_i \le x_i$$

is called a **Riemann sum** of f for the partition Δ. (The sums in Section 4.2 are examples of Riemann sums, but there are more general Riemann sums than those covered there.)

Insight

On the AP® Exam, a Riemann sum is called a *left Riemann sum* when c_i is the left endpoint of $[x_{i-1}, x_i]$, a *right Riemann sum* when c_i is the right endpoint of $[x_{i-1}, x_i]$, and a *midpoint Riemann sum* when c_i is the midpoint of $[x_{i-1}, x_i]$.

The width of the largest subinterval of a partition Δ is the **norm** of the partition and is denoted by $\|\Delta\|$. If every subinterval is of equal width, then the partition is **regular** and the norm is denoted by

$$\|\Delta\| = \Delta x = \frac{b - a}{n}. \quad \text{Regular partition}$$

For a **general partition,** the norm is related to the number of subintervals of $[a, b]$ in the following way.

$$\frac{b - a}{\|\Delta\|} \le n \quad \text{General partition}$$

So, the number of subintervals in a partition approaches infinity as the norm of the partition approaches 0. That is, $\|\Delta\| \to 0$ implies that $n \to \infty$.

The converse of this statement is not true. For example, let Δ_n be the partition of the interval $[0, 1]$ given by

$$0 < \frac{1}{2^n} < \frac{1}{2^{n-1}} < \cdots < \frac{1}{8} < \frac{1}{4} < \frac{1}{2} < 1.$$

As shown in Figure 4.20, for any positive value of n, the norm of the partition Δ_n is $\frac{1}{2}$. So, letting n approach infinity does not force $\|\Delta\|$ to approach 0. In a regular partition, however, the statements

$$\|\Delta\| \to 0 \quad \text{and} \quad n \to \infty$$

are equivalent.

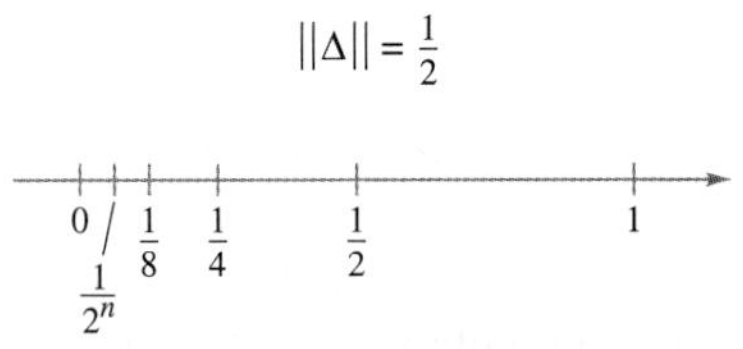

$$\|\Delta\| = \tfrac{1}{2}$$

$n \to \infty$ does not imply that $\|\Delta\| \to 0$.

Figure 4.20

Definite Integrals

To define the definite integral, consider the limit

$$\lim_{\|\Delta\| \to 0} \sum_{i=1}^{n} f(c_i)\,\Delta x_i = L.$$

To say that this limit exists means there exists a real number L such that for each $\varepsilon > 0$, there exists a $\delta > 0$ such that for every partition with $\|\Delta\| \le \delta$, it follows that

$$\left| L - \sum_{i=1}^{n} f(c_i)\,\Delta x_i \right| < \varepsilon$$

regardless of the choice of c_i in the ith subinterval of each partition Δ.

Definition of Definite Integral

If f is defined on the closed interval $[a, b]$ and the limit of Riemann sums over partitions Δ

$$\lim_{\|\Delta\| \to 0} \sum_{i=1}^{n} f(c_i)\,\Delta x_i$$

exists (as described above), then f is said to be **integrable** on $[a, b]$ and the limit is denoted by

$$\lim_{\|\Delta\| \to 0} \sum_{i=1}^{n} f(c_i)\,\Delta x_i = \int_{a}^{b} f(x)\,dx.$$

The limit is called the **definite integral** of f from a to b. The number a is the **lower limit** of integration, and the number b is the **upper limit** of integration.

Remark

Later in this chapter, you will learn convenient methods for calculating $\int_{a}^{b} f(x)\,dx$ for continuous functions. For now, you must use the limit definition.

It is not a coincidence that the notation for definite integrals is similar to that used for indefinite integrals. You will see why in the next section when the Fundamental Theorem of Calculus is introduced. For now, it is important to see that definite integrals and indefinite integrals are different concepts. A definite integral is a *number*, whereas an indefinite integral is a *family of functions*.

Though Riemann sums were defined for functions with very few restrictions, a sufficient condition for a function f to be integrable on $[a, b]$ is that it is continuous on $[a, b]$. A proof of this theorem is beyond the scope of this text.

Theorem 4.4 Continuity Implies Integrability

If a function f is continuous on the closed interval $[a, b]$, then f is integrable on $[a, b]$. That is, $\int_{a}^{b} f(x)\,dx$ exists.

Exploration

The Converse of Theorem 4.4 Is the converse of Theorem 4.4 true? That is, when a function is integrable, does it have to be continuous? Explain your reasoning and give examples.

Describe the relationships among continuity, differentiability, and integrability. Which is the strongest condition? Which is the weakest? Which conditions imply other conditions?

EXAMPLE 2   Evaluating a Definite Integral as a Limit

Evaluate the definite integral.

$$\int_{-2}^{1} 2x \, dx$$

Solution

The function $f(x) = 2x$ is integrable on the interval $[-2, 1]$ because it is continuous on $[-2, 1]$. Moreover, the definition of integrability implies that any partition whose norm approaches 0 can be used to determine the limit. For computational convenience, define Δ by subdividing $[-2, 1]$ into n subintervals of equal width

$$\Delta x_i = \Delta x = \frac{b - a}{n} = \frac{3}{n}.$$

Choosing c_i as the right endpoint of each subinterval produces

$$c_i = a + i(\Delta x) = -2 + \frac{3i}{n}.$$

So, the definite integral is

$$\int_{-2}^{1} 2x \, dx = \lim_{\|\Delta\| \to 0} \sum_{i=1}^{n} f(c_i) \, \Delta x_i$$

$$= \lim_{n \to \infty} \sum_{i=1}^{n} f(c_i) \, \Delta x$$

$$= \lim_{n \to \infty} \sum_{i=1}^{n} 2\left(-2 + \frac{3i}{n}\right)\left(\frac{3}{n}\right)$$

$$= \lim_{n \to \infty} \frac{6}{n} \sum_{i=1}^{n} \left(-2 + \frac{3i}{n}\right)$$

$$= \lim_{n \to \infty} \frac{6}{n} \left(-2 \sum_{i=1}^{n} 1 + \frac{3}{n} \sum_{i=1}^{n} i\right)$$

$$= \lim_{n \to \infty} \frac{6}{n} \left\{-2n + \frac{3}{n}\left[\frac{n(n + 1)}{2}\right]\right\}$$

$$= \lim_{n \to \infty} \left(-12 + 9 + \frac{9}{n}\right)$$

$$= -3.$$

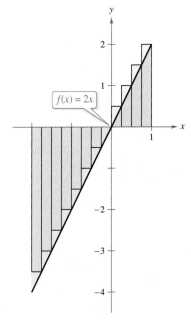

Because the definite integral is negative, it does not represent the area of the region.

Figure 4.21

Because the definite integral in Example 2 is negative, it *does not* represent the area of the region shown in Figure 4.21. Definite integrals can be positive, negative, or zero. For a definite integral to be interpreted as an area (as defined in Section 4.2), the function f must be continuous and nonnegative on $[a, b]$, as stated in the next theorem. The proof of this theorem is straightforward—you simply use the definition of area given in Section 4.2, because it is a Riemann sum.

Algebra Review

For help on the algebra in Example 2, see Example 1(c) in the *Chapter 4 Algebra Review* on page A42.

Theorem 4.5   The Definite Integral as the Area of a Region

If f is continuous and nonnegative on the closed interval $[a, b]$, then the area of the region bounded by the graph of f, the x-axis, and the vertical lines $x = a$ and $x = b$ is

$$\text{Area} = \int_{a}^{b} f(x) \, dx.$$

(See Figure 4.22.)

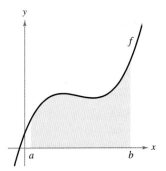

You can use a definite integral to find the area of the region bounded by the graph of f, the x-axis, $x = a$, and $x = b$.

Figure 4.22

As an example of Theorem 4.5, consider the region bounded by the graph of

$$f(x) = 4x - x^2$$

and the *x*-axis, as shown in Figure 4.23. Because f is continuous and nonnegative on the closed interval $[0, 4]$, the area of the region is

$$\text{Area} = \int_0^4 (4x - x^2)\, dx.$$

A straightforward technique for evaluating a definite integral such as this will be discussed in Section 4.4. For now, however, you can evaluate a definite integral in two ways—you can use the limit definition *or* you can check to see whether the definite integral represents the area of a common geometric region, such as a rectangle, triangle, or semicircle.

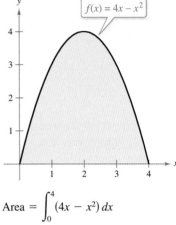

$$\text{Area} = \int_0^4 (4x - x^2)\, dx$$

Figure 4.23

EXAMPLE 3 Areas of Common Geometric Figures

Sketch the region corresponding to each definite integral. Then evaluate each integral using a geometric formula.

a. $\displaystyle\int_1^3 4\, dx$ **b.** $\displaystyle\int_0^3 (x + 2)\, dx$ **c.** $\displaystyle\int_{-2}^2 \sqrt{4 - x^2}\, dx$

Solution

A sketch of each region is shown in Figure 4.24.

a. This region is a rectangle of height 4 and width 2.

$$\int_1^3 4\, dx = (\text{Area of rectangle}) = 4(2) = 8$$

b. This region is a trapezoid with an altitude of 3 and parallel bases of lengths 2 and 5. The formula for the area of a trapezoid is $\frac{1}{2}h(b_1 + b_2)$.

$$\int_0^3 (x + 2)\, dx = (\text{Area of trapezoid}) = \frac{1}{2}(3)(2 + 5) = \frac{21}{2}$$

c. This region is a semicircle of radius 2. The formula for the area of a semicircle is $\frac{1}{2}\pi r^2$.

$$\int_{-2}^2 \sqrt{4 - x^2}\, dx = (\text{Area of semicircle}) = \frac{1}{2}\pi(2^2) = 2\pi$$

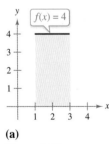

(a)

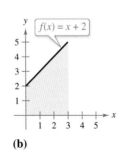

(b)

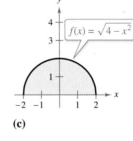

(c)

Figure 4.24

The variable of integration in a definite integral is sometimes called a *dummy variable* because it can be replaced by any other variable without changing the value of the integral. For instance, the definite integrals

$$\int_0^3 (x + 2)\, dx \quad \text{and} \quad \int_0^3 (t + 2)\, dt$$

have the same value.

Properties of Definite Integrals

The definition of the definite integral of f on the interval $[a, b]$ specifies that $a < b$. Now, however, it is convenient to extend the definition to cover cases in which $a = b$ or $a > b$. Geometrically, the next two definitions seem reasonable. For instance, it makes sense to define the area of a region of zero width and finite height to be 0.

> ### Definitions of Two Special Definite Integrals
>
> **1.** If f is defined at $x = a$, then $\displaystyle\int_a^a f(x)\,dx = 0$.
>
> **2.** If f is integrable on $[a, b]$, then $\displaystyle\int_b^a f(x)\,dx = -\int_a^b f(x)\,dx$.

> ### Insight
>
> Understanding the properties of integrals will help you develop the graphical interpretation skills that are emphasized on the AP® Exam.

EXAMPLE 4   Evaluating Definite Integrals

See LarsonCalculusforAP.com for an interactive version of this type of example.

Evaluate each definite integral.

a. $\displaystyle\int_\pi^\pi \sin x\,dx$ **b.** $\displaystyle\int_3^0 (x + 2)\,dx$

Solution

a. Because the sine function is defined at $x = \pi$, and the upper and lower limits of integration are equal, you can write

$$\int_\pi^\pi \sin x\,dx = 0.$$

b. The integral $\int_3^0 (x + 2)\,dx$ is the same as that given in Example 3(b) except that the upper and lower limits are interchanged. Because the integral in Example 3(b) has a value of $\frac{21}{2}$, you can write

$$\int_3^0 (x + 2)\,dx = -\int_0^3 (x + 2)\,dx = -\frac{21}{2}.$$ ∎

In Figure 4.25, the larger region can be divided at $x = c$ into two subregions whose intersection is a line segment. Because the line segment has zero area, it follows that the area of the larger region is equal to the sum of the areas of the two smaller regions.

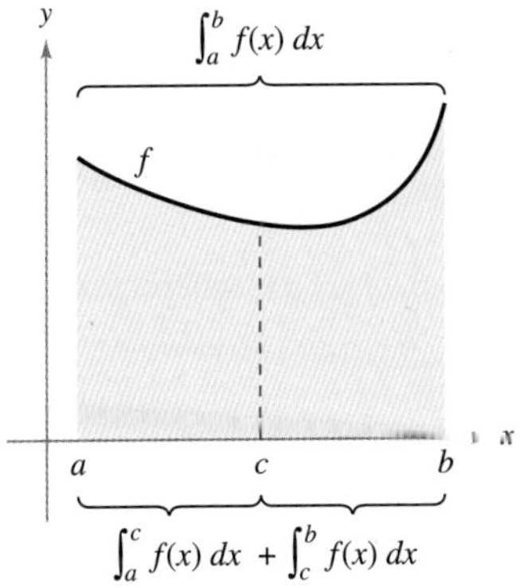

> ### Theorem 4.6   Additive Interval Property
>
> If f is integrable on the three closed intervals determined by a, b, and c, then
>
> $$\int_a^b f(x)\,dx = \int_a^c f(x)\,dx + \int_c^b f(x)\,dx. \qquad \text{See Figure 4.25.}$$

$\displaystyle\int_a^b f(x)\,dx$

f

$\displaystyle\int_a^c f(x)\,dx + \int_c^b f(x)\,dx$

Figure 4.25

EXAMPLE 5   Using the Additive Interval Property

$$\int_{-1}^1 |x|\,dx = \int_{-1}^0 -x\,dx + \int_0^1 x\,dx \qquad \text{Theorem 4.6}$$

$$= \frac{1}{2} + \frac{1}{2} \qquad \text{Area of a triangle}$$

$$= 1$$ ∎

Because the definite integral is defined as the limit of a sum, it inherits the properties of summation given at the top of page 291.

Theorem 4.7 Properties of Definite Integrals

If f and g are integrable on $[a, b]$ and k is a constant, then the functions kf and $f \pm g$ are integrable on $[a, b]$, and

1. $\displaystyle\int_a^b kf(x)\, dx = k \int_a^b f(x)\, dx$ **2.** $\displaystyle\int_a^b [f(x) \pm g(x)]\, dx = \int_a^b f(x)\, dx \pm \int_a^b g(x)\, dx.$

> **Remark**
>
> Property 2 of Theorem 4.7 can be extended to cover any finite number of functions. (See Example 6.)

EXAMPLE 6 **Evaluating a Definite Integral**

Evaluate $\displaystyle\int_1^3 (-x^2 + 4x - 3)\, dx$ using each of the following values.

$$\int_1^3 x^2\, dx = \frac{26}{3}, \qquad \int_1^3 x\, dx = 4, \qquad \int_1^3 dx = 2$$

Algebraic Solution

$$\int_1^3 (-x^2 + 4x - 3)\, dx = \int_1^3 (-x^2)\, dx + \int_1^3 4x\, dx + \int_1^3 (-3)\, dx$$

$$= -\int_1^3 x^2\, dx + 4\int_1^3 x\, dx - 3\int_1^3 dx$$

$$= -\left(\frac{26}{3}\right) + 4(4) - 3(2)$$

$$= \frac{4}{3}$$

Graphical Solution

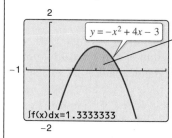

Use the *integral* feature to determine that the value of the definite integral is about $1.333 \approx 4/3$.

Theorem 4.4 guarantees that continuous functions are integrable. Some functions that have removable or jump discontinuities are also integrable. A function is integrable when it has a finite number of points of discontinuity but is otherwise continuous.

EXAMPLE 7 **Integrating a Function That Has a Discontinuity**

Evaluate $\displaystyle\int_0^5 f(x)\, dx$, where $f(x) = \begin{cases} -2x + 7, & x \le 3 \\ 4, & x > 3 \end{cases}$.

Solution

Notice in Figure 4.26 that the graph of f has one discontinuity at $x = 3$, where it jumps from 1 to 4. Otherwise, it is continuous. By Theorem 4.6, you can write

$$\int_0^5 f(x)\, dx = \int_0^3 f(x)\, dx + \int_3^5 f(x)\, dx.$$

The region that corresponds to $\int_0^3 f(x)\, dx$ is a trapezoid with an altitude of 3 and parallel bases of lengths 1 and 7. The region that corresponds to $\int_3^5 f(x)\, dx$ is a rectangle of height 4 and width 2, as shown in Figure 4.26. So,

$$\int_0^5 f(x)\, dx = \int_0^3 f(x)\, dx + \int_3^5 f(x)\, dx$$

$$= \frac{1}{2}(3)(1 + 7) + 4(2)$$

$$= 20.$$

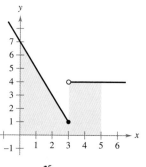

$$\text{Area} = \int_0^5 f(x)\, dx$$

Figure 4.26

If f and g are continuous on the closed interval $[a, b]$ and $0 \le f(x) \le g(x)$ for $a \le x \le b$, then the following properties are true. First, the area of the region bounded by the graph of f and the x-axis (between a and b) must be nonnegative. Second, this area must be less than or equal to the area of the region bounded by the graph of g and the x-axis (between a and b), as shown in Figure 4.27. These two properties are generalized in Theorem 4.8.

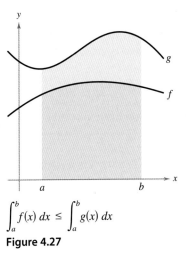

$$\int_a^b f(x)\, dx \le \int_a^b g(x)\, dx$$

Figure 4.27

> **Theorem 4.8   Preservation of Inequality**
>
> **1.** If f is integrable and nonnegative on the closed interval $[a, b]$, then
>
> $$0 \le \int_a^b f(x)\, dx.$$
>
> **2.** If f and g are integrable on the closed interval $[a, b]$ and $f(x) \le g(x)$ for every x in $[a, b]$, then
>
> $$\int_a^b f(x)\, dx \le \int_a^b g(x)\, dx.$$
>
> A proof of this theorem is given in Appendix A.

The Trapezoidal Rule

Some elementary functions simply do not have antiderivatives that are elementary functions. When you need to evaluate a definite integral involving a function whose antiderivative cannot be found, you can use an approximation technique.

One way to approximate a definite integral is to use n trapezoids, as shown in Figure 4.28. In the development of this method, assume that f is continuous and positive on the interval $[a, b]$. So, the definite integral $\int_a^b f(x)\, dx$ represents the area of the region bounded by the graph of f and the x-axis, from $x = a$ to $x = b$. First, partition the interval $[a, b]$ into n subintervals, each of width $\Delta x = (b - a)/n$, such that $a = x_0 < x_1 < x_2 < \ldots < x_n = b$. Then form a trapezoid for each subinterval. (See Figure 4.29.) The area of the ith trapezoid is

$$\text{Area of } i\text{th trapezoid} = \left[\frac{f(x_{i-1}) + f(x_i)}{2}\right]\left(\frac{b - a}{n}\right).$$

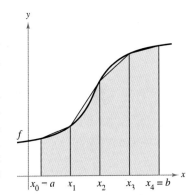

The area of the region can be approximated using four trapezoids.

Figure 4.28

This implies that the sum of the areas of the n trapezoids is

$$\text{Area} = \left(\frac{b - a}{n}\right)\left[\frac{f(x_0) + f(x_1)}{2} + \cdots + \frac{f(x_{n-1}) + f(x_n)}{2}\right]$$

$$= \left(\frac{b - a}{2n}\right)\left[f(x_0) + f(x_1) + f(x_1) + f(x_2) + \cdots + f(x_{n-1}) + f(x_n)\right]$$

$$= \left(\frac{b - a}{2n}\right)\left[f(x_0) + 2f(x_1) + 2f(x_2) + \cdots + 2f(x_{n-1}) + f(x_n)\right].$$

Letting $\Delta x = (b - a)/n$, you can take the limit as $n \to \infty$ to obtain

$$\lim_{n \to \infty}\left(\frac{b - a}{2n}\right)\left[f(x_0) + 2f(x_1) + \cdots + 2f(x_{n-1}) + f(x_n)\right]$$

$$= \lim_{n \to \infty}\left[\frac{[f(a) - f(b)]\,\Delta x}{2} + \sum_{i=1}^n f(x_i)\,\Delta x\right]$$

$$= \lim_{n \to \infty}\frac{[f(a) - f(b)](b - a)}{2n} + \lim_{n \to \infty}\sum_{i=1}^n f(x_i)\,\Delta x$$

$$= 0 + \int_a^b f(x)\, dx.$$

The result is summarized in Theorem 4.9 on the next page.

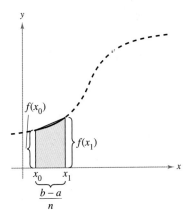

The area of the first trapezoid is

$$\left[\frac{f(x_0) + f(x_1)}{2}\right]\left(\frac{b - a}{n}\right).$$

Figure 4.29

Theorem 4.9 The Trapezoidal Rule

Let f be continuous on $[a, b]$. The Trapezoidal Rule for approximating $\int_a^b f(x)\, dx$ is

$$\int_a^b f(x)\, dx \approx \frac{b-a}{2n}[f(x_0) + 2f(x_1) + 2f(x_2) + \cdots + 2f(x_{n-1}) + f(x_n)].$$

Moreover, as $n \to \infty$, the right-hand side approaches $\int_a^b f(x)\, dx$.

Remark

Observe that the coefficients in the Trapezoidal Rule have the following pattern.

$$1\ 2\ 2\ 2\ \ldots\ 2\ 2\ 1$$

Note that the Trapezoidal Rule will overestimate $\int_a^b f(x)\, dx$ when the graph of f is concave upward on (a, b), and it will underestimate the integral when the graph of f is concave downward on (a, b).

EXAMPLE 8 Using the Trapezoidal Rule

Use the Trapezoidal Rule to approximate $\int_0^\pi \sin x\, dx$. Compare the results for $n = 4$ and $n = 8$, as shown in Figure 4.30.

Solution

When $n = 4$, $\Delta x = \pi/4$, and you obtain

$$\int_0^\pi \sin x\, dx \approx \frac{\pi}{8}\left(\sin 0 + 2\sin\frac{\pi}{4} + 2\sin\frac{\pi}{2} + 2\sin\frac{3\pi}{4} + \sin\pi\right)$$

$$= \frac{\pi}{8}\left(0 + \sqrt{2} + 2 + \sqrt{2} + 0\right)$$

$$= \frac{\pi(1 + \sqrt{2})}{4}$$

$$\approx 1.896.$$

When $n = 8$, $\Delta x = \pi/8$, and you obtain

$$\int_0^\pi \sin x\, dx \approx \frac{\pi}{16}\left(\sin 0 + 2\sin\frac{\pi}{8} + 2\sin\frac{\pi}{4} + 2\sin\frac{3\pi}{8} + 2\sin\frac{\pi}{2}\right.$$

$$\left. + 2\sin\frac{5\pi}{8} + 2\sin\frac{3\pi}{4} + 2\sin\frac{7\pi}{8} + \sin\pi\right)$$

$$= \frac{\pi}{16}\left(2 + 2\sqrt{2} + 4\sin\frac{\pi}{8} + 4\sin\frac{3\pi}{8}\right)$$

$$\approx 1.974.$$

In the next section, you will use the Fundamental Theorem of Calculus to find that the exact value of $\int_0^\pi \sin x\, dx$ is 2. [See Example 1(c) on page 319.]

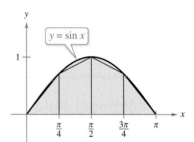

Four subintervals

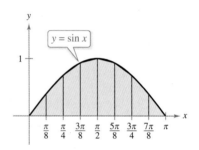

Eight subintervals

Trapezoidal approximations
Figure 4.30

It is interesting to compare the Trapezoidal Rule with the Midpoint Rule given in Section 4.2. For the Trapezoidal Rule, you average the function values at the endpoints of the subintervals, but for the Midpoint Rule, you take the function values of the subinterval midpoints.

$$\int_a^b f(x)\, dx \approx \sum_{i=1}^n f\left(\frac{x_{i-1} + x_i}{2}\right)\Delta x \qquad \text{Midpoint Rule}$$

$$\int_a^b f(x)\, dx \approx \sum_{i=1}^n \left(\frac{f(x_{i-1}) + f(x_i)}{2}\right)\Delta x \qquad \text{Trapezoidal Rule}$$

When using the Trapezoidal Rule (or the Midpoint Rule), note that the approximation tends to become more accurate as n increases. For instance, in Example 8, when $n = 16$, the Trapezoidal Rule yields an approximation of 1.994.

Insight

The Trapezoidal Rule is a useful formula when the intervals are of equal width. When the AP® Exam asks for a *trapezoidal sum* and the intervals are not of equal width, the Trapezoidal Rule does not apply. You must calculate each trapezoidal area separately and add them together.

Error Analysis

When you use an approximation technique such as the Trapezoidal Rule, it is important to know how accurate you can expect the approximation to be. The next theorem, which is listed without proof, gives the formula for estimating the error involved in the use of the Trapezoidal Rule. In general, when using an approximation, you can think of the error E as the difference between $\int_a^b f(x)\, dx$ and the approximation.

Theorem 4.10   Error in the Trapezoidal Rule

If f has a continuous second derivative on $[a, b]$, then the error E in approximating $\int_a^b f(x)\, dx$ by the Trapezoidal Rule is

$$|E| \le \frac{(b-a)^3}{12n^2}[\max |f''(x)|], \quad a \le x \le b. \qquad \text{Trapezoidal Rule}$$

◄ **Communication and Notation**

In Theorem 4.10, $\max |f''(x)|$ is the least upper bound of the absolute value of the second derivative on $[a, b]$.

Theorem 4.10 states that the error generated by the Trapezoidal Rule has an upper bound dependent on the extreme value of $f''(x)$ in the interval $[a, b]$. Furthermore, this error can be made arbitrarily small by *increasing n*, provided that f'' is continuous and therefore bounded on $[a, b]$.

EXAMPLE 9   The Approximate Error in the Trapezoidal Rule

Determine a value of n such that the Trapezoidal Rule will approximate the value of

$$\int_0^1 \sqrt{1 + x^2}\, dx$$

with an error that is less than or equal to 0.01.

Algebra Review

For help on the algebra in Example 9, see Example 3 in the *Chapter 4 Algebra Review* on page A43.

Solution

Begin by letting $f(x) = \sqrt{1 + x^2}$ and finding the second derivative of f.

$$f'(x) = x(1 + x^2)^{-1/2} \quad \text{and} \quad f''(x) = (1 + x^2)^{-3/2}$$

The maximum value of $|f''(x)|$ on the interval $[0, 1]$ is $|f''(0)| = 1$. So, by Theorem 4.10, you can write

$$|E| \le \frac{(b-a)^3}{12n^2}|f''(0)| = \frac{1}{12n^2}(1) = \frac{1}{12n^2}.$$

To obtain an error E that is less than or equal to 0.01, you must choose n such that $1/(12n^2) \le 1/100$.

$$100 \le 12n^2 \quad \Longrightarrow \quad n \ge \sqrt{\frac{100}{12}} \approx 2.89$$

So, you can choose $n = 3$ (because n must be greater than or equal to 2.89) and apply the Trapezoidal Rule, as shown in Figure 4.31, to obtain

$$\int_0^1 \sqrt{1 + x^2}\, dx \approx \frac{1}{6}\left[\sqrt{1 + 0^2} + 2\sqrt{1 + \left(\frac{1}{3}\right)^2} + 2\sqrt{1 + \left(\frac{2}{3}\right)^2} + \sqrt{1 + 1^2}\right]$$

$$\approx 1.154.$$

So, by adding and subtracting the error from this estimate, you know that

$$1.144 \le \int_0^1 \sqrt{1 + x^2}\, dx \le 1.164.$$

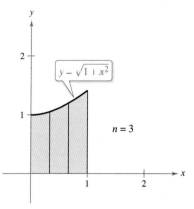

$$1.144 \le \int_0^1 \sqrt{1 + x^2}\, dx \le 1.164$$

Figure 4.31

4.3 Exercises

See *CalcChat.com* for tutorial help and worked-out solutions to odd-numbered exercises.

Evaluating a Limit In Exercises 1 and 2, use Example 1 as a model to evaluate the limit

$$\lim_{n\to\infty} \sum_{i=1}^{n} f(c_i)\, \Delta x_i$$

over the region bounded by the graphs of the equations.

1. $f(x) = \sqrt{x},\ y = 0,\ x = 0,\ x = 3$ $\left(\textit{Hint: Let } c_i = \dfrac{3i^2}{n^2}.\right)$

2. $f(x) = \sqrt[3]{x},\ y = 0,\ x = 0,\ x = 1$ $\left(\textit{Hint: Let } c_i = \dfrac{i^3}{n^3}.\right)$

Evaluating a Definite Integral as a Limit In Exercises 3–8, evaluate the definite integral by the limit definition.

3. $\displaystyle\int_{2}^{6} 8\, dx$

4. $\displaystyle\int_{-2}^{3} x\, dx$

5. $\displaystyle\int_{-1}^{1} x^3\, dx$

6. $\displaystyle\int_{1}^{4} 4x^2\, dx$

7. $\displaystyle\int_{1}^{2} (x^2 + 1)\, dx$

8. $\displaystyle\int_{-2}^{1} (2x^2 + 3)\, dx$

Writing a Limit as a Definite Integral In Exercises 9–14, write the limit as a definite integral on the given interval, where c_i is any point in the ith subinterval.

9. $\displaystyle\lim_{\|\Delta\|\to 0} \sum_{i=1}^{n} (3c_i + 10)\, \Delta x_i,\ [-1, 5]$

10. $\displaystyle\lim_{\|\Delta\|\to 0} \sum_{i=1}^{n} 6c_i(4 - c_i)^2\, \Delta x_i,\ [0, 4]$

11. $\displaystyle\lim_{\|\Delta\|\to 0} \sum_{i=1}^{n} \sqrt{c_i^2 + 4}\, \Delta x_i,\ [0, 3]$

12. $\displaystyle\lim_{\|\Delta\|\to 0} \sum_{i=1}^{n} \left(\dfrac{3}{c_i^2}\right) \Delta x_i,\ [1, 3]$

13. $\displaystyle\lim_{\|\Delta\|\to 0} \sum_{i=1}^{n} \left(1 + \dfrac{3}{c_i}\right) \Delta x_i,\ [1, 5]$

14. $\displaystyle\lim_{\|\Delta\|\to 0} \sum_{i=1}^{n} (2^{-c_i} \sin c_i)\, \Delta x_i,\ [0, \pi]$

Writing a Definite Integral In Exercises 15–26, write a definite integral that represents the area of the region. (Do not evaluate the integral.)

15. $f(x) = 5$

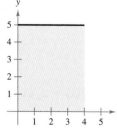

16. $f(x) = 6 - 3x$

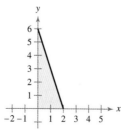

17. $f(x) = 25 - x^2$

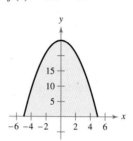

18. $f(x) = 4 - |x|$

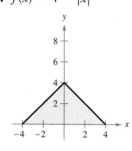

19. $f(x) = \dfrac{2}{x}$

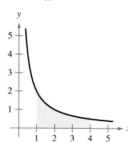

20. $f(x) = 2e^{-x}$

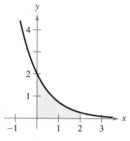

21. $f(x) = \cos x$

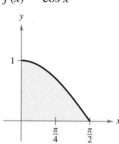

22. $f(x) = \tan x$

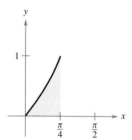

23. $f(y) = 3$

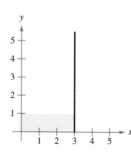

24. $g(y) = \dfrac{y - 1}{2}$

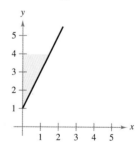

25. $g(y) = y^3$

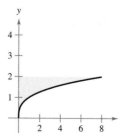

26. $f(y) = (y - 2)^2$

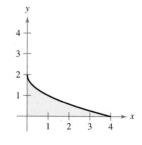

Evaluating a Definite Integral Using a Geometric Formula In Exercises 27–38, sketch the region whose area is given by the definite integral. Then use a geometric formula to evaluate the integral ($a > 0, r > 0$).

27. $\int_0^3 4\, dx$

28. $\int_{-5}^0 8\, dy$

29. $\int_0^4 x\, dx$

30. $\int_0^8 \dfrac{x}{4}\, dx$

31. $\int_0^6 \left(\dfrac{1}{3}y + 4\right) dy$

32. $\int_0^3 (8 - 2x)\, dx$

33. $\int_{-1}^1 (1 - |x|)\, dx$

34. $\int_{-a}^a (a - |x|)\, dx$

35. $\int_{-7}^7 \sqrt{49 - x^2}\, dx$

36. $\int_{-r}^r \sqrt{r^2 - x^2}\, dx$

37. $\int_{-4}^4 \left(\sqrt{16 - y^2} + 3\right) dy$

38. $\int_{-2}^2 \left(4 - \sqrt{4 - x^2}\right) dx$

39. Using Properties of Definite Integrals Given

$$\int_0^5 f(x)\, dx = 10 \quad \text{and} \quad \int_5^7 f(x)\, dx = 3$$

evaluate

(a) $\int_0^7 f(x)\, dx.$

(b) $\int_5^0 f(x)\, dx.$

(c) $\int_5^5 f(x)\, dx.$

(d) $\int_7^0 f(x)\, dx.$

40. Using Properties of Definite Integrals Given

$$\int_{-3}^3 g(x)\, dx = 12 \text{ evaluate}$$

(a) $\int_{-3}^{-3} g(x)\, dx.$

(b) $\int_3^{-3} g(x)\, dx.$

(c) $\int_{-3}^1 g(x)\, dx + \int_1^3 g(x)\, dx.$

(d) $\int_0^{-3} g(x)\, dx - \int_0^3 g(x)\, dx.$

Using Properties of Definite Integrals In Exercises 41–50, evaluate the integral using the following values, if possible. Use a graphing utility to verify your result.

$$\int_2^4 x^3\, dx = 60, \quad \int_2^4 x\, dx = 6, \quad \int_2^4 dx = 2$$

41. $\int_4^2 x\, dx$

42. $\int_2^2 x^3\, dx$

43. $\int_2^4 8x\, dx$

44. $\int_4^2 25\, dx$

45. $\int_4^2 (x - 9)\, dx$

46. $\int_2^4 (x^3 + 4)\, dx$

47. $\int_2^4 x^4\, dx$

48. $\int_2^4 (x^2 - x)\, dx$

49. $\int_2^4 \left(\tfrac{1}{2}x^3 - 3x + 2\right) dx$

50. $\int_2^4 (10 + 4x - 3x^3)\, dx$

51. Estimating a Definite Integral The table gives the values of a decreasing function f for various values of x. Use Riemann sums to find lower and upper estimates of $\int_0^{10} f(x)\, dx$. Did you use left, right, or midpoint Riemann sums for each estimate?

x	0	2	4	6	8	10
$f(x)$	32	24	12	-4	-20	-36

52. Estimating a Definite Integral The table gives the values of an increasing function f for various values of x. Estimate

$$\int_0^6 f(x)\, dx$$

using three equal subintervals and (a) a left Riemann sum, (b) a right Riemann sum, and (c) a midpoint Riemann sum. If possible, compare each estimate with the actual value. Explain your reasoning.

x	0	1	2	3	4	5	6
$f(x)$	-6	0	8	18	30	50	80

53. Think About It The graph of f consists of line segments and a semicircle, as shown in the figure. Evaluate each definite integral by using geometric formulas.

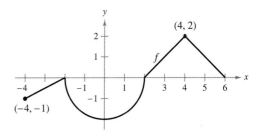

(a) $\int_0^2 f(x)\, dx$

(b) $\int_2^6 f(x)\, dx$

(c) $\int_{-4}^2 f(x)\, dx$

(d) $\int_{-4}^6 f(x)\, dx$

(e) $\int_{-4}^6 |f(x)|\, dx$

(f) $\int_{-4}^6 [f(x) + 2]\, dx$

54. Think About It The graph of f consists of line segments, as shown in the figure. Evaluate each definite integral by using geometric formulas.

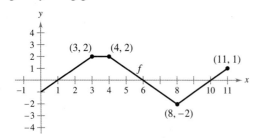

(a) $\int_0^1 -f(x)\,dx$

(b) $\int_3^4 [3 + f(x)]\,dx$

(c) $\int_0^7 f(x)\,dx$

(d) $\int_5^{11} f(x)\,dx$

(e) $\int_0^{11} f(x)\,dx$

(f) $\int_4^{10} f(x)\,dx$

 Integrating a Function that has a Discontinuity In Exercises 55–60, (a) find the x-value(s) at which the function is not continuous, and (b) evaluate the integral. Use a graphing utility to verify your result.

55. $\int_{-3}^2 \frac{|x|}{x}\,dx$

56. $\int_{-5}^6 \frac{x}{|x|}\,dx$

57. $\int_{-4}^5 \frac{x^2 - 4}{x + 2}\,dx$

58. $\int_{-6}^1 \frac{1 - x^2}{x + 1}\,dx$

59. $\int_0^4 f(x)\,dx$, where $f(x) = \begin{cases} 3x + 1, & x \le 2 \\ 2, & x > 2 \end{cases}$

60. $\int_0^5 g(x)\,dx$, where $g(x) = \begin{cases} 8, & x < 3 \\ \dfrac{1}{2}x, & x \ge 3 \end{cases}$

 Using the Trapezoidal Rule In Exercises 61–68, use the Trapezoidal Rule to approximate the value of the definite integral for the given value of n. Round your answer to four decimal places.

61. $\int_0^2 x^2\,dx$, $n = 4$

62. $\int_1^4 (4 - x^2)\,dx$, $n = 6$

63. $\int_0^2 x^3\,dx$, $n = 4$

64. $\int_1^3 x^3\,dx$, $n = 6$

65. $\int_4^9 \sqrt{x}\,dx$, $n = 8$

66. $\int_0^8 \sqrt[3]{x}\,dx$, $n = 8$

67. $\int_0^{\pi/2} \sin 2x\,dx$, $n = 8$

68. $\int_2^3 \frac{2}{x^2}\,dx$, $n = 8$

 Using the Trapezoidal Rule In Exercises 69–80, approximate the definite integral using the Trapezoidal Rule with $n = 4$. Compare the result with the approximation of the integral using a graphing utility.

69. $\int_1^3 \ln x\,dx$

70. $\int_0^{\pi/2} \cos x\,dx$

71. $\int_0^2 \frac{1}{\sqrt{1 + x^3}}\,dx$

72. $\int_0^2 \sqrt{1 + x^3}\,dx$

73. $\int_0^1 \sqrt{x}\,\sqrt{1 - x}\,dx$

74. $\int_0^4 \sqrt{x}\,e^x\,dx$

75. $\int_0^{\sqrt{\pi/2}} \sin x^2\,dx$

76. $\int_0^{\sqrt{\pi/4}} \tan x^2\,dx$

77. $\int_3^{3.1} \cos x^2\,dx$

78. $\int_0^{\pi/2} \sqrt{1 + \sin^2 x}\,dx$

79. $\int_0^2 x \ln(x + 1)\,dx$

80. $\int_0^\pi f(x)\,dx$, $f(x) = \begin{cases} \dfrac{\sin x}{x}, & x > 0 \\ 1, & x = 0 \end{cases}$

 Estimating Errors In Exercises 81–84, use the error formula in Theorem 4.10 to estimate the error in approximating the integral, with $n = 4$, using the Trapezoidal Rule.

81. $\int_1^3 2x^3\,dx$

82. $\int_3^5 (5x + 2)\,dx$

83. $\int_2^4 \frac{1}{(x - 1)^2}\,dx$

84. $\int_0^\pi \cos x\,dx$

Estimating Errors In Exercises 85–88, use the error formula in Theorem 4.10 to find n such that the error in the approximation of the definite integral is less than or equal to 0.00001 using the Trapezoidal Rule.

85. $\int_1^3 \frac{1}{x}\,dx$

86. $\int_0^1 \frac{1}{1 + x}\,dx$

87. $\int_0^2 \sqrt{x + 2}\,dx$

88. $\int_0^{\pi/2} \sin x\,dx$

Error Analysis In Exercises 89 and 90, describe and correct the error in approximating the definite integral using the Trapezoidal Rule with $n = 4$.

89. $\int_0^\pi \cos \frac{x}{2}\,dx \approx \frac{\pi}{8}\left(\cos 0 + \cos \frac{\pi}{8} + \cos \frac{\pi}{4} \right.$
$\left. + \cos \frac{3\pi}{8} + \cos \frac{\pi}{2}\right)$

90. $\int_0^{\pi/2} \sin 2x\,dx \approx \frac{\pi}{8}\left(\sin 0 + 2 \sin \frac{\pi}{4} + 2 \sin \frac{\pi}{2} \right.$
$\left. + 2 \sin \frac{3\pi}{4} + \sin \pi\right)$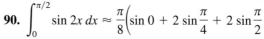

91. Think About It Graph the function $y = 3\sqrt{1 - (x^2/36)}$. Determine whether each sum is an overestimate or underestimate of $\int_0^6 f(x)\,dx$, where $[0, 6]$ is partitioned into 6 subintervals and $\Delta x_i = 1$ for each i.

(a) The left Riemann sum

(b) The right Riemann sum

(c) The trapezoidal sum

92. HOW DO YOU SEE IT? Use the figure to fill in each blank with the symbol $<$, $>$, or $=$. Explain your reasoning.

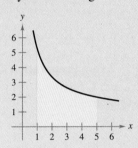

(a) The interval $[1, 5]$ is partitioned into n subintervals of equal width Δx, and x_i is the left endpoint of the ith subinterval.

$$\sum_{i=1}^{n} f(x_i)\,\Delta x \qquad \int_1^5 f(x)\,dx$$

(b) The interval $[1, 5]$ is partitioned into n subintervals of equal width Δx, and x_i is the right endpoint of the ith subinterval.

$$\sum_{i=1}^{n} f(x_i)\,\Delta x \qquad \int_1^5 f(x)\,dx$$

93. Approximating a Function The table lists several measurements gathered in an experiment to approximate an unknown continuous function $y = f(x)$.

x	0.00	0.50	0.75	1.00	1.50	1.75	2.00
y	4.32	4.58	5.79	6.14	7.64	8.08	8.14

(a) Can you use the Trapezoidal Rule with $n = 6$ to approximate the integral $\int_0^2 f(x)\,dx$? Why or why not?

(b) Approximate the integral $\int_0^2 f(x)\,dx$ using the Trapezoidal Rule or a trapezoidal sum.

(c) Use a graphing utility to find a model of the form $y = ax^3 + bx^2 + cx + d$ for the data. Integrate the resulting polynomial over $[0, 2]$ and compare the result with the integral from part (b).

94. SURVEYING

Use the Trapezoidal Rule to estimate the number of square meters of land, where x and y are measured in meters, as shown in the figure. The land is bounded by a stream and two straight roads that meet at right angles.

x	0	100	200	300	400	500
y	125	125	120	112	90	90

x	600	700	800	900	1000
y	95	88	75	35	0

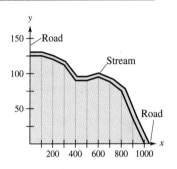

EXPLORING CONCEPTS

95. Justifying Suppose you know the value of $\int_0^4 f(x)\,dx$. Explain how to find each value.

(a) $\displaystyle\int_2^6 f(x - 2)\,dx$

(b) $\displaystyle\int_{-4}^4 f(x)\,dx$, where f is even.

(c) $\displaystyle\int_{-4}^4 f(x)\,dx$, where f is odd.

96. Applying a Definition Describe a partition of $[-1, 1]$ such that $\|\Delta\|$ does not approach zero when $n \to \infty$.

97. Justifying Can you use Theorem 4.5 to find the area of the region bounded by the x-axis and the graphs of $y = 1/(x - 4)$, $x = 3$, and $x = 5$? Explain.

98. Describing an Error Describe the size of the error when the Trapezoidal Rule is used to approximate $\int_a^b f(x)\,dx$ when $f(x)$ is a linear function. Use a graph to explain your answer.

Finding Values In Exercises 99–102, find possible values of a and b that make the statement true. If possible, use a graph to support your answer. (There may be more than one correct answer.)

99. $\displaystyle\int_{-2}^{1} f(x)\,dx + \int_{1}^{5} f(x)\,dx + \int_{5}^{8} f(x)\,dx = \int_{a}^{b} f(x)\,dx$

100. $\displaystyle\int_{-3}^{3} f(x)\,dx + \int_{3}^{6} f(x)\,dx - \int_{a}^{b} f(x)\,dx = \int_{-1}^{6} f(x)\,dx$

101. $\displaystyle\int_{a}^{b} \sin x\,dx < 0$ **102.** $\displaystyle\int_{a}^{b} \cos x\,dx = 0$

True or False? In Exercises 103 and 104, determine whether the statement is true or false. If it is false, explain why or give an example that shows it is false.

103. The Riemann sum $\displaystyle\sum_{i=1}^{n} f(c_i)\Delta x_i$ only approaches the exact value of a definite integral $\int_{a}^{b} f(x)\,dx$ as $\|\Delta\| \to 0$ if the partitions of the sum are of equal width.

104. If f is increasing on $[a, b]$, then the minimum value of $f(x)$ on $[a, b]$ is $f(a)$.

105. Finding a Riemann Sum Find the Riemann sum for $f(x) = x^2 + 3x$ over the interval $[0, 8]$, where $x_0 = 0$, $x_1 = 1$, $x_2 = 3$, $x_3 = 7$, and $x_4 = 8$ and where $c_1 = 1$, $c_2 = 2$, $c_3 = 5$, and $c_4 = 8$.

106. Finding a Riemann Sum Find the Riemann sum for $f(x) = \sin x$ over the interval $[0, 2\pi]$, where $x_0 = 0$, $x_1 = \pi/4$, $x_2 = \pi/3$, $x_3 = \pi$, and $x_4 = 2\pi$, and where $c_1 = \pi/6$, $c_2 = \pi/3$, $c_3 = 2\pi/3$, and $c_4 = 3\pi/2$.

107. Think About It Determine whether the Dirichlet function

$$f(x) = \begin{cases} 1, & x \text{ is rational} \\ 0, & x \text{ is irrational} \end{cases}$$

is integrable on the interval $[0, 1]$. Explain.

108. Finding a Definite Integral The function

$$f(x) = \begin{cases} 0, & x = 0 \\ \dfrac{1}{x}, & 0 < x \le 1 \end{cases}$$

is defined on $[0, 1]$, as shown in the figure. Show that $\int_{0}^{1} f(x)\,dx$ does not exist. Does this contradict Theorem 4.4? Why or why not?

109. Proof Prove that $\displaystyle\int_{a}^{b} x\,dx = \frac{b^2 - a^2}{2}$.

110. Proof Prove that $\displaystyle\int_{a}^{b} x^2\,dx = \frac{b^3 - a^3}{3}$.

111. Finding Values Find the constants a and b, where $a < b$, that maximize the value of $\int_{a}^{b} (1 - x^2)\,dx$. Explain your reasoning.

112. Think About It Find b in terms of k such that $\int_{0}^{b} \sin(kx)\,dx = 0$.

113. Using a Riemann Sum Determine

$$\lim_{n \to \infty} \frac{1}{n^3}\left(1^2 + 2^2 + 3^2 + \ldots + n^2\right)$$

by using an appropriate Riemann sum.

Calculus AP® – Exam Preparation Questions

114. Multiple Choice $\displaystyle\int_{-3}^{6}\left(-\frac{2}{3}x + 5\right)dx =$

(A) 25 (B) 32

(C) 36 (D) 45

115. Multiple Choice The expression

$$\frac{1}{10}\left[\left(\frac{1}{10}\right)^2 + \left(\frac{2}{10}\right)^2 + \left(\frac{3}{10}\right)^2 + \ldots + \left(\frac{10}{10}\right)^2\right]$$

is a Reimann sum approximation for

(A) $\displaystyle\int_{0}^{1} x^2\,dx$. (B) $\displaystyle\frac{1}{10}\int_{0}^{1} x^2\,dx$.

(C) $\displaystyle\int_{1}^{10} x^2\,dx$. (D) $\displaystyle\int_{0}^{10} x^2\,dx$.

116. Multiple Choice The table shows selected values for a continuous function f over the interval $[2, 8]$. Using the subintervals $[2, 3]$, $[3, 5]$, and $[5, 8]$, what is the trapezoidal approximation of $\int_{2}^{8} f(x)\,dx$?

x	2	3	5	8
$f(x)$	8	22	72	142

(A) 268 (B) 338

(C) 430 (D) 592

117. Free Response Consider the function

$$f(x) = \begin{cases} x^3 - 6x^2 + 12x - 6, & x < 2 \\ x^2 - 4x, & x \ge 2 \end{cases}.$$

(a) Graph f on the interval $[0, 4]$.

(b) Is f differentiable at $x = 2$? Justify your answer.

(c) Is f integrable on the interval $[0, 4]$? If so, use your graph to approximate $\int_{0}^{4} f(x)\,dx$. Show the work that leads to your answer.

4.4   The Fundamental Theorem of Calculus

▶ Evaluate a definite integral using the Fundamental Theorem of Calculus.
▶ Understand and use the Mean Value Theorem for Integrals.
▶ Find the average value of a function over a closed interval.
▶ Understand and use the Second Fundamental Theorem of Calculus.

The Fundamental Theorem of Calculus

You have now been introduced to the two major branches of calculus: differential calculus (introduced with the tangent line problem) and integral calculus (introduced with the area problem). So far, these two problems might seem unrelated—but there is a very close connection. The connection was discovered independently by Isaac Newton and Gottfried Leibniz and is stated in the **Fundamental Theorem of Calculus.**

Informally, the theorem states that differentiation and (definite) integration are inverse operations, in the same sense that division and multiplication are inverse operations. To see how Newton and Leibniz might have anticipated this relationship, consider the approximations shown in Figure 4.32. The slope of the tangent line was defined using the *quotient* $\Delta y/\Delta x$ (the slope of the secant line). Similarly, the area of a region under a curve was defined using the *product* $\Delta y \Delta x$ (the area of a rectangle). So, at least in the primitive approximation stage, the operations of differentiation and definite integration appear to have an inverse relationship in the same sense that division and multiplication are inverse operations. The Fundamental Theorem of Calculus states that the limit processes (used to define the derivative and definite integral) preserve this inverse relationship.

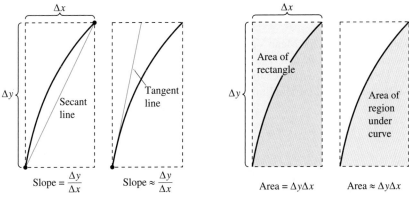

(a) Differentiation   **(b)** Definite integration
Differentiation and definite integration have an "inverse" relationship.
Figure 4.32

Throughout this chapter, you have been using the integral sign to denote an antiderivative (a family of functions) and a definite integral (a number).

Antidifferentiation: $\displaystyle\int f(x)\,dx$ A family of functions

Definite integration: $\displaystyle\int_{a}^{b} f(x)\,dx$ A number

The use of the same symbol for both operations makes it appear that they are related. In the early work with calculus, however, it was not known that the two operations were related. The symbol $\int$ was first applied to the definite integral by Leibniz and was derived from the letter S. (Leibniz calculated area as an infinite sum, thus, the letter S.)

Theorem 4.11   The Fundamental Theorem of Calculus

If a function f is continuous on the closed interval $[a, b]$ and F is an antiderivative of f on the interval $[a, b]$, then

$$\int_a^b f(x)\,dx = F(b) - F(a).$$

Insight

The AP® exam will assess your understanding of the Fundamental Theorem of Calculus from multiple perspectives—graphical, analytic, numerical, and verbal.

Proof

The key to the proof is writing the difference $F(b) - F(a)$ in a convenient form. Let Δ be any partition of $[a, b]$.

$$a = x_0 < x_1 < x_2 < \cdots < x_{n-1} < x_n = b$$

By pairwise subtraction and addition of like terms, you can write

$$F(b) - F(a) = F(x_n) - F(x_{n-1}) + F(x_{n-1}) - \cdots - F(x_1) + F(x_1) - F(x_0)$$

$$= \sum_{i=1}^{n} [F(x_i) - F(x_{i-1})].$$

By the Mean Value Theorem, you know that there exists a number c_i in the ith subinterval such that

$$F'(c_i) = \frac{F(x_i) - F(x_{i-1})}{x_i - x_{i-1}}.$$

Because $F'(c_i) = f(c_i)$, you can let $\Delta x_i = x_i - x_{i-1}$ and obtain

$$F(b) - F(a) = \sum_{i=1}^{n} f(c_i)\,\Delta x_i.$$

This important equation tells you that by repeatedly applying the Mean Value Theorem, you can always find a collection of c_i's such that the *constant* $F(b) - F(a)$ is a Riemann sum of f on $[a, b]$ for any partition. Theorem 4.4 guarantees that the limit of Riemann sums over the partition with $\|\Delta\| \to 0$ exists. So, taking the limit (as $\|\Delta\| \to 0$) produces

$$F(b) - F(a) = \int_a^b f(x)\,dx.$$

■

Guidelines for Using the Fundamental Theorem of Calculus

1. *Provided you can find* an antiderivative of f, you now have a way to evaluate a definite integral without having to use the limit of a sum.

2. When applying the Fundamental Theorem of Calculus, the notation shown below is convenient.

$$\int_a^b f(x)\,dx = F(x)\Big]_a^b = F(b) - F(a)$$

For instance, to evaluate $\int_1^3 x^3\,dx$, you can write

$$\int_1^3 x^3\,dx = \frac{x^4}{4}\Big]_1^3 = \frac{3^4}{4} - \frac{1^4}{4} = \frac{81}{4} - \frac{1}{4} = 20.$$

3. It is not necessary to include a constant of integration C in the antiderivative.

$$\int_a^b f(x)\,dx = \Big[F(x) + C\Big]_a^b = [F(b) + C] - [F(a) + C] = F(b) - F(a)$$

Communication and Notation

Other common notations used when applying the Fundamental Theorem of Calculus are

$$\Big[F(x)\Big]_a^b \quad \text{and} \quad F(x)\Big|_a^b.$$

EXAMPLE 1   Evaluating Definite Integrals

See LarsonCalculusforAP.com for an interactive version of this type of example.

Evaluate each definite integral.

a. $\displaystyle\int_1^2 (x^2 - 3)\, dx$ **b.** $\displaystyle\int_1^4 3\sqrt{x}\, dx$ **c.** $\displaystyle\int_0^\pi \sin x\, dx$

Solution

a. $\displaystyle\int_1^2 (x^2 - 3)\, dx = \left[\frac{x^3}{3} - 3x\right]_1^2 = \left(\frac{8}{3} - 6\right) - \left(\frac{1}{3} - 3\right) = -\frac{2}{3}$

b. $\displaystyle\int_1^4 3\sqrt{x}\, dx = 3\int_1^4 x^{1/2}\, dx = 3\left[\frac{x^{3/2}}{3/2}\right]_1^4 = 2(4)^{3/2} - 2(1)^{3/2} = 14$

c. $\displaystyle\int_0^\pi \sin x\, dx = -\cos x\Big]_0^\pi = -\cos \pi - (-\cos 0) = 2$

EXAMPLE 2   A Definite Integral Involving Absolute Value

Evaluate $\displaystyle\int_0^2 |2x - 1|\, dx$.

Solution

Using Figure 4.33 and the definition of absolute value, you can rewrite the integrand as shown.

$$|2x - 1| = \begin{cases} -(2x - 1), & x < \frac{1}{2} \\ 2x - 1, & x \geq \frac{1}{2} \end{cases}$$

From this, you can rewrite the integral in two parts.

$$\int_0^2 |2x - 1|\, dx = \int_0^{1/2} -(2x - 1)\, dx + \int_{1/2}^2 (2x - 1)\, dx$$

$$= \left[-x^2 + x\right]_0^{1/2} + \left[x^2 - x\right]_{1/2}^2$$

$$= \left(-\frac{1}{4} + \frac{1}{2}\right) - (0 + 0) + (4 - 2) - \left(\frac{1}{4} - \frac{1}{2}\right)$$

$$= \frac{5}{2}$$

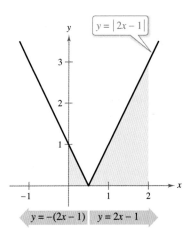

The definite integral of y on $[0, 2]$ is $\frac{5}{2}$.
Figure 4.33

EXAMPLE 3   Using the Fundamental Theorem to Find Area

Find the area of the region bounded by the graph of $y = 1/x$, the x-axis, and the vertical lines $x = 1$ and $x = e$.

Algebraic Solution

Note that $y > 0$ on the interval $[1, e]$.

$$\text{Area} = \int_1^e \frac{1}{x}\, dx \qquad \text{Integrate between } x = 1 \text{ and } x = e.$$

$$= \left[\ln x\right]_1^e \qquad \text{Find antiderivative.}$$

$$= \ln e - \ln 1 \qquad \text{Apply Fundamental Theorem of Calculus.}$$

$$= 1 \qquad \text{Simplify.}$$

Graphical Solution

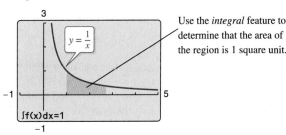

Use the *integral* feature to determine that the area of the region is 1 square unit.

The Mean Value Theorem for Integrals

In Section 4.2, you saw that the area of a region under a curve is greater than the area of an inscribed rectangle and less than the area of a circumscribed rectangle. The Mean Value Theorem for Integrals states that somewhere "between" the inscribed and circumscribed rectangles, there is a rectangle whose area is precisely equal to the area of the region under the curve, as shown in Figure 4.34.

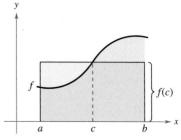

> **Theorem 4.12 Mean Value Theorem for Integrals**
>
> If f is continuous on the closed interval $[a, b]$, then there exists a number c in the closed interval $[a, b]$ such that
>
> $$\int_a^b f(x)\, dx = f(c)(b - a).$$

Mean value rectangle:

$$f(c)(b - a) = \int_a^b f(x)\, dx$$

Figure 4.34

Proof

Case 1: If f is constant on the interval $[a, b]$, then the theorem is clearly valid because c can be any point in $[a, b]$.

Case 2: If f is not constant on $[a, b]$, then, by the Extreme Value Theorem, you can choose $f(m)$ and $f(M)$ to be the minimum and maximum values of f on $[a, b]$. Because

$$f(m) \le f(x) \le f(M)$$

for all x in $[a, b]$, you can apply Theorem 4.8 to write the following.

$$\int_a^b f(m)\, dx \le \quad \int_a^b f(x)\, dx \quad \le \int_a^b f(M)\, dx \qquad \text{See Figure 4.35.}$$

$$f(m)(b - a) \le \quad \int_a^b f(x)\, dx \quad \le f(M)(b - a) \qquad \text{Apply Fundamental Theorem.}$$

$$f(m) \le \frac{1}{b - a}\int_a^b f(x)\, dx \le f(M) \qquad \text{Divide by } b - a.$$

From the third inequality, you can apply the Intermediate Value Theorem to conclude that there exists some c in $[a, b]$ such that

$$f(c) = \frac{1}{b - a}\int_a^b f(x)\, dx \quad \text{or} \quad f(c)(b - a) = \int_a^b f(x)\, dx.$$

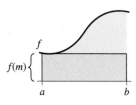 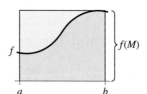

Inscribed rectangle
(less than actual area)

$$\int_a^b f(m)\, dx = f(m)(b - a)$$

Mean value rectangle
(equal to actual area)

$$\int_a^b f(x)\, dx$$

Circumscribed rectangle
(greater than actual area)

$$\int_a^b f(M)\, dx = f(M)(b - a)$$

Figure 4.35

Notice that Theorem 4.12 does not specify how to determine c. It merely guarantees the existence of at least one number c in the interval.

Average Value of a Function

The value of $f(c)$ given in the Mean Value Theorem for Integrals is called the **average value** of f on the interval $[a, b]$.

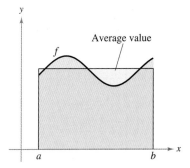

Average value $= \dfrac{1}{b-a} \displaystyle\int_a^b f(x)\, dx$

Figure 4.36

> ### Definition of the Average Value of a Function on an Interval
>
> If f is integrable on the closed interval $[a, b]$, then the **average value** of f on the interval is
>
> $$\frac{1}{b-a} \int_a^b f(x)\, dx.$$
>
> See Figure 4.36.

To see why the average value of f is defined in this way, partition $[a, b]$ into n subintervals of equal width $\Delta x = (b-a)/n$. If c_i is any point in the ith subinterval, then the arithmetic average (or mean) of the function values at the c_i's is

$$a_n = \frac{1}{n}[f(c_1) + f(c_2) + \cdots + f(c_n)]. \qquad \text{Average of } f(c_1), \ldots, f(c_n)$$

By writing the sum using summation notation and then multiplying and dividing by $(b-a)$, you can write the average as

$$a_n = \frac{1}{n} \sum_{i=1}^{n} f(c_i) \qquad \text{Rewrite using summation notation.}$$

$$= \frac{1}{n} \sum_{i=1}^{n} f(c_i)\left(\frac{b-a}{b-a}\right) \qquad \text{Multiply and divide by } (b-a).$$

$$= \frac{1}{b-a} \sum_{i=1}^{n} f(c_i)\left(\frac{b-a}{n}\right) \qquad \text{Rewrite.}$$

$$= \frac{1}{b-a} \sum_{i=1}^{n} f(c_i)\, \Delta x. \qquad \Delta x = \frac{b-a}{n}$$

Finally, taking the limit as $n \to \infty$ produces the average value of f on the interval $[a, b]$, as given in the definition above. In Figure 4.36, notice that the area of the region under the graph of f is equal to the area of the rectangle whose height is the average value.

This development of the average value of a function on an interval is only one of many practical uses of definite integrals to represent summation processes. In Chapter 6, you will study other applications, such as volume and arc length.

Communication and Notation

Be sure you understand the difference between the *average value* of a function on an interval (definite integral application) and the *average rate of change* of a function over an interval (derivative application).

EXAMPLE 4   Finding the Average Value of a Function

Find the average value of $f(x) = 3x^2 - 2x$ on the interval $[1, 4]$.

Solution

The average value is

$$\frac{1}{b-a} \int_a^b f(x)\, dx = \frac{1}{4-1} \int_1^4 (3x^2 - 2x)\, dx$$

$$= \frac{1}{3}\Big[x^3 - x^2\Big]_1^4$$

$$= \frac{1}{3}[64 - 16 - (1 - 1)]$$

$$= \frac{48}{3}$$

$$= 16. \qquad \text{See Figure 4.37.}$$

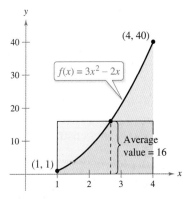

Figure 4.37

EXAMPLE 5 The Speed of Sound

At different altitudes in Earth's atmosphere, sound travels at different speeds. The speed of sound $s(x)$, in meters per second, can be modeled by

$$s(x) = \begin{cases} -4x + 341, & 0 \le x < 11.5 \\ 295, & 11.5 \le x < 22 \\ \frac{3}{4}x + 278.5, & 22 \le x < 32 \\ \frac{3}{2}x + 254.5, & 32 \le x < 50 \\ -\frac{3}{2}x + 404.5, & 50 \le x \le 80 \end{cases}$$

where x is the altitude in kilometers. (See Figure 4.38.) What is the average speed of sound over the interval $[0, 80]$?

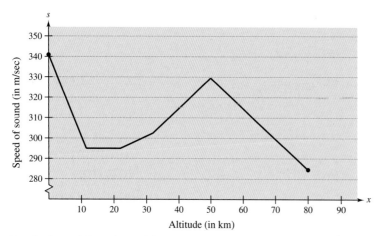

Speed of sound depends on altitude.
Figure 4.38

The first person to fly at a speed greater than the speed of sound was Charles Yeager. On October 14, 1947, Yeager was clocked at 295.9 meters per second at an altitude of 12.2 kilometers. If Yeager had been flying at an altitude below 11.275 kilometers, this speed would not have "broken the sound barrier." The photo shows an F/A-18F Super Hornet, a supersonic twin-engine strike fighter. A "Green Hornet" using a 50/50 mixture of biofuel made from camelina oil became the first U.S. naval tactical aircraft to exceed 1 mach (the speed of sound).

Solution

Begin by integrating $s(x)$ over the interval $[0, 80]$. To do this, you can break the integral into five parts.

$$\int_0^{11.5} s(x)\,dx = \int_0^{11.5} (-4x + 341)\,dx = \left[-2x^2 + 341x\right]_0^{11.5} = 3657$$

$$\int_{11.5}^{22} s(x)\,dx = \int_{11.5}^{22} 295\,dx = \left[295x\right]_{11.5}^{22} = 3097.5$$

$$\int_{22}^{32} s(x)\,dx = \int_{22}^{32} \left(\frac{3}{4}x + 278.5\right) dx = \left[\frac{3}{8}x^2 + 278.5x\right]_{22}^{32} = 2987.5$$

$$\int_{32}^{50} s(x)\,dx = \int_{32}^{50} \left(\frac{3}{2}x + 254.5\right) dx = \left[\frac{3}{4}x^2 + 254.5x\right]_{32}^{50} = 5688$$

$$\int_{50}^{80} s(x)\,dx = \int_{50}^{80} \left(-\frac{3}{2}x + 404.5\right) dx = \left[-\frac{3}{4}x^2 + 404.5x\right]_{50}^{80} = 9210$$

By adding the values of the five integrals, you have

$$\int_0^{80} s(x)\,dx = 24{,}640.$$

So, the average speed of sound from an altitude of 0 kilometers to an altitude of 80 kilometers is

$$\text{Average speed} = \frac{1}{80}\int_0^{80} s(x)\,dx = \frac{24{,}640}{80} = 308 \text{ meters per second.}$$

Insight

The average value of a function is frequently tested on the multiple-choice and the free-response sections of the AP® exam.

The Second Fundamental Theorem of Calculus

Earlier, you saw that the definite integral of f on the interval $[a, b]$ was defined using the constant b as the upper limit of integration and x as the variable of integration. However, a slightly different situation may arise in which the variable x is used in the upper limit of integration. To avoid the confusion of using x in two different ways, t is temporarily used as the variable of integration. (Remember that the definite integral is *not* a function of its variable of integration.)

The Definite Integral as a Number   *The Definite Integral as a Function of x*

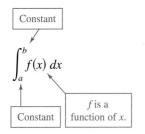

EXAMPLE 6   The Definite Integral as a Function

Evaluate the function

$$F(x) = \int_0^x \cos t \, dt$$

at $x = 0, \pi/6, \pi/4, \pi/3,$ and $\pi/2$.

Exploration

Use a graphing utility to graph the function

$$F(x) = \int_0^x \cos t \, dt$$

for $0 \le x \le 2\pi$. Do you recognize this graph? Explain.

Solution

You could solve this problem by evaluating five different definite integrals, one for each of the given upper limits. It is much simpler, however, to fix x (as a constant) temporarily to obtain

$$\int_0^x \cos t \, dt = \sin t \Big]_0^x$$

$$= \sin x - \sin 0$$

$$= \sin x.$$

Now, using $F(x) = \sin x$, you can obtain the results shown in Figure 4.39.

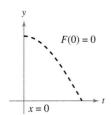 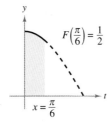 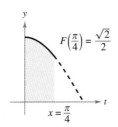 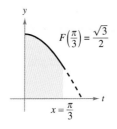 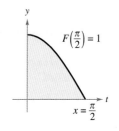

$F(x) = \int_0^x \cos t \, dt$ is the area under the curve $f(t) = \cos t$ from 0 to x.

Figure 4.39

You can think of the function $F(x)$ as *accumulating* the area under the curve $f(t) = \cos t$ from $t = 0$ to $t = x$. For $x = 0$, the area is 0 and $F(0) = 0$. For $x = \pi/2$, $F(\pi/2) = 1$ gives the accumulated area under the cosine curve on the entire interval $[0, \pi/2]$. This interpretation of an integral as an **accumulation function** is used often in applications of integration.

In Example 6, note that the derivative of F is the original integrand (with only the variable changed). That is,

$$\frac{d}{dx}[F(x)] = \frac{d}{dx}[\sin x] = \frac{d}{dx}\left[\int_0^x \cos t \, dt\right] = \cos x.$$

This result is generalized in the next theorem, called the **Second Fundamental Theorem of Calculus.**

Theorem 4.13   The Second Fundamental Theorem of Calculus

If f is continuous on an open interval I containing a, then, for every x in the interval,

$$\frac{d}{dx}\left[\int_a^x f(t) \, dt\right] = f(x).$$

Insight

The Second Fundamental Theorem of Calculus is frequently tested on the multiple-choice and the free-response sections of the AP® Calculus Exam. Remember to apply the Chain Rule when necessary.

Proof   Begin by defining F as

$$F(x) = \int_a^x f(t) \, dt.$$

Then, by the definition of the derivative, you can write

$$F'(x) = \lim_{\Delta x \to 0} \frac{F(x + \Delta x) - F(x)}{\Delta x}$$

$$= \lim_{\Delta x \to 0} \frac{1}{\Delta x}\left[\int_a^{x+\Delta x} f(t) \, dt - \int_a^x f(t) \, dt\right]$$

$$= \lim_{\Delta x \to 0} \frac{1}{\Delta x}\left[\int_a^{x+\Delta x} f(t) \, dt + \int_x^a f(t) \, dt\right]$$

$$= \lim_{\Delta x \to 0} \frac{1}{\Delta x}\left[\int_x^{x+\Delta x} f(t) \, dt\right].$$

From the Mean Value Theorem for Integrals (assuming $\Delta x > 0$), you know there exists a number c in the interval $[x, x + \Delta x]$ such that the integral in the expression above is equal to $f(c) \, \Delta x$. Moreover, because $x \le c \le x + \Delta x$, it follows that $c \to x$ as $\Delta x \to 0$. So, you obtain

$$F'(x) = \lim_{\Delta x \to 0}\left[\frac{1}{\Delta x}f(c) \, \Delta x\right] = \lim_{\Delta x \to 0} f(c) = f(x).$$

A similar argument can be made for $\Delta x < 0$.

Using the area model for definite integrals, the approximation

$$f(x) \, \Delta x \approx \int_x^{x+\Delta x} f(t) \, dt$$

can be viewed as saying that the area of the rectangle of height $f(x)$ and width Δx is approximately equal to the area of the region lying between the graph of f and the x-axis on the interval

$$[x, x + \Delta x]$$

as shown in the figure at the right.

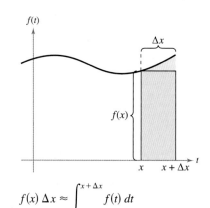

$$f(x) \, \Delta x \approx \int_x^{x+\Delta x} f(t) \, dt$$

Note that the Second Fundamental Theorem of Calculus tells you that when a function is continuous, you can be sure that it has an antiderivative. However, this antiderivative need not be an elementary function. (Recall the discussion of elementary functions in Section P.3.)

EXAMPLE 7 The Second Fundamental Theorem of Calculus

Evaluate $\dfrac{d}{dx}\left[\displaystyle\int_0^x \sqrt{t^2 + 1}\, dt\right]$.

Solution

Note that $f(t) = \sqrt{t^2 + 1}$ is continuous on the entire real number line. So, using the Second Fundamental Theorem of Calculus, you can write

$$\frac{d}{dx}\left[\int_0^x \sqrt{t^2 + 1}\, dt\right] = \sqrt{x^2 + 1}.$$

The differentiation shown in Example 7 is a straightforward application of the Second Fundamental Theorem of Calculus. The next example shows how this theorem can be combined with the Chain Rule to find the derivative of a function.

EXAMPLE 8 The Second Fundamental Theorem of Calculus

Find the derivative of $F(x) = \displaystyle\int_{\pi/2}^{x^3} \cos t\, dt$.

Solution

Using $u = x^3$, you can apply the Second Fundamental Theorem of Calculus with the Chain Rule as shown.

$$\begin{aligned}
F'(x) &= \frac{dF}{du}\frac{du}{dx} & &\text{Chain Rule}\\[4pt]
&= \frac{d}{du}[F(x)]\frac{du}{dx} & &\text{Definition of } \frac{dF}{du}\\[4pt]
&= \frac{d}{du}\left[\int_{\pi/2}^{x^3}\cos t\, dt\right]\frac{du}{dx} & &\text{Substitute } \int_{\pi/2}^{x^3}\cos t\, dt \text{ for } F(x).\\[4pt]
&= \frac{d}{du}\left[\int_{\pi/2}^{u}\cos t\, dt\right]\frac{du}{dx} & &\text{Substitute } u \text{ for } x^3.\\[4pt]
&= (\cos u)(3x^2) & &\text{Apply Second Fundamental Theorem of Calculus.}\\[4pt]
&= (\cos x^3)(3x^2) & &\text{Rewrite as function of } x.
\end{aligned}$$

Because the integrand in Example 8 is easily integrated, you can verify the derivative as follows.

$$\begin{aligned}
F(x) &= \int_{\pi/2}^{x^3}\cos t\, dt\\[4pt]
&= \sin t \Big]_{\pi/2}^{x^3}\\[4pt]
&= \sin x^3 - \sin\frac{\pi}{2}\\[4pt]
&= \sin x^3 - 1
\end{aligned}$$

In this form, you can apply the Chain Rule to verify that the derivative of F is the same as that obtained in Example 8.

$$\frac{d}{dx}[\sin x^3 - 1] = (\cos x^3)(3x^2) \qquad \text{Derivative of } F$$

4.4 Exercises

See *CalcChat.com* for tutorial help and worked-out solutions to odd-numbered exercises.

 Graphical Reasoning   In Exercises 1–4, use a graphing utility to graph the integrand. Use the graph to determine whether the definite integral is positive, negative, or zero.

1. $\displaystyle\int_0^\pi \frac{4}{x^2 + 1}\, dx$

2. $\displaystyle\int_0^\pi \cos x \, dx$

3. $\displaystyle\int_{-2}^2 x\sqrt{x^2 + 1}\, dx$

4. $\displaystyle\int_{-2}^2 x\sqrt{2 - x}\, dx$

 Evaluating a Definite Integral   In Exercises 5–28, evaluate the definite integral. Use a graphing utility to verify your result.

5. $\displaystyle\int_{-1}^0 (2x - 1)\, dx$

6. $\displaystyle\int_{-1}^2 (7 - 3t)\, dt$

7. $\displaystyle\int_{-1}^1 (t^2 - 5)\, dt$

8. $\displaystyle\int_1^2 (6x^2 - 3x)\, dx$

9. $\displaystyle\int_0^1 (2t - 1)^2\, dt$

10. $\displaystyle\int_1^4 (8x^3 - x)\, dx$

11. $\displaystyle\int_1^2 \left(\frac{3}{x^2} - 1\right) dx$

12. $\displaystyle\int_{-2}^{-1} \left(u - \frac{1}{u^2}\right) du$

13. $\displaystyle\int_{-1}^1 (\sqrt[3]{t} - 2)\, dt$

14. $\displaystyle\int_1^8 \left(\sqrt{\frac{2}{x}} + \sqrt{8}\right) dx$

15. $\displaystyle\int_{-1}^0 (t^{1/3} - t^{2/3})\, dt$

16. $\displaystyle\int_{-8}^{-1} \frac{x - x^2}{2\sqrt[3]{x}}\, dx$

17. $\displaystyle\int_0^5 |2x - 5|\, dx$

18. $\displaystyle\int_1^4 (3 - |x - 3|)\, dx$

19. $\displaystyle\int_0^4 |x^2 - 9|\, dx$

20. $\displaystyle\int_0^4 |x^2 - 4x + 3|\, dx$

21. $\displaystyle\int_0^\pi (\sin x - 7)\, dx$

22. $\displaystyle\int_0^\pi (2 + \cos x)\, dx$

23. $\displaystyle\int_0^{\pi/4} \frac{1 - \sin^2 \theta}{\cos^2 \theta}\, d\theta$

24. $\displaystyle\int_0^{\pi/4} \frac{\sec^2 \theta}{\tan^2 \theta + 1}\, d\theta$

25. $\displaystyle\int_{-\pi/6}^{\pi/6} \sec^2 x \, dx$

26. $\displaystyle\int_{-\pi/3}^{\pi/3} 4 \sec \theta \tan \theta \, d\theta$

27. $\displaystyle\int_0^2 (2^x + 6)\, dx$

28. $\displaystyle\int_0^3 (t - 5^t)\, dt$

 Finding the Area of a Region   In Exercises 29–32, determine the area of the given region.

29. $y = x - x^2$

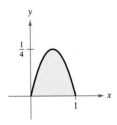

30. $y = \dfrac{1}{x^2}$

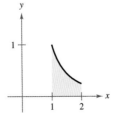

31. $y = \cos x$

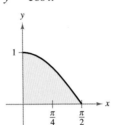

32. $y = x + \sin x$

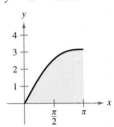

 Finding the Area of a Region   In Exercises 33–38, find the area of the region bounded by the graphs of the equations.

33. $y = 5x^2 + 2$, $x = 0$, $x = 2$, $y = 0$

34. $y = x^3 + 6x$, $x = 2$, $y = 0$

35. $y = 1 + \sqrt[3]{x}$, $x = 0$, $x = 8$, $y = 0$

36. $y = 2\sqrt{x} - x$, $y = 0$

37. $y = \dfrac{4}{x}$, $x = 1$, $x = e$, $y = 0$

38. $y = e^x$, $x = 0$, $x = 2$, $y = 0$

 Using the Mean Value Theorem for Integrals   In Exercises 39–44, find the value(s) of c guaranteed by the Mean Value Theorem for Integrals for the function over the given interval.

39. $f(x) = x^3$, $[0, 3]$

40. $y = \dfrac{x^2}{4}$, $[0, 6]$

41. $f(x) = 5 - \dfrac{1}{x}$, $[1, 4]$

42. $f(x) = 10 - 2^x$, $[0, 3]$

43. $f(x) = 2 \sec^2 x$, $\left[-\dfrac{\pi}{4}, \dfrac{\pi}{4}\right]$

44. $f(x) = \cos x$, $\left[-\dfrac{\pi}{3}, \dfrac{\pi}{3}\right]$

 Finding the Average Value of a Function   In Exercises 45–50, find the average value of the function over the given interval and all values of x in the interval for which the function equals its average value.

45. $f(x) = 4 - x^2$, $[-2, 2]$

46. $f(x) = \dfrac{4(x^2 + 1)}{x^2}$, $[1, 3]$

47. $f(x) = 4e^x$, $[-1, 1]$

48. $f(x) = \dfrac{6}{x}$, $[1, 4]$

49. $f(x) = \sin x$, $[0, \pi]$

50. $f(x) = \cos x$, $\left[0, \dfrac{\pi}{2}\right]$

Evaluating a Definite Integral   In Exercises 51–54, find F as a function of x and evaluate it at $x = 2$, $x = 5$, and $x = 8$.

51. $F(x) = \displaystyle\int_0^x (4t - 7)\, dt$ **52.** $F(x) = \displaystyle\int_2^x (t^3 + 2t)\, dt$

53. $F(x) = \displaystyle\int_1^x \dfrac{20}{v^2}\, dv$ **54.** $F(x) = \displaystyle\int_2^x -\dfrac{2}{t^3}\, dt$

Evaluate a Definite Integral   In Exercises 55 and 56, find F as a function of x and evaluate it as $x = 0$, $x = \pi/4$, and $x = \pi/2$.

55. $F(x) = \displaystyle\int_{-\pi/2}^x \cos\theta\, d\theta$ **56.** $F(x) = \displaystyle\int_{-\pi}^x \sin\theta\, d\theta$

 Finding and Checking an Integral   In Exercises 57–62, (a) integrate to find F as a function of x, and (b) demonstrate the Second Fundamental Theorem of Calculus by differentiating the result in part (a).

57. $F(x) = \displaystyle\int_0^x (t + 2)\, dt$ **58.** $F(x) = \displaystyle\int_0^x t(t^2 + 1)\, dt$

59. $F(x) = \displaystyle\int_8^x \sqrt[3]{t}\, dt$ **60.** $F(x) = \displaystyle\int_{-1}^x e^t\, dt$

61. $F(x) = \displaystyle\int_{\pi/4}^x \sec^2 t\, dt$ **62.** $F(x) = \displaystyle\int_{\pi/3}^x \sec t \tan t\, dt$

 The Second Fundamental Theorem of Calculus   In Exercises 63–68, use the Second Fundamental Theorem of Calculus to find $F'(x)$.

63. $F(x) = \displaystyle\int_{-2}^x (t^2 - 2t)\, dt$ **64.** $F(x) = \displaystyle\int_1^x \dfrac{t^3}{t^2 + 1}\, dt$

65. $F(x) = \displaystyle\int_{-1}^x \sqrt{t^3 + 1}\, dt$ **66.** $F(x) = \displaystyle\int_1^x \sqrt[4]{t}\, dt$

67. $F(x) = \displaystyle\int_1^x \sqrt{t}\csc t\, dt$ **68.** $F(x) = \displaystyle\int_0^x \sec^3 t\, dt$

Finding a Derivative   In Exercises 69–74, find $F'(x)$.

69. $F(x) = \displaystyle\int_x^{x+2} (4t + 1)\, dt$ **70.** $F(x) = \displaystyle\int_{-x}^x t^3\, dt$

71. $F(x) = \displaystyle\int_0^{\sin x} \sqrt{t}\, dt$ **72.** $F(x) = \displaystyle\int_2^{x^2} \dfrac{1}{t^3}\, dt$

73. $F(x) = \displaystyle\int_0^{x^3} \sin t^2\, dt$ **74.** $F(x) = \displaystyle\int_0^{2x} \cos t^4\, dt$

Error Analysis   In Exercises 75 and 76, describe the error. Correct the error, if possible.

75. $\displaystyle\int_{-2}^1 \dfrac{2}{x^3}\, dx = \left[-\dfrac{1}{x^2}\right]_{-2}^1 = -\dfrac{3}{4}$ ✗

76. $\dfrac{d}{dx}\displaystyle\int_2^{x^2} t^4\, dt = (x^2)^4 = x^8$ ✗

77. Force   The force F (in newtons) of a hydraulic cylinder in a press is proportional to the square of $\sec x$, where x is the distance (in meters) that the cylinder is extended in its cycle. The domain of F is $[0, \pi/3]$, and $F(0) = 500$.

(a) Find F as a function of x.

(b) Find the average force exerted by the press over the interval $[0, \pi/3]$.

78. Blood Flow   The velocity v of the flow of blood at a distance r from the central axis of an artery of radius R is $v = k(R^2 - r^2)$, where k is the constant of proportionality. Find the average rate of flow of blood along a radius of the artery. (Use 0 and R as the limits of integration.)

79. Respiratory Cycle   The volume V, in liters, of air in the lungs during a five-second respiratory cycle is approximated by the model $V = 0.1729t + 0.1522t^2 - 0.0374t^3$, where t is the time in seconds. Approximate the average volume of air in the lungs during one cycle.

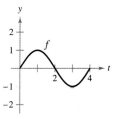 **80. HOW DO YOU SEE IT?**   The graph of f is shown in the figure. The shaded region A has an area of 1.5, and $\int_0^6 f(x)\, dx = 3.5$. Use this information to fill in the blanks.

(a) $\displaystyle\int_0^2 f(x)\, dx = $ [ ]

(b) $\displaystyle\int_2^6 f(x)\, dx = $ [ ]

(c) $\displaystyle\int_0^6 |f(x)|\, dx = $ [ ]

(d) $\displaystyle\int_0^2 -2f(x)\, dx = $ [ ]

(e) $\displaystyle\int_0^6 [2 + f(x)]\, dx = $ [ ]

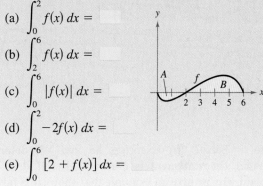

(f) The average value of f over the interval $[0, 6]$ is [ ].

EXPLORING CONCEPTS

81. Graphical Analysis   Sketch an approximate graph of g on the interval $0 \le x \le 4$, where

$$g(x) = \int_0^x f(t)\, dt.$$

Identify the x-coordinate of an extremum of g. To print an enlarged copy of the graph, go to *MathGraphs.com.*

EXPLORING CONCEPTS (CONTINUED)

82. Connecting Representations The graph of f is shown in the figure.

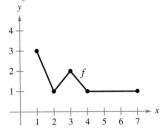

(a) Evaluate $\int_1^7 f(x)\, dx$.

(b) Find the average value of f on the interval $[1, 7]$.

(c) Determine the answers to parts (a) and (b) when the graph is translated two units upward.

Graphical Reasoning In Exercises 83 and 84, let $g(x) = \int_0^x f(t)\, dt$, where f is the function whose graph is shown in the figure.

(a) Estimate $g(0)$, $g(2)$, $g(4)$, $g(6)$, and $g(8)$.

(b) Find the largest open intervals on which g is increasing and decreasing.

(c) Identify any extrema of g.

(d) Sketch a rough graph of g.

83.
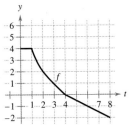

84.
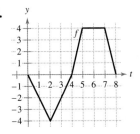

True or False? In Exercises 85 and 86, determine whether the statement is true or false. If it is false, explain why or give an example that shows it is false.

85. If $F'(x) = G'(x)$ on the interval $[a, b]$, then

$$F(b) - F(a) = G(b) - G(a).$$

86. If f is a continuous even function, then $F(x) = \int_0^x f(t)\, dt$ is an odd function.

87. Justifying Show that the function

$$f(x) = \int_0^{1/x} \frac{1}{t^2 + 1}\, dt + \int_0^x \frac{1}{t^2 + 1}\, dt$$

is constant for $x > 0$.

88. Implementing Processes Find the function $f(t)$ and all values of c such that

$$\int_c^x f(t)\, dt = x^2 + x - 2.$$

Calculus AP® – Exam Preparation Questions

89. Multiple Choice If $f(x) = x^3$ has an average value of 12 on the interval $[0, k]$, then $k =$

  (A) $12^{1/3}$.   (B) $48^{1/4}$.   (C) $24^{1/3}$.   (D) $48^{1/3}$.

90. Multiple Choice $\dfrac{d}{dx}\left[\displaystyle\int_0^{x^2} e^{t^2}\, dt \right] =$

  (A) 0   (B) $2e^{x^4}$ (C) $2xe^{x^4}$ (D) e^{x^4}

91. Free Response The velocity $v(t)$ (in feet per second) of a high-speed rail train is positive over $0 \le t \le 60$ seconds. The velocities at time t are given as ordered pairs $(t, v(t))$: $(0, 0)$, $(10, 45)$, $(20, 105)$, $(30, 140)$, $(40, 165)$, $(50, 195)$, and $(60, 210)$.

(a) Estimate the acceleration of the train at $t = 25$. Indicate units of measure.

(b) Use a left Riemann sum with three subintervals of equal length to approximate $\int_{20}^{50} v(t)\, dt$. Using correct units, explain the meaning of the integral in the context of this problem.

(c) Evaluate $\int_{20}^{50} v'(t)\, dt$. Using correct units, explain the meaning of the integral in the context of this problem.

(d) Estimate the average velocity of the train over the 60-second period of time using a midpoint Riemann sum with 3 subintervals.

SECTION PROJECT

Demonstrating the Fundamental Theorem

Use a graphing utility to graph the function $y_1 = \sin^2 t$ on the interval $0 \le t \le \pi$. Let $F(x) = \int_0^x \sin^2 t\, dt$.

(a) Complete the table. Explain why the values of F are increasing.

x	0	$\dfrac{\pi}{6}$	$\dfrac{\pi}{3}$	$\dfrac{\pi}{2}$	$\dfrac{2\pi}{3}$	$\dfrac{5\pi}{6}$	π
$F(x)$							

(b) Use the integration capabilities of a graphing utility to graph F.

(c) Use the differentiation capabilities of a graphing utility to graph F'. How is this graph related to the graph in part (b)?

(d) Verify that the derivative of $y = \frac{1}{2}t - \frac{1}{4}\sin 2t$ is $\sin^2 t$. Graph y and write a short paragraph about how this graph is related to those in parts (b) and (c).

4.5   The Net Change Theorem

▶ Understand and use the Net Change Theorem.

Net Change Theorem

The Fundamental Theorem of Calculus (Theorem 4.11) states that if f is continuous on the closed interval $[a, b]$ and F is an antiderivative of f on $[a, b]$, then

$$\int_a^b f(x)\, dx = F(b) - F(a).$$

But because $F'(x) = f(x)$, this statement can be rewritten as

$$\int_a^b F'(x)\, dx = F(b) - F(a)$$

where the quantity $F(b) - F(a)$ represents the *net change of F* on the interval $[a, b]$.

Theorem 4.14   The Net Change Theorem

If $F'(x)$ is the rate of change of a quantity $F(x)$, then the definite integral of $F'(x)$ from a to b gives the total change, or **net change,** of $F(x)$ on the interval $[a, b]$.

$$\int_a^b F'(x)\, dx = F(b) - F(a) \qquad \text{Net change of } F$$

EXAMPLE 1   Using the Net Change Theorem

A chemical flows into a storage tank at a rate of $(180 + 3t)$ liters per minute, where t is the time in minutes and $0 \le t \le 60$. Find the amount of the chemical that flows into the tank during the first 20 minutes.

Solution

Let $c(t)$ be the amount of the chemical in the tank at time t. Then $c'(t)$ represents the rate at which the chemical flows into the tank at time t. During the first 20 minutes, the amount that flows into the tank is

$$\int_0^{20} c'(t)\, dt = \int_0^{20} (180 + 3t)\, dt$$

$$= \left[180t + \frac{3}{2}t^2 \right]_0^{20}$$

$$= 3600 + 600$$

$$= 4200.$$

So, the amount that flows into the tank during the first 20 minutes is 4200 liters.   ■

A common application of the Net Change Theorem is a particle motion problem. Consider a particle moving along a straight line, where $s(t)$ is the position at time t. The velocity of the particle is $v(t) = s'(t)$ and

$$\int_a^b v(t)\, dt - s(b) - s(a) \qquad \text{Displacement on } [a, b]$$

is the net change in position, or **displacement,** of the particle on the time interval $a \le t \le b$.

Exploration

A car enters a highway at mile marker 98 and travels for t hours at a constant velocity of $v(t) = 65$ miles per hour.

a. Find the distance traveled by the car after 2 hours.

b. Sketch the graph of v for $0 \le t \le 2$. Write an integral that represents the region under the curve.

c. What mile marker is the car at after 2 hours? Does the integral from part (b) give the car's position after 2 hours? Why or why not?

d. Write an expression involving an integral that gives the car's position after 2 hours.

e. Repeat part (d) when the car's velocity after t hours is $v(t) = 5\sqrt{t} + 17t^2 - t^3$. What mile marker is the car at after 2 hours?

To calculate the **total distance** the particle travels on the time interval $a \le t \le b$, you must consider the intervals where $v(t) < 0$ and the intervals where $v(t) > 0$. When $v(t) < 0$, the particle moves to the left. When $v(t) > 0$, the particle moves to the right. In both cases, the distance is found by integrating the **speed** of the particle, $|v(t)|$.

Total distance traveled on $[a, b] = \displaystyle\int_a^b |v(t)|\, dt.$

Figure 4.40 shows how both displacement and total distance traveled can be interpreted as areas under a velocity curve.

Displacement on $[a, b] = \displaystyle\int_a^b v(t)\, dt = A_1 - A_2 + A_3$

Total distance traveled on $[a, b] = \displaystyle\int_a^b |v(t)|\, dt = A_1 + A_2 + A_3$

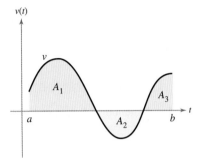

A_1, A_2, and A_3 are the areas of the shaded regions.

Figure 4.40

EXAMPLE 2   Solving a Particle Motion Problem

The velocity (in feet per second) of a particle moving along a line is

$$v(t) = t^3 - 10t^2 + 29t - 20$$

where t is the time in seconds.

a. What is the displacement of the particle on the time interval $1 \le t \le 5$?

b. What is the total distance traveled by the particle on the time interval $1 \le t \le 5$?

Solution

a. The displacement of the particle on $1 \le t \le 5$ is

$$\int_1^5 v(t)\, dt = \int_1^5 (t^3 - 10t^2 + 29t - 20)\, dt$$

$$= \left[\frac{1}{4}t^4 - \frac{10}{3}t^3 + \frac{29}{2}t^2 - 20t \right]_1^5$$

$$= \frac{25}{12} - \left(-\frac{103}{12} \right)$$

$$= \frac{32}{3} \text{ feet.}$$

So, the particle moves about 10.667 feet to the right.

b. To find the total distance traveled, calculate $\int_1^5 |v(t)|\, dt$. Using Figure 4.41 and the fact that $v(t)$ can be factored as $(t - 1)(t - 4)(t - 5)$, you can determine that $v(t) > 0$ on the interval $(1, 4)$ and $v(t) < 0$ on the interval $(4, 5)$. So, the total distance traveled on $1 \le t \le 5$ is

$$\int_1^5 |v(t)|\, dt = \int_1^4 v(t)\, dt + \int_4^5 -v(t)\, dt$$

$$= \int_1^4 (t^3 - 10t^2 + 29t - 20)\, dt + \int_4^5 -(t^3 - 10t^2 + 29t - 20)\, dt$$

$$= \left[\frac{1}{4}t^4 - \frac{10}{3}t^3 + \frac{29}{2}t^2 - 20t \right]_1^4 + \left[-\frac{1}{4}t^4 + \frac{10}{3}t^3 - \frac{29}{2}t^2 + 20t \right]_4^5$$

$$= \frac{45}{4} + \frac{7}{12}$$

$$= \frac{71}{6} \text{ feet}$$

or about 11.833 feet.

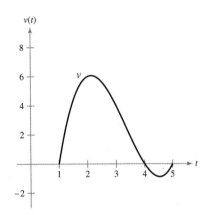

Figure 4.41

Communication and Notation

The unit for the area of a region defined by a rate of change is the unit for the rate of change multiplied by the unit for the independent variable. For instance, in Example 2, the unit for $v(t)$ is feet per second and the unit for t is seconds, so the unit for the area is

$$\frac{\text{feet}}{\text{second}} \cdot \text{second} = \text{feet}.$$

EXAMPLE 3   Falling Object

Neglecting air resistance, the velocity (in feet per second) of an object after it is dropped from a hovering helicopter is $v(t) = -32t$. What is the displacement of the object after 2 seconds?

Solution

Integrate $v(t)$ on the interval $[0, 2]$ to find the displacement of the object.

$$\int_0^2 v(t) \, dt = \int_0^2 -32t \, dt$$

$$= -16t^2 \Big]_0^2$$

$$= -16(4 - 0)$$

$$= -64 \text{ feet}$$

After 2 seconds, the displacement of the object is -64 feet. This means the object is 64 feet *below* where it was dropped from the helicopter. ■

Recall from Example 6 in Section 3.6 that the rate of change of revenue R with respect to the number of units sold x is called the marginal revenue. A common application of a revenue function is to find the increase or decrease in revenue obtained by selling one or several additional units. For instance, suppose you are asked to find the additional revenue obtained by increasing sales from x_1 to x_2 units. When you know the revenue function R, you can find the additional revenue by subtracting $R(x_1)$ from $R(x_2)$. When you do not know R, you can use the marginal revenue function dR/dx to find the additional revenue by using the Net Change Theorem.

$$\int_{x_1}^{x_2} \frac{dR}{dx} \, dx = R(x_2) - R(x_1)$$

Similarly, you can use the Net Change Theorem to find the increase or decrease in profit or cost obtained by selling one or several additional units.

EXAMPLE 4   Analyzing a Profit Function

The rate of change of profit P with respect to the number of units sold x is called the *marginal profit*. The marginal profit for a product is modeled by

$$\frac{dP}{dx} = -0.0005x + 12.2$$

where P is the profit in dollars. Find the change in profit when sales increase from 100 to 200 units.

Solution

Find the change in profit when sales increase from 100 to 200 units.

$$\int_{100}^{200} \frac{dP}{dx} \, dx = \int_{100}^{200} (-0.0005x + 12.2) \, dx$$

$$= \left[-0.00025x^2 + 12.2x \right]_{100}^{200}$$

$$= 2430 - 1217.5$$

$$= 1212.5$$

So, the change in profit is $1212.50. ■

Connecting Representations

If a rate of change is positive (or negative) on an interval, then the accumulated change is positive (or negative). For instance, in Example 4, dP/dx is positive on $[100, 200]$, so the accumulated change in profit, $1215.50, is positive (see figure).

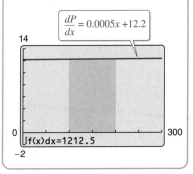

4.5 Exercises

See *CalcChat.com* for tutorial help and worked-out solutions to odd-numbered exercises.

1. Velocity The graph shows the velocity, in feet per second, of a car accelerating from rest. Use the graph to estimate the distance the car travels in 8 seconds.

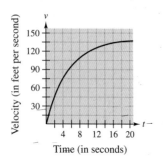

Time (in seconds)

2. Velocity The graph shows the velocity, in feet per second, of a decelerating car after the driver applies the brakes. Use the graph to estimate how far the car travels before it comes to a stop.

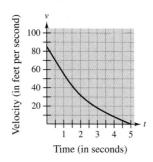

Time (in seconds)

3. Water Flow Water flows from a storage tank at a rate of $(500 - 5t)$ liters per minute. Find the amount of water that flows out of the tank during the first 18 minutes.

4. Oil Leak At 1:00 P.M., oil begins leaking from a tank at a rate of $(4 + 0.75t)$ gallons per hour.

(a) How much oil is lost from 1:00 P.M. to 4:00 P.M.?

(b) How much oil is lost from 4:00 P.M. to 7:00 P.M.?

(c) Compare your answers to parts (a) and (b). What do you notice?

 Particle Motion In Exercises 5–10, the velocity function, in feet per second, is given for a particle moving along a straight line. Find (a) the displacement and (b) the total distance that the particle travels over the given interval.

5. $v(t) = 5t - 7, \quad 0 \le t \le 3$

6. $v(t) = t^2 - t - 12, \quad 1 \le t \le 5$

7. $v(t) = t^3 - 10t^2 + 27t - 18, \quad 1 \le t \le 7$

8. $v(t) = t^3 - 8t^2 + 15t, \quad 0 \le t \le 5$

9. $v(t) = \dfrac{1}{\sqrt{t}}, \quad 1 \le t \le 4$

10. $v(t) = \cos t, \quad 0 \le t \le 3\pi$

11. Particle Motion A particle is moving along the x-axis. The position of the particle at time t is given by $x(t) = t^3 - 6t^2 + 9t - 2, \ 0 \le t \le 5$. Find the total distance the particle travels in 5 units of time.

12. Particle Motion Repeat Exercise 11 for the position function given by $x(t) = (t - 1)(t - 3)^2, \ 0 \le t \le 5$.

Error Analysis In Exercises 13 and 14, the velocity (in inches per second) of a particle moving along a line is $v(t) = \sin t \ dt$.

13. Describe and correct the error in finding the total distance traveled by the particle on the time interval $0 \le t \le 4$.

$$\int_0^4 \sin t \ dt = \Big[-\cos t \Big]_0^4$$

$$= -\cos 4 - (-\cos 0)$$

$$\approx 1.6536 \text{ inches} \qquad ✗$$

14. Describe and correct the error in finding the displacement of the particle on the time interval $4 \le t \le 7$.

$$\int_4^7 |\sin t| \ dt = \int_4^{2\pi} -\sin t \ dt + \int_{2\pi}^7 \sin t \ dt$$

$$= \Big[\cos t \Big]_4^{2\pi} + \Big[-\cos t \Big]_{2\pi}^7$$

$$= 1 - \cos 4 - \cos 7 + 1$$

$$\approx 1.8997 \text{ inches} \qquad ✗$$

15. Falling Object A coin is dropped from the roof of a skyscraper. Neglecting air resistance, the velocity v (in meters per second) of the coin after it is dropped is $v(t) = -9.8t$. What is the displacement of the coin after 3 seconds?

16. Vertical Motion A baseball is batted straight upward. Neglecting air resistance, the velocity v (in feet per second) of the baseball t seconds after it is batted is $v(t) = -32t + 64$.

(a) What is the displacement of the baseball after 3 seconds?

(b) What is the total distance traveled by the baseball in 3 seconds?

17. Analyzing Profit The marginal profit for a product is modeled by

$$\frac{dP}{dx} = -0.0008x + 76.8$$

where P is the profit in dollars and x is the number of units sold. Find the change in profit when sales increase from 400 to 460 units.

18. Modeling Data An experimental vehicle is tested on a straight track. It starts from rest, and its velocity v (in meters per second) is recorded every 10 seconds for 1 minute (see table).

t	0	10	20	30	40	50	60
v	0	5	21	40	62	78	83

(a) Use a graphing utility to find a model of the form $v = at^3 + bt^2 + ct + d$ for the data.

(b) Use a graphing utility to plot the data and graph the model.

(c) Approximate the distance traveled by the vehicle during the test.

EXPLORING CONCEPTS

19. Connecting Representations Describe a situation where the displacement and the total distance traveled for a particle are equal.

20. Notation Let $r'(t)$ represent the rate of growth of a dog, in pounds per year. What does $r(t)$ represent? What does $\int_2^6 r'(t)\,dt$ represent about the dog?

21. Notation Let $r(t)$ represent the number of gallons of oil produced by an oil well after t hours. Interpret $r'(t)$ and $\int_5^{12} r'(t)\,dt$ in the context of this situation.

22. HOW DO YOU SEE IT? Let $v(t)$ represent the velocity (in feet per second) of a particle moving along a straight line at time t (in seconds). The graph of v is shown in the figure. Describe what each expression represents in the context of the situation.

(a) $v'(t)$

(b) $\int_a^c v(t)\,dt$

(c) $\int_a^c |v(t)|\,dt$

(d) $\dfrac{d}{dx}\int_a^x v(t)\,dt$

(e) $A - B$

(f) $\int_a^b v(t)\,dt + \int_b^c v(t)\,dt$

True or False? In Exercises 23 and 24, determine whether the statement is true or false. If it is false, explain why or give an example that shows it is false.

23. The total distance traveled by a moving object is sometimes greater than the displacement of the object.

24. If $F(b) - F(a) = G(b) - G(a)$, then $F'(x) = G'(x)$ on the interval $[a, b]$.

Calculus AP® – Exam Preparation Questions

25. Multiple Choice A motorcycle is traveling at a velocity of 30 meters per second. The rider applies the brakes at time $t = 0$ seconds. The velocity of the motorcycle from time $t = 0$ until it comes to a stop is given by

$$v(t) = -2t^2 + t + 30$$

meters per second. How far does the motorcycle travel during this time interval?

(A) 61.966 m

(B) 70.499 m

(C) 85.465 m

(D) 93.998 m

26. Free Response The rate at which people enter a stadium through a given turnstile is called the turnstile rate. In the 60 minutes leading up to a stadium event, the turnstile rate for turnstile A is modeled by the function F defined by

$$F(t) = 14 + 18 \sin\left(\frac{t}{17}\right) \quad \text{for} \quad 0 \le t \le 60$$

where F is measured in people per minute and t is measured in minutes.

(a) To the nearest whole number, how many people enter through turnstile A during the 60-minute time interval?

(b) Is the turnstile rate increasing or decreasing at $t = 30$? Explain.

(c) What is the average turnstile rate during the time period $40 \le t \le 50$? Indicate units of measure.

(d) What is the average rate of change of the turnstile rate during the time period $40 \le t \le 50$? Indicate units of measure.

27. Free Response For $0 \le t \le 6$, the acceleration of a particle moving along a straight line is given by

$$a(t) = 2t - 6.$$

The velocity of the particle is given by $v(t)$ and its position is given by $s(t)$. When $t = 1$, $v(1) = 3$ and $s(1) = \frac{4}{3}$.

(a) Find the average velocity of the particle for the time interval $0 \le t \le 6$.

(b) When is the particle moving to the left? Explain.

(c) Find the total distance traveled by the particle from time $t = 0$ to $t = 6$.

(d) Find the time t at which the particle is farthest to the left. Explain.

4.6 Integration by Substitution

▶ Use pattern recognition to find an indefinite integral.
▶ Use a change of variables to find an indefinite integral.
▶ Use the General Power Rule for Integration to find an indefinite integral.
▶ Use a change of variables to evaluate a definite integral.
▶ Evaluate a definite integral involving an even or odd function.

Pattern Recognition

In this section, you will study techniques for integrating composite functions. The discussion is split into two parts—*pattern recognition* and *change of variables*. Both techniques involve a **u-substitution.** With pattern recognition, you perform the substitution mentally, and with change of variables, you write the substitution steps.

The role of substitution in integration is comparable to the role of the Chain Rule in differentiation. Recall that for the differentiable functions

$$y = F(u) \quad \text{and} \quad u = g(x)$$

the Chain Rule states that

$$\frac{d}{dx}[F(g(x))] = F'(g(x))g'(x).$$

From the definition of an antiderivative, it follows that

$$\int F'(g(x))g'(x)\, dx = F(g(x)) + C.$$

These results are summarized in the next theorem.

Theorem 4.15 Antidifferentiation of a Composite Function

Let g be a function whose range is an interval I, and let f be a function that is continuous on I. If g is differentiable on its domain and F is an antiderivative of f on I, then

$$\int f(g(x))g'(x)\, dx = F(g(x)) + C.$$

Letting $u = g(x)$ gives $du = g'(x)\, dx$ and

$$\int f(u)\, du = F(u) + C.$$

Implementing Processes

The statement of Theorem 4.15 does not tell how to distinguish between $f(g(x))$ and $g'(x)$ in the integrand. As you become more experienced at integration, your skill in doing this will increase. Of course, part of the key is familiarity with derivatives.

Examples 1 and 2 show how to apply Theorem 4.15 *directly*, by recognizing the presence of $f(g(x))$ and $g'(x)$. Note that the composite function in the integrand has an *outside function f* and an *inside function g.* Moreover, the derivative $g'(x)$ is present as a factor of the integrand.

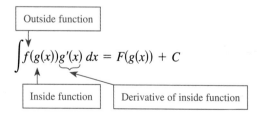

EXAMPLE 1   Recognizing the $f(g(x))g'(x)$ Pattern

Find $\int (x^2 + 1)^2(2x)\, dx$.

Solution

Letting $g(x) = x^2 + 1$, you obtain

$$g'(x) = 2x$$

and

$$f(g(x)) = f(x^2 + 1) = (x^2 + 1)^2.$$

From this, you can recognize that the integrand follows the $f(g(x))g'(x)$ pattern. Using the Power Rule for Integration and Theorem 4.15, you can write

$$\int \overbrace{(x^2 + 1)^2}^{f(g(x))}\,\overbrace{(2x)}^{g'(x)}\, dx = \frac{1}{3}(x^2 + 1)^3 + C.$$

Try using the Chain Rule to check that the derivative of $\frac{1}{3}(x^2 + 1)^3 + C$ is the integrand of the original integral.

EXAMPLE 2   Recognizing the $f(g(x))g'(x)$ Pattern

Find $\int 5e^{5x}\, dx$.

Solution

Letting $g(x) = 5x$, you obtain

$$g'(x) = 5$$

and

$$f(g(x)) = f(5x) = e^{5x}.$$

From this, you can recognize that the integrand follows the $f(g(x))g'(x)$ pattern. Using the Exponential Rule for Integration and Theorem 4.15, you can write

$$\int \overset{f(g(x))}{e^{5x}}\,\overset{g'(x)}{(5)}\, dx = e^{5x} + C.$$

You can check this by differentiating $e^{5x} + C$ to obtain the original integrand.   ∎

Technology

Try using a computer algebra system, such as *Maple*, *Mathematica*, or the *TI-Nspire*, to find the integrals given in Examples 1 and 2. Do you obtain the same antiderivatives that are listed in the examples?

Exploration

Recognizing Patterns   The integrand in each of the integrals labeled (a)–(c) fits the pattern $f(g(x))g'(x)$. Identify $f(g(x))$ and $g'(x)$, and then find the integral.

a. $\int 5x^4(x^5 + 1)^3\, dx$ **b.** $\int 3x^2\sqrt{x^3 + 1}\, dx$ **c.** $\int (\sec^2 x)(\tan x + 3)\, dx$

The integrals labeled (d)–(f) are similar to (a)–(c). Show how you can multiply and divide by a constant to find these integrals.

d. $\int x^4(x^5 + 1)^3\, dx$ **e.** $\int x^2\sqrt{x^3 + 1}\, dx$ **f.** $\int (2\sec^2 x)(\tan x + 3)\, dx$

The integrands in Examples 1 and 2 fit the $f(g(x))g'(x)$ pattern exactly—you only had to recognize the pattern. You can extend this technique considerably with the Constant Multiple Rule

$$\int kf(x)\,dx = k\int f(x)\,dx.$$

Many integrands contain the essential part (the variable part) of $g'(x)$ but are missing a constant multiple. In such cases, you can multiply and divide by the necessary constant multiple, as shown in Example 3.

EXAMPLE 3   Multiplying and Dividing by a Constant

Find the indefinite integral.

$$\int x(x^2 + 1)^2\,dx$$

Solution

This is similar to the integral given in Example 1, except that the integrand is missing a factor of 2. Recognizing that $2x$ is the derivative of $x^2 + 1$, you can let

$$g(x) = x^2 + 1$$

and supply the $2x$ as shown.

$$\int x(x^2 + 1)^2\,dx = \int (x^2 + 1)^2 \left(\frac{1}{2}\right)(2x)\,dx \qquad \text{Multiply and divide by 2.}$$

$$= \frac{1}{2}\int \overbrace{(x^2 + 1)^2}^{f(g(x))}\overbrace{(2x)}^{g'(x)}\,dx \qquad \text{Constant Multiple Rule}$$

$$= \frac{1}{2}\left[\frac{(x^2 + 1)^3}{3}\right] + C \qquad \text{Integrate.}$$

$$= \frac{1}{6}(x^2 + 1)^3 + C \qquad \text{Simplify.}$$

In practice, most people would not write as many steps as are shown in Example 3. For instance, you could evaluate the integral by simply writing

$$\int x(x^2 + 1)^2\,dx = \frac{1}{2}\int (x^2 + 1)^2(2x)\,dx$$

$$= \frac{1}{2}\left[\frac{(x^2 + 1)^3}{3}\right] + C$$

$$= \frac{1}{6}(x^2 + 1)^3 + C.$$

Be sure you see that the *Constant* Multiple Rule applies only to *constants*. You cannot multiply and divide by a variable and then move the variable outside the integral sign. For instance,

$$\int (x^2 + 1)^2\,dx \neq \frac{1}{2x}\int (x^2 + 1)^2(2x)\,dx.$$

After all, if it were legitimate to move variable quantities outside the integral sign, you could move the entire integrand out and simplify the whole process. But the result would be incorrect.

Change of Variables for Indefinite Integrals

With a formal **change of variables,** you completely rewrite the integral in terms of u and du (or any other convenient variable). Although this procedure can involve more written steps than the pattern recognition illustrated in Examples 1 to 3, it is useful for complicated integrands. The change of variables technique uses the Leibniz notation for the differential. That is, if $u = g(x)$, then $du = g'(x)\,dx$, and the integral in Theorem 4.15 takes the form

$$\int f(g(x))g'(x)\,dx = \int f(u)\,du = F(u) + C.$$

EXAMPLE 4   Change of Variables

Find $\displaystyle\int \sqrt{2x - 1}\,dx.$

Solution

First, let u be the inner function, $u = 2x - 1$. Then calculate the differential du to be $du = 2\,dx$. Now, using $\sqrt{2x - 1} = \sqrt{u}$ and $dx = du/2$, substitute to obtain

$$\int \sqrt{2x - 1}\,dx = \int \sqrt{u}\left(\frac{du}{2}\right) \qquad \text{Integral in terms of } u$$

$$= \frac{1}{2}\int u^{1/2}\,du \qquad \text{Constant Multiple Rule}$$

$$= \frac{1}{2}\left(\frac{u^{3/2}}{3/2}\right) + C \qquad \text{Antiderivative in terms of } u$$

$$= \frac{1}{3}u^{3/2} + C \qquad \text{Simplify.}$$

$$= \frac{1}{3}(2x - 1)^{3/2} + C. \qquad \text{Antiderivative in terms of } x$$

> **Justification**
>
> Because integration is usually more difficult than differentiation, you should always check your answer to an integration problem by differentiating. For instance, in Example 4, you should differentiate $\frac{1}{3}(2x - 1)^{3/2} + C$ to verify that you obtain the original integrand.

EXAMPLE 5   Change of Variables

See LarsonCalculusforAP.com for an interactive version of this type of example.

Find $\displaystyle\int x\sqrt{2x - 1}\,dx.$

Solution

As in the previous example, let $u = 2x - 1$ and obtain $dx = du/2$. Because the integrand contains a factor of x, you must also solve for x in terms of u, as shown.

$$u = 2x - 1 \quad \Longrightarrow \quad x = \frac{u + 1}{2} \qquad \text{Solve for } x \text{ in terms of } u.$$

Now, using substitution, you obtain

$$\int x\sqrt{2x - 1}\,dx = \int \left(\frac{u + 1}{2}\right)u^{1/2}\left(\frac{du}{2}\right)$$

$$= \frac{1}{4}\int (u^{3/2} + u^{1/2})\,du$$

$$= \frac{1}{4}\left(\frac{u^{5/2}}{5/2} + \frac{u^{3/2}}{3/2}\right) + C$$

$$= \frac{1}{10}(2x - 1)^{5/2} + \frac{1}{6}(2x - 1)^{3/2} + C.$$

To complete the change of variables in Example 5, you solved for x in terms of u. Sometimes this is very difficult. Fortunately, it is not always necessary, as shown in the next example.

EXAMPLE 6 Change of Variables

Find $\displaystyle\int \sin^2 3x \cos 3x \, dx$.

Solution

Because $\sin^2 3x = (\sin 3x)^2$, you can let $u = \sin 3x$. Then

$$du = (\cos 3x)(3) \, dx.$$

Now, because $\cos 3x \, dx$ is part of the original integral, you can write

$$\frac{du}{3} = \cos 3x \, dx.$$

Substituting u and $du/3$ in the original integral yields

$$\begin{aligned}
\int \sin^2 3x \cos 3x \, dx &= \int u^2 \frac{du}{3} \\
&= \frac{1}{3} \int u^2 \, du \\
&= \frac{1}{3}\left(\frac{u^3}{3}\right) + C \\
&= \frac{1}{9} \sin^3 3x + C.
\end{aligned}$$

You can check this by differentiating.

$$\begin{aligned}
\frac{d}{dx}\left[\frac{1}{9}\sin^3 3x + C\right] &= \left(\frac{1}{9}\right)(3)(\sin 3x)^2(\cos 3x)(3) \\
&= \sin^2 3x \cos 3x
\end{aligned}$$

Because differentiation produces the original integrand, you know that you have obtained the correct antiderivative. ∎

The steps used for integration by substitution are summarized in the following guidelines.

> ### Implementing Processes
>
> When making a change of variables, be sure that your answer is written using the same variables as in the original integrand. For instance, in Example 6, you should not leave your answer as
>
> $$\frac{1}{9}u^3 + C$$
>
> but rather, you should replace u by $\sin 3x$.

Guidelines for Making a Change of Variables

1. Choose a substitution $u = g(x)$. Usually, it is best to choose the *inner* part of a composite function, such as a quantity raised to a power.

2. Compute $du = g'(x) \, dx$.

3. Rewrite the integral in terms of the variable u.

4. Find the resulting integral in terms of u.

5. Replace u by $g(x)$ to obtain an antiderivative in terms of x.

6. Check your answer by differentiating.

So far, you have seen two techniques for applying substitution, and you will see more techniques in the remainder of this section. Each technique differs slightly from the others. You should remember, however, that the goal is the same with each technique—*you are trying to find an antiderivative of the integrand.*

The General Power Rule for Integration

One of the most common *u*-substitutions involves quantities in the integrand that are raised to a power. Because of the importance of this type of substitution, it is given a special name—the **General Power Rule for Integration.** A proof of this rule follows directly from the (simple) Power Rule for Integration, together with Theorem 4.15.

Theorem 4.16   The General Power Rule for Integration

If g is a differentiable function of x, then

$$\int [g(x)]^n g'(x)\, dx = \frac{[g(x)]^{n+1}}{n+1} + C, \quad n \neq -1.$$

Equivalently, if $u = g(x)$, then

$$\int u^n\, du = \frac{u^{n+1}}{n+1} + C, \quad n \neq -1.$$

EXAMPLE 7   **Substitution and the General Power Rule**

a. $\displaystyle \int 3(3x-1)^4\, dx = \int \overbrace{(3x-1)^4}^{u^4}\overbrace{(3)\, dx}^{du} = \overbrace{\frac{(3x-1)^5}{5}}^{u^5/5} + C$

b. $\displaystyle \int (e^x+1)(e^x+x)\, dx = \int \overbrace{(e^x+x)}^{u^1}\overbrace{(e^x+1)\, dx}^{du} = \overbrace{\frac{(e^x+x)^2}{2}}^{u^2/2} + C$

c. $\displaystyle \int 3x^2\sqrt{x^3-2}\, dx = \int \overbrace{(x^3-2)^{1/2}}^{u^{1/2}}\overbrace{(3x^2)\, dx}^{du} = \overbrace{\frac{(x^3-2)^{3/2}}{3/2}}^{u^{3/2}/(3/2)} + C = \frac{2}{3}(x^3-2)^{3/2} + C$

d. $\displaystyle \int \frac{-4x}{(1-2x^2)^2}\, dx = \int \overbrace{(1-2x^2)^{-2}}^{u^{-2}}\overbrace{(-4x)\, dx}^{du} = \overbrace{\frac{(1-2x^2)^{-1}}{-1}}^{u^{-1}/(-1)} + C = -\frac{1}{1-2x^2} + C$

e. $\displaystyle \int \cos^2 x \sin x\, dx = -\int \overbrace{(\cos x)^2}^{u^2}\overbrace{(-\sin x)\, dx}^{du} = -\overbrace{\frac{(\cos x)^3}{3}}^{u^3/3} + C$ ∎

Some integrals whose integrands involve quantities raised to powers cannot be found by the General Power Rule. Consider the two integrals

$$\int x(x^2+1)^2\, dx \quad \text{and} \quad \int (x^2+1)^2\, dx.$$

The substitution

$$u = x^2 + 1$$

works in the first integral but not in the second. In the second, the substitution fails because the integrand lacks the factor x needed for du. Fortunately, *for this particular integral,* you can expand the integrand as

$$(x^2+1)^2 = x^4 + 2x^2 + 1$$

and use the (simple) Power Rule to integrate each term.

Change of Variables for Definite Integrals

When using u-substitution with a definite integral, it is often convenient to determine the limits of integration for the variable u rather than to convert the antiderivative back to the variable x and evaluate at the original limits. This change of variables is stated explicitly in the next theorem. The proof follows from Theorem 4.15, combined with the Fundamental Theorem of Calculus.

Theorem 4.17 Change of Variables for Definite Integrals

If the function $u = g(x)$ has a continuous derivative on the closed interval $[a, b]$ and f is continuous on the range of g, then

$$\int_a^b f(g(x))g'(x)\,dx = \int_{g(a)}^{g(b)} f(u)\,du.$$

EXAMPLE 8 Change of Variables

Evaluate the definite integral.

$$\int_0^1 x(x^2 + 1)^3\,dx$$

Algebraic Solution

To evaluate this integral, let $u = x^2 + 1$. Then, you obtain

$$u = x^2 + 1 \quad \Longrightarrow \quad du = 2x\,dx.$$

Before substituting, determine the new upper and lower limits of integration.

Lower Limit	Upper Limit
When $x = 0$, $u = 0^2 + 1 = 1$.	When $x = 1$, $u = 1^2 + 1 = 2$.

Now, you can substitute to obtain

$$\int_0^1 x(x^2 + 1)^3\,dx = \frac{1}{2}\int_0^1 (x^2 + 1)^3(2x)\,dx \qquad \text{Integration limits for } x$$

$$= \frac{1}{2}\int_1^2 u^3\,du \qquad \text{Integration limits for } u$$

$$= \frac{1}{2}\left[\frac{u^4}{4}\right]_1^2$$

$$= \frac{1}{2}\left(4 - \frac{1}{4}\right)$$

$$= \frac{15}{8}.$$

Graphical Solution

Use a graphing utility to graph $y = x(x^2 + 1)^3$.

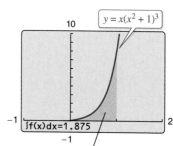

$y = x(x^2 + 1)^3$

∫f(x)dx=1.875

Use the *integral* feature to determine that the value of $\int_0^1 x(x^2 + 1)^3\,dx$ is 1.875.

Note that the result can be written as

$$\int_0^1 x(x^2 + 1)^3\,dx = 1.875 = \frac{15}{8}.$$

Notice in Example 8 that you obtain the same result when you rewrite the antiderivative $\frac{1}{2}(u^4/4)$ in terms of the variable x and evaluate the definite integral at the original limits of integration, as shown.

$$\frac{1}{2}\left[\frac{u^4}{4}\right]_1^2 = \frac{1}{2}\left[\frac{(x^2 + 1)^4}{4}\right]_0^1 = \frac{1}{2}\left(4 - \frac{1}{4}\right) = \frac{15}{8}$$

EXAMPLE 9   **Change of Variables**

Evaluate the definite integral.

$$\int_1^5 \frac{x}{\sqrt{2x-1}}\, dx$$

Solution

To evaluate this integral, let $u = \sqrt{2x-1}$. Then, you obtain

$$u^2 = 2x - 1$$
$$u^2 + 1 = 2x$$
$$\frac{u^2 + 1}{2} = x$$
$$u\, du = dx. \qquad \text{Differentiate each side.}$$

Before substituting, determine the new upper and lower limits of integration.

Lower Limit	*Upper Limit*
When $x = 1$, $u = \sqrt{2-1} = 1$.	When $x = 5$, $u = \sqrt{10-1} = 3$.

Now, substitute to obtain

$$\int_1^5 \frac{x}{\sqrt{2x-1}}\, dx = \int_1^3 \frac{1}{u}\left(\frac{u^2+1}{2}\right)u\, du$$
$$= \frac{1}{2}\int_1^3 (u^2 + 1)\, du$$
$$= \frac{1}{2}\left[\frac{u^3}{3} + u\right]_1^3$$
$$= \frac{1}{2}\left(9 + 3 - \frac{1}{3} - 1\right)$$
$$= \frac{16}{3}.$$

Geometrically, you can interpret the equation

$$\int_1^5 \frac{x}{\sqrt{2x-1}}\, dx = \int_1^3 \frac{u^2+1}{2}\, du$$

to mean that the two *different* regions shown in Figures 4.42 and 4.43 have the *same* area.

When evaluating definite integrals by substitution, it is possible for the upper limit of integration of the u-variable form to be smaller than the lower limit. When this happens, do not rearrange the limits. Simply evaluate as usual. For example, after substituting $u = \sqrt{1-x}$ in the integral

$$\int_0^1 x^2(1-x)^{1/2}\, dx$$

you obtain $u = \sqrt{1-1} = 0$ when $x = 1$, and $u = \sqrt{1-0} = 1$ when $x = 0$. So, the correct u-variable form of this integral is

$$-2\int_1^0 (1-u^2)^2 u^2\, du.$$

Expanding the integrand, you can evaluate this integral as shown.

$$-2\int_1^0 (u^2 - 2u^4 + u^6)\, du = -2\left[\frac{u^3}{3} - \frac{2u^5}{5} + \frac{u^7}{7}\right]_1^0 = -2\left(-\frac{1}{3} + \frac{2}{5} - \frac{1}{7}\right) = \frac{16}{105}$$

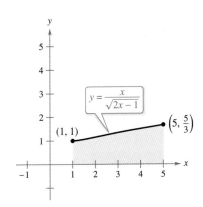

The region before substitution has an area of $\frac{16}{3}$.

Figure 4.42

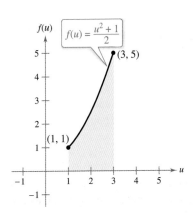

The region after substitution has an area of $\frac{16}{3}$.

Figure 4.43

Integration of Even and Odd Functions

Even with a change of variables, integration can be difficult. Occasionally, you can simplify the evaluation of a definite integral over an interval that is symmetric about the y-axis or about the origin by recognizing the integrand to be an even or odd function. (See Figure 4.44.)

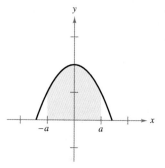

Even function

Theorem 4.18   Integration of Even and Odd Functions

Let f be integrable on the closed interval $[-a, a]$.

1. If f is an *even* function, then $\displaystyle\int_{-a}^{a} f(x)\, dx = 2 \int_{0}^{a} f(x)\, dx$.

2. If f is an *odd* function, then $\displaystyle\int_{-a}^{a} f(x)\, dx = 0$.

Proof   Here is the proof of the first property. (The proof of the second property is left to you. [See Exercise 116.]) Because f is even, you know that $f(x) = f(-x)$. Using Theorem 4.15 with the substitution $u = -x$ produces

$$\int_{-a}^{0} f(x)\, dx = \int_{a}^{0} f(-u)(-du) = -\int_{a}^{0} f(u)\, du = \int_{0}^{a} f(u)\, du = \int_{0}^{a} f(x)\, dx.$$

Finally, using Theorem 4.6, you obtain

$$\int_{-a}^{a} f(x)\, dx = \int_{-a}^{0} f(x)\, dx + \int_{0}^{a} f(x)\, dx$$

$$= \int_{0}^{a} f(x)\, dx + \int_{0}^{a} f(x)\, dx$$

$$= 2\int_{0}^{a} f(x)\, dx.$$

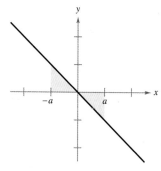

Odd function
Figure 4.44

EXAMPLE 10   Integration of an Odd Function

Evaluate the definite integral.

$$\int_{-\pi/2}^{\pi/2} (\sin^3 x \cos x + \sin x \cos x)\, dx$$

Solution

Letting $f(x) = \sin^3 x \cos x + \sin x \cos x$ produces

$$f(-x) = \sin^3(-x) \cos(-x) + \sin(-x) \cos(-x)$$

$$= -\sin^3 x \cos x - \sin x \cos x$$

$$= -f(x).$$

So, f is an odd function, and because f is symmetric about the origin over $[-\pi/2, \pi/2]$, you can apply Theorem 4.18 to conclude that

$$\int_{-\pi/2}^{\pi/2} (\sin^3 x \cos x + \sin x \cos x)\, dx = 0.$$

From Figure 4.45, you can see that the two regions on either side of the y-axis have the same area. However, because one lies below the x-axis and one lies above it, integration produces a cancellation effect. (More will be said about areas below the x-axis in Section 6.1.)

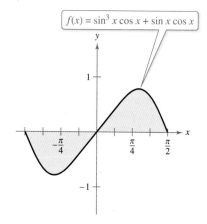

Because f is an odd function,
$$\int_{-\pi/2}^{\pi/2} f(x)\, dx = 0.$$
Figure 4.45

4.6 Exercises

See *CalcChat.com* for tutorial help and worked-out solutions to odd-numbered exercises.

 Finding u **and** du **In Exercises 1–4, complete the table by identifying** u **and** du **for the integral.**

$$\int f(g(x))g'(x)\,dx \qquad u = g(x) \qquad du = g'(x)\,dx$$

1. $\int (5x^2 + 1)^2\,(10x)\,dx$

2. $\int 3x^2\sqrt{x^3 + 5}\,dx$

3. $\int \tan^2 x \sec^2 x\,dx$

4. $\int \dfrac{\cos x}{\sin^2 x}\,dx$

 Finding an Indefinite Integral In Exercises 5–26, find the indefinite integral and check the result by differentiation.

5. $\int (1 + 6x)^4\,(6)\,dx$

6. $\int (x^2 - 9)^3(2x)\,dx$

7. $\int \sqrt{25 - x^2}(-2x)\,dx$

8. $\int \sqrt[3]{3 - 4x^2}(-8x)\,dx$

9. $\int x^3(x^4 + 3)^2\,dx$

10. $\int x^2(6 - x^3)^5\,dx$

11. $\int x^2(2x^3 - 1)^4\,dx$

12. $\int x(5x^2 + 4)^3\,dx$

13. $\int t\sqrt{t^2 + 2}\,dt$

14. $\int t^3\sqrt{2t^4 + 3}\,dt$

15. $\int 5x\sqrt[3]{1 - x^2}\,dx$

16. $\int -2u^2\sqrt{u^3 + 2}\,du$

17. $\int \dfrac{x}{(1 - x^2)^3}\,dx$

18. $\int \dfrac{x^3}{(1 - x^4)^2}\,dx$

19. $\int \dfrac{9x^2}{(1 + x^3)^2}\,dx$

20. $\int \dfrac{6x^2}{(4x^3 - 9)^3}\,dx$

21. $\int \dfrac{x}{\sqrt{1 - x^2}}\,dx$

22. $\int \dfrac{x^3}{\sqrt{1 + x^4}}\,dx$

23. $\int \left(1 + \dfrac{1}{t}\right)^3\left(\dfrac{1}{t^2}\right)\,dt$

24. $\int \left(\dfrac{1}{\sqrt{t}}\right)(1 - \sqrt{t})^2\,dt$

25. $\int \dfrac{x + 3}{\sqrt{x^2 + 6x}}\,dx$

26. $\int \dfrac{4x - 10}{(x^2 - 5x + 1)^3}\,dx$

 Differential Equation In Exercises 27–30, solve the differential equation.

27. $\dfrac{dy}{dx} = 4x + \dfrac{4x}{\sqrt{16 - x^2}}$

28. $\dfrac{dy}{dx} = \dfrac{10x^2}{\sqrt{1 + x^3}}$

29. $\dfrac{dy}{dx} = \dfrac{x + 1}{(x^2 + 2x - 3)^2}$

30. $\dfrac{dy}{dx} = \dfrac{x - 4}{\sqrt{x^2 - 8x + 1}}$

Finding an Indefinite Integral In Exercises 31–50, find the indefinite integral.

31. $\int \pi \sin \pi x\,dx$

32. $\int \cos 8x\,dx$

33. $\int \dfrac{\sin\sqrt{x}}{\sqrt{x}}\,dx$

34. $\int \dfrac{1}{\theta^2}\cos\dfrac{1}{\theta}\,d\theta$

35. $\int \sin 2x \cos 2x\,dx$

36. $\int \sqrt{\tan x}\,\sec^2 x\,dx$

37. $\int \dfrac{\csc^2 x}{\cot^3 x}\,dx$

38. $\int \dfrac{\sin x}{\cos^3 x}\,dx$

39. $\int 9e^{9x}\,dx$

40. $\int e^x(e^x + 1)^2\,dx$

41. $\int (x + 1)e^{x^2 + 2x}\,dx$

42. $\int \dfrac{2e^x - 2e^{-x}}{(e^x + e^{-x})^2}\,dx$

43. $\int \dfrac{5 - e^x}{e^{2x}}\,dx$

44. $\int \dfrac{e^{2x} + 2e^x + 1}{e^x}\,dx$

45. $\int e^{\sin \pi x}\cos \pi x\,dx$

46. $\int e^{\tan 2x}\sec^2 2x\,dx$

47. $\int e^{-x}\sec^2(e^{-x})\,dx$

48. $\int \sin(\ln x^2)\left(\dfrac{1}{x}\right)\,dx$

49. $\int 3^{x/2}\,dx$

50. $\int (3 - x)7^{(3-x)^2}\,dx$

 Finding an Equation In Exercises 51–56, find an equation for the function f **that has the given derivative and whose graph passes through the given point.**

51. $f'(x) = -\sin\dfrac{x}{2}$, $(0, 6)$

52. $f'(x) = 0.4^{x/3}$, $\left(0, \tfrac{1}{2}\right)$

53. $f'(x) = 2e^{-x/4}$, $(0, 1)$

54. $f'(x) = x^2 e^{-0.2x^3}$, $\left(0, \tfrac{3}{2}\right)$

55. $f'(x) = 2x(4x^2 - 10)^2$, $(2, 10)$

56. $f'(x) = -2x\sqrt{8 - x^2}$, $(2, 7)$

 Change of Variables In Exercises 57–68, find the indefinite integral by the method shown in Examples 4–6.

57. $\int \sqrt{3x + 5}\,dx$

58. $\int \dfrac{1}{\sqrt{4x + 7}}\,dx$

59. $\int x\sqrt{x + 6}\,dx$

60. $\int x\sqrt{3x - 4}\,dx$

61. $\int x^2\sqrt{1 - x}\,dx$

62. $\int (x + 1)\sqrt{2 - x}\,dx$

63. $\int \dfrac{x^2 - 1}{\sqrt{2x - 1}}\,dx$

64. $\int \dfrac{2x + 1}{\sqrt{x + 4}}\,dx$

65. $\int \dfrac{-x}{(x + 1) - \sqrt{x + 1}}\,dx$

66. $\int t\sqrt[3]{t + 10}\,dt$

67. $\int \cos^2 4x \sin 4x\,dx$

68. $\int \sec^2(-x)\tan^3(-x)\,dx$

Evaluating a Definite Integral In Exercises 69–80, evaluate the definite integral. Use a graphing utility to verify your result.

69. $\int_{-1}^{1} x(x^2 + 1)^4 \, dx$

70. $\int_{0}^{1} x^3(2x^4 + 1)^2 \, dx$

71. $\int_{0}^{4} \frac{1}{\sqrt{2x + 1}} \, dx$

72. $\int_{0}^{2} \frac{x}{\sqrt{1 + 2x^2}} \, dx$

73. $\int_{0}^{1} e^{-2x} \, dx$

74. $\int_{0}^{\sqrt{2}} xe^{-x^2/2} \, dx$

75. $\int_{0}^{4} (t + 2)\sqrt{4 - t} \, dt$

76. $\int_{-1}^{1} 2x^2\sqrt{x + 1} \, dx$

77. $\int_{3}^{7} \frac{5 + 2x}{\sqrt{x - 3}} \, dx$

78. $\int_{3}^{6} \frac{t}{\sqrt{t - 3}} \, dt$

79. $\int_{-14}^{-6} (t - 1)\sqrt[3]{t + 6} \, dt$

80. $\int_{1}^{10} \frac{1 + \sqrt{x - 1}}{\sqrt{x - 1} + x - 1} \, dx$

Error Analysis In Exercises 81 and 82, describe and correct the error in finding the indefinite integral.

81. $\int x(x^2 + 1) \, dx = \frac{1}{2}\int (x^2 + 1)(2x) \, dx$

$$= \frac{1}{2}(x^2 + 1)^2 + C \quad \text{✗}$$

82. $\int_{5}^{9} x\sqrt{x - 5} \, dx = \int_{5}^{9} (u + 5)\sqrt{u} \, du$

$$= \int_{5}^{9} u^{3/2} + 5u^{1/2} \, du$$

$$= \left[\frac{2}{5}u^{5/2} + \frac{10}{3}u^{3/2}\right]_{5}^{9}$$

$$\approx 127.57 \quad \text{✗}$$

Finding the Area of a Region In Exercises 83–86, find the area of the region. Use a graphing utility to verify your result.

83. $\int_{0}^{7} x\sqrt[3]{x + 1} \, dx$

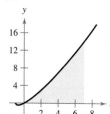

84. $\int_{-2}^{6} x^2\sqrt[3]{x + 2} \, dx$

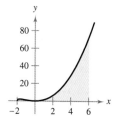

85. $\int_{\pi/2}^{2\pi/3} \sec^2 \frac{x}{2} \, dx$

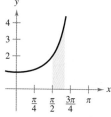

86. $\int_{\pi/12}^{\pi/4} \csc 2x \cot 2x \, dx$

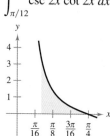

Area In Exercises 87–90, find the area of the region bounded by the graphs of the equations. Use a graphing utility to graph the region and verify your result.

87. $y = e^x$, $y = 0$, $x = 0$, $x = 5$

88. $y = e^{-x}$, $y = 0$, $x = a$, $x = b$

89. $y = xe^{-x^2/4}$, $y = 0$, $x = 0$, $x = \sqrt{6}$

90. $y = e^{-2x} + 2$, $y = 0$, $x = 0$, $x = 2$

Even and Odd Functions In Exercises 91–94, evaluate the integral using the properties of even and odd functions as an aid.

91. $\int_{-2}^{2} x^2(x^2 + 1) \, dx$

92. $\int_{-2}^{2} x(x^2 + 1)^3 \, dx$

93. $\int_{-\pi/2}^{\pi/2} \sin x \cos x \, dx$

94. $\int_{-\pi/2}^{\pi/2} \sin^2 x \cos x \, dx$

95. Using an Even Function Use $\int_{0}^{4} x^2 \, dx = \frac{64}{3}$ to evaluate each definite integral without using the Fundamental Theorem of Calculus.

(a) $\int_{-4}^{0} x^2 \, dx$

(b) $\int_{-4}^{4} x^2 \, dx$

(c) $\int_{0}^{4} -x^2 \, dx$

(d) $\int_{-4}^{0} 3x^2 \, dx$

96. Using Symmetry Use the symmetry of the graphs as an aid in evaluating each definite integral.

(a) $\int_{-\pi/4}^{\pi/4} \sin x \, dx$

(b) $\int_{-\pi/4}^{\pi/4} \sec^2 x \, dx$

(c) $\int_{-\pi/2}^{\pi/2} \cos x \, dx$

(d) $\int_{-3\pi/2}^{3\pi/2} \sin x \cos x \, dx$

Even and Odd Functions In Exercises 97 and 98, write the integral as the sum of the integral of an odd function and the integral of an even function. Use this simplification to evaluate the integral.

97. $\int_{-3}^{3} (x^3 + 4x^2 - 3x - 6) \, dx$

98. $\int_{-\pi/2}^{\pi/2} (\sin 4x + \cos 4x) \, dx$

EXPLORING CONCEPTS

99. Using Substitution   Describe why

$$\int x(5 - x^2)^3 \, dx \neq \int u^3 \, du$$

where $u = 5 - x^2$.

100. Justifying   What problem do you face when you try to use Theorem 4.16 to find $\int 2x(x^2 + 1)^{-1} \, dx$?

101. Choosing an Integral   You are asked to find one of the integrals. Which one would you choose? Explain.

(a) $\int \sqrt{x^3 + 1} \, dx$ or $\int x^2 \sqrt{x^3 + 1} \, dx$

(b) $\int \tan 3x \sec^2 3x \, dx$ or $\int \tan 3x \, dx$

(c) $\int e^{4x-3} \, dx$ or $\int x e^{x+4} \, dx$

102. Comparing Methods   Find each indefinite integral in two ways. Explain any difference in the forms of the answers.

(a) $\int (2x - 1)^2 \, dx$ (b) $\int \tan x \sec^2 x \, dx$

---

103. Depreciation   The rate of depreciation dV/dt of a machine is inversely proportional to the square of $(t + 1)$, where V is the value of the machine t years after it was purchased. The initial value of the machine was \$500,000, and its value decreased \$100,000 in the first year. Estimate its value after 4 years.

104. HOW DO YOU SEE IT?   The graph shows the flow rate of water at a pumping station for one day.

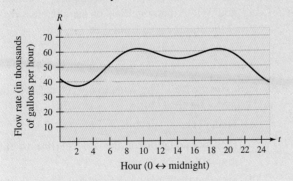

Hour (0 ↔ midnight)

(a) Approximate the maximum flow rate at the pumping station. At what times does this occur?

(b) Explain how you can find the amount of water used during the day.

(c) Approximate the two-hour period when the least amount of water is used. Explain your reasoning.

105. Sales   The sales S (in thousands of units) of a seasonal product are given by the model

$$S = 74.50 + 43.75 \sin \frac{\pi t}{6}$$

where t is the time in months, with $t = 1$ corresponding to January. Find the average sales for each time period.

(a) The first quarter $(0 \leq t \leq 3)$

(b) The second quarter $(3 \leq t \leq 6)$

(c) The entire year $(0 \leq t \leq 12)$

106. Electricity   The oscillating current in an electrical circuit is $I = 2 \sin(60\pi t) + \cos(120\pi t)$, where I is measured in amperes and t is measured in seconds. Find the average current for each time interval.

(a) $0 \leq t \leq \dfrac{1}{60}$ (b) $0 \leq t \leq \dfrac{1}{240}$ (c) $0 \leq t \leq \dfrac{1}{30}$

Probability   In Exercises 107 and 108, the function $f(x) = kx^n(1 - x)^m$, $0 \leq x \leq 1$, where $n > 0$, $m > 0$, and k is a constant, can be used to represent various probability distributions. If k is chosen such that

$$\int_0^1 f(x) \, dx = 1$$

then the probability that x will fall between a and b $(0 \leq a \leq b \leq 1)$ is

$$P_{a, b} = \int_a^b f(x) \, dx.$$

107. The probability that a person will remember between $100a\%$ and $100b\%$ of material learned in an experiment is

$$P_{a, b} = \int_a^b \frac{15}{4} x \sqrt{1 - x} \, dx$$

where x represents the proportion remembered. (See figure.)

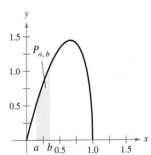

(a) For a randomly chosen individual, what is the probability that he or she will recall between 50% and 75% of the material?

(b) What is the median percent recall? That is, for what value of b is it true that the probability of recalling 0 to b is 0.5?

108. The probability that ore samples taken from a region contain between $100a\%$ and $100b\%$ iron is

$$P_{a,b} = \int_a^b \frac{1155}{32} x^3 (1 - x)^{3/2} \, dx$$

where x represents the proportion of iron. (See figure.) What is the probability that a sample will contain between

(a) 0% and 25% iron?   (b) 50% and 100% iron?

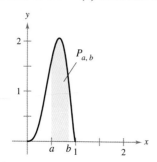

109. **Graphical Analysis** Consider the functions f and g, where $f(x) = 6 \sin x \cos^2 x$ and $g(t) = \int_0^t f(x) \, dx$.

(a) Use a graphing utility to graph f and g in the same viewing window.

(b) Explain why g is nonnegative.

(c) Identify the points on the graph of g that correspond to the extrema of f.

(d) Does each of the zeros of f correspond to an extremum of g? Explain.

(e) Consider the function

$$h(t) = \int_{\pi/2}^t f(x) \, dx.$$

Use a graphing utility to graph h. What is the relationship between g and h? Verify your conjecture.

110. **Finding a Limit Using a Definite Integral** Find

$$\lim_{n \to \infty} \sum_{i=1}^n \frac{\sin(i\pi/n)}{n}$$

by evaluating an appropriate definite integral over the interval $[0, 1]$.

111. **Rewriting Integrals**

(a) Show that $\displaystyle\int_0^1 x^2(1 - x)^5 \, dx = \int_0^1 x^5(1 - x)^2 \, dx.$

(b) Show that $\displaystyle\int_0^1 x^a(1 - x)^b \, dx = \int_0^1 x^b(1 - x)^a \, dx.$

112. **Rewriting Integrals**

(a) Show that $\displaystyle\int_0^{\pi/2} \sin^2 x \, dx = \int_0^{\pi/2} \cos^2 x \, dx.$

(b) Show that $\displaystyle\int_0^{\pi/2} \sin^n x \, dx = \int_0^{\pi/2} \cos^n x \, dx,$ where n is a positive integer.

True or False? **In Exercises 113 and 114, determine whether the statement is true or false. If it is false, explain why or give an example that shows it is false.**

113. $\displaystyle\int_{-10}^{10} (ax^3 + bx^2 + cx + d) \, dx = 2 \int_0^{10} (bx^2 + d) \, dx$

114. $\displaystyle\int_a^b \sin x \, dx = \int_a^{b+2\pi} \sin x \, dx$

115. **Rewriting Integrals** Assume that f is continuous everywhere and that c is a constant. Show that

$$\int_{ca}^{cb} f(x) \, dx = c \int_a^b f(cx) \, dx.$$

116. **Proof** Prove the second property of Theorem 4.18.

Calculus AP® – Exam Preparation Questions

117. **Multiple Choice** Which expression could be a solution of the differential equation

$$\frac{dy}{dx} = \frac{1}{\sqrt[3]{x^2}} e^{\sqrt[3]{x}}?$$

(A) $y = e^{x^{1/3}} - 1$ (B) $y = 3e^{x^{1/3}} + e$

(C) $y = \dfrac{3}{4} e^{x^{4/3}}$ (D) $y = \dfrac{9}{4} e^{x^{4/3}} - 3e$

118. **Multiple Choice** What is the average value of $h(x) = (\sec^2 x)(1 + 2 \tan x)^3$ on the interval $[0, \pi/4]$?

(A) $\dfrac{40}{\pi}$ (B) 10

(C) $\dfrac{81}{2\pi}$ (D) $\dfrac{80}{\pi}$

119. **Multiple Choice** A chemical is leaking from a storage area at the rate of $f(t) = 1600e^{-0.12t}$ gallons per hour. How many gallons of the chemical leak out of the storage area from time $t = 0$ to $t = 12$?

(A) 379   (B) 1221

(C) 3159   (D) 10,174

120. **Free Response** The function f is defined by $f(x) = \sqrt{100 - x^2}$ for $-10 \le x \le 10$.

(a) Find $f'(x)$.

(b) Find an equation of the tangent line to the graph of f at $x = -6$.

(c) Let g be the function defined by

$$g(x) = \begin{cases} f(x), & -10 \le x \le -6 \\ -\dfrac{1}{2}x + 5, & -6 < x \le 10 \end{cases}.$$

Is g continuous at $x = -6$? Use the definition of continuity to explain your answer.

(d) Find the value of $\int_0^{10} x\sqrt{100 - x^2} \, dx$.

4.7   The Natural Logarithmic Function: Integration

▶ Use the Log Rule for Integration to integrate a rational function.
▶ Integrate trigonometric functions.

Log Rule for Integration

In Chapter 2, you studied two differentiation rules for logarithms. The differentiation rule $d/dx[\ln x] = 1/x$ produces the Log Rule for Integration that you learned in Section 4.1. The differentiation rule $d/dx[\ln u] = u'/u$ produces the integration rule $\int 1/u \, du = \ln|u| + C$. These rules are summarized below. (See Exercise 103.)

> **Insight**
>
> The Log Rule for Integration is frequently tested on the AP® Exam.

Theorem 4.19   Log Rule for Integration

Let u be a differentiable function of x.

1. $\displaystyle\int \frac{1}{x} \, dx = \ln|x| + C$

2. $\displaystyle\int \frac{1}{u} \, du = \ln|u| + C$

Because $du = u' \, dx$, the second formula can also be written as

$$\int \frac{u'}{u} \, dx = \ln|u| + C. \qquad \text{Alternative form of Log Rule}$$

EXAMPLE 1   Using the Log Rule for Integration

$$
\begin{aligned}
\int \frac{2}{x} \, dx &= 2 \int \frac{1}{x} \, dx && \text{Constant Multiple Rule} \\
&= 2 \ln|x| + C && \text{Log Rule for Integration} \\
&= \ln x^2 + C && \text{Property of logarithms}
\end{aligned}
$$

Because x^2 cannot be negative, the absolute value notation is unnecessary in the final form of the antiderivative.

EXAMPLE 2   Using the Log Rule with a Change of Variables

Find $\displaystyle\int \frac{1}{4x - 1} \, dx$.

Solution

If you let $u = 4x - 1$, then $du = 4 \, dx$.

$$
\begin{aligned}
\int \frac{1}{4x - 1} \, dx &= \frac{1}{4} \int \left(\frac{1}{4x - 1} \right) 4 \, dx && \text{Multiply and divide by 4.} \\
&= \frac{1}{4} \int \frac{1}{u} \, du && \text{Substitute: } u = 4x - 1. \\
&= \frac{1}{4} \ln|u| + C && \text{Apply Log Rule.} \\
&= \frac{1}{4} \ln|4x - 1| + C && \text{Back-substitute.}
\end{aligned}
$$

> **Exploration**
>
> *Integrating Rational Functions*
>
> Earlier in this chapter, you learned rules that allowed you to integrate *any* polynomial function. The Log Rule presented in this section goes a long way toward enabling you to integrate rational functions. For instance, each of the following functions can be integrated with the Log Rule.
>
> $\dfrac{2}{x}$ Example 1
>
> $\dfrac{1}{4x - 1}$ Example 2
>
> $\dfrac{x}{x^2 + 1}$ Example 3
>
> $\dfrac{3x^2 + 1}{x^3 + x}$ Example 4(a)
>
> $\dfrac{x + 1}{x^2 + 2x}$ Example 4(c)
>
> $\dfrac{1}{3x + 2}$ Example 4(d)
>
> $\dfrac{x^2 + x + 1}{x^2 + 1}$ Example 5
>
> $\dfrac{2x}{(x + 1)^2}$ Example 6
>
> There are still some rational functions that cannot be integrated using the Log Rule. Give examples of these functions, and explain your reasoning.

Example 3 uses the alternative form of the Log Rule. To apply this rule, look for quotients in which the numerator is the derivative of the denominator.

EXAMPLE 3   Finding Area with the Log Rule

Find the area of the region bounded by the graph of

$$y = \frac{x}{x^2 + 1}$$

the x-axis, and the line $x = 3$.

Solution

In Figure 4.46, you can see that the area of the region is given by the definite integral

$$\int_0^3 \frac{x}{x^2 + 1} \, dx.$$

If you let $u = x^2 + 1$, then $u' = 2x$. To apply the Log Rule, multiply and divide by 2, as shown.

$$\int_0^3 \frac{x}{x^2 + 1} \, dx = \frac{1}{2} \int_0^3 \frac{2x}{x^2 + 1} \, dx \qquad \text{Multiply and divide by 2.}$$

$$= \frac{1}{2} \left[\ln(x^2 + 1) \right]_0^3 \qquad \int \frac{u'}{u} \, dx = \ln|u| + C$$

$$= \frac{1}{2} (\ln 10 - \ln 1)$$

$$= \frac{1}{2} \ln 10 \qquad \qquad \ln 1 = 0$$

$$\approx 1.151$$

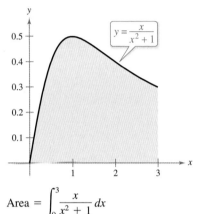

$$\text{Area} = \int_0^3 \frac{x}{x^2 + 1} \, dx$$

The area of the region bounded by the graph of y, the x-axis, and $x = 3$ is $\frac{1}{2} \ln 10$.

Figure 4.46

EXAMPLE 4   Recognizing Quotient Forms of the Log Rule

a. $\displaystyle\int \frac{3x^2 + 1}{x^3 + x} \, dx = \ln|x^3 + x| + C \qquad u = x^3 + x$

b. $\displaystyle\int \frac{\sec^2 x}{\tan x} \, dx = \ln|\tan x| + C \qquad u = \tan x$

c. $\displaystyle\int \frac{x + 1}{x^2 + 2x} \, dx = \frac{1}{2} \int \frac{2x + 2}{x^2 + 2x} \, dx \qquad u = x^2 + 2x$

$$= \frac{1}{2} \ln|x^2 + 2x| + C$$

d. $\displaystyle\int \frac{1}{3x + 2} \, dx = \frac{1}{3} \int \frac{3}{3x + 2} \, dx \qquad u = 3x + 2$

$$= \frac{1}{3} \ln|3x + 2| + C$$

With antiderivatives involving logarithms, it is easy to obtain forms that look quite different but are still equivalent. For instance, both

$$\ln|(3x + 2)^{1/3}| + C$$

and

$$\ln|3x + 2|^{1/3} + C$$

are equivalent to the antiderivative listed in Example 4(d).

Integrals to which the Log Rule can be applied often appear in disguised form. For instance, when a rational function has a *numerator of degree greater than or equal to that of the denominator*, division may reveal a form to which you can apply the Log Rule. This is shown in Example 5.

EXAMPLE 5 Using Long Division Before Integrating

See LarsonCalculusforAP.com for an interactive version of this type of example.

Find $\displaystyle\int \frac{x^2 + x + 1}{x^2 + 1}\, dx$.

Solution

Begin by using long division to rewrite the integrand.

$$\frac{x^2 + x + 1}{x^2 + 1} \implies x^2 + 1 \overline{\smash{\big)}\ \begin{array}{c} 1 \\ x^2 + x + 1 \\ \underline{x^2 \qquad + 1} \\ x \end{array}} \implies 1 + \frac{x}{x^2 + 1}$$

Now, you can integrate to obtain

$$\int \frac{x^2 + x + 1}{x^2 + 1}\, dx = \int \left(1 + \frac{x}{x^2 + 1}\right) dx \qquad \text{Rewrite using long division.}$$

$$= \int dx + \frac{1}{2}\int \frac{2x}{x^2 + 1}\, dx \qquad \text{Rewrite as two integrals.}$$

$$= x + \frac{1}{2}\ln(x^2 + 1) + C. \qquad \text{Integrate.}$$

Check this result by differentiating to obtain the original integrand. ■

The next example presents another instance in which the use of the Log Rule is disguised. In this case, a change of variables helps you recognize the Log Rule.

EXAMPLE 6 Change of Variables with the Log Rule

Find $\displaystyle\int \frac{2x}{(x + 1)^2}\, dx$.

Solution

If you let $u = x + 1$, then $du = dx$ and $x = u - 1$.

$$\int \frac{2x}{(x + 1)^2}\, dx = \int \frac{2(u - 1)}{u^2}\, du \qquad \text{Substitute.}$$

$$= 2\int \left(\frac{u}{u^2} - \frac{1}{u^2}\right) du \qquad \text{Rewrite as two fractions.}$$

$$= 2\int \frac{du}{u} - 2\int u^{-2}\, du \qquad \text{Rewrite as two integrals.}$$

$$= 2\ln|u| - 2\left(\frac{u^{-1}}{-1}\right) + C \qquad \text{Integrate.}$$

$$= 2\ln|u| + \frac{2}{u} + C \qquad \text{Simplify.}$$

$$= 2\ln|x + 1| + \frac{2}{x + 1} + C \qquad \text{Back-substitute.}$$

Check this result by differentiating to obtain the original integrand. ■

As you study the methods shown in Examples 5 and 6, be aware that both methods involve rewriting a disguised integrand so that it fits one or more of the basic integration formulas. Throughout the remaining sections of Chapter 4 and in Chapter 7, much time will be devoted to integration techniques. To master these techniques, you must recognize the "form-fitting" nature of integration. In this sense, integration is not nearly as straightforward as differentiation. Differentiation takes the form

"Here is the question; what is the answer?"

Integration is more like

"Here is the answer; what is the question?"

Here are some guidelines you can use for integration.

Guidelines for Integration

1. Learn a basic list of integration formulas.

2. Find an integration formula that resembles all or part of the integrand, and, by trial and error, find a choice of u that will make the integrand conform to the formula.

3. When you cannot find a u-substitution that works, try altering the integrand. You might try a trigonometric identity, multiplication and division by the same quantity, addition and subtraction of the same quantity, or long division. Be creative.

4. If you have access to computer software that will find antiderivatives symbolically, use it.

5. Check your result by differentiating to obtain the original integrand.

EXAMPLE 7   *u*-Substitution and the Log Rule

Solve the differential equation

$$\frac{dy}{dx} = \frac{1}{x \ln x}.$$

Solution

The solution can be written as an indefinite integral.

$$y = \int \frac{1}{x \ln x} \, dx$$

Because the integrand is a quotient whose denominator is raised to the first power, you should try the Log Rule. There are three basic choices for u. The choices

$$u = x \quad \text{and} \quad u = x \ln x$$

fail to fit the u'/u form of the Log Rule. However, the third choice does fit. Letting $u = \ln x$ produces $u' = 1/x$, and you obtain the following.

$$\int \frac{1}{x \ln x} \, dx = \int \frac{1/x}{\ln x} \, dx \qquad \text{Divide numerator and denominator by } x.$$

$$= \int \frac{u'}{u} \, dx \qquad \text{Substitute: } u = \ln x.$$

$$= \ln|u| + C \qquad \text{Apply Log Rule.}$$

$$= \ln|\ln x| + C \qquad \text{Back-substitute.}$$

So, the solution is $y = \ln|\ln x| + C.$

Justification

Keep in mind that you can check your answer to an integration problem by differentiating the answer. For instance, in Example 7, the derivative of $y = \ln|\ln x| + C$ is $y' = 1/(x \ln x)$.

Integrals of Trigonometric Functions

In Section 4.1, you looked at six trigonometric integration rules—the six that correspond directly to differentiation rules. With the Log Rule, you can now complete the set of basic trigonometric integration formulas.

EXAMPLE 8 Using a Trigonometric Identity

Find $\int \tan x \, dx$.

Solution

This integral does not seem to fit any formulas on our basic list. However, by using a trigonometric identity, you obtain

$$\int \tan x \, dx = \int \frac{\sin x}{\cos x} \, dx.$$

Knowing that $D_x[\cos x] = -\sin x$, you can let $u = \cos x$ and write

$$
\begin{aligned}
\int \tan x \, dx &= -\int \frac{-\sin x}{\cos x} \, dx && \text{Apply trigonometric identity and} \\
&&& \text{multiply and divide by } -1. \\
&= -\int \frac{u'}{u} \, dx && \text{Substitute: } u = \cos x. \\
&= -\ln|u| + C && \text{Apply Log Rule.} \\
&= -\ln|\cos x| + C. && \text{Back-substitute.} \quad \blacksquare
\end{aligned}
$$

Example 8 used a trigonometric identity to derive an integration rule for the tangent function. The next example takes a rather unusual step (multiplying and dividing by the same quantity) to derive an integration rule for the secant function.

EXAMPLE 9 Derivation of the Secant Formula

Find $\int \sec x \, dx$.

Solution

Consider the following procedure.

$$
\begin{aligned}
\int \sec x \, dx &= \int (\sec x)\left(\frac{\sec x + \tan x}{\sec x + \tan x}\right) dx && \text{Multiply and divide by } \sec x + \tan x. \\
&= \int \frac{\sec^2 x + \sec x \tan x}{\sec x + \tan x} \, dx && \text{Simplify.}
\end{aligned}
$$

Letting u be the denominator of this quotient produces

$$u = \sec x + \tan x \quad \text{and} \quad u' = \sec x \tan x + \sec^2 x.$$

So, you can conclude that

$$
\begin{aligned}
\int \sec x \, dx &= \int \frac{\sec^2 x + \sec x \tan x}{\sec x + \tan x} \, dx && \text{Rewrite integrand.} \\
&= \int \frac{u'}{u} \, dx && \text{Substitute: } u = \sec x + \tan x. \\
&= \ln|u| + C && \text{Apply Log Rule.} \\
&= \ln|\sec x + \tan x| + C. && \text{Back-substitute.} \quad \blacksquare
\end{aligned}
$$

> **Insight**
>
> It is possible that integrals similar to the one in Example 9 will appear on the AP® Exam. The exam can include derivatives and integrals of any trigonometric function.

With the results of Examples 8 and 9, you now have integration formulas for $\sin x$, $\cos x$, $\tan x$, and $\sec x$. The integrals of the six basic trigonometric functions are summarized below. (For proofs of $\cot u$ and $\csc u$, see Exercises 87 and 88.)

Integrals of the Six Basic Trigonometric Functions

$$\int \sin u \, du = -\cos u + C \qquad \int \cos u \, du = \sin u + C$$

$$\int \tan u \, du = -\ln|\cos u| + C \qquad \int \cot u \, du = \ln|\sin u| + C$$

$$\int \sec u \, du = \ln|\sec u + \tan u| + C \qquad \int \csc u \, du = -\ln|\csc u + \cot u| + C$$

Connecting Representations

Using trigonometric identities and properties of logarithms, you could rewrite these six integration rules in other forms. For instance, you could write

$$\int \csc u \, du$$
$$= \ln|\csc u - \cot u| + C.$$

(See Exercises 89 and 90.)

EXAMPLE 10 Integrating a Trigonometric Function

Evaluate $\displaystyle\int_0^{\pi/4} \sqrt{1 + \tan^2 x} \, dx.$

Solution

Using $1 + \tan^2 x = \sec^2 x$, you can write

$$\int_0^{\pi/4} \sqrt{1 + \tan^2 x} \, dx = \int_0^{\pi/4} \sqrt{\sec^2 x} \, dx$$

$$= \int_0^{\pi/4} \sec x \, dx \qquad \sec x \geq 0 \text{ for } 0 \leq x \leq \frac{\pi}{4}$$

$$= \ln|\sec x + \tan x| \Big]_0^{\pi/4}$$

$$= \ln(\sqrt{2} + 1) - \ln 1$$

$$\approx 0.881.$$

EXAMPLE 11 Finding an Average Value

Find the average value of $f(x) = \tan x$ on the interval $[0, \pi/4]$.

Solution

$$\text{Average value} = \frac{1}{(\pi/4) - 0} \int_0^{\pi/4} \tan x \, dx \qquad \text{Average value} = \frac{1}{b-a}\int_a^b f(x)\,dx$$

$$= \frac{4}{\pi} \int_0^{\pi/4} \tan x \, dx \qquad \text{Simplify.}$$

$$= \frac{4}{\pi}\left[-\ln|\cos x| \right]_0^{\pi/4} \qquad \text{Integrate. (See Example 8.)}$$

$$= -\frac{4}{\pi}\left[\ln \frac{\sqrt{2}}{2} - \ln 1 \right]$$

$$= -\frac{4}{\pi} \ln \frac{\sqrt{2}}{2}$$

$$\approx 0.441$$

The average value is about 0.441, as shown in Figure 4.47.

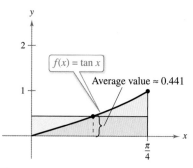

Figure 4.47

4.7 Exercises

See *CalcChat.com* for tutorial help and worked-out solutions to odd-numbered exercises.

Finding an Indefinite Integral In Exercises 1–26, find the indefinite integral.

1. $\int \dfrac{3}{x}\,dx$

2. $\int \dfrac{-12}{x}\,dx$

3. $\int \dfrac{1}{7-x}\,dx$

4. $\int \dfrac{5}{x+2}\,dx$

5. $\int \dfrac{2}{3x+5}\,dx$

6. $\int \dfrac{9}{5-4x}\,dx$

7. $\int \dfrac{x}{-x^2+1}\,dx$

8. $\int \dfrac{x^2}{10+x^3}\,dx$

9. $\int \dfrac{4x^3+3}{x^4+3x}\,dx$

10. $\int \dfrac{x^2-2x}{x^3-3x^2}\,dx$

11. $\int \dfrac{6x^2-4}{x}\,dx$

12. $\int \dfrac{x^5-8x}{x^2}\,dx$

13. $\int \dfrac{x^2+2x+3}{x^3+3x^2+9x}\,dx$

14. $\int \dfrac{x^2+4x}{x^3+6x^2+5}\,dx$

15. $\int \dfrac{x^2-3x+2}{x+1}\,dx$

16. $\int \dfrac{2x^2+7x-3}{x-2}\,dx$

17. $\int \dfrac{x^3-3x^2+5}{3-x}\,dx$

18. $\int \dfrac{x^3-6x-20}{x+5}\,dx$

19. $\int \dfrac{x^4+x-4}{x^2+2}\,dx$

20. $\int \dfrac{x^3-4x^2-4x+20}{x^2-5}\,dx$

21. $\int \dfrac{1}{\sqrt{x}\left(1-3\sqrt{x}\right)}\,dx$

22. $\int \dfrac{1}{x^{2/3}(1+x^{1/3})}\,dx$

23. $\int \dfrac{2x}{(x-1)^2}\,dx$

24. $\int \dfrac{x(x-2)}{(x-1)^3}\,dx$

25. $\int \dfrac{(\ln x)^2}{x}\,dx$

26. $\int \dfrac{1}{x\ln x^3}\,dx$

Finding an Indefinite Integral by *u*-Substitution In Exercises 27–30, find the indefinite integral by *u*-substitution. (*Hint:* Let *u* be the denominator of the integrand.)

27. $\int \dfrac{1}{1+\sqrt{2x}}\,dx$

28. $\int \dfrac{1}{1+\sqrt{3x}}\,dx$

29. $\int \dfrac{\sqrt{x}}{\sqrt{x}-3}\,dx$

30. $\int \dfrac{\sqrt[3]{x}}{\sqrt[3]{x}-1}\,dx$

Finding an Indefinite Integral of a Trigonometric Function In Exercises 31–42, find the indefinite integral.

31. $\int \cot \dfrac{\theta}{3}\,d\theta$

32. $\int \tan 5\theta\,d\theta$

33. $\int \csc 2x\,dx$

34. $\int \sec \dfrac{x}{2}\,dx$

35. $\int \left(\sec^2 \dfrac{\theta}{4} - \tan \dfrac{\theta}{4}\right)d\theta$

36. $\int (\cos 3\theta - \cot 3\theta)\,d\theta$

37. $\int \dfrac{\cos t}{1+\sin t}\,dt$

38. $\int \dfrac{\csc^2 t}{\cot t}\,dt$

39. $\int \dfrac{1-\tan x}{\sin x}\,dx$

40. $\int \dfrac{\tan \theta + \cot \theta}{\cos \theta}\,d\theta$

41. $\int e^{-x}\tan(e^{-x})\,dx$

42. $\int \dfrac{2}{x}\sec(\ln x^2)\,dx$

Error Analysis In Exercises 43 and 44, describe and correct the error.

43. $\displaystyle\int \dfrac{x^2-5x-6}{x+3}\,dx = \int \left(x-8+\dfrac{18}{x+3}\right)dx$
$$= \dfrac{x^2}{2} - 8x + 18\ln(x+3) + C \quad ✗$$

44. $\displaystyle\int \dfrac{1}{2x+3}\,dx = \ln|2x+3| + C \quad ✗$

 Differential Equation In Exercises 45–48, solve the differential equation. Use a graphing utility to graph three solutions, one of which passes through the given point.

45. $\dfrac{dy}{dx} = \dfrac{3}{2-x}$, $(1,0)$

46. $\dfrac{dy}{dx} = \dfrac{2x}{x^2-9}$, $(0,4)$

47. $\dfrac{dy}{dt} = \dfrac{\ln(t+1)}{t+1}$, $(0,-1)$

48. $\dfrac{dr}{dt} = \dfrac{\sec^2 t}{\tan t + 1}$, $(\pi, 4)$

Finding a Particular Solution In Exercises 49 and 50, find the particular solution that satisfies the differential equation and the initial equations.

49. $f''(x) = \dfrac{2}{x^2}$, $f'(1) = 1$, $f(1) = 1$, $x > 0$

50. $f''(x) = -\dfrac{4}{(x-1)^2} - 2$, $f'(2) = 0$, $f(2) = 3$, $x > 1$

Evaluating a Definite Integral In Exercises 51–60, evaluate the definite integral. Use a graphing utility to verify your result.

51. $\displaystyle\int_0^4 \dfrac{5}{3x+1}\,dx$

52. $\displaystyle\int_{-1}^0 \dfrac{x^3-2x}{1+4x^2-x^4}\,dx$

53. $\displaystyle\int_0^2 \dfrac{x^2-2}{x+1}\,dx$

54. $\displaystyle\int_0^1 \dfrac{x-1}{x+1}\,dx$

55. $\displaystyle\int_1^e \dfrac{(1+\ln x)^2}{x}\,dx$

56. $\displaystyle\int_e^{e^2} \dfrac{1}{x\ln x}\,dx$

57. $\displaystyle\int_{\pi/4}^{\pi/2} \sqrt{1+\cot^2 x}\,dx$

58. $\displaystyle\int_0^{\pi/8} \dfrac{2\tan x}{1-\tan^2 x}\,dx$

59. $\displaystyle\int_1^2 \dfrac{1-\cos\theta}{\theta-\sin\theta}\,d\theta$

60. $\displaystyle\int_{\pi/8}^{\pi/4} (\csc 2\theta - \cot 2\theta)\,d\theta$

Using Technology to Find an Integral **In Exercises 61–64, use a computer algebra system to find or evaluate the integral.**

61. $\displaystyle\int \frac{1}{1 + \sqrt{x}}\, dx$

62. $\displaystyle\int \frac{x^2}{x - 1}\, dx$

63. $\displaystyle\int_{\pi/4}^{\pi/2} (\csc x - \sin x)\, dx$

64. $\displaystyle\int_{-\pi/4}^{\pi/4} \frac{\sin^2 x - \cos^2 x}{\cos x}\, dx$

Finding a Derivative **In Exercises 65–68, find $F'(x)$.**

65. $\displaystyle F(x) = \int_{1}^{x} \frac{1}{t}\, dt$

66. $\displaystyle F(x) = \int_{0}^{x} \tan t\, dt$

67. $\displaystyle F(x) = \int_{1}^{3x} \frac{1}{t}\, dt$

68. $\displaystyle F(x) = \int_{1}^{x^2} \frac{1}{t}\, dt$

 Area **In Exercises 69–72, find the area of the given region. Use a graphing utility to verify your result.**

69. $y = \dfrac{6}{x}$

70. $y = \dfrac{2}{x \ln x}$

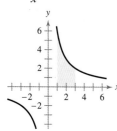

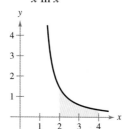

71. $y = \tan x$

72. $y = \dfrac{\sin x}{1 + \cos x}$

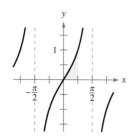

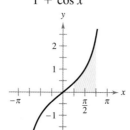

 Area **In Exercises 73–76, find the area of the region bounded by the graphs of the equations. Use a graphing utility to verify your result.**

73. $y = \dfrac{x^2 + 4}{x}, \quad x = 1, \quad x = 4, \quad y = 0$

74. $y = \dfrac{5x}{x^2 + 2}, \quad x = 1, \quad x = 5, \quad y = 0$

75. $y = 2 \sec \dfrac{\pi x}{6}, \quad x = 0, \quad x = 2, \quad y = 0$

76. $y = 2x - \tan 0.3x, \quad x = 1, \quad x = 4, \quad y = 0$

Numerical Integration **In Exercises 77–80, use the Trapezoidal Rule to approximate the value of the definite integral. Let $n = 4$ and round your answer to four decimal places. Use a graphing utility to verify your result.**

77. $\displaystyle\int_{1}^{5} \frac{12}{x}\, dx$

78. $\displaystyle\int_{0}^{4} \frac{8x}{x^2 + 4}\, dx$

79. $\displaystyle\int_{2}^{6} \ln x\, dx$

80. $\displaystyle\int_{-\pi/3}^{\pi/3} \sec x\, dx$

EXPLORING CONCEPTS

81. Choosing a Formula State the integration techniques and formulas you would use to perform each integration. Do not integrate.

   (a) $\displaystyle\int \frac{x}{(x^2 + 4)^3}\, dx$ (b) $\displaystyle\int \frac{x}{x^2 + 4}\, dx$

   (c) $\displaystyle\int \frac{x^2 + x + 4}{x^2 + 4}\, dx$ (d) $\displaystyle\int \frac{2x}{(x^2 + 4) \ln(x^2 + 4)}\, dx$

82. Think About It What problem do you face when you try to use the Log Rule to find $\int_{0}^{3} 2x/(x^2 - 9)\, dx$?

Approximation **In Exercises 83 and 84, determine which value best approximates the area of the region between the x-axis and the graph of the function over the given interval. (Make your selection on the basis of a sketch of the region, not by performing any calculations.)**

83. $f(x) = \sec x, \quad [0, 1]$

   (a) 6   (b) -6 (c) $\frac{1}{2}$ (d) 1.25   (e) 3

84. $f(x) = \dfrac{2x}{x^2 + 1}, \quad [0, 4]$

   (a) 3   (b) 7   (c) -2 (d) 5   (e) 1

85. Finding a Value Find a value of x such that

$$\int_{1}^{x} \frac{3}{t}\, dt = \int_{1/4}^{x} \frac{1}{t}\, dt.$$

86. Think About It Write an expression whose antiderivative is $\ln\left|\sqrt{x^2 - 1}\right| + C$.

87. Proof Prove that $\int \cot u\, du = \ln|\sin u| + C$.

88. Proof Prove that

$$\int \csc u\, du = -\ln|\csc u + \cot u| + C.$$

Using Properties of Logarithms and Trigonometric Identities **In Exercises 89 and 90, show that the two formulas are equivalent.**

89. $\displaystyle\int \tan x\, dx = -\ln|\cos x| + C$

   $\displaystyle\int \tan x\, dx = \ln|\sec x| + C$

90. $\displaystyle\int \csc x\, dx = -\ln|\csc x + \cot x| + C$

   $\displaystyle\int \csc x\, dx = \ln|\csc x - \cot x| + C$

Finding the Average Value of a Function In Exercises 91–94, find the average value of the function over the given interval.

91. $f(x) = \dfrac{x^2}{8 - x^3}$, $[-2, 1]$ **92.** $f(x) = \dfrac{4(x + 1)}{x^2}$, $[2, 4]$

93. $f(x) = \dfrac{2 \ln x}{x}$, $[1, e]$ **94.** $f(x) = \sec \dfrac{\pi x}{6}$, $[0, 2]$

95. Population Growth A population of bacteria P is changing at a rate of

$$\frac{dP}{dt} = \frac{3000}{1 + 0.25t}$$

where t is the time in days. The initial population (when $t = 0$) is 1000 bacteria. Write an equation that gives the population at any time t. Then find the population when $t = 3$ days.

96. Sales The rate of change in sales S is inversely proportional to time t ($t > 1$), measured in weeks. Find S as a function of t when the sales after 2 and 4 weeks are 200 units and 300 units, respectively.

97. HEAT TRANSFER

Find the time required for an object to cool from 300°F to 250°F by evaluating

$$t = \frac{10}{\ln 2} \int_{250}^{300} \frac{1}{T - 100} \, dT$$

where t is time in minutes and T is the temperature in degrees Fahrenheit.

98. Average Price The demand equation for a product is

$$p = \frac{90,000}{400 + 3x}$$

where p is the price (in dollars) and x is the number of units (in thousands). Find the average price p on the interval $40 \le x \le 50$.

99. Area and Slope Graph the function

$$f(x) = \frac{x}{1 + x^2}$$

on the interval $[0, \infty)$.

(a) Find the area bounded by the graph of f and the line $y = \frac{1}{2}x$.

(b) Determine the values of the slope m such that the line $y = mx$ and the graph of f enclose a finite region.

(c) Calculate the area of this region as a function of m.

100. HOW DO YOU SEE IT? Use the graph of f' shown in the figure to answer the following.

(a) Approximate the slope of f at $x = -1$. Explain.

(b) Approximate any open intervals in which the graph of f is increasing and any open intervals in which it is decreasing. Explain.

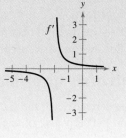

True or False? In Exercises 101 and 102, determine whether the statement is true or false. If it is false, explain why or give an example that shows it is false.

101. $\displaystyle\int \frac{1}{x} \, dx = \ln|cx|$, $c \ne 0$ **102.** $\displaystyle\int \ln x \, dx = \frac{1}{x} + C$

103. Proof Prove Theorem 4.19.

Calculus AP® – Exam Preparation Questions

104. Multiple Choice $\displaystyle\int \frac{12}{7 - 8x} \, dx =$

(A) $-\frac{3}{2} \ln|7 - 8x| + C$ (B) $\frac{3}{2} \ln|7 - 8x| + C$

(C) $12 \ln|7 - 8x| + C$ (D) $\ln|7 - 8x| + C$

105. Multiple Choice Let $F(x)$ be an antiderivative of $f(x) = 2(\ln x)^4/x$. If $F(1) = 0$, then what is the value of $F(6)$?

(A) 3.693   (B) 6.156

(C) 7.387   (D) 36.934

106. Free Response Let $f(x) = -\tan x + 1$.

(a) Find an equation of the tangent line to the graph of f at $x = \pi/6$.

(b) Find an expression that represents the area of the region bounded by the graph of f, the x-axis, and the y-axis.

(c) Find the average value of f on the interval $\left[\dfrac{\pi}{6}, \dfrac{\pi}{4}\right]$.

107. Free Response Consider the differential equation

$$f'(x) = -\frac{3}{x - 2} + x, \quad x > 2.$$

(a) Find the particular solution $y = f(x)$ to the differential equation with the initial condition $f(3) = 4$.

(b) For the particular solution described in part (a), find $\lim_{x \to \infty} f(x)$, if possible. Explain your reasoning.

4.8   Inverse Trigonometric Functions: Integration

▶ Integrate functions whose antiderivatives involve inverse trigonometric functions.
▶ Use the method of completing the square to integrate a function.
▶ Review the basic integration rules involving elementary functions.

Integrals Involving Inverse Trigonometric Functions

The derivatives of the six inverse trigonometric functions fall into three pairs. In each pair, the derivative of one function is the negative of the other. For example,

$$\frac{d}{dx}[\arcsin x] = \frac{1}{\sqrt{1 - x^2}}$$

and

$$\frac{d}{dx}[\arccos x] = -\frac{1}{\sqrt{1 - x^2}}.$$

When listing the *antiderivative* that corresponds to each of the inverse trigonometric functions, you need to use only one member from each pair. It is conventional to use $\arcsin x$ as the antiderivative of $1/\sqrt{1 - x^2}$, rather than $-\arccos x$. The next theorem gives one antiderivative formula for each of the three pairs. The proofs of these integration rules are left to you. (See Exercises 67–69.)

Theorem 4.20   Integrals Involving Inverse Trigonometric Functions

Let u be a differentiable function of x, and let $a > 0$.

1. $\displaystyle\int \frac{du}{\sqrt{a^2 - u^2}} = \arcsin \frac{u}{a} + C$

2. $\displaystyle\int \frac{du}{a^2 + u^2} = \frac{1}{a} \arctan \frac{u}{a} + C$

3. $\displaystyle\int \frac{du}{u\sqrt{u^2 - a^2}} = \frac{1}{a} \operatorname{arcsec} \frac{|u|}{a} + C$

Insight

The integration formulas in Theorem 4.20 are rarely tested on the AP® Exam. The formulas that are most likely to be tested are the ones involving arcsine and arctangent.

EXAMPLE 1   Integration with Inverse Trigonometric Functions

a. $\displaystyle\int \frac{dx}{\sqrt{4 - x^2}} = \arcsin \frac{x}{2} + C$ $u = x, \ a = 2$

b. $\displaystyle\int \frac{dx}{2 + 9x^2} = \frac{1}{3}\int \frac{3 \, dx}{(\sqrt{2})^2 + (3x)^2}$ $u = 3x, \ a = \sqrt{2}$

$\displaystyle\qquad = \frac{1}{3\sqrt{2}} \arctan \frac{3x}{\sqrt{2}} + C$

c. $\displaystyle\int \frac{dx}{x\sqrt{4x^2 - 9}} = \int \frac{2 \, dx}{2x\sqrt{(2x)^2 - 3^2}}$ $u = 2x, \ a = 3$

$\displaystyle\qquad = \frac{1}{3} \operatorname{arcsec} \frac{|2x|}{3} + C$

The integrals in Example 1 are fairly straightforward applications of integration formulas. Unfortunately, this is not typical. The integration formulas for inverse trigonometric functions can be disguised in many ways.

EXAMPLE 2   **Integration by Substitution**

Find $\displaystyle\int \frac{dx}{\sqrt{e^{2x}-1}}$.

Solution   As it stands, this integral does not fit any of the three inverse trigonometric formulas. Using the substitution $u = e^x$, however, produces

$$u = e^x \quad\Longrightarrow\quad du = e^x\,dx \quad\Longrightarrow\quad dx = \frac{du}{e^x} = \frac{du}{u}.$$

With this substitution, you can integrate as shown.

$$\int \frac{dx}{\sqrt{e^{2x}-1}} = \int \frac{dx}{\sqrt{(e^x)^2 - 1}} \qquad \text{Write } e^{2x} \text{ as } (e^x)^2.$$

$$= \int \frac{du/u}{\sqrt{u^2 - 1}} \qquad \text{Substitute.}$$

$$= \int \frac{du}{u\sqrt{u^2 - 1}} \qquad \text{Rewrite to fit Arcsecant Rule.}$$

$$= \operatorname{arcsec}\frac{|u|}{1} + C \qquad \text{Apply Arcsecant Rule.}$$

$$= \operatorname{arcsec} e^x + C \qquad \text{Back-substitute.} \qquad\blacksquare$$

Technology Pitfall

A symbolic integration utility can be useful for integrating functions. The utility may fail to find an antiderivative, however, often for two reasons. First, some elementary functions do not have antiderivatives that are elementary functions. Second, every utility has limitations—you might have entered a function that the utility was not programmed to handle. Also, remember that antiderivatives can be written in many different forms. For instance, a utility was used to find the integral in Example 2, and the result is shown below. Try showing that this result is equivalent to the one found in Example 2.

$$\int \frac{dx}{\sqrt{e^{2x}-1}} = \arctan\sqrt{e^{2x}-1} + C.$$

EXAMPLE 3   **Rewriting as the Sum of Two Quotients**

Find $\displaystyle\int \frac{x+2}{\sqrt{4-x^2}}\,dx$.

Solution   This integral does not appear to fit any of the basic integration formulas. By splitting the integrand into two parts, however, you can see that the first part can be found with the Power Rule, and the second part yields an inverse sine function.

$$\int \frac{x+2}{\sqrt{4-x^2}}\,dx = \int \frac{x}{\sqrt{4-x^2}}\,dx + \int \frac{2}{\sqrt{4-x^2}}\,dx$$

$$= -\frac{1}{2}\int (4-x^2)^{-1/2}(-2x)\,dx + 2\int \frac{1}{\sqrt{4-x^2}}\,dx$$

$$= -\frac{1}{2}\left[\frac{(4-x^2)^{1/2}}{1/2}\right] + 2\arcsin\frac{x}{2} + C$$

$$= -\sqrt{4-x^2} + 2\arcsin\frac{x}{2} + C \qquad\qquad\blacksquare$$

Completing the Square

Completing the square helps when quadratic functions are involved in the integrand. For example, the quadratic $x^2 + bx + c$ can be written as the difference of two squares by adding and subtracting $(b/2)^2$.

$$x^2 + bx + c = x^2 + bx + \left(\frac{b}{2}\right)^2 - \left(\frac{b}{2}\right)^2 + c = \left(x + \frac{b}{2}\right)^2 - \left(\frac{b}{2}\right)^2 + c$$

EXAMPLE 4   Completing the Square

See LarsonCalculusforAP.com for an interactive version of this type of example.

Find $\displaystyle\int \frac{dx}{x^2 - 4x + 7}$.

Solution You can write the denominator as the sum of two squares, as shown.

$$x^2 - 4x + 7 = (x^2 - 4x + 4) - 4 + 7 = (x - 2)^2 + 3 = u^2 + a^2$$

Now, in this completed square form, let $u = x - 2$ and $a = \sqrt{3}$.

$$\int \frac{dx}{x^2 - 4x + 7} = \int \frac{dx}{(x - 2)^2 + 3} = \frac{1}{\sqrt{3}} \arctan \frac{x - 2}{\sqrt{3}} + C$$

When the leading coefficient is not 1, it helps to factor before completing the square. For instance, you can complete the square of $2x^2 - 8x + 10$ by factoring first.

$$2x^2 - 8x + 10 = 2(x^2 - 4x + 5) = 2(x^2 - 4x + 4 - 4 + 5) = 2[(x - 2)^2 + 1]$$

To complete the square when the coefficient of x^2 is negative, use the same factoring process shown above. For instance, you can complete the square for $3x - x^2$, as shown.

$$3x - x^2 = -(x^2 - 3x) = -\left[x^2 - 3x + \left(\frac{3}{2}\right)^2 - \left(\frac{3}{2}\right)^2\right] = \left(\frac{3}{2}\right)^2 - \left(x - \frac{3}{2}\right)^2$$

EXAMPLE 5   Completing the Square

Find the area of the region bounded by the graph of

$$f(x) = \frac{1}{\sqrt{3x - x^2}}$$

the x-axis, and the lines $x = \frac{3}{2}$ and $x = \frac{9}{4}$.

Algebraic Solution

Using the completed square derived above, the area is

$$\text{Area} = \int_{3/2}^{9/4} \frac{1}{\sqrt{3x - x^2}}\, dx$$

$$= \int_{3/2}^{9/4} \frac{dx}{\sqrt{(3/2)^2 - [x - (3/2)]^2}}$$

$$= \arcsin \frac{x - (3/2)}{3/2} \Bigg]_{3/2}^{9/4}$$

$$= \arcsin \frac{1}{2} - \arcsin 0$$

$$= \frac{\pi}{6}$$

$$\approx 0.524.$$

Graphical Solution

Use a graphing utility to graph $f(x) = \dfrac{1}{\sqrt{3x - x^2}}$.

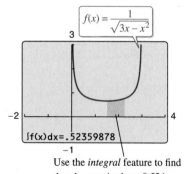

Use the *integral* feature to find that the area is about 0.524.

Review of Basic Integration Rules

You have now completed the introduction of the **basic integration rules.** To be efficient at applying these rules, you should have practiced enough so that each rule is committed to memory.

Basic Integration Rules ($a > 0$)

1. $\int kf(u)\, du = k\int f(u)\, du$

2. $\int [f(u) \pm g(u)]\, du = \int f(u)\, du \pm \int g(u)\, du$

3. $\int du = u + C$

4. $\int u^n\, du = \dfrac{u^{n+1}}{n+1} + C, \quad n \neq -1$

5. $\int \dfrac{du}{u} = \ln|u| + C$

6. $\int e^u\, du = e^u + C$

7. $\int a^u\, du = \left(\dfrac{1}{\ln a}\right)a^u + C$

8. $\int \sin u\, du = -\cos u + C$

9. $\int \cos u\, du = \sin u + C$

10. $\int \tan u\, du = -\ln|\cos u| + C$

11. $\int \cot u\, du = \ln|\sin u| + C$

12. $\int \sec u\, du = \ln|\sec u + \tan u| + C$

13. $\int \csc u\, du = -\ln|\csc u + \cot u| + C$

14. $\int \sec^2 u\, du = \tan u + C$

15. $\int \csc^2 u\, du = -\cot u + C$

16. $\int \sec u \tan u\, du = \sec u + C$

17. $\int \csc u \cot u\, du = -\csc u + C$

18. $\int \dfrac{du}{\sqrt{a^2 - u^2}} = \arcsin \dfrac{u}{a} + C$

19. $\int \dfrac{du}{a^2 + u^2} = \dfrac{1}{a}\arctan \dfrac{u}{a} + C$

20. $\int \dfrac{du}{u\sqrt{u^2 - a^2}} = \dfrac{1}{a}\text{arcsec} \dfrac{|u|}{a} + C$

You can learn a lot about the nature of integration by comparing this list with the summary of differentiation rules given in Section 2.6. For differentiation, you now have rules that allow you to differentiate *any* elementary function. For integration, this is far from true.

The integration rules listed above are primarily those that were happened on during the development of differentiation rules. So far, you have not learned any rules or techniques for finding the antiderivative of a general product or quotient, the natural logarithmic function, or the inverse trigonometric functions. More important, you cannot apply any of the rules in this list unless you can create the proper *du* corresponding to the *u* in the formula. The point is that you need to work more on integration techniques, which you will do in Chapter 7. The next two examples should give you a better feeling for the integration problems that you *can* and *cannot* solve with the techniques and rules you now know.

EXAMPLE 6 Comparing Integration Problems

Find as many of the following integrals as you can using the formulas and techniques you have studied so far in the text.

a. $\displaystyle\int \frac{dx}{x\sqrt{x^2 - 1}}$

b. $\displaystyle\int \frac{x\,dx}{\sqrt{x^2 - 1}}$

c. $\displaystyle\int \frac{dx}{\sqrt{x^2 - 1}}$

Solution

a. You *can* find this integral (it fits the Arcsecant Rule).

$$\int \frac{dx}{x\sqrt{x^2 - 1}} = \text{arcsec}|x| + C$$

b. You *can* find this integral (it fits the Power Rule).

$$\int \frac{x\,dx}{\sqrt{x^2 - 1}} = \frac{1}{2}\int (x^2 - 1)^{-1/2}(2x)\,dx$$

$$= \frac{1}{2}\left[\frac{(x^2 - 1)^{1/2}}{1/2}\right] + C$$

$$= \sqrt{x^2 - 1} + C$$

c. You *cannot* find this integral using the techniques you have studied so far. (You should scan the list of basic integration rules to verify this conclusion.)

EXAMPLE 7 Comparing Integration Problems

Find as many of the following integrals as you can using the formulas and techniques you have studied so far in the text.

a. $\displaystyle\int \frac{dx}{x \ln x}$

b. $\displaystyle\int \frac{\ln x\,dx}{x}$

c. $\displaystyle\int \ln x\,dx$

Solution

a. You *can* find this integral (it fits the Log Rule).

$$\int \frac{dx}{x \ln x} = \int \frac{1/x}{\ln x}\,dx$$

$$= \ln|\ln x| + C$$

b. You *can* find this integral (it fits the Power Rule).

$$\int \frac{\ln x\,dx}{x} = \int \left(\frac{1}{x}\right)(\ln x)^1\,dx$$

$$= \frac{(\ln x)^2}{2} + C$$

c. You *cannot* find this integral using the techniques you have studied so far.

> **Remark**
>
> Notice in Examples 6 and 7 that the *simplest* functions are the ones that you cannot yet integrate. The integral in Example 7(c) is covered in the BC course and can be solved using a method called *integration by parts* (see Section 7.2).

4.8 Exercises

See *CalcChat.com* for tutorial help and worked-out solutions to odd-numbered exercises.

Finding an Indefinite Integral **In Exercises 1–20, find the indefinite integral.**

1. $\displaystyle\int \frac{dx}{\sqrt{9 - x^2}}$

2. $\displaystyle\int \frac{dx}{\sqrt{1 - 4x^2}}$

3. $\displaystyle\int \frac{1}{x\sqrt{4x^2 - 1}}\, dx$

4. $\displaystyle\int \frac{12}{1 + 9x^2}\, dx$

5. $\displaystyle\int \frac{1}{\sqrt{1 - (x + 1)^2}}\, dx$

6. $\displaystyle\int \frac{7}{4 + (3 - x)^2}\, dx$

7. $\displaystyle\int \frac{t}{\sqrt{1 - t^4}}\, dt$

8. $\displaystyle\int \frac{1}{x\sqrt{x^4 - 4}}\, dx$

9. $\displaystyle\int \frac{t}{t^4 + 25}\, dt$

10. $\displaystyle\int \frac{1}{x\sqrt{1 - (\ln x)^2}}\, dx$

11. $\displaystyle\int \frac{e^{2x}}{4 + e^{4x}}\, dx$

12. $\displaystyle\int \frac{5}{x\sqrt{9x^2 - 11}}\, dx$

13. $\displaystyle\int \frac{\sec^2 x}{\sqrt{25 - \tan^2 x}}\, dx$

14. $\displaystyle\int \frac{\sin x}{7 + \cos^2 x}\, dx$

15. $\displaystyle\int \frac{1}{\sqrt{x}\sqrt{1 - x}}\, dx$

16. $\displaystyle\int \frac{3}{2\sqrt{x}(1 + x)}\, dx$

17. $\displaystyle\int \frac{x - 3}{x^2 + 1}\, dx$

18. $\displaystyle\int \frac{x^2 + 8}{x\sqrt{x^2 - 4}}\, dx$

19. $\displaystyle\int \frac{x + 5}{\sqrt{9 - (x - 3)^2}}\, dx$

20. $\displaystyle\int \frac{x - 2}{(x + 1)^2 + 4}\, dx$

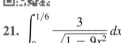

Evaluating a Definite Integral **In Exercises 21–32, evaluate the definite integral.**

21. $\displaystyle\int_0^{1/6} \frac{3}{\sqrt{1 - 9x^2}}\, dx$

22. $\displaystyle\int_0^{\sqrt{2}} \frac{1}{\sqrt{4 - x^2}}\, dx$

23. $\displaystyle\int_0^{\sqrt{3}/2} \frac{1}{1 + 4x^2}\, dx$

24. $\displaystyle\int_{\sqrt{3}}^{3} \frac{1}{x\sqrt{4x^2 - 9}}\, dx$

25. $\displaystyle\int_1^7 \frac{1}{9 + (x + 2)^2}\, dx$

26. $\displaystyle\int_1^4 \frac{1}{x\sqrt{16x^2 - 5}}\, dx$

27. $\displaystyle\int_0^{\ln 5} \frac{e^x}{1 + e^{2x}}\, dx$

28. $\displaystyle\int_{\ln 2}^{\ln 4} \frac{e^{-x}}{\sqrt{1 - e^{-2x}}}\, dx$

29. $\displaystyle\int_{\pi/2}^{\pi} \frac{\sin x}{1 + \cos^2 x}\, dx$

30. $\displaystyle\int_0^{\pi/2} \frac{\cos x}{1 + \sin^2 x}\, dx$

31. $\displaystyle\int_0^{1/\sqrt{2}} \frac{\arcsin x}{\sqrt{1 - x^2}}\, dx$

32. $\displaystyle\int_0^{1/\sqrt{2}} \frac{\arccos x}{\sqrt{1 - x^2}}\, dx$

Completing the Square **In Exercises 33–42, find or evaluate the integral by completing the square. If the integral is definite, then use the Trapezoidal Rule with $n = 4$ to verify your result.**

33. $\displaystyle\int_0^2 \frac{dx}{x^2 - 2x + 2}$

34. $\displaystyle\int_{-2}^2 \frac{dx}{x^2 + 4x + 13}$

35. $\displaystyle\int \frac{dx}{\sqrt{-2x^2 + 8x + 4}}$

36. $\displaystyle\int \frac{dx}{3x^2 - 6x + 12}$

37. $\displaystyle\int \frac{1}{\sqrt{-x^2 - 4x}}\, dx$

38. $\displaystyle\int \frac{2}{\sqrt{-x^2 + 4x}}\, dx$

39. $\displaystyle\int_2^3 \frac{2x - 3}{\sqrt{4x - x^2}}\, dx$

40. $\displaystyle\int_3^4 \frac{1}{(x - 1)\sqrt{x^2 - 2x}}\, dx$

41. $\displaystyle\int \frac{x}{x^4 + 2x^2 + 2}\, dx$

42. $\displaystyle\int \frac{x}{\sqrt{9 + 8x^2 - x^4}}\, dx$

Integration by Substitution **In Exercises 43–46, use the specified substitution to find or evaluate the integral.**

43. $\displaystyle\int \sqrt{e^t - 3}\, dt$

$u = \sqrt{e^t - 3}$

44. $\displaystyle\int \frac{\sqrt{x - 2}}{x + 1}\, dx$

$u = \sqrt{x - 2}$

45. $\displaystyle\int_1^3 \frac{dx}{\sqrt{x}(1 + x)}$

$u = \sqrt{x}$

46. $\displaystyle\int_0^1 \frac{dx}{2\sqrt{3 - x}\sqrt{x + 1}}$

$u = \sqrt{x + 1}$

Comparing Integration Problems **In Exercises 47–50, find the indefinite integrals, if possible, using the formulas and techniques you have studied so far in the text.**

47. (a) $\displaystyle\int \frac{1}{\sqrt{1 - x^2}}\, dx$

(b) $\displaystyle\int \frac{x}{\sqrt{1 - x^2}}\, dx$

(c) $\displaystyle\int \frac{1}{x\sqrt{1 - x^2}}\, dx$

48. (a) $\displaystyle\int e^{x^2}\, dx$

(b) $\displaystyle\int x e^{x^2}\, dx$

(c) $\displaystyle\int \frac{1}{x^2} e^{1/x}\, dx$

49. (a) $\displaystyle\int \sqrt{x - 1}\, dx$

(b) $\displaystyle\int x\sqrt{x - 1}\, dx$

(c) $\displaystyle\int \frac{x}{\sqrt{x - 1}}\, dx$

50. (a) $\displaystyle\int \frac{1}{1 + x^4}\, dx$

(b) $\displaystyle\int \frac{x}{1 + x^4}\, dx$

(c) $\displaystyle\int \frac{x^3}{1 + x^4}\, dx$

EXPLORING CONCEPTS

Connecting Representations **In Exercises 51 and 52, show that the antiderivatives are equivalent.**

51. $\displaystyle\int \frac{3x^2}{\sqrt{1 - x^6}}\, dx = \arcsin x^3 + C$ or $\arccos \sqrt{1 - x^6} + C$

52. $\displaystyle\int \frac{6}{4 + 9x^2}\, dx = \arctan \frac{3x}{2} + C$ or $\operatorname{arccsc} \frac{\sqrt{4 + 9x^2}}{3x} + C$

53. **Connecting Representations** The indefinite integral $\int (1/\sqrt{1 - x^2})\, dx$ can be either $\arcsin x + C$ or $-\arccos x + C$. Does this mean that $\arcsin x = -\arccos x$? Explain.

54. **HOW DO YOU SEE IT?** Using the graph, which value best approximates the area of the region between the x-axis and the function over the interval $\left[-\frac{1}{2}, \frac{1}{2}\right]$? Explain.

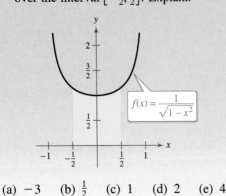

$$f(x) = \frac{1}{\sqrt{1 - x^2}}$$

(a) -3 (b) $\frac{1}{2}$ (c) 1 (d) 2 (e) 4

Error Analysis In Exercises 55 and 56, describe and correct the error.

55. $\displaystyle\int \frac{x - 5}{\sqrt{1 - x^2}}\, dx$

$$= \int \frac{x}{\sqrt{1 - x^2}}\, dx + \int \frac{5}{\sqrt{1 - x^2}}\, dx$$

$$= -\frac{1}{2}\int (1 - x^2)^{-1/2}(-2x)\, dx + 5\int \frac{1}{\sqrt{1 - x^2}}\, dx$$

$$= -\frac{1}{2}\left[\frac{(1 - x^2)^{1/2}}{1/2}\right] + 5\arcsin x + C$$

$$= -\sqrt{1 - x^2} + 5\arcsin x + C \qquad \textbf{✗}$$

56. $\displaystyle\int_{-1}^{3} \frac{dx}{x^2 + 2x + 3} = \int_{-1}^{3} \frac{dx}{(x + 1)^2 + 2}$

$$= \left[\frac{1}{2}\arctan \frac{x + 1}{2}\right]_{-1}^{3}$$

$$= \frac{1}{2}\arctan 2 \qquad \textbf{✗}$$

Area In Exercises 57–60, find the area of the shaded region. Use a graphing utility to verify your result.

57. $y = \dfrac{2}{\sqrt{4 - x^2}}$

58. $y = \dfrac{1}{x\sqrt{x^2 - 1}}$

59. $y = \dfrac{1}{x^2 - 2x + 5}$

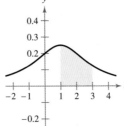

60. $y = \dfrac{3\cos x}{1 + \sin^2 x}$

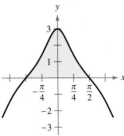

Solving a Differential Equation In Exercises 61 and 62, find the particular solution of the differential equation that satisfies the initial condition.

61. $\dfrac{dy}{dx} = \dfrac{1}{\sqrt{4 - x^2}}$

$y(0) = \pi$

62. $\dfrac{dy}{dx} = \dfrac{1}{4 + x^2}$

$y(2) = \pi$

True or False? In Exercises 63–66, determine whether the statement is true or false. If it is false, explain why or give an example that shows it is false.

63. $\displaystyle\int \frac{dx}{3x\sqrt{9x^2 - 16}} = \frac{1}{4}\operatorname{arcsec} \frac{3x}{4} + C$

64. $\displaystyle\int \frac{dx}{\sqrt{4 - x^2}} = -\arccos \frac{x}{2} + C$

65. $\dfrac{d}{dx}[\arctan x] = \dfrac{d}{dx}[\operatorname{arccot} x]$

66. One way to find $\displaystyle\int \frac{2e^{2x}}{\sqrt{9 - e^{2x}}}\, dx$ is to use the Arcsine Rule.

Verifying an Integration Rule In Exercises 67–69, verify the rule by differentiating. Let $a > 0$.

67. $\displaystyle\int \frac{du}{\sqrt{a^2 - u^2}} = \arcsin \frac{u}{a} + C$

68. $\displaystyle\int \frac{du}{a^2 + u^2} = \frac{1}{a}\arctan \frac{u}{a} + C$

69. $\displaystyle\int \frac{du}{u\sqrt{u^2 - a^2}} = \frac{1}{a}\operatorname{arcsec} \frac{|u|}{a} + C$

70. Connecting Representations Consider the integral

$$\int \frac{1}{\sqrt{6x - x^2}}\, dx.$$

(a) Find the integral by completing the square of the radicand.

(b) Find the integral by making the substitution $u = \sqrt{x}$.

(c) The antiderivatives in parts (a) and (b) appear to be significantly different. Use a graphing utility to graph each antiderivative in the same viewing window and determine the relationship between them. Find the domain of each.

71. Investigation Consider the function

$$F(x) = \frac{1}{2}\int_{x}^{x+2} \frac{2}{t^2 + 1}\, dt.$$

(a) Write a brief statement giving a geometric interpretation of the function $F(x)$ relative to the function

$$f(x) = \frac{2}{x^2 + 1}.$$

Use your statement to estimate the value of x that maximizes $F(x)$.

(b) Perform the specified integration to find an alternative form of $F(x)$. Use calculus to locate the value of x that maximizes $F(x)$ and compare the result with your estimate in part (a).

72. Vertical Motion An object is projected upward from ground level with an initial velocity of 500 feet per second. In this exercise, the goal is to analyze the motion of the object during its upward flight.

(a) If air resistance is neglected, find the velocity of the object as a function of time. Use a graphing utility to graph this function.

(b) Use the result of part (a) to find the position function and determine the maximum height attained by the object.

(c) If the air resistance is proportional to the square of the velocity, you obtain the equation $dv/dt = -(32 + kv^2)$, where 32 feet per second per second is the acceleration due to gravity and k is a constant. Find the velocity as a function of time by solving the equation

$$\int \frac{dv}{32 + kv^2} = -\int dt.$$

(d) Use a graphing utility to graph the velocity function $v(t)$ in part (c) for $k = 0.001$. Use the graph to approximate the time t_0 at which the object reaches its maximum height.

(e) Use the integration capabilities of a graphing utility to approximate the integral $\int_{0}^{t_0} v(t)\, dt$, where $v(t)$ and t_0 are those found in part (d). This is the approximation of the maximum height of the object.

(f) Explain the difference between the results in parts (b) and (e).

73. Approximating Pi

(a) Show that $\int_{0}^{1} \frac{4}{1 + x^2}\, dx = \pi.$

(b) Approximate the number π using the Trapezoidal Rule (with $n = 6$) and the integral in part (a).

(c) Approximate the number π by using the integration capabilities of a graphing utility.

Calculus AP® – Exam Preparation Questions

74. Multiple Choice Which of the following is the solution of the differential equation

$$y' = \frac{4}{\sqrt{16 - x^2}}?$$

(A) $y = \arcsin \dfrac{x}{4} + C$

(B) $y = 4 \arcsin \dfrac{x}{4} + C$

(C) $y = \dfrac{1}{4} \arcsin \dfrac{x}{16} + C$

(D) $y = 16 \arcsin \dfrac{x}{4} + C$

75. Multiple Choice Which integral has a value of π?

I. $\displaystyle\int_{5/2}^{5} \frac{2}{\sqrt{5x - x^2}}\, dx$

II. $\displaystyle\int_{\pi}^{2\pi} \frac{\pi}{2} \sin \frac{x}{2}\, dx$

III. $\displaystyle\int_{3}^{8} \frac{\pi}{2\sqrt{x + 1}}\, dx$

(A) I and II only   (B) I and III only

(C) II and III only   (D) I, II, and III

76. Free Response Let $f(x) = \arccos x$ and let $g(x) = x^2$. Define $h(x) = f(g(x))$.

(a) At what values of x does $h(x)$ have a relative maximum?

(b) Write, but do not evaluate, an expression that can be used to determine the area of the region bounded by the graphs of $h(x)$ and the horizontal line $y = \pi/3$.

(c) Evaluate $\dfrac{d}{dx}\left[f^{-1}\left(\dfrac{\pi}{3}\right)\right]$.

77. Free Response The function f is defined by

$$f(x) = \frac{1}{\sqrt{4 - x^2}}$$

for $-2 < x < 2$. Let g be the function defined by

$$g(x) = \begin{cases} f(x), & -2 < x \le 0 \\ x + \dfrac{1}{2}, & 0 < x \le 2 \end{cases}.$$

(a) Is g continuous at $x = 0$? Use the definition of continuity to explain your answer.

(b) What is the area of the region bounded by f, the x-axis, the y-axis, and the line $x = 1$?

(c) Find the value of

$$\int_{-1}^{1} g(x)\, dx.$$

Finding an Indefinite Integral   In Exercises 1–6, find the indefinite integral.

1. $\int (4x^2 + x + 3)\, dx$

2. $\int \dfrac{6}{\sqrt[3]{x}}\, dx$

3. $\int \dfrac{x^4 + 8}{x^5}\, dx$

4. $\int (5 \cos x - 2 \sec^2 x)\, dx$

5. $\int (5 - e^x)\, dx$

6. $\int (10^x + x^{3/2})\, dx$

Finding a Particular Solution   In Exercises 7–10, find the particular solution that satisfies the differential equation and the initial condition.

7. $f'(x) = -6x,\ f(1) = -2$

8. $f'(x) = 9x^2 + 1,\ f(0) = 7$

9. $f''(x) = e^{-x},\ f'(0) = 0,\ f(0) = 8$

10. $f''(x) = 2 \cos x,\ f'(0) = 4,\ f(0) = -5$

11. **Velocity and Acceleration**   A ball is thrown vertically upward from ground level with an initial velocity of 96 feet per second. Assume that the acceleration is $a(t) = -32$ feet per second per second. (Neglect air resistance.)

   (a) How long will it take the ball to rise to its maximum height? What is the maximum height?

   (b) After how many seconds is the velocity of the ball one-half the initial velocity?

   (c) What is the height of the ball when its velocity is one-half the initial velocity?

12. **Velocity and Acceleration**   The speed of a car traveling in a straight line is reduced from 45 to 30 miles per hour in a distance of 264 feet. Find the distance in which the car can be brought to rest from 30 miles per hour, assuming the same constant deceleration.

Evaluating a Sum   In Exercises 13–18, use the properties of summation and Theorem 4.2 to evaluate the sum.

13. $\displaystyle\sum_{i=1}^{20} 2i$

14. $\displaystyle\sum_{i=1}^{30} (3i - 4)$

15. $\displaystyle\sum_{i=1}^{5} (5i - 3)$

16. $\displaystyle\sum_{k=0}^{3} (k^2 + k)$

17. $\displaystyle\sum_{i=1}^{20} (i + 1)^2$

18. $\displaystyle\sum_{i=1}^{12} i(i^2 - 1)$

Finding Area by the Limit Definition   In Exercises 19–22, use the limit process to find the area of the region bounded by the graph of the function and the x-axis over the given interval. Sketch the region.

19. $y = 8 - 2x,\ \ [0, 3]$

20. $y = x^2 + 3,\ \ [0, 2]$

21. $y = 5 - x^2,\ \ [-2, 1]$

22. $y = \frac{1}{4}x^3,\ \ [2, 4]$

23. **Finding Area by the Limit Definition**   Use the limit process to find the area of the region bounded by $x = 5y - y^2,\ x = 0,\ y = 2,$ and $y = 5$.

24. **Upper and Lower Sums**   Consider the region bounded by $y = mx,\ y = 0,\ x = 0,$ and $x = b$.

   (a) Find the upper and lower sums to approximate the area of the region when $\Delta x = b/4$.

   (b) Find the upper and lower sums to approximate the area of the region when $\Delta x = b/n$.

   (c) Find the area of the region by letting n approach infinity in both sums in part (b). Show that, in each case, you obtain the formula for the area of a triangle.

Evaluating a Definite Integral Using a Geometric Formula   In Exercises 25 and 26, sketch the region whose area is given by the definite integral. Then use a geometric formula to evaluate the integral.

25. $\displaystyle\int_0^5 (5 - |x - 5|)\, dx$

26. $\displaystyle\int_{-6}^6 \sqrt{36 - x^2}\, dx$

Using Properties of Definite Integrals   In Exercises 27–30, evaluate the expression, given

$$\int_4^8 f(x)\, dx = 12 \quad \text{and} \quad \int_4^8 g(x)\, dx = 5.$$

27. $\displaystyle\int_4^8 [f(x) + g(x)]\, dx$

28. $\displaystyle\int_4^8 [2f(x) - 3g(x)]\, dx$

29. $\displaystyle\int_4^4 [f(x) - g(x)]\, dx$

30. $\displaystyle\int_8^4 7f(x)\, dx$

Integrating a Function that has a Discontinuity   In Exercises 31 and 32, (a) find the x-value(s) at which the function is not continuous, and (b) evaluate the integral.

31. $\displaystyle\int_{-6}^8 \dfrac{x^2 - 25}{5 + x}\, dx$

32. $\displaystyle\int_{3/2}^6 h(x)\, dx,$ where $h(x) = \begin{cases} 4, & x < 4 \\ \frac{3}{4}x - 2,\, x \geq 4 \end{cases}$

Using the Trapezoidal Rule   In Exercises 33–36, approximate the definite integral using the Trapezoidal Rule with $n = 4$. Compare the result with the approximation of the integral using a graphing utility.

33. $\displaystyle\int_2^3 \dfrac{2}{1 + x^2}\, dx$

34. $\displaystyle\int_0^1 \dfrac{x^{3/2}}{3 - x^2}\, dx$

35. $\displaystyle\int_0^3 \sqrt{x} \ln(x + 1)\, dx$

36. $\displaystyle\int_0^\pi \sqrt{1 + \sin^2 x}\, dx$

Evaluating a Definite Integral   In Exercises 37–42, use the Fundamental Theorem of Calculus to evaluate the definite integral.

37. $\displaystyle\int_0^6 (x - 1)\, dx$

38. $\displaystyle\int_{-2}^1 (4x^4 - x)\, dx$

39. $\displaystyle\int_4^9 x\sqrt{x}\, dx$

40. $\displaystyle\int_1^4 \left(\frac{1}{x^3} + x\right) dx$

41. $\displaystyle\int_0^{3\pi/4} \sin\theta\, d\theta$

42. $\displaystyle\int_{-\pi/4}^{\pi/4} \sec^2 t\, dt$

Finding the Area of a Region   In Exercises 43–46, find the area of the region bounded by the graphs of the equations.

43. $y = 8 - x,\ x = 0,\ x = 6,\ y = 0$

44. $y = 16 - x^{4/3},\ x = 0,\ y = 0$

45. $y = \dfrac{2}{x},\ y = 0,\ x = 1,\ x = 3$

46. $y = 1 + e^x,\ y = 0,\ x = 0,\ x = 2$

Finding the Average Value of a Function   In Exercises 47 and 48, find the average value of the function over the given interval and all values of x in the interval for which the function equals its average value.

47. $f(x) = \dfrac{1}{\sqrt{x}},\quad [4, 9]$ **48.** $f(x) = x^3,\quad [0, 2]$

Particle Motion   In Exercises 49 and 50, the velocity function, in feet per second, is given for a particle moving along a straight line. Find (a) the displacement and (b) the total distance that the particle travels over the given interval.

49. $v(t) = \dfrac{t}{4} - 2,\quad 0 \le t \le 10$

50. $v(t) = -t^2 + 4t + 12,\quad 2 \le t \le 7$

51. Particle Motion   A particle is moving along the x-axis. The position of the particle after t seconds is given by $x(t) = t^3 - 10t^2 + 28t - 24,\ 0 \le t \le 6$. Find the total distance the particle travels in 6 seconds.

52. Profit   The marginal profit for a product is modeled by

$$\frac{dP}{dx} = 20 - 0.008x$$

where P is the profit in dollars and x is the number of units sold. Find the change in profit when sales decrease from 550 to 500 units.

The Second Fundamental Theorem of Calculus   In Exercises 53 and 54, use the Second Fundamental Theorem of Calculus to find $F'(x)$.

53. $F(x) = \displaystyle\int_0^x \csc^2 t\, dt$

54. $F(x) = \displaystyle\int_1^x \frac{1}{t^2}\, dt$

Finding an Indefinite Integral   In Exercises 55–66, find the indefinite integral.

55. $\displaystyle\int x(1 - 3x^2)^4\, dx$

56. $\displaystyle\int \frac{x + 4}{(x^2 + 8x - 7)^2}\, dx$

57. $\displaystyle\int \frac{x^2}{\sqrt{x^3 + 3}}\, dx$

58. $\displaystyle\int 6x^3\sqrt{3x^4 + 2}\, dx$

59. $\displaystyle\int \sin^3 x \cos x\, dx$

60. $\displaystyle\int x \sin 3x^2\, dx$

61. $\displaystyle\int (\sin 4\theta)e^{\cos 4\theta}\, d\theta$

62. $\displaystyle\int \frac{e^{1/x}}{x^2}\, dx$

63. $\displaystyle\int (x + 1)5^{(x+1)^2}\, dx$

64. $\displaystyle\int \frac{1}{t^2}(2^{-1/t})\, dt$

65. $\displaystyle\int (1 + \sec \pi x)^2 \sec \pi x \tan \pi x\, dx$

66. $\displaystyle\int \sec 2x \tan 2x\, dx$

Evaluating a Definite Integral   In Exercises 67–74, evaluate the definite integral. Use a graphing utility to verify your result.

67. $\displaystyle\int_0^1 (3x + 1)^5\, dx$

68. $\displaystyle\int_0^1 x^2(x^3 - 2)^3\, dx$

69. $\displaystyle\int_0^3 \frac{1}{\sqrt{1 + x}}\, dx$

70. $\displaystyle\int_3^6 \frac{x}{3\sqrt{x^2 - 8}}\, dx$

71. $\displaystyle\int_0^\pi \cos \frac{x}{2}\, dx$

72. $\displaystyle\int_{-\pi/4}^{\pi/4} \sin 2x\, dx$

73. $\displaystyle 2\pi \int_0^1 (y + 1)\sqrt{1 - y}\, dy$ **74.** $\displaystyle 2\pi \int_{-1}^0 x^2\sqrt{x + 1}\, dx$

Finding an Indefinite Integral   In Exercises 75–78, find the indefinite integral.

75. $\displaystyle\int \frac{1}{7x - 2}\, dx$

76. $\displaystyle\int \frac{x^2}{x^3 + 1}\, dx$

77. $\displaystyle\int \frac{\sin x}{1 + \cos x}\, dx$

78. $\displaystyle\int \frac{1}{x^{1/3}(x^{2/3} - 3)}\, dx$

Evaluating a Definite Integral   In Exercises 79–82, evaluate the definite integral.

79. $\displaystyle\int_1^4 \frac{2x + 1}{2x}\, dx$

80. $\displaystyle\int_1^e \frac{\ln x}{x}\, dx$

81. $\displaystyle\int_0^{\pi/3} \sec\theta\, d\theta$

82. $\displaystyle\int_0^\pi \tan \frac{\theta}{3}\, d\theta$

Finding an Indefinite Integral   In Exercises 83–88, find the indefinite integral.

83. $\displaystyle\int \frac{1}{e^{2x} + e^{-2x}}\, dx$

84. $\displaystyle\int \frac{1}{3 + 25x^2}\, dx$

85. $\displaystyle\int \frac{x}{\sqrt{1 - x^4}}\, dx$

86. $\displaystyle\int \frac{1}{x\sqrt{9x^2 - 49}}\, dx$

87. $\displaystyle\int \frac{\arctan (x/2)}{4 + x^2}\, dx$

88. $\displaystyle\int \frac{\arcsin 2x}{\sqrt{1 - 4x^2}}\, dx$

What You Need to Know

- Approximating the area under a curve using rectangles and basic geometry is often tested on the AP® Exam.

- Be prepared to approximate definite integrals using left, right, or midpoint Riemann sums, or trapezoidal sums.

- An alternative form of the Fundamental Theorem of Calculus, $f(b) = f(a) + \int_a^b f'(x)\,dx$, is also emphasized on the AP® Exam.

- Some questions where technology is permitted not only encourage but also require the use of a graphing utility in evaluating definite integrals. This is the case for functions with no elementary antiderivative.

Practice Questions

Section 1, Part A, Multiple Choice, No Technology

1. The table shows selected values for a continuous function g that is increasing over the interval $[0, 4]$. Which of the following could be the value of $\int_0^4 g(x)\,dx$?

x	0	$\frac{1}{2}$	1	$\frac{3}{2}$	2	$\frac{5}{2}$	3	$\frac{7}{2}$	4
$g(x)$	0	3	7	12	18	25	33	42	52

(A) 70 (B) 80

(C) 96 (D) 100

2. The graph of f is shown for $0 \le x \le 5$. What is the value of $\int_0^5 f(x)\,dx$?

(A) −1

(B) 7

(C) 8

(D) 16

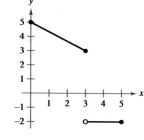

3. $\displaystyle\int \frac{4}{(x-5)^2 + 9}\,dx =$

(A) $\dfrac{4}{3}\tan^{-1}\dfrac{x-5}{3} + C$ (B) $4\tan^{-1}\dfrac{x-5}{3} + C$

(C) $\tan^{-1}\dfrac{x-5}{3} + C$ (D) $\dfrac{1}{3}\tan^{-1}\dfrac{x-5}{3} + C$

4. The velocity of a particle is given by $v(t) = 4t^3 - 4t$ for the times $0 \le t \le 2$ in seconds. What is the average velocity of the particle over that interval?

(A) 4 (B) 5

(C) 10 (D) 24

5.

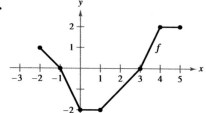

The graph of a piecewise linear function f is shown above. If g is the function defined by

$$g(x) = \int_4^x f(t)\,dt$$

find $g(-1)$.

(A) −6   (B) −4

(C) 4   (D) 6

Section 1, Part B, Multiple Choice, Technology Permitted

6. If $0 \le b \le \pi$, and the area under the curve $y = \sin x$ from $x = b$ to $x = \pi$ is 0.4, what is the value of b?

(A) 0.927   (B) 1.159

(C) 1.982   (D) 2.214

7. Let $f(x)$ be a continuous function such that $f(1) = 2$ and $f'(x) = \sqrt{x^3 + 6}$. What is the value of $f(5)$?

(A) 11.446   (B) 13.446

(C) 24.672   (D) 26.672

8. What is the average value of the function

$$y = \frac{2x}{x^2 + 1} + \sin x$$

on the interval $\left[0, \dfrac{3\pi}{2}\right]$?

(A) 0.220   (B) 0.879   (C) 1.979   (D) 2.170

Section 2, Part A, Free Response, Technology Permitted

9. As a pot of coffee cools down, the temperature of the coffee is modeled by a differentiable function C, for $0 \le t \le 12$, where time t is measured in minutes and the temperature $C(t)$ is measured in degrees Celsius. Selected values of t are shown in the table.

t (minutes)	0	3	5	7	8	12
$C(t)$ (degrees Celsius)	65	57	50	46	44	40

(a) Evaluate $\int_0^{12} C'(t)\, dt$. Explain the meaning of your answer in the context of the problem. Indicate units of measure.

(b) Explain the meaning of $\frac{1}{12}\int_0^{12} C(t)\, dt$ in the context of the problem. Use a trapezoidal sum with 5 subintervals indicated by the table to approximate $\frac{1}{12}\int_0^{12} C(t)\, dt$. Indicate units of measure.

(c) Use the data in the table to approximate the rate at which the temperature is changing at time $t = 4$. Show the work that leads to your answer.

(d) For $12 \le t \le 15$, the rate of cooling is modeled by

$$C'(t) = -2\cos(0.5t).$$

Based on the model, what is the temperature of the coffee when $t = 15$? Assume $C(t)$ is continuous at $t = 12$.

10. On a typical day, the snow on a mountain melts at a rate modeled by the function

$$M(t) = \frac{\pi}{6}\sin\frac{\pi t}{12}.$$

A snow maker adds snow at a rate modeled by the function

$$S(t) = 0.006t^2 - 0.12t + 0.87.$$

Both M and S have units in inches per hour and t is measured in hours for $0 \le t \le 6$. At $t = 0$, the mountain has 40 inches of snow.

(a) How much snow will melt during the 6 hour period? Indicate units of measure.

(b) Find the rate of change of the total amount of snow when $t = 3$.

(c) Write an expression for $I(t)$, the total number of inches of snow at any time t.

(d) For $0 \le t \le 6$, at what time t is the amount of snow a maximum? What is the maximum value? Justify your answers.

11. For $0 \le t \le 9$, a particle moves along the x-axis. The velocity of the particle is given by $v(t) = \sin(\pi t/4)$. The particle is at position $x = -4$ when $t = 0$.

(a) For $0 \le t \le 9$, when is the particle moving to the right? Justify your answer.

(b) Write, but do not evaluate, an integral expression that gives the total distance traveled by the particle from time $t = 0$ to $t = 9$.

(c) Find the acceleration of the particle at time $t = 3$. Is the particle speeding up, slowing down, or neither at $t = 3$? Justify your answer.

(d) Find the position of the particle at time $t = 3$.

Section 2, Part B, Free Response, No Technology

12. Let $F(x) = \int_3^x f(t)\, dt$. The graph of f on the interval $[-3, 4]$ consists of two line segments and a semicircle, as shown in the figure.

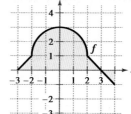

(a) Find $F(0)$, $F'(0)$, and $F(4)$.

(b) Find all relative minimum values of $F(x)$ on the interval $[-3, 4]$. Justify your answer.

(c) Find the x-coordinate of each inflection point of the graph of F on the interval $[-3, 4]$. Justify your answer.

(d) Write an equation of the line tangent to the graph of F at $x = 2$.

13. The graph of a continuous function f is shown. The three regions between the graph of f and the x-axis are marked A, B, and C, and have unsigned areas 5.5, 6, and 15.5, respectively. Let $F(x)$ be an antiderivative of f that is differentiable on $(0, 4)$ such that $F(1) = 9$.

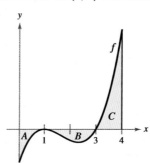

(a) Find $F(0)$ and $F(4)$.

(b) What is the minimum number of times F equals 5 on the interval $[0, 4]$? Show the work that leads to your answer.

(c) Find all intervals where F is increasing. Justify your answer.

4   Performance Task

The Wankel Rotary Engine

Named for Felix Wankel, who developed its basic principles in the 1950s, the Wankel rotary engine presents an alternative to the piston engine commonly used in automobiles. Some of its advantages over the piston engine are its size and weight compared with that of a piston engine of equivalent power, and it has very few moving parts.

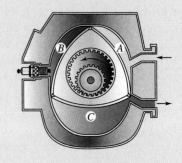

The most common configuration for the rotary engine is a two-lobed housing surrounding a rotor, which is shaped like a slightly bulged equilateral triangle, as shown at the right. The size of the rotor in comparison with the size of the housing cavity is critical in determining the compression ratio and thus the combustion efficiency. The rotor moves, pressing its corners against the walls of the housing, forming three chambers: *A*, *B*, and *C*. As each side of the rotor moves closer and farther from the walls of the housing, the combustion chamber is compressed and expanded to produce power, like the strokes of a piston in a piston engine.

One interesting use of the Wankel design is in the seat-belt pretensioner system for some automobiles. Small Wankel engines tighten up the slack in seat-belt systems, which help secure the driver and passengers firmly in their seats before a collision.

Exercises

In Exercises 1 and 2, use the scale drawing of a rotor in a Wankel engine and its corresponding figure.

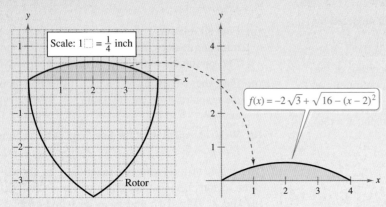

$$f(x) = -2\sqrt{3} + \sqrt{16 - (x - 2)^2}$$

1. **Estimating an Area**   Estimate the area of the entire rotor (a) by counting grid squares and (b) by using common geometric figures. (c) Then inscribe and circumscribe an equilateral triangle on the rotor in the scale drawing. Find the areas of the triangles. Use these areas to determine whether your estimates are reasonable. Show the work that leads to your answer.

2. **Connecting Representations**   The region shown in the figure on the right above is bounded by the graph of

$$f(x) = -2\sqrt{3} + \sqrt{16 - (x - 2)^2}$$

   and the *x*-axis.

   (a) Use the Trapezoidal Rule with four subintervals to approximate $\int_0^4 f(x)\, dx$. Estimate the error in your approximation. Then use your approximation to estimate the area of the rotor. How can you improve your approximation? Explain your reasoning.

   (b) Use a graphing utility to approximate $\int_0^4 f(x)\, dx$. Then approximate the area of the rotor. Compare this area with your estimates in Exercises 1 and 2.

5 Differential Equations

5.1   Slope Fields and Euler's Method
5.2   Growth and Decay
5.3   Separation of Variables
5.4   The Logistic Equation

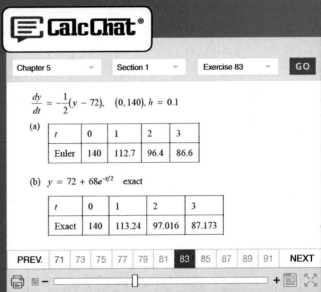

$$\frac{dy}{dt} = -\frac{1}{2}(y - 72), \quad (0, 140), h = 0.1$$

(a)

t	0	1	2	3
Euler	140	112.7	96.4	86.6

(b) $y = 72 + 68e^{-t/2}$ exact

t	0	1	2	3
Exact	140	113.24	97.016	87.173

PREV. 71 73 75 77 79 81 **83** 85 87 89 91 NEXT

5.2 Radioactive Decay (*Example 3, p. 381*)

5.4 Elk Population (*Example 6, p. 401*)

5.1 Slope Fields and Euler's Method

▶ Use initial conditions to find particular solutions of differential equations.
▶ Use slope fields to approximate solutions of differential equations.
▶ Use Euler's Method to approximate solutions of differential equations.

General and Particular Solutions

In this text, you will learn that physical phenomena can be described by differential equations. Recall that a **differential equation** in x and y is an equation that involves x, y, and derivatives of y. For example,

$$2xy' - 3y = 0 \qquad \text{Differential equation}$$

is a differential equation. In the next section, you will see that problems involving radioactive decay, population growth, and Newton's Law of Cooling can be formulated in terms of differential equations.

A function $y = f(x)$ is called a **solution** of a differential equation if the equation is satisfied when y and its derivatives are replaced by $f(x)$ and its derivatives. For example, differentiation and substitution would show that $y = e^{-2x}$ is a solution of the differential equation $y' + 2y = 0$. It can be shown that every solution of this differential equation is of the form

$$y = Ce^{-2x} \qquad \text{General solution of } y' + 2y = 0$$

where C is any real number. This solution is called the **general solution.** Some differential equations have **singular solutions** that cannot be written as special cases of the general solution. Such solutions, however, are not considered in this text. The **order** of a differential equation is determined by the highest-order derivative in the equation. For instance, $y' = 4y$ is a first-order differential equation.

In Section 4.1, Example 9, you saw that the second-order differential equation $s''(t) = -32$ has the general solution

$$s(t) = -16t^2 + C_1 t + C_2 \qquad \text{General solution of } s''(t) = -32$$

which contains two arbitrary constants. It can be shown that a differential equation of order n has a general solution with n arbitrary constants.

EXAMPLE 1   Verifying Solutions

Determine whether each function is a solution of the differential equation $y'' - y = 0$.

a. $y = \sin x$ **b.** $y = 4e^{-x}$ **c.** $y = Ce^x$

Solution

a. Because $y = \sin x$, $y' = \cos x$, and $y'' = -\sin x$, it follows that

$$y'' - y = -\sin x - \sin x = -2 \sin x \neq 0.$$

So, $y = \sin x$ is *not* a solution.

b. Because $y = 4e^{-x}$, $y' = -4e^{-x}$, and $y'' = 4e^{-x}$, it follows that

$$y'' - y = 4e^{-x} - 4e^{-x} = 0.$$

So, $y = 4e^{-x}$ is a solution.

c. Because $y = Ce^x$, $y' = Ce^x$, and $y'' = Ce^x$, it follows that

$$y'' - y = Ce^x - Ce^x = 0.$$

So, $y = Ce^x$ is a solution for any value of C.

Geometrically, the general solution of a first-order differential equation represents a family of curves known as **solution curves,** one for each value assigned to the arbitrary constant. For instance, you can verify that every function of the form

$$y = Ce^{-2x} \qquad \text{General solution of } y' + 2y = 0$$

is a solution of the differential equation

$$y' + 2y = 0.$$

Figure 5.1 shows four of the solution curves corresponding to different values of C.

As discussed in Section 4.1, **particular solutions** of a differential equation are obtained from **initial conditions** that give the values of the dependent variable or one of its derivatives for particular values of the independent variable. The term "initial condition" stems from the fact that, often in problems involving time, the value of the dependent variable or one of its derivatives is known at the *initial* time $t = 0$. For instance, the second-order differential equation

$$s''(t) = -32$$

having the general solution

$$s(t) = -16t^2 + C_1 t + C_2 \qquad \text{General solution of } s''(t) = -32$$

might have the following initial conditions.

$$s(0) = 80, \quad s'(0) = 64 \qquad \text{Initial conditions}$$

In this case, the initial conditions yield the particular solution

$$s(t) = -16t^2 + 64t + 80. \qquad \text{Particular solution}$$

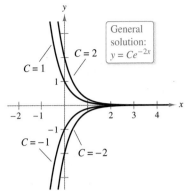

Several solution curves for $y' + 2y = 0$

Figure 5.1

EXAMPLE 2   Finding a Particular Solution

See LarsonCalculusforAP.com for an interactive version of this type of example.

For the differential equation

$$xy' - 3y = 0$$

verify that $y = Cx^3$ is a solution. (Assume $x > 0$.) Then find the particular solution determined by the initial condition $y = 2$ when $x = 3$.

Solution

You know that $y = Cx^3$ is a solution because $y' = 3Cx^2$ and

$$xy' - 3y = x(3Cx^2) - 3(Cx^3) = 0.$$

Furthermore, the initial condition $y = 2$ when $x = 3$ yields

$$y = Cx^3 \qquad \text{General solution}$$

$$2 = C(3)^3 \qquad \text{Substitute initial condition.}$$

$$\frac{2}{27} = C \qquad \text{Solve for } C.$$

and you can conclude that the particular solution is

$$y = \frac{2x^3}{27}, \ x > 0 \qquad \text{Particular solution}$$

as shown in Figure 5.2. Try checking this solution by substituting for y and y' in the original differential equation.

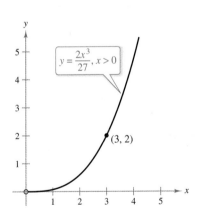

For the initial condition $y = 2$ when $x = 3$, the particular solution of the differential equation $xy' - 3y = 0$, $x > 0$, is $y = (2x^3)/27$.

Figure 5.2

Note that to determine a particular solution, the number of initial conditions must match the number of constants in the general solution.

Slope Fields

Solving a differential equation analytically can be difficult or even impossible. However, there is a graphical approach you can use to learn a lot about the solution of a differential equation. Consider a differential equation of the form

$$y' = F(x, y) \qquad \text{Differential equation}$$

where $F(x, y)$ is some expression in x and y. At each point (x, y) in the xy-plane where F is defined, the differential equation determines the slope $y' = F(x, y)$ of the solution at that point. If you draw short line segments with slope $F(x, y)$ at selected points (x, y) in the domain of F, then these line segments form a **slope field,** or a *direction field,* for the differential equation $y' = F(x, y)$. Each line segment has the same slope as the solution curve through that point. A slope field shows the general shape of all the solutions and can be helpful in getting a visual perspective of the directions of the solutions of a differential equation.

EXAMPLE 3   Sketching a Slope Field

Sketch a slope field for the differential equation $y' = x - y$ for the points $(-1, 1)$, $(0, 1)$, and $(1, 1)$.

Solution

The slope of the solution curve at any point (x, y) is

$$F(x, y) = x - y. \qquad \text{Slope at } (x, y)$$

So, the slope at each point can be found as shown.

Slope at $(-1, 1)$: $y' = -1 - 1 = -2$
Slope at $(0, 1)$: $y' = 0 - 1 = -1$
Slope at $(1, 1)$: $y' = 1 - 1 = 0$

Draw short line segments at the three points with their respective slopes, as shown in Figure 5.3.

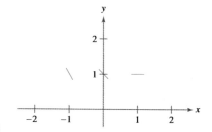

Figure 5.3

EXAMPLE 4   Identifying Slope Fields for Differential Equations

Match each slope field with its differential equation.

a.

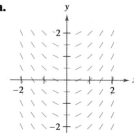

i. $y' = x + y$

b.

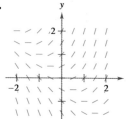

ii. $y' = x$

c.

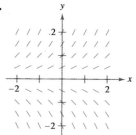

iii. $y' = y$

Solution

a. You can see that the slope at any point along the y-axis is 0. The only equation that satisfies this condition is $y' = x$. So, the graph matches equation (ii).

b. You can see that the slope at the point $(1, -1)$ is 0. The only equation that satisfies this condition is $y' = x + y$. So, the graph matches equation (i).

c. You can see that the slope at any point along the x-axis is 0. The only equation that satisfies this condition is $y' = y$. So, the graph matches equation (iii).

A solution curve of a differential equation $y' = F(x, y)$ is simply a curve in the xy-plane whose tangent line at each point (x, y) has slope equal to $F(x, y)$. This is illustrated in Example 5.

EXAMPLE 5   Sketching a Solution Using a Slope Field

Sketch a slope field for the differential equation $y' = 2x + y$. Use the slope field to sketch the solution that passes through the point $(1, 1)$.

Solution

Make a table showing the slopes at several points. The table shown is a small sample. The slopes at many other points should be calculated to get a representative slope field.

x	-2	-2	-1	-1	0	0	1	1	2	2
y	-1	1	-1	1	-1	1	-1	1	-1	1
$y' = 2x + y$	-5	-3	-3	-1	-1	1	1	3	3	5

Next, draw line segments at the points with their respective slopes, as shown in Figure 5.4.

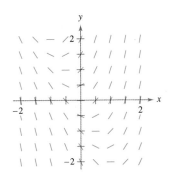

Slope field for $y' = 2x + y$

Figure 5.4

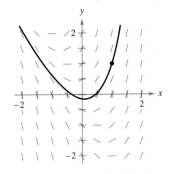

Particular solution for $y' = 2x + y$ passing through $(1, 1)$

Figure 5.5

After the slope field is drawn, start at the initial point $(1, 1)$ and move to the right in the direction of the line segment. Continue to draw the solution curve so that it moves parallel to the nearby line segments. Do the same to the left of $(1, 1)$. The resulting solution is shown in Figure 5.5.

In Example 5, note that the slope field shows that y' increases to infinity as x increases.

Technology

Drawing a slope field by hand is tedious. In practice, slope fields are usually drawn using a graphing utility. If you have access to a graphing utility that can graph slope fields, try graphing the slope field for the differential equation in Example 5. One example of a slope field drawn by a graphing utility is shown at the right.

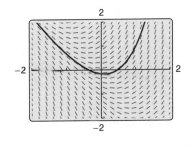

Euler's Method

Euler's Method is a numerical approach to approximating the particular solution of the differential equation

$$y' = F(x, y)$$

that passes through the point (x_0, y_0). From the given information, you know that the graph of the solution passes through the point (x_0, y_0) and has a slope of $F(x_0, y_0)$ at this point. This gives you a "starting point" for approximating the solution.

From this starting point, you can proceed in the direction indicated by the slope. Using a small step h, move along the tangent line until you arrive at the point (x_1, y_1), where

$$x_1 = x_0 + h \quad \text{and} \quad y_1 = y_0 + hF(x_0, y_0)$$

as shown in Figure 5.6. Then, using (x_1, y_1) as a new starting point, you can repeat the process to obtain a second point (x_2, y_2). The values of x_i and y_i are shown below.

$$x_1 = x_0 + h \qquad y_1 = y_0 + hF(x_0, y_0)$$
$$x_2 = x_1 + h \qquad y_2 = y_1 + hF(x_1, y_1)$$
$$\vdots \qquad\qquad \vdots$$
$$x_n = x_{n-1} + h \qquad y_n = y_{n-1} + hF(x_{n-1}, y_{n-1})$$

When using this method, note that you can obtain better approximations of the exact solution by choosing smaller and smaller step sizes.

Insight

Euler's Method is tested only on the AP® Calculus BC Exam.

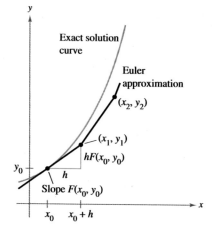

Figure 5.6

EXAMPLE 6   **Approximating a Solution Using Euler's Method**

Use Euler's Method to approximate the particular solution of the differential equation

$$y' = x - y$$

passing through the point $(0, 1)$. Use a step of $h = 0.1$.

Solution

Using $h = 0.1$, $x_0 = 0$, $y_0 = 1$, and $F(x, y) = x - y$, you have

$$x_0 = 0, \quad x_1 = 0.1, \quad x_2 = 0.2, \quad x_3 = 0.3$$

and the first three approximations are

$$y_1 = y_0 + hF(x_0, y_0) = 1 + (0.1)(0 - 1) = 0.9$$
$$y_2 = y_1 + hF(x_1, y_1) = 0.9 + (0.1)(0.1 - 0.9) = 0.82$$
$$y_3 = y_2 + hF(x_2, y_2) = 0.82 + (0.1)(0.2 - 0.82) = 0.758.$$

The first ten approximations are shown in the table. You can plot these values to see a graph of the approximate solution, as shown in Figure 5.7.

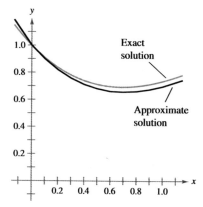

Figure 5.7

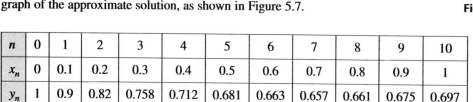

n	0	1	2	3	4	5	6	7	8	9	10
x_n	0	0.1	0.2	0.3	0.4	0.5	0.6	0.7	0.8	0.9	1
y_n	1	0.9	0.82	0.758	0.712	0.681	0.663	0.657	0.661	0.675	0.697

For the differential equation in Example 6, you can verify the exact solution to be the equation

$$y = x - 1 + 2e^{-x}.$$

Figure 5.7 compares this exact solution with the approximate solution obtained in Example 6.

Verifying a Solution   In Exercises 1–8, verify that the function is a solution of the differential equation.

Function	Differential Equation
1. $y = Ce^{5x}$	$y' = 5y$
2. $y = e^{-2x}$	$3y' + 5y = -e^{-2x}$
3. $x^2 + y^2 = Cy$	$y' = \dfrac{2xy}{x^2 - y^2}$
4. $y^2 - 2\ln y = x^2$	$\dfrac{dy}{dx} = \dfrac{xy}{y^2 - 1}$
5. $y = C_1 \sin x - C_2 \cos x$	$y'' + y = 0$
6. $y = C_1 e^{-x} \cos x + C_2 e^{-x} \sin x$	$y'' + 2y' + 2y = 0$
7. $y = -\cos x \ln|\sec x + \tan x|$	$y'' + y = \tan x$
8. $y = \frac{2}{5}(e^{-4x} + e^x)$	$y'' + 4y' = 2e^x$

 Verifying a Particular Solution   In Exercises 9–12, verify that the function is a particular solution of the differential equation.

Function	Differential Equation and Initial Condition
9. $y = \sin x \cos x - \cos^2 x$	$2y + y' = 2 \sin 2x - 1$ $y\left(\dfrac{\pi}{4}\right) = 0$
10. $y = 6x - 4 \sin x + 1$	$y' = 6 - 4 \cos x$ $y(0) = 1$
11. $y = 4e^{-6x^2}$	$y' = -12xy$ $y(0) = 4$
12. $y = e^{-\cos x}$	$y' = y \sin x$ $y\left(\dfrac{\pi}{2}\right) = 1$

 Determining a Solution   In Exercises 13–20, determine whether the function is a solution of the differential equation $y^{(4)} - 16y = 0$.

13. $y = 3 \cos x$ 14. $y = 2 \sin x$
15. $y = 2 \cos 3x$ 16. $y = 3 \sin 2x$
17. $y = e^{-2x}$ 18. $y = 5 \ln x$
19. $y = C_1 e^{2x} + C_2 e^{-2x} + C_3 \sin 2x + C_4 \cos 2x$
20. $y = 3e^{2x} - 4 \sin 2x$

Determining a Solution   In Exercises 21–28, determine whether the function is a solution of the differential equation $xy' - 2y = x^3 e^x,\ x > 0$.

21. $y = x^2$ 22. $y = \cos x$
23. $y = x^2 e^x$ 24. $y = x^2(2 + e^x)$
25. $y = \ln x$ 26. $y = x^2 e^x - 5x^2$
27. $y = C_1 x^2 + x^2 e^x$ 28. $y = C_1(x^2 + x^2 e^x),\ C_1 \neq 1$

 Finding a Particular Solution   In Exercises 29 and 30, some of the curves corresponding to different values of C in the general solution of the differential equation are shown in the graph. Find the particular solution that passes through the point shown on the graph.

29. $y = Ce^{-x/2}$
$2y' + y = 0$

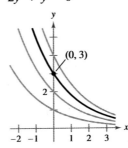

30. $2x^2 - y^2 = C$
$yy' - 2x = 0$

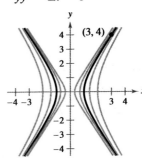

 Graphs of Particular Solutions   In Exercises 31 and 32, the general solution of the differential equation is given. Use a graphing utility to graph the particular solutions for the given values of C. Determine the domain of each particular solution.

31. $4yy' - x = 0$
$4y^2 - x^2 = C$
$C = 0,\ C = \pm 1,\ C = \pm 4$

32. $yy' + x = 0$
$x^2 + y^2 = C$
$C = 0,\ C = 1,\ C = 4$

 Finding a Particular Solution   In Exercises 33–38, verify that the general solution satisfies the differential equation. Then find the particular solution that satisfies the initial condition(s).

33. $y = Ce^{-6x}$
$y' + 6y = 0$
$y = 3$ when $x = 0$

34. $3x^2 + 2y^2 = C$
$3x + 2yy' = 0$
$y = 3$ when $x = 1$

35. $y = C_1 x + C_2 x^3$
$x^2 y'' - 3xy' + 3y = 0$
$y = 0$ when $x = 2$
$y' = 4$ when $x = 2$

36. $y = C_1 + C_2 \ln x$
$xy'' + y' = 0$
$y = 0$ when $x = 2$
$y' = \frac{1}{2}$ when $x = 2$

37. $y = C_1 \sin 3x + C_2 \cos 3x$
$y'' + 9y = 0$
$y = 2$ when $x = \pi/6$
$y' = 1$ when $x = \pi/6$

38. $y = e^{2x/3}(C_1 + C_2 x)$
$9y'' - 12y' + 4y = 0$
$y = 4$ when $x = 0$
$y = 0$ when $x = 3$

Finding a General Solution In Exercises 39–54, use integration to find a general solution of the differential equation.

39. $\dfrac{dy}{dx} = 12x^2$ **40.** $\dfrac{dy}{dx} = 4x^{5/3}$

41. $\dfrac{dy}{dx} = 10x^4 - 2x^3$ **42.** $\dfrac{dy}{dx} = 3x^8 - 2x$

43. $\dfrac{dy}{dx} = \dfrac{x}{1 + x^2}$ **44.** $\dfrac{dy}{dx} = \dfrac{e^x}{4 + e^x}$

45. $\dfrac{dy}{dx} = \dfrac{x - 2}{x}$ **46.** $\dfrac{dy}{dx} = x \cos x^2$

47. $\dfrac{dy}{dx} = \sin 2x$ **48.** $\dfrac{dy}{dx} = \tan^2 x$

49. $\dfrac{dy}{dx} = x\sqrt{x - 6}$ **50.** $\dfrac{dy}{dx} = 2x\sqrt{4x^2 + 1}$

51. $\dfrac{dy}{dx} = xe^{x^2}$ **52.** $\dfrac{dy}{dx} = 5e^{-x/2}$

53. $\dfrac{dy}{dx} = \cos x\, e^{\sin x}$ **54.** $\dfrac{dy}{dx} = 5(\sin x)e^{\cos x}$

Slope Field In Exercises 55–58, a differential equation and its slope field are given. Complete the table by determining the slopes (if possible) in the slope field at the given points.

x	-4	-2	0	2	4	8
y	2	0	4	4	6	8
dy/dx						

55. $\dfrac{dy}{dx} = \dfrac{2x}{y}$ **56.** $\dfrac{dy}{dx} = y - x$

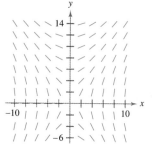 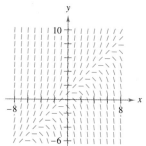

57. $\dfrac{dy}{dx} = x \cos \dfrac{\pi y}{8}$ **58.** $\dfrac{dy}{dx} = \tan \dfrac{\pi y}{6}$

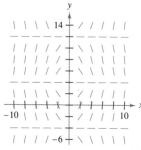 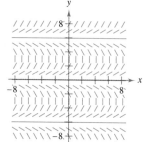

Matching In Exercises 59–62, match the differential equation with its slope field. [The slope fields are labeled (a), (b), (c), and (d).]

(a) 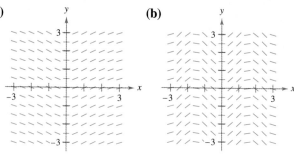 **(b)**

(c) 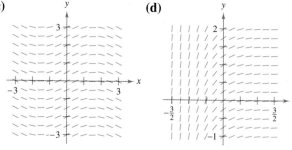 **(d)**

59. $y' = \sin 2x$ **60.** $y' = \frac{1}{2} \cos x$

61. $y' = e^{-2x}$ **62.** $y' = \dfrac{x}{x^2 + 1}$

Using a Slope Field In Exercises 63 and 64, use the slope field for the differential equation to sketch the graph of the solution that passes through the given point. Then determine the domain of the solution and discuss the graph of the solution as $x \to \infty$. To print an enlarged copy of the graph, go to *MathGraphs.com*.

63. $y' = \dfrac{1}{x}, \; x > 0; \; (1, 0)$ **64.** $y' = \dfrac{1}{y}, \; y > 0; \; (0, 1)$

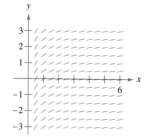 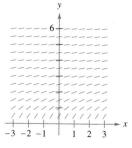

Slope Field In Exercises 65–68, (a) sketch the slope field for the differential equation, (b) use the slope field to sketch the solution that passes through the given point, and (c) discuss the graph of the solution as $x \to \infty$ and $x \to -\infty$. Use a graphing utility to verify your results. To print a blank coordinate plane, go to *MathGraphs.com*.

65. $y' = 3 - x, \; (4, 2)$ **66.** $y' = \frac{1}{3}x^2 - \frac{1}{2}x, \; (1, 1)$

67. $y' = y - 4x, \; (2, 2)$ **68.** $y' = y + xy, \; (0, -4)$

Slope Field **In Exercises 69–72, use a computer algebra system to (a) graph the slope field for the differential equation, (b) graph the solution satisfying the specified initial condition, and (c) determine the domain of the solution found in part (b).**

69. $\dfrac{dy}{dx} = 0.25y$

$y(0) = 4$

70. $\dfrac{dy}{dx} = 0.02y(10 - y)$

$y(0) = 2$

71. $\dfrac{dy}{dx} = 0.4y(3 - x)$

$y(0) = 1$

72. $\dfrac{dy}{dx} = \dfrac{1}{2}e^{-x/8} \sin \dfrac{\pi y}{4}$

$y(0) = 2$

Euler's Method **In Exercises 73–78, use Euler's Method to make a table of values for the approximate solution of the differential equation with the specified initial value. Use n steps of size h.**

73. $y' = x + y$, $y(0) = 2$, $n = 10$, $h = 0.1$

74. $y' = x + y$, $y(0) = 2$, $n = 20$, $h = 0.05$

75. $y' = 3x - 2y$, $y(0) = 3$, $n = 10$, $h = 0.05$

76. $y' = 0.5x(3 - y)$, $y(0) = 1$, $n = 5$, $h = 0.4$

77. $y' = e^{xy}$, $y(0) = 1$, $n = 10$, $h = 0.1$

78. $y' = \cos x + \sin y$, $y(0) = 5$, $n = 10$, $h = 0.1$

Euler's Method **In Exercises 79–82, complete the table using the exact solution of the differential equation and two approximations obtained using Euler's Method to approximate the particular solution of the differential equation. Use $h = 0.2$ and $h = 0.1$, and compute each approximation to four decimal places. Compare the values of the approximations with the values given by the exact solution. How does the error change as h decreases?**

x	0	0.2	0.4	0.6	0.8	1
$y(x)$ (exact)						
$y(x)$ ($h = 0.2$)						
$y(x)$ ($h = 0.1$)						

	Differential Equation	Initial Condition	Exact Solution
79.	$\dfrac{dy}{dx} = y$	$(0, 3)$	$y = 3e^x$
80.	$\dfrac{dy}{dx} = \dfrac{2x}{y}$	$(0, 2)$	$y = \sqrt{2x^2 + 4}$
81.	$\dfrac{dy}{dx} = y + \cos x$	$(0, 0)$	$y = \dfrac{1}{2}(\sin x - \cos x + e^x)$
82.	$\dfrac{dy}{dx} = 2x + 3y$	$(0, 1)$	$y = -\dfrac{2}{3}x - \dfrac{2}{9} + \dfrac{11}{9}e^{3x}$

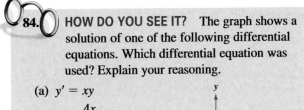 **83. Temperature** At time $t = 0$ minutes, the temperature of an object is $140°F$. The temperature of the object is changing at the rate given by the differential equation $y' = -\dfrac{1}{2}(y - 72)$.

(a) Use a graphing utility and Euler's Method to approximate the particular solutions of this differential equation at $t = 1, 2,$ and 3. Use a step size of $h = 0.1$. (A graphing utility program for Euler's Method is available at *LarsonCalculusforAP.com*.)

(b) Compare your results with the exact solution, $y = 72 + 68e^{-t/2}$.

(c) Repeat parts (a) and (b) using a step size of $h = 0.05$. Compare the results.

84. HOW DO YOU SEE IT? The graph shows a solution of one of the following differential equations. Which differential equation was used? Explain your reasoning.

(a) $y' = xy$

(b) $y' = \dfrac{4x}{y}$

(c) $y' = -4xy$

(d) $y' = 4 - xy$

EXPLORING CONCEPTS

85. Communicating Explain why the general solution of $y' = 1/x$ is $y = \ln |x| + C$.

86. Reasoning In Exercise 85, determine the domain of the solution. Does the domain depend on the value of C? Explain.

87. Reasoning Explain when Euler's Method produces an exact particular solution of a differential equation.

88. Reasoning It is known that $y = Ce^{kx}$ is a solution of the differential equation $y' = 0.07y$. If possible, determine the values of the constants C and k from the information given. If not possible, explain what additional information is needed.

89. Error Analysis Describe and correct the error in determining whether $y = e^{-4x}$ is a solution of $y'' - 3y' + 4y = 0$.

$$y'' - 3y' + 4y = -16e^{-4x} - 3(-4e^{-4x}) + 4(e^{-4x})$$
$$= -16e^{-4x} + 12e^{-4x} + 4e^{-4x}$$
$$= -16e^{-4x} + 16e^{-4x}$$
$$= 0$$

So, $y = e^{-4x}$ is a solution.

90. Error Analysis Describe and correct the error in determining whether $y = x^3 + 4x + (2/x)$ is a solution of $xy' + y = 4x(x^2 + 2)$.

$$xy' + y = x\left(3x^2 + 4 + \frac{2}{x^2}\right) + \left(x^3 + 4x + \frac{2}{x}\right)$$

$$= 3x^3 + 4x + \frac{2}{x} + x^3 + 4x + \frac{2}{x}$$

$$= 4x^3 + 8x + \frac{4}{x}$$

So, $y = x^3 + 4x + \frac{2}{x}$ is *not* a solution. ✗

True or False? **In Exercises 91–94, determine whether the statement is true or false. If it is false, explain why or give an example that shows it is false.**

91. If $y = f(x)$ is a solution of a first-order differential equation, then $y = f(x) + C$ must also be a solution.

92. The general solution of a differential equation is $y = -4.9x^2 + C_1x + C_2$. To find a particular solution, you must be given two initial conditions.

93. Slope fields represent the general solutions of differential equations.

94. A slope field shows that the slope at the point $(1, 1)$ is 6. This slope field must represent the family of solutions for the differential equation $y' = 4x + 2y$.

95. Errors and Euler's Method The exact solution of the differential equation $y' = -2y$, where $y(0) = 4$, is $y = 4e^{-2x}$.

 (a) Use a graphing utility to complete the table, where y is the exact value of the solution, y_1 is the approximate solution using Euler's Method with $h = 0.1$, y_2 is the approximate solution using Euler's Method with $h = 0.2$, e_1 is the absolute error $|y - y_1|$, e_2 is the absolute error $|y - y_2|$, and r is the ratio e_1/e_2.

x	0	0.2	0.4	0.6	0.8	1
y						
y_1						
y_2						
e_1						
e_2						
r						

(b) What can you conclude about the ratio r as h changes?

(c) Predict the absolute error when $h = 0.05$.

96. Errors and Euler's Method Repeat Exercise 95 for which the exact solution of the differential equation $y' = x - y$, where $y(0) = 1$, is $y = x - 1 + 2e^{-x}$.

97. Think About It Find the values of k for which $y = e^{kt}$ is a solution of the differential equation $y'' - 16y = 0$.

98. Think About It Find the values of ω for which $y = A \sin \omega t$ is a solution of the differential equation $y'' + 16y = 0$.

Calculus AP® – Exam Preparation Questions

99. Multiple Choice Which differential equation corresponds to the slope field below?

(A) $\dfrac{dy}{dx} = \dfrac{1}{x \ln x}$

(B) $\dfrac{dy}{dx} = x^2 - 1$

(C) $\dfrac{dy}{dx} = \ln x$

(D) $\dfrac{dy}{dx} = \dfrac{\ln x}{x}$

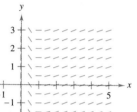

100. Multiple Choice Consider the differential equation $y' = y - 6x$. Let $y = f(x)$ be the particular solution of the differential equation with $f(0) = -1$. If Euler's Method, starting at $x = 0$ with three steps of equal size, is used to approximate $f(0.6)$, what is the resulting approximation?

(A) -3.7152 (B) -2.496

(C) -1.68 (D) -1.2

101. Free Response Consider the differential equation

$$\frac{dy}{dx} = (4 - y)\cos x.$$

Let $y = f(x)$ be the particular solution of the differential equation with the initial condition $f(0) = 1$. The function f is defined for all real numbers.

(a) A portion of the slope field of the differential equation is shown below. Sketch the solution curve through the point $(0, 1)$.

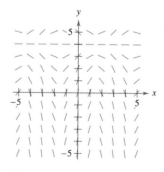

(b) Write an equation of the tangent line to the solution curve in part (a) at the point $(\pi, 1)$. Use the equation to approximate $f(3.2)$.

5.2 Growth and Decay

▶ Use separation of variables to solve a simple differential equation.
▶ Use exponential functions to model growth and decay in applied problems.

Differential Equations

In Section 5.1, you learned to analyze the solutions of differential equations visually using slope fields and to approximate solutions numerically using Euler's Method. Analytically, you have learned to solve only two types of differential equations—those of the forms $y' = f(x)$ and $y'' = f(x)$. In this section, you will learn how to solve a more general type of differential equation. The strategy is to rewrite the equation so that each variable occurs on only one side of the equation. This strategy is called *separation of variables*. (You will study this strategy in detail in Section 5.3.)

EXAMPLE 1 Solving a Differential Equation

$$y' = \frac{2x}{y} \qquad \text{Original equation}$$

$$yy' = 2x \qquad \text{Multiply each side by } y.$$

$$\int yy'\,dx = \int 2x\,dx \qquad \text{Integrate each side with respect to } x.$$

$$\int y\,dy = \int 2x\,dx \qquad dy = y'dx$$

$$\frac{1}{2}y^2 = x^2 + C_1 \qquad \text{Apply Power Rule.}$$

$$y^2 - 2x^2 = C \qquad \text{Rewrite, letting } C = 2C_1.$$

So, the general solution is $y^2 - 2x^2 = C$.

When you integrate each side of the equation in Example 1, you do not need to add a constant of integration to each side. When you do, you still obtain the same result.

$$\int y\,dy = \int 2x\,dx$$

$$\frac{1}{2}y^2 + C_2 = x^2 + C_3$$

$$\frac{1}{2}y^2 = x^2 + (C_3 - C_2)$$

$$\frac{1}{2}y^2 = x^2 + C_1 \qquad \text{Rewrite, letting } C_1 = C_3 - C_2.$$

Some people prefer to use Leibniz notation and differentials when applying separation of variables. The solution to Example 1 is shown below using this notation.

$$\frac{dy}{dx} = \frac{2x}{y}$$

$$y\,dy = 2x\,dx$$

$$\int y\,dy = \int 2x\,dx$$

$$\frac{1}{2}y^2 = x^2 + C_1$$

$$y^2 - 2x^2 = C$$

Justification

You can use implicit differentiation to check the solution to Example 1.

Exploration

In Example 1, the general solution of the differential equation is

$$y^2 - 2x^2 = C.$$

Use a graphing utility to sketch the particular solutions for $C = \pm 2$, $C = \pm 1$, and $C = 0$. Describe the solutions graphically. Is the following statement true of each solution?

The slope of the graph at the point (x, y) is equal to twice the ratio of x and y.

Explain your reasoning. Are all curves for which this statement is true represented by the general solution?

Growth and Decay Models

In many applications, the rate of change of a variable y is proportional to the value of y. When y is a function of time t, the proportion can be written as shown.

Rate of change of y is   proportional to y.

$$\frac{dy}{dt} = ky$$

The general solution of this differential equation is given in the next theorem.

Theorem 5.1   **Exponential Growth and Decay**

If y is a differentiable function of t such that $y > 0$ and $dy/dt = ky$ for some constant k, then

$$y = Ce^{kt}$$

where C is the **initial value** of y, and k is the **proportionality constant. Exponential growth** occurs when $k > 0$, and **exponential decay** occurs when $k < 0$.

Proof

$\dfrac{dy}{dt} = ky$	Write original equation.
$\dfrac{dy}{y} = k\,dt$	Separate variables.
$\displaystyle\int \dfrac{dy}{y} = \int k\,dt$	Integrate each side.
$\ln y = kt + C_1$	Find antiderivative of each side.
$y = e^{kt + C_1}$	Exponentiate each side.
$y = e^{kt}e^{C_1}$	Property of exponents
$y = Ce^{kt}$	Let $C = e^{C_1}$.

> **Justification**
>
> Notice that you do not need to write $\ln |y|$ because $y > 0$.

So, all solutions of $y' = ky$ are of the form $y = Ce^{kt}$. Remember that you can differentiate the function $y = Ce^{kt}$ with respect to t to verify that $y' = ky$. ∎

EXAMPLE 2   Using an Exponential Growth Model

The rate of change of y is proportional to y. When $t = 0$, $y = 2$, and when $t = 2$, $y = 4$. What is the value of y when $t = 3$?

Solution

Because $y' = ky$, you know that y and t are related by the equation $y = Ce^{kt}$. You can find the values of the constants C and k by applying the initial conditions.

$2 = Ce^0 \implies C = 2$ When $t = 0$, $y = 2$.

$4 = 2e^{2k} \implies k = \dfrac{1}{2}\ln 2 \approx 0.3466$ When $t = 2$, $y = 4$.

So, the model is $y = 2e^{0.3466t}$. When $t = 3$, the value of y is $2e^{0.3466(3)} \approx 5.657$. (See Figure 5.8.) ∎

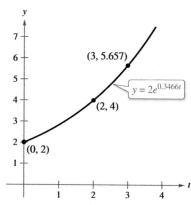

If the rate of change of y is proportional to y, then y follows an exponential model.

Figure 5.8

Using logarithmic properties, the value of k in Example 2 can also be written as $\ln \sqrt{2}$. So, the model becomes $y = 2e^{(\ln \sqrt{2})t}$, which can be rewritten as $y = 2\left(\sqrt{2}\right)^t$.

Technology

Most graphing utilities have curve-fitting capabilities that can be used to find models that represent data. Use the *exponential regression* feature of a graphing utility and the information in Example 2 to find a model for the data. How does your model compare with the given model?

Radioactive decay is measured in terms of *half-life*—the number of years required for half of the atoms in a sample of radioactive material to decay. The rate of decay is proportional to the amount present. The half-lives of some common radioactive isotopes are listed below.

Uranium (^{238}U)	4,470,000,000 years
Plutonium (^{239}Pu)	24,100 years
Carbon (^{14}C)	5715 years
Radium (^{226}Ra)	1599 years
Einsteinium (^{254}Es)	276 days
Nobelium (^{257}No)	25 seconds

EXAMPLE 3   Radioactive Decay

Ten grams of the plutonium isotope ^{239}Pu were released in a nuclear accident. How long will it take for the 10 grams to decay to 1 gram?

Solution   Let y represent the mass (in grams) of the plutonium. Because the rate of decay is proportional to y, you know that $y = Ce^{kt}$, where t is the time in years. To find the values of the constants C and k, apply the initial conditions. Using the fact that $y = 10$ when $t = 0$, you can write

$$10 = Ce^{k(0)} \implies 10 = Ce^0$$

which implies that $C = 10$. Next, using the fact that the half-life of ^{239}Pu is 24,100 years, you have $y = 10/2 = 5$ when $t = 24,100$. So, you can write

$$5 = 10e^{k(24,100)} \qquad \text{Substitute.}$$

$$\frac{1}{2} = e^{24,100k} \qquad \text{Divide each side by 10.}$$

$$\ln \frac{1}{2} = \ln e^{24,100k} \qquad \text{Take natural log of each side.}$$

$$\ln \frac{1}{2} = 24,100k \qquad \text{Apply inverse property.}$$

$$\frac{1}{24,100} \ln \frac{1}{2} = k \qquad \text{Divide each side by 24,100.}$$

$$-0.000028761 \approx k. \qquad \text{Use a calculator.}$$

So, the model is

$$y = 10e^{-0.000028761t}. \qquad \text{Half-life model}$$

To find the time it would take for 10 grams to decay to 1 gram, you can solve for t in the equation $1 = 10e^{-0.000028761t}$. The solution is approximately 80,059 years. ∎

From Example 3, notice that in an exponential growth or decay problem, it is easy to solve for C when you are given the value of y at $t = 0$. The next example demonstrates a procedure for solving for C and k when you do not know the value of y at $t = 0$.

In a conventional nuclear reactor, 1 kilogram of ^{239}Pu can generate enough electricity to power about 900 homes for a year. *(Source: World Nuclear Association, U.S. Energy Information Administration)*

Connecting Representations

The model in Example 3 can also be written as

$$y = 10\left(\frac{1}{2}\right)^{t/24,100}.$$

This model is much easier to derive, but for some applications it is not as convenient to use.

EXAMPLE 4 Population Growth

See LarsonCalculusforAP.com for an interactive version of this type of example.

An experimental population of fruit flies increases according to the law of exponential growth. There were 100 flies after the second day of the experiment and 300 flies after the fourth day. Approximately how many flies were in the original population?

Solution

Let $y = Ce^{kt}$ be the number of flies at time t, where t is measured in days. Note that y is continuous, whereas the number of flies is discrete. Because $y = 100$ when $t = 2$ and $y = 300$ when $t = 4$, you can write $100 = Ce^{2k}$ and $300 = Ce^{4k}$. From the first equation, you know that $C = 100e^{-2k}$. Substituting this value into the second equation produces the following.

$$300 = 100e^{-2k}e^{4k} \qquad \text{Substitute.}$$
$$300 = 100e^{2k} \qquad \text{Property of exponents}$$
$$3 = e^{2k} \qquad \text{Divide each side by 100.}$$
$$\ln 3 = \ln e^{2k} \qquad \text{Take natural log of each side.}$$
$$\ln 3 = 2k \qquad \text{Apply inverse property.}$$
$$\frac{1}{2}\ln 3 = k \qquad \text{Divide each side by 2.}$$
$$0.5493 \approx k \qquad \text{Use a calculator.}$$

So, the exponential growth model is

$$y = Ce^{0.5493t}.$$

To solve for C, reapply the condition $y = 100$ when $t = 2$ and obtain

$$100 = Ce^{0.5493(2)}$$
$$100e^{-1.0986} = C$$
$$33 \approx C.$$

So, the original population (when $t = 0$) consisted of approximately $y = C = 33$ flies, as shown in Figure 5.9.

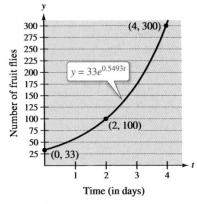

Figure 5.9

EXAMPLE 5 Declining Sales

Four months after it stops advertising, a manufacturing company notices that its sales have dropped from 100,000 units per month to 80,000 units per month. The sales follow an exponential pattern of decline. What will the sales be after another 2 months?

Solution

Use the exponential decay model $y = Ce^{kt}$, where t is measured in months. From the initial condition ($t = 0$), you know that $C = 100{,}000$. Moreover, because $y = 80{,}000$ when $t = 4$, you have

$$80{,}000 = 100{,}000e^{4k} \qquad \text{Substitute.}$$
$$0.8 = e^{4k} \qquad \text{Divide each side by 100,000.}$$
$$\ln 0.8 = \ln e^{4k} \qquad \text{Take natural log of each side.}$$
$$\ln 0.8 = 4k \qquad \text{Apply inverse property.}$$
$$-0.0558 \approx k. \qquad \text{Divide each side by 4. Then use a calculator.}$$

So, after 2 more months ($t = 6$), you can expect the monthly sales to be

$$y = 100{,}000e^{-0.0558(6)} \approx 71{,}500 \text{ units.}$$

See Figure 5.10.

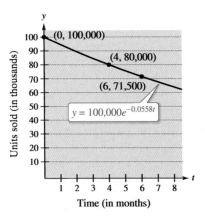

Figure 5.10

In Examples 2 through 5, you did not actually have to solve the differential equation $dy/dt = ky$. (This was done once in the proof of Theorem 5.1.) The next example demonstrates a problem whose solution involves the separation of variables technique. The example concerns **Newton's Law of Cooling,** which states that the rate of change in the temperature of an object is proportional to the difference between the object's temperature and the temperature of the surrounding medium.

EXAMPLE 6   Newton's Law of Cooling

Let y represent the temperature (in °F) of an object in a room whose temperature is kept at a constant 60°F. The object cools from 100°F to 90°F in 10 minutes. How much longer will it take for the temperature of the object to decrease to 80°F?

Solution

From Newton's Law of Cooling, you know that the rate of change in y is proportional to the difference between y and 60. This can be written as $dy/dt = k(y - 60)$, $80 \le y \le 100$. To solve this differential equation, use separation of variables, as shown.

$$\frac{dy}{dt} = k(y - 60) \qquad \text{Differential equation}$$

$$\left(\frac{1}{y - 60}\right) dy = k\, dt \qquad \text{Separate variables.}$$

$$\int \frac{1}{y - 60}\, dy = \int k\, dt \qquad \text{Integrate each side.}$$

$$\ln|y - 60| = kt + C_1 \qquad \text{Find antiderivative of each side.}$$

Because $y > 60$, $|y - 60| = y - 60$, and you can omit the absolute value signs. Using exponential notation, you have

$$y - 60 = e^{kt + C_1}$$

$$y = 60 + Ce^{kt}. \qquad C = e^{C_1}$$

Using $y = 100$ when $t = 0$, you obtain

$$100 = 60 + Ce^{k(0)} \implies 100 = 60 + C \implies 40 = C.$$

Because $y = 90$ when $t = 10$, the value of k is

$$90 = 60 + 40e^{k(10)} \qquad \text{Substitute.}$$

$$30 = 40e^{10k} \qquad \text{Subtract 60 from each side.}$$

$$\ln\frac{3}{4} = \ln e^{10k} \qquad \text{Divide each side by 40. Then take natural log of each side.}$$

$$\frac{1}{10}\ln\frac{3}{4} = k. \qquad \text{Apply inverse property and solve for } k.$$

So, $k \approx -0.02877$ and the cooling model is $y = 60 + 40e^{-0.02877t}$. When $y = 80$, you obtain

$$80 = 60 + 40e^{-0.02877t} \qquad \text{Substitute.}$$

$$20 = 40e^{-0.02877t} \qquad \text{Subtract 60 from each side.}$$

$$\ln\frac{1}{2} = \ln e^{-0.02877t} \qquad \text{Divide each side by 40. Then take natural log of each side.}$$

$$\ln\frac{1}{2} = -0.02877t \qquad \text{Apply inverse property.}$$

$$24.09 \text{ minutes} \approx t. \qquad \text{Divide each side by } -0.02877. \text{ Then use a calculator.}$$

So, it will require about 14.09 *more* minutes for the object to cool to a temperature of 80°F. (See Figure 5.11.)

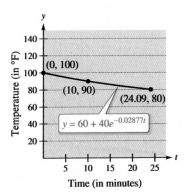

Figure 5.11

5.2 Exercises

See *CalcChat.com* for tutorial help and worked-out solutions to odd-numbered exercises.

 Solving a Differential Equation In Exercises 1–10, find the general solution of the differential equation.

1. $\dfrac{dy}{dx} = x + 3$

2. $\dfrac{dy}{dx} = 5 - 8x$

3. $y' = y + 3$

4. $y' = 6 - y$

5. $y' = \dfrac{5x}{y}$

6. $y' = -\dfrac{\sqrt{x}}{4y}$

7. $y' = \sqrt{x}\,y$

8. $y' = x(1 + y)$

9. $(1 + x^2)y' - 2xy = 0$

10. $xy + y' = 100x$

Writing and Solving a Differential Equation In Exercises 11 and 12, write and find the general solution of the differential equation that models the verbal statement.

11. The rate of change of Q with respect to t is inversely proportional to the square of t.

12. The rate of change of P with respect to t is proportional to $25 - t$.

 Slope Field In Exercises 13 and 14, a differential equation, a point, and a slope field are given. (a) Sketch two approximate solutions of the differential equation on the slope field, one of which passes through the given point. To print an enlarged copy of the graph, go to *MathGraphs.com*. (b) Use integration and the given point to find the particular solution of the differential equation and use a graphing utility to graph the solution. Compare the result with the sketch in part (a) that passes through the given point.

13. $\dfrac{dy}{dx} = x(6 - y), \quad (0, 0)$

14. $\dfrac{dy}{dx} = xy, \quad \left(0, \dfrac{1}{2}\right)$

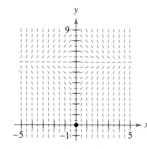

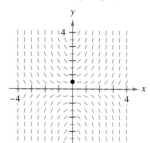

 Finding a Particular Solution In Exercises 15–18, find the function $y = f(t)$ passing through the point $(0, 10)$ with the given differential equation. Use a graphing utility to graph the solution.

15. $\dfrac{dy}{dt} = \dfrac{1}{2}t$

16. $\dfrac{dy}{dt} = -9\sqrt{t}$

17. $\dfrac{dy}{dt} = -\dfrac{1}{2}y$

18. $\dfrac{dy}{dt} = \dfrac{3}{4}y$

 Writing and Solving a Differential Equation In Exercises 19 and 20, write and find the general solution of the differential equation that models the verbal statement. Evaluate the solution at the specified value of the independent variable.

19. The rate of change of N is proportional to N. When $t = 0$, $N = 250$, and when $t = 1$, $N = 400$. What is the value of N when $t = 4$?

20. The rate of change of P is proportional to P. When $t = 0$, $P = 5000$, and when $t = 1$, $P = 4750$. What is the value of P when $t = 5$?

 Finding an Exponential Function In Exercises 21–24, find the exponential function $y = Ce^{kt}$ that passes through the given points.

21.

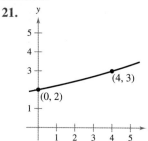

22.

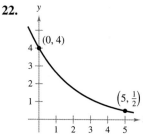

23.

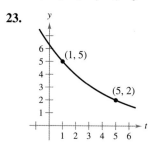

24.

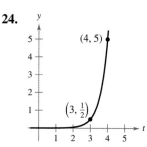

25. **Error Analysis** Describe and correct the error when finding the particular solution of the differential equation

$y' = x^2/y$

where $y(0) = 1$.

$y\,dy = x^2\,dx$

$\displaystyle\int y\,dy = \int x^2\,dx$

$\dfrac{1}{2}y^2 = \dfrac{1}{3}x^3 + C$

$\dfrac{1}{2}(0)^2 = \dfrac{1}{3}(1)^3 + C \implies C = -\dfrac{1}{3}$

$\dfrac{1}{2}y^2 = \dfrac{1}{3}x^3 - \dfrac{1}{3} \implies 2x^3 - 3y^2 = 2$

26. Error Analysis Describe and correct the error when finding the exponential function $y = Ce^{kx}$ that passes through the points $(0, 1)$ and $(2, 8)$.

$$y = Ce^{kx}$$
$$1 = Ce^{k(0)} \implies C = 1$$
$$y = e^{kx}$$
$$8 = e^{k(2)}$$
$$\ln 8 = 2k \implies k = \ln 4$$
$$y = e^{(\ln 4)x} \qquad \text{✗}$$

EXPLORING CONCEPTS ———————

Reasoning In Exercises 27 and 28, determine the quadrants in which the solution of the differential equation is an increasing function. Explain. (Do not solve the differential equation.)

27. $\dfrac{dy}{dx} = \dfrac{1}{2}xy$ **28.** $\dfrac{dy}{dx} = \dfrac{1}{2}x^2y$

———————————————————

Radioactive Decay In Exercises 29–32, complete the table for the radioactive isotope.

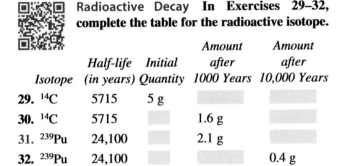

Isotope	Half-life (in years)	Initial Quantity	Amount after 1000 Years	Amount after 10,000 Years
29. ^{14}C	5715	5 g		
30. ^{14}C	5715		1.6 g	
31. ^{239}Pu	24,100		2.1 g	
32. ^{239}Pu	24,100			0.4 g

Radioactive Decay In Exercises 33–36, complete the table for the radioactive isotope.

Isotope	Half-life (in years)	Initial Quantity	Amount after 1000 Years	Time to decay to 1 gram
33. ^{226}Ra	1599	20 g		
34. ^{226}Ra	1599		1.5 g	
35. ^{226}Ra	1599			10,000 yr
36. ^{14}C	5715			5000 yr

37. Radioactive Decay Radioactive radium has a half-life of approximately 1599 years. What percent of a given amount remains after 100 years?

38. Carbon Dating Carbon-14 dating assumes that the carbon dioxide on Earth today has the same radioactive content as it did centuries ago. If this is true, the amount of ^{14}C absorbed by a tree that grew centuries ago should be the same as the amount of ^{14}C absorbed by a tree growing today. A piece of ancient charcoal contains 15% as much of the radioactive carbon as a piece of modern charcoal. How long ago was the tree burned to make the ancient charcoal? (The half-life of ^{14}C is 5715 years.)

Compound Interest In Exercises 39–42, complete the table for a fund in which interest is compounded continuously. Use the formula $A = Pe^{rt}$, where P is the initial investment, r is the annual rate, and A is the amount in the fund after t years.

	Initial Investment	Annual Rate	Time to Double	Amount after 10 Years
39.	$1000	12%		
40.	$750		$7\frac{3}{4}$ yr	
41.	$500			$1292.85
42.	$6000			$8950.95

Population In Exercises 43–46, the population (in millions) of a country in 2018 and the expected annual growth rate k of the population are given. (*Source: U.S. Census Bureau, International Data Base*)

(a) Find the exponential growth model $P = Ce^{kt}$ for the population by letting $t = 0$ correspond to 2010.

(b) Use the model to predict the population of the country in 2028.

(c) Discuss the relationship between the sign of k and the change in population for the country.

	Country	2018 Population	k
43.	Latvia	1.9	-0.011
44.	Egypt	99.4	0.024
45.	Uganda	40.8	0.032
46.	Hungary	9.8	-0.003

47. Bacteria Growth The number of bacteria in a culture is increasing according to the law of exponential growth. There are 125 bacteria in the culture after 2 hours and 350 bacteria after 4 hours.

(a) Find the initial population.

(b) Write an exponential growth model for the bacteria population. Let t represent the time in hours.

(c) Use the model to determine the number of bacteria after 8 hours.

(d) After how many hours will the bacteria count be 25,000?

48. Bacteria Growth The number of bacteria in a culture is increasing according to the law of exponential growth. The initial population is 250 bacteria, and the population after 10 hours is double the population after 1 hour.

(a) Write an exponential growth model for the bacteria population. Let t represent the time in hours.

(b) Use the model to determine the number of bacteria after 6 hours.

(c) After how many hours will the bacteria count be 10,000?

49. Modeling Data The number N of bacteria in a culture is counted each hour for 5 hours. The results are shown in the table, where t is the time in hours.

t	0	1	2	3	4	5
N	100	126	151	198	243	297

(a) Use the regression capabilities of a graphing utility to find an exponential model $y = Ce^{kx}$ for the data.

(b) Use the model to estimate the time required for the population to quadruple in size.

50. HOW DO YOU SEE IT? The functions f and g are both of the form $y = Ce^{kt}$.

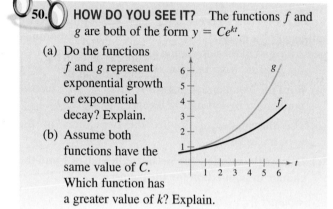

(a) Do the functions f and g represent exponential growth or exponential decay? Explain.

(b) Assume both functions have the same value of C. Which function has a greater value of k? Explain.

51. Insect Population An insect population increases by a constant number each month. Explain why the number of insects can be represented by a linear function.

52. Insect Population An insect population increases by a constant percentage each month. Explain why the number of insects can be represented by an exponential function.

53. Newton's Law of Cooling When an object is removed from a furnace and placed in an environment with a constant temperature of 80°F, its core temperature is 1500°F. One hour after it is removed, the core temperature is 1120°F.

(a) Write an equation for the core temperature y of the object t hours after it is removed from the furnace.

(b) What is the core temperature of the object 6 hours after it is removed from the furnace?

54. Newton's Law of Cooling A container of hot liquid is placed in a freezer that is kept at a constant temperature of 20°F. The initial temperature of the liquid is 160°F. After 5 minutes, the liquid's temperature is 60°F.

(a) Write an equation for the temperature y of the liquid t minutes after it is placed in the freezer.

(b) How much longer will it take for the temperature of the liquid to decrease to 25°F?

55. Learning Curve The management at a factory has determined that the rate of change of the number of units N that a new employee can produce per day after having worked t days is proportional to $N - 30$. After 0 days on the job, the employee produces 0 units and after 15 days on the job, the employee produces 15 units.

(a) Write and find the general solution of the differential equation that models this situation.

(b) According to your model, how many days pass before the employee produces 25 units per day?

56. Learning Curve Repeat Exercise 55 when the new employee produces 0 units after 0 days on the job and 20 units after 19 days on the job.

True or False? In Exercises 57 and 58, determine whether the statement is true or false. If it is false, explain why or give an example that shows it is false.

57. Half of the atoms in a sample of radioactive radium decay in 799.5 years.

58. In exponential growth, the rate of growth is constant.

Calculus AP® – Exam Preparation Questions

59. Multiple Choice Which statement corresponds to the differential equation $dP/dt = k/(xy)$?

(A) The rate of change of P is inversely proportional to both x and y.

(B) The rate of change of P is proportional to y and inversely proportional to x.

(C) The rate of change of P is proportional to both x and y.

(D) The rate of change of P is proportional to x and inversely proportional to y.

60. Multiple Choice Which of the following is the solution of $dy/dx = 8x/y$, where $y(2) = -4$?

(A) $y = -\sqrt{8x^2 - 16}$ for $x > \sqrt{2}$

(B) $y = \sqrt{8x^2 - 16}$ for $x > \sqrt{2}$

(C) $y = \sqrt{8x^2 - 8}$ for $x > 1$

(D) $y = -\sqrt{8x^2 - 8}$ for $x > 1$

61. Multiple Choice Let $y = f(t)$ be a solution of $dy/dt = ky$, where k is a constant. Values of f for selected values of t are given in the table below. Which of the following is an expression for $f(t)$?

t	0	4
$f(t)$	2	10

(A) $2t + 2$

(B) $\frac{1}{2}t^2 + 2$

(C) $e^{(t/2)\ln 3} + 1$

(D) $2e^{(t/4)\ln 5}$

5.3   Separation of Variables

▶ Recognize and solve differential equations that can be solved by separation of variables.
▶ Use differential equations to model and solve applied problems.

Separation of Variables

Consider a differential equation that can be written in the form

$$M(x) + N(y)\frac{dy}{dx} = 0$$

where M is a continuous function of x alone and N is a continuous function of y alone. As you saw in Section 5.2, for this type of equation, all x terms can be collected with dx and all y terms with dy, and a solution can be obtained by integration. Such equations are said to be **separable,** and the solution procedure is called **separation of variables.** Below are some examples of differential equations that are separable.

Original Differential Equation	*Rewritten with Variables Separated*
$\dfrac{dy}{dx} = \dfrac{x}{y^2 + 1}$	$(y^2 + 1)\, dy = x\, dx$
$x^2 + 3y\dfrac{dy}{dx} = 0$	$3y\, dy = -x^2\, dx$
$(\sin x)y' = \cos x$	$dy = \cot x\, dx$
$\dfrac{xy'}{e^y + 1} = 2$	$\dfrac{1}{e^y + 1}\, dy = \dfrac{2}{x}\, dx$

> **Insight**
>
> Separable differential equations appear on both the AP® Calculus AB and BC Exams.

EXAMPLE 1   Separation of Variables

See LarsonCalculusforAP.com for an interactive version of this type of example.

Find the general solution of $(x^2 + 4)\dfrac{dy}{dx} = xy$.

Solution

To begin, note that $y = 0$ is a solution. To find other solutions, assume that $y \neq 0$ and separate variables as shown.

$(x^2 + 4)\, dy = xy\, dx$	Differential form
$\dfrac{dy}{y} = \dfrac{x}{x^2 + 4}\, dx$	Separate variables.
$\displaystyle\int \dfrac{dy}{y} = \int \dfrac{x}{x^2 + 4}\, dx$	Integrate each side.
$\ln\lvert y\rvert = \dfrac{1}{2}\ln(x^2 + 4) + C_1$	Find antiderivative of each side.
$\ln\lvert y\rvert = \ln\sqrt{x^2 + 4} + C_1$	Logarithmic property
$\lvert y\rvert = e^{\ln\sqrt{x^2+4}+C_1}$	Exponentiate each side.
$\lvert y\rvert = e^{C_1}e^{\ln\sqrt{x^2+4}}$	Property of exponents
$\lvert y\rvert = e^{C_1}\sqrt{x^2 + 4}$	Apply inverse property.
$y = \pm e^{C_1}\sqrt{x^2 + 4}.$	Definition of absolute value.

Because $y = 0$ is also a solution, you can write the general solution as

$$y = C\sqrt{x^2 + 4}. \qquad \text{General solution}$$

> **Justification**
>
> In Example 1, you can check the solution
>
> $$y = C\sqrt{x^2} + 4$$
>
> by differentiating and substituting into the original equation.
>
> $$(x^2 + 4)\frac{dy}{dx} = xy$$
>
> $$(x^2 + 4)\frac{Cx}{\sqrt{x^2 + 4}} \overset{?}{=} x\left(C\sqrt{x^2 + 4}\right)$$
>
> $$Cx\sqrt{x^2 + 4} = Cx\sqrt{x^2 + 4}$$
>
> So, the solution checks.

In some cases, it is not feasible to write the general solution in the explicit form $y = f(x)$. The next example illustrates such a solution.

EXAMPLE 2 Finding a Particular Solution

Given the initial condition $y(0) = 1$, find the particular solution of the equation

$$xy \, dx + e^{-x^2}(y^2 - 1) \, dy = 0.$$

Solution

Note that $y = 0$ is a solution of the differential equation—but this solution does not satisfy the initial condition. So, you can assume that $y \neq 0$. To separate variables, you must rid the first term of y and the second term of e^{-x^2}. So, you should multiply by e^{x^2}/y and obtain the following.

$$xy \, dx + e^{-x^2}(y^2 - 1) \, dy = 0 \qquad \text{Write original equation.}$$

$$e^{-x^2}(y^2 - 1) \, dy = -xy \, dx \qquad \text{Subtract } xy \, dx \text{ from each side.}$$

$$\left(y - \frac{1}{y}\right) dy = -xe^{x^2} \, dx \qquad \text{Separate variables.}$$

$$\int \left(y - \frac{1}{y}\right) dy = \int -xe^{x^2} \, dx \qquad \text{Integrate each side.}$$

$$\frac{y^2}{2} - \ln|y| = -\frac{1}{2}e^{x^2} + C \qquad \text{Find antiderivative of each side.}$$

From the initial condition $y(0) = 1$, you have

$$\frac{1^2}{2} - \ln|1| = -\frac{1}{2}e^{0^2} + C \quad \Longrightarrow \quad \frac{1}{2} - 0 = -\frac{1}{2} + C$$

which implies that $C = 1$. So, the particular solution has the implicit form

$$\frac{y^2}{2} - \ln|y| = -\frac{1}{2}e^{x^2} + 1 \quad \Longrightarrow \quad y^2 - \ln y^2 + e^{x^2} = 2.$$

You can check this by differentiating and rewriting to get the original equation.

EXAMPLE 3 Finding a Particular Solution Curve

Find the equation of the curve that passes through the point $(1, 3)$ and has a slope of y/x^2 at any point (x, y), where $x > 0$ and $y > 0$.

Solution

Because the slope of the curve is y/x^2, you have $dy/dx = y/x^2$ with the initial condition $y(1) = 3$. Separating variables and integrating produces

$$\int \frac{dy}{y} = \int \frac{dx}{x^2}, \quad x > 0, y > 0 \qquad \text{Separate variables and integrate each side.}$$

$$\ln y = -\frac{1}{x} + C_1 \qquad \text{Find antiderivative of each side.}$$

$$y = e^{-(1/x) + C_1} \qquad \text{Exponentiate each side.}$$

$$y = e^{C_1}e^{-1/x} \qquad \text{Property of exponents}$$

$$y = Ce^{-1/x}. \qquad \text{Rewrite, letting } C = e^{C_1}.$$

Because $y = 3$ when $x = 1$, it follows that $3 = Ce^{-1}$ and $C = 3e$. So, the equation of the specified curve is

$$y = (3e)e^{-1/x} \quad \Longrightarrow \quad y = 3e^{(x-1)/x}, \quad x > 0.$$

See Figure 5.12.

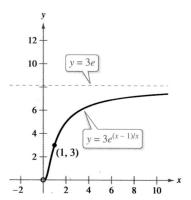

Figure 5.12

Applications

EXAMPLE 4   **Wildlife Population**

The rate of change of the number of coyotes $N(t)$ in a population is directly proportional to $650 - N(t)$, where t is the time in years. When $t = 0$, the population is 300, and when $t = 2$, the population has increased to 500. Find the population when $t = 3$.

Solution

Because the rate of change of the population is proportional to $650 - N(t)$, or $650 - N$, you can write the differential equation

$$\frac{dN}{dt} = k(650 - N).$$

You can solve this equation using separation of variables.

$$dN = k(650 - N)\, dt \qquad \text{Differential form}$$

$$\frac{dN}{650 - N} = k\, dt \qquad \text{Separate variables.}$$

$$-\ln|650 - N| = kt + C_1 \qquad \text{Integrate each side.}$$

$$\ln|650 - N| = -kt - C_1 \qquad \text{Multiply each side by } -1.$$

$$650 - N = e^{-kt - C_1} \qquad \text{Exponentiate each side. Assume } N < 650.$$

$$650 - N = e^{-C_1} e^{-kt} \qquad \text{Property of exponents}$$

$$N = 650 - Ce^{-kt} \qquad \text{General solution}$$

Using $N = 300$ when $t = 0$, you can conclude that $C = 350$, which produces

$$N = 650 - 350e^{-kt}.$$

Then, using $N = 500$ when $t = 2$, it follows that

$$500 = 650 - 350e^{-2k} \implies e^{-2k} = \frac{3}{7} \implies k \approx 0.4236.$$

So, the model for the coyote population is

$$N = 650 - 350e^{-0.4236t}. \qquad \text{Model for population}$$

When $t = 3$, you can approximate the population to be

$$N = 650 - 350e^{-0.4236(3)} \approx 552 \text{ coyotes.}$$

The model for the population is shown in Figure 5.13. Note that $N = 650$ is the horizontal asymptote of the graph and is the *carrying capacity* of the model. You will learn more about carrying capacity in Section 5.4.

> **Algebra Review**
>
> For help with the algebra in solving for C in Example 4, see Example 1 in the *Chapter 5 Algebra Review* on page A44. For help with the algebra in solving for k in Example 4, see Example 4(a) in the *Chapter 5 Algebra Review* on page A45.

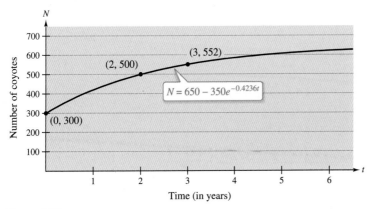

Figure 5.13

EXAMPLE 5 **Modeling Advertising Awareness**

A new cereal product is introduced through an advertising campaign to a population of 1 million potential customers. The rate at which the population hears about the product is assumed to be proportional to the number of people who are not yet aware of the product. By the end of 1 year, half of the population has heard of the product. How many will have heard of it by the end of 2 years?

Solution

Let y be the number of people (in millions) at time t who have heard of the product. This means that $(1 - y)$ is the number of people (in millions) who have not heard of it, and dy/dt is the rate at which the population hears about the product. From the given assumption, you can write the differential equation as shown.

$$\frac{dy}{dt} = k(1 - y)$$

Rate of change of y — is proportional to — the difference between 1 and y.

You can solve this equation using separation of variables.

$dy = k(1 - y)\, dt$	Differential form
$\dfrac{dy}{1 - y} = k\, dt$	Separate variables.
$-\ln\lvert 1 - y\rvert = kt + C_1$	Integrate each side.
$\ln\lvert 1 - y\rvert = -kt - C_1$	Multiply each side by -1.
$1 - y = e^{-kt - C_1}$	Exponentiate each side. Assume $y < 1$.
$y = 1 - Ce^{-kt}$	General solution

To solve for the constants C and k, use the initial conditions. That is, because $y = 0$ when $t = 0$, you can determine that $C = 1$. Similarly, because $y = 0.5$ when $t = 1$, it follows that $0.5 = 1 - e^{-k}$, which implies that

$$k = -\ln 0.5 \approx 0.693.$$

So, the particular solution is

$$y = 1 - e^{-0.693t}. \qquad \text{Particular solution}$$

This model is shown in Figure 5.14. Using the model, you can determine that the number of people who have heard of the product after 2 years is

$$y = 1 - e^{-0.693(2)}$$

$$\approx 0.75 \text{ or } 750{,}000 \text{ people.}$$

Algebra Review

For help with the algebra in solving for C in Example 5, see Example 2 in the *Chapter 5 Algebra Review* on page A44. For help with the algebra in solving for k in Example 5, see Example 4(b) in the *Chapter 5 Algebra Review* on page A45.

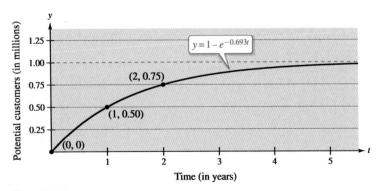

Figure 5.14

EXAMPLE 6 Modeling a Chemical Reaction

During a chemical reaction, substance A is converted into substance B at a rate that is proportional to the square of the amount of A. When $t = 0$, 60 grams of A is present, and after 1 hour ($t = 1$), only 10 grams of A remains unconverted. How much of A is present after 2 hours?

Solution

Let y be the amount of unconverted substance A at any time t. From the given assumption about the conversion rate, you can write the differential equation as shown.

$$\frac{dy}{dt} = ky^2$$

Rate of change of y is proportional to   the square of y.

You can solve this equation using separation of variables.

$dy = ky^2\, dt$	Differential form
$\dfrac{dy}{y^2} = k\, dt$	Separate variables.
$-\dfrac{1}{y} = kt + C$	Integrate each side.
$y = \dfrac{-1}{kt + C}$	General solution

To solve for the constants C and k, use the initial conditions. That is, because $y = 60$ when $t = 0$, you can determine that $C = -\frac{1}{60}$. Similarly, because $y = 10$ when $t = 1$, it follows that

$$10 = \frac{-1}{k - (1/60)}$$

which implies that $k = -\frac{1}{12}$. So, the particular solution is

$$y = \frac{-1}{(-1/12)t - (1/60)} \qquad \text{Substitute for } k \text{ and } C.$$

$$= \frac{60}{5t + 1}. \qquad \text{Particular solution}$$

Using the model, you can determine that the unconverted amount of substance A after 2 hours is

$$y = \frac{60}{5(2) + 1}$$

$$\approx 5.45 \text{ grams.}$$

In Figure 5.15, note that the chemical conversion is occurring rapidly during the first hour. Then, as more and more of substance A is converted, the conversion rate slows down.

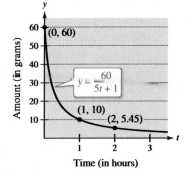

Figure 5.15

Exploration

In Example 6, the rate of conversion was assumed to be proportional to the *square* of the unconverted amount. How does the result change when the conversion is proportional to the unconverted amount?

The next example describes a growth model called a **Gompertz growth model.** This model assumes that the rate of change of y is proportional to the product of y and the natural log of L/y, where L is the population limit.

EXAMPLE 7 Modeling Population Growth

A population of 20 wolves has been introduced into a national park. The forest service estimates that the maximum population the park can sustain is 200 wolves. After 3 years, the population is estimated to be 40 wolves. According to a Gompertz growth model, how many wolves will there be 10 years after their introduction?

Solution

Let y be the number of wolves at any time t. From the given assumption about the rate of growth of the population, you can write the differential equation as shown.

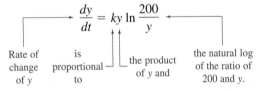

$$\frac{dy}{dt} = ky \ln \frac{200}{y}$$

| Rate of change of y | is proportional to | the product of y and | the natural log of the ratio of 200 and y. |

Using separation of variables *or* a computer algebra system, you can find the general solution to be

$$y = 200e^{-Ce^{-kt}}. \qquad \text{General solution}$$

To solve for the constants C and k, use the initial conditions. That is, because $y = 20$ when $t = 0$, you can determine that

$$C = \ln 10$$
$$\approx 2.3026.$$

Similarly, because $y = 40$ when $t = 3$, it follows that

$$40 = 200e^{-2.3026e^{-3k}}$$

which implies that $k \approx 0.1194$. So, the particular solution is

$$y = 200e^{-2.3026e^{-0.1194t}}. \qquad \text{Particular solution}$$

Using the model, you can estimate the wolf population after 10 years to be

$$y = 200e^{-2.3026e^{-0.1194(10)}}$$
$$\approx 100 \text{ wolves.}$$

In Figure 5.16, note that after 10 years the population has reached about half of the estimated maximum population. Try checking the growth model to see that it yields $y = 20$ when $t = 0$ and $y = 40$ when $t = 3$.

> **Algebra Review**
>
> For help with the algebra in solving for C in Example 7, see Example 3 in the *Chapter 5 Algebra Review* on page A44. For help with the algebra in solving for k in Example 7, see Example 4(c) in the *Chapter 5 Algebra Review* on page A45.

> **Technology**
>
> If you have access to a computer algebra system, try using it to find the general solution and the particular solution to Example 7.

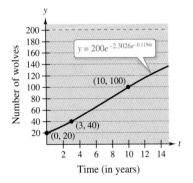

Number of wolves — Time (in years)

$y = 200e^{-2.3026e^{-0.1194t}}$

(10, 100)

(3, 40)

(0, 20)

Figure 5.16

5.3 Exercises

 Finding a General Solution Using Separation of Variables In Exercises 1–14, find the general solution of the differential equation.

1. $\dfrac{dy}{dt} = \dfrac{3}{2}y$

2. $\dfrac{dy}{dt} = \dfrac{3}{2}t$

3. $\dfrac{dy}{dx} = \dfrac{x}{y}$

4. $\dfrac{dy}{dx} = \dfrac{5x^2}{y^2}$

5. $\dfrac{dy}{dx} = \dfrac{x-1}{y^3}$

6. $\dfrac{dy}{dx} = \dfrac{6-x^2}{2y^3}$

7. $(2+x)y' = -2y$

8. $xy' = y$

9. $yy' = 4\sin x$

10. $yy' = -8\cos \pi x$

11. $\sqrt{1-4x^2}\,y' = x$

12. $\sqrt{x^2-16}\,y' = 11x$

13. $y\ln x - xy' = 0$

14. $12y'/x - 7e^{x^2} = 0$

 Finding a Particular Solution Using Separation of Variables In Exercises 15–24, find the particular solution that satisfies the initial condition.

Differential Equation	*Initial Condition*
15. $yy' - 2e^x = 0$	$y(0) = 6$
16. $\sqrt{x} + \sqrt{y}\,y' = 0$	$y(1) = 9$
17. $y(x+1) + y' = 0$	$y(-2) = 1$
18. $2xy' - \ln x^2 = 0$	$y(1) = 2$
19. $y(1+x^2)y' - x(1+y^2) = 0$	$y(0) = \sqrt{3}$
20. $y\sqrt{1-x^2}\,y' - x\sqrt{1-y^2} = 0$	$y\left(\frac{1}{2}\right) = \frac{1}{2}$
21. $\dfrac{du}{dv} = uv\sin v^2$	$u(0) = 1$
22. $\dfrac{dr}{ds} = e^{r-2s}$	$r(0) = 0$
23. $x\ln x^4\,dy - dx = 0$	$y(e) = 4$
24. $\sec^2 t\,dt = \cos P\tan t\,dP$	$P\left(\dfrac{\pi}{4}\right) = \dfrac{\pi}{2}$

 Finding a Particular Solution Curve In Exercises 25–28, find an equation of the graph that passes through the point and has the given slope, where $x > 0$ and $y > 0$.

25. $(0,2)$, $y' = \dfrac{x}{4y}$

26. $(1,1)$, $y' = \dfrac{1-9x^2}{16y}$

27. $(1,2)$, $y' = \dfrac{y}{2x^2}$

28. $\left(\sqrt{5},1\right)$, $y' = \dfrac{xy}{x^2-1}$

Using Slope In Exercises 29 and 30, find all functions f having the indicated property.

29. The tangent to the graph of f at the point (x, y) intersects the x-axis at $(x + 2, 0)$.

30. All tangents to the graph of f pass through the origin.

Slope Field In Exercises 31–34, sketch a few solutions of the differential equation on the slope field and then find the general solution analytically. To print an enlarged copy of the graph, go to *MathGraphs.com*.

31. $\dfrac{dy}{dx} = x$

32. $\dfrac{dy}{dx} = -\dfrac{x}{y}$

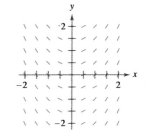 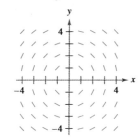

33. $\dfrac{dy}{dx} = 4 - y$

34. $\dfrac{dy}{dx} = 0.25x(4 - y)$

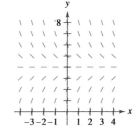 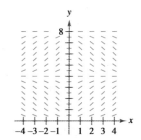

Euler's Method In Exercises 35–38, (a) use Euler's Method with a step size of $h = 0.1$ to approximate the particular solution of the initial value problem at the given x-value, (b) find the exact solution of the differential equation analytically, and (c) compare the solutions at the given x-value.

Differential Equation	*Initial Condition*	*x-Value*
35. $\dfrac{dy}{dx} = -6xy$	$(0,5)$	$x = 1$
36. $\dfrac{dy}{dx} + 6xy^2 = 0$	$(0,3)$	$x = 1$
37. $\dfrac{dy}{dx} = \dfrac{2x+12}{3y^2-4}$	$(1,2)$	$x = 2$
38. $\dfrac{dy}{dx} = 2x(1+y^2)$	$(1,0)$	$x = 1.5$

Error Analysis In Exercises 39 and 40, describe and correct the error in finding the general solution of the differential equation.

39. $\dfrac{y'}{y} = xy$

$\displaystyle\int \dfrac{dy}{y} = \int xy\,dx$

$\ln|y| = \dfrac{1}{2}x^2 y + C$ ✗

40. $\dfrac{dy}{dx} = \dfrac{3y}{x^2}$

$\displaystyle\int 3y\,dy = \int x^2\,dx$

$\dfrac{3}{2}y^2 = \dfrac{1}{3}x^3 + C$ ✗

Slope Field In Exercises 41–44, (a) write a differential equation for the statement and (b) match the differential equation with a possible slope field. Verify your result by using a graphing utility to graph a slope field for the differential equation. [The slope fields are labeled (i), (ii), (iii), and (iv).] To print an enlarged copy of the graph, go to *MathGraphs.com*.

(i)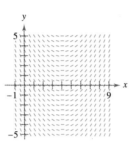

(ii)

(iii)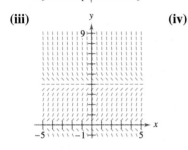

(iv)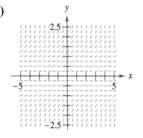

41. The rate of change of y with respect to x is proportional to the difference between y and 4.

42. The rate of change of y with respect to x is proportional to the difference between x and 4.

43. The rate of change of y with respect to x is proportional to the product of y and the difference between y and 4.

44. The rate of change of y with respect to x is proportional to y^2.

45. Weight Gain A calf that weighs 60 pounds at birth gains weight at the rate

$$\frac{dw}{dt} = k(1200 - w)$$

where w is weight in pounds and t is time in years.

(a) Find the general solution of the differential equation.

(b) Use a graphing utility to graph the particular solutions for $k = 0.8, 0.9,$ and 1.

(c) The animal is sold when its weight reaches 800 pounds. Find the time of sale for each of the models in part (b).

(d) What is the maximum weight of the animal for each of the models in part (b)?

46. Weight Gain A calf that weighs w_0 pounds at birth gains weight at the rate

$$\frac{dw}{dt} = 1200 - w$$

where w is weight in pounds and t is time in years. Find the general solution of the differential equation.

47. Biology At any time t, the rate of growth of the population N of deer in a state park is proportional to the product of N and $L - N$, where $L = 500$ is the maximum number of deer the park can sustain. When $t = 0$, $N = 100$, and when $t = 4$, $N = 200$. Write N as a function of t. (*Hint:* Use partial fractions.)

48. Sales Growth The rate of change in sales S (in thousands of units) of a new product is proportional to the product of S and $L - S$, where L (in thousands of units) is the estimated maximum level of sales. When $t = 0$, $S = 10$. Write and solve the differential equation for this sales model. (*Hint:* Use partial fractions.)

Advertising Awareness In Exercises 49 and 50, use the advertising awareness model described in Example 5 to find the number of people y (in millions) aware of the product as a function of time t (in years).

49. $y = 0$ when $t = 0$; $y = 0.75$ when $t = 1$

50. $y = 0$ when $t = 0$; $y = 0.9$ when $t = 2$

Chemical Reaction In Exercises 51 and 52, use the chemical reaction model given in Example 6 to find the amount y as a function of t, and use a graphing utility to graph the function.

51. $y = 45$ grams when $t = 0$; $y = 4$ grams when $t = 2$

52. $y = 75$ grams when $t = 0$; $y = 12$ grams when $t = 1$

Using a Gompertz Growth Model In Exercises 53 and 54, use the Gompertz growth model described on page 392 to find the growth function, and sketch its graph.

53. $L = 500$; $y = 100$ when $t = 0$; $y = 150$ when $t = 2$

54. $L = 5000$; $y = 500$ when $t = 0$; $y = 625$ when $t = 1$

55. Biology A population of eight beavers has been introduced into a new wetlands area. Biologists estimate that the maximum population the wetlands can sustain is 60 beavers. After 3 years, the population is 15 beavers. According to a Gompertz growth model, how many beavers will be present in the wetlands after 10 years?

56. Biology A population of 30 rabbits has been introduced into a new region. It is estimated that the maximum population the region can sustain is 400 rabbits. After 1 year, the population is estimated to be 90 rabbits. According to a Gompertz growth model, how many rabbits will be present after 3 years?

57. Chemical Mixture A 100-gallon tank is full of a solution containing 25 pounds of a concentrate. Starting at time $t = 0$, distilled water is admitted to the tank at the rate of 5 gallons per minute, and the well-stirred solution is withdrawn at the same rate.

(a) Find the amount Q of the concentrate in the solution as a function of t. (*Hint:* $Q' + Q/20 = 0$)

(b) Find the time when the amount of concentrate in the tank reaches 15 pounds.

58. Chemical Mixture A 200-gallon tank is half full of distilled water. At time $t = 0$, a solution containing 0.5 pound of concentrate per gallon enters the tank at the rate of 5 gallons per minute, and the well-stirred mixture is withdrawn at the same rate. Find the amount Q of concentrate in the tank after 30 minutes.

$$\left(Hint:\ Q' + \frac{Q}{20} = \frac{5}{2} \right)$$

59. Snow Removal The rate of change in the number of miles s of road cleared per hour by a snowplow is inversely proportional to the depth h of snow. That is,

$$\frac{ds}{dh} = \frac{k}{h}.$$

Find s as a function of h given that $s = 25$ miles when $h = 2$ inches and $s = 12$ miles when $h = 6$ inches $(2 \le h \le 15)$.

60. Biology Let x and y be the sizes of two internal organs of a particular mammal at time t. Empirical data indicate that the relative growth rates of these two organs are equal, and can be modeled by

$$\frac{1}{x}\frac{dx}{dt} = \frac{1}{y}\frac{dy}{dt}.$$

Use this differential equation to write y as a function of x.

61. Investment A large corporation starts at time $t = 0$ to invest part of its receipts at a rate of P dollars per year in a fund for future corporate expansion. The fund earns r percent interest per year compounded continuously. The rate of growth of the amount A in the fund is given by

$$\frac{dA}{dt} = rA + P$$

where $A = 0$ when $t = 0$. Solve this differential equation for A as a function of t.

Investment In Exercises 62–64, use the result of Exercise 61.

62. Find A for $P = \$275,000$, $r = 8\%$, and $t = 10$ years.

63. The corporation needs $\$260,000,000$ in 8 years and the fund earns $7\frac{1}{4}\%$ interest compounded continuously. Find P.

64. The corporation needs $\$1,000,000$ and it can invest $\$125,000$ per year in a fund earning 8% interest compounded continuously. Find t.

Using a Gompertz Growth Model In Exercises 65 and 66, use the Gompertz growth model described on page 392.

65. (a) Use a graphing utility to graph the slope field for the growth model when $k = 0.02$ and $L = 5000$.

(b) Describe the behavior of the graph as $t \to \infty$.

(c) Solve the growth model for $L = 5000$, $y_0 = 500$, and $k = 0.02$.

(d) Graph the equation you found in part (c). Determine the concavity of the graph.

66. (a) Use a graphing utility to graph the slope field for the growth model when $k = 0.05$ and $L = 1000$.

(b) Describe the behavior of the graph as $t \to \infty$.

(c) Solve the growth model for $L = 1000$, $y_0 = 100$, and $k = 0.05$.

(d) Graph the equation you found in part (c). Determine the concavity of the graph.

EXPLORING CONCEPTS

67. Separation of Variables Is an equation of the form

$$\frac{dy}{dx} = f(x)g(y) - f(x)h(y), \quad g(y) \ne h(y)$$

separable? Explain.

68. Finding a General Solution Find the general solution of

$$\frac{dy}{dx} = \frac{ay + b}{cy + d},$$

where a, b, c, and d are nonzero constants.

Separation of Variables In Exercises 69–74, determine whether the differential equation is separable. If the equation is separable, rewrite it in the form $N(y)\,dy = M(x)\,dx$. (Do not solve the differential equation.)

69. $y(1 + x)\,dx + x\,dy = 0$ **70.** $y' = y^{1/2}$

71. $y' + xy = 5$ **72.** $y' = x - xy - y + 1$

73. $y' = (x^3 y^5)^{-1}$ **74.** $e^{x-1} - y = x^2 y^t$

75. SAILING

Ignoring resistance, a sailboat starting from rest accelerates (dv/dt) at a rate proportional to the difference between the velocities of the wind and the boat.

(a) The wind is blowing at 20 knots, and after 1 half-hour, the boat is moving at 10 knots. Write the velocity v as a function of time t.

(b) Use the result of part (a) to write the distance traveled by the boat as a function of time.

76. **HOW DO YOU SEE IT?**   Recall from Example 1 that the general solution of

$$(x^2 + 4)\frac{dy}{dx} = xy$$

is $y = C\sqrt{x^2 + 4}$. The graphs below show the particular solutions for $C = 0.5, 1, 2,$ and 3. Match the value of C with each graph. Explain your reasoning.

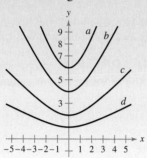

True or False? **In Exercises 77 and 78, determine whether the statement is true or false. If it is false, explain why or give an example that shows it is false.**

77. The function $y = 0$ is always a solution of a differential equation that can be solved by separation of variables.

78. The differential equation $y' = xy - 2y + x - 2$ can be written in separated variables form.

Calculus AP® – Exam Preparation Questions

79. Multiple Choice   If $\dfrac{dy}{dx} = \dfrac{y^2 + 1}{x + 2}$, then $y =$

(A) $\tan[\ln(x + 2) + C]$.

(B) $\tan[\ln(x + 2)] + C$.

(C) $\ln(x + 2) + C$.

(D) $\tan\left(\ln x + \dfrac{x}{2} + C\right)$.

80. Multiple Choice   If

$$\frac{dy}{dt} = y \sec^2 t$$

and $y = 4$ when $t = 0$, then $y =$

(A) $e^{\tan t} + 3$.   (B) $4e^{\tan t}$.

(C) $e^{\tan t} + 4$.   (D) $\tan t + 4$.

81. Free Response   Consider the differential equation

$$\frac{dy}{dx} = \frac{y - 4}{x^2}.$$

(a) Find the particular solution $y = f(x)$ to the differential equation with the initial condition $f(3) = 0$.

(b) For the particular solution $y = f(x)$ described in part (a), find $\lim\limits_{x \to \infty} f(x)$.

SECTION PROJECT

Orthogonal Trajectories

A common problem in electrostatics, thermodynamics, and hydrodynamics involves finding a family of curves, each of which is orthogonal to all members of a given family of curves. For example, the figure shows a family of circles $x^2 + y^2 = C$, each of which intersects the lines in the family $y = Kx$ at right angles.

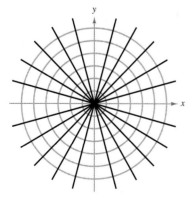

Each line $y = Kx$ is an orthogonal trajectory of the family of circles.

Two such families of curves are said to be **mutually orthogonal,** and each curve in one of the families is called an **orthogonal trajectory** of the other family. In electrostatics, lines of force are orthogonal to the *equipotential curves*. In thermodynamics, the flow of heat across a plane surface is orthogonal to the *isothermal curves*. In hydrodynamics, the flow (stream) lines are orthogonal trajectories of the *velocity potential curves*.

In (a)–(f), find the orthogonal trajectories of each family. Use a graphing utility to graph several members of each family.

(a) $y = Ce^x$

(b) $x^2 - 2y^2 = C$

(c) $x^2 = Cy$

(d) $y^2 = 2Cx$

(e) $y^2 = Cx^3$

(f) $y = \dfrac{C}{x}$

5.4   The Logistic Equation

▶ Solve and analyze logistic differential equations.
▶ Use logistic differential equations to model and solve applied problems.

Logistic Differential Equation

In Section 5.2, the exponential growth model was derived from the fact that the rate of change of a variable y is proportional to the value of y. You observed that the differential equation $dy/dt = ky$ has the general solution $y = Ce^{kt}$. Exponential growth is unlimited, but when describing a population, there often exists some upper limit L past which growth cannot occur. This upper limit L is called the **carrying capacity,** which is the maximum population $y(t)$ that can be sustained or supported as time t increases. A model that is often used to describe this type of growth is the **logistic differential equation**

$$\frac{dy}{dt} = ky\left(1 - \frac{y}{L}\right) \qquad \text{Logistic differential equation}$$

where k and L are positive constants. A population that satisfies this equation does not grow without bound, but approaches the carrying capacity L as t increases.

From the equation, you can see that if y is between 0 and the carrying capacity L, then $dy/dt > 0$, and the population increases. If y is greater than L, then $dy/dt < 0$, and the population decreases. The general solution of the logistic differential equation is derived in the next example.

> **Insight**
>
> Logistic differential equations appear only on the AP® Calculus BC Exam. On the free-response section, you may be asked to solve a logistic differential equation by separating variables. You may also be asked to find the carrying capacity and the inflection point (if any), and then explain what they represent in the context of the problem.

EXAMPLE 1   Deriving the General Solution

Solve the logistic differential equation $\dfrac{dy}{dt} = ky\left(1 - \dfrac{y}{L}\right)$.

Solution

Begin by separating variables.

$$\frac{dy}{dt} = ky\left(1 - \frac{y}{L}\right) \qquad \text{Write differential equation.}$$

$$\frac{1}{y(1 - y/L)}\,dy = k\,dt \qquad \text{Separate variables.}$$

$$\int \frac{1}{y(1 - y/L)}\,dy = \int k\,dt \qquad \text{Integrate each side.}$$

$$\int \left(\frac{1}{y} + \frac{1}{L - y}\right) dy = \int k\,dt \qquad \text{Rewrite left side using partial fractions.}$$

$$\ln|y| - \ln|L - y| = kt + C \qquad \text{Find antiderivative of each side.}$$

$$\ln\left|\frac{L - y}{y}\right| = -kt - C \qquad \text{Multiply each side by } -1 \text{ and simplify.}$$

$$\left|\frac{L - y}{y}\right| = e^{-kt - C} \qquad \text{Exponentiate each side.}$$

$$\left|\frac{L - y}{y}\right| = e^{-C}e^{-kt} \qquad \text{Property of exponents}$$

$$\frac{L - y}{y} = be^{-kt} \qquad \text{Let } \pm e^{-C} = b.$$

> **Remark**
>
> A review of the method of partial fractions is given in Section 7.5.

Solving this equation for y produces the general solution $y = \dfrac{L}{1 + be^{-kt}}$. ■

From Example 1, you can conclude that all solutions of the logistic differential equation are of the general form

$$y = \frac{L}{1 + be^{-kt}}.$$

The graph of the function y is called the *logistic curve,* as shown in Figure 5.17. In the next example, you will verify a particular solution of a logistic differential equation and find the initial condition.

Exploration

Use a graphing utility to investigate the effects of the values of L, b, and k on the graph of

$$y = \frac{L}{1 + be^{-kt}}.$$

Include some examples to support your results.

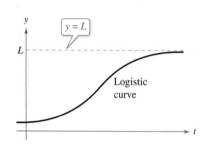

Note that as $t \to \infty$, $y \to L$.

Figure 5.17

EXAMPLE 2 Verifying a Particular Solution

Verify that the equation

$$y = \frac{4}{1 + 2e^{-3t}}$$

satisfies the logistic differential equation, and find the initial condition.

Solution

Comparing the given equation with the general form derived in Example 1, you know that $L = 4$, $b = 2$, and $k = 3$. You can verify that y satisfies the logistic differential equation as follows.

$$y = 4(1 + 2e^{-3t})^{-1} \qquad \text{Rewrite using negative exponent.}$$
$$y' = 4(-1)(1 + 2e^{-3t})^{-2}(-6e^{-3t}) \qquad \text{Apply Power Rule.}$$
$$= 3\left(\frac{4}{1 + 2e^{-3t}}\right)\left(\frac{2e^{-3t}}{1 + 2e^{-3t}}\right) \qquad \text{Rewrite.}$$
$$= 3y\left(\frac{2e^{-3t}}{1 + 2e^{-3t}}\right) \qquad \text{Rewrite using } y = \frac{4}{1 + 2e^{-3t}}.$$
$$= 3y\left(1 - \frac{1}{1 + 2e^{-3t}}\right) \qquad \text{Rewrite fraction using long division.}$$
$$= 3y\left(1 - \frac{4}{4(1 + 2e^{-3t})}\right) \qquad \text{Multiply fraction by } \frac{4}{4}.$$
$$= 3y\left(1 - \frac{y}{4}\right) \qquad \text{Rewrite using } y = \frac{4}{1 + 2e^{-3t}}.$$

So, y satisfies the logistic differential equation

$$y' = 3y\left(1 - \frac{y}{4}\right).$$

The initial condition can be found by letting $t = 0$ in the given equation.

$$y = \frac{4}{1 + 2e^{-3(0)}} = \frac{4}{3}$$

So, the initial condition is $y(0) = \frac{4}{3}$.

EXAMPLE 3   Verifying the Upper Limit

Verify that the upper limit of $y = \dfrac{4}{1 + 2e^{-3t}}$ is 4.

Algebraic Solution

To verify the upper limit, find the limit of y as $t \to \infty$.

$$\lim_{t \to \infty} y = \lim_{t \to \infty} \frac{4}{1 + 2e^{-3t}}$$

$$= \frac{\displaystyle\lim_{t \to \infty} 4}{\displaystyle\lim_{t \to \infty} (1 + 2e^{-3t})}$$

$$= \frac{4}{1 + 0}$$

$$= 4$$

So, the upper limit of y is 4, which is also the carrying capacity $L = 4$.

Numerical Solution

Let $y_1 = \dfrac{4}{1 + 2e^{-3x}}$.

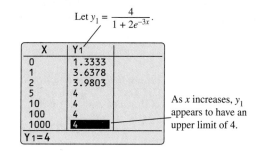

X	Y₁
0	1.3333
1	3.6378
2	3.9803
5	4
10	4
100	4
1000	4

Y1=4

As x increases, y_1 appears to have an upper limit of 4.

So, the upper limit of y appears to be 4, which is also the carrying capacity $L = 4$.

EXAMPLE 4   Determining the Point of Inflection

Sketch a graph of

$$y = \frac{4}{1 + 2^{-3t}}.$$

Calculate y'' in terms of y and y'. Then determine the point of inflection.

Solution

From Example 2, you know that

$$y' = 3y\left(1 - \frac{y}{4}\right).$$

Now calculate y'' in terms of y and y'.

$$y'' = 3y\left(-\frac{y'}{4}\right) + \left(1 - \frac{y}{4}\right)(3y') \qquad \text{Differentiate using Product Rule.}$$

$$y'' = 3y'\left(1 - \frac{y}{2}\right) \qquad \text{Factor and simplify.}$$

When $2 < y < 4$, $y'' < 0$ and the graph of y is concave downward. When $0 < y < 2$, $y'' > 0$ and the graph of y is concave upward. So, a point of inflection must occur at $y = 2$. The corresponding t-value is

$$2 = \frac{4}{1 + 2e^{-3t}}$$

$$1 + 2e^{-3t} = 2$$

$$e^{-3t} = \frac{1}{2}$$

$$t = \frac{1}{3} \ln 2.$$

The point of inflection is $\left(\frac{1}{3} \ln 2, 2\right)$, as shown in Figure 5.18.

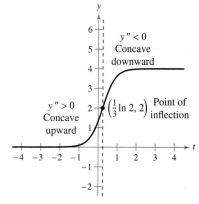

Figure 5.18

In Example 4, the point of inflection occurs at $y = L/2$. This is true for any logistic growth curve for which the solution starts below the carrying capacity L. (See Exercise 28.)

EXAMPLE 5 Graphing a Slope Field and Solution Curves

Graph a slope field for the logistic differential equation

$$y' = 0.05y\left(1 - \frac{y}{800}\right).$$

Then graph solution curves for the initial conditions $y(0) = 200$, $y(0) = 1200$, and $y(0) = 800$.

Solution

The slope field is shown in Figure 5.19. The solution curves for the initial conditions

$$y(0) = 200, \quad y(0) = 1200, \quad \text{and} \quad y(0) = 800$$

are shown in Figures 5.20–5.22.

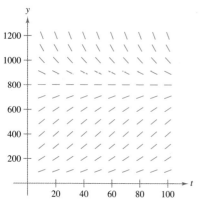

Slope field for

$$y' = 0.05y\left(1 - \frac{y}{800}\right)$$

Figure 5.19

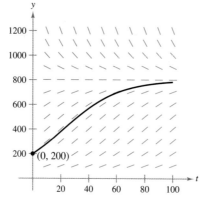

Particular solution for

$$y' = 0.05y\left(1 - \frac{y}{800}\right)$$

and initial condition $y(0) = 200$

Figure 5.20

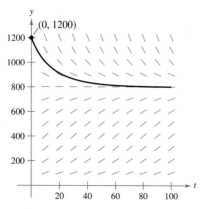

Particular solution for

$$y' = 0.05y\left(1 - \frac{y}{800}\right)$$

and initial condition $y(0) = 1200$

Figure 5.21

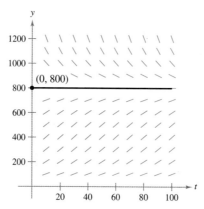

Particular solution for

$$y' = 0.05y\left(1 - \frac{y}{800}\right)$$

and initial condition $y(0) = 800$

Figure 5.22

Note that as t increases without bound, the solution curves in Figures 5.20–5.22 all tend to the same limit, which is the carrying capacity of 800. ■

Application

EXAMPLE 6   Solving a Logistic Differential Equation

A state game commission releases 40 elk into a game refuge. After 5 years, the elk population is 104. The commission believes that the environment can support no more than 4000 elk. The growth rate of the elk population p is

$$\frac{dp}{dt} = kp\left(1 - \frac{p}{4000}\right), \quad 40 \le p \le 4000$$

where t is the number of years.

a. Write a model for the elk population in terms of t.

b. Graph the slope field for the differential equation and the solution that passes through the point $(0, 40)$.

c. Use the model to estimate the elk population after 15 years.

d. Find the limit of the model as $t \to \infty$.

Solution

a. You know that $L = 4000$. So, the solution of the equation is of the form

$$p = \frac{4000}{1 + be^{-kt}}.$$

Because $p(0) = 40$, you can solve for b as follows.

$$40 = \frac{4000}{1 + be^{-k(0)}} \implies 40 = \frac{4000}{1 + b} \implies b = 99$$

Then, because $p = 104$ when $t = 5$, you can solve for k.

$$104 = \frac{4000}{1 + 99e^{-k(5)}} \implies k \approx 0.194$$

So, a model for the elk population is

$$p = \frac{4000}{1 + 99e^{-0.194t}}.$$

b. Using a graphing utility, you can graph the slope field of

$$\frac{dp}{dt} = 0.194p\left(1 - \frac{p}{4000}\right)$$

and the solution that passes through $(0, 40)$, as shown in Figure 5.23.

c. To estimate the elk population after 15 years, substitute 15 for t in the model.

$$p = \frac{4000}{1 + 99e^{-0.194(15)}} \qquad \text{Substitute 15 for } t.$$

$$= \frac{4000}{1 + 99e^{-2.91}} \qquad \text{Simplify.}$$

$$\approx 626 \qquad \text{Simplify.}$$

d. As t increases without bound, the denominator of

$$\frac{4000}{1 + 99e^{-0.194t}}$$

gets closer and closer to 1. So,

$$\lim_{t \to \infty} \frac{4000}{1 + 99e^{-0.194t}} = 4000.$$

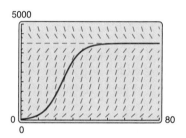

Slope field for

$$\frac{dp}{dt} = 0.194p\left(1 - \frac{p}{4000}\right)$$

and the solution passing through $(0, 40)$

Figure 5.23

5.4 Exercises

Connecting Representations In Exercises 1–4, match the logistic equation with its graph. [The graphs are labeled (a), (b), (c), and (d).]

(a)

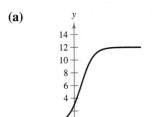

(b)

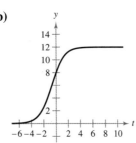

(c)

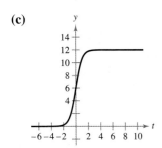

(d)

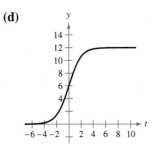

1. $y = \dfrac{12}{1 + e^{-t}}$

2. $y = \dfrac{12}{1 + 3e^{-t}}$

3. $y = \dfrac{12}{1 + \frac{1}{2}e^{-t}}$

4. $y = \dfrac{12}{1 + e^{-2t}}$

 Verifying a Particular Solution In Exercises 5–8, verify that the equation satisfies the logistic differential equation

$$\frac{dy}{dt} = ky\left(1 - \frac{y}{L}\right).$$

Then find the initial condition.

5. $y = \dfrac{8}{1 + e^{-2t}}$

6. $y = \dfrac{10}{1 + 3e^{-4t}}$

7. $y = \dfrac{12}{1 + 6e^{-t}}$

8. $y = \dfrac{14}{1 + 5e^{-3t}}$

 Using a Logistic Equation In Exercises 9–12, the logistic equation models the growth of a population. Use the equation to (a) find the value of k, (b) find the carrying capacity, (c) find the initial population, (d) determine when the population will reach 50% of its carrying capacity, and (e) write a logistic differential equation that has the solution $P(t)$.

9. $P(t) = \dfrac{2100}{1 + 29e^{-0.75t}}$

10. $P(t) = \dfrac{5000}{1 + 39e^{-0.2t}}$

11. $P(t) = \dfrac{6000}{1 + 4999e^{-0.8t}}$

12. $P(t) = \dfrac{1000}{1 + 8e^{-0.2t}}$

 Using a Logistic Differential Equation In Exercises 13–16, the logistic differential equation models the growth rate of a population. Use the equation to (a) find the value of k, (b) find the carrying capacity, (c) use a computer algebra system to graph a slope field, and (d) determine the value of P at which the population growth rate is the greatest.

13. $\dfrac{dP}{dt} = 3P\left(1 - \dfrac{P}{100}\right)$

14. $\dfrac{dP}{dt} = 0.5P\left(1 - \dfrac{P}{250}\right)$

15. $\dfrac{dP}{dt} = 0.1P - 0.0004P^2$

16. $\dfrac{dP}{dt} = 0.4P - 0.00025P^2$

Solving a Logistic Differential Equation In Exercises 17–20, find the logistic equation that satisfies the initial condition. Then use the logistic equation to find y when $t = 5$ and $t = 100$.

Logistic Differential Equation   *Initial Condition*

17. $\dfrac{dy}{dt} = y\left(1 - \dfrac{y}{36}\right)$ $(0, 4)$

18. $\dfrac{dy}{dt} = 2.8y\left(1 - \dfrac{y}{10}\right)$ $(0, 7)$

19. $\dfrac{dy}{dt} = \dfrac{4y}{5} - \dfrac{y^2}{150}$ $(0, 8)$

20. $\dfrac{dy}{dt} = \dfrac{3y}{20} - \dfrac{y^2}{1600}$ $(0, 15)$

EXPLORING CONCEPTS

21. Communication and Notation Describe the values of $y(0)$ for which the logistic differential equation

$$\frac{dy}{dt} = 4y\left(1 - \frac{y}{3000}\right)$$

describes the growth of a population with a carrying capacity of 3000.

22. Communication and Notation Let

$$y = \frac{L}{1 + be^{-kt}}$$

be a solution of the logistic differential equation

$$\frac{dy}{dt} = 0.75y\left(1 - \frac{y}{2500}\right).$$

Is it possible to determine L, k, and b from the information given? If so, find their values. If not, which value(s) cannot be determined and what information do you need to determine the value(s)?

23. Slope Field Describe the slope field for a logistic differential equation. Explain your reasoning.

24. **HOW DO YOU SEE IT?** The growth of a population is modeled by a logistic equation as shown in the graph below. What happens to the rate of growth as the population increases? How and why is the pattern of growth different for this logistic equation than for an exponential growth function?

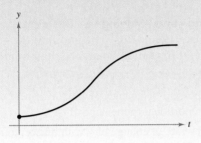

25. Endangered Species A conservation organization releases 25 Florida panthers into a game preserve. After 2 years, there are 39 panthers in the preserve. The Florida preserve has a carrying capacity of 200 panthers.

  (a) Write a logistic equation that models the population of panthers in the preserve.

  (b) Find the population after 5 years.

  (c) When will the population reach 100?

  (d) Write a logistic differential equation that models the growth rate of the panther population. Then repeat part (b) using Euler's Method with a step size of $h = 1$. Compare the approximation with the exact answer.

  (e) When is the panther population growing most rapidly? Explain. What is the maximum rate of growth?

26. Bacteria Growth At time $t = 0$, a bacterial culture weighs 1 gram. Two hours later, the culture weighs 4 grams. The maximum weight of the culture is 20 grams.

  (a) Write a logistic equation that models the weight of the bacterial culture.

  (b) Find the culture's weight after 5 hours.

  (c) When will the culture's weight reach 18 grams?

  (d) Write a logistic differential equation that models the growth rate of the culture's weight. Then repeat part (b) using Euler's Method with a step size of $h = 1$. Compare the approximation with the exact answer.

  (e) When is the culture's weight increasing most rapidly? Explain. What is the maximum rate of increase?

27. Finding a Derivative Show that if

$$y = \frac{1}{1 + be^{-kt}}$$

then $dy/dt = ky(1 - y)$.

28. Justifying For any logistic growth curve, show that the point of inflection occurs at $y = L/2$ when the solution starts below the carrying capacity L.

True or False? In Exercises 29 and 30, determine whether the statement is true or false. If it is false, explain why or give an example that shows it is false.

29. The carrying capacity for R is greater than the carrying capacity for S, where

$$R(t) = \frac{8}{1 + 6e^{-2t}} \quad \text{and} \quad \frac{dS}{dt} = 2S\left(1 - \frac{S}{7}\right).$$

30. For the logistic differential equation

$$\frac{dy}{dt} = ky\left(1 - \frac{y}{L}\right)$$

if $y > L$, then $dy/dt > 0$ and the population increases.

Calculus AP® – Exam Preparation Questions

31. Free Response The model for a population is a function P that satisfies

$$\frac{dP}{dt} = 2P\left(1 - \frac{P}{5}\right).$$

  (a) Suppose $P(0) = 3$. What is $\lim\limits_{t\to\infty} P(t)$?

  (b) Suppose $P(0) = 8$. What is $\lim\limits_{t\to\infty} P(t)$?

  (c) When $P(0) = 3$, for what value of P is the population growing the fastest?

  (d) Find the particular solution satisfying $P(0) = 3$.

32. Free Response Consider the differential equation

$$\frac{dy}{dt} = 0.9y\left(1 - \frac{y}{200}\right).$$

Let $y = f(t)$ be the particular solution of the differential equation with $f(0) = 240$.

  (a) A slope field for this differential equation is given below. Sketch possible solution curves through the points $(0, 240)$ and $(4, 100)$. To print an enlarged copy of the graph, go to *MathGraphs.com*.

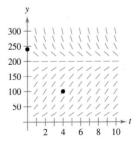

  (b) Use Euler's Method, starting at $t = 0$ with two steps of equal size, to approximate $f(1)$.

  (c) What is the range of f for $t \geq 0$?

5　Review Exercises

1. **Determining a Solution**　Determine whether the function $y = x^3$ is a solution of the differential equation $2xy' + 4y = 10x^3$.

2. **Determining a Solution**　Determine whether the function $y = 2 \sin 2x$ is a solution of the differential equation $y''' - 8y = 0$.

Finding a General Solution　In Exercises 3–8, use integration to find a general solution of the differential equation.

3. $\dfrac{dy}{dx} = 4x^2 + 7$

4. $\dfrac{dy}{dx} = 3x^3 - 8x$

5. $\dfrac{dy}{dx} = \cos 2x$

6. $\dfrac{dy}{dx} = 2 \sec^2 x$

7. $\dfrac{dy}{dx} = e^{2-x}$

8. $\dfrac{dy}{dx} = 2e^{3x}$

Slope Field　In Exercises 9 and 10, a differential equation and its slope field are given. Complete the table by determining the slopes (if possible) in the slope field at the given points.

x	-4	-2	0	2	4	8
y	2	0	4	4	6	8
dy/dx						

9. $\dfrac{dy}{dx} = 2x - y$

10. $\dfrac{dy}{dx} = x \sin \dfrac{\pi y}{4}$

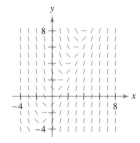
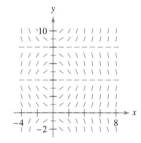

Slope Field　In Exercises 11 and 12, (a) sketch the slope field for the differential equation and (b) use the slope field to sketch the solution that passes through the given point. To print a blank coordinate plane, go to *MathGraphs.com*.

11. $y' = 2x^2y$, $\ (0, 2)$

12. $y' = x^4y^2$, $\ (-1, 1)$

Euler's Method　In Exercises 13 and 14, use Euler's Method to make a table of values for the approximate solution of the differential equation with the specified initial value. Use n steps of size h.

13. $y' = x - y$, $\ y(0) = 4$, $\ n = 10$, $\ h = 0.05$

14. $y' = 5x - 2y$, $\ y(0) = 2$, $\ n = 10$, $\ h = 0.1$

Solving a Differential Equation　In Exercises 15–18, find the general solution of the differential equation.

15. $dy/dx = (3 + y)^2$

16. $dy/dx = 10\sqrt{y}$

17. $(2 + x)y' - xy = 0$

18. $xy' - (x + 1)y = 0$

Writing and Solving a Differential Equation　In Exercises 19 and 20, write and find the general solution of the differential equation that models the verbal statement.

19. The rate of change of y with respect to t is inversely proportional to the cube of t.

20. The rate of change of y with respect to t is proportional to $50 - t$.

Finding an Exponential Function　In Exercises 21–24, find the exponential function $y = Ce^{kt}$ that passes through the given points.

21.
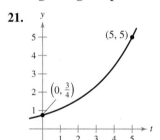

22.
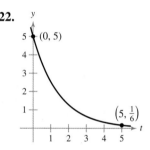

23.
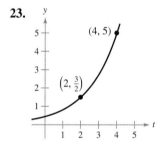

24.
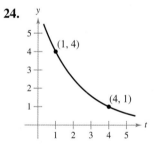

25. **Radioactive Decay**　Radioactive radon has a half-life of approximately 3.82 days. The initial quantity is 15 grams. How much remains after 7 days?

26. **Population Growth**　A population grows continuously at a rate of 1.85%. Use the exponential growth model, where k is the expected annual growth rate, to determine how long will it take the population to double.

27. **Sales**　The sales S (in thousands of units) of a new product after it has been on the market for t years is given by $S = Ce^{k/t}$.

(a) Find S as a function of t when 5000 units have been sold after 1 year and the saturation point for the market is 30,000 units (that is, $\lim\limits_{t \to \infty} S = 30$).

(b) How many units will have been sold after 5 years?

28. Sales The sales S (in thousands of units) of a new product after it has been on the market for t years is given by

$$S = 25(1 - e^{kt}).$$

(a) Find S as a function of t when 4000 units have been sold after 1 year.

(b) After how many years will 18,805 units be sold?

Finding a General Solution Using Separation of Variables In Exercises 29–32, find the general solution of the differential equation.

29. $\dfrac{dy}{dx} = \dfrac{5x}{y}$ **30.** $\dfrac{dy}{dx} = \dfrac{x^3}{2y^2}$

31. $y' - 16xy = 0$ **32.** $y' - e^y \sin x = 0$

Finding a Particular Solution Using Separation of Variables In Exercises 33–36, find the particular solution that satisfies the initial condition.

Differential Equation	Initial Condition
33. $y^3 y' - 3x = 0$	$y(2) = 2$
34. $yy' - 5e^{2x} = 0$	$y(0) = -3$
35. $y^3(x^4 + 1)y' - x^3(y^4 + 1) = 0$	$y(0) = 1$
36. $yy' - x \cos x^2 = 0$	$y(0) = -2$

Slope Field In Exercises 37 and 38, sketch a few solutions of the differential equation on the slope field and then find the general solution analytically. To print an enlarged copy of the graph, go to *MathGraphs.com*.

37. $\dfrac{dy}{dx} = -\dfrac{4x}{y}$ **38.** $\dfrac{dy}{dx} = 3 - 2y$

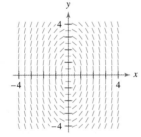 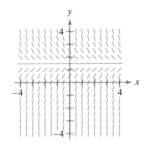

39. Chemical Reaction In a chemical reaction, a certain substance is converted into another substance at a rate proportional to the square of the unchanged amount. There is 65 grams of the original substance initially and 15 grams after 1 hour. How much of the original substance is present after 6 hours?

40. Biology A population of 10 foxes has been introduced into a new region. It is estimated that the maximum population the region can sustain is 100 foxes. After 5 years, the population is 37 foxes. According to a Gompertz growth model, how many foxes will be present after 15 years?

Using a Logistic Equation In Exercises 41 and 42, the logistic equation models the growth of a population. Use the equation to (a) find the value of k, (b) find the carrying capacity, (c) find the initial population, (d) determine when the population will reach 50% of its carrying capacity, and (e) write a logistic differential equation that has the solution $P(t)$.

41. $P(t) = \dfrac{5250}{1 + 34e^{-0.55t}}$ **42.** $P(t) = \dfrac{4800}{1 + 14e^{-0.15t}}$

Solving a Logistic Differential Equation In Exercises 43 and 44, find the logistic equation that passes through the given point.

43. $\dfrac{dy}{dt} = 4.2y\left(1 - \dfrac{y}{21}\right),$

$(0, 9)$

44. $\dfrac{dy}{dt} = 2.3y\left(1 - \dfrac{y}{12}\right),$

$(0, 2)$

45. Environment A conservation department releases 1200 brook trout into a lake. The estimated carrying capacity of the lake for the species is 20,400. After the first year, there are 2000 brook trout in the lake.

(a) Write a logistic equation that models the number of brook trout in the lake. When will the number of brook trout reach 10,000?

(b) Find the number of brook trout in the lake after 8 years.

46. Environment Write a logistic differential equation that models the growth rate of the brook trout population in Exercise 45. Then repeat part (b) using Euler's Method with a step size of $h = 0.5$. Compare the approximation with the exact answer.

47. Sales Growth The rate of change in sales S (in thousands of units) of a new product is proportional to $L - S$ at any time t (in years), where L is the estimated maximum level of sales (in thousands of units). When $t = 0$, $s = 0$. Write and solve the differential equation for this sales model.

48. Sales Growth Use the result of Exercise 47 to write S as a function of t for (a) $L = 100$ and $S = 25$ when $t = 2$, and (b) $L = 500$ and $S = 50$ when $t = 1$.

Learning Theory In Exercises 49 and 50, assume that the rate of change in the proportion P of correct responses after n trials is proportional to the product of P and $L - P$, where L is the limiting proportion of correct responses.

49. Write and find the general solution of the differential equation for this learning theory model.

50. Use the solution of Exercise 49 to write P as a function of n, and then use a graphing utility to graph the solution.

(a) $L = 1.00$

$P = 0.50$ when $n = 0$

$P = 0.85$ when $n = 4$

(b) $L = 0.80$

$P = 0.25$ when $n = 0$

$P = 0.60$ when $n = 10$

What You Need to Know

- You may have to sketch a slope field for a given differential equation at a specified number of points.
- Given a slope field, you may be asked to sketch a solution curve through a point. When sketching the curve, make sure that it follows the slope field appropriately and passes through the indicated point.
- Be prepared to solve differential equations completely using separation of variables with a given initial condition. The final answer should be of the form $y = f(x)$.
- On the AP® Calculus BC Exam, be prepared to do at least two iterations of Euler's Method, showing all of your work without using a calculator.

Practice Questions

Section 1, Part A, Multiple Choice, No Technology

1. Which figure is a slope field for $\dfrac{dy}{dx} = y - \dfrac{x}{5}$?

(A)

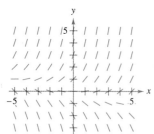

(B)

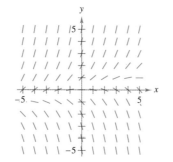

(C)

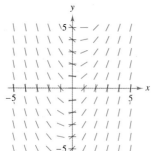

(D)

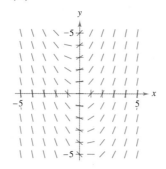

2. A population P grows according to the equation $dP/dt = kP$, where k is a constant and t is measured in years. If the population triples every 15 years, what is the value of k?

(A) $\ln \frac{1}{5}$ (B) $\frac{1}{15} \ln 3$

(C) $\ln 3$ (D) 5

3. Let $y = f(x)$ be a solution of the differential equation $y' = ky$, where k is a constant. If $f(0) = 8$ and $f(6) = 2$, which of the following is an expression for $f(x)$?

(A) $8e^{(x/6)\ln(1/4)}$ (B) $-e^{(x/6)\ln 7} + 9$

(C) $-x + 8$ (D) $x^2 + 8$

4. For $dy/dx = 2xy^2$ and $y(-1) = 2$, find $y(2)$.

(A) $-4e^3$ (B) $-\dfrac{3}{2}$

(C) $-\dfrac{2}{5}$ (D) $-\dfrac{1}{4}$

5. Which of the following is the solution of the differential equation

$$\frac{dy}{dx} = \frac{3y}{x}$$

with the initial condition $y(1) = -1$?

(A) $y = x^3$ (B) $y - -x^3$

(C) $y = x^3 - 2$ (D) $y = -x^3 - 2$

6. Which of the following differential equations produces the slope field shown below?

(A) $\dfrac{dy}{dx} = 10y\left(1 - \dfrac{y}{3}\right)$

(B) $\dfrac{dy}{dx} = \dfrac{y}{2}\left(1 - \dfrac{y}{3}\right)$

(C) $\dfrac{dy}{dx} = y\left(1 - \dfrac{y}{3}\right)$

(D) $\dfrac{dy}{dx} = 5y\left(1 - \dfrac{y}{6}\right)$

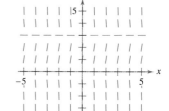

Section 1, Part B, Multiple Choice, Technology Permitted

7. Consider the differential equation

$$y' = 0.5(y - 1)(t + 1)$$

with an initial value of $y(0) = -3$. Using Euler's Method with a step of $h = \frac{1}{3}$, what is the approximate value of $y(1)$?

(A) -6.288 (B) -6.125

(C) -4.753 (D) -4.703

8. The rate of growth of the number of bacteria y is given by $dy/dt = 0.5y$, where t is the time in hours and $t \geq 0$. Initially, there are 200 bacteria.

    (a) Solve for y, the number of bacteria present, at any time $t \geq 0$.

    (b) Write and evaluate an expression to find the average number of bacteria in the population for $0 \leq t \leq 10$.

Section 2, Part B, Free Response, No Technology

9. Let $y = f(x)$ be a particular solution of the differential equation

$$\frac{dy}{dx} = \frac{1}{xy}$$

with $f(1) = 2$.

    (a) Find d^2y/dx^2 at the point $(1, 2)$.

    (b) Write an equation for the line tangent to the graph of f at $(1, 2)$ and use it to approximate $f(1.1)$. Is the approximation for $f(1.1)$ greater than or less than $f(1.1)$? Explain your reasoning.

    (c) Find the solution of the given differential equation that satisfies the initial condition $f(1) = 2$.

10. Consider the differential equation $dy/dx = x^2(1 - y)$.

    (a) On the axes provided, sketch a slope field for the given differential equation at the nine points indicated.

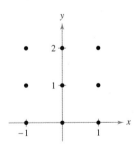

    (b) While the slope field in part (a) is drawn only at nine points, it is defined at every point in the xy-plane. Describe all points in the xy-plane for which the slopes are positive.

    (c) Find the particular solution in the form of $y = f(x)$ to the given differential equation with the initial condition $f(0) = 2$.

    (d) Find d^2y/dx^2 in terms of x and y. Then determine if the particular solution from part (c) has a relative minimum, a relative maximum, or neither at $x = 0$.

11. Consider the differential equation $y' = (2x)/y$ with a particular solution in the form of $y = f(x)$ that satisfies the initial condition $f(1) = 2$.

    (a) Use Euler's Method, starting at $x = 1$ with two steps of equal size, to approximate $f(1.4)$. Show the work that leads to your answer.

    (b) Find the particular solution of the given differential equation that passes through $(1, 2)$ and state its domain.

12. Consider the differential equation $dy/dx = xy$.

    (a) Let $y = f(x)$ be the function that satisfies the differential equation with initial condition $f(1) = 1$. Use Euler's Method, starting at $x = 1$ with a step size of 0.1, to approximate $f(1.2)$. Show the work that leads to your answer.

    (b) Find d^2y/dx^2. Determine whether the approximation found in part (a) is less than or greater than $f(1.2)$. Justify your answer.

    (c) Find the particular solution of the given differential equation that passes through $(1, 1)$.

13. At any time $t \geq 0$, the rate of the spread of a disease is modeled by the differential equation

$$\frac{dy}{dt} = \frac{1}{10}y\left(1 - \frac{y}{1000}\right)$$

where y is the number of people who have the disease. In an isolated town of 1000 inhabitants, 100 people have the disease at the beginning of the week.

    (a) Is the disease spreading faster when 100 people have the disease or when 200 people have the disease? Explain your reasoning.

    (b) Write a model of the form $y = L/(1 + Ce^{-kt})$ for the population $y = f(t)$ at any time $t \geq 0$.

    (c) What is $\lim\limits_{t \to \infty} y(t)$?

14. Consider the differential equation $dy/dx = x/y^2$, where $y \neq 0$.

    (a) On the axes provided, sketch a slope field for the given differential equation at the indicated points.

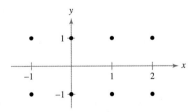

    (b) Find d^2y/dx^2 in terms of x and y.

    (c) Find the particular solution of the given differential equation that satisfies the initial condition $y(0) = 2$.

5　Performance Task

Spread of an Influenza Virus

Throughout history, influenza viruses have caused pandemics or global epidemics. The influenza pandemic of 1918–1919 occurred in three waves. The first wave occurred in the late spring and summer of 1918, the second wave occurred in the fall of 1918, and the final wave occurred in the spring of 1919. By the time it ended, approximately 21.5 million people across the world had died as a result of the pandemic, with an estimated 675,000 deaths in the United States alone.

Exercises

In Exercises 1–3, use the following information. On a small college campus with 800 students, ten students return from spring break with a contagious flu virus. The rate at which the virus spreads through the campus is given by the differential equation

$$\frac{dS}{dt} = 0.434S\left(1 - \frac{S}{800}\right)$$

where S is the number of infected students and t is the number of days.

1. **Writing a Logistic Equation**　Write a logistic equation that models the number of students infected with the virus after t days.

2. **Using a Logistic Equation**　Use the equation you wrote in Exercise 1.

    (a) What is $\lim\limits_{t \to \infty} S(t)$? What does this value represent?

    (b) How many students are infected with the virus on Day 3?

3. **Using a Logistic Differential Equation**　The slope field for the given differential equation is shown. To print an enlarged copy of the graph, go to *MathGraphs.com*.

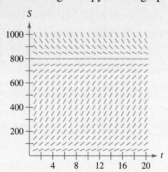

    (a) Sketch the solution that satisfies the initial condition.

    (b) On what day is the virus spreading most rapidly? How many students are infected with the virus at this point? Justify your answer.

    (c) What is the rate of change of the number of students infected with the virus when the virus is spreading most rapidly? Interpret your answer.

    (d) What are all values of S for which the rate of change of the number of people infected is decreasing? Justify your answer.

    (e) Repeat Exercise 2(b) using Euler's Method with a step size of $h = 1$. Compare your results.

6 Applications of Integration

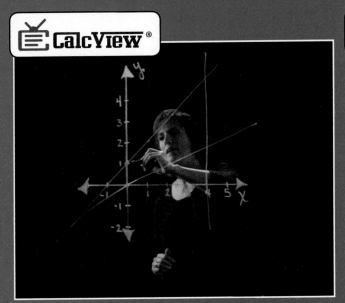

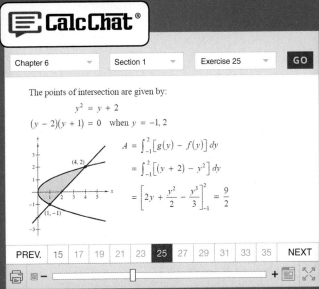

CalcChat®

Chapter 6 ▾   Section 1 ▾   Exercise 25 ▾   GO

The points of intersection are given by:

$$y^2 = y + 2$$

$$(y - 2)(y + 1) = 0 \quad \text{when } y = -1, 2$$

$$A = \int_{-1}^{2} \left[g(y) - f(y) \right] dy$$

$$= \int_{-1}^{2} \left[(y + 2) - y^2 \right] dy$$

$$= \left[2y + \frac{y^2}{2} - \frac{y^3}{3} \right]_{-1}^{2} = \frac{9}{2}$$

PREV.   15   17   19   21   23   **25**   27   29   31   33   35   NEXT

6.1 Building Design *(Exercise 73, p. 418)*

6.3 Saturn *(Section Project, p. 439)*

6.1   Area of a Region Between Two Curves

▶ Find the area of a region between two curves using integration.
▶ Find the area of a region between intersecting curves using integration.
▶ Describe integration as an accumulation process.

Area of a Region Between Two Curves

With a few modifications, you can extend the application of definite integrals from the area of a region *under* a curve to the area of a region *between* two curves. Consider two functions f and g that are continuous on the interval $[a, b]$. Also, the graphs of both f and g lie above the x-axis, and the graph of g lies below the graph of f, as shown in Figure 6.1. You can geometrically interpret the area of the region between the graphs as the area of the region under the graph of g subtracted from the area of the region under the graph of f, as shown in Figure 6.2.

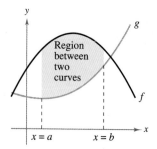

Figure 6.1

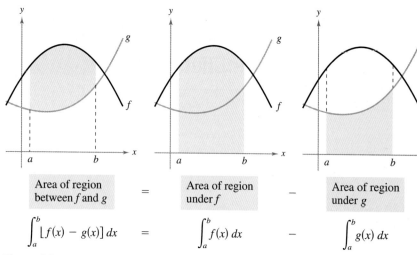

Area of region between f and g	$=$	Area of region under f	$-$	Area of region under g
$\displaystyle\int_a^b [f(x) - g(x)]\, dx$	$=$	$\displaystyle\int_a^b f(x)\, dx$	$-$	$\displaystyle\int_a^b g(x)\, dx$

Figure 6.2

To verify the reasonableness of the result shown in Figure 6.2, you can partition the interval $[a, b]$ into n subintervals, each of width Δx. Then, as shown in Figure 6.3, sketch a **representative rectangle** of width Δx and height $f(x_i) - g(x_i)$, where x_i is in the ith subinterval. The area of this representative rectangle is

$$\Delta A_i = (\text{height})(\text{width}) = [f(x_i) - g(x_i)]\, \Delta x.$$

By adding the areas of the n rectangles and taking the limit as $\|\Delta\| \to 0$ $(n \to \infty)$, you obtain

$$\lim_{n \to \infty} \sum_{i=1}^{n} [f(x_i) - g(x_i)]\, \Delta x.$$

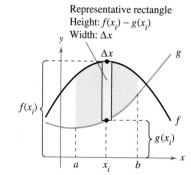

Representative rectangle
Height: $f(x_i) - g(x_i)$
Width: Δx

Figure 6.3

Because f and g are continuous on $[a, b]$, $f - g$ is also continuous on $[a, b]$ and the limit exists. So, the area of the region is

$$\text{Area} = \lim_{n \to \infty} \sum_{i=1}^{n} [f(x_i) - g(x_i)]\, \Delta x$$

$$= \int_a^b [f(x) - g(x)]\, dx.$$

Communication and Notation

Recall from Section 4.3 that $\|\Delta\|$ is the norm of the partition. In a regular partition, the statements $\|\Delta\| \to 0$ and $n \to \infty$ are equivalent.

Area of a Region Between Two Curves

If f and g are continuous on $[a, b]$ and $g(x) \leq f(x)$ for all x in $[a, b]$, then the area of the region bounded by the graphs of f and g and the vertical lines $x = a$ and $x = b$ is

$$A = \int_a^b [f(x) - g(x)]\, dx.$$

Insight

Finding the area of a region between two curves is tested on both the AP® Calculus AB and BC Exams.

In Figure 6.1, the graphs of f and g are shown above the x-axis. This, however, is not necessary. The same integrand $[f(x) - g(x)]$ can be used as long as f and g are continuous and $g(x) \leq f(x)$ for all x in the interval $[a, b]$. This is summarized graphically in Figure 6.4. Notice in Figure 6.4 that the height of a representative rectangle is $f(x) - g(x)$ regardless of the relative position of the x-axis.

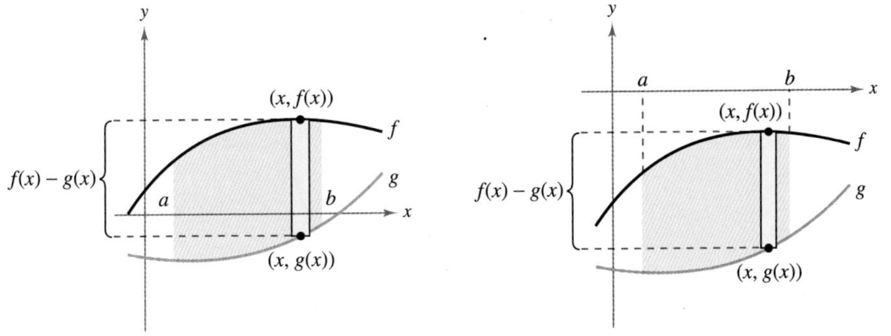

Figure 6.4

Representative rectangles are used throughout this chapter in various applications of integration. A vertical rectangle (of width Δx) implies integration with respect to x, whereas a horizontal rectangle (of width Δy) implies integration with respect to y.

EXAMPLE 1 Finding the Area of a Region Between Two Curves

Find the area of the region bounded by the graphs of $y = x^2 + 2$, $y = -x$, $x = 0$, and $x = 1$.

Solution

Let $g(x) = -x$ and $f(x) = x^2 + 2$. Then $g(x) \leq f(x)$ for all x in $[0, 1]$, as shown in Figure 6.5. So, the area of the representative rectangle is

$$\begin{aligned}\Delta A &= [f(x) - g(x)]\,\Delta x \\ &= [(x^2 + 2) - (-x)]\,\Delta x\end{aligned}$$

and the area of the region is

$$\begin{aligned}A &= \int_a^b [f(x) - g(x)]\, dx \\ &= \int_0^1 [(x^2 + 2) - (-x)]\, dx \\ &= \left[\frac{x^3}{3} + \frac{x^2}{2} + 2x\right]_0^1 \\ &= \frac{1}{3} + \frac{1}{2} + 2 \\ &= \frac{17}{6}.\end{aligned}$$

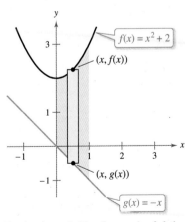

Region bounded by the graph of f, the graph of g, $x = 0$, and $x = 1$

Figure 6.5

Area of a Region Between Intersecting Curves

In Example 1, the graphs of $f(x) = x^2 + 2$ and $g(x) = -x$ do not intersect, and the values of a and b are given explicitly. A more common problem involves the area of a region bounded by two *intersecting* graphs, where the values of a and b must be calculated.

EXAMPLE 2   A Region Lying Between Two Intersecting Graphs

Find the area of the region bounded by the graphs of $f(x) = 2 - x^2$ and $g(x) = x$.

Solution

In Figure 6.6, notice that the graphs of f and g have two points of intersection. To find the x-coordinates of these points, set $f(x)$ and $g(x)$ equal to each other and solve for x.

$$2 - x^2 = x \qquad \text{Set } f(x) \text{ equal to } g(x).$$
$$-x^2 - x + 2 = 0 \qquad \text{Write in general form.}$$
$$-(x + 2)(x - 1) = 0 \qquad \text{Factor.}$$
$$x = -2 \text{ or } 1 \qquad \text{Solve for } x.$$

So, $a = -2$ and $b = 1$. Because $g(x) \leq f(x)$ for all x in the interval $[-2, 1]$, the representative rectangle has an area of

$$\Delta A = [f(x) - g(x)] \, \Delta x = [(2 - x^2) - x] \, \Delta x$$

and the area of the region is

$$A = \int_{-2}^{1} [(2 - x^2) - x] \, dx$$
$$= \left[-\frac{x^3}{3} - \frac{x^2}{2} + 2x \right]_{-2}^{1}$$
$$= \frac{9}{2}.$$

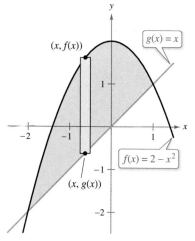

Region bounded by the graph of f and the graph of g

Figure 6.6

EXAMPLE 3   A Region Lying Between Two Intersecting Graphs

The sine and cosine curves intersect infinitely many times, bounding regions of equal areas, as shown in Figure 6.7. Find the area of one of these regions.

Solution

Let $g(x) = \cos x$ and $f(x) = \sin x$. Then $g(x) \leq f(x)$ for all x in the interval corresponding to the shaded region in Figure 6.7. To find the two points of intersection on this interval, set $f(x)$ and $g(x)$ equal to each other and solve for x.

$$\sin x = \cos x \qquad \text{Set } f(x) \text{ equal to } g(x).$$
$$\frac{\sin x}{\cos x} = 1 \qquad \text{Divide each side by } \cos x.$$
$$\tan x = 1 \qquad \text{Trigonometric identity}$$
$$x = \frac{\pi}{4} \text{ or } \frac{5\pi}{4}, \quad 0 \leq x \leq 2\pi \qquad \text{Solve for } x.$$

So, $a = \pi/4$ and $b = 5\pi/4$. Because $\sin x \geq \cos x$ for all x in the interval $[\pi/4, 5\pi/4]$, the area of the region is

$$A = \int_{\pi/4}^{5\pi/4} [\sin x - \cos x] \, dx$$
$$= \Big[-\cos x - \sin x \Big]_{\pi/4}^{5\pi/4}$$
$$= 2\sqrt{2}.$$

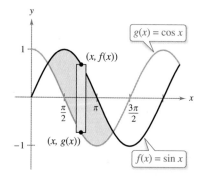

One of the regions bounded by the graphs of the sine and cosine functions

Figure 6.7

To find the area of the region between two curves that intersect at *more* than two points, first determine all points of intersection. Then check to see which curve is above the other in each interval determined by these points, as shown in Example 4.

EXAMPLE 4   Curves That Intersect at More than Two Points

See LarsonCalculusforAP.com for an interactive version of this type of example.

Find the area of the region between the graphs of

$$f(x) = 3x^3 - x^2 - 10x \quad \text{and} \quad g(x) = -x^2 + 2x.$$

Solution

Begin by setting $f(x)$ and $g(x)$ equal to each other and solving for x. This yields the x-values at all points of intersection of the two graphs.

$3x^3 - x^2 - 10x = -x^2 + 2x$	Set $f(x)$ equal to $g(x)$.
$3x^3 - 12x = 0$	Write in general form.
$3x(x - 2)(x + 2) = 0$	Factor.
$x = -2, 0, 2$	Solve for x.

So, the two graphs intersect when $x = -2, 0$, and 2. In Figure 6.8, notice that $g(x) \le f(x)$ on the interval $[-2, 0]$. The two graphs switch at the origin, however, and $f(x) \le g(x)$ on the interval $[0, 2]$. So, you need two integrals—one for the interval $[-2, 0]$ and one for the interval $[0, 2]$.

$$A = \int_{-2}^{0} [f(x) - g(x)]\, dx + \int_{0}^{2} [g(x) - f(x)]\, dx$$

$$= \int_{-2}^{0} (3x^3 - 12x)\, dx + \int_{0}^{2} (-3x^3 + 12x)\, dx$$

$$= \left[\frac{3x^4}{4} - 6x^2\right]_{-2}^{0} + \left[\frac{-3x^4}{4} + 6x^2\right]_{0}^{2}$$

$$= -(12 - 24) + (-12 + 24)$$

$$= 24$$

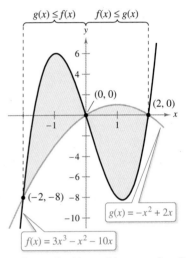

Algebra Review

For help on the algebra in Example 4, see Example 1 in the *Chapter 6 Algebra Review* on page A46.

On $[-2, 0]$, $g(x) \le f(x)$, and on $[0, 2]$, $f(x) \le g(x)$.

Figure 6.8

> **Justification**   In Example 4, notice that you obtain an incorrect result when you integrate from -2 to 2. Such integration produces
>
> $$\int_{-2}^{2} [f(x) - g(x)]\, dx = \int_{-2}^{2} (3x^3 - 12x)\, dx = 0.$$

When the graph of a function of y is a boundary of a region, it is often convenient to use representative rectangles that are *horizontal* and find the area by integrating with respect to y. In general, to determine the area between two curves, you can use

$$A = \underbrace{\int_{x_1}^{x_2} [(\text{top curve}) - (\text{bottom curve})]}_{\text{in variable } x}\, dx \qquad \text{Vertical rectangles}$$

or

$$A = \underbrace{\int_{y_1}^{y_2} [(\text{right curve}) - (\text{left curve})]}_{\text{in variable } y}\, dy \qquad \text{Horizontal rectangles}$$

where (x_1, y_1) and (x_2, y_2) are either adjacent points of intersection of the two curves involved or points on the specified boundary lines.

EXAMPLE 5   Horizontal Representative Rectangles

Find the area of the region bounded by the graphs of $x = 3 - y^2$ and $x = y + 1$.

Solution

Consider

$$g(y) = 3 - y^2 \quad \text{and} \quad f(y) = y + 1.$$

These two curves intersect when $y = -2$ and $y = 1$, as shown in Figure 6.9. Because $f(y) \le g(y)$ on this interval, you have

$$\Delta A = [g(y) - f(y)]\,\Delta y = [(3 - y^2) - (y + 1)]\,\Delta y.$$

So, the area is

$$
\begin{aligned}
A &= \int_{-2}^{1} [(3 - y^2) - (y + 1)]\,dy \\
&= \int_{-2}^{1} (-y^2 - y + 2)\,dy \\
&= \left[\frac{-y^3}{3} - \frac{y^2}{2} + 2y \right]_{-2}^{1} \\
&= \left(-\frac{1}{3} - \frac{1}{2} + 2 \right) - \left(\frac{8}{3} - 2 - 4 \right) \\
&= \frac{9}{2}.
\end{aligned}
$$

> **Algebra Review**
>
> For help on the algebra in Example 5, see Example 2 in the *Chapter 6 Algebra Review* on page A46.

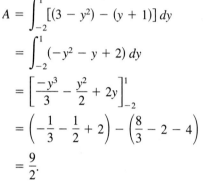

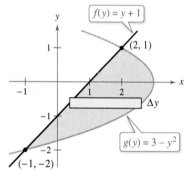

Horizontal rectangles (integration with respect to y)
Figure 6.9

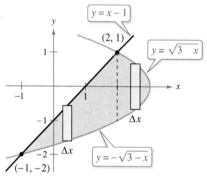

Vertical rectangles (integration with respect to x)
Figure 6.10

In Example 5, notice that by integrating with respect to y, you need only one integral. To integrate with respect to x, you would need two integrals because the upper boundary changes at $x = 2$, as shown in Figure 6.10.

$$
\begin{aligned}
A &= \int_{-1}^{2} \left[(x - 1) + \sqrt{3 - x} \right] dx + \int_{2}^{3} \left(\sqrt{3 - x} + \sqrt{3 - x} \right) dx \\
&= \int_{-1}^{2} \left[x - 1 + (3 - x)^{1/2} \right] dx + 2 \int_{2}^{3} (3 - x)^{1/2}\,dx \\
&= \left[\frac{x^2}{2} - x - \frac{(3 - x)^{3/2}}{3/2} \right]_{-1}^{2} - 2 \left[\frac{(3 - x)^{3/2}}{3/2} \right]_{2}^{3} \\
&= \left(2 - 2 - \frac{2}{3} \right) - \left(\frac{1}{2} + 1 - \frac{16}{3} \right) - 2(0) + 2\left(\frac{2}{3} \right) \\
&= \frac{9}{2}
\end{aligned}
$$

Integration as an Accumulation Process

In this section, the integration formula for the area between two curves was developed by using a rectangle as the *representative element*. For each new application in the remaining sections of this chapter, an appropriate representative element will be constructed using precalculus formulas you already know. Each integration formula will then be obtained by summing or accumulating these representative elements.

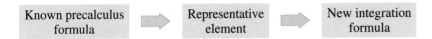

For example, the area formula in this section was developed as follows.

$$A = (\text{height})(\text{width}) \quad \Longrightarrow \quad \Delta A = [f(x) - g(x)]\,\Delta x \quad \Longrightarrow \quad A = \int_a^b [f(x) - g(x)]\,dx$$

EXAMPLE 6   Integration as an Accumulation Process

Find the area of the region bounded by the graph of $y = 4 - x^2$ and the x-axis. Describe the integration as an accumulation process.

Solution

The area of the region is

$$A = \int_{-2}^{2} (4 - x^2)\,dx.$$

You can think of the integration as an accumulation of the areas of the rectangles formed as the representative rectangle slides from $x = -2$ to $x = 2$, as shown in Figure 6.11.

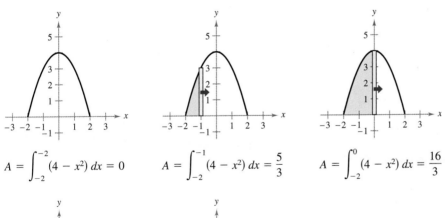

$$A = \int_{-2}^{-2} (4 - x^2)\,dx = 0 \qquad A = \int_{-2}^{-1} (4 - x^2)\,dx = \frac{5}{3} \qquad A = \int_{-2}^{0} (4 - x^2)\,dx = \frac{16}{3}$$

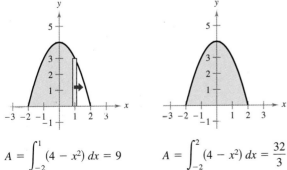

$$A = \int_{-2}^{1} (4 - x^2)\,dx = 9 \qquad A = \int_{-2}^{2} (4 - x^2)\,dx = \frac{32}{3}$$

Figure 6.11

Writing a Definite Integral In Exercises 1–6, write the definite integral that gives the area of the region.

1. $y_1 = x^2 - 6x$
$y_2 = 0$

2. $y_1 = x^2 + 2x + 1$
$y_2 = 2x + 5$

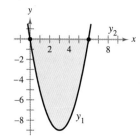
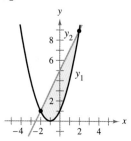

3. $y_1 = x^2 - 4x + 3$
$y_2 = -x^2 + 2x + 3$

4. $y_1 = x^2$
$y_2 = x^3$

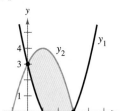
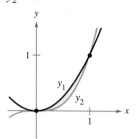

5. $y_1 = 3(x^3 - x)$
$y_2 = 0$

6. $y_1 = (x - 1)^3$
$y_2 = x - 1$

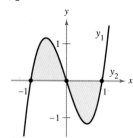
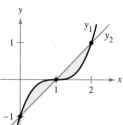

Finding a Region In Exercises 7–12, the integrand of the definite integral is a difference of two functions. Sketch the graph of each function and shade the region whose area is represented by the integral.

7. $\int_0^4 \left[(x + 1) - \dfrac{x}{2} \right] dx$

8. $\int_{-1}^1 [(2 - x^2) - x^2] \, dx$

9. $\int_2^3 \left[\left(\dfrac{x^3}{3} - x \right) - \dfrac{x}{3} \right] dx$

10. $\int_{-\pi/4}^{\pi/4} (\sec^2 x - \cos x) \, dx$

11. $\int_{-2}^1 [(2 - y) - y^2] \, dy$

12. $\int_0^4 (2\sqrt{y} - y) \, dy$

Error Analysis In Exercises 13 and 14, let R and S be the two regions enclosed by the graphs of $f(x) = 2x^3 + x^2 + 2$ and $g(x) = -x^2 + 4x + 2$, as shown. Describe and correct the error in the statement.

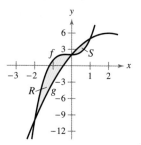

13. The area of R is given by

$$\int_{-2}^0 [g(x) - f(x)] \, dx = \int_{-2}^0 (-2x^3 - 2x^2 + 4x) \, dx. \ ✗$$

14. The sum of the areas of regions R and S is given by

$$\int_{-2}^1 [f(x) - g(x)] \, dx = \int_{-2}^1 (2x^3 + 2x^2 - 4x) \, dx. \ ✗$$

Finding the Area of a Region In Exercises 15–30, sketch the region bounded by the graphs of the equations and find the area of the region.

15. $y = x^2 - 1$, $y = -x + 2$, $x = 0$, $x = 1$

16. $y = -x^3 + 2$, $y = x - 3$, $x = -1$, $x = 1$

17. $f(x) = \dfrac{1}{9x^2}$, $y = 1$, $x = 1$, $x = 2$

18. $f(x) = -\dfrac{4}{x^3}$, $y = 0$, $x = -3$ $x = -1$

19. $y = -x^3 + 3$, $y = x$, $x = -1$, $x = 1$

20. $y = -\dfrac{3}{8}x(x - 8)$, $y = 10 - \dfrac{1}{2}x$, $x = 2$, $x = 8$

21. $f(x) = x^2 + 2x$, $g(x) = x + 2$

22. $f(x) = -x^2 + 3x + 1$, $g(x) = -x + 1$

23. $f(x) = x^5 + 2$, $g(x) = x + 2$

24. $f(x) = \sqrt[3]{x - 1}$, $g(x) = x - 1$

25. $f(y) = y^2$, $g(y) = y + 2$

26. $f(y) = y(2 - y)$, $g(y) = -y$

27. $f(y) = y^2 + 1$, $g(y) = 0$, $y = -1$, $y = 2$

28. $f(y) = \dfrac{y}{\sqrt{16 - y^2}}$, $g(y) = 0$, $y = 3$

29. $f(x) = \dfrac{10}{x}$, $x = 0$, $y = 2$, $y = 10$

30. $f(x) = x$, $g(x) = 4 - x$, $y = 0$

Connecting Representations In Exercises 31 and 32, find the area of the region by integrating (a) with respect to x and (b) with respect to y. (c) Compare your results. Which method is simpler? Explain why you found this method simpler to use.

31. $x = 4 - y^2$
    $x = y - 2$

32. $y = x^2$
    $y = 6 - x$

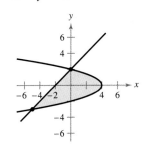 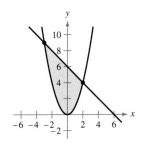

 Finding the Area of a Region In Exercises 33–42, (a) use a graphing utility to graph the region bounded by the graphs of the equations, (b) find the area of the region analytically, and (c) use the integration capabilities of the graphing utility to verify your results.

33. $f(x) = x(x^2 - 3x + 3), \quad g(x) = x^2$

34. $y = x^4 - 2x^2, \quad y = 2x^2$

35. $f(x) = x^4 - 4x^2, \quad g(x) = x^2 - 4$

36. $f(x) = x^4 - 9x^2, \quad g(x) = x^3 - 9x$

37. $f(x) = \dfrac{1}{1 + x^2}, \quad g(x) = \dfrac{1}{2}x^2$

38. $f(x) = \dfrac{6x}{x^2 + 1}, \quad y = 0, \quad 0 \le x \le 3$

39. $f(x) = 2 \sin x + \sin 2x, \quad y = 0, \quad 0 \le x \le \pi$

40. $f(x) = 2 \sin x + \cos 2x, \quad y = 0, \quad 0 \le x \le \pi$

41. $f(x) = \dfrac{1}{x^2} e^{1/x}, \quad y = 0, \quad 1 \le x \le 3$

42. $g(x) = \dfrac{4 \ln x}{x}, \quad y = 0, \quad x = 5$

 Finding the Area of a Region In Exercises 43–48, sketch the region bounded by the graphs of the functions and find the area of the region.

43. $f(x) = \cos x, \quad g(x) = 2 - \cos x, \quad 0 \le x \le 2\pi$

44. $f(x) = \sin x, \quad g(x) = \cos 2x, \quad -\dfrac{\pi}{2} \le x \le \dfrac{\pi}{6}$

45. $f(x) = 2 \sin x, \quad g(x) = \tan x, \quad -\dfrac{\pi}{3} \le x \le \dfrac{\pi}{3}$

46. $f(x) = \sec \dfrac{\pi x}{4} \tan \dfrac{\pi x}{4}, \quad g(x) = (\sqrt{2} - 4)x + 4, \quad x = 0$

47. $f(x) = xe^{-x^2}, \quad y = 0, \quad 0 \le x \le 1$

48. $f(x) = 3^x, \quad g(x) = 2x + 1$

Finding the Area of a Region In Exercises 49–52, (a) use a graphing utility to graph the region bounded by the graphs of the equations, (b) explain why the area of the region is difficult to find by hand, and (c) use the integration capabilities of the graphing utility to approximate the area to four decimal places.

49. $y = \sqrt{\dfrac{x^3}{4 - x}}, \quad y = 0, \quad x = 3$

50. $y = \sqrt{x} \, e^x, \quad y = 0, \quad x = 0, \quad x = 1$

51. $y = x^2, \quad y = 4 \cos x$ **52.** $y = x^2, \quad y = \sqrt{3 + x}$

Integration as an Accumulation Process In Exercises 53–56, find the accumulation function F. Then evaluate F at each value of the independent variable and graphically show the accumulated area that each function value represents.

53. $F(x) = \displaystyle\int_0^x \left(\dfrac{1}{2}t + 1\right) dt$ (a) $F(0)$ (b) $F(3)$ (c) $F(6)$

54. $F(x) = \displaystyle\int_0^x \left(\dfrac{1}{2}t^2 + 2\right) dt$ (a) $F(0)$ (b) $F(3)$ (c) $F(6)$

55. $F(\alpha) = \displaystyle\int_{-1}^{\alpha} \cos \dfrac{\pi \theta}{2} \, d\theta$ (a) $F\left(-\dfrac{1}{2}\right)$ (b) $F(0)$ (c) $F\left(\dfrac{1}{2}\right)$

56. $F(y) = \displaystyle\int_{-1}^{y} 4e^{x/2} \, dx$ (a) $F(0)$ (b) $F(2)$ (c) $F(4)$

57. Finding the Area of a Region Find the area of the given region bounded by the graphs of y_1, y_2, and y_3, as shown in the figure.

$$y_1 = x^2 + 2, \quad y_2 = 4 - x^2, \quad y_3 = 2 - x$$

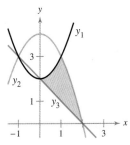 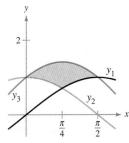

Figure for 57   Figure for 58

58. Finding the Area of a Region Find the area of the given region bounded by the graphs of y_1, y_2, and y_3, as shown in the figure.

$$y_1 = \sin x, \quad y_2 = \cos x, \quad y_3 = \sin x + \cos x$$

Finding Area In Exercises 59–62, use integration to find the area of the polygon having the given vertices.

59. $(2, -3), (4, 6), (6, 1)$ **60.** $(0, 0), (6, 0), (4, 3)$

61. $(0, 2), (4, 2), (0, -2), (-4, -2)$

62. $(0, 0), (1, 2), (3, -2), (1, -3)$

EXPLORING CONCEPTS

63. Communicating The graphs of $y = 1 - x^2$ and $y = x^4 - 2x^2 + 1$ intersect at three points, but the area between the curves can be represented by a single integral. Explain why. Then write and evaluate an integral to find the area.

64. Using Symmetry The area of the region bounded by the graphs of $y = x^3$ and $y = x$ *cannot* be found by the single integral $\int_{-1}^{1} (x^3 - x)\, dx$. Explain why this is so. Use symmetry to write a single integral that does represent the area. Then find the area.

65. Interpreting Integrals Two cars start a race side-by-side and travel with velocities v_1 and v_2 (in meters per second). Use the following information, where t represents the time (in seconds).

$$\int_0^5 [v_1(t) - v_2(t)]\, dt = 10 \quad \int_0^{10} [v_1(t) - v_2(t)]\, dt = 30$$

$$\int_{20}^{30} [v_1(t) - v_2(t)]\, dt = -5$$

(a) Write a verbal interpretation of each integral.

(b) Which car is ahead when $t = 10$ seconds? How far ahead is the car?

(c) Car 1 has velocity v_1 and is ahead of Car 2 by 13 meters when $t = 20$ seconds. How far ahead or behind is Car 1 when $t = 30$ seconds?

(d) Is it possible to determine which car is traveling faster when $t = 30$ seconds? Explain.

66. HOW DO YOU SEE IT? A state has an annual budget deficit of $60 billion. Two proposals for eliminating the annual deficit in 10 years are shown in the figure.

(a) What does the area between the two curves represent?

(b) From the viewpoint of minimizing the cumulative state deficit, which is the better proposal? Explain.

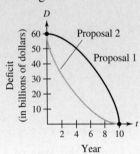

Connecting Limits and Integrals In Exercises 67 and 68, evaluate the limit and sketch the graph of the region whose area is represented by the limit.

67. $\displaystyle\lim_{\|\Delta\| \to 0} \sum_{i=1}^{n} (x_i - x_i^2)\, \Delta x$, where $x_i = \dfrac{i}{n}$ and $\Delta x = \dfrac{1}{n}$

68. $\displaystyle\lim_{\|\Delta\| \to 0} \sum_{i=1}^{n} (4 - x_i^2)\, \Delta x$, where $x_i = -2 + \dfrac{4i}{n}$ and $\Delta x = \dfrac{4}{n}$

Dividing a Region In Exercises 69 and 70, find b such that the line $y = b$ divides the region bounded by the graphs of the two equations into two regions of equal area.

69. $y = 9 - x^2,\ y = 0$ **70.** $y = 9 - |x|,\ y = 0$

Dividing a Region In Exercises 71 and 72, find a such that the line $x = a$ divides the region bounded by the graphs of the equations into two regions of equal area.

71. $y = x,\ y = 4,\ x = 0$ **72.** $y^2 = 4 - x,\ x = 0$

73. BUILDING DESIGN

Concrete sections for a new building have the dimensions (in meters) and shape shown in the figure.

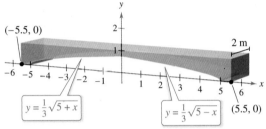

(a) Find the area of the face of the section superimposed on the rectangular coordinate system.

(b) Find the volume of concrete in one of the sections by multiplying the area in part (a) by 2 meters.

(c) One cubic meter of concrete weighs 5000 pounds. Find the weight of the section.

74. Mechanical Design The surface of a machine part is the region between the graphs of $y_1 = |x|$ and $y_2 = 0.08x^2 + k$ (see figure).

(a) Find k where the parabola is tangent to the graph of y_1.

(b) Find the area of the surface of the machine part.

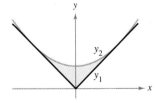

75. Profit A company reports that profits for the past fiscal year were $15.9 million. The company predicts that profits for the next 5 years will grow at a continuous annual rate somewhere between $3\frac{1}{2}\%$ and 5%. Estimate the cumulative difference in total profit over the 5 years based on the predicted range of growth rates.

76. Lorenz Curve   Economists use *Lorenz curves* to illustrate the distribution of income in a country. Each point on a Lorenz curve shows the percent y of all earned income that is earned by the least-earning x percent of families in the country. The model $y = x$ represents a country in which each family has the same income. The area between these two models, where $0 \le x \le 100$, indicates a country's "income inequality." The *Gini coefficient* is the ratio of the income inequality to the area under the graph of $y = x$ for $0 \le x \le 100$. The table shows selected Lorenz curve data for a country. For example, the *poorest* 20% of families earn 6.07% of the total income.

x	10	20	30	40	50
y	3.35	6.07	9.17	13.39	19.45

x	60	70	80	90
y	28.03	39.77	55.28	75.12

(a) Use a graphing utility to find a cubic model for the Lorenz curve.

(b) Plot the data and graph the model.

(c) Graph the model $y = x$. How does this model compare with the model in part (a)?

(d) Use the integration capabilities of a graphing utility to approximate the "income inequality" and the Gini Coefficient for the country.

(e) Ecuador had a Gini Coefficient of 0.459 in 2017. Compare the distribution of wealth of the given country to that of Ecuador.

77. Area   Find the area between the graph of

$$y = \sin x$$

and the line segment joining the points $(0, 0)$ and $(7\pi/6, -1/2)$, as shown in the figure.

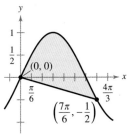

Figure for 77

Figure for 78

78. Area   The horizontal line $y = c$ intersects the graph of $y = 6x - x^3$ in the first quadrant, as shown in the figure. Find c so that the areas of the two shaded regions are equal.

True or False?   In Exercises 79–82, determine whether the statement is true or false. If it is false, explain why or give an example that shows it is false.

79. The area of the region bounded by the graphs of f and g is equal to the area bounded by the graphs of

$$h(x) = f(x) + C \quad \text{and} \quad k(x) = g(x) + C.$$

80. If $\int_a^b [f(x) - g(x)]\, dx = A$, then

$$\int_a^b [g(x) - f(x)]\, dx = -A.$$

81. If the graphs of f and g intersect midway between $x = a$ and $x = b$, then

$$\int_a^b [f(x) - g(x)]\, dx = 0.$$

82. The line $y = \left(1 - \sqrt[3]{0.5}\right)x$ divides the region under the curve $f(x) = x(1 - x)$ on $[0, 1]$ into two regions of equal area.

Calculus AP® – Exam Preparation Questions

83. Multiple Choice   The figure below shows the graphs of $y = 2 - 4x - x^2$ and $y = -2x - 1$. What is the area of the shaded region?

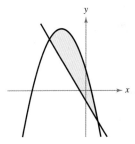

(A) $\dfrac{5}{3}$ (B) 10   (C) $\dfrac{32}{3}$ (D) $\dfrac{86}{3}$

84. Multiple Choice   What is the area of the region bounded by the graphs of $x = y^2 - 2y$ and $y = -x + 2$?

(A) $\dfrac{3}{2}$ (B) $\dfrac{10}{3}$ (C) $\dfrac{9}{2}$ (D) $\dfrac{31}{6}$

85. Multiple Choice   Which integral gives the area A of the region bounded by the graph of $f(x) = x^3 - 2x$ and the tangent line to the graph of f at $(-1, 1)$?

(A) $A = \displaystyle\int_{-1}^{2} (x^3 + 3x + 2)\, dx$

(B) $A = \displaystyle\int_{-1}^{2} (x^3 - 3x - 2)\, dx$

(C) $A = \displaystyle\int_{-1}^{4} (-x^3 + 3x + 2)\, dx$

(D) $A = \displaystyle\int_{-1}^{2} (-x^3 + 3x + 2)\, dx$

6.2 Volume: The Disk and Washer Methods

▶ Find the volume of a solid of revolution using the disk method.
▶ Find the volume of a solid of revolution using the washer method.
▶ Find the volume of a solid with known cross sections.

The Disk Method

You have already learned that area is only one of the *many* applications of the definite integral. Another important application is its use in finding the volume of a three-dimensional solid. In this section, you will study a particular type of three-dimensional solid—one whose cross sections are similar. Solids of revolution are used commonly in engineering and manufacturing. Some examples are axles, funnels, pills, bottles, and pistons, as shown in Figure 6.12.

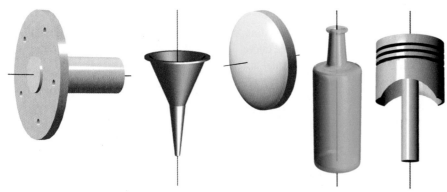

Solids of revolution
Figure 6.12

When a region in the plane is revolved about a line, the resulting solid is a **solid of revolution,** and the line is called the **axis of revolution.** The simplest such solid is a right circular cylinder or **disk,** which is formed by revolving a rectangle about an axis adjacent to one side of the rectangle, as shown in Figure 6.13. The volume of such a disk is

Volume of disk = (area of disk)(width of disk) = $\pi R^2 w$

where R is the radius of the disk and w is the width.

To see how to use the volume of a disk to find the volume of a general solid of revolution, consider a solid of revolution formed by revolving the plane region in Figure 6.14 about the indicated axis, as shown on the next page. To determine the volume of this solid, consider a representative rectangle in the plane region. When this rectangle is revolved about the axis of revolution, it generates a representative disk whose volume is

$$\Delta V = \pi R^2 \, \Delta x.$$

Approximating the volume of the solid by n such disks of width Δx and radius $R(x_i)$ produces

Volume of solid $\approx \sum_{i=1}^{n} \pi [R(x_i)]^2 \, \Delta x$

$$= \pi \sum_{i=1}^{n} [R(x_i)]^2 \, \Delta x.$$

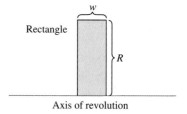

Rectangle

Axis of revolution

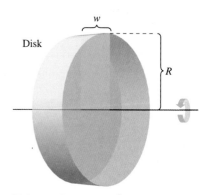

Disk

Volume of a disk: $\pi R^2 w$
Figure 6.13

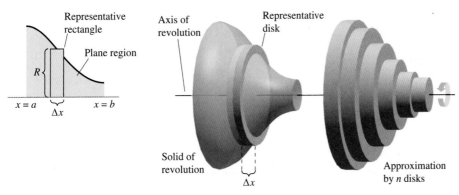

Disk method
Figure 6.14

This approximation appears to become better and better as $\|\Delta\| \to 0$ $(n \to \infty)$. So, you can define the volume of the solid as

$$\text{Volume of solid} = \lim_{\|\Delta\| \to 0} \pi \sum_{i=1}^{n} [R(x_i)]^2 \, \Delta x = \pi \int_a^b [R(x)]^2 \, dx.$$

Schematically, the disk method looks like this.

Known Precalculus Formula	*Representative Element*	*New Integration Formula*
Volume of disk $V = \pi R^2 w$	$\Delta V = \pi [R(x_i)]^2 \, \Delta x$	Solid of revolution $V = \pi \int_a^b [R(x)]^2 \, dx$

A similar formula can be derived when the axis of revolution is vertical.

The Disk Method

To find the volume of a solid of revolution with the **disk method,** use one of the formulas below. (See Figure 6.15.)

Horizontal Axis of Revolution

$$\text{Volume} = V = \pi \int_a^b [R(x)]^2 \, dx$$

Vertical Axis of Revolution

$$\text{Volume} = V = \pi \int_c^d [R(y)]^2 \, dy$$

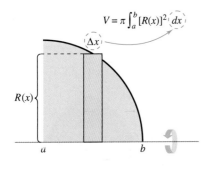

Horizontal axis of revolution
Figure 6.15

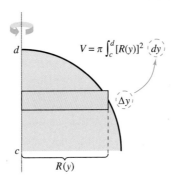

Vertical axis of revolution

Implementing Processes

In Figure 6.15, note that you can determine the variable of integration by placing a representative rectangle in the plane region "perpendicular" to the axis of revolution. When the width of the rectangle is Δx, integrate with respect to x, and when the width of the rectangle is Δy, integrate with respect to y.

The simplest application of the disk method involves a plane region bounded by the graph of f and the x-axis. When the axis of revolution is the x-axis, the radius $R(x)$ is simply $f(x)$.

EXAMPLE 1   Using the Disk Method

Find the volume of the solid formed by revolving the region bounded by the graph of

$$f(x) = \sqrt{\sin x}$$

and the x-axis $(0 \le x \le \pi)$ about the x-axis.

Solution

From the representative rectangle in the upper graph in Figure 6.16, you can see that the radius of this solid is

$$R(x) = f(x)$$
$$= \sqrt{\sin x}.$$

So, the volume of the solid of revolution is

$$V = \pi \int_a^b [R(x)]^2 \, dx \qquad \text{Apply disk method.}$$

$$= \pi \int_0^\pi (\sqrt{\sin x})^2 \, dx \qquad \text{Substitute } \sqrt{\sin x} \text{ for } R(x).$$

$$= \pi \int_0^\pi \sin x \, dx \qquad \text{Simplify.}$$

$$= \pi \left[-\cos x \right]_0^\pi \qquad \text{Integrate.}$$

$$= \pi(1 + 1)$$

$$= 2\pi.$$

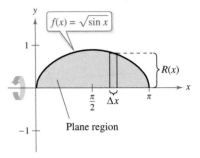

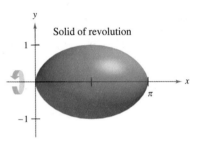

Figure 6.16

EXAMPLE 2   Using a Line That Is Not a Coordinate Axis

Find the volume of the solid formed by revolving the region bounded by the graphs of $f(x) = 2 - x^2$ and $g(x) = 1$ about the line $y = 1$, as shown in Figure 6.17.

Solution

By equating $f(x)$ and $g(x)$, you can determine that the two graphs intersect when $x = \pm 1$. To find the radius, subtract $g(x)$ from $f(x)$.

$$R(x) = f(x) - g(x)$$
$$= (2 - x^2) - 1$$
$$= 1 - x^2$$

To find the volume, integrate between -1 and 1.

$$V = \pi \int_a^b [R(x)]^2 \, dx \qquad \text{Apply disk method.}$$

$$= \pi \int_{-1}^1 (1 - x^2)^2 \, dx \qquad \text{Substitute } 1 - x^2 \text{ for } R(x).$$

$$= \pi \int_{-1}^1 (1 - 2x^2 + x^4) \, dx \qquad \text{Simplify.}$$

$$= \pi \left[x - \frac{2x^3}{3} + \frac{x^5}{5} \right]_{-1}^1 \qquad \text{Integrate.}$$

$$= \frac{16\pi}{15}$$

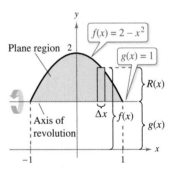

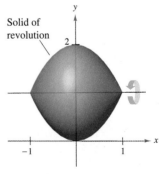

Figure 6.17

The Washer Method

The disk method can be extended to cover solids of revolution with holes by replacing the representative disk with a representative **washer.** The washer is formed by revolving a rectangle about an axis, as shown in Figure 6.18. If r and R are the inner and outer radii of the washer and w is the width of the washer, then the volume is

Volume of washer $= \pi(R^2 - r^2)w.$

To see how this concept can be used to find the volume of a solid of revolution, consider a region bounded by an **outer radius** $R(x)$ and an **inner radius** $r(x)$, as shown in Figure 6.19. If the region is revolved about its axis of revolution, then the volume of the resulting solid is

$$V = \pi \int_a^b ([R(x)]^2 - [r(x)]^2)\, dx. \qquad \text{Washer method}$$

Note that the integral involving the inner radius represents the volume of the hole and is *subtracted* from the integral involving the outer radius.

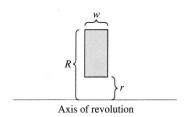

Axis of revolution

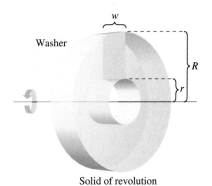

Solid of revolution

Figure 6.18

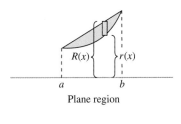

Plane region

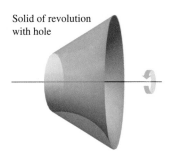

Solid of revolution with hole

Figure 6.19

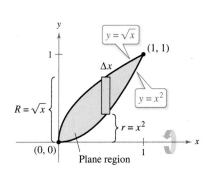

Plane region

EXAMPLE 3   **Using the Washer Method**

Find the volume of the solid formed by revolving the region bounded by the graphs of

$$y = \sqrt{x} \quad \text{and} \quad y = x^2$$

about the x-axis, as shown in Figure 6.20.

Solution

In Figure 6.20, you can see that the outer and inner radii are as follows.

$$R(x) = \sqrt{x} \qquad \qquad \text{Outer radius}$$
$$r(x) = x^2 \qquad \qquad \text{Inner radius}$$

Integrating between 0 and 1 produces

$$V = \pi \int_a^b ([R(x)]^2 - [r(x)]^2)\, dx \qquad \text{Apply washer method.}$$

$$= \pi \int_0^1 \left[(\sqrt{x})^2 - (x^2)^2\right] dx \qquad \text{Substitute } \sqrt{x} \text{ for } R(x) \text{ and } x^2 \text{ for } r(x).$$

$$= \pi \int_0^1 (x - x^4)\, dx \qquad \text{Simplify.}$$

$$= \pi \left[\frac{x^2}{2} - \frac{x^5}{5}\right]_0^1 \qquad \text{Integrate.}$$

$$= \frac{3\pi}{10}.$$

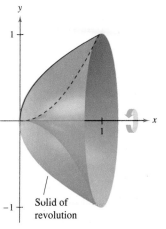

Solid of revolution

Solid of revolution
Figure 6.20

In each example so far, the axis of revolution has been *horizontal* and you have integrated with respect to x. In the next example, the axis of revolution is *vertical* and you integrate with respect to y. In this example, you need two separate integrals to compute the volume.

EXAMPLE 4   Integrating with Respect to y: Two-Integral Case

Find the volume of the solid formed by revolving the region bounded by the graphs of $y = x^2 + 1$, $y = 0$, $x = 0$, and $x = 1$ about the y-axis, as shown in Figure 6.21.

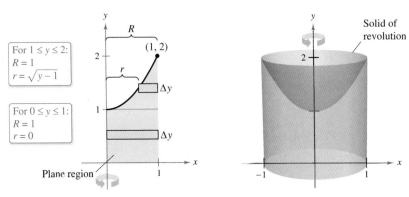

Figure 6.21

Solution

For the region shown in Figure 6.21, the outer radius is simply $R = 1$. There is, however, no convenient formula that represents the inner radius. When $0 \le y \le 1$, $r = 0$, but when $1 \le y \le 2$, r is determined by the equation $y = x^2 + 1$, which implies that $r = \sqrt{y-1}$.

$$r(y) = \begin{cases} 0, & 0 \le y \le 1 \\ \sqrt{y-1}, & 1 \le y \le 2 \end{cases}$$

Using this definition of the inner radius, you can use two integrals to find the volume.

$$V = \pi \int_0^1 (1^2 - 0^2)\, dy + \pi \int_1^2 \left[1^2 - \left(\sqrt{y-1}\right)^2\right] dy \qquad \text{Apply washer method.}$$

$$= \pi \int_0^1 1\, dy + \pi \int_1^2 (2 - y)\, dy \qquad \text{Simplify.}$$

$$= \pi\left[y\right]_0^1 + \pi\left[2y - \frac{y^2}{2}\right]_1^2 \qquad \text{Integrate.}$$

$$= \pi + \pi\left(4 - 2 - 2 + \frac{1}{2}\right)$$

$$= \frac{3\pi}{2}$$

Note that the first integral $\pi \int_0^1 1\, dy$ represents the volume of a right circular cylinder of radius 1 and height 1. This portion of the volume could have been determined without using calculus.

> ### Algebra Review
>
> For help on the algebra in Example 4, see Example 3(a) in the *Chapter 6 Algebra Review* on page A46.

Technology

Some graphing utilities have the capability of generating (or have built-in software capable of generating) a solid of revolution. If you have access to such a utility, use it to graph some of the solids of revolution described in this section. For instance, the solid in Example 4 might appear like that shown in Figure 6.22.

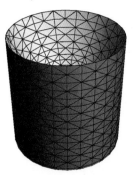

Generated by Mathematica

Figure 6.22

EXAMPLE 5   Manufacturing

See LarsonCalculusforAP.com for an interactive version of this type of example.

A manufacturer drills a hole through the center of a metal sphere of radius 5 inches, as shown in Figure 6.23(a). The hole has a radius of 3 inches. What is the volume of the resulting metal ring?

Solution

You can imagine the ring to be generated by a segment of the circle whose equation is $x^2 + y^2 = 25$, as shown in Figure 6.23(b). Because the radius of the hole is 3 inches, you can let $y = 3$ and solve the equation $x^2 + y^2 = 25$ to determine that the limits of integration are $x = \pm 4$. So, the inner and outer radii are $r(x) = 3$ and $R(x) = \sqrt{25 - x^2}$, and the volume is

$$V = \pi \int_a^b ([R(x)]^2 - [r(x)]^2)\, dx \qquad \text{Apply washer method.}$$

$$= \pi \int_{-4}^{4} \left[\left(\sqrt{25 - x^2} \right)^2 - (3)^2 \right] dx \qquad \text{Substitute } \sqrt{25 - x^2} \text{ for } R(x) \text{ and 3 for } r(x).$$

$$= \pi \int_{-4}^{4} (16 - x^2)\, dx \qquad \text{Simplify.}$$

$$= \pi \left[16x - \frac{x^3}{3} \right]_{-4}^{4} \qquad \text{Integrate.}$$

$$= \frac{256\pi}{3} \text{ cubic inches.}$$

Solid of revolution

(a)

Plane region

(b)

Figure 6.23

Solids with Known Cross Sections

With the disk method, you can find the volume of a solid having a circular cross section whose area is $A = \pi R^2$. This method can be generalized to solids of any shape, as long as you know a formula for the area of an arbitrary cross section. Some common cross sections are squares, rectangles, triangles, semicircles, and trapezoids.

Algebra Review

For help on the algebra in Example 5, see Example 3(b) in the *Chapter 6 Algebra Review* on page A46.

Volumes of Solids with Known Cross Sections

1. For cross sections of area $A(x)$ taken perpendicular to the *x*-axis,

$$\text{Volume} = \int_a^b A(x)\, dx. \qquad \text{See Figure 6.24(a).}$$

2. For cross sections of area $A(y)$ taken perpendicular to the *y*-axis,

$$\text{Volume} = \int_c^d A(y)\, dy. \qquad \text{See Figure 6.24(b).}$$

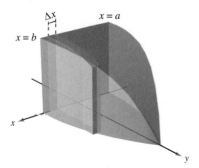

(a) Cross sections perpendicular to *x*-axis

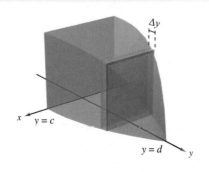

(b) Cross sections perpendicular to *y*-axis

Figure 6.24

EXAMPLE 6 **Triangular Cross Sections**

Find the volume of the solid shown in Figure 6.25. The base of the solid is the region bounded by the lines

$$f(x) = 1 - \frac{x}{2}, \quad g(x) = -1 + \frac{x}{2}, \quad \text{and} \quad x = 0.$$

The cross sections perpendicular to the x-axis are equilateral triangles.

Solution

The base and area of each triangular cross section are as follows.

$$\text{Base} = \left(1 - \frac{x}{2}\right) - \left(-1 + \frac{x}{2}\right) = 2 - x \qquad \text{Length of base}$$

$$\text{Area} = \frac{\sqrt{3}}{4}(\text{base})^2 \qquad \text{Area of equilateral triangle}$$

$$A(x) = \frac{\sqrt{3}}{4}(2 - x)^2 \qquad \text{Area of cross section}$$

Because x ranges from 0 to 2, the volume of the solid is

$$V = \int_a^b A(x)\, dx = \int_0^2 \frac{\sqrt{3}}{4}(2-x)^2\, dx = -\frac{\sqrt{3}}{4}\left[\frac{(2-x)^3}{3}\right]_0^2 = \frac{2\sqrt{3}}{3}.$$

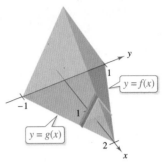

Cross sections are equilateral triangles.

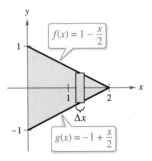

Triangular base in xy-plane
Figure 6.25

EXAMPLE 7 **An Application to Geometry**

Prove that the volume of a pyramid with a square base is $V = \frac{1}{3}hB$, where h is the height of the pyramid and B is the area of the base.

Solution

As shown in Figure 6.26, you can intersect the pyramid with a plane parallel to the base at height y to form a square cross section whose sides are of length b'. Using similar triangles, you can show that

$$\frac{b'}{b} = \frac{h - y}{h} \quad \text{or} \quad b' = \frac{b}{h}(h - y)$$

where b is the length of the sides of the base of the pyramid. So,

$$A(y) = (b')^2 = \frac{b^2}{h^2}(h - y)^2.$$

Integrating between 0 and h produces

$$V = \int_0^h A(y)\, dy \qquad \text{Cross sections perpendicular to } y\text{-axis}$$

$$= \int_0^h \frac{b^2}{h^2}(h - y)^2\, dy \qquad \text{Substitute.}$$

$$= \frac{b^2}{h^2}\int_0^h (h - y)^2\, dy \qquad \text{Constant Multiple Rule}$$

$$= -\left(\frac{b^2}{h^2}\right)\left[\frac{(h - y)^3}{3}\right]_0^h \qquad \text{Integrate.}$$

$$= \frac{b^2}{h^2}\left(\frac{h^3}{3}\right)$$

$$= \frac{1}{3}hB. \qquad B = b^2$$

Algebra Review

For help on the algebra in Example 7, see Example 5 in the *Chapter 6 Algebra Review* on page A47.

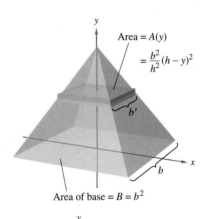

Area of base $= B = b^2$

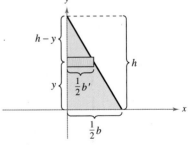

Figure 6.26

6.2 Exercises

See *CalcChat.com* for tutorial help and worked-out solutions to odd-numbered exercises.

 Finding the Volume of a Solid   In Exercises 1–10, write and evaluate the definite integral that represents the volume of the solid formed by revolving the region bounded by the graphs of the equations about the *x*-axis.

1. $y = -x + 1$, $y = 0$,   **2.** $y = 4 - x^2$, $y = 0$,
   $x = 0$ $x = 0$

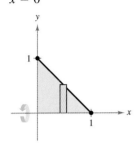
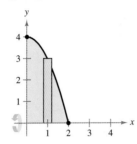

3. $y = \sqrt{x}$, $y = 0$, $x = 1$,   **4.** $y = \sqrt{9 - x^2}$, $y = 0$,
   $x = 4$ $x = 1$

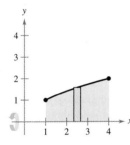
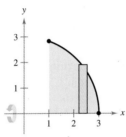

5. $y = \dfrac{1}{\sqrt{x + 1}}$, $y = 0$, $x = 0$, $x = 4$

6. $y = x\sqrt{4 - x^2}$, $y = 0$, $x = 0$, $x = 2$

7. $y = 1/x$, $y = 0$, $x = 1$, $x = 3$

8. $y = \dfrac{2}{x + 1}$, $y = 0$, $x = 0$, $x = 6$

9. $y = e^{-x}$, $y = 0$, $x = 0$, $y = 1$

10. $y = e^{x/4}$, $y = 0$, $x = 0$, $x = 6$

 Finding the Volume of a Solid   In Exercises 11–18, write and evaluate the definite integral that represents the volume of the solid formed by revolving the region bounded by the graphs of the equations about the *y*-axis.

11. $y = x^2$, $y = 4$, $x = 0$ **12.** $y = \sqrt{16 - x^2}$, $y = 0$,
                                         $x = 0$

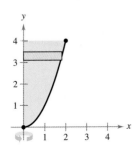
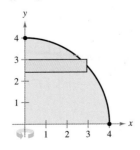

13. $x = y^{3/2}$, $x = 0$, $y = 1$ **14.** $x = -y^2 + 4y$, $x = 0$

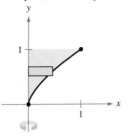
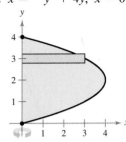

15. $y = 3(2 - x)$, $y = 0$, $x = 0$

16. $y = 8 - x^3$, $y = 0$, $x = 0$

17. $y = \sqrt{5x + 1}$, $y = 6$, $x = 0$

18. $y = 8/(x - 2)$, $y = 1$, $y = 8$, $x = 0$

Finding the Volume of a Solid   In Exercises 19–24, find the volume of the solid generated by revolving the region bounded by the graphs of the equations about the line $y = 4$.

19. $y = x + 4$, $y = 4$,   **20.** $y = x^2 + 5$, $y = 4$,
   $x = 4$ $x = -2$, $x = 2$

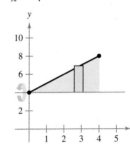
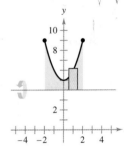

21. $y = \sqrt{x + 16}$, $y = 4$, $x = 9$

22. $y = \sqrt{3x} + 4$, $y = 4$, $x = 3$

23. $y = \frac{1}{2}x^3$, $y = 4$, $x = 0$ **24.** $y = x^{2/3}$, $y = 4$, $x = 0$

 Finding the Volume of a Solid   In Exercises 25–28, find the volume of the solid generated by revolving the region bounded by the graphs of the equations about the line $x = 5$.

25. $y = (x - 8)^2$, $y = 0$, $x = 5$

26. $y = x$, $y = 0$, $y = 4$, $x = 5$

27. $xy = 3$, $y = 1$, $y = 4$, $x = 5$

28. $x - 5 = \sqrt{25 - y^2}$, $x = 5$

Error Analysis   In Exercises 29 and 30, describe and correct the error in using the disk method to write an integral representing the volume of the solid formed by revolving the region bounded by $y = \ln x$, $y = 1$, and $x = 1$ about the line $x = 1$.

29. $\pi \displaystyle\int_0^1 (\ln x)^2 \, dx$ ✗   **30.** $\pi \displaystyle\int_0^1 (e^y)^2 \, dy$

Finding the Volume of a Solid In Exercises 31–44, find the volume of the solid generated by revolving the region bounded by the graphs of the equations about the given axis.

31. $y = x^2$, $y = x^5$, x-axis   **32.** $y = 2$, $y = 4 - \dfrac{x^2}{4}$, x-axis

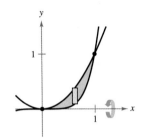 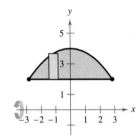

33. $y = \sqrt{x}$, $y = 2$, $x = 16$, x-axis
34. $y = (x/2) + 1$, $y = 3x + 1$, $x = 3$, x-axis
35. $y = (x - 1)^3$, $y = 17 - x^2$, $x = 1$, x-axis
36. $y = \sqrt{6x - 6}$, $y = \frac{1}{6}(x - 1)^2$, x-axis
37. $y = (x/2) + 1$, $y = 3x + 1$, $y = 7$, y-axis
38. $y = 9 - x^2$, $y = 0$, $x = 2$, $x = 3$, y-axis
39. $\sqrt{y} = \sqrt[3]{x}$, $2x + y^2 = 8y$, y-axis
40. $y = x^2$, $y = 4x - x^2$, y-axis
41. $y = 1 - x^3$, $y = 2$, $x = 0$, $x = 2$, y-axis
42. $y = \sqrt{x - 2} + 5$, $x = -y^2 + 10y - 15$, $y = 5$, $y = 8$, y-axis
43. $y = x^2 + 1$, $y = -x^2 + 2x + 5$, $x = 0$, $x = 3$, x-axis
44. $y = \sqrt{x}$, $y = -\frac{1}{2}x + 4$, $x = 0$, $x = 8$, x-axis

 Finding the Volume of a Solid In Exercises 45–48, find the volume of the solid generated by revolving the region bounded by the graphs of the equations about the x-axis. Verify your results using the integration capabilities of a graphing utility.

45. $y = \sin x$, $y = 0$, $x = 0$, $x = \pi$
46. $y = \cos 2x$, $y = 0$, $x = 0$, $x = \dfrac{\pi}{4}$
47. $y = e^{x-1}$, $y = 0$, $x = 1$, $x = 2$
48. $y = e^{x/2} + e^{-x/2}$, $y = 0$, $x = -1$, $x = 2$

Finding the Volume of a Solid In Exercises 49–52, use the integration capabilities of a graphing utility to approximate the volume of the solid generated by revolving the region bounded by the graphs of the equations about the x-axis.

49. $y = e^{-x^2}$, $y = 0$, $x = 0$, $x = 2$
50. $y = \ln x$, $y = 0$, $x = 1$, $x = 3$
51. $y = 2 \arctan 0.2x$, $y = 0$, $x = 0$, $x = 5$
52. $y = \sqrt{2x}$, $y = x^2$

Finding the Volume of a Solid In Exercises 53–60, find the volume generated by revolving the given region about the specified line.

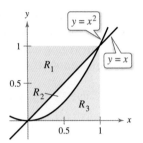

53. R_1 about $x = 0$ **54.** R_1 about $x = 1$
55. R_2 about $y = 0$ **56.** R_2 about $y = 1$
57. R_3 about $x = 0$ **58.** R_3 about $x = 1$
59. R_2 about $x = 0$ **60.** R_2 about $x = 1$

EXPLORING CONCEPTS

Describing a Solid In Exercises 61 and 62, the integral represents the volume of a solid. Describe the solid.

61. $\pi \displaystyle\int_0^{\pi/2} \sin^2 x\, dx$ **62.** $\pi \displaystyle\int_2^4 y^4\, dy$

63. Comparing Volumes A region bounded by the parabola $y = 4x - x^2$ and the x-axis is revolved about the x-axis. A second region bounded by the parabola $y = 4 - x^2$ and the x-axis is revolved about the x-axis. Without integrating, how do the volumes of the two solids compare? Explain.

64. HOW DO YOU SEE IT? Use the graph to match the integral for the volume with the axis of revolution.

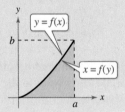

(a) $V = \pi \displaystyle\int_0^b (a^2 - [f(y)]^2)\, dy$ (i) x-axis

(b) $V = \pi \displaystyle\int_0^a (b^2 - [b - f(x)]^2)\, dx$ (ii) y-axis

(c) $V = \pi \displaystyle\int_0^a [f(x)]^2\, dx$ (iii) $x = a$

(d) $V = \pi \displaystyle\int_0^b [a - f(y)]^2\, dy$ (iv) $y = b$

Dividing a Solid In Exercises 65 and 66, consider the solid formed by revolving the region bounded by $y = \sqrt{x}, y = 0$, and $x = 4$ about the x-axis.

65. Find the value of x in the interval $[0, 4]$ that divides the solid into two parts of equal volume.

66. Find the values of x in the interval $[0, 4]$ that divide the solid into three parts of equal volume.

67. Manufacturing A manufacturer drills a hole through the center of a metal sphere of radius R. The hole has a radius r. Find the volume of the resulting ring.

68. Manufacturing For the metal sphere in Exercise 67, let $R = 6$. What value of r will produce a ring whose volume is exactly half the volume of the sphere?

69. Volume of a Cone Use the disk method to verify that the volume of a right circular cone is $\frac{1}{3}\pi r^2 h$, where r is the radius of the base and h is the height.

70. Volume of a Sphere Use the disk method to verify that the volume of a sphere is $\frac{4}{3}\pi r^3$, where r is the radius.

71. Using a Cone A cone of height H with a base of radius r is cut by a plane parallel to and h units above the base, where $h < H$. Find the volume of the solid (frustum of a cone) below the plane.

72. Using a Sphere A sphere of radius r is cut by a plane h units above the equator, where $h < r$. Find the volume of the solid (spherical segment) above the plane.

73. Volume of a Fuel Tank A fuel tank is formed by revolving the region bounded by the x-axis and the graph of $y = \frac{1}{8}x^2\sqrt{2 - x}$ about the x-axis, where x and y are measured in meters. Use a graphing utility to graph the function. Find the volume of the tank analytically.

74. Volume of a Container A container can be modeled by revolving the graph of

$$y = \begin{cases} \sqrt{0.1x^3 - 2.2x^2 + 10.9x + 22.2}, & 0 \le x \le 11.5 \\ 2.95, & 11.5 < x \le 15 \end{cases}$$

about the x-axis, where x and y are measured in centimeters. Use a graphing utility to graph the function. Find the volume of the container analytically.

75. Finding Volumes of Solids Find the volumes of the solids (see figures) generated when the ellipse $9x^2 + 25y^2 = 225$ is revolved about (a) the x-axis to form a prolate spheroid (shaped like a football), and (b) the y-axis to form an oblate spheroid.

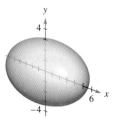

Figure for 75(a)

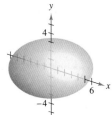

Figure for 75(b)

76. 3D PRINTING

A 3D printer is used to create a plastic drinking glass. The equations given to the printer for the inside of the glass are

$$x = \left(\frac{y}{4}\right)^{1/32} \quad \text{and} \quad y = 5$$

where x and y are measured in inches. What is the total volume that the drinking glass can hold when the region bounded by the graphs of the equations is revolved about the y-axis?

77. Minimum Volume The function $y = 4 - (x^2/4)$ on the interval $[0, 4]$ is revolved about the line $y = b$ (see figure).

(a) Find the volume of the resulting solid as a function of b.

(b) Use a graphing utility to graph the function in part (a), and use the graph to approximate the value of b that minimizes the volume of the solid.

(c) Use calculus to find the value of b that minimizes the volume of the solid, and compare the result with the answer to part (b).

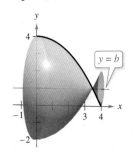

78. Think About It Match each integral with the solid whose volume it represents.

(a) Right circular cylinder   (b) Ellipsoid

(c) Sphere   (d) Right circular cone   (e) Torus

(i) $\pi \displaystyle\int_0^h \left(\frac{rx}{h}\right)^2 dx$ (ii) $\pi \displaystyle\int_0^h r^2 \, dx$

(iii) $\pi \displaystyle\int_{-r}^r \left(\sqrt{r^2 - x^2}\right)^2 dx$

(iv) $\pi \displaystyle\int_{-b}^b \left(a\sqrt{1 - \frac{x^2}{b^2}}\right)^2 dx$

(v) $\pi \displaystyle\int_{-r}^r \left[\left(R + \sqrt{r^2 - x^2}\right)^2 - \left(R - \sqrt{r^2 - x^2}\right)^2\right] dx$

79. Cavalieri's Theorem Prove that if two solids have equal altitudes and all cross sections parallel to their bases and at equal distances from their bases have equal areas, then the solids have the same volume (see figure).

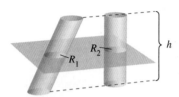

Area of R_1 = area of R_2

80. Using Cross Sections Find the volumes of the solids whose bases are bounded by the graphs of $y = x + 1$ and $y = x^2 - 1$, with the indicated cross sections taken perpendicular to the x-axis.

(a) Squares

(b) Rectangles of height 1

81. Using Cross Sections Find the volumes of the solids whose bases are bounded by the circle $x^2 + y^2 = 4$, with the indicated cross sections taken perpendicular to the x-axis.

(a) Squares

(b) Equilateral triangles

(c) Semicircles

(d) Isosceles right triangles

82. Using Cross Sections The solid shown in the figure has cross sections bounded by the graph of $|x|^a + |y|^a = 1$, where $1 \le a \le 2$. (a) Describe the cross section when $a = 1$ and $a = 2$. (b) Describe a procedure for approximating the volume of the solid.

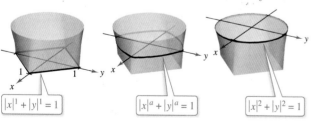

Calculus AP® – Exam Preparation Questions

83. Multiple Choice The region shown in the figure is revolved about the x-axis, the y-axis, and the line $x = 3$. Which of the following orders the volumes of the resulting solids from least to greatest?

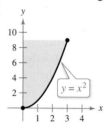

(A) y-axis, x-axis, $x = 3$

(B) x-axis, y-axis, $x = 3$

(C) y-axis, $x = 3$, x-axis

(D) $x = 3$, y-axis, x-axis

84. Multiple Choice Let R be the region bounded by the graphs of $y = 3x$ and $y = 4x^2$ for $0 \le x \le \frac{3}{4}$. What is the volume of the solid generated when R is revolved about the line $y = 4$?

(A) $\pi \int_0^{3/4} \left[(4 - 3x)^2 - \left(4 - 4x^2\right)^2 \right] dx$

(B) $\pi \int_0^{3/4} \left[\left(4 - 4x^2\right)^2 - (4 - 3x)^2 \right] dx$

(C) $\pi \int_0^{3/4} \left(9x^2 - 16x^4\right) dx$

(D) $\pi \int_0^{9/4} \left[\left(4 - \frac{\sqrt{y}}{2}\right)^2 - \left(4 - \frac{y}{3}\right)^2 \right] dy$

85. Free Response Let f and g be the functions defined by $f(x) = x^4 - 4x^2 + 2x + 2$ and $g(x) = 2 - \sin(\pi x)$. Let A and B be the two regions enclosed by the graphs of f and g shown in the figure.

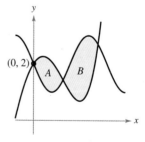

(a) Find the sum of the areas of regions A and B.

(b) Region B is the base of a solid whose cross sections perpendicular to the x-axis are squares. Find the volume of the solid.

(c) Let h be the vertical distance between the graphs of f and g in region B. Find the rate at which h changes with respect to x when $x = 1.2$.

6.3   Volume: The Shell Method

▶ Find the volume of a solid of revolution using the shell method.
▶ Compare the uses of the disk, washer, and shell methods.

The Shell Method

In this section, you will study an alternative method for finding the volume of a solid of revolution. This method is called the **shell method** because it uses cylindrical shells. A comparison of the advantages of the disk and shell methods is given later in this section.

To begin, consider a representative rectangle as shown in Figure 6.27, where w is the width of the rectangle, h is the height of the rectangle, and p is the distance between the axis of revolution and the *center* of the rectangle. When this rectangle is revolved about its axis of revolution, it forms a cylindrical shell (or tube) of thickness w. To find the volume of this shell, consider two cylinders. The radius of the larger cylinder corresponds to the outer radius of the shell, and the radius of the smaller cylinder corresponds to the inner radius of the shell. Because p is the average radius of the shell, you know the outer radius is

$$p + \frac{w}{2} \qquad \text{Outer radius}$$

and the inner radius is

$$p - \frac{w}{2}. \qquad \text{Inner radius}$$

So, the volume of the shell is

$$\text{Volume of shell} = (\text{volume of cylinder}) - (\text{volume of hole})$$
$$= \pi\left(p + \frac{w}{2}\right)^2 h - \pi\left(p - \frac{w}{2}\right)^2 h$$
$$= 2\pi p h w$$
$$= 2\pi(\text{average radius})(\text{height})(\text{thickness}).$$

You can use this formula to find the volume of a solid of revolution. For instance, the plane region in Figure 6.28 is revolved about a line to form the indicated solid. Consider a horizontal rectangle of width Δy. As the plane region is revolved about a line parallel to the x-axis, the rectangle generates a representative shell whose volume is

$$\Delta V = 2\pi[p(y)h(y)]\,\Delta y.$$

You can approximate the volume of the solid by n such shells of thickness Δy, height $h(y_i)$, and average radius $p(y_i)$.

$$\text{Volume of solid} \approx \sum_{i=1}^{n} 2\pi[p(y_i)h(y_i)]\,\Delta y = 2\pi \sum_{i=1}^{n}[p(y_i)h(y_i)]\,\Delta y$$

This approximation appears to become better and better as $\|\Delta\| \to 0 \ (n \to \infty)$. So, the volume of the solid is

$$\text{Volume of solid} = \lim_{\|\Delta\| \to 0} 2\pi \sum_{i=1}^{n}[p(y_i)h(y_i)]\,\Delta y$$
$$= 2\pi \int_{c}^{d} [p(y)h(y)]\,dy.$$

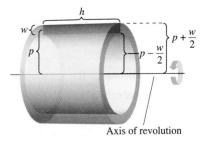

Figure 6.27

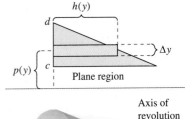

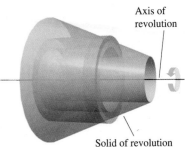

Figure 6.28

The Shell Method

To find the volume of a solid of revolution with the **shell method,** use one of the formulas below. (See Figure 6.29.)

Horizontal Axis of Revolution

$$\text{Volume} = V = 2\pi \int_c^d p(y)h(y)\, dy$$

Vertical Axis of Revolution

$$\text{Volume} = V = 2\pi \int_a^b p(x)h(x)\, dx$$

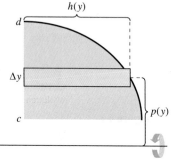

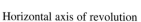

Horizontal axis of revolution

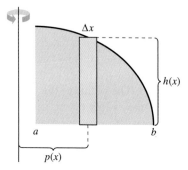

Vertical axis of revolution

Figure 6.29

EXAMPLE 1 Using the Shell Method to Find Volume

Find the volume of the solid formed by revolving the region bounded by

$$y = x - x^3$$

and the x-axis $(0 \le x \le 1)$ about the y-axis.

Solution

Because the axis of revolution is vertical, use a vertical representative rectangle, as shown in Figure 6.30. The width Δx indicates that x is the variable of integration. The distance from the center of the rectangle to the axis of revolution is $p(x) = x$, and the height of the rectangle is

$$h(x) = x - x^3.$$

Because x ranges from 0 to 1, apply the shell method to find the volume of the solid.

$$V = 2\pi \int_a^b p(x)h(x)\, dx$$

$$= 2\pi \int_0^1 x(x - x^3)\, dx$$

$$= 2\pi \int_0^1 (-x^4 + x^2)\, dx \qquad \text{Simplify.}$$

$$= 2\pi \left[-\frac{x^5}{5} + \frac{x^3}{3} \right]_0^1 \qquad \text{Integrate.}$$

$$= 2\pi \left(-\frac{1}{5} + \frac{1}{3} \right)$$

$$= \frac{4\pi}{15}$$

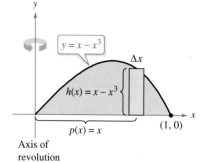

Figure 6.30

EXAMPLE 2   Using the Shell Method to Find Volume

Find the volume of the solid formed by revolving the region bounded by the graph of $x = e^{-y^2}$ and the y-axis ($0 \le y \le 1$) about the x-axis.

Solution

Because the axis of revolution is horizontal, use a horizontal representative rectangle, as shown in Figure 6.31. The width Δy indicates that y is the variable of integration. The distance from the center of the rectangle to the axis of revolution is $p(y) = y$, and the height of the rectangle is $h(y) = e^{-y^2}$. Because y ranges from 0 to 1, the volume of the solid is

$$V = 2\pi \int_c^d p(y)h(y)\,dy \qquad \text{Apply shell method.}$$

$$= 2\pi \int_0^1 ye^{-y^2}\,dy$$

$$= -\pi \left[e^{-y^2} \right]_0^1 \qquad \text{Integrate.}$$

$$= \pi\left(1 - \frac{1}{e}\right)$$

$$\approx 1.986.$$

Check this result using a graphing utility, as shown below.

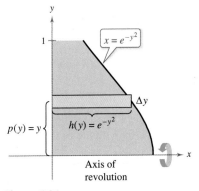

Figure 6.31

$$2\pi \int_0^1 (Ye^{-Y^2})\,dY$$
$$1.985865304$$

Comparison of Disk, Washer, and Shell Methods

The disk, washer, and shell methods can be distinguished as follows. For the disk and washer methods, the representative rectangle is always *perpendicular* to the axis of revolution, whereas for the shell method, the representative rectangle is always *parallel* to the axis of revolution. The washer method and the shell method are compared in Figure 6.32.

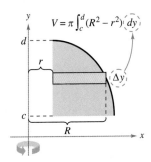

Vertical axis of revolution

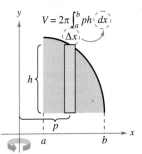

Horizontal axis of revolution

Vertical axis of revolution

Horizontal axis of revolution

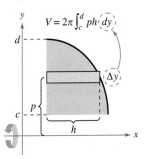

Washer method: Representative rectangle is perpendicular to the axis of revolution.

Shell method: Representative rectangle is parallel to the axis of revolution.

Figure 6.32

Often, one method is more convenient to use than the other. The next example illustrates a case in which the shell method is preferable.

EXAMPLE 3 Shell Method Preferable

See LarsonCalculusforAP.com for an interactive version of this type of example.

Find the volume of the solid formed by revolving the region bounded by the graphs of

$$y = x^2 + 1, \quad y = 0, \quad x = 0, \quad \text{and} \quad x = 1$$

about the *y*-axis.

Solution

In Example 4 in Section 6.2, you saw that the washer method requires two integrals to determine the volume of this solid. See Figure 6.33(a).

$$V = \pi \int_0^1 (1^2 - 0^2)\, dy + \pi \int_1^2 \left[1^2 - \left(\sqrt{y - 1} \right)^2 \right] dy \qquad \text{Apply washer method.}$$

$$= \pi \int_0^1 1\, dy + \pi \int_1^2 (2 - y)\, dy \qquad \text{Simplify.}$$

$$= \pi \Big[y \Big]_0^1 + \pi \left[2y - \frac{y^2}{2} \right]_1^2 \qquad \text{Integrate.}$$

$$= \pi + \pi \left(4 - 2 - 2 + \frac{1}{2} \right)$$

$$= \frac{3\pi}{2}$$

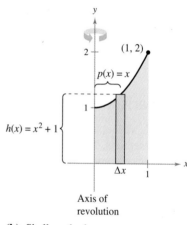

For $1 \le y \le 2$:
$R = 1$
$r = \sqrt{y - 1}$

For $0 \le y \le 1$:
$R = 1$
$r = 0$

Axis of revolution

(a) Disk method

In Figure 6.33(b), you can see that the shell method requires only one integral to find the volume.

$$V = 2\pi \int_a^b p(x)h(x)\, dx \qquad \text{Apply shell method.}$$

$$= 2\pi \int_0^1 x(x^2 + 1)\, dx$$

$$= 2\pi \int_0^1 (x^3 + x)\, dx \qquad \text{Simplify.}$$

$$= 2\pi \left[\frac{x^4}{4} + \frac{x^2}{2} \right]_0^1 \qquad \text{Integrate.}$$

$$= 2\pi \left(\frac{3}{4} \right)$$

$$= \frac{3\pi}{2}$$

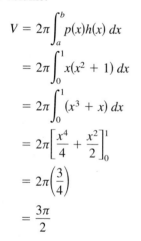

$p(x) = x$

$h(x) = x^2 + 1$

Axis of revolution

(b) Shell method

Figure 6.33

Consider the solid formed by revolving the region in Example 3 about the vertical line $x = 1$. Would the resulting solid of revolution have a greater volume or a smaller volume than the solid in Example 3? Without integrating, you should be able to reason that the resulting solid would have a smaller volume because "more" of the revolved region would be closer to the axis of revolution. To confirm this, try solving the integral

$$V = 2\pi \int_0^1 (1 - x)(x^2 + 1)\, dx \qquad\qquad p(x) = 1 - x$$

which gives the volume of the solid.

EXAMPLE 4 Volume of a Pontoon

A pontoon is to be made in the shape shown in Figure 6.34. The pontoon is designed by revolving the graph of $y = 1 - x^2/16$, $-4 \leq x \leq 4$, about the x-axis, where x and y are measured in feet. Find the volume of the pontoon.

Solution

Refer to Figure 6.35 and use the disk method as shown.

$$V = \pi \int_{-4}^{4} \left(1 - \frac{x^2}{16}\right)^2 dx \qquad \text{Apply disk method.}$$

$$= \pi \int_{-4}^{4} \left(1 - \frac{x^2}{8} + \frac{x^4}{256}\right) dx \qquad \text{Simplify.}$$

$$= \pi \left[x - \frac{x^3}{24} + \frac{x^5}{1280}\right]_{-4}^{4} \qquad \text{Integrate.}$$

$$= \frac{64\pi}{15}$$

$$\approx 13.4 \text{ cubic feet}$$

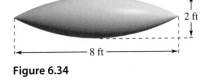

Figure 6.34

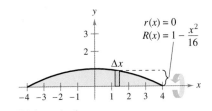

Disk method
Figure 6.35

To use the shell method in Example 4, you would have to solve for x in terms of y in the equation

$$y = 1 - \frac{x^2}{16}$$

and then evaluate an integral that requires a u-substitution.

Sometimes, solving for x is very difficult (or even impossible). In such cases, you must use a vertical rectangle (of width Δx), thus making x the variable of integration. The position (horizontal or vertical) of the axis of revolution then determines the method to be used. This is shown in Example 5.

EXAMPLE 5 Shell Method Necessary

Find the volume of the solid formed by revolving the region bounded by the graphs of $y = x^3 + x + 1$, $y = 1$, and $x = 1$ about the line $x = 2$, as shown in Figure 6.36.

Solution

In the equation $y = x^3 + x + 1$, you cannot easily solve for x in terms of y. Therefore, the variable of integration must be x, and you should choose a vertical representative rectangle. Because the rectangle is parallel to the axis of revolution, use the shell method.

$$V = 2\pi \int_{a}^{b} p(x)h(x) \, dx \qquad \text{Apply shell method.}$$

$$= 2\pi \int_{0}^{1} (2 - x)(x^3 + x + 1 - 1) \, dx$$

$$= 2\pi \int_{0}^{1} (-x^4 + 2x^3 - x^2 + 2x) \, dx \qquad \text{Simplify.}$$

$$= 2\pi \left[-\frac{x^5}{5} + \frac{x^4}{2} - \frac{x^3}{3} + x^2\right]_{0}^{1} \qquad \text{Integrate.}$$

$$= 2\pi \left(-\frac{1}{5} + \frac{1}{2} - \frac{1}{3} + 1\right)$$

$$= \frac{29\pi}{15}$$

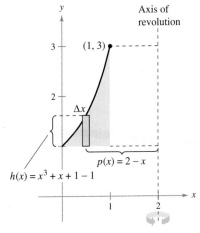

Figure 6.36

6.3   Exercises

See *CalcChat.com* for tutorial help and worked-out solutions to odd-numbered exercises.

Finding the Volume of a Solid In Exercises 1–14, use the shell method to write and evaluate the definite integral that represents the volume of the solid generated by revolving the plane region bounded by the graphs of the equations about the *y*-axis.

1. $y = x$, $y = 0$, $x = 2$ **2.** $y = 1 - x$, $y = 0$, $x = 0$

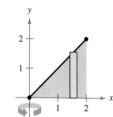 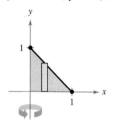

3. $y = \sqrt{x}$, $y = 0$, $x = 4$ **4.** $y = \frac{1}{2}x^2 + 1$, $y = 3$, $x = 0$

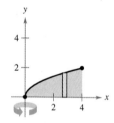 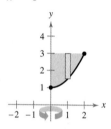

5. $y = \frac{1}{4}x^2$, $y = 0$, $x = 4$ **6.** $y = \frac{1}{2}x^3$, $y = 0$, $x = 3$

7. $y = x^2$, $y = 4x - x^2$ **8.** $y = 9 - x^2$, $y = x^2 + 1$

9. $y = 4x - x^2$, $x = 0$, $y = 4$

10. $y = x^{3/2}$, $y = 8$, $x = 0$

11. $y = \dfrac{1}{\sqrt{2\pi}}e^{-x^2/2}$, $y = 0$, $x = 0$, $x = 1$

12. $y = \begin{cases} \dfrac{\sin x}{x}, & x > 0 \\ 1, & x = 0 \end{cases}$, $y = 0$, $x = 0$, $x = \pi$

Finding the Volume of a Solid In Exercises 13–20, use the shell method to write and evaluate the definite integral that represents the volume of the solid generated by revolving the plane region bounded by the graphs of the equations about the *x*-axis.

13. $y = x$, $y = 0$, $x = 2$ **14.** $y = 1 - x$, $y = 0$, $x = 3$

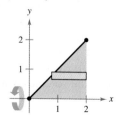 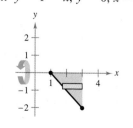

15. $y = \dfrac{1}{x}$, $y = 0$, $x = 1$,   **16.** $x + y^2 = 4$, $y = 0$,
$x = 2$ $x = 0$

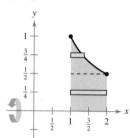 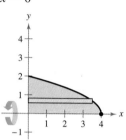

17. $y = x^3$, $x = 0$, $y = 8$

18. $y = 4x^2$, $x = 0$, $y = 4$

19. $y = 1 - \sqrt{x}$, $y = x + 1$, $y = 0$

20. $y = \sqrt{x + 2}$, $y = x$, $y = 0$

Finding the Volume of a Solid In Exercises 21–24, use the shell method to find the volume of the solid generated by revolving the region bounded by the graphs of the equations about the given line.

21. $y = 2x - x^2$, $y = 0$, about the line $x = 4$

22. $y = \sqrt{x}$, $y = 0$, $x = 4$, about the line $x = 6$

23. $y = x^2 + x$, $y = 5x - x^2$, about the line $x = 4$

24. $y = \frac{1}{3}x^3$, $y = 6x - x^2$, about the line $x = 3$

Error Analysis Let *A* be the region enclosed by the graphs of $y = \sqrt{x - 1}$, $y = 0$, $x = 5$, as shown. In Exercises 25–28, describe and correct the error in using the shell method to write the given integral that represents the volume *V* of the solid formed by revolving the region about the line $y = 4$.

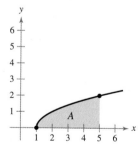

25. $V = 2\pi \displaystyle\int_0^2 y(4 - y^2)\,dy$ ✗

26. $V = 2\pi \displaystyle\int_0^2 (4 + y)(4 - y^2)\,dy$ ✗

27. $V = 2\pi \displaystyle\int_0^2 (4 - y)(y^2 + 1)\,dy$ ✗

28. $V = 2\pi \displaystyle\int_1^5 (4 - y)(4 - y^2)\,dy$ ✗

Choosing a Method   In Exercises 29 and 30, decide whether it is more convenient to use the disk method or the shell method to find the volume of the solid of revolution. Explain your reasoning. (Do not find the volume.)

29. $(y - 2)^2 = 4 - x$ **30.** $y = 4 - e^x$

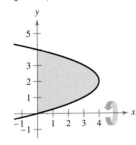   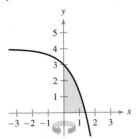

Choosing a Method   In Exercises 31–34, use the disk method *or* the shell method to find the volumes of the solids generated by revolving the region bounded by the graphs of the equations about the given lines.

31. $y = x^3$, $y = 0$, $x = 2$

   (a) x-axis   (b) y-axis   (c) $x = 4$

32. $y = \dfrac{10}{x^2}$, $y = 0$, $x = 1$, $x = 5$

   (a) x-axis   (b) y-axis   (c) $y = 10$

33. $x^{1/2} + y^{1/2} = a^{1/2}$, $x = 0$, $y = 0$

   (a) x-axis   (b) y-axis   (c) $x = a$

34. $x^{2/3} + y^{2/3} = a^{2/3}$, $a > 0$ (hypocycloid)

   (a) x-axis   (b) y-axis

Finding the Volume of a Solid   In Exercises 35–38, (a) use a graphing utility to graph the plane region bounded by the graphs of the equations, and (b) use the integration capabilities of the graphing utility to approximate the volume of the solid generated by revolving the region about the *y*-axis.

35. $x^{4/3} + y^{4/3} = 1$, $x = 0$, $y = 0$,   first quadrant

36. $y = \sqrt{1 - x^3}$, $y = 0$, $x = 0$

37. $y = \sqrt[3]{(x - 2)^2(x - 6)^2}$, $y = 0$, $x = 2$, $x = 6$

38. $y = \dfrac{2}{1 + e^{1/x}}$, $y = 0$, $x = 1$, $x = 3$

EXPLORING CONCEPTS

39. Communicating   Consider a solid that is generated by revolving a plane region about the *y*-axis. Describe the position of a representative rectangle when using (a) the shell method and (b) the disk method to find the volume of the solid.

40. Reasoning   Consider the plane region bounded by the graphs of $y = k$, $y = 0$, $x = 0$, and $x = b$, where $k > 0$ and $b > 0$. What are the heights and radii of the cylinders generated when this region is revolved about (a) the x-axis and (b) the y-axis?

EXPLORING CONCEPTS (continued)

41. Comparing Integrals   Give a geometric argument that explains why the integrals have equal values.

   (a) $\pi \displaystyle\int_1^5 (x - 1)\, dx = 2\pi \int_0^2 y[5 - (y^2 + 1)]\, dy$

   (b) $\pi \displaystyle\int_0^2 [16 - (2y)^2]\, dy = 2\pi \int_0^4 x\!\left(\frac{x}{2}\right) dx$

 42. HOW DO YOU SEE IT?   Use the graph to answer the following.

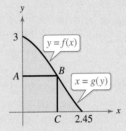

   (a) Describe the figure generated by revolving segment AB about the y-axis.

   (b) Describe the figure generated by revolving segment BC about the y-axis.

   (c) A solid is generated by revolving the region bounded by the curve, $y = 0$, and $x = 0$ about the y-axis. Write integrals to find the volume of this solid using the disk method and the shell method. (Do not integrate.)

Analyzing an Integral   In Exercises 43–48, the integral represents the volume of a solid of revolution. Identify (a) the plane region that is revolved and (b) the axis of revolution.

43. $2\pi \displaystyle\int_0^2 x^3\, dx$ **44.** $2\pi \displaystyle\int_0^1 (y - y^{3/2})\, dy$

45. $2\pi \displaystyle\int_0^1 (4 - x)e^x\, dx$ **46.** $2\pi \displaystyle\int_0^6 (y + 2)\sqrt{6 - y}\, dy$

47. $2\pi \displaystyle\int_1^8 \left(\frac{4x + 5}{2x}\right) dx$ **48.** $2\pi \displaystyle\int_{1/2}^5 (3x^2 + 2)\, dx$

49. Comparing Volumes   Two types of buckets are available at a hardware store. The first bucket has a shape that can be generated by revolving the region bounded by the graphs of $y = 5$ and $y = 5x^4/16$ about the y-axis. The second bucket can be generated by revolving the region bounded by the graphs of $y = 4$ and $y = x^8/64$ about the y-axis. Which bucket holds more water? Find the difference in the volumes, where the volume is measured in cups.

50. Comparing Volumes   You have two different soup bowls. One bowl has a shape that can be generated by revolving the region bounded by the graphs of $y = 9/2$ and $y = x^2/2$ about the y-axis. The other bowl can be generated by revolving the region bounded by the graphs of $y = 4$ and $y = x^2/4$ about the y-axis. Which bowl holds more soup? Find the difference in the volumes, where the volume is measured in ounces.

51. Volume of a Solid   A bead is formed by drilling a round hole with a radius of 1 centimeter through a sphere generated by revolving the graph of $y = \sqrt{9 - x^2}$ about the x-axis. What is the volume of the bead?

52. Volume of a Solid   A bead is formed by drilling a round hole through a solid generated by revolving the graph of $y = \sqrt{16 - x^4}$ about the x-axis. The volume of the finished bead is about 133 cubic millimeters. What is the volume of the section removed to create the hole?

53. Machine Part   A solid is generated by revolving the region bounded by $y = \frac{1}{2}x^2$ and $y = 2$ about the y-axis. A hole, centered along the axis of revolution, is drilled through this solid so that one-fourth of the volume is removed. Find the diameter of the hole.

54. Machine Part   A solid is generated by revolving the region bounded by $y = \sqrt{9 - x^2}$ and $y = 0$ about the y-axis. A hole, centered along the axis of revolution, is drilled through this solid so that one-third of the volume is removed. Find the diameter of the hole.

55. Finding Volumes of Solids   Use differentiation to verify that $\int x \sin x \, dx = \sin x - x \cos x + C$. Use this result to find the volume of the solid generated by revolving each plane region about the y-axis.

(a) 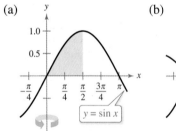   (b)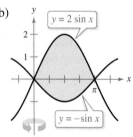

56. Finding Volumes of Solids   Use differentiation to verify that $\int x \cos x \, dx = \cos x + x \sin x + C$. Use this result to find the volume of the solid generated by revolving each plane region about the y-axis.

(a) 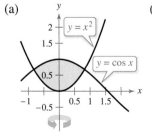   (b)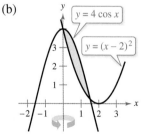

57. Volume of a Torus   A torus is formed by revolving the region bounded by the circle $x^2 + y^2 = 1$ about the line $x = 2$ (see figure). Find the volume of this "doughnut-shaped" solid. (*Hint:* The integral $\int_{-1}^{1} \sqrt{1 - x^2} \, dx$ represents the area of a semicircle.)

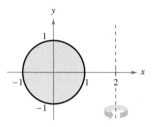

58. Volume of a Torus   Repeat Exercise 57 for a torus formed by revolving the region bounded by the circle $x^2 + y^2 = r^2$ about the line $x = R$, where $r < R$.

59. Equal Volumes   Let V_1 and V_2 be the volumes of the solids that result when the plane region bounded by $y = 1/x$, $y = 0$, $x = \frac{1}{4}$, and $x = c$ $\left(\text{where } c > \frac{1}{4}\right)$ is revolved about the x-axis and the y-axis, respectively. Find the value of c for which $V_1 = V_2$.

60. Volume of a Segment of a Paraboloid   The region bounded by $y = r^2 - x^2$, $y = 0$, and $x = 0$ is revolved about the y-axis to form a paraboloid. A hole, centered along the axis of revolution, is drilled through this solid. The hole has a radius k, $0 < k < r$. Find the volume of the resulting ring (a) by integrating with respect to x and (b) by integrating with respect to y.

61. Connecting Concepts   Consider the region bounded by the graphs of $y = ax^n$, $y = ab^n$, and $x = 0$, as shown in the figure.

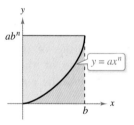

(a) Find the ratio $R_1(n)$ of the area of the region to the area of the circumscribed rectangle. Then find $\lim\limits_{n \to \infty} R_1(n)$.

(b) Find the volume of the solid of revolution formed by revolving the region about the y-axis. Find the ratio $R_2(n)$ of this volume to the volume of the circumscribed right circular cylinder. Then find $\lim\limits_{n \to \infty} R_2(n)$.

(c) Use the results of the limits from parts (a) and (b) to make a conjecture about the shape of the region bounded by the graphs of $y = ab^n$, $x = 0$, and $y = ax^n$ $(0 \le x \le b)$ as $n \to \infty$ for the following values of b.

  (i) $b < 1$ (ii) $b = 1$ (iii) $b > 1$

62. Connecting Concepts   Match each integral with the solid whose volume it represents.

(a) Right circular cone   (b) Torus   (c) Sphere

(d) Right circular cylinder   (e) Ellipsoid

(i) $2\pi \displaystyle\int_0^r hx \, dx$ (ii) $2\pi \displaystyle\int_0^r hx\left(1 - \dfrac{x}{r}\right) dx$

(iii) $2\pi \displaystyle\int_0^r 2x\sqrt{r^2 - x^2} \, dx$

(iv) $2\pi \displaystyle\int_0^b 2ax\sqrt{1 - \dfrac{x^2}{b^2}} \, dx$

(v) $2\pi \displaystyle\int_{-r}^r (R - x)\left(2\sqrt{r^2 - x^2}\right) dx$

63. Finding Volumes of Solids   Use a graphing utility to graph the function $y^2 = x(4 - x)^2$. Find the volumes of the solids that are generated when the loop of this graph is revolved about (a) the x-axis, (b) the y-axis, and (c) the line $x = 4$.

Calculus AP® – Exam Preparation Questions

64. Multiple Choice   The region shown in the figure is revolved about the x-axis, the y-axis, and the line $x = 4$. Which of the following orders the volumes of the resulting solids from least to greatest?

(A) x-axis, $x = 4$, y-axis

(B) x-axis, y-axis, $x = 4$

(C) $x = 4$, x-axis, y-axis

(D) $x = 4$, y-axis, x-axis

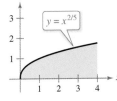

$y = x^{2/5}$

65. Multiple Choice   Let A be the region bounded by the graphs of $y = 4\sqrt{x}$, $y = 4$, and $x = 0$. What is the volume of the solid formed when A is revolved about the line $x = -\frac{3}{2}$?

(A) $\dfrac{4\pi}{5}$ (B) $\dfrac{16\pi}{5}$ (C) $\dfrac{24\pi}{5}$ (D) $\dfrac{56\pi}{5}$

66. Multiple Choice   Let R be the region enclosed by the graphs of $y = \frac{1}{8}(x - 4)^2$ and $y = 2$. What is the volume of the solid formed when R is revolved about the line $x = 10$?

(A) $\dfrac{128\pi}{3}$ (B) 128π (C) $\dfrac{256\pi}{3}$ (D) 256π

67. Free Response   Let T be the region bounded by the graphs of $y = 4/(x + 2)$ and $y = 2 - \frac{2}{5}x$.

(a) Find the area of the region.

(b) What is the volume of the solid formed when T is revolved about the y-axis?

(c) What is the volume of the solid formed when T is revolved about the x-axis?

Saturn

The Oblateness of Saturn   Saturn is the most oblate of the planets in our solar system. Its equatorial radius is 60,268 kilometers and its polar radius is 54,364 kilometers. The color-enhanced photograph of Saturn was taken by Voyager 1. In the photograph, the oblateness of Saturn is clearly visible.

(a) Find the ratio of the volumes of the sphere and the oblate ellipsoid shown below.

(b) If a planet were spherical and had the same volume as Saturn, what would its radius be?

Computer model of "spherical Saturn," whose equatorial radius is equal to its polar radius. The equation of the cross section passing through the pole is

$x^2 + y^2 = 60{,}268^2.$

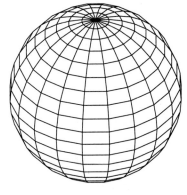

Computer model of "oblate Saturn," whose equatorial radius is greater than its polar radius. The equation of the cross section passing through the pole is

$\dfrac{x^2}{60{,}268^2} + \dfrac{y^2}{54{,}364^2} = 1.$

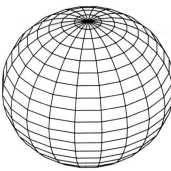

6.4 Arc Length and Surfaces of Revolution

▶ Find the arc length of a smooth curve.
▶ Find the area of a surface of revolution.

Arc Length

In this section, definite integrals are used to find the arc lengths of curves and the areas of surfaces of revolution. In either case, an arc (a segment of a curve) is approximated by straight line segments whose lengths are given by the familiar Distance Formula

$$d = \sqrt{(x_2 - x_1)^2 + (y_2 - y_1)^2}.$$

A **rectifiable** curve is one that has a finite arc length. You will see that a sufficient condition for the graph of a function f to be rectifiable between $(a, f(a))$ and $(b, f(b))$ is that f' be continuous on $[a, b]$. Such a function is **continuously differentiable** on $[a, b]$, and its graph on the interval $[a, b]$ is a **smooth curve.**

Consider a function $y = f(x)$ that is continuously differentiable on the interval $[a, b]$. You can approximate the graph of f by n line segments whose endpoints are determined by the partition

$$a = x_0 < x_1 < x_2 < \cdots < x_n = b$$

as shown in Figure 6.37. By letting $\Delta x_i = x_i - x_{i-1}$ and $\Delta y_i = y_i - y_{i-1}$, you can approximate the length of the graph by

$$s \approx \sum_{i=1}^{n} \sqrt{(x_i - x_{i-1})^2 + (y_i - y_{i-1})^2}$$

$$= \sum_{i=1}^{n} \sqrt{(\Delta x_i)^2 + (\Delta y_i)^2}$$

$$= \sum_{i=1}^{n} \sqrt{(\Delta x_i)^2 + \left(\frac{\Delta y_i}{\Delta x_i}\right)^2 (\Delta x_i)^2}$$

$$= \sum_{i=1}^{n} \sqrt{1 + \left(\frac{\Delta y_i}{\Delta x_i}\right)^2} (\Delta x_i).$$

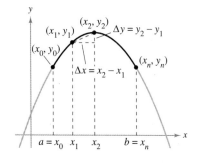

This approximation appears to become better and better as $\|\Delta\| \to 0$ $(n \to \infty)$. So, the length of the graph is

$$s = \lim_{\|\Delta\| \to 0} \sum_{i=1}^{n} \sqrt{1 + \left(\frac{\Delta y_i}{\Delta x_i}\right)^2} (\Delta x_i).$$

Because $f'(x)$ exists for each x in (x_{i-1}, x_i), the Mean Value Theorem guarantees the existence of c_i in (x_{i-1}, x_i) such that

$$\frac{f(x_i) - f(x_{i-1})}{x_i - x_{i-1}} = f'(c_i)$$

$$\frac{\Delta y_i}{\Delta x_i} = f'(c_i).$$

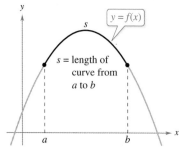

Figure 6.37

Because f' is continuous on $[a, b]$, it follows that $\sqrt{1 + [f'(x)]^2}$ is also continuous (and therefore integrable) on $[a, b]$, which implies that

$$s = \lim_{\|\Delta\| \to 0} \sum_{i=1}^{n} \sqrt{1 + [f'(c_i)]^2} (\Delta x_i)$$

$$= \int_a^b \sqrt{1 + [f'(x)]^2}\, dx$$

where s is called the **arc length** of f between a and b.

Definition of Arc Length

Let the function $y = f(x)$ represent a smooth curve on the interval $[a, b]$. The **arc length** of f between a and b is

$$s = \int_a^b \sqrt{1 + [f'(x)]^2}\, dx.$$

Similarly, for a smooth curve $x = g(y)$, the **arc length** of g between c and d is

$$s = \int_c^d \sqrt{1 + [g'(y)]^2}\, dy.$$

Insight

Finding the arc length of the graph of a function on an interval is tested on the AP® Calculus BC Exam.

Because the definition of arc length can be applied to a linear function, you can check to see that this new definition agrees with the standard Distance Formula for the length of a line segment. This is shown in Example 1.

EXAMPLE 1   The Length of a Line Segment

Find the arc length from (x_1, y_1) to (x_2, y_2) on the graph of $f(x) = mx + b$, as shown in the figure.

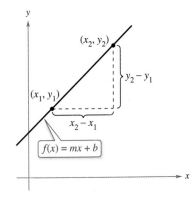

Solution

Because

$$f'(x) = m = \frac{y_2 - y_1}{x_2 - x_1}$$

it follows that

$$
\begin{aligned}
s &= \int_{x_1}^{x_2} \sqrt{1 + [f'(x)]^2}\, dx && \text{Formula for arc length} \\
&= \int_{x_1}^{x_2} \sqrt{1 + \left(\frac{y_2 - y_1}{x_2 - x_1}\right)^2}\, dx \\
&= \sqrt{\frac{(x_2 - x_1)^2 + (y_2 - y_1)^2}{(x_2 - x_1)^2}}\, (x) \Big]_{x_1}^{x_2} && \text{Integrate and simplify.} \\
&= \sqrt{\frac{(x_2 - x_1)^2 + (y_2 - y_1)^2}{(x_2 - x_1)^2}}\, (x_2 - x_1) \\
&= \sqrt{(x_2 - x_1)^2 + (y_2 - y_1)^2}
\end{aligned}
$$

which is the formula for the distance between two points in the plane.

Technology

Definite integrals representing arc length often are very difficult to evaluate. In this section, a few examples are presented. In the next chapter, with more advanced integration techniques, you will be able to tackle more difficult arc length problems. In the meantime, remember that you can always use a numerical integration program to approximate an arc length. For instance, use the *integral* feature of a graphing utility to approximate the arc lengths in Examples 2 and 3.

EXAMPLE 2   Finding Arc Length

Find the arc length of the graph of $y = x^3/6 + 1/(2x)$ on the interval $\left[\frac{1}{2}, 2\right]$, as shown in Figure 6.38.

Solution

Using $\dfrac{dy}{dx} = \dfrac{3x^2}{6} - \dfrac{1}{2x^2} = \dfrac{1}{2}\left(x^2 - \dfrac{1}{x^2}\right)$ yields an arc length of

$$
\begin{aligned}
s &= \int_a^b \sqrt{1 + \left(\frac{dy}{dx}\right)^2}\, dx && \text{Formula for arc length}\\
&= \int_{1/2}^2 \sqrt{1 + \left[\frac{1}{2}\left(x^2 - \frac{1}{x^2}\right)\right]^2}\, dx\\
&= \int_{1/2}^2 \sqrt{\frac{1}{4}\left(x^4 + 2 + \frac{1}{x^4}\right)}\, dx\\
&= \frac{1}{2}\int_{1/2}^2 \left(x^2 + \frac{1}{x^2}\right) dx && \text{Simplify.}\\
&= \frac{1}{2}\left[\frac{x^3}{3} - \frac{1}{x}\right]_{1/2}^2 && \text{Integrate.}\\
&= \frac{1}{2}\left(\frac{13}{6} + \frac{47}{24}\right)\\
&= \frac{33}{16}.
\end{aligned}
$$

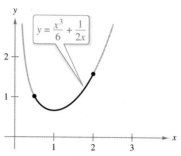

The arc length of the graph of y on $\left[\frac{1}{2}, 2\right]$
Figure 6.38

Algebra Review

For help on the algebra in Example 2, see Example 4(a) in the *Chapter 6 Algebra Review* on page A47.

EXAMPLE 3   Finding Arc Length

Find the arc length of the graph of $(y - 1)^3 = x^2$ on the interval $[0, 8]$, as shown in Figure 6.39.

Solution

On the interval $[0, 8]$, $dy/dx = \frac{2}{3}x^{-1/3}$ is not defined at 0. So, solve for x in terms of y: $x = \pm(y - 1)^{3/2}$. Choosing the positive value of x produces

$$\frac{dx}{dy} = \frac{3}{2}(y - 1)^{1/2}.$$

The x-interval $[0, 8]$ corresponds to the y-interval $[1, 5]$, and the arc length is

$$
\begin{aligned}
s &= \int_c^d \sqrt{1 + \left(\frac{dx}{dy}\right)^2}\, dy && \text{Formula for arc length}\\
&= \int_1^5 \sqrt{1 + \left[\frac{3}{2}(y - 1)^{1/2}\right]^2}\, dy\\
&= \int_1^5 \sqrt{\frac{9}{4}y - \frac{5}{4}}\, dy\\
&= \frac{1}{2}\int_1^5 \sqrt{9y - 5}\, dy && \text{Simplify.}\\
&= \frac{1}{18}\left[\frac{(9y - 5)^{3/2}}{3/2}\right]_1^5 && \text{Integrate.}\\
&= \frac{1}{27}(40^{3/2} - 4^{3/2})\\
&\approx 9.073.
\end{aligned}
$$

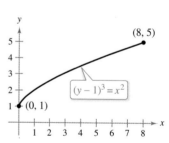

The arc length of the graph of y on $[0, 8]$
Figure 6.39

Algebra Review

For help on the algebra in Example 3, see Example 4(b) in the *Chapter 6 Algebra Review* on page A47.

EXAMPLE 4   Finding Arc Length

See LarsonCalculusforAP.com for an interactive version of this type of example.

Find the arc length of the graph of $y = \ln(\cos x)$ from $x = 0$ to $x = \pi/4$, as shown in Figure 6.40.

Solution

Using

$$\frac{dy}{dx} = -\frac{\sin x}{\cos x} = -\tan x$$

yields an arc length of

$$\begin{aligned}
s &= \int_a^b \sqrt{1 + \left(\frac{dy}{dx}\right)^2}\, dx && \text{Formula for arc length}\\
&= \int_0^{\pi/4} \sqrt{1 + \tan^2 x}\, dx \\
&= \int_0^{\pi/4} \sqrt{\sec^2 x}\, dx && \text{Trigonometric identity}\\
&= \int_0^{\pi/4} \sec x\, dx && \text{Simplify.}\\
&= \Big[\ln|\sec x + \tan x|\Big]_0^{\pi/4} && \text{Integrate.}\\
&= \ln\left(\sqrt{2} + 1\right) - \ln 1 \\
&\approx 0.881.
\end{aligned}$$

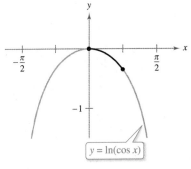

The arc length of the graph of y on $\left[0, \dfrac{\pi}{4}\right]$

Figure 6.40

EXAMPLE 5   Length of a Cable

An electric cable is hung between two towers that are 200 feet apart, as shown in Figure 6.41. The cable takes the shape of a catenary whose equation is

$$y = 75\left(e^{x/150} + e^{-x/150}\right).$$

Find the arc length of the cable between the two towers.

Solution

Because $y' = \frac{1}{2}\left(e^{x/150} - e^{-x/150}\right)$, you can write

$$(y')^2 = \frac{1}{4}\left(e^{x/75} - 2 + e^{-x/75}\right)$$

and

$$1 + (y')^2 = \frac{1}{4}\left(e^{x/75} + 2 + e^{-x/75}\right) = \left[\frac{1}{2}\left(e^{x/150} + e^{-x/150}\right)\right]^2.$$

Therefore, the arc length of the cable is

$$\begin{aligned}
s &= \int_a^b \sqrt{1 + (y')^2}\, dx && \text{Formula for arc length}\\
&= \frac{1}{2}\int_{-100}^{100}\left(e^{x/150} + e^{-x/150}\right) dx \\
&= 75\left[e^{x/150} - e^{-x/150}\right]_{-100}^{100} && \text{Integrate.}\\
&= 150\left(e^{2/3} - e^{-2/3}\right) \\
&\approx 215 \text{ feet.}
\end{aligned}$$

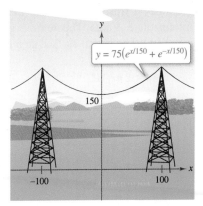

$y = 75\left(e^{x/150} + e^{-x/150}\right)$

Figure 6.41

Area of a Surface of Revolution

In Sections 6.2 and 6.3, integration was used to calculate the volume of a solid of revolution. You will now look at a procedure for finding the area of a surface of revolution.

> ### Definition of Surface of Revolution
>
> When the graph of a continuous function is revolved about a line, the resulting surface is a **surface of revolution.**

The area of a surface of revolution is derived from the formula for the lateral surface area of the frustum of a right circular cone. Consider the line segment in Figure 6.42, where L is the length of the line segment, r_1 is the radius at the left end of the line segment, and r_2 is the radius at the right end of the line segment. When the line segment is revolved about its axis of revolution, it forms a frustum of a right circular cone, with

$$S = 2\pi r L \qquad \text{Lateral surface area of frustum}$$

where

$$r = \frac{1}{2}(r_1 + r_2). \qquad \text{Average radius of frustum}$$

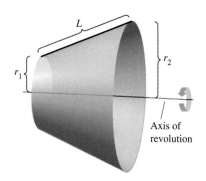

Figure 6.42

(In Exercise 52, you are asked to verify the formula for S.)

Consider a function f that has a continuous derivative on the interval $[a, b]$. The graph of f is revolved about the x-axis to form a surface of revolution, as shown in Figure 6.43. Let Δ be a partition of $[a, b]$, with subintervals of width Δx_i. Then the line segment of length

$$\Delta L_i = \sqrt{(\Delta x_i)^2 + (\Delta y_i)^2}$$

generates a frustum of a cone. Let r_i be the average radius of this frustum. By the Intermediate Value Theorem, a point d_i exists (in the ith subinterval) such that $r_i = f(d_i)$. The lateral surface area ΔS_i of the frustum is

$$\Delta S_i = 2\pi r_i \, \Delta L_i = 2\pi f(d_i)\sqrt{(\Delta x_i)^2 + (\Delta y_i)^2} = 2\pi f(d_i)\sqrt{1 + \left(\frac{\Delta y_i}{\Delta x_i}\right)^2}\, \Delta x_i.$$

By the Mean Value Theorem, a number c_i exists in (x_{i-1}, x_i) such that

$$f'(c_i) = \frac{f(x_i) - f(x_{i-1})}{x_i - x_{i-1}}$$

$$= \frac{\Delta y_i}{\Delta x_i}.$$

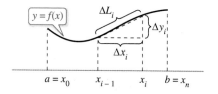

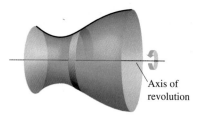

Figure 6.43

So, $\Delta S_i = 2\pi f(d_i)\sqrt{1 + [f'(c_i)]^2}\, \Delta x_i$, and the total surface area can be approximated by

$$S \approx 2\pi \sum_{i=1}^{n} f(d_i)\sqrt{1 + [f'(c_i)]^2}\, \Delta x_i.$$

It can be shown that the limit of the right side as $\|\Delta\| \to 0 \ (n \to \infty)$ is

$$S = 2\pi \int_a^b f(x)\sqrt{1 + [f'(x)]^2}\, dx. \qquad f \text{ is revolved about the } x\text{-axis.}$$

In a similar manner, if the graph of f is revolved about the y-axis, then S is

$$S = 2\pi \int_a^b x\sqrt{1 + [f'(x)]^2}\, dx. \qquad f \text{ is revolved about the } y\text{-axis.}$$

(See Figure 6.44 on the next page.)

In the two formulas for S on the preceding page, you can regard the products $2\pi f(x)$ and $2\pi x$ as the circumferences of the circles traced by a point (x, y) on the graph of f as it is revolved about the x-axis and the y-axis (see Figure 6.44). In one case, the radius is $r = f(x)$, and in the other case, the radius is $r = x$. Moreover, by appropriately adjusting r, you can generalize the formula for surface area to cover *any* horizontal or vertical axis of revolution, as indicated in the next definition.

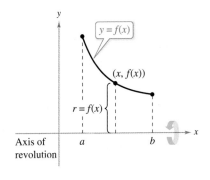

Definition of the Area of a Surface of Revolution

Let $y = f(x)$ have a continuous derivative on the interval $[a, b]$. The area S of the surface of revolution formed by revolving the graph of f about a horizontal or vertical axis is

$$S = 2\pi \int_a^b r(x) \sqrt{1 + [f'(x)]^2}\, dx \qquad y \text{ is a function of } x.$$

where $r(x)$ is the distance between the graph of f and the axis of revolution. If $x = g(y)$ on the interval $[c, d]$, then the surface area is

$$S = 2\pi \int_c^d r(y) \sqrt{1 + [g'(y)]^2}\, dy \qquad x \text{ is a function of } y.$$

where $r(y)$ is the distance between the graph of g and the axis of revolution.

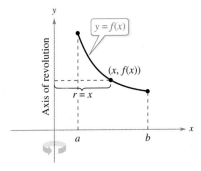

Figure 6.44

The formulas in this definition are sometimes written as

$$S = 2\pi \int_a^b r(x)\, ds \qquad y \text{ is a function of } x.$$

and

$$S = 2\pi \int_c^d r(y)\, ds \qquad x \text{ is a function of } y.$$

where $ds = \sqrt{1 + [f'(x)]^2}\, dx$ and $ds = \sqrt{1 + [g'(y)]^2}\, dy$, respectively.

EXAMPLE 6   The Area of a Surface of Revolution

Find the area of the surface formed by revolving the graph of $f(x) = x^3$ on the interval $[0, 1]$ about the x-axis, as shown in Figure 6.45.

Solution

The distance between the x-axis and the graph of f is $r(x) = f(x)$, and because $f'(x) = 3x^2$, the surface area is

$$S = 2\pi \int_a^b r(x) \sqrt{1 + [f'(x)]^2}\, dx \qquad \text{Formula for surface area}$$

$$= 2\pi \int_0^1 x^3 \sqrt{1 + (3x^2)^2}\, dx$$

$$= \frac{2\pi}{36} \int_0^1 (36x^3)(1 + 9x^4)^{1/2}\, dx \qquad \text{Simplify.}$$

$$= \frac{\pi}{18} \left[\frac{(1 + 9x^4)^{3/2}}{3/2} \right]_0^1 \qquad \text{Integrate.}$$

$$= \frac{\pi}{27}(10^{3/2} - 1)$$

$$\approx 3.563.$$

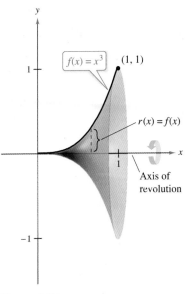

Figure 6.45

6.4 Exercises

Finding Distance Using Two Methods In Exercises 1 and 2, find the distance between the points using (a) the Distance Formula and (b) integration.

1. $(0, 0)$, $(12, 9)$

2. $(-1, 4)$, $(3, 1)$

Finding Arc Length In Exercises 3–18, find the arc length of the graph of the function over the indicated interval.

3. $y = \frac{2}{3}x^{3/2} + 1$

4. $y = 2x^{3/2} + 3$

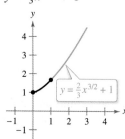
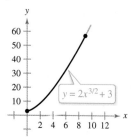

5. $y = \frac{2}{3}(x^2 + 1)^{3/2}$

6. $y = \frac{x^3}{3} + \frac{1}{4x}$

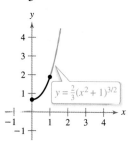
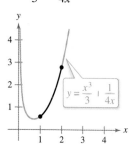

7. $y = \frac{3}{2}x^{2/3}$, $[1, 8]$

8. $y = \frac{3}{2}x^{2/3} + 4$, $[1, 27]$

9. $y = \frac{x^5}{10} + \frac{1}{6x^3}$, $[2, 5]$

10. $y = \frac{x^4}{8} + \frac{1}{4x^2}$, $[1, 3]$

11. $y = \ln(\sin x)$, $\left[\frac{\pi}{4}, \frac{3\pi}{4}\right]$

12. $y = \ln(2 \cos x)$, $\left[-\frac{\pi}{3}, \frac{\pi}{3}\right]$

13. $y = \frac{1}{2}(e^x + e^{-x})$, $[-1, 0]$

14. $y = 4e^x + \frac{1}{16}e^{-x}$, $[\ln 2, \ln 4]$

15. $(x - 5)^2 = 4y^3$, $5 \le x \le 7$

16. $(y + 3)^3 = (x - 1)^2$, $1 \le x \le 9$

17. $x = \frac{1}{3}(y^2 + 2)^{3/2}$, $0 \le y \le 4$

18. $x = \frac{1}{3}\sqrt{y}(y - 3)$, $1 \le y \le 4$

Approximation In Exercises 19 and 20, determine which value best approximates the arc length represented by the integral. Make your selection on the basis of a sketch of the arc, not by performing calculations.

19. $\int_0^2 \sqrt{1 + \left[\frac{d}{dx}\left(\frac{5}{x^2 + 1}\right)\right]^2}\, dx$

(a) 1 (b) 3 (c) 5 (d) 7

20. $\int_0^{\pi/4} \sqrt{1 + \left[\frac{d}{dx}(\tan x)\right]^2}\, dx$

(a) 1 (b) 2 (c) 3 (d) 4

Finding Arc Length In Exercises 21–30, (a) sketch the graph of the function, highlighting the given interval, (b) write a definite integral that represents the arc length of the curve over the indicated interval and observe that the integral cannot be evaluated with the techniques studied so far, and (c) use the integration capabilities of a graphing utility to approximate the arc length.

21. $y = 4 - x^2$, $0 \le x \le 2$

22. $y = x^2 + x - 2$, $-2 \le x \le 1$

23. $y = \frac{1}{x}$, $1 \le x \le 3$

24. $y = \frac{1}{x + 1}$, $0 \le x \le 1$

25. $y = \sin x$, $0 \le x \le \pi$

26. $y = \cos x$, $-\frac{\pi}{2} \le x \le \frac{\pi}{2}$

27. $x = e^{-y}$, $0 \le y \le 2$

28. $y = \ln x$, $1 \le x \le 5$

29. $y = 2 \arctan x$, $0 \le x \le 1$

30. $x = \sqrt{36 - y^2}$, $0 \le y \le 3$

31. Error Analysis Describe and correct the error in finding the integral that gives the arc length s of the graph of $y = \tan x$ over the interval $[a, b]$, where $0 < a < b < \pi/2$.

$$s = \int_a^b \sqrt{1 + \left(\frac{dy}{dx}\right)^2}\, dx$$
$$= \int_a^b \sqrt{1 + (\sec x)^2}\, dx$$
$$= \int_a^b \sqrt{1 + \sec^2 x}\, dx \quad ✗$$

32. Error Analysis Describe and correct the error in finding the integral that gives the arc length s of the graph of $y = x^{1/3}$ over the interval $[-2, 2]$.

$$s = \int_{-2}^2 \sqrt{1 + (y')^2}\, dx$$
$$= \int_{-2}^2 \sqrt{1 + \left(\frac{1}{3x^{2/3}}\right)^2}\, dx$$
$$= \int_{-2}^2 \sqrt{1 + \frac{1}{9x^{4/3}}}\, dx \quad ✗$$

33. Length of a Catenary Electrical wires suspended between two towers form a catenary (see figure) modeled by the equation $y = 10(e^{x/20} + e^{-x/20})$, $-20 \le x \le 20$, where x and y are measured in meters. The towers are 40 meters apart. Find the length of the suspended cable.

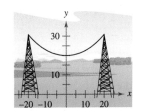

34. ROOF AREA

A barn is 100 feet long and 40 feet wide (see figure).

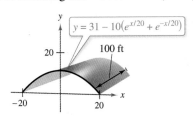

$$y = 31 - 10(e^{x/20} + e^{-x/20})$$

A cross section of the roof is the inverted catenary $y = 31 - 10(e^{x/20} + e^{-x/20})$. Find the number of square feet of roofing on the barn.

35. Astroid Find the total length of the graph of the astroid $x^{2/3} + y^{2/3} = 4$.

36. Arc Length of a Sector of a Circle Find the arc length from $(-3, 4)$ clockwise to $(4, 3)$ along the circle $x^2 + y^2 = 25$. Show that the result is one-fourth the circumference of the circle.

 Finding the Area of a Surface of Revolution In Exercises 37–42, write and evaluate the definite integral that represents the area of the surface generated by revolving the curve on the indicated interval about the x-axis.

37. $y = 3x$, $0 \le x \le 3$

38. $y = -2x + 1$, $2 \le x \le 6$

39. $y = \dfrac{1}{3}x^3$, $0 \le x \le 3$

40. $y = 2\sqrt{x}$, $4 \le x \le 9$

41. $y = \sqrt{4 - x^2}$, $-1 \le x \le 1$

42. $y = \sqrt{9 - x^2}$, $-2 \le x \le 2$

 Finding the Area of a Surface of Revolution In Exercises 43–46, write and evaluate the definite integral that represents the area of the surface generated by revolving the curve on the indicated interval about the y-axis.

43. $y = \sqrt[3]{x} + 2$, $[1, 8]$ **44.** $y = 9 - x^2$, $[0, 3]$

45. $y = 1 - \dfrac{x^2}{4}$, $[0, 2]$ **46.** $y = \dfrac{x}{2} + 3$, $[1, 5]$

EXPLORING CONCEPTS

47. Notation What precalculus formula and representative element are used to develop the integration formula for (a) arc length and (b) area of a surface of revolution?

48. Reasoning Can the arc length of any function f that is continuous on $[a, b]$ be calculated by evaluating $s = \int_a^b \sqrt{1 + [f'(x)]^2}\, dx$? Explain why or why not.

49. Exploring Relationships Consider the function $f(x) = \frac{1}{4}e^x + e^{-x}$. Compare the definite integral of f on the interval $[a, b]$ with the arc length of f over the interval $[a, b]$.

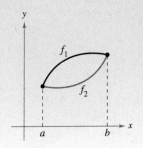 **HOW DO YOU SEE IT?** The graphs of the functions f_1 and f_2 on the interval $[a, b]$ are shown in the figure. The graph of each function is revolved about the x-axis. Which surface of revolution has the greater surface area? Explain.

51. Think About It The figure shows the graphs of the functions $y_1 = x$, $y_2 = \frac{1}{2}x^{3/2}$, $y_3 = \frac{1}{4}x^2$, and $y_4 = \frac{1}{8}x^{5/2}$ on the interval $[0, 4]$. Label the functions. Without calculating, list the functions in order of increasing arc length. Verify your answer by using the integration capabilities of a graphing utility. To print an enlarged copy of the graph, go to *MathGraphs.com*.

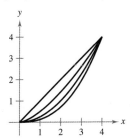

52. Verifying a Formula

(a) Given a circular sector with radius L and central angle θ (see figure), show that the area of the sector is given by

$$S = \frac{1}{2}L^2\theta.$$

(b) By joining the straight-line edges of the sector in part (a), a right circular cone is formed (see figure) and the lateral surface area of the cone is the same as the area of the sector. Show that the area is $S = \pi r L$, where r is the radius of the base of the cone. (*Hint:* The arc length of the sector equals the circumference of the base of the cone.)

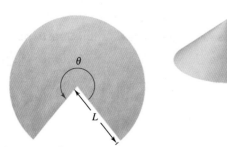

Figure for 52(a)   Figure for 52(b)

(c) Use the result of part (b) to verify that the formula for the lateral surface area of the frustum of a cone with slant height L and radii r_1 and r_2 (see figure) is $S = \pi(r_1 + r_2)L$.

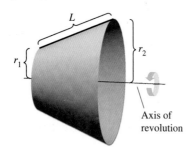

Axis of revolution

53. Lateral Surface Area of a Cone A right circular cone is generated by revolving the region bounded by $y = 3x/4$, $y = 3$, and $x = 0$ about the y-axis. Find the lateral surface area of the cone.

54. Lateral Surface Area of a Cone A right circular cone is generated by revolving the region bounded by $y = hx/r$, $y = h$, and $x = 0$ about the y-axis. Verify that the lateral surface area of the cone is

$$S = \pi r\sqrt{r^2 + h^2}.$$

55. Using a Sphere Find the area of the segment of a sphere formed by revolving the graph of $y = \sqrt{9 - x^2}$, $0 \le x \le 2$, about the y-axis.

56. Using a Sphere Find the area of the segment of a sphere formed by revolving the graph of $y = \sqrt{r^2 - x^2}$, $0 \le x \le a$, about the y-axis. Assume that $a < r$.

57. Modeling Data The circumference C (in inches) of a vase is measured at three-inch intervals starting at its base. The measurements are shown in the table, where y is the vertical distance in inches from the base.

y	0	3	6	9	12	15	18
C	50	65.5	70	66	58	51	48

(a) Use the data to approximate the volume of the vase by summing the volumes of approximating disks.

(b) Use the data to approximate the outside surface area (excluding the base) of the vase by summing the outside surface areas of approximating frustums of right circular cones.

(c) Use the regression capabilities of a graphing utility to find a cubic model for the points (y, r), where $r = C/(2\pi)$. Use the graphing utility to plot the points and graph the model.

(d) Use the model in part (c) and the integration capabilities of a graphing utility to approximate the volume and outside surface area of the vase. Compare the results with your answers in parts (a) and (b).

58. Modeling Data Property bounded by two perpendicular roads and a stream is shown in the figure. All distances are measured in feet.

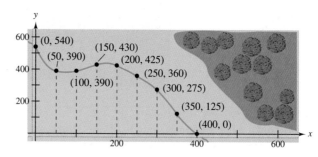

(a) Use the regression capabilities of a graphing utility to fit a fourth-degree polynomial to the path of the stream.

(b) Use the model in part (a) to approximate the area of the property in acres.

(c) Use the integration capabilities of a graphing utility to find the length of the stream that bounds the property.

59. Volume and Surface Area Let R be the region bounded by $y = 1/x$, the x-axis, $x = 1$, and $x = b$, where $b > 1$. Let D be the solid formed when R is revolved about the x-axis.

(a) Find the volume V of D.

(b) Write a definite integral that represents the surface area S of D.

(c) Show that V approaches a finite limit as $b \to \infty$.

(d) Show that $S \to \infty$ as $b \to \infty$.

60. Think About It   Consider the equation $\dfrac{x^2}{9} + \dfrac{y^2}{4} = 1$.

(a) Use a graphing utility to graph the equation.

(b) Write the definite integral for finding the first-quadrant arc length of the graph in part (a).

(c) Compare the interval of integration in part (b) and the domain of the integrand. Is it possible to evaluate the definite integral? Explain. (You will learn how to evaluate this type of integral in Section 7.8.)

Approximating Arc Length or Surface Area   In Exercises 61 and 62, write the definite integral for finding the indicated arc length or surface area. Do not integrate. (You will learn how to evaluate this type of integral in Section 7.8.)

61. Length of Pursuit   A fleeing object leaves the origin and moves up the y-axis (see figure). At the same time, a pursuer leaves the point $(1, 0)$ and always moves toward the fleeing object. The equation of the path is modeled by $y = \frac{1}{3}(x^{3/2} - 3x^{1/2} + 2)$. How far has the fleeing object traveled when it is caught? Show that the pursuer has traveled twice as far.

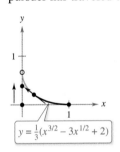

$y = \frac{1}{3}(x^{3/2} - 3x^{1/2} + 2)$

Figure for 61   Figure for 62

62. Bulb Design   An ornamental light bulb is designed by revolving the graph of $y = \frac{1}{3}x^{1/2} - x^{3/2}$, $0 \le x \le \frac{1}{3}$, about the x-axis, where x and y are measured in feet (see figure). Find the surface area of the bulb and use the result to approximate the amount of glass needed to make the bulb. (Assume that the glass is 0.015 inch thick.)

63. Suspension Bridge   A cable for a suspension bridge has the shape of a parabola with equation $y = kx^2$. Let h represent the height of the cable from its lowest point to its highest point and let $2w$ represent the total span of the bridge (see figure). Show that the length C of the cable is given by $C = 2\int_0^w \sqrt{1 + (4h^2/w^4)x^2}\, dx$.

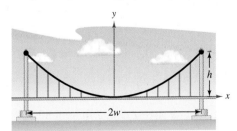

64. SUSPENSION BRIDGE

The Humber Bridge, located in the United Kingdom and opened in 1981, has a main span of about 1400 meters. Each of its towers has a height of about 155 meters. Use these dimensions, the integral in Exercise 63, and the integration capabilities of a graphing utility to approximate the length of a parabolic cable along the main span.

Calculus AP® – Exam Preparation Questions

65. Multiple Choice   Which of the following integrals gives the arc length of the graph of $y = 2\cos\sqrt{x}$ between a and b, where $0 < a < b$?

(A) $\displaystyle\int_a^b \sqrt{1 + 4\cos^2\sqrt{x}}\, dx$

(B) $\displaystyle\int_a^b \sqrt{1 + \frac{1}{x}\sin^2\sqrt{x}}\, dx$

(C) $\displaystyle\int_a^b \sqrt{\frac{1 + \sin^2\sqrt{x}}{x}}\, dx$

(D) $\displaystyle\int_a^b \sqrt{4\cos^2\sqrt{x} + \frac{1}{x}\sin^2\sqrt{x}}\, dx$

66. Multiple Choice   The length of a curve from $x = 1$ to $x = 5$ is given by $\int_1^5 \sqrt{1 + 36x^4}\, dx$. The curve contains the point $(1, 9)$. Which of the following could be an equation for this curve?

(A) $y = 2x^3 + 7$ (B) $y = 6x^2 + 3$

(C) $y = \dfrac{36}{5}x^5 + \dfrac{9}{5}$ (D) $y = x^3 + 8$

67. Multiple Choice   The figure shows the graphs of $f(x) = 5 - x^3$ and $g(x) = -4x + 5$. What is the length of the curve $y = f(x)$ between the points of intersection shown in the figure?

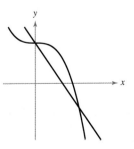

(A) 8   (B) 8.246   (C) 8.630   (D) 27.658

6 Review Exercises

See *CalcChat.com* for tutorial help and worked-out solutions to odd-numbered exercises.

Writing a Definite Integral In Exercises 1–4, write the definite integral that gives the area of the region.

1. $y_1 = \sin \pi x$
$y_2 = x^3 - 4x$

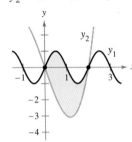

2. $y_1 = x^2 - 4x + 4$
$y_2 = e$

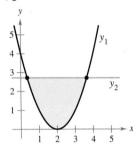

3. $y_1 = -2x^3 + 8x$
$y_2 = 0$

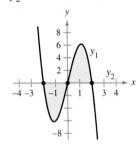

4. $y_1 = -(x - 2)^3 + 1$
$y_2 = -x + 3$

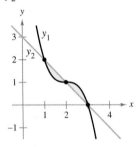

Finding the Area of a Region In Exercises 5–14, sketch the region bounded by the graphs of the equations and find the area of the region.

5. $y = 6 - \frac{1}{2}x^2$, $y = \frac{3}{4}x$, $x = -2$, $x = 2$

6. $y = \frac{1}{x^2}$, $y = 4$, $x = 5$

7. $y = \frac{1}{x^2 + 1}$, $y = 0$, $x = -1$, $x = 1$

8. $x = y^2 - 2y$, $x = -1$, $y = 0$

9. $y = x$, $y = x^3$

10. $x = -y^5$, $x = -y^3$

11. $y = e^x$, $y = e^2$, $x = 0$

12. $y = -e^{2x}$, $y = -e^2$, $x = -1$

13. $y = \sin 2x$, $y = \cos x$, $\frac{\pi}{2} \le x \le \frac{3\pi}{2}$

14. $x = \cos y$, $x = \frac{1}{2}$, $\frac{\pi}{3} \le y \le \frac{7\pi}{3}$

Finding the Area of a Region In Exercises 15–18, (a) use a graphing utility to graph the region bounded by the graphs of the equations, and (b) use the integration capabilities of the graphing utility to approximate the area of the region to four decimal places.

15. $y = x^2 - 8x + 3$, $y = 3 + 8x - x^2$

16. $y = x^2 - 4x + 3$, $y = x^3$, $x = 0$

17. $\sqrt{x} + \sqrt{y} = 1$, $y = 0$, $x = 0$

18. $y = x^4 - x^2$, $y = \frac{3}{2}x^3$

Revenue In Exercises 19 and 20, two models R_1 and R_2 are given for the projected revenue (in millions of dollars) for a corporation for the years 2020 through 2025, with $t = 0$ corresponding to 2020. Which model projects greater total revenue? How much more total revenue does that model project over this time period?

19. $R_1 = 3.17 + 0.45t$
$R_2 = 3.17 + 0.54t$

20. $R_1 = 1.76 + 0.18t + 0.08t^2$
$R_2 = 1.76 + 0.17t + 0.02t^2$

Integration as an Accumulation Process In Exercises 21 and 22, find the accumulation function F. Then evaluate F at each value of the independent variable and show graphically the area given by each value of the independent variable.

21. $F(x) = \int_0^x (4t^2 + 1)\, dt$

(a) $F(0)$ (b) $F\left(\frac{3}{2}\right)$ (c) $F(3)$

22. $F(x) = \int_0^x \left(\frac{8t + 3}{4t^2 + 3t + 5}\right) dt$

(a) $F(0)$ (b) $F(3)$ (c) $F(5)$

Finding the Volume of a Solid In Exercises 23–25, use the disk method to find the volume of the solid generated by revolving the region bounded by the graphs of the equations about the x-axis.

23. $y = \frac{1}{\sqrt{1 + x^2}}$, $y = 0$, $x = -1$, $x = 1$

24. $y = e^{-x}$, $y = 0$, $x = 0$, $x = 1$

25. $y = \sec x$, $y = 0$, $x = 0$, $x = \frac{\pi}{6}$

Finding the Volume of a Solid In Exercises 26–28, use the shell method to find the volume of the solid generated by revolving the region bounded by the graphs of the equations about the y-axis.

26. $y = \frac{1}{x^4 + 1}$, $y = 0$, $x = 0$, $x = 1$

27. $y = \frac{1}{x^2}$, $y = 0$, $x = 2$, $x = 5$

28. $y = x - x^4$, $y = 0$

Finding the Volume of a Solid In Exercises 29 and 30, use the disk method *or* the shell method to find the volumes of the solids generated by revolving the region bounded by the graphs of the equations about the given lines.

29. $y = x$, $y = 0$, $x = 3$
   (a) x-axis (b) y-axis (c) $x = 3$ (d) $x = 6$

30. $y = \sqrt{x}$, $y = 2$, $x = 0$
   (a) x-axis (b) $y = 2$ (c) y-axis (d) $x = -1$

31. **Gasoline Tank** A gasoline tank is an oblate spheroid generated by revolving the region bounded by the graph of

$$\frac{x^2}{16} + \frac{y^2}{9} = 1$$

about the y-axis, where x and y are measured in feet. How much gasoline can the tank hold?

32. **Using Cross Sections** Find the volume of the solid whose base is bounded by the circle $x^2 + y^2 = 9$ and the cross sections perpendicular to the x-axis are equilateral triangles.

33. **Volume of a Segment of a Sphere** Let a sphere of radius r be cut by a plane, thereby forming a segment of height h. Show that the volume of this segment is $\frac{1}{3}\pi h^2(3r - h)$.

34. **Volume of an Ellipsoid** Consider the plane region bounded by the graph of

$$\left(\frac{x}{a}\right)^2 + \left(\frac{y}{b}\right)^2 = 1$$

where $a > 0$ and $b > 0$. Show that the volume of the ellipsoid formed when this region is revolved about the y-axis is $\frac{4}{3}\pi a^2 b$. What is the volume when the region is revolved about the x-axis?

Finding Distance Using Two Methods In Exercises 35 and 36, find the distance between the points using (a) the Distance Formula and (b) integration.

35. $(0, 0), (5, 12)$ 36. $(1, 3), (9, 18)$

Finding Arc Length In Exercises 37 and 38, find the arc length of the graph of the function over the indicated interval.

37. $f(x) = \frac{4}{5}x^{5/4}$ 38. $y = \frac{1}{2\sqrt{2}}(x^2 - \ln x)$

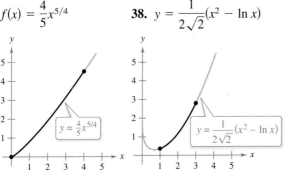

39. **Length of a Catenary** A wire hung between two poles forms a catenary modeled by the equation

$$y = 50(e^{x/100} + e^{-x/100}), \ -50 \le x \le 50$$

where x and y are measured in feet. Find the length of the wire between the two poles.

40. **Approximation** Determine which value best approximates the length of the arc represented by the integral

$$\int_0^1 \sqrt{1 + \left[\frac{d}{dx}\left(\frac{4}{x + 1}\right)\right]^2} \ dx.$$

(Make your selection on the basis of a sketch of the arc and not by performing any calculations.)

   (a) 5 (b) 7 (c) 2 (d) 4

41. **Arc Length of a Sector of a Circle** Find the arc length from $(0, 3)$ clockwise to $(2, \sqrt{5})$ along the circle $x^2 + y^2 = 9$.

42. **Arc Length of a Sector of a Circle** Find the arc length from $(-2, 2\sqrt{3})$ clockwise to $(3, \sqrt{7})$ along the circle $x^2 + y^2 = 16$.

43. **Surface Area** Use integration to find the lateral surface area of a right circular cone of height 4 and radius 3.

44. **Surface Area** The region bounded by the graphs of $y = 2\sqrt{x}$, $y = 0$, $x = 3$, and $x = 8$ is revolved about the x-axis. Find the surface area of the solid generated.

45. **Astroid** Write the definite integral for finding the area of the surface formed by revolving the portion in the first quadrant of the graph of

$$x^{2/3} + y^{2/3} = 4, \ 0 \le y \le 8$$

about the y-axis (see figure). Do not integrate.

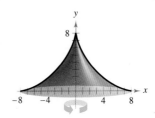

46. **Using a Loop** Consider the graph of $y^2 = \frac{1}{12}x(4 - x)^2$ shown in the figure. Write the definite integral for finding the area of the surface formed when the loop of this graph is revolved about the x-axis. Do not integrate.

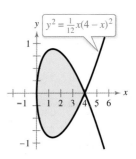

AP® Exam Practice Questions

See *LarsonCalculusforAP.com* for worked-out solutions to these questions.

What You Need to Know

- The shell method is not required on the AP® Exam, but some free-response questions may be solvable by the shell method in addition to the disk method.
- The shell method is particularly advantageous when it is difficult to express one variable in terms of the other and when more than one integral is required to find a volume.
- On the AP® Calculus BC Exam, you may need to use the concept of arc length to find the perimeter of a given region.
- When limits of integration are irrational numbers, you can assign variables to represent each limit of integration. You can then write the correct integral expression using the variables, instead of writing out each integral in its entirety. This will help you save time.
- You may be asked to set up the correct integral for a problem but not to evaluate the integral.

Practice Questions

Section 1, Part A, Multiple Choice, No Technology

1. What is the area of the region bounded by the y-axis, the line $y = e$, and the graph of the function $y = e^{3x}$?

   (A) $\dfrac{1}{3}$

   (B) $e^{3e} - \dfrac{1}{3}$

   (C) $1 - \dfrac{2}{3}e$

   (D) $3 - \dfrac{8}{3}e$

2. What is the area enclosed by the curves $y = x^3 - 7x^2 + 12x + 4$ and $y = 2x + 4$?

   (A) $\dfrac{125}{12}$

   (B) $\dfrac{63}{4}$

   (C) $\dfrac{253}{12}$

   (D) $\dfrac{445}{12}$

In Exercises 3 and 4, let R be the region bounded by the graphs of $y = 4 \cos x$, $y = 4 \sin x$, and the y-axis, as shown in the figure.

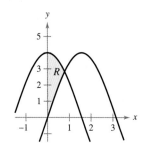

3. Which expression represents the area of R?

   (A) $4\left(\sqrt{2} - 1\right)$

   (B) $\sqrt{2} - 1$

   (C) $4\left(\sqrt{3} - 1\right)$

   (D) $2\sqrt{2} - 1$

4. The horizontal line $y = 2$ splits the region R into two parts. What is the area of the part of R that is below this horizontal line?

   (A) $\dfrac{2\pi}{3} - 2$

   (B) $\dfrac{\pi}{3} + 2\sqrt{3} - 4$

   (C) $\dfrac{2\pi}{3} + 2$

   (D) $\dfrac{\pi}{3} + 2\sqrt{3}$

5. What is the area of the region bounded by the curves $x = y^2 - 4y$ and $y = -x + 4$?

   (A) $\dfrac{95}{6}$

   (B) 18

   (C) $\dfrac{56}{3}$

   (D) $\dfrac{125}{6}$

6. Which of the following integrals gives the length of the graph of $y = \ln(\sec x)$ from $x = 0$ to $x = \pi/4$?

   (A) $\displaystyle\int_0^{\pi/4} \sec^2 x \, dx$

   (B) $\displaystyle\int_0^{\pi/4} \sec x \, dx$

   (C) $\displaystyle\int_0^{\pi/4} \sec x \tan x \, dx$

   (D) $\displaystyle\int_0^{\pi/4} \sqrt{1 + \cos^2 x} \, dx$

7. Which of the following integrals gives the length of the graph of $y = 4e^{0.5x}$ from $x = 1$ to $x = 4$?

   (A) $\displaystyle\int_1^4 \sqrt{1 + 4e^x} \, dx$

   (B) $\displaystyle\int_1^4 \sqrt{1 + 16e^x} \, dx$

   (C) $\displaystyle\int_1^4 \sqrt{1 + 2e^{0.5x}} \, dx$

   (D) $\displaystyle\int_1^4 \sqrt{x + 16e^x} \, dx$

8. What is the arc length of the graph of $y = \frac{2}{3}x^{3/2}$ from $x = 3$ to $x = 8$?

   (A) $\dfrac{32}{3}$

   (B) $\dfrac{38}{3}$

   (C) $\dfrac{40}{3}$

   (D) 28

Section 1, Part B, Multiple Choice, Technology Permitted

9. The base of a solid is the region in the first quadrant bounded above by the line $y = 2$, below by $y = \sin^{-1} x$, and to the right by the line $x = 1$. For this solid, each cross section perpendicular to the x-axis is a square. What is the volume of the solid?

   (A) 1.429

   (B) 2

   (C) 2.184

   (D) 4

Section 2, Part A, Free Response, Technology Permitted

10. Consider the region bounded by the y-axis,

    $y = 10$,   and $y = 1 + 6x^{3/2}$.

    (a) Write, but do not evaluate, an integral equation that will find the value of k so that $x = k$ divides the region into two parts of equal area.

    (b) Find the length of the curve

    $$y = 1 + 6x^{3/2}$$

    on the interval $[0, 1]$.

    (c) The region is the base of a solid. For this solid, the cross sections perpendicular to the x-axis are rectangles with a height of 3 times that of its width. Find the volume of this solid.

11. Let R be the region bounded by the graphs of

    $y = \ln x$ and $y = 2x - 3$.

    (a) Find the area of R.

    (b) Find the volume of the solid generated when R is revolved about the horizontal line $y = -3$.

    (c) Write, but do not evaluate, an expression involving one or more integrals that can be used to find the volume of the solid generated when R is revolved about the y-axis.

12. Let R be the region bounded by the graphs of

    $y = x^2 - 1$ and $x = y^2$.

    (a) Find the area of R.

    (b) Find the volume of the solid generated when R is revolved about the vertical line $x = 2$.

    (c) Write, but do not evaluate, an expression involving one or more integrals that can be used to find the volume of the solid generated when R is revolved about the horizontal line $y = -1$.

Section 2, Part B, Free Response, No Technology

13. A region in the xy-plane is bounded by

    $$y = 2x + 2, \quad x = \frac{y^2}{2} + 2, \quad y = -2, \quad \text{and} \quad y = 2.$$

    (a) Sketch the bounded region. Label each boundary curve and shade the bounded region.

    (b) Find the area of the bounded region. Show the work that leads to your answer.

14. The region shown below is bounded by $y = \sqrt{x}, y = 0$, $x = 0$, and $x = 2$.

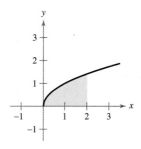

    (a) Find the volume of the solid formed by revolving the region about the x-axis.

    (b) Find the volume of the solid formed by revolving the region about the y-axis.

    (c) Write, but do not evaluate, an expression involving one or more integrals that gives the volume of the solid formed by revolving the region about the line $y = -2$.

    (d) The region shown is the base of a solid. For this solid, each cross section perpendicular to the x-axis is an equilateral triangle. Find the volume of this solid.

15. Consider the region R bounded by the graphs of $y = x^3$, $y = 8$, and the y-axis. The region S is bounded by $y = x^3$, $x = 2$, and the x-axis.

    (a) Find the area of R.

    (b) Find the volume of the solid formed by revolving R about the y-axis.

    (c) The region S is the base of a solid. For this solid, each cross section perpendicular to the x-axis is a semicircle with diameters extending from $y = x^3$ to the x-axis. Find the volume of this solid.

16. Consider the region T bounded by the graphs of $y = x^2$, $y = -2x$, and $x = 2$.

    (a) Find the area of T.

    (b) Find the volume of the solid formed by revolving T about the horizontal line $y = -4$.

    (c) Write, but do not evaluate, an expression involving one or more integrals that gives the perimeter of T.

6   Performance Task

Constructing an Arch Dam

One design used in dam construction is the arch dam. This design curves toward the water it contains, and is usually built in narrow canyons. The force of the water presses the edges of the dam against the walls of the canyon, so that the natural rock helps support the structure. Shown at the right is a famous use of this design, the Hoover Dam in the Black Canyon of the Colorado River.

Exercises

In Exercises 1–3, use the following information. A cross section of an arch dam can be modeled as shown in the figure at the right. The model for this cross section is

$$f(x) = \begin{cases} 0.03x^2 + 7.1x + 350, & -70 \le x \le -16 \\ 389, & -16 < x < 0 \\ -6.593x + 389, & 0 \le x \le 59 \end{cases}.$$

To form the arch dam, this cross section is swung through an arc, revolving it about the y-axis (see figure below). The cross section is rotated 150° and the axis of rotation is the vertical line 150 feet from the innermost point of the dam.

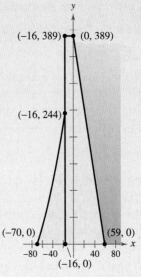

A cross section of an arch dam

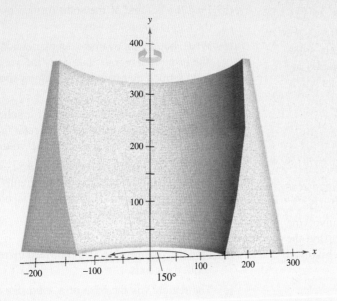

1. **Calculating Area without Calculus**   Explain how you would calculate the area of a cross section of the dam *without* using calculus. Use your explanation to calculate the area of the cross section. Is the area you found exact? Why or why not?

2. **Calculating Area with Calculus**   Explain how you would calculate the area of a cross section of the dam *with* calculus. Use your explanation to calculate the area of the cross section. Is the area you found exact? Why or why not?

3. **Calculating Volume**   Explain how you would calculate the volume of concrete needed to build the dam. Use your explanation to calculate this volume.

7 Integration Techniques, L'Hôpital's Rule, and Improper Integrals

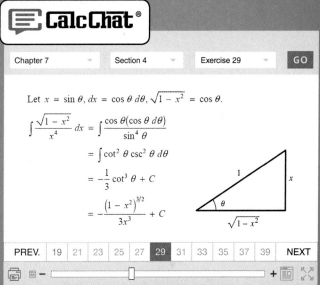

7.4 Mechanical Design *(Exercise 56, p. 489)*

7.5 Chemical Reaction *(Exercise 46, p. 499)*

7.1   Basic Integration Rules

▶ Review procedures for fitting an integrand to one of the basic integration rules.

Fitting Integrands to Basic Integration Rules

In this chapter, you will study several integration techniques that greatly expand the set of integrals to which the basic integration rules can be applied. These rules are reviewed at the right. A major step in solving any integration problem is recognizing which basic integration rule to use.

EXAMPLE 1   A Comparison of Three Similar Integrals

See LarsonCalculusforAP.com for an interactive version of this type of example.

Find each integral.

a. $\displaystyle\int \frac{4}{x^2 + 9}\, dx$ **b.** $\displaystyle\int \frac{4x}{x^2 + 9}\, dx$ **c.** $\displaystyle\int \frac{4x^2}{x^2 + 9}\, dx$

Solution

a. Use the Arctangent Rule and let $u = x$ and $a = 3$.

$$\int \frac{4}{x^2 + 9}\, dx = 4 \int \frac{1}{x^2 + 3^2}\, dx \qquad \text{Constant Multiple Rule}$$

$$= 4\left(\frac{1}{3} \arctan \frac{x}{3}\right) + C \qquad \text{Arctangent Rule}$$

$$= \frac{4}{3} \arctan \frac{x}{3} + C \qquad \text{Simplify.}$$

b. The Arctangent Rule does not apply because the numerator contains a factor of x. Consider the Log Rule and let $u = x^2 + 9$. Then $du = 2x\, dx$, and you have

$$\int \frac{4x}{x^2 + 9}\, dx = 2 \int \frac{2x\, dx}{x^2 + 9} \qquad \text{Constant Multiple Rule}$$

$$= 2 \int \frac{du}{u} \qquad \text{Substitute: } u = x^2 + 9.$$

$$= 2 \ln|u| + C \qquad \text{Log Rule}$$

$$= 2 \ln(x^2 + 9) + C. \qquad \text{Rewrite as a function of } x.$$

c. Because the degree of the numerator is equal to the degree of the denominator, you should first use division to rewrite the improper rational function as the sum of a polynomial and a proper rational function. (For help on rewriting the integrand using long division, see Example 1 in the *Chapter 7 Algebra Review* on page A48.)

$$\int \frac{4x^2}{x^2 + 9}\, dx = \int \left(4 + \frac{-36}{x^2 + 9}\right) dx \qquad \text{Rewrite using long division.}$$

$$= \int 4\, dx - 36 \int \frac{1}{x^2 + 9}\, dx \qquad \text{Rewrite as two integrals.}$$

$$= 4x - 36 \left(\frac{1}{3} \arctan \frac{x}{3}\right) + C \qquad \text{Integrate.}$$

$$= 4x - 12 \arctan \frac{x}{3} + C \qquad \text{Simplify.} \qquad ■$$

Note in Example 1(c) that some algebra is required before applying any integration rules, and more than one rule is needed to find the resulting integral.

Review of Basic Integration Rules ($a > 0$)

1. $\displaystyle\int kf(u)\, du = k \int f(u)\, du$

2. $\displaystyle\int [f(u) \pm g(u)]\, du =$
   $\displaystyle\int f(u)\, du \pm \int g(u)\, du$

3. $\displaystyle\int du = u + C$

4. $\displaystyle\int u^n\, du = \frac{u^{n+1}}{n+1} + C,$
   $n \neq -1$

5. $\displaystyle\int \frac{du}{u} = \ln|u| + C$

6. $\displaystyle\int e^u\, du = e^u + C$

7. $\displaystyle\int a^u\, du = \left(\frac{1}{\ln a}\right) a^u + C$

8. $\displaystyle\int \sin u\, du = -\cos u + C$

9. $\displaystyle\int \cos u\, du = \sin u + C$

10. $\displaystyle\int \tan u\, du = -\ln|\cos u| + C$

11. $\displaystyle\int \cot u\, du = \ln|\sin u| + C$

12. $\displaystyle\int \sec u\, du =$
    $\ln|\sec u + \tan u| + C$

13. $\displaystyle\int \csc u\, du =$
    $-\ln|\csc u + \cot u| + C$

14. $\displaystyle\int \sec^2 u\, du = \tan u + C$

15. $\displaystyle\int \csc^2 u\, du = -\cot u + C$

16. $\displaystyle\int \sec u \tan u\, du = \sec u + C$

17. $\displaystyle\int \csc u \cot u\, du = -\csc u + C$

18. $\displaystyle\int \frac{du}{\sqrt{a^2 - u^2}} = \arcsin \frac{u}{a} + C$

19. $\displaystyle\int \frac{du}{a^2 + u^2} = \frac{1}{a} \arctan \frac{u}{a} + C$

20. $\displaystyle\int \frac{du}{u\sqrt{u^2 - a^2}} =$
    $\frac{1}{a} \operatorname{arcsec} \frac{|u|}{a} + C$

EXAMPLE 2   Using Two Basic Rules to Solve a Single Integral

Evaluate $\displaystyle\int_0^1 \frac{x + 3}{\sqrt{4 - x^2}}\,dx$.

Solution   Begin by writing the integral as the sum of two integrals. Then apply the Power Rule and the Arcsine Rule.

$$\int_0^1 \frac{x + 3}{\sqrt{4 - x^2}}\,dx = \int_0^1 \frac{x}{\sqrt{4 - x^2}}\,dx + \int_0^1 \frac{3}{\sqrt{4 - x^2}}\,dx$$

$$= -\frac{1}{2}\int_0^1 (4 - x^2)^{-1/2}(-2x)\,dx + 3\int_0^1 \frac{1}{\sqrt{2^2 - x^2}}\,dx$$

$$= \left[-(4 - x^2)^{1/2} + 3\arcsin\frac{x}{2} \right]_0^1$$

$$= \left(-\sqrt{3} + \frac{\pi}{2} \right) - (-2 + 0)$$

$$\approx 1.839 \qquad\qquad \text{See Figure 7.1.}$$

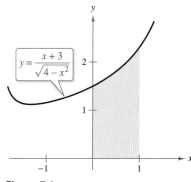

$$y = \frac{x + 3}{\sqrt{4 - x^2}}$$

Figure 7.1

Technology

The Trapezoidal Rule can be used to give a good approximation of the value of the integral in Example 2 (for $n = 10$, the approximation is 1.839). When using numerical integration, however, you should be aware that the Trapezoidal Rule does not always give good approximations when one or both of the limits of integration are near a vertical asymptote. For instance, using the Fundamental Theorem of Calculus, you can obtain

$$\int_0^{1.99} \frac{x + 3}{\sqrt{4 - x^2}}\,dx \approx 6.213.$$

For $n = 10$, the Trapezoidal Rule gives an approximation of 7.500.

Rules 18, 19, and 20 of the basic integration rules on the preceding page all have expressions involving the sum or difference of two squares: $a^2 - u^2$, $a^2 + u^2$, and $u^2 - a^2$. These expressions are often apparent after a u-substitution, as shown in Example 3.

EXAMPLE 3   A Substitution Involving $a^2 - u^2$

Find $\displaystyle\int \frac{x^2}{\sqrt{16 - x^6}}\,dx$.

Solution   Because the radical in the denominator can be written in the form $\sqrt{a^2 - u^2} = \sqrt{4^2 - (x^3)^2}$, you can try the substitution $u = x^3$. Then $du = 3x^2\,dx$, and

$$\int \frac{x^2}{\sqrt{16 - x^6}}\,dx = \frac{1}{3}\int \frac{3x^2\,dx}{\sqrt{4^2 - (x^3)^2}} \qquad \text{Rewrite integral.}$$

$$= \frac{1}{3}\int \frac{du}{\sqrt{4^2 - u^2}} \qquad \text{Substitute: } u = x^3.$$

$$= \frac{1}{3}\arcsin\frac{u}{4} + C \qquad \text{Arcsine Rule}$$

$$= \frac{1}{3}\arcsin\frac{x^3}{4} + C. \qquad \text{Rewrite as a function of } x.$$

Exploration

A Comparison of Three Similar Integrals   Which, if any, of the integrals listed below can be found using the 20 basic integration rules? For any that can be found, do so. For any that cannot, explain why not.

a. $\displaystyle\int \frac{3}{\sqrt{1 - x^2}}\,dx$

b. $\displaystyle\int \frac{3x}{\sqrt{1 - x^2}}\,dx$

c. $\displaystyle\int \frac{3x^2}{\sqrt{1 - x^2}}\,dx$

Two of the most commonly overlooked integration rules are the Log Rule and the Power Rule. Notice in the next two examples how these two integration rules can be disguised.

EXAMPLE 4   A Disguised Form of the Log Rule

Find $\displaystyle\int \frac{1}{1 + e^x}\, dx$.

Solution

The integral does not appear to fit any of the basic rules. The quotient form, however, suggests the Log Rule. If you let $u = 1 + e^x$, then $du = e^x\, dx$. You can obtain the required du by adding and subtracting e^x in the numerator.

$$
\begin{aligned}
\int \frac{1}{1 + e^x}\, dx &= \int \frac{1 + e^x - e^x}{1 + e^x}\, dx && \text{Add and subtract } e^x \text{ in numerator.}\\[2mm]
&= \int \left(\frac{1 + e^x}{1 + e^x} - \frac{e^x}{1 + e^x} \right) dx && \text{Rewrite as two fractions.}\\[2mm]
&= \int dx - \int \frac{e^x\, dx}{1 + e^x} && \text{Rewrite as two integrals.}\\[2mm]
&= x - \ln(1 + e^x) + C && \text{Integrate.}
\end{aligned}
$$

There is usually more than one way to solve an integration problem. For instance, in Example 4, try integrating by multiplying the numerator and denominator by e^{-x} to obtain an integral of the form $-\int du/u$. See if you can get the same answer by this procedure. (Be careful, the answer will appear in a different form.)

EXAMPLE 5   A Disguised Form of the Power Rule

Find $\displaystyle\int (\cot x)[\ln(\sin x)]\, dx$.

Solution

Again, the integral does not appear to fit any of the basic rules. However, considering the two primary choices for u

$$
u = \cot x \quad \text{or} \quad u = \ln(\sin x)
$$

you can see that the second choice is the appropriate one because

$$
u = \ln(\sin x) \quad \text{and} \quad du = \frac{\cos x}{\sin x}\, dx = \cot x\, dx.
$$

So,

$$
\begin{aligned}
\int (\cot x)[\ln(\sin x)]\, dx &= \int u\, du && \text{Substitute: } u = \ln(\sin x).\\[2mm]
&= \frac{u^2}{2} + C && \text{Integrate.}\\[2mm]
&= \frac{1}{2}[\ln(\sin x)]^2 + C. && \text{Rewrite as a function of } x.
\end{aligned}
$$

In Example 5, try checking that the derivative of

$$
\frac{1}{2}[\ln(\sin x)]^2 + C
$$

is the integrand of the original integral.

Implementing Processes

Remember that you can separate numerators but not denominators. Watch out for this common error when fitting integrands to basic rules. For instance, you cannot separate denominators in Example 4.

$$
\frac{1}{1 + e^x} \neq \frac{1}{1} + \frac{1}{e^x}
$$

Trigonometric identities can often be used to fit integrals to one of the basic integration rules.

EXAMPLE 6   Using Trigonometric Identities

Find $\int \tan^2 2x \, dx$.

Solution

Note that $\tan^2 u$ is not in the list of basic integration rules. However, $\sec^2 u$ is in the list. This suggests the trigonometric identity $\tan^2 u = \sec^2 u - 1$. If you let $u = 2x$, then $du = 2 \, dx$ and

$$\int \tan^2 2x \, dx = \frac{1}{2} \int \tan^2 u \, du \qquad \text{Substitute: } u = 2x.$$

$$= \frac{1}{2} \int (\sec^2 u - 1) \, du \qquad \text{Trigonometric identity}$$

$$= \frac{1}{2} \int \sec^2 u \, du - \frac{1}{2} \int du \qquad \text{Rewrite as two integrals.}$$

$$= \frac{1}{2} \tan u - \frac{u}{2} + C \qquad \text{Integrate.}$$

$$= \frac{1}{2} \tan 2x - x + C. \qquad \text{Rewrite as a function of } x.$$

> **Technology**
>
> If you have access to a computer algebra system, try using it to find the integrals in this section. Compare the *forms* of the antiderivatives given by the software with the forms obtained by hand. Sometimes the forms will be the same, but often they will differ. For instance, why is the antiderivative $\ln 2x + C$ equivalent to the antiderivative $\ln x + C$?

This section concludes with a summary of the common procedures for fitting integrands to the basic integration rules.

Procedures for Fitting Integrands to Basic Integration Rules

Technique	*Example*
Expand (numerator).	$(1 + e^x)^2 = 1 + 2e^x + e^{2x}$
Separate numerator.	$\dfrac{1 + x}{x^2 + 1} = \dfrac{1}{x^2 + 1} + \dfrac{x}{x^2 + 1}$
Complete the square.	$\dfrac{1}{\sqrt{2x - x^2}} = \dfrac{1}{\sqrt{1 - (x - 1)^2}}$
Divide improper rational function.	$\dfrac{x^2}{x^2 + 1} = 1 - \dfrac{1}{x^2 + 1}$
Add and subtract terms in numerator.	$\dfrac{2x}{x^2 + 2x + 1} = \dfrac{2x + 2 - 2}{x^2 + 2x + 1}$
	$= \dfrac{2x + 2}{x^2 + 2x + 1} - \dfrac{2}{(x + 1)^2}$
Use trigonometric identities.	$\cot^2 x = \csc^2 x - 1$
Multiply and divide by Pythagorean conjugate.	$\dfrac{1}{1 + \sin x} = \left(\dfrac{1}{1 + \sin x} \right)\left(\dfrac{1 - \sin x}{1 - \sin x} \right)$
	$= \dfrac{1 - \sin x}{1 - \sin^2 x}$
	$= \dfrac{1 - \sin x}{\cos^2 x}$
	$= \sec^2 x - \dfrac{\sin x}{\cos^2 x}$

7.1 Exercises

See *CalcChat.com* for tutorial help and worked-out solutions to odd-numbered exercises.

Choosing a Formula In Exercises 1–10, state the basic integration formula(s) you can use to find the indefinite integral, and identify *u* and *a* when appropriate. Do not integrate.

1. $\displaystyle\int \frac{4 - x^2}{2x}\, dx$

2. $\displaystyle\int \frac{2x}{4 - x^2}\, dx$

3. $\displaystyle\int \frac{2x}{\sqrt{4 - x^2}}\, dx$

4. $\displaystyle\int \frac{1}{\sqrt{4 - x^2}}\, dx$

5. $\displaystyle\int \frac{1}{\sqrt{x}(1 - 2\sqrt{x})}\, dx$

6. $\displaystyle\int \frac{2}{(2t - 1)^2 + 4}\, dt$

7. $\displaystyle\int t \sin t^2 \, dt$

8. $\displaystyle\int \sec 5x \tan 5x \, dx$

9. $\displaystyle\int (\cos x)e^{\sin x}\, dx$

10. $\displaystyle\int \frac{1}{x\sqrt{x^2 - 4}}\, dx$

Finding an Indefinite Integral In Exercises 11–42, find the indefinite integral.

11. $\displaystyle\int \frac{7}{(z - 10)^7}\, dz$

12. $\displaystyle\int 14(x - 5)^6 \, dx$

13. $\displaystyle\int \left[v + \frac{1}{(3v - 1)^3}\right] dv$

14. $\displaystyle\int \left[4x - \frac{2}{(2x + 3)^2}\right] dx$

15. $\displaystyle\int t^3 \sqrt{t^4 + 1}\, dt$

16. $\displaystyle\int \frac{-y}{(6 + y^2)^3}\, dy$

17. $\displaystyle\int \frac{t^2 - 3}{-t^3 + 9t + 1}\, dt$

18. $\displaystyle\int \frac{x + 1}{\sqrt{3x^2 + 6x}}\, dx$

19. $\displaystyle\int \frac{x^2}{x - 1}\, dx$

20. $\displaystyle\int \frac{3x}{x + 4}\, dx$

21. $\displaystyle\int \frac{e^x}{1 + e^x}\, dx$

22. $\displaystyle\int \left(\frac{1}{2x + 5} - \frac{1}{2x - 5}\right) dx$

23. $\displaystyle\int (5 + 4x^2)^2 \, dx$

24. $\displaystyle\int x\left(3 + \frac{2}{x}\right)^2 dx$

25. $\displaystyle\int x \cos 2\pi x^2 \, dx$

26. $\displaystyle\int \csc \pi x \cot \pi x \, dx$

27. $\displaystyle\int \frac{\sin \theta + \cos^3 \theta}{\cos^2 \theta}\, d\theta$

28. $\displaystyle\int (\csc^2 x)e^{\cot x}\, dx$

29. $\displaystyle\int \frac{2}{e^{-x} + 1}\, dx$

30. $\displaystyle\int \frac{2}{7e^x + 4}\, dx$

31. $\displaystyle\int \frac{\cot y}{[\ln(\sin y)]^2}\, dy$

32. $\displaystyle\int (\tan x)[\ln(\cos x)]\, dx$

33. $\displaystyle\int \frac{1 + \cos \alpha}{\sin \alpha}\, d\alpha$

34. $\displaystyle\int \frac{1}{\cos \theta - 1}\, d\theta$

35. $\displaystyle\int \frac{-1}{\sqrt{1 - (4t + 1)^2}}\, dt$

36. $\displaystyle\int \frac{1}{25 + 4x^2}\, dx$

37. $\displaystyle\int \frac{\tan(2/t)}{t^2}\, dt$

38. $\displaystyle\int \frac{e^{1/t}}{t^2}\, dt$

39. $\displaystyle\int \frac{6}{\sqrt{10x - x^2}}\, dx$

40. $\displaystyle\int \frac{1}{(x - 1)\sqrt{4x^2 - 8x + 3}}\, dx$

41. $\displaystyle\int \frac{4}{4x^2 + 4x + 65}\, dx$

42. $\displaystyle\int \frac{1}{x^2 - 4x + 9}\, dx$

Slope Field In Exercises 43 and 44, a differential equation, a point, and a slope field are given. (a) Sketch two approximate solutions of the differential equation on the slope field, one of which passes through the given point. To print an enlarged copy of the graph, go to *MathGraphs.com*. (b) Use integration and the given point to find the particular solution of the differential equation and use a graphing utility to graph the solution. Compare the result with the sketch in part (a) that passes through the given point.

43. $\displaystyle\frac{ds}{dt} = \frac{t}{\sqrt{1 - t^4}}$

$\left(0, -\dfrac{1}{2}\right)$

44. $\displaystyle\frac{dy}{dx} = \frac{1}{\sqrt{4x - x^2}}$

$\left(2, \dfrac{1}{2}\right)$

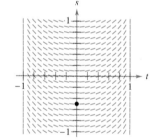

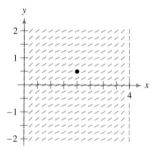

Differential Equation In Exercises 45–50, find the general solution of the differential equation.

45. $\displaystyle\frac{dy}{dx} = (4 - e^{2x})^2$

46. $\displaystyle\frac{dr}{dt} = \frac{(1 + e^t)^2}{e^{3t}}$

47. $\displaystyle\frac{dr}{dt} = \frac{10e^t}{\sqrt{1 - e^{2t}}}$

48. $\displaystyle\frac{dy}{dt} = \frac{\ln t^2}{t}$

49. $(4 + \tan^2 x)y' = \sec^2 x$

50. $\displaystyle y' = \frac{1}{x\sqrt{4x^2 - 9}}$

Error Analysis In Exercises 51 and 52, describe and correct the error in finding the indefinite integral.

51. $\displaystyle\int \frac{1}{2x\sqrt{x^2 - 16}}\, dx = 2\sqrt{x^2 - 16} + C$ ✗

52. $\displaystyle\int \frac{1}{1 + e^{-3x}}\, dx = \int \frac{1}{1} + \int \frac{1}{e^{-3x}}\, dx = x + \frac{1}{3}e^{3x} + C$ ✗

Evaluating a Definite Integral In Exercises 53–64, evaluate the definite integral. Use a graphing utility to verify your result.

53. $\displaystyle\int_0^{\pi/8} \frac{\sin 2x + 1}{\cos 2x}\, dx$

54. $\displaystyle\int_0^{\pi} \sin^2 t \cos t\, dt$

55. $\displaystyle\int_0^1 xe^{-x^2}\, dx$

56. $\displaystyle\int_1^e \frac{1 - \ln x}{x}\, dx$

57. $\displaystyle\int_0^8 \frac{2x}{\sqrt{x^2 + 36}}\, dx$

58. $\displaystyle\int_1^3 \frac{2x^2 + 3x - 2}{x}\, dx$

59. $\displaystyle\int_0^{2/\sqrt{3}} \frac{1}{4 + 9x^2}\, dx$

60. $\displaystyle\int_0^7 \frac{1 + x}{\sqrt{100 - x^2}}\, dx$

61. $\displaystyle\int_3^5 \frac{2t}{t^2 - 4t + 4}\, dt$

62. $\displaystyle\int_2^4 \frac{4x^3}{x^4 - 6x^2 + 9}\, dx$

63. $\displaystyle\int_{-4}^0 3^{1-x}\, dx$

64. $\displaystyle\int_0^1 7^{x^2 + 2x}(x + 1)\, dx$

Area In Exercises 65–68, find the area of the region.

65. $y = (-4x + 6)^{3/2}$

66. $y = \dfrac{3x + 2}{x^2 + 9}$

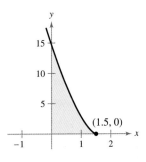

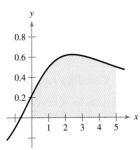

67. $y^2 = x^2(1 - x^2)$

68. $y = \sin 2x$

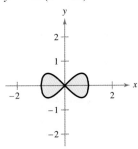

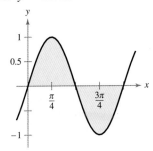

EXPLORING CONCEPTS ────────

Implementing Processes In Exercises 69–71, state the integration formula you would use to perform the integration. Explain why you chose that formula. Do not integrate.

69. $\displaystyle\int x \sec(x^2 + 1) \tan(x^2 + 1)\, dx$

70. $\displaystyle\int \frac{x}{x^2 + 1}\, dx$

71. $\displaystyle\int \frac{1}{x^2 + 1}\, dx$

EXPLORING CONCEPTS (continued)

72. Implementing Processes Find

$$\int \frac{x^2}{x - 4}\, dx$$

by (a) using the substitution $u = x - 4$ and (b) first dividing the improper fraction. (c) Compare the two methods. Is the result the same? Explain.

───────────────

73. Finding Constants Determine the constants a and b such that

$$\sin x + \cos x = a \sin(x + b).$$

Use this result to integrate

$$\int \frac{dx}{\sin x + \cos x}.$$

74. Deriving a Rule Show that

$$\sec x = \frac{\sin x}{\cos x} + \frac{\cos x}{1 + \sin x}.$$

Then use this identity to derive the basic integration rule

$$\int \sec x\, dx = \ln|\sec x + \tan x| + C.$$

75. Area The graphs of $f(x) = x$ and $g(x) = ax^2$ intersect at the points $(0, 0)$ and $(1/a, 1/a)$. Find a $(a > 0)$ such that the area of the region bounded by the graphs of these two functions is $\frac{2}{3}$.

76. Implementing Processes When evaluating $\int_{-1}^1 x^2\, dx$ is it correct to substitute $u = x^2$, $x = \sqrt{u}$, and $dx = du/(2\sqrt{u})$ to obtain $\frac{1}{2}\int_1^1 \sqrt{u}\, du = 0$? Explain.

77. Comparing Antiderivatives

(a) Explain why the antiderivative $y_1 = e^{x + C_1}$ is equivalent to the antiderivative $y_2 = Ce^x$.

(b) Explain why the antiderivative $y_1 = \sec^2 x + C_1$ is equivalent to the antiderivative $y_2 = \tan^2 x + C$.

78. HOW DO YOU SEE IT? Using the graph, is

$$\int_0^5 f(x)\, dx$$

positive or negative? Explain.

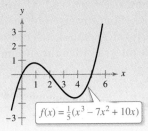

$f(x) = \frac{1}{5}(x^3 - 7x^2 + 10x)$

Approximation In Exercises 79 and 80, determine which value best approximates the area of the region between the x-axis and the function over the given interval. (Make your selection on the basis of a sketch of the region and not by integrating.)

79. $f(x) = \dfrac{4x}{x^2 + 1}$, $[0, 2]$

   (a) 3   (b) 1   (c) -8 (d) 8   (e) 10

80. $f(x) = \dfrac{4}{x^2 + 1}$, $[0, 2]$

   (a) 3   (b) 1   (c) -4 (d) 4   (e) 10

Average Value of a Function In Exercises 81 and 82, find the average value of the function over the given interval.

81. $f(x) = \dfrac{1}{1 + x^2}$, $-3 \le x \le 3$

82. $f(x) = \sin nx$, $0 \le x \le \dfrac{\pi}{n}$, n is a positive integer.

83. Volume The region bounded by $y = e^{-x^2}$, $y = 0$, $x = 0$, and $x = b$ $(b > 0)$ is revolved about the y-axis.

   (a) Find the volume of the solid generated when $b = 1$.

   (b) Find b such that the volume of the generated solid is $\frac{4}{3}$ cubic units.

84. Volume Consider the region bounded by the graphs of $x = 0$, $y = \cos x^2$, $y = \sin x^2$, and $x = \sqrt{\pi}/2$. Find the volume of the solid generated by revolving the region about the y-axis.

85. Arc Length Find the arc length of the graph of $y = \ln(\sin x)$ from $x = \pi/4$ to $x = \pi/2$.

86. Arc Length Find the arc length of the graph of $y = \ln(\cos x)$ from $x = 0$ to $x = \pi/3$.

87. Surface Area Find the area of the surface formed by revolving the graph of

$$y = 2\sqrt{x}$$

on the interval $[0, 9]$ about the x-axis.

88. Surface Area Find the area of the surface formed by revolving the graph of $y = 36 - x^2$ on the interval $[0, 6]$ about the y-axis.

Interpreting Integrals In Exercises 89 and 90, (a) sketch the region whose area is given by the integral, (b) sketch the solid whose volume is given by the integral when the disk method is used, and (c) sketch the solid whose volume is given by the integral when the shell method is used.

89. $\displaystyle\int_0^2 2\pi x^2\, dx$

90. $\displaystyle\int_0^4 \pi y\, dy$

Arc Length In Exercises 91 and 92, use the integration capabilities of a graphing utility to approximate the arc length of the curve over the given interval.

91. $y = \tan \pi x$, $\left[0, \frac{1}{4}\right]$

92. $y = x^{2/3}$, $[1, 8]$

93. Finding a Pattern

   (a) Find $\displaystyle\int \cos^3 x\, dx$.

   (b) Find $\displaystyle\int \cos^5 x\, dx$.

   (c) Find $\displaystyle\int \cos^7 x\, dx$.

   (d) Explain how to find $\int \cos^{15} x\, dx$ without actually integrating.

94. Finding a Pattern

   (a) Write $\int \tan^3 x\, dx$ in terms of $\int \tan x\, dx$. Then find $\int \tan^3 x\, dx$.

   (b) Write $\int \tan^5 x\, dx$ in terms of $\int \tan^3 x\, dx$.

   (c) Write $\int \tan^{2k+1} x\, dx$, where k is a positive integer, in terms of $\int \tan^{2k-1} x\, dx$.

   (d) Explain how to find $\int \tan^{15} x\, dx$ without actually integrating.

Calculus AP® – Exam Preparation Questions

Multiple Choice In Exercises 95–98, select the correct antiderivative.

95. $\dfrac{dy}{dx} = \dfrac{x}{\sqrt{x^2 + 1}}$

   (A) $2\sqrt{x^2 + 1} + C$ (B) $\sqrt{x^2 + 1} + C$

   (C) $\frac{1}{2}\sqrt{x^2 + 1} + C$ (D) $\ln(x^2 + 1) + C$

96. $\dfrac{dy}{dx} = \dfrac{x}{x^2 + 1}$

   (A) $\ln\sqrt{x^2 + 1} + C$ (B) $\dfrac{2x}{(x^2 + 1)^2} + C$

   (C) $\arctan x + C$ (D) $\ln(x^2 + 1) + C$

97. $\dfrac{dy}{dx} = \dfrac{1}{x^2 + 1}$

   (A) $\ln\sqrt{x^2 + 1} + C$ (B) $\dfrac{2x}{(x^2 + 1)^2} + C$

   (C) $\arctan x + C$ (D) $\ln(x^2 + 1) + C$

98. $\dfrac{dy}{dx} = x\cos(x^2 + 1)$

   (A) $2x \sin(x^2 + 1) + C$

   (B) $-\frac{1}{2}\sin(x^2 + 1) + C$

   (C) $\frac{1}{2}\sin(x^2 + 1) + C$

   (D) $-2x \sin(x^2 + 1) + C$

7.2   Integration by Parts

▶ Find an antiderivative using integration by parts.

Integration by Parts

In this section, you will study an important integration technique called **integration by parts.** This technique can be applied to a wide variety of functions and is particularly useful for integrands involving *products* of algebraic and transcendental functions. For instance, integration by parts works well with integrals such as

$$\int x \ln x \, dx, \quad \int x^2 \, e^x \, dx, \quad \text{and} \quad \int e^x \sin x \, dx.$$

Integration by parts is based on the formula for the derivative of a product

$$\frac{d}{dx}[uv] = u \frac{dv}{dx} + v \frac{du}{dx}$$

$$= uv' + vu'$$

where both u and v are differentiable functions of x. When u' and v' are continuous, you can integrate both sides of this equation to obtain

$$uv = \int uv' \, dx + \int vu' \, dx$$

$$= \int u \, dv + \int v \, du.$$

By rewriting this equation, you obtain the next theorem.

Theorem 7.1   Integration by Parts

If u and v are functions of x and have continuous derivatives, then

$$\int u \, dv = uv - \int v \, du.$$

> **Insight**
>
> Integration by parts is tested on the AP® Calculus BC Exam.

This formula expresses the original integral in terms of another integral. Depending on the choices of u and dv, it may be easier to find the second integral than the original one. Because the choices of u and dv are critical in the integration by parts process, the guidelines below are provided.

Guidelines for Integration by Parts

1. Try letting dv be the most complicated portion of the integrand that fits a basic integration rule. Then u will be the remaining portion of the integrand.

2. Try letting u be the portion of the integrand whose derivative is a function simpler than u. Then dv will be the remaining portion of the integrand.

Note that dv always includes the dx of the original integrand.

When using integration by parts, note that you can first choose dv or first choose u. After you choose, however, the choice of the other factor is determined—it must be the remaining portion of the integrand. Also note that dv must contain the differential dx of the original integral.

EXAMPLE 1 Integration by Parts

Find $\int xe^x\,dx.$

Solution

To apply integration by parts, you need to write the integral in the form $\int u\,dv$. There are several ways to do this.

$$\int \underbrace{(x)}_{u}\,\underbrace{(e^x\,dx)}_{dv}, \quad \int \underbrace{(e^x)}_{u}\underbrace{(x\,dx)}_{dv}, \quad \int \underbrace{(1)}_{u}\,\underbrace{(xe^x\,dx)}_{dv}, \quad \int \underbrace{(xe^x)}_{u}\,\underbrace{(dx)}_{dv}$$

The guidelines on the preceding page suggest the first option because the derivative of $u = x$ is simpler than x, and $dv = e^x\,dx$ is the most complicated portion of the integrand that fits a basic integration formula.

$$dv = e^x\,dx \quad\Longrightarrow\quad v = \int dv = \int e^x\,dx = e^x$$

$$u = x \quad\Longrightarrow\quad du = dx$$

Now, integration by parts produces

$$\int u\,dv = uv - \int v\,du \qquad \text{Integration by parts formula}$$

$$\int xe^x\,dx = xe^x - \int e^x\,dx \qquad \text{Substitute.}$$

$$= xe^x - e^x + C. \qquad \text{Integrate.}$$

To check this, differentiate $xe^x - e^x + C$ to see that you obtain the original integrand.

EXAMPLE 2 Integration by Parts

Find $\int x^2 \ln x\,dx.$

Solution

In this case, x^2 is more easily integrated than $\ln x$. Furthermore, the derivative of $\ln x$ is simpler than $\ln x$. So, you should let $dv = x^2\,dx$.

$$dv = x^2\,dx \quad\Longrightarrow\quad v = \int x^2\,dx = \frac{x^3}{3}$$

$$u = \ln x \quad\Longrightarrow\quad du = \frac{1}{x}\,dx$$

Integration by parts produces

$$\int u\,dv = uv - \int v\,du \qquad \text{Integration by parts formula}$$

$$\int x^2 \ln x\,dx = \frac{x^3}{3}\ln x - \int \left(\frac{x^3}{3}\right)\left(\frac{1}{x}\right)dx \qquad \text{Substitute.}$$

$$= \frac{x^3}{3}\ln x - \frac{1}{3}\int x^2\,dx \qquad \text{Simplify.}$$

$$= \frac{x^3}{3}\ln x - \frac{x^3}{9} + C. \qquad \text{Integrate.}$$

You can check this result by differentiating.

$$\frac{d}{dx}\left[\frac{x^3}{3}\ln x - \frac{x^3}{9} + C\right] = \frac{x^3}{3}\left(\frac{1}{x}\right) + (\ln x)(x^2) - \frac{x^2}{3} = x^2 \ln x$$

> **Justification**
>
> In Example 1, note that it is not necessary to include a constant of integration when solving
>
> $$v = \int e^x\,dx = e^x + C_1.$$
>
> To illustrate this, replace $v = e^x$ by $v = e^x + C_1$ and apply integration by parts to see that you obtain the same result.

Surprisingly, integration by parts is useful for integrands that do *not* involve a product, such as $\int \ln x \, dx$ and $\int \arcsin x \, dx$. In these cases, try letting $dv = dx$, as shown in the next two examples.

EXAMPLE 3 Integration by Parts

Find $\int \ln x \, dx$.

Solution   The integrand is not a product, so let $dv = dx$.

$$dv = dx \quad \Longrightarrow \quad v = \int dx = x$$

$$u = \ln x \quad \Longrightarrow \quad du = \frac{1}{x} dx$$

Integration by parts produces

$$\int u \, dv = uv - \int v \, dv \qquad \text{Integration by parts.}$$

$$\int \ln x \, dx = (\ln x)(x) - \int x \left(\frac{1}{x}\right) dx \qquad \text{Substitute.}$$

$$= x \ln x - \int dx \qquad \text{Simplify.}$$

$$= x \ln x - x + C. \qquad \text{Integrate.}$$

EXAMPLE 4 Integration by Parts with a Definite Integral

Evaluate $\int_0^1 \arcsin x \, dx$.

Algebraic Solution

Let $dv = dx$.

$$dv = dx \quad \Longrightarrow \quad v = \int dx = x$$

$$u = \arcsin x \quad \Longrightarrow \quad du = \frac{1}{\sqrt{1 - x^2}} dx$$

Integration by parts produces

$$\int u \, dv = uv - \int v \, du$$

$$\int \arcsin x \, dx = x \arcsin x - \int \frac{x}{\sqrt{1 - x^2}} dx$$

$$= x \arcsin x + \frac{1}{2}\int (1 - x^2)^{-1/2}(-2x) \, dx$$

$$= x \arcsin x + \sqrt{1 - x^2} + C.$$

Using this antiderivative, you can evaluate the definite integral as shown.

$$\int_0^1 \arcsin x \, dx = \left[x \arcsin x + \sqrt{1 - x^2} \right]_0^1$$

$$= \frac{\pi}{2} - 1$$

$$\approx 0.571$$

Graphical Solution

Use a graphing utility set in *radian mode* to graph $y = \arcsin x$, as shown below.

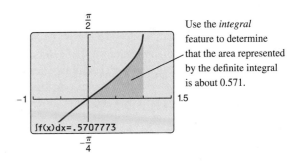

Use the *integral* feature to determine that the area represented by the definite integral is about 0.571.

$\int f(x)dx = .5707773$

Some integrals require repeated use of the integration by parts formula, as shown in the next example.

EXAMPLE 5 Repeated Use of Integration by Parts

Find $\int x^2 \sin x \, dx$.

Solution

The factors x^2 and $\sin x$ are equally easy to integrate. However, the derivative of x^2 becomes simpler, whereas the derivative of $\sin x$ does not. So, you should let $u = x^2$.

$$dv = \sin x \, dx \quad \Longrightarrow \quad v = \int \sin x \, dx = -\cos x$$

$$u = x^2 \quad \Longrightarrow \quad du = 2x \, dx$$

Now, integration by parts produces

$$\int x^2 \sin x \, dx = -x^2 \cos x + \int 2x \cos x \, dx. \qquad \text{First use of integration by parts}$$

This first use of integration by parts has succeeded in simplifying the original integral, but the integral on the right still does not fit a basic integration rule. To find that integral, you can apply integration by parts again. This time, let $u = 2x$.

$$dv = \cos x \, dx \quad \Longrightarrow \quad v = \int \cos x \, dx = \sin x$$

$$u = 2x \quad \Longrightarrow \quad du = 2 \, dx$$

Now, integration by parts produces

$$\int 2x \cos x \, dx = 2x \sin x - \int 2 \sin x \, dx \qquad \text{Second use of integration by parts}$$

$$= 2x \sin x + 2 \cos x + C.$$

Combining these two results, you can write

$$\int x^2 \sin x \, dx = -x^2 \cos x + 2x \sin x + 2 \cos x + C. \qquad \blacksquare$$

When making repeated applications of integration by parts, you need to be careful not to interchange the substitutions in successive applications. For instance, in Example 5, the first substitution was $u = x^2$ and $dv = \sin x \, dx$. If, in the second application, you had switched the substitution to $u = \cos x$ and $dv = 2x \, dx$, you would have obtained

$$\int x^2 \sin x \, dx = -x^2 \cos x + \int 2x \cos x \, dx$$

$$= -x^2 \cos x + x^2 \cos x + \int x^2 \sin x \, dx$$

$$= \int x^2 \sin x \, dx$$

thereby undoing the previous integration and returning to the *original* integral. When making repeated applications of integration by parts, you should also watch for the appearance of a *constant multiple* of the original integral. For instance, this occurs when you use integration by parts to find $\int e^x \cos 2x \, dx$, and it also occurs in Example 6 on the next page.

The integral in Example 6 is an important one. In Section 7.4 (Example 6), you will see that it is used to find the arc length of a parabolic segment.

EXAMPLE 6   **Integration by Parts**

Find $\displaystyle\int \sec^3 x \, dx$.

Solution

The most complicated portion of the integrand that can be easily integrated is $\sec^2 x$, so you should let $dv = \sec^2 x \, dx$ and $u = \sec x$.

$$dv = \sec^2 x \, dx \quad\Longrightarrow\quad v = \int \sec^2 x \, dx = \tan x$$

$$u = \sec x \quad\Longrightarrow\quad du = \sec x \tan x \, dx$$

Integration by parts produces

$$\int u \, dv = uv - \int v \, du \qquad\qquad \text{Integration by parts formula}$$

$$\int \sec^3 x \, dx = \sec x \tan x - \int \sec x \tan^2 x \, dx \qquad\qquad \text{Substitute.}$$

$$\int \sec^3 x \, dx = \sec x \tan x - \int (\sec x)(\sec^2 x - 1) \, dx \qquad\qquad \text{Trigonometric identity}$$

$$\int \sec^3 x \, dx = \sec x \tan x - \int \sec^3 x \, dx + \int \sec x \, dx \qquad\qquad \text{Rewrite.}$$

$$2\int \sec^3 x \, dx = \sec x \tan x + \int \sec x \, dx \qquad\qquad \text{Collect like integrals.}$$

$$2\int \sec^3 x \, dx = \sec x \tan x + \ln|\sec x + \tan x| + C \qquad\qquad \text{Integrate.}$$

$$\int \sec^3 x \, dx = \frac{1}{2} \sec x \tan x + \frac{1}{2} \ln|\sec x + \tan x| + C. \qquad\qquad \text{Divide by 2.}$$

EXAMPLE 7   **Finding a Particular Solution**

Given the initial condition $y(0) = 4$, find the particular solution of the differential equation

$$\frac{dy}{dx} = \frac{x}{2y} \sin x.$$

Solution

Begin by separating variables.

$$2y \, dy = x \sin x \, dx \qquad\qquad \text{Separate variables.}$$

$$\int 2y \, dy = \int x \sin x \, dx \qquad\qquad \text{Integrate each side.}$$

You can find the integral on the left using the Power Rule. To find the integral on the right, use integration by parts. To do this, let $dv = \sin x \, dx$ and $u = x$. This produces $v = -\cos x$ and $du = dx$. Using the Power Rule and integration by parts, you can write

$$y^2 = -x \cos x + \int \cos x \, dx \qquad\qquad \text{Apply integration rules.}$$

$$y^2 = -x \cos x + \sin x + C. \qquad\qquad \text{General solution}$$

From the initial condition $y(0) = 4$, you have $4^2 = 0 + 0 + C$, which implies $C = 16$. So, the particular solution has the implicit form

$$y^2 = -x \cos x + \sin x + 16$$

$$y^2 + x \cos x - \sin x = 16. \qquad\qquad \text{Particular solution} \ \blacksquare$$

As you gain experience in using integration by parts, your skill in determining u and dv will increase. The next summary lists several common integrals with suggestions for the choices of u and dv.

Summary: Common Integrals Using Integration by Parts

1. For integrals of the form

$$\int x^n e^{ax}\, dx, \quad \int x^n \sin ax\, dx, \quad \text{or} \quad \int x^n \cos ax\, dx$$

let $u = x^n$ and let $dv = e^{ax}\, dx$, $\sin ax\, dx$, or $\cos ax\, dx$.

2. For integrals of the form

$$\int x^n \ln x\, dx, \quad \int x^n \arcsin ax\, dx, \quad \text{or} \quad \int x^n \arctan ax\, dx$$

let $u = \ln x$, $\arcsin ax$, or $\arctan ax$ and let $dv = x^n\, dx$.

3. For integrals of the form

$$\int e^{ax} \sin bx\, dx \quad \text{or} \quad \int e^{ax} \cos bx\, dx$$

let $u = \sin bx$ or $\cos bx$ and let $dv = e^{ax}\, dx$.

Implementing Processes

You can use the acronym LIATE as a guideline for choosing u in integration by parts. In order, check the integrand for the following.

Is there a **L**ogarithmic part?

Is there an **I**nverse trigonometric part?

Is there an **A**lgebraic part?

Is there a **T**rigonometric part?

Is there an **E**xponential part?

In problems involving repeated applications of integration by parts, a tabular method, illustrated in Example 8, can help to organize the work. This method works well for integrals of the form

$$\int x^n \sin ax\, dx, \quad \int x^n \cos ax\, dx, \quad \text{and} \quad \int x^n e^{ax}\, dx.$$

EXAMPLE 8   Using the Tabular Method

See LarsonCalculusforAP.com for an interactive version of this type of example.

Find $\displaystyle\int x^2 \sin 4x\, dx$.

Solution

Begin as usual by letting $u = x^2$ and

$$dv = v'\, dx = \sin 4x\, dx.$$

Next, create a table consisting of three columns, as shown.

Alternate Signs	u and Its Derivatives	v' and Its Antiderivatives
$+$	x^2	$\sin 4x$
$-$	$2x$	$-\frac{1}{4}\cos 4x$
$+$	2	$-\frac{1}{16}\sin 4x$
$-$	0	$\frac{1}{64}\cos 4x$

Differentiate until you obtain 0 as a derivative.

Insight

The tabular method is not tested on the AP® Exam, but you may find this method helpful in solving some free-response questions.

The solution is obtained by adding the signed products of the diagonal entries:

$$\int x^2 \sin 4x\, dx = -\frac{1}{4}x^2 \cos 4x + \frac{1}{8}x \sin 4x + \frac{1}{32}\cos 4x + C.$$

7.2 Exercises

 Setting Up Integration by Parts   In Exercises 1–8, identify *u* and *dv* for finding the integral using integration by parts. Do not integrate.

1. $\int xe^{9x}\,dx$

2. $\int x^2 e^{2x}\,dx$

3. $\int (\ln x)^2\,dx$

4. $\int \ln 5x\,dx$

5. $\int x\sec^2 x\,dx$

6. $\int x^2 \cos x\,dx$

7. $\int x^3 \arcsin 4x\,dx$

8. $\int e^{2x}\cos 4x\,dx$

 Using Integration by Parts   In Exercises 9–14, find the indefinite integral using integration by parts with the given choices of *u* and *dv*.

9. $\int x^3 \ln x\,dx;\quad u = \ln x,\quad dv = x^3\,dx$

10. $\int x^5 \ln x\,dx;\quad u = \ln x,\quad dv = x^5\,dx$

11. $\int xe^{8x}\,dx;\quad u = x,\quad dv = e^{8x}\,dx$

12. $\int (4x + 7)e^x\,dx;\quad u = 4x + 7,\quad dv = e^x\,dx$

13. $\int x\sin 3x\,dx;\quad u = x,\quad dv = \sin 3x\,dx$

14. $\int x\cos 4x\,dx;\quad u = x,\quad dv = \cos 4x\,dx$

 Finding an Indefinite Integral   In Exercises 15–36, find the indefinite integral. (*Note:* Solve by the simplest method—not all require integration by parts.)

15. $\int xe^{4x}\,dx$

16. $\int \dfrac{5x}{e^{2x}}\,dx$

17. $\int x^3 e^x\,dx$

18. $\int \dfrac{e^{1/t}}{t^2}\,dt$

19. $\int t\ln(t + 1)\,dt$

20. $\int x^5 \ln 3x\,dx$

21. $\int \dfrac{(\ln x)^2}{x}\,dx$

22. $\int \dfrac{\ln x}{x^3}\,dx$

23. $\int \dfrac{xe^{2x}}{(2x + 1)^2}\,dx$

24. $\int \dfrac{x^3 e^{x^2}}{(x^2 + 1)^2}\,dx$

25. $\int x\sqrt{x - 5}\,dx$

26. $\int \dfrac{2x}{\sqrt{1 - 6x}}\,dx$

27. $\int x\csc^2 x\,dx$

28. $\int t\csc t\cot t\,dt$

29. $\int \ln 2x\,dx$

30. $\int \ln x^2\,dx$

31. $\int \arctan x\,dx$

32. $\int 4\arccos x\,dx$

33. $\int x^3 \sin x\,dx$

34. $\int x^2 \cos x\,dx$

35. $\int e^{-3x}\sin 5x\,dx$

36. $\int e^{4x}\cos 2x\,dx$

37. Error Analysis Describe and correct the error in finding the indefinite integral $\int x\sin x\,dx$.

$\int x\sin x\,dx = x(-\cos x) - \int(-\cos x)\,dx$

$\qquad\qquad = -x\cos x + \sin x$

38. Error Analysis Describe and correct the error in finding the indefinite integral $\int x^4 \ln x\,dx$ using $u = \ln x$ and $dv = x^4\,dx$.

$\int x^4 \ln x\,dx = \dfrac{x^5}{5}\ln x - \dfrac{x^5}{5}\int \dfrac{1}{x}\,dx$

$\qquad\qquad = \dfrac{x^5}{5}\ln x - \dfrac{x^5}{5}\ln x + C = C$ ✗

Differential Equation   In Exercises 39–42, find the general solution of the differential equation.

39. $y' = 2\ln x$

40. $y' = \arctan \dfrac{x}{2}$

41. $\dfrac{dy}{dt} = \dfrac{t^2}{\sqrt{3 + 5t}}$

42. $\dfrac{dy}{dx} = x^2 \sqrt{x - 3}$

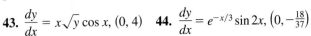 **Slope Field   In Exercises 43 and 44, a differential equation, a point, and a slope field are given. (a) Sketch two approximate solutions of the differential equation on the slope field, one of which passes through the given point. To print an enlarged copy of the graph, go to *MathGraphs.com*. (b) Use integration and the given point to find the particular solution of the differential equation and use a graphing utility to graph the solution. Compare the result with the sketch in part (a) that passes through the given point.**

43. $\dfrac{dy}{dx} = x\sqrt{y}\cos x,\ (0, 4)$

44. $\dfrac{dy}{dx} = e^{-x/3}\sin 2x,\ \left(0, -\tfrac{18}{37}\right)$

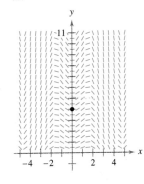

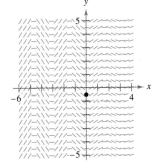

Finding a Particular Solution In Exercises 45–48, find the particular solution that satisfies the initial condition.

Differential Equation   Initial Condition

45. $\dfrac{dy}{dx} = xe^{2x}$ $y(0) = 4$

46. $\dfrac{dy}{dx} = (x - 4)\cos x$ $y(0) = 2$

47. $\dfrac{dy}{dx} = \dfrac{x}{4y} \ln x^3$ $y(1) = 2$

48. $\dfrac{dy}{dx} = e^{-x}e^y \sec y$ $y(1) = 0$

 Evaluating a Definite Integral In Exercises 49–58, evaluate the definite integral. Use a graphing utility to confirm your result.

49. $\displaystyle\int_0^3 xe^{x/2}\, dx$

50. $\displaystyle\int_0^2 x^2 e^{-2x}\, dx$

51. $\displaystyle\int_0^{\pi/4} x \cos 2x\, dx$

52. $\displaystyle\int_0^{\pi} x \sin 2x\, dx$

53. $\displaystyle\int_0^{1/2} \arccos x\, dx$

54. $\displaystyle\int_0^1 x \arcsin x^2\, dx$

55. $\displaystyle\int_0^1 e^x \sin x\, dx$

56. $\displaystyle\int_0^1 \ln(4 + x^2)\, dx$

57. $\displaystyle\int_2^4 x \,\text{arcsec}\, x\, dx$

58. $\displaystyle\int_0^{\pi/8} x \sec^2 2x\, dx$

 Using the Tabular Method In Exercises 59–64, use the tabular method to find the indefinite integral.

59. $\displaystyle\int x^2 e^{2x}\, dx$

60. $\displaystyle\int (1 - x)(e^{-x} + 1)\, dx$

61. $\displaystyle\int x^3 \sin x\, dx$

62. $\displaystyle\int x^3 \cos 2x\, dx$

63. $\displaystyle\int (x + 2)^2 \sin x\, dx$

64. $\displaystyle\int (6 + x)\sqrt{4x + 9}\, dx$

Using Two Methods Together In Exercises 65–68, find the indefinite integral by using substitution followed by integration by parts.

65. $\displaystyle\int \sin \sqrt{x}\, dx$

66. $\displaystyle\int 2x^3 \cos x^2\, dx$

67. $\displaystyle\int x^5 e^{x^2}\, dx$

68. $\displaystyle\int e^{\sqrt{2x}}\, dx$

69. Using Two Methods Integrate $\displaystyle\int \dfrac{x^3}{\sqrt{4 + x^2}}\, dx$

 (a) by parts, letting $dv = \dfrac{x}{\sqrt{4 + x^2}}\, dx$.

 (b) by substitution, letting $u = 4 + x^2$.

70. Using Two Methods Integrate $\displaystyle\int x\sqrt{4 - x}\, dx$

 (a) by parts, letting $dv = \sqrt{4 - x}\, dx$.

 (b) by substitution, letting $u = 4 - x$.

EXPLORING CONCEPTS

71. Communicating Integration by parts is based on what differentiation rule? Explain.

72. Implementing Processes In your own words, state how you determine which parts of the integrand should be u and dv.

73. Implementing Processes When finding $\int x \sin x\, dx$, explain how letting $u = \sin x$ and $dv = x\, dx$ makes the solution more difficult to find.

74. Justifying Write an integral that requires three applications of integration by parts. Explain why three applications are needed.

75. Implementing Processes State whether you would use integration by parts to find each integral. If so, identify what you would use for u and dv. Explain your reasoning.

 (a) $\displaystyle\int \dfrac{\ln x}{x}\, dx$ (b) $\displaystyle\int x^8 \ln x\, dx$ (c) $\displaystyle\int x^2 e^{-3x}\, dx$

 (d) $\displaystyle\int 2xe^{x^2}\, dx$ (e) $\displaystyle\int \dfrac{x}{\sqrt{x + 1}}\, dx$ (f) $\displaystyle\int \dfrac{x}{\sqrt{x^2 + 1}}\, dx$

 76. HOW DO YOU SEE IT? Use the graph of f' shown in the figure to answer the following.

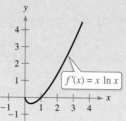

$f'(x) = x \ln x$

 (a) Approximate the slope of f at $x = 2$. Explain.

 (b) Approximate any open intervals on which the graph of f is increasing and any open intervals on which it is decreasing. Explain.

Finding a General Rule In Exercises 77 and 78, find the integral for $n = 0, 1, 2,$ and 3. Use the result to make a conjecture of a general rule for the integral for any positive integer n. Test your results for $n = 4$.

77. $\displaystyle\int x^n \ln x\, dx$

78. $\displaystyle\int x^n e^x\, dx$

Proof   In Exercises 79–84, use integration by parts to prove the formula. (For Exercises 79–82, assume that n is a positive integer.)

79. $\displaystyle\int x^n \sin x \, dx = -x^n \cos x + n \int x^{n-1} \cos x \, dx$

80. $\displaystyle\int x^n \cos x \, dx = x^n \sin x - n \int x^{n-1} \sin x \, dx$

81. $\displaystyle\int x^n \ln x \, dx = \frac{x^{n+1}}{(n+1)^2}\left[-1 + (n+1)\ln x\right] + C$

82. $\displaystyle\int x^n e^{ax} \, dx = \frac{x^n e^{ax}}{a} - \frac{n}{a}\int x^{n-1} e^{ax} \, dx$

83. $\displaystyle\int e^{ax} \sin bx \, dx = \frac{e^{ax}(a \sin bx - b \cos bx)}{a^2 + b^2} + C$

84. $\displaystyle\int e^{ax} \cos bx \, dx = \frac{e^{ax}(a \cos bx + b \sin bx)}{a^2 + b^2} + C$

Implementing Processes   In Exercises 85–90, find the indefinite integral by using the appropriate formula from Exercises 79–84.

85. $\displaystyle\int x^2 \sin x \, dx$ **86.** $\displaystyle\int x^2 \cos x \, dx$

87. $\displaystyle\int x^5 \ln x \, dx$ **88.** $\displaystyle\int x^3 e^{2x} \, dx$

89. $\displaystyle\int e^{-3x} \sin 4x \, dx$ **90.** $\displaystyle\int e^{2x} \cos 3x \, dx$

Area   In Exercises 91–94, use a graphing utility to graph the region bounded by the graphs of the equations. Then find the area of the region analytically.

91. $y = 2xe^{-x}, \quad y = 0, \quad x = 3$

92. $y = \dfrac{1}{10}xe^{3x}, \quad y = 0, \quad x = 0, \quad x = 2$

93. $y = e^{-x} \sin \pi x, \quad y = 0, \quad x = 1$

94. $y = x^3 \ln x, \quad y = 0, \quad x = 1, \quad x = 3$

95. MEMORY MODEL

A model for the ability M of a child to memorize, measured on a scale from 0 to 10, is given by $M = 1 + 1.6t \ln t$, $0 < t \le 4$, where t is the child's age in years. Find the average value of this model

(a) between the child's first and second birthdays.

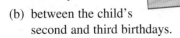

(b) between the child's second and third birthdays.

(c) between the child's third and fourth birthdays.

96. Average Displacement   A damping force affects the vibration of a spring so that the displacement of the spring is given by $y = e^{-2t}(\cos 2t + 5 \sin 2t)$. Find the average value of y on the interval from $t = 0$ to $t = \pi$.

Present Value   In Exercises 97 and 98, find the present value P of the amount accumulated after t_1 years from a continuous income flow of $c(t)$ dollars per year using

$$P = \int_0^{t_1} c(t)e^{-rt} \, dt$$

where t is the time in years and r is the annual interest rate compounded continuously that *could* be earned for t_1 years on the present value amount P.

97. $c(t) = 100{,}000 + 4000t, \ r = 9\%, \ t_1 = 10$

98. $c(t) = 40{,}000 + 1000t, \ r = 7\%, \ t_1 = 5$

Integrals Used to Find Fourier Coefficients   In Exercises 99 and 100, verify the value of the definite integral, where n is a positive integer.

99. $\displaystyle\int_{-\pi}^{\pi} x \sin nx \, dx = \begin{cases} \dfrac{2\pi}{n}, & n \text{ is odd} \\[2mm] -\dfrac{2\pi}{n}, & n \text{ is even} \end{cases}$

100. $\displaystyle\int_{-\pi}^{\pi} x^2 \cos nx \, dx = \dfrac{(-1)^n 4\pi}{n^2}$

101. Vibrating String   A string stretched between the two points $(0, 0)$ and $(2, 0)$ is plucked by displacing the string h units at its midpoint. The motion of the string is modeled by a **Fourier Sine Series** whose coefficients are given by

$$b_n = h\int_0^1 x \sin \frac{n\pi x}{2} \, dx + h\int_1^2 (-x + 2) \sin \frac{n\pi x}{2} \, dx.$$

Find b_n.

102. Particle Motion   The velocity (in meters per second) of a particle moving along the x-axis is

$$v(t) = t^6 \ln t \, dt$$

where t is the time in seconds.

(a) Find the position function $x(t)$ for the particle given that $x(1) = 48/49$.

(b) Find the total distance traveled by the particle from time $t = 1$ to $t = 2$.

103. Finding a Pattern   Find the area bounded by the graphs of $y = x \sin x$ and $y = 0$ over each interval.

(a) $[0, \pi]$ (b) $[\pi, 2\pi]$ (c) $[2\pi, 3\pi]$

Describe any patterns that you notice. What is the area between the graphs of $y = x \sin x$ and $y = 0$ over the interval $[n\pi, (n + 1)\pi]$, where n is any nonnegative integer? Explain.

104. Area and Volume Given the region bounded by the graphs of $y = x \sin x$, $y = 0$, $x = 0$, and $x = \pi$, find

(a) the volume of the solid generated by revolving the region about the x-axis.

(b) the volume of the solid generated by revolving the region about the y-axis.

105. Connecting Representations Give a geometric explanation of why

$$\int_0^{\pi/2} x \sin x \, dx \leq \int_0^{\pi/2} x \, dx.$$

Verify the inequality by evaluating the integrals.

Calculus AP® – Exam Preparation Questions

106. Multiple Choice $\int x \sin 8x \, dx =$

(A) $-\dfrac{x}{8} \cos 8x + \dfrac{1}{64} \sin 8x + C$

(B) $-\dfrac{x}{8} \cos 8x - \dfrac{1}{64} \sin 8x + C$

(C) $-\dfrac{x}{8} \cos 8x + \dfrac{1}{8} \sin 8x + C$

(D) $\dfrac{x}{8} \cos 8x + \dfrac{1}{64} \sin 8x + C$

107. Free Response Consider the region S bounded by the graphs of $y = \ln x$, $y = 0$, and $x = e$.

(a) Find the area of S.

(b) Find the volume of the solid formed by revolving S about the x-axis.

(c) Find the volume of the solid formed by revolving S about the y-axis.

Exam Preparation Questions (continued)

108. Free Response Let f be a function defined for $x > 0$, with $f(e) = 4$ and $f'(x) = x \ln x$.

(a) Write an equation for the line tangent to the graph of f at the point $(e, 4)$.

(b) Does the graph of f have any relative extrema? If so, where do they occur? Show the work that leads to your answer.

(c) Determine the open interval(s) on which the graph of f is concave upward or concave downward.

(d) Use antidifferentiation to find $f(x)$.

109. Free Response Consider the region R bounded by the graphs of

$$y = xe^{-x}, \quad y = -x, \quad \text{and} \quad x = 1.$$

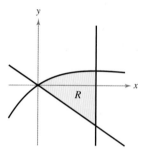

(a) Find the area of R.

(b) Find the volume of the solid formed by revolving R about the horizontal line $y = -1$.

(c) Write, but do not evaluate, an expression involving one or more integrals that gives the perimeter of R.

SECTION PROJECT

Rocket Velocity

The velocity v (in feet per second) of a rocket whose initial mass m (including fuel) is given by

$$v = -gt + u \ln \frac{m}{m - rt}, \quad t < \frac{m}{r}$$

where u is the expulsion speed of the fuel, r is the rate at which the fuel is consumed, and $g = 32$ feet per second per second is the acceleration due to gravity. Find the position equation for a rocket for which $m = 50,000$ pounds, $u = 12,000$ feet per second, and $r = 400$ pounds per second. What is the height of the rocket when $t = 100$ seconds? (Assume that the rocket was fired from ground level and is moving straight upward.)

In 2018, the private spaceflight company SpaceX launched its first Falcon Heavy rocket. The launch was billed as a test flight to prepare for launching large payloads such as commercial satellites.

7.3 Trigonometric Integrals

▶ Solve trigonometric integrals involving powers of sine and cosine.
▶ Solve trigonometric integrals involving powers of secant and tangent.
▶ Solve trigonometric integrals involving sines and cosines of different angles.

Integrals Involving Powers of Sine and Cosine

In this section, you will study techniques for finding integrals of the form

$$\int \sin^m x \cos^n x \, dx \quad \text{and} \quad \int \sec^m x \tan^n x \, dx$$

where either m or n is a positive integer. To find antiderivatives for these forms, try to break them into combinations of trigonometric integrals to which you can apply the Power Rule.

For instance, you can find

$$\int \sin^5 x \cos x \, dx$$

with the Power Rule by letting $u = \sin x$. Then, $du = \cos x \, dx$ and you have

$$\int \sin^5 x \cos x \, dx = \int u^5 \, du = \frac{u^6}{6} + C = \frac{\sin^6 x}{6} + C.$$

To break up $\int \sin^m x \cos^n x \, dx$ into forms to which you can apply the Power Rule, use the relationships listed below.

$\sin^2 x + \cos^2 x = 1$	Pythagorean identity
$\sin^2 x = \dfrac{1 - \cos 2x}{2}$	Power-reducing formula for $\sin^2 x$
$\cos^2 x = \dfrac{1 + \cos 2x}{2}$	Power-reducing formula for $\cos^2 x$

Guidelines for Finding Integrals Involving Powers of Sine and Cosine

1. When the power of the sine is odd and positive, save one sine factor and convert the remaining factors to cosines. Then, expand and integrate.

$$\int \sin^{\overbrace{2k+1}^{\text{Odd}}} x \cos^n x \, dx = \int \overbrace{(\sin^2 x)^k}^{\text{Convert to cosines}} \cos^n x \overbrace{\sin x \, dx}^{\text{Save for } du} = \int (1 - \cos^2 x)^k \cos^n x \sin x \, dx$$

2. When the power of the cosine is odd and positive, save one cosine factor and convert the remaining factors to sines. Then, expand and integrate.

$$\int \sin^m x \cos^{\overbrace{2k+1}^{\text{Odd}}} x \, dx = \int (\sin^m x)\overbrace{(\cos^2 x)^k}^{\text{Convert to sines}} \overbrace{\cos x \, dx}^{\text{Save for } du} = \int (\sin^m x)(1 - \sin^2 x)^k \cos x \, dx$$

3. When the powers of both the sine and cosine are even and nonnegative, make repeated use of the formulas

$$\sin^2 x = \frac{1 - \cos 2x}{2} \quad \text{and} \quad \cos^2 x = \frac{1 + \cos 2x}{2}$$

to convert the integrand to odd powers of the cosine. Then proceed as in the second guideline.

EXAMPLE 1   Power of Sine Is Odd and Positive

Find $\displaystyle\int \sin^3 x \cos^4 x \, dx$.

Solution   Because you expect to use the Power Rule with $u = \cos x$, *save one sine factor* to form du and convert the remaining sine factors to cosines.

$$\int \sin^3 x \cos^4 x \, dx = \int (\sin^2 x \cos^4 x) \sin x \, dx \qquad \text{Rewrite.}$$

$$= \int (1 - \cos^2 x) \cos^4 x \sin x \, dx \qquad \text{Trigonometric identity}$$

$$= \int (\cos^4 x - \cos^6 x) \sin x \, dx \qquad \text{Multiply.}$$

$$= \int \cos^4 x \sin x \, dx - \int \cos^6 x \sin x \, dx \qquad \text{Rewrite.}$$

$$= -\int (\cos^4 x)(-\sin x) \, dx + \int (\cos^6 x)(-\sin x) \, dx$$

$$= -\frac{\cos^5 x}{5} + \frac{\cos^7 x}{7} + C \qquad \text{Integrate.} \qquad \blacksquare$$

Technology

A computer algebra system used to find the integral in Example 1 yielded $\int \sin^3 x \cos^4 x \, dx = (-\cos^5 x)\left(\frac{1}{7} \sin^2 x + \frac{2}{35}\right) + C$. Is this equivalent to the result obtained in Example 1?

In Example 1, *both* of the powers m and n happened to be positive integers. This strategy will work as long as either m or n is odd and positive. For instance, in the next example, the power of the cosine is 3, but the power of the sine is $-\frac{1}{2}$.

EXAMPLE 2   Power of Cosine Is Odd and Positive

See LarsonCalculusforAP.com for an interactive version of this type of example.

Evaluate $\displaystyle\int_{\pi/6}^{\pi/3} \frac{\cos^3 x}{\sqrt{\sin x}} \, dx$.

Solution   Because you expect to use the Power Rule with $u = \sin x$, *save one cosine factor* to form du and convert the remaining cosine factors to sines.

$$\int_{\pi/6}^{\pi/3} \frac{\cos^3 x}{\sqrt{\sin x}} \, dx = \int_{\pi/6}^{\pi/3} \frac{\cos^2 x \cos x}{\sqrt{\sin x}} \, dx \qquad \text{Rewrite.}$$

$$= \int_{\pi/6}^{\pi/3} \frac{(1 - \sin^2 x)(\cos x)}{\sqrt{\sin x}} \, dx \qquad \text{Trigonometric identity}$$

$$= \int_{\pi/6}^{\pi/3} [(\sin x)^{-1/2} - (\sin x)^{3/2}] \cos x \, dx \qquad \text{Divide.}$$

$$= \left[\frac{(\sin x)^{1/2}}{1/2} - \frac{(\sin x)^{5/2}}{5/2} \right]_{\pi/6}^{\pi/3} \qquad \text{Integrate.}$$

$$= 2\left(\frac{\sqrt{3}}{2}\right)^{1/2} - \frac{2}{5}\left(\frac{\sqrt{3}}{2}\right)^{5/2} - \sqrt{2} + \frac{\sqrt{32}}{80}$$

$$\approx 0.239$$

Figure 7.2 shows the region whose area is represented by this integral.

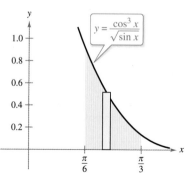

The area of the region is approximately 0.239.

Figure 7.2

EXAMPLE 3   Power of Cosine Is Even and Nonnegative

Find $\displaystyle\int \cos^4 x\,dx$.

Solution

Because m and n are both even and nonnegative ($m = 0$), you can replace $\cos^4 x$ by

$$\left(\frac{1 + \cos 2x}{2}\right)^2.$$

So, you can integrate as shown.

$$
\begin{aligned}
\int \cos^4 x\,dx &= \int \left(\frac{1 + \cos 2x}{2}\right)^2 dx && \text{Power-reducing formula}\\[2mm]
&= \int \left(\frac{1}{4} + \frac{\cos 2x}{2} + \frac{\cos^2 2x}{4}\right) dx && \text{Expand.}\\[2mm]
&= \int \left[\frac{1}{4} + \frac{\cos 2x}{2} + \frac{1}{4}\left(\frac{1 + \cos 4x}{2}\right)\right] dx && \text{Power-reducing formula}\\[2mm]
&= \frac{3}{8}\int dx + \frac{1}{4}\int 2\cos 2x\,dx + \frac{1}{32}\int 4\cos 4x\,dx && \text{Rewrite.}\\[2mm]
&= \frac{3x}{8} + \frac{\sin 2x}{4} + \frac{\sin 4x}{32} + C && \text{Integrate.}
\end{aligned}
$$

Use a symbolic differentiation utility to verify this. Can you simplify the derivative to obtain the original integrand?

In Example 3, when you evaluate the definite integral from 0 to $\pi/2$, you obtain

$$
\begin{aligned}
\int_0^{\pi/2} \cos^4 x\,dx &= \left[\frac{3x}{8} + \frac{\sin 2x}{4} + \frac{\sin 4x}{32}\right]_0^{\pi/2}\\[2mm]
&= \left(\frac{3\pi}{16} + 0 + 0\right) - (0 + 0 + 0)\\[2mm]
&= \frac{3\pi}{16}.
\end{aligned}
$$

Note that the only term that contributes to the solution is

$$\frac{3x}{8}.$$

This observation is generalized in the following formulas developed by John Wallis (1616–1703).

Wallis's Formulas
---

1. If n is odd ($n \geq 3$), then

$$\int_0^{\pi/2} \cos^n x\,dx = \left(\frac{2}{3}\right)\left(\frac{4}{5}\right)\left(\frac{6}{7}\right) \cdots \left(\frac{n-1}{n}\right).$$

2. If n is even ($n \geq 2$), then

$$\int_0^{\pi/2} \cos^n x\,dx = \left(\frac{1}{2}\right)\left(\frac{3}{4}\right)\left(\frac{5}{6}\right) \cdots \left(\frac{n-1}{n}\right)\left(\frac{\pi}{2}\right).$$

These formulas are also valid when $\cos^n x$ is replaced by $\sin^n x$. (You are asked to prove both formulas in Exercise 86.)

Integrals Involving Powers of Secant and Tangent

The guidelines below can help you find integrals of the form

$$\int \sec^m x \tan^n x \, dx.$$

Guidelines for Finding Integrals Involving Powers of Secant and Tangent

1. When the power of the secant is even and positive, save a secant-squared factor and convert the remaining factors to tangents. Then, expand and integrate.

$$\int \overbrace{\sec^{2k} x}^{\text{Even}} \tan^n x \, dx = \int \underbrace{(\sec^2 x)^{k-1}}_{\text{Convert to tangents}} \tan^n x \overbrace{\sec^2 x \, dx}^{\text{Save for } du} = \int (1 + \tan^2 x)^{k-1} \tan^n x \sec^2 x \, dx$$

2. When the power of the tangent is odd and positive, save a secant-tangent factor and convert the remaining factors to secants. Then, expand and integrate.

$$\int \sec^m x \overbrace{\tan^{2k+1} x}^{\text{Odd}} \, dx = \int (\sec^{m-1} x) \underbrace{(\tan^2 x)^k}_{\text{Convert to secants}} \overbrace{\sec x \tan x \, dx}^{\text{Save for } du} = \int (\sec^{m-1} x)(\sec^2 x - 1)^k \sec x \tan x \, dx$$

3. When there are no secant factors and the power of the tangent is even and positive, convert a tangent-squared factor to a secant-squared factor, then expand and repeat if necessary.

$$\int \tan^n x \, dx = \int (\tan^{n-2} x) \overbrace{(\tan^2 x)}^{\text{Convert to secants}} \, dx = \int (\tan^{n-2} x)(\sec^2 x - 1) \, dx$$

4. When the integral is of the form

$$\int \sec^m x \, dx$$

where m is odd and positive, use integration by parts, as illustrated in Example 6 in Section 7.2.

5. When the first four guidelines do not apply, try converting to sines and cosines.

EXAMPLE 4   Power of Tangent Is Odd and Positive

Find $\displaystyle \int \frac{\tan^3 x}{\sqrt{\sec x}} \, dx$.

Solution

Because you expect to use the Power Rule with $u = \sec x$, *save a factor of* $(\sec x \tan x)$ to form du and convert the remaining tangent factors to secants.

$$\int \frac{\tan^3 x}{\sqrt{\sec x}} \, dx = \int (\sec x)^{-1/2} \tan^3 x \, dx \qquad \text{Rewrite.}$$

$$= \int (\sec x)^{-3/2} (\tan^2 x)(\sec x \tan x) \, dx \qquad \text{Rewrite.}$$

$$= \int (\sec x)^{-3/2}(\sec^2 x - 1)(\sec x \tan x) \, dx \qquad \text{Trigonometric identity}$$

$$= \int [(\sec x)^{1/2} - (\sec x)^{-3/2}](\sec x \tan x) \, dx \qquad \text{Multiply.}$$

$$= \frac{2}{3}(\sec x)^{3/2} + 2(\sec x)^{-1/2} + C \qquad \text{Integrate.} \qquad \blacksquare$$

EXAMPLE 5   **Power of Secant Is Even and Positive**

Find the indefinite integral.

$$\int \sec^4 3x \tan^3 3x \, dx$$

Solution

Let $u = \tan 3x$, then $du = 3 \sec^2 3x \, dx$ and you can write

$$\int \sec^4 3x \tan^3 3x \, dx = \int \sec^2 3x \tan^3 3x \sec^2 3x \, dx \qquad \text{Rewrite.}$$

$$= \int (1 + \tan^2 3x) \tan^3 3x \sec^2 3x \, dx \qquad \text{Trigonometric identity}$$

$$= \frac{1}{3} \int (\tan^3 3x + \tan^5 3x)(3 \sec^2 3x) \, dx \qquad \text{Multiply.}$$

$$= \frac{1}{3} \left(\frac{\tan^4 3x}{4} + \frac{\tan^6 3x}{6} \right) + C \qquad \text{Integrate.}$$

$$= \frac{\tan^4 3x}{12} + \frac{\tan^6 3x}{18} + C.$$

In Example 5, the power of the tangent is odd and positive. So, you could also find the integral using the procedure described in the second guideline on the preceding page. In Exercises 73 and 74, you are asked to show that the results obtained by these two procedures differ only by a constant.

EXAMPLE 6   **Power of Tangent Is Even**

Evaluate the definite integral.

$$\int_0^{\pi/4} \tan^4 x \, dx$$

Algebraic Solution

Because there are no secant factors, you can begin by converting a tangent-squared factor to a secant-squared factor.

$$\int \tan^4 x \, dx = \int \tan^2 x \tan^2 x \, dx$$

$$= \int (\tan^2 x)(\sec^2 x - 1) \, dx$$

$$= \int \tan^2 x \sec^2 x \, dx - \int \tan^2 x \, dx$$

$$= \int \tan^2 x \sec^2 x \, dx - \int (\sec^2 x - 1) \, dx$$

$$= \frac{\tan^3 x}{3} - \tan x + x + C$$

Next, evaluate the definite integral.

$$\int_0^{\pi/4} \tan^4 x \, dx = \left[\frac{\tan^3 x}{3} - \tan x + x \right]_0^{\pi/4}$$

$$= \frac{1}{3} - 1 + \frac{\pi}{4}$$

$$\approx 0.119$$

Graphical Solution

Use a graphing utility set in *radian mode* to graph $y = \tan^4 x$, as shown below.

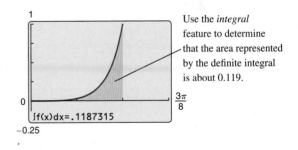

Use the *integral* feature to determine that the area represented by the definite integral is about 0.119.

For integrals involving powers of cotangents and cosecants, you can follow a strategy similar to that used for powers of tangents and secants. Also, when integrating trigonometric functions, remember that it sometimes helps to convert the entire integrand to powers of sines and cosines.

EXAMPLE 7 Converting to Sines and Cosines

Find the indefinite integral.

$$\int \frac{\sec x}{\tan^2 x} \, dx$$

Solution

Because the first four guidelines on page 476 do not apply, try converting the integrand to sines and cosines. In this case, you are able to integrate the resulting powers of sine and cosine as shown.

$$\int \frac{\sec x}{\tan^2 x} \, dx = \int \sec x \cot^2 x \, dx \qquad \text{Trigonometric identity}$$

$$= \int \left(\frac{1}{\cos x}\right)\left(\frac{\cos x}{\sin x}\right)^2 \, dx \qquad \text{Convert to sines and cosines.}$$

$$= \int (\sin x)^{-2}(\cos x) \, dx \qquad \text{Rewrite.}$$

$$= -(\sin x)^{-1} + C \qquad \text{Integrate.}$$

$$= -\csc x + C \qquad \text{Trigonometric identity}$$

Integrals Involving Sines and Cosines of Different Angles

Integrals involving the products of sines and cosines of two *different* angles occur in many applications. In such instances, you can use integration by parts. However, you may find it simpler to use the product-to-sum formulas listed below.

$$\sin mx \sin nx = \frac{1}{2}(\cos[(m - n)x] - \cos[(m + n)x])$$

$$\sin mx \cos nx = \frac{1}{2}(\sin[(m - n)x] + \sin[(m + n)x])$$

$$\cos mx \cos nx = \frac{1}{2}(\cos[(m - n)x] + \cos[(m + n)x])$$

EXAMPLE 8 Using a Product-to-Sum Formula

Find the indefinite integral.

$$\int \sin 5x \cos 4x \, dx$$

Solution

Considering the second product-to-sum formula above, you can write

$$\int \sin 5x \cos 4x \, dx = \frac{1}{2}\int (\sin x + \sin 9x) \, dx \qquad \text{Product-to-sum formula}$$

$$= \frac{1}{2}\left(-\cos x - \frac{\cos 9x}{9}\right) + C \qquad \text{Integrate.}$$

$$= -\frac{\cos x}{2} - \frac{\cos 9x}{18} + C. \qquad \text{Multiply.}$$

7.3 Exercises

See *CalcChat.com* for tutorial help and worked-out solutions to odd-numbered exercises.

 Finding an Indefinite Integral Involving Sine and Cosine In Exercises 1–12, find the indefinite integral.

1. $\displaystyle\int \cos^5 x \sin x \, dx$ 2. $\displaystyle\int \cos^3 x \sin^4 x \, dx$

3. $\displaystyle\int \sin^7 2x \cos 2x \, dx$ 4. $\displaystyle\int \sin^3 3x \, dx$

5. $\displaystyle\int \sin^3 x \cos^2 x \, dx$ 6. $\displaystyle\int \cos^3 \frac{x}{3} \, dx$

7. $\displaystyle\int \sin^3 2\theta \sqrt{\cos 2\theta} \, d\theta$ 8. $\displaystyle\int \frac{\cos^5 t}{\sqrt{\sin t}} \, dt$

9. $\displaystyle\int \cos^4 3x \, dx$ 10. $\displaystyle\int \sin^4 6\theta \, d\theta$

11. $\displaystyle\int 4x \cos^2 x \, dx$ 12. $\displaystyle\int 6x^2 \sin^2 2x \, dx$

Using Wallis's Formulas In Exercises 13–18, use Wallis's Formulas to evaluate the integral.

13. $\displaystyle\int_0^{\pi/2} \cos^3 x \, dx$ 14. $\displaystyle\int_0^{\pi/2} \cos^5 x \, dx$

15. $\displaystyle\int_0^{\pi/2} \cos^{12} x \, dx$ 16. $\displaystyle\int_0^{\pi/2} \sin^7 x \, dx$

17. $\displaystyle\int_0^{\pi/2} \sin^4 x \, dx$ 18. $\displaystyle\int_0^{\pi/2} \sin^{10} x \, dx$

 Finding an Indefinite Integral Involving Secant and Tangent In Exercises 19–32, find the indefinite integral.

19. $\displaystyle\int \sec 4x \, dx$ 20. $\displaystyle\int \sec^4 x \, dx$

21. $\displaystyle\int \sec^3 \pi x \, dx$ 22. $\displaystyle\int \tan^6 3x \, dx$

23. $\displaystyle\int \tan^5 \frac{x}{2} \, dx$ 24. $\displaystyle\int \tan^3 \frac{\pi x}{2} \sec^2 \frac{\pi x}{2} \, dx$

25. $\displaystyle\int \tan^3 2t \sec^3 2t \, dt$ 26. $\displaystyle\int \tan^5 x \sec^4 x \, dx$

27. $\displaystyle\int \sec^6 4x \tan 4x \, dx$ 28. $\displaystyle\int \sec^2 \frac{x}{2} \tan \frac{x}{2} \, dx$

29. $\displaystyle\int \sec^5 x \tan^3 x \, dx$ 30. $\displaystyle\int \tan^3 3x \, dx$

31. $\displaystyle\int \frac{\tan^2 x}{\sec x} \, dx$ 32. $\displaystyle\int \frac{\tan^2 x}{\sec^5 x} \, dx$

Differential Equation In Exercises 33–36, find the general solution of the differential equation.

33. $\dfrac{dr}{d\theta} = \sin^4 \pi\theta$ 34. $\dfrac{ds}{d\alpha} = \sin^2 \dfrac{\alpha}{2} \cos^2 \dfrac{\alpha}{2}$

35. $y' = \tan^3 3x \sec 3x$ 36. $y' = \sqrt{\tan x} \sec^4 x$

Slope Field In Exercises 37 and 38, (a) sketch two approximate solutions of the given differential equation on the slope field, one of which passes through the given point. To print an enlarged copy of the graph, go to *MathGraphs.com*. (b) Use integration and the given point to find the particular solution of the differential equation and use a graphing utility to graph the solution. Compare the result with the sketch in part (a) that passes through the given point.

37. $\dfrac{dy}{dx} = \sin^2 x, \ (0, 0)$ 38. $\dfrac{dy}{dx} = \sec^2 x \tan^2 x, \left(0, -\dfrac{1}{4}\right)$

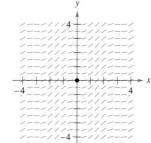 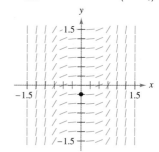

Slope Field In Exercises 39 and 40, use a computer algebra system to graph the slope field for the differential equation, and graph the solution satisfying the specified initial condition.

39. $\dfrac{dy}{dx} = \dfrac{3 \sin x}{y}$, 40. $\dfrac{dy}{dx} = 3\sqrt{y} \tan^2 x$,

$\quad y(0) = 2$ $\quad y(0) = 3$

 Using a Product-to-Sum Formula In Exercises 41–46, find the indefinite integral.

41. $\displaystyle\int \cos 2x \cos 6x \, dx$ 42. $\displaystyle\int \cos 5\theta \cos 3\theta \, d\theta$

43. $\displaystyle\int \sin 9t \cos 4t \, dt$ 44. $\displaystyle\int 2 \sin 5\alpha \cos 8\alpha \, d\alpha$

45. $\displaystyle\int \sin \theta \sin 3\theta \, d\theta$ 46. $\displaystyle\int \sin 5x \sin 4x \, dx$

Finding an Indefinite Integral In Exercises 47–54, find the indefinite integral. Use a computer algebra system to confirm your result.

47. $\displaystyle\int \cot^5 2x \, dx$ 48. $\displaystyle\int \tan^5 \frac{x}{4} \sec^4 \frac{x}{4} \, dx$

49. $\displaystyle\int \csc^6 5x \, dx$ 50. $\displaystyle\int \cot^3 \frac{x}{2} \csc^4 \frac{x}{2} \, dx$

51. $\displaystyle\int \frac{1}{\sec x \tan x} \, dx$ 52. $\displaystyle\int \frac{\sin^2 x - \cos^2 x}{\cos x} \, dx$

53. $\displaystyle\int (\tan^4 t - \sec^4 t) \, dt$ 54. $\displaystyle\int \frac{1 - \sec t}{\cos t - 1} \, dt$

55. Error Analysis Describe and correct the error in finding the integral $\int \cos^2 x \tan^3 x \, dx$ using $u = \cos x$ and $du = -\sin x \, dx$.

$$\int \cos^2 x \tan^3 x \, dx = \int (\cos^2 x)\left(\frac{\sin^3 x}{\cos^3 x}\right) dx$$

$$= \int \left(\frac{\sin^2 x}{\cos x}\right) \sin x \, dx$$

$$= \int \left(\frac{1 + \cos^2 x}{\cos x}\right) \sin x \, dx$$

$$= \int \left(\frac{1}{\cos x} + \cos x\right) \sin x \, dx$$

$$= -\ln|\cos x| - \frac{\cos^2 x}{2} + C \quad \textbf{✗}$$

56. Error Analysis Describe and correct the error in finding the indefinite integral.

$$\int \cos 7x \cos 5x \, dx = \frac{1}{2} \int (\cos 2x + \cos 12x) \, dx$$

$$= \frac{1}{2}\left(\frac{\sin 2x}{2} + \frac{\sin 12x}{2}\right) + C$$

$$= \frac{\sin 2x}{4} + \frac{\sin 12x}{4} + C$$

$$= \frac{\sin 2x + \sin 12x}{4} + C \quad \textbf{✗}$$

Area In Exercises 57–60, find the area of the region bounded by the graphs of the equations.

57. $y = \sin x, \quad y = \sin^3 x, \quad x = 0, \quad x = \dfrac{\pi}{2}$

58. $y = \sin^2 \pi x, \quad y = 0, \quad x = 0, \quad x = 1$

59. $y = \cos^2 x, \quad y = \sin^2 x, \quad x = -\dfrac{\pi}{4}, \quad x = \dfrac{\pi}{4}$

60. $y = \cos^2 x, \quad y = \sin x \cos x, \quad x = -\dfrac{\pi}{2}, \quad x = \dfrac{\pi}{4}$

Volume In Exercises 61 and 62, find the volume of the solid generated by revolving the region bounded by the graphs of the equations about the *x*-axis.

61. $y = \tan x, \quad y = 0, \quad x = -\dfrac{\pi}{4}, \quad x = \dfrac{\pi}{4}$

62. $y = \cos \dfrac{x}{2}, \quad y = \sin \dfrac{x}{2}, \quad x = 0, \quad x = \dfrac{\pi}{2}$

Particle Motion In Exercises 63 and 64, the velocity function, in feet per second, is given for a particle moving along a line. Find (a) the displacement and (b) the total distance the particle travels over the given interval.

63. $v(t) = \dfrac{1}{8} - \sin^2 \dfrac{\pi t}{4} \cos^2 \dfrac{\pi t}{4}, \quad 0 \le t \le \dfrac{7}{2}$

64. $v(t) = \dfrac{\pi}{5}\left(\cos^2 \dfrac{\pi t}{2} - \sin^2 \dfrac{\pi t}{3} - \dfrac{1}{4}\right), \quad 0 \le t \le 4$

 Evaluating a Definite Integral In Exercises 65–72, evaluate the definite integral.

65. $\displaystyle\int_{-\pi}^{\pi} \sin^2 x \, dx$

66. $\displaystyle\int_{0}^{\pi/3} \tan^2 x \, dx$

67. $\displaystyle\int_{0}^{\pi/4} 6 \tan^3 x \, dx$

68. $\displaystyle\int_{0}^{\pi/3} \sec^{3/2} x \tan x \, dx$

69. $\displaystyle\int_{0}^{\pi/2} \dfrac{\cos t}{1 + \sin^2 t} \, dt$

70. $\displaystyle\int_{\pi/6}^{\pi/3} \sin 6x \cos 4x \, dx$

71. $\displaystyle\int_{-\pi/2}^{\pi/2} 3 \cos^3 x \, dx$

72. $\displaystyle\int_{0}^{\pi} \sin^5 x \, dx$

EXPLORING CONCEPTS

Comparing Methods In Exercises 73 and 74, (a) find the indefinite integral in two different ways. (b) Use a graphing utility to graph the antiderivative (without the constant of integration) obtained by each method to show that the results differ only by a constant. (c) Verify analytically that the results differ only by a constant.

73. $\displaystyle\int \sec^4 3x \tan^3 3x \, dx$

74. $\displaystyle\int \sec^2 x \tan x \, dx$

75. Comparing Methods Find $\int \sin x \cos x \, dx$ using the given method. Explain how your answers differ for each method.

(a) Substitution where $u = \sin x$

(b) Substitution where $u = \cos x$

(c) Integration by parts

(d) Using the double-angle formula $\sin 2x = 2 \sin x \cos x$

 76. HOW DO YOU SEE IT? Use the graph of f' shown in the figure to answer the following.

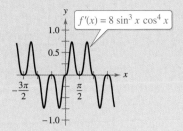

$f'(x) = 8 \sin^3 x \cos^4 x$

(a) Using the interval shown in the graph, approximate the value(s) of *x* where *f* is maximum. Explain.

(b) Using the interval shown in the graph, approximate the value(s) of *x* where *f* is minimum. Explain.

Verifying In Exercises 77–80, use integration by parts to verify the reduction formula.

77. $\displaystyle\int \sin^n x \, dx = -\frac{\sin^{n-1} x \cos x}{n} + \frac{n-1}{n} \int \sin^{n-2} x \, dx$

78. $\displaystyle\int \cos^n x \, dx = \frac{\cos^{n-1} x \sin x}{n} + \frac{n-1}{n} \int \cos^{n-2} x \, dx$

79. $\displaystyle\int \cos^m x \sin^n x \, dx = -\frac{\cos^{m+1} x \sin^{n-1} x}{m+n}$
$$+ \frac{n-1}{m+n} \int \cos^m x \sin^{n-2} x \, dx$$

80. $\displaystyle\int \sec^n x \, dx = \frac{1}{n-1} \sec^{n-2} x \tan x$
$$+ \frac{n-2}{n-1} \int \sec^{n-2} x \, dx$$

Implementing Processes In Exercises 81–84, find the indefinite integral by using the appropriate formula from Exercises 77–80.

81. $\displaystyle\int \sin^5 x \, dx$

82. $\displaystyle\int \cos^4 x \, dx$

83. $\displaystyle\int \sec^4 \frac{2\pi x}{5} \, dx$

84. $\displaystyle\int \sin^4 x \cos^2 x \, dx$

85. **Modeling Data** The table shows the normal maximum (high) and minimum (low) temperatures (in degrees Fahrenheit) in Erie, Pennsylvania, for each month of the year. (*Source: NOAA*)

Month	Jan	Feb	Mar	Apr	May	Jun
Max	33.7	35.5	43.8	56.1	66.6	75.7
Min	20.8	21.1	27.5	38.1	48.2	58.4

Month	Jul	Aug	Sep	Oct	Nov	Dec
Max	79.8	78.6	71.9	60.8	49.9	38.1
Min	63.5	62.5	55.8	45.3	36.6	26.6

The maximum and minimum temperatures can be modeled by $f(t) = a_0 + a_1 \cos(\pi t/6) + b_1 \sin(\pi t/6)$, where $t = 0$ corresponds to January 1, and

$$a_0 = \frac{1}{12} \int_0^{12} f(t) \, dt, \quad a_1 = \frac{1}{6} \int_0^{12} f(t) \cos \frac{\pi t}{6} \, dt, \text{ and}$$

$$b_1 = \frac{1}{6} \int_0^{12} f(t) \sin \frac{\pi t}{6} \, dt.$$

(a) Approximate the models $H(t)$ for the maximum temperatures and $L(t)$ for the minimum temperatures. (*Hint:* Use the Trapezoidal Rule to approximate the integrals and use the January data twice.)

(b) Use a graphing utility to graph each model. During what part of the year is the difference between the maximum and minimum temperatures greatest?

86. **Wallis's Formulas** Use the result of Exercise 78 to prove the following versions of Wallis's Formulas.

(a) If n is odd ($n \geq 3$), then
$$\int_0^{\pi/2} \cos^n x \, dx = \left(\frac{2}{3}\right)\left(\frac{4}{5}\right)\left(\frac{6}{7}\right) \cdots \left(\frac{n-1}{n}\right).$$

(b) If n is even ($n \geq 2$), then
$$\int_0^{\pi/2} \cos^n x \, dx = \left(\frac{1}{2}\right)\left(\frac{3}{4}\right)\left(\frac{5}{6}\right) \cdots \left(\frac{n-1}{n}\right)\left(\frac{\pi}{2}\right).$$

87. **Orthogonal Functions** The **inner product** of two functions f and g on $[a, b]$ is given by
$$\langle f, g \rangle = \int_a^b f(x)g(x) \, dx.$$

Two distinct functions f and g are said to be **orthogonal** if $\langle f, g \rangle = 0$. Show that the following set of functions is orthogonal on $[-\pi, \pi]$.

$$\{\sin x, \sin 2x, \sin 3x, \ldots, \cos x, \cos 2x, \cos 3x, \ldots\}$$

88. **Fourier Series** The following sum is a *finite Fourier series*.

$$f(x) = \sum_{i=1}^{N} a_i \sin ix$$
$$= a_1 \sin x + a_2 \sin 2x + \cdots + a_N \sin Nx$$

(a) Use Exercise 87 to show that the nth coefficient a_n is given by
$$a_n = \frac{1}{\pi} \int_{-\pi}^{\pi} f(x) \sin nx \, dx.$$

(b) Let $f(x) = x$. Find a_1, a_2, and a_3.

Calculus AP® – Exam Preparation Questions

89. **Multiple Choice** $\displaystyle\int \sin^3 x \, dx =$

(A) $\cos x + \dfrac{\cos^3 x}{3} + C$

(B) $-\cos x + \dfrac{\cos^3 x}{3} + C$

(C) $-\cos x - \dfrac{\cos^3 x}{3} + C$

(D) $\dfrac{\sin^4 x}{4} + C$

90. **Multiple Choice** What is the area of the region bounded by the graphs of $y = \tan^5 x$, $y = 0$, $x = 0$, and $x = \pi/4$?

(A) $-\dfrac{1}{4} + \ln\sqrt{2}$

(B) $\ln\sqrt{2}$

(C) $\dfrac{1}{4} + \ln\sqrt{2}$

(D) $\dfrac{1 + \ln\sqrt{2}}{2}$

7.4 Trigonometric Substitution

▶ Use trigonometric substitution to find an integral.
▶ Use integrals to model and solve real-life applications.

Trigonometric Substitution

Now that you can find integrals involving powers of trigonometric functions, you can use **trigonometric substitution** to find integrals involving the radicals

$$\sqrt{a^2 - u^2}, \quad \sqrt{a^2 + u^2}, \quad \text{and} \quad \sqrt{u^2 - a^2}.$$

The objective with trigonometric substitution is to eliminate the radical in the integrand. You do this by using the Pythagorean identities.

$$\cos^2 \theta = 1 - \sin^2 \theta$$
$$\sec^2 \theta = 1 + \tan^2 \theta$$
$$\tan^2 \theta = \sec^2 \theta - 1$$

For example, for $a > 0$, let $u = a \sin \theta$, where $-\pi/2 \le \theta \le \pi/2$. Then

$$\sqrt{a^2 - u^2} = \sqrt{a^2 - a^2 \sin^2 \theta}$$
$$= \sqrt{a^2(1 - \sin^2 \theta)}$$
$$= \sqrt{a^2 \cos^2 \theta}$$
$$= a \cos \theta.$$

Note that $\cos \theta \ge 0$, because $-\pi/2 \le \theta \le \pi/2$.

Exploration

Integrating a Radical Function Up to this point in the text, you have not evaluated the integral

$$\int_{-1}^{1} \sqrt{1 - x^2} \, dx.$$

From geometry, you should be able to find the exact value of this integral—what is it? Using the Trapezoidal Rule, you cannot be sure of the accuracy of the approximation. Why? Try finding the exact value using the substitution

$$x = \sin \theta$$

and

$$dx = \cos \theta \, d\theta.$$

Does your answer agree with the value you obtained using geometry?

Trigonometric Substitution ($a > 0$)

1. For integrals involving $\sqrt{a^2 - u^2}$, let

   $$u = a \sin \theta.$$

   Then $\sqrt{a^2 - u^2} = a \cos \theta$, where

   $$-\pi/2 \le \theta \le \pi/2.$$

   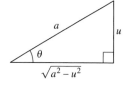

2. For integrals involving $\sqrt{a^2 + u^2}$, let

   $$u = a \tan \theta.$$

   Then $\sqrt{a^2 + u^2} = a \sec \theta$, where

   $$-\pi/2 < \theta < \pi/2.$$

   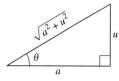

3. For integrals involving $\sqrt{u^2 - a^2}$, let

   $$u = a \sec \theta.$$

   Then

   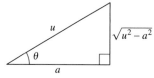

   $$\sqrt{u^2 - a^2} = \begin{cases} a \tan \theta \text{ for } u > a, \text{ where } 0 \le \theta < \pi/2 \\ -a \tan \theta \text{ for } u < -a, \text{ where } \pi/2 < \theta \le \pi. \end{cases}$$

The restrictions on θ ensure that the function that defines the substitution is one-to-one. In fact, these are the same intervals over which the arcsine, arctangent, and arcsecant are defined.

> **EXAMPLE 1**   **Trigonometric Substitution: $u = a \sin \theta$**

Find $\displaystyle\int \frac{dx}{x^2\sqrt{9 - x^2}}.$

Solution

First, note that the basic integration rules do not apply. To use trigonometric substitution, you should observe that

$$\sqrt{9 - x^2}$$

is of the form $\sqrt{a^2 - u^2}$. So, you can use the substitution

$$x = a \sin \theta = 3 \sin \theta.$$

Using differentiation and the triangle shown in Figure 7.3, you obtain $dx = 3 \cos \theta \, d\theta$, $\sqrt{9 - x^2} = 3 \cos \theta$, and $x^2 = 9 \sin^2 \theta$. So, trigonometric substitution yields

$$
\begin{aligned}
\int \frac{dx}{x^2\sqrt{9 - x^2}} &= \int \frac{3 \cos \theta \, d\theta}{(9 \sin^2 \theta)(3 \cos \theta)} && \text{Substitute.} \\
&= \frac{1}{9}\int \frac{d\theta}{\sin^2 \theta} && \text{Simplify.} \\
&= \frac{1}{9}\int \csc^2 \theta \, d\theta && \text{Trigonometric identity} \\
&= -\frac{1}{9}\cot \theta + C && \text{Apply Cosecant Rule.} \\
&= -\frac{1}{9}\left(\frac{\sqrt{9 - x^2}}{x}\right) + C && \text{Substitute for } \cot \theta. \\
&= -\frac{\sqrt{9 - x^2}}{9x} + C. &&
\end{aligned}
$$

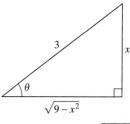

$\sin \theta = \dfrac{x}{3}, \cot \theta = \dfrac{\sqrt{9 - x^2}}{x}$

Figure 7.3

Note that the triangle in Figure 7.3 can be used to convert the θ's back to x's, as shown.

$$\cot \theta = \frac{\text{adj.}}{\text{opp.}} = \frac{\sqrt{9 - x^2}}{x}$$

> **EXAMPLE 2**   **Trigonometric Substitution: $u = a \tan \theta$**

Find $\displaystyle\int \frac{dx}{\sqrt{4x^2 + 1}}.$

Solution

Let $u = 2x$, $a = 1$, and $2x = \tan \theta$, as shown in Figure 7.4. Then,

$$dx = \frac{1}{2}\sec^2 \theta \, d\theta \quad \text{and} \quad \sqrt{4x^2 + 1} = \sec \theta.$$

Trigonometric substitution produces

$$
\begin{aligned}
\int \frac{dx}{\sqrt{4x^2 + 1}} &= \frac{1}{2}\int \frac{\sec^2 \theta \, d\theta}{\sec \theta} && \text{Substitute.} \\
&= \frac{1}{2}\int \sec \theta \, d\theta && \text{Simplify.} \\
&= \frac{1}{2}\ln|\sec \theta + \tan \theta| + C && \text{Apply Secant Rule.} \\
&= \frac{1}{2}\ln\left|\sqrt{4x^2 + 1} + 2x\right| + C. && \text{Back-substitute.}
\end{aligned}
$$

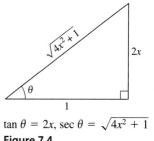

$\tan \theta = 2x, \sec \theta = \sqrt{4x^2 + 1}$

Figure 7.4

For definite integrals, it is often convenient to determine integration limits for θ that avoid converting back to x. You might want to review this procedure in Section 4.6, Examples 8 and 9.

EXAMPLE 3   Converting the Limits of Integration

Evaluate $\displaystyle\int_{\sqrt{3}}^{2} \frac{\sqrt{x^2 - 3}}{x}\, dx.$

Solution

Because $\sqrt{x^2 - 3}$ has the form $\sqrt{u^2 - a^2}$, you can consider

$$u = x, \quad a = \sqrt{3}, \quad \text{and} \quad x = \sqrt{3}\sec\theta$$

as shown in Figure 7.5. Then,

$$dx = \sqrt{3}\sec\theta\tan\theta\, d\theta \quad \text{and} \quad \sqrt{x^2 - 3} = \sqrt{3}\tan\theta.$$

To determine the upper and lower limits of integration, use the substitution $x = \sqrt{3}\sec\theta$, as shown.

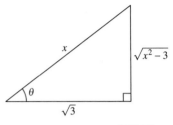

$$\sec\theta = \frac{x}{\sqrt{3}}, \tan\theta = \frac{\sqrt{x^2 - 3}}{\sqrt{3}}$$

Figure 7.5

Lower Limit	*Upper Limit*
When $x = \sqrt{3}$, $\sec\theta = 1$ and $\theta = 0$.	When $x = 2$, $\sec\theta = \dfrac{2}{\sqrt{3}}$ and $\theta = \dfrac{\pi}{6}$.

So, you have

Integration limits for x →

Integration limits for θ →

$$\int_{\sqrt{3}}^{2} \frac{\sqrt{x^2 - 3}}{x}\, dx = \int_{0}^{\pi/6} \frac{\left(\sqrt{3}\tan\theta\right)\left(\sqrt{3}\sec\theta\tan\theta\right) d\theta}{\sqrt{3}\sec\theta}$$

$$= \int_{0}^{\pi/6} \sqrt{3}\tan^2\theta\, d\theta$$

$$= \sqrt{3}\int_{0}^{\pi/6} (\sec^2\theta - 1)\, d\theta$$

$$= \sqrt{3}\left[\tan\theta - \theta\right]_{0}^{\pi/6}$$

$$= \sqrt{3}\left(\frac{1}{\sqrt{3}} - \frac{\pi}{6}\right)$$

$$= 1 - \frac{\sqrt{3}\pi}{6}$$

$$\approx 0.0931.$$

In Example 3, try converting back to the variable x and evaluating the antiderivative at the original limits of integration. You should obtain

$$\int_{\sqrt{3}}^{2} \frac{\sqrt{x^2 - 3}}{x}\, dx = \sqrt{3}\left[\frac{\sqrt{x^2 - 3}}{\sqrt{3}} - \operatorname{arcsec}\frac{x}{\sqrt{3}}\right]_{\sqrt{3}}^{2}$$

$$= \sqrt{3}\left(\frac{1}{\sqrt{3}} - \frac{\pi}{6}\right)$$

$$\approx 0.0931.$$

When using trigonometric substitution to evaluate definite integrals, you must be careful to check that the values of θ lie in the intervals discussed at the beginning of this section. For instance, if in Example 3 you had been asked to evaluate the definite integral

$$\int_{-2}^{-\sqrt{3}} \frac{\sqrt{x^2 - 3}}{x} \, dx$$

then using $u = x$ and $a = \sqrt{3}$ in the interval $\left[-2, -\sqrt{3}\right]$ would imply that $u < -a$. So, when determining the upper and lower limits of integration, you would have to choose θ such that $\pi/2 < \theta \le \pi$. In this case, the integral would be evaluated as shown.

$$\int_{-2}^{-\sqrt{3}} \frac{\sqrt{x^2 - 3}}{x} \, dx = \int_{5\pi/6}^{\pi} \frac{(-\sqrt{3} \tan \theta)(\sqrt{3} \sec \theta \tan \theta) \, d\theta}{\sqrt{3} \sec \theta}$$

$$= \int_{5\pi/6}^{\pi} -\sqrt{3} \tan^2 \theta \, d\theta$$

$$= -\sqrt{3} \int_{5\pi/6}^{\pi} (\sec^2 \theta - 1) \, d\theta$$

$$= -\sqrt{3} \left[\tan \theta - \theta \right]_{5\pi/6}^{\pi}$$

$$= -\sqrt{3} \left[(0 - \pi) - \left(-\frac{1}{\sqrt{3}} - \frac{5\pi}{6} \right) \right]$$

$$= -1 + \frac{\sqrt{3}\pi}{6}$$

$$\approx -0.0931$$

> ### Algebra Review
>
> For help on the algebra in evaluating the integral at the left, see Example 2(a) in the *Chapter 7 Algebra Review* on page A48.

You can extend the use of trigonometric substitution to cover integrals involving expressions such as $(a^2 - u^2)^{n/2}$ by writing the expression as

$$(a^2 - u^2)^{n/2} = \left(\sqrt{a^2 - u^2} \right)^n.$$

EXAMPLE 4   Trigonometric Substitution: Rational Powers

See LarsonCalculusforAP.com for an interactive version of this type of example.

Find $\displaystyle \int \frac{dx}{(x^2 + 1)^{3/2}}.$

Solution

Begin by writing $(x^2 + 1)^{3/2}$ as $\left(\sqrt{x^2 + 1} \right)^3$. Then, let $a = 1$ and $u = x = \tan \theta$, as shown in Figure 7.6. Using $dx = \sec^2 \theta \, d\theta$ and $\sqrt{x^2 + 1} = \sec \theta$ you can apply trigonometric substitution, as shown.

$$\int \frac{dx}{(x^2 + 1)^{3/2}} = \int \frac{dx}{\left(\sqrt{x^2 + 1} \right)^3} \qquad \text{Rewrite denominator.}$$

$$= \int \frac{\sec^2 \theta \, d\theta}{\sec^3 \theta} \qquad \text{Substitute.}$$

$$= \int \frac{d\theta}{\sec \theta} \qquad \text{Simplify.}$$

$$= \int \cos \theta \, d\theta \qquad \text{Trigonometric identity}$$

$$= \sin \theta + C \qquad \text{Apply Cosine Rule.}$$

$$= \frac{x}{\sqrt{x^2 + 1}} + C \qquad \text{Back-substitute.}$$

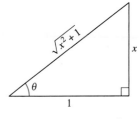

$$\tan \theta = x, \ \sin \theta = \frac{x}{\sqrt{x^2 + 1}}$$

Figure 7.6

You can further expand the range of problems to which trigonometric substitution applies by completing the square, as shown in the next example. (You can review the procedure of completing the square in Section 4.8).

EXAMPLE 5   Trigonometric Substitution: Completing the Square

Find the indefinite integral.

$$\int \frac{dx}{\sqrt{x^2 - 4x}}$$

Solution

To obtain an expression where you can use trigonometric substitution, complete the square to write $x^2 - 4x$ as the difference of two squares, as shown.

$$x^2 - 4x = (x^2 - 4x + 4) - 4$$
$$= (x - 2)^2 - 4$$

Because $\sqrt{x^2 - 4x} = \sqrt{(x - 2)^2 - 4}$ has the form $\sqrt{u^2 - a^2}$, let

$$u = x - 2, \quad a = 2, \quad \text{and} \quad x - 2 = 2 \sec \theta$$

as shown in Figure 7.7. Using

$$dx = 2 \sec \theta \tan \theta \, d\theta$$

and

$$\sqrt{(x - 2)^2 - 4} = 2 \tan \theta$$

you can apply trigonometric substitution, as shown.

$$\int \frac{dx}{\sqrt{x^2 - 4x}} = \int \frac{dx}{\sqrt{(x - 2)^2 - 4}} \qquad \text{Rewrite denominator.}$$

$$= \int \frac{2 \sec \theta \tan \theta \, d\theta}{2 \tan \theta} \qquad \text{Substitute.}$$

$$= \int \sec \theta \, d\theta \qquad \text{Simplify.}$$

$$= \ln|\sec \theta + \tan \theta| + C \qquad \text{Apply Secant Rule.}$$

$$= \ln\left|\frac{x - 2}{2} + \frac{\sqrt{(x - 2)^2 - 4}}{2}\right| + C \qquad \text{Back-substitute.}$$

Note that you can write this result as $\ln|x - 2 + \sqrt{x^2 - 4x}| + C_1$, where $C_1 = C - \ln 2$.

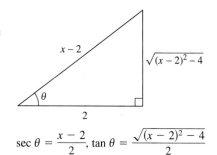

$$\sec \theta = \frac{x - 2}{2}, \quad \tan \theta = \frac{\sqrt{(x - 2)^2 - 4}}{2}$$

Figure 7.7

> ### Algebra Review
>
> For help on the algebra in Example 5, see Example 2(b) in the *Chapter 7 Algebra Review* on page A48.

Trigonometric substitution can be used to find the three integrals listed in Theorem 7.2. These integrals will be encountered several times in the remainder of the text. When this happens, there will be a reference to Theorem 7.2. (In Exercise 67, you are asked to verify the formulas given in the theorem.)

> Theorem 7.2   **Special Integration Formulas ($a > 0$)**
>
> **1.** $\displaystyle\int \sqrt{a^2 - u^2} \, du = \frac{1}{2}\left(u\sqrt{a^2 - u^2} + a^2 \arcsin \frac{u}{a}\right) + C$
>
> **2.** $\displaystyle\int \sqrt{u^2 - a^2} \, du = \frac{1}{2}\left(u\sqrt{u^2 - a^2} - a^2 \ln|u + \sqrt{u^2 - a^2}|\right) + C$
>
> **3.** $\displaystyle\int \sqrt{u^2 + a^2} \, du = \frac{1}{2}\left(u\sqrt{u^2 + a^2} + a^2 \ln|u + \sqrt{u^2 + a^2}|\right) + C$

Applications

EXAMPLE 6   Finding Arc Length

Find the arc length of the graph of

$$f(x) = \frac{1}{2}x^2$$

from $x = 0$ to $x = 1$. (See Figure 7.8.)

Solution

Refer to the arc length formula in Section 6.4.

$$s = \int_0^1 \sqrt{1 + [f'(x)]^2}\, dx \qquad \text{Formula for arc length}$$

$$= \int_0^1 \sqrt{1 + x^2}\, dx \qquad f'(x) = x$$

$$= \int_0^{\pi/4} \sec^3 \theta\, d\theta \qquad \text{Let } a = 1 \text{ and } x = \tan \theta.$$

$$= \frac{1}{2}\left[\sec \theta \tan \theta + \ln|\sec \theta + \tan \theta| \right]_0^{\pi/4} \qquad \text{Example 6, Section 7.2}$$

$$= \frac{1}{2}\left[\sqrt{2} + \ln\left(\sqrt{2} + 1 \right) \right]$$

$$\approx 1.148$$

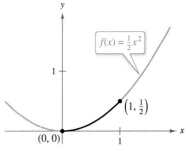

The arc length of the curve from $(0, 0)$ to $\left(1, \frac{1}{2}\right)$

Figure 7.8

EXAMPLE 7   Area of an Ellipse

Find the area enclosed by the ellipse

$$\frac{x^2}{a^2} + \frac{y^2}{b^2} = 1.$$

Solution

Because the ellipse is symmetric with respect to both axes, find the area of the region bounded by the ellipse in the first quadrant and multiply by 4 to obtain the total area of the ellipse (see figure). In the first quadrant, the ellipse is given by the equation

$$y = b\sqrt{1 - \left(\frac{x}{a}\right)^2}, \quad 0 \leq x \leq a.$$

So, the total area of the ellipse is

$$A = 4\int_0^a b\sqrt{1 - \left(\frac{x}{a}\right)^2}\, dx$$

$$= \frac{4b}{a}\int_0^a \sqrt{a^2 - x^2}\, dx$$

$$= \left(\frac{4b}{a}\right)\left(\frac{1}{2}\right)\left[x\sqrt{a^2 - x^2} + a^2 \arcsin \frac{x}{a} \right]_0^a \qquad \text{Apply Theorem 7.2.}$$

$$= \left(\frac{2b}{a}\right)\left[a^2\left(\frac{\pi}{2}\right) \right]$$

$$= \pi ab.$$

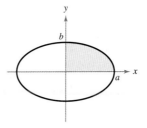

The area bounded by the ellipse in Quadrant I is one-fourth the total area enclosed by the ellipse.

Algebra Review

For help on the algebra in Example 7, see Examples 3 and 4 in the *Chapter 7 Algebra Review* on page A49.

7.4 Exercises

See *CalcChat.com* for tutorial help and worked-out solutions to odd-numbered exercises.

 Trigonometric Substitution   **In Exercises 1–4, state the trigonometric substitution you would use to find the indefinite integral. Do not integrate.**

1. $\int (9 + x^2)^{-2} \, dx$ **2.** $\int \sqrt{4 - x^2} \, dx$

3. $\int \dfrac{x^2}{\sqrt{25 - x^2}} \, dx$ **4.** $\int x^2(x^2 - 64)^{3/2} \, dx$

Using Trigonometric Substitution   **In Exercises 5–8, find the indefinite integral using the substitution $x = 4 \sin \theta$.**

5. $\int \dfrac{\sqrt{16 - x^2}}{x} \, dx$ **6.** $\int \dfrac{4}{x^2\sqrt{16 - x^2}} \, dx$

7. $\int \dfrac{1}{16 - x^2} \, dx$ **8.** $\int \dfrac{x^3}{\sqrt{16 - x^2}} \, dx$

Using Trigonometric Substitution   **In Exercises 9–12, find the indefinite integral using the substitution $x = \tan \theta$.**

9. $\int x\sqrt{1 + x^2} \, dx$ **10.** $\int \dfrac{9x^3}{\sqrt{1 + x^2}} \, dx$

11. $\int \dfrac{1}{(1 + x^2)^2} \, dx$ **12.** $\int \dfrac{x^2}{(1 + x^2)^2} \, dx$

 **Using Trigonometric Substitution**   **In Exercises 13–16, find the indefinite integral using the substitution $x = 5 \sec \theta$.**

13. $\int \dfrac{1}{\sqrt{x^2 - 25}} \, dx$ **14.** $\int \dfrac{\sqrt{x^2 - 25}}{x} \, dx$

15. $\int x^3\sqrt{x^2 - 25} \, dx$ **16.** $\int \dfrac{x^3}{(x^2 - 25)^3} \, dx$

Completing the Square   **In Exercises 17–20, complete the square and find the indefinite integral.**

17. $\int \dfrac{x^2}{\sqrt{2x - x^2}} \, dx$ **18.** $\int \dfrac{1}{\sqrt{4x - x^2}} \, dx$

19. $\int \dfrac{x}{\sqrt{x^2 + 6x + 12}} \, dx$

20. $\int \dfrac{x}{\sqrt{x^2 - 6x + 5}} \, dx$

Using Formulas   **In Exercises 21–24, use the Special Integration Formulas (Theorem 7.2) to find the indefinite integral.**

21. $\int \sqrt{36 - x^2} \, dx$ **22.** $\int \sqrt{9x^2 - 2} \, dx$

23. $\int 2\sqrt{25 + 3x^2} \, dx$ **24.** $\int \sqrt{36x^2 + 45} \, dx$

 Finding an Indefinite Integral   **In Exercises 25–40, find the indefinite integral.**

25. $\int \sqrt{16 - 4x^2} \, dx$ **26.** $\int \dfrac{1}{\sqrt{x^2 - 4}} \, dx$

27. $\int \dfrac{1}{\sqrt{16 - x^2}} \, dx$ **28.** $\int \dfrac{x}{\sqrt{x^2 - 36}} \, dx$

29. $\int \dfrac{\sqrt{1 - x^2}}{x^4} \, dx$ **30.** $\int \dfrac{\sqrt{25x^2 + 4}}{x^4} \, dx$

31. $\int \dfrac{1}{x\sqrt{4x^2 + 9}} \, dx$ **32.** $\int \dfrac{1}{x\sqrt{9x^2 + 1}} \, dx$

33. $\int \dfrac{x}{(16 - x^2)^{5/2}} \, dx$ **34.** $\int \dfrac{1}{(x^2 + 5)^{3/2}} \, dx$

35. $\int e^x\sqrt{1 - e^{2x}} \, dx$ **36.** $\int \dfrac{\sqrt{1 - x}}{\sqrt{x}} \, dx$

37. $\int \dfrac{1}{4 + 4x^2 + x^4} \, dx$ **38.** $\int \dfrac{x^3 + x + 1}{x^4 + 2x^2 + 1} \, dx$

39. $\int \operatorname{arcsec} 2x \, dx, \ x > \dfrac{1}{2}$ **40.** $\int x \arcsin x \, dx$

 Converting Limits of Integration   **In Exercises 41–46, evaluate the definite integral using (a) the given integration limits and (b) the limits obtained by trigonometric substitution.**

41. $\displaystyle\int_0^{\sqrt{3}/2} \dfrac{t^2}{(1 - t^2)^{3/2}} \, dt$ **42.** $\displaystyle\int_0^{\sqrt{3}/2} \dfrac{1}{(1 - t^2)^{5/2}} \, dt$

43. $\displaystyle\int_0^3 \dfrac{x^3}{\sqrt{x^2 + 9}} \, dx$ **44.** $\displaystyle\int_0^{3/5} \sqrt{9 - 25x^2} \, dx$

45. $\displaystyle\int_4^6 \dfrac{x^2}{\sqrt{x^2 - 9}} \, dx$ **46.** $\displaystyle\int_4^8 \dfrac{\sqrt{x^2 - 16}}{x^2} \, dx$

EXPLORING CONCEPTS

47. Implementing Processes   State the substitution you would make if you used trigonometric substitution for an integral involving the given radical, where $a > 0$. Explain your reasoning.

(a) $\sqrt{a^2 - u^2}$

(b) $\sqrt{a^2 + u^2}$

(c) $\sqrt{u^2 - a^2}$

48. Justifying   State the method of integration you would use to perform each integration. Explain why you chose that method. Do not integrate.

(a) $\int x\sqrt{x^2 + 1} \, dx$

(b) $\int x^2\sqrt{x^2 - 1} \, dx$

EXPLORING CONCEPTS (continued)

49. Comparing Methods

(a) Find the integral

$$\int \frac{x}{x^2 + 9}\, dx$$

using u-substitution. Then find the integral using trigonometric substitution. Discuss the results.

(b) Find the integral

$$\int \frac{x^2}{x^2 + 9}\, dx$$

algebraically using $x^2 = (x^2 + 9) - 9$. Then find the integral using trigonometric substitution. Discuss the results.

50. HOW DO YOU SEE IT?   Use the graph of f' shown in the figure to answer the following.

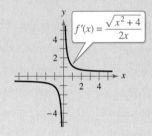

$$f'(x) = \frac{\sqrt{x^2 + 4}}{2x}$$

(a) Identify the open interval(s) on which the graph of f is increasing or decreasing. Explain.

(b) Identify the open interval(s) on which the graph of f is concave upward or concave downward. Explain.

True or False?   In Exercises 51–54, determine whether the statement is true or false. If it is false, explain why or give an example that shows it is false.

51. If $x = \sin\theta$, then $\displaystyle\int \frac{dx}{\sqrt{1 - x^2}} = \int d\theta.$

52. If $x = \sec\theta$, then

$$\int \frac{\sqrt{x^2 - 1}}{x}\, dx = \int \sec\theta \tan\theta \, d\theta.$$

53. If $x = \tan\theta$, then

$$\int_0^{\sqrt{3}} \frac{dx}{(1 + x^2)^{3/2}} = \int_0^{4\pi/3} \cos\theta \, d\theta.$$

54. If $x = \sec\theta$, then

$$\int_{-2}^{-1} x^2\sqrt{x^2 - 1}\, dx = \int_{2\pi/3}^{\pi} -\sec^3\theta \tan^2\theta \, d\theta.$$

55. Area   Find the area of the shaded region of the circle of radius a when the chord is h units $(0 < h < a)$ from the center of the circle (see figure).

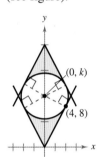

56. MECHANICAL DESIGN

The surface of a machine part is the four regions between the graphs of $y = |2x|$, $y = 20 - |2x|$, and $x^2 + (y - 10)^2 = 20$ (see figure).

(a) Find k when the circle is tangent to the graph of $y = |2x|$.

(b) Find the area of the surface of the machine part.

Volume of a Torus   In Exercises 57 and 58, find the volume of the torus generated by revolving the region bounded by the graph of the circle about the y-axis.

57. $(x - 3)^2 + y^2 = 1$

58. $(x - h)^2 + y^2 = r^2, \quad h > r$

Arc Length   In Exercises 59–62, find the arc length of the curve over the given interval.

59. $y = \frac{1}{2}x^2, \quad [0, 4]$

60. $y = \frac{x^2}{4} - 2x, \quad [4, 8]$

61. $y = \ln x, \quad [1, 5]$

62. $y = \ln x^2, \quad [-3, -1]$

63. Arc Length   Show that the length of one arch of the sine curve is equal to the length of one arch of the cosine curve.

64. Conjecture

(a) Find formulas for the distances between $(0, 0)$ and (a, a^2) along the line between these points and along the parabola $y = x^2$.

(b) Use the formulas from part (a) to find the distances for $a = 1$ and $a = 10$.

(c) Make a conjecture about the ratio between the two distances as a increases.

65. Surface Area Find the surface area of the solid generated by revolving the region bounded by the graphs of $y = x^2$, $y = 0$, $x = 0$, and $x = \sqrt{2}$ about the x-axis.

66. Field Strength The field strength H of a magnet of length $2L$ on a particle r units from the center of the magnet is

$$H = \frac{2mL}{(r^2 + L^2)^{3/2}}$$

where $\pm m$ are the poles of the magnet (see figure). Find the average field strength as the particle moves from 0 to R units from the center by evaluating the integral

$$\frac{1}{R} \int_0^R \frac{2mL}{(r^2 + L^2)^{3/2}} \, dr.$$

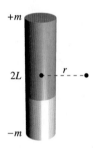

67. Verifying Use trigonometric substitution to verify the integration formulas given in Theorem 7.2.

68. Arc Length Show that the arc length of the graph of $y = \sin x$ on the interval $[0, 2\pi]$ is equal to the circumference of the ellipse $x^2 + 2y^2 = 2$ (see figure).

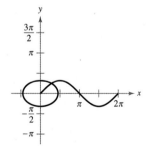
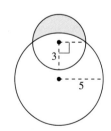

Figure for 68   Figure for 69

69. Area of a Lune The crescent-shaped region bounded by two circles forms a *lune* (see figure). Find the area of the lune given that the radius of the smaller circle is 3 and the radius of the larger circle is 5.

70. Area Two circles of radius 3, with centers at $(-2, 0)$ and $(2, 0)$ intersect as shown in the figure. Find the area of the shaded region.

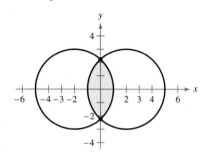

Calculus AP® – Exam Preparation Questions

71. Multiple Choice What is the general solution of the differential equation $y'\sqrt{9x^2 + 1} = x^3$?

(A) $y = \frac{1}{9}x^2\sqrt{9x^2 + 1} + C$

(B) $y = \frac{1}{27}x^2\sqrt{9x^2 + 1} + C$

(C) $y = \frac{1}{81}(9x^2 - 2)\sqrt{9x^2 + 1} + C$

(D) $y = \frac{1}{243}(9x^2 - 2)\sqrt{9x^2 + 1} + C$

72. Multiple Choice What is the average value of the function $f(x) = \dfrac{\sqrt{16x^2 - 1}}{x}$ on the interval $\left[\frac{1}{4}, \frac{1}{2}\right]$?

(A) 0.685   (B) 1.370

(C) 2.739   (D) 3.787

73. Free Response The figure below shows the graphs of

$$y = \frac{1}{(16 + x^2)^{3/2}} \quad \text{and} \quad y = \frac{x}{\sqrt{25 + x^2}}.$$

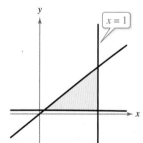

(a) Use a geometric formula to estimate the value of

$$\int_0^1 \frac{x}{\sqrt{25 + x^2}} \, dx.$$

Then evaluate this integral. How close is your estimate?

(b) Use a geometric formula to estimate the value of

$$\int_0^1 \frac{1}{(16 + x^2)^{3/2}} \, dx.$$

Then evaluate this integral. How close is your estimate?

(c) Estimate the area of the shaded region.

7.5   Partial Fractions

▶ Understand the concept of partial fraction decomposition.
▶ Use partial fraction decomposition with linear factors to integrate rational functions.
▶ Use partial fraction decomposition with quadratic factors to integrate rational functions.

Partial Fractions

This section examines a procedure for decomposing a rational function into simpler rational functions to which you can apply the basic integration formulas. This procedure is called the **method of partial fractions.** To see the benefit of the method of partial fractions, consider the integral

$$\int \frac{1}{x^2 - 5x + 6}\,dx.$$

To find this integral *without* partial fractions, you can complete the square and use trigonometric substitution (see Figure 7.9) to obtain

$$\int \frac{1}{x^2 - 5x + 6}\,dx = \int \frac{dx}{(x - 5/2)^2 - (1/2)^2} \qquad a = \tfrac{1}{2},\ x - \tfrac{5}{2} = \tfrac{1}{2}\sec\theta$$

$$= \int \frac{(1/2)\sec\theta \tan\theta\,d\theta}{(1/4)\tan^2\theta} \qquad dx = \tfrac{1}{2}\sec\theta\tan\theta\,d\theta$$

$$= 2 \int \csc\theta\,d\theta$$

$$= 2 \ln|\csc\theta - \cot\theta| + C$$

$$= 2 \ln\left|\frac{2x - 5}{2\sqrt{x^2 - 5x + 6}} - \frac{1}{2\sqrt{x^2 - 5x + 6}}\right| + C$$

$$= 2 \ln\left|\frac{x - 3}{\sqrt{x^2 - 5x + 6}}\right| + C$$

$$= \ln\left|\frac{(x - 3)^2}{x^2 - 5x + 6}\right| + C$$

$$= \ln\left|\frac{(x - 3)^2}{(x - 2)(x - 3)}\right| + C$$

$$= \ln\left|\frac{x - 3}{x - 2}\right| + C$$

$$= \ln|x - 3| - \ln|x - 2| + C.$$

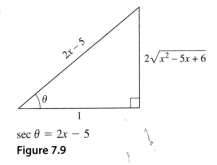

$\sec\theta = 2x - 5$

Figure 7.9

Now, suppose you had observed that

$$\frac{1}{x^2 - 5x + 6} = \frac{1}{x - 3} - \frac{1}{x - 2}. \qquad \text{Partial fraction decomposition}$$

Then you could find the integral, as shown.

$$\int \frac{1}{x^2 - 5x + 6}\,dx = \int \left(\frac{1}{x - 3} - \frac{1}{x - 2}\right) dx = \ln|x - 3| - \ln|x - 2| + C$$

This method is clearly preferable to trigonometric substitution. Its use, however, depends on the ability to factor the denominator, $x^2 - 5x + 6$, and to find the **partial fractions**

$$\frac{1}{x - 3} \quad \text{and} \quad -\frac{1}{x - 2}.$$

In this section, you will study techniques for finding partial fraction decompositions.

Recall from algebra that every polynomial with real coefficients can be factored into linear and irreducible quadratic factors.* For instance, the polynomial

$$x^5 + x^4 - x - 1$$

can be written as

$$
\begin{aligned}
x^5 + x^4 - x - 1 &= x^4(x + 1) - (x + 1) \\
&= (x^4 - 1)(x + 1) \\
&= (x^2 + 1)(x^2 - 1)(x + 1) \\
&= (x^2 + 1)(x + 1)(x - 1)(x + 1) \\
&= (x - 1)(x + 1)^2(x^2 + 1)
\end{aligned}
$$

where $(x - 1)$ is a linear factor, $(x + 1)^2$ is a repeated linear factor, and $(x^2 + 1)$ is an irreducible quadratic factor. Using this factorization, you can write the partial fraction decomposition of the rational expression

$$\frac{N(x)}{x^5 + x^4 - x - 1}$$

where $N(x)$ is a polynomial of degree less than 5, as shown.

$$\frac{N(x)}{(x - 1)(x + 1)^2(x^2 + 1)} = \frac{A}{x - 1} + \frac{B}{x + 1} + \frac{C}{(x + 1)^2} + \frac{Dx + E}{x^2 + 1}$$

Decomposition of $N(x)/D(x)$ into Partial Fractions

1. **Divide when improper:** When $N(x)/D(x)$ is an improper fraction (that is, when the degree of the numerator is greater than or equal to the degree of the denominator), divide the denominator into the numerator to obtain

   $$\frac{N(x)}{D(x)} = (\text{a polynomial}) + \frac{N_1(x)}{D(x)}$$

   where the degree of $N_1(x)$ is less than the degree of $D(x)$. Then apply Steps 2, 3, and 4 to the proper rational expression $N_1(x)/D(x)$.

2. **Factor denominator:** Completely factor the denominator into factors of the form

   $$(px + q)^m \quad \text{and} \quad (ax^2 + bx + c)^n$$

   where $ax^2 + bx + c$ is irreducible.

3. **Linear factors:** For each factor of the form $(px + q)^m$, the partial fraction decomposition must include the following sum of m fractions.

   $$\frac{A_1}{(px + q)} + \frac{A_2}{(px + q)^2} + \cdots + \frac{A_m}{(px + q)^m}$$

4. **Quadratic factors:** For each factor of the form $(ax^2 + bx + c)^n$, the partial fraction decomposition must include the following sum of n fractions.

   $$\frac{B_1x + C_1}{ax^2 + bx + c} + \frac{B_2x + C_2}{(ax^2 + bx + c)^2} + \cdots + \frac{B_nx + C_n}{(ax^2 + bx + c)^n}$$

Connecting Representations

In precalculus, you learned how to combine fractions such as

$$\frac{1}{x - 2} + \frac{-1}{x + 3} = \frac{5}{(x - 2)(x + 3)}.$$

The method of partial fractions shows you how to reverse this process.

$$\frac{5}{(x - 2)(x + 3)} = \frac{?}{x - 2} + \frac{?}{x + 3}$$

---

* For a review of factorization techniques, see *Precalculus with Limits*, 4th edition, or *Precalculus with Limits: A Graphing Approach*, 8th edition, both by Ron Larson and Paul Battaglia (Boston, Massachusetts: Cengage, 2018 and 2020, respectively).

Linear Factors

Algebraic techniques for determining the constants in the numerators of a partial fraction decomposition with linear or repeated linear factors are shown in Examples 1 and 2.

EXAMPLE 1   Distinct Linear Factors

Write the partial fraction decomposition for

$$\frac{1}{x^2 - 5x + 6}.$$

Solution

Because $x^2 - 5x + 6 = (x - 3)(x - 2)$, you should include one partial fraction for each factor and write

$$\frac{1}{x^2 - 5x + 6} = \frac{A}{x - 3} + \frac{B}{x - 2}$$

where A and B are to be determined. Multiplying this equation by the least common denominator $(x - 3)(x - 2)$ yields the **basic equation**

$$1 = A(x - 2) + B(x - 3). \qquad \text{Basic equation}$$

Because this equation is to be true for all x, you can substitute any *convenient* values for x to obtain equations in A and B. The most convenient values are the ones that make particular factors equal to 0. To solve for A, let $x = 3$.

$$1 = A(3 - 2) + B(3 - 3) \qquad \text{Let } x = 3 \text{ in basic equation.}$$
$$1 = A(1) + B(0)$$
$$1 = A$$

To solve for B, let $x = 2$.

$$1 = A(2 - 2) + B(2 - 3) \qquad \text{Let } x = 2 \text{ in basic equation.}$$
$$1 = A(0) + B(-1)$$
$$-1 = B$$

So, the decomposition is

$$\frac{1}{x^2 - 5x + 6} = \frac{1}{x - 3} - \frac{1}{x - 2}$$

as shown at the beginning of this section.

Justification

Note that the substitutions for x in Example 1 are chosen for their convenience in determining values for A and B; $x = 3$ is chosen to eliminate the term $B(x - 3)$, and $x = 2$ is chosen to eliminate the term $A(x - 2)$. The goal is to make *convenient* substitutions whenever possible.

Be sure you see that the method of partial fractions is practical only for integrals of rational functions whose denominators factor "nicely." For instance, when the denominator in Example 1 is changed to

$$x^2 - 5x + 5$$

its factorization as

$$x^2 - 5x + 5 = \left(x - \frac{5 + \sqrt{5}}{2}\right)\left(x - \frac{5 - \sqrt{5}}{2}\right)$$

would be too cumbersome to use with partial fractions. In such cases, you should use completing the square or a computer algebra system to perform the integration. When you do this, you should obtain

$$\int \frac{1}{x^2 - 5x + 5}\, dx = \frac{\sqrt{5}}{5} \ln|2x - \sqrt{5} - 5| - \frac{\sqrt{5}}{5} \ln|2x + \sqrt{5} - 5| + C.$$

EXAMPLE 2 **Repeated Linear Factors**

Find $\displaystyle \int \frac{5x^2 + 20x + 6}{x^3 + 2x^2 + x}\,dx$.

Solution

The denominator factors as

$$x^3 + 2x^2 + x = x(x^2 + 2x + 1) = x(x + 1)^2$$

so you should include one fraction for *each power* of x and $(x + 1)$ and write

$$\frac{5x^2 + 20x + 6}{x(x + 1)^2} = \frac{A}{x} + \frac{B}{x + 1} + \frac{C}{(x + 1)^2}.$$

Multiplying by the least common denominator $x(x + 1)^2$ yields the basic equation

$$5x^2 + 20x + 6 = A(x + 1)^2 + Bx(x + 1) + Cx. \qquad \text{Basic equation}$$

To solve for A, let $x = 0$. This eliminates the B and C terms and yields

$$5(0)^2 + 20(0) + 6 = A(0 + 1)^2 + B(0)(0 + 1) + C(0)$$
$$6 = A(1) + 0 + 0$$
$$6 = A.$$

To solve for C, let $x = -1$. This eliminates the A and B terms and yields

$$5(-1)^2 + 20(-1) + 6 = A(-1 + 1)^2 + B(-1)(-1 + 1) + C(-1)$$
$$5 - 20 + 6 = 0 + 0 - C$$
$$9 = C.$$

The most convenient choices for x have been used, so to find the value of B, you can use *any other value* of x along with the calculated values of A and C. Using $x = 1$, $A = 6$, and $C = 9$ produces

$$5(1)^2 + 20(1) + 6 = 6(1 + 1)^2 + B(1)(1 + 1) + 9(1)$$
$$31 = 6(4) + 2B + 9$$
$$-2 = 2B$$
$$-1 = B.$$

So, the decomposition is

$$\frac{5x^2 + 20x + 6}{x(x + 1)^2} = \frac{6}{x} - \frac{1}{x + 1} + \frac{9}{(x + 1)^2}.$$

Now, find the integral.

$$\int \frac{5x^2 + 20x + 6}{x(x + 1)^2}\,dx = \int \left(\frac{6}{x} - \frac{1}{x + 1} + \frac{9}{(x + 1)^2} \right) dx$$
$$= 6 \ln|x| - \ln|x + 1| + 9\frac{(x + 1)^{-1}}{-1} + C$$
$$= \ln\left| \frac{x^6}{x + 1} \right| - \frac{9}{x + 1} + C$$

Try checking this result by differentiating. Include algebra in your check, simplifying the derivative until you have obtained the original integrand. ▪

It is necessary to make as many substitutions for x as there are unknowns ($A, B, C, \ldots$) to be determined. For instance, in Example 2, three substitutions ($x = 0$, $x = -1$, and $x = 1$) were made to solve for A, B, and C.

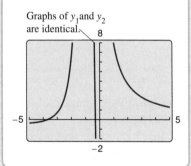

Quadratic Factors

When using the method of partial fractions with *linear* factors, a convenient choice of x immediately yields a value for one of the coefficients. With *quadratic* factors, a system of linear equations usually has to be solved, regardless of the choice of x.

EXAMPLE 3   Distinct Linear and Quadratic Factors

See LarsonCalculusforAP.com for an interactive version of this type of example.

Find $\displaystyle\int \frac{2x^3 - 4x - 8}{(x^2 - x)(x^2 + 4)}\, dx$.

Solution

Because $(x^2 - x)(x^2 + 4) = x(x - 1)(x^2 + 4)$, you should include one partial fraction for each factor and write

$$\frac{2x^3 - 4x - 8}{x(x - 1)(x^2 + 4)} = \frac{A}{x} + \frac{B}{x - 1} + \frac{Cx + D}{x^2 + 4}.$$

Multiplying by the least common denominator

$$x(x - 1)(x^2 + 4)$$

yields the basic equation

$$2x^3 - 4x - 8 = A(x - 1)(x^2 + 4) + Bx(x^2 + 4) + (Cx + D)(x)(x - 1).$$

To solve for A, let $x = 0$ and obtain

$$-8 = A(-1)(4) + B(0)(4) + D(0)(-1)$$
$$-8 = -4A + 0 + 0$$
$$2 = A.$$

To solve for B, let $x = 1$ and obtain

$$-10 = A(0)(5) + B(5) + (C + D)(1)(0)$$
$$-10 = 0 + 5B + 0$$
$$-2 = B.$$

At this point, C and D are yet to be determined. You can find these remaining constants by choosing two other values for x and solving the resulting system of linear equations. Using $x = -1$, $A = 2$, and $B = -2$, you can write

$$-6 = (2)(-2)(5) + (-2)(-1)(5) + (-C + D)(-1)(-2)$$
$$2 = -C + D.$$

For $x = 2$, $A = 2$, and $B = -2$, you have

$$0 = (2)(1)(8) + (-2)(2)(8) + (2C + D)(2)(1)$$
$$8 = 2C + D.$$

Solving the linear system by subtracting the first equation from the second

$$-C + D = 2$$
$$2C + D = 8$$

yields $C = 2$. Consequently, $D = 4$, and it follows that

$$\int \frac{2x^3 - 4x - 8}{x(x - 1)(x^2 + 4)}\, dx = \int \left(\frac{2}{x} - \frac{2}{x - 1} + \frac{2x}{x^2 + 4} + \frac{4}{x^2 + 4}\right) dx$$

$$= 2\ln|x| - 2\ln|x - 1| + \ln(x^2 + 4) + 2\arctan\frac{x}{2} + C.$$

In Examples 1, 2, and 3, the solution of the basic equation began with substituting values of x that made the linear factors equal to 0. This method works well when the partial fraction decomposition involves linear factors. When the decomposition involves only quadratic factors, however, an alternative procedure is often more convenient. For instance, try writing the right side of the basic equation in polynomial form and *equating the coefficients* of like terms. This method is shown in Example 4.

EXAMPLE 4   Repeated Quadratic Factors

Evaluate $\displaystyle\int_1^2 \frac{8x^3 + 13x}{(x^2 + 2)^2}\, dx$.

Solution

Include one partial fraction for each power of $(x^2 + 2)$ and write

$$\frac{8x^3 + 13x}{(x^2 + 2)^2} = \frac{Ax + B}{x^2 + 2} + \frac{Cx + D}{(x^2 + 2)^2}.$$

Multiplying by the least common denominator $(x^2 + 2)^2$ yields the basic equation

$$8x^3 + 13x = (Ax + B)(x^2 + 2) + Cx + D.$$

Expanding the basic equation and collecting like terms produces

$$8x^3 + 13x = Ax^3 + 2Ax + Bx^2 + 2B + Cx + D$$
$$8x^3 + 13x = Ax^3 + Bx^2 + (2A + C)x + (2B + D).$$

Now, you can equate the coefficients of like terms on opposite sides of the equation.

$$8 = A \qquad\qquad\qquad 0 = 2B + D$$

$$8x^3 + 0x^2 + 13x + 0 = Ax^3 + Bx^2 + (2A + C)x + (2B + D)$$

$$0 = B$$

$$13 = 2A + C$$

Using the known values $A = 8$ and $B = 0$, you can solve for C and D as shown.

$$13 = 2A + C \implies 13 = 2(8) + C \implies -3 = C$$
$$0 = 2B + D \implies 0 = 2(0) + D \implies 0 = D$$

Now, evaluate the integral.

$$\int_1^2 \frac{8x^3 + 13x}{(x^2 + 2)^2}\, dx = \int_1^2 \left(\frac{8x}{x^2 + 2} + \frac{-3x}{(x^2 + 2)^2}\right) dx$$

$$= \left[4 \ln(x^2 + 2) + \frac{3}{2(x^2 + 2)}\right]_1^2$$

$$= \left(4 \ln 6 + \frac{1}{4}\right) - \left(4 \ln 3 + \frac{1}{2}\right)$$

$$\approx 2.523$$

Use a graphing utility to check your result.

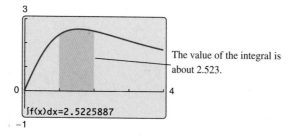

The value of the integral is about 2.523.

∫f(x)dx=2.5225887

When integrating rational expressions, keep in mind that for *improper* rational expressions such as

$$\frac{N(x)}{D(x)} = \frac{2x^3 + x^2 - 7x + 7}{x^2 + x - 2}$$

you must first divide to obtain

$$\frac{N(x)}{D(x)} = 2x - 1 + \frac{-2x + 5}{x^2 + x - 2}.$$

The proper rational expression is then decomposed into its partial fractions by the usual methods.

Here are some guidelines for solving the basic equation that is obtained in a partial fraction decomposition.

Guidelines for Solving the Basic Equation

Linear Factors

1. Substitute the roots of the distinct linear factors in the basic equation.
2. For repeated linear factors, use the coefficients determined in the first guideline to rewrite the basic equation. Then substitute other convenient values of x and solve for the remaining coefficients.

Quadratic Factors

1. Expand the basic equation.
2. Collect terms according to powers of x.
3. Equate the coefficients of like powers to obtain a system of linear equations involving A, B, C, and so on.
4. Solve the system of linear equations.

Before concluding this section, here are a few things you should remember. First, it is not necessary to use the partial fractions technique on all rational functions. For instance, the following integral is found more easily by the Log Rule.

$$\int \frac{x^2 + 1}{x^3 + 3x - 4} \, dx = \frac{1}{3} \int \frac{3x^2 + 3}{x^3 + 3x - 4} \, dx$$

$$= \frac{1}{3} \ln|x^3 + 3x - 4| + C$$

Second, when the integrand is not in reduced form, reducing it may eliminate the need for partial fractions, as shown in the following integral.

$$\int \frac{x^2 - x - 2}{x^3 - 2x - 4} \, dx = \int \frac{(x + 1)(x - 2)}{(x - 2)(x^2 + 2x + 2)} \, dx$$

$$= \int \frac{x + 1}{x^2 + 2x + 2} \, dx$$

$$= \frac{1}{2} \ln|x^2 + 2x + 2| + C$$

Finally, partial fractions can be used with some quotients involving transcendental functions. For instance, the substitution $u = \sin x$ allows you to write

$$\int \frac{\cos x}{(\sin x)(\sin x - 1)} \, dx = \int \frac{du}{u(u - 1)}. \qquad u = \sin x, \, du = \cos x \, dx$$

7.5 Exercises

See *CalcChat.com* for tutorial help and worked-out solutions to odd-numbered exercises.

Partial Fraction Decomposition In Exercises 1–4, write the form of the partial fraction decomposition of the rational expression. Do not solve for the constants.

1. $\dfrac{4}{x^2 - 8x}$

2. $\dfrac{2x^2 + 1}{(x-3)^3}$

3. $\dfrac{2x - 3}{x^3 + 10x}$

4. $\dfrac{2x - 1}{x(x^2 + 1)^2}$

Using Partial Fractions In Exercises 5–22, use partial fractions to find the indefinite integral.

5. $\displaystyle\int \dfrac{1}{x^2 - 9}\, dx$

6. $\displaystyle\int \dfrac{2}{9x^2 - 1}\, dx$

7. $\displaystyle\int \dfrac{5}{x^2 + 3x - 4}\, dx$

8. $\displaystyle\int \dfrac{3 - x}{3x^2 - 2x - 1}\, dx$

9. $\displaystyle\int \dfrac{x^2 + 12x + 12}{x^3 - 4x}\, dx$

10. $\displaystyle\int \dfrac{x^3 - x + 3}{x^2 + x - 2}\, dx$

11. $\displaystyle\int \dfrac{x^3 - 11x - 15}{x^2 - 2x - 8}\, dx$

12. $\displaystyle\int \dfrac{x + 2}{x^2 + 5x}\, dx$

13. $\displaystyle\int \dfrac{4x^2 + 2x - 1}{x^3 + x^2}\, dx$

14. $\displaystyle\int \dfrac{5x - 2}{(x - 2)^2}\, dx$

15. $\displaystyle\int \dfrac{x^2 + x + 2}{x^3 - 2x^2 - 4x + 8}\, dx$

16. $\displaystyle\int \dfrac{5x - 1}{x^3 + x^2 - x - 1}\, dx$

17. $\displaystyle\int \dfrac{3x^2 + x - 1}{x^3 + x}\, dx$

18. $\displaystyle\int \dfrac{6x}{x^3 - 8}\, dx$

19. $\displaystyle\int \dfrac{x^2}{x^4 - 2x^2 - 8}\, dx$

20. $\displaystyle\int \dfrac{x}{16x^4 - 1}\, dx$

21. $\displaystyle\int \dfrac{x^2 + 5}{x^3 - x^2 + x + 3}\, dx$

22. $\displaystyle\int \dfrac{x^2 + 6x + 4}{x^4 + 8x^2 + 16}\, dx$

Evaluating a Definite Integral In Exercises 23–26, evaluate the definite integral. Use a graphing utility to verify your result.

23. $\displaystyle\int_0^2 \dfrac{3}{4x^2 + 5x + 1}\, dx$

24. $\displaystyle\int_1^5 \dfrac{x - 1}{x^2(x + 1)}\, dx$

25. $\displaystyle\int_1^2 \dfrac{x + 1}{x(x^2 + 1)}\, dx$

26. $\displaystyle\int_0^1 \dfrac{3x^2 - 3x}{x^2 - x - 2}\, dx$

Error Analysis In Exercises 27 and 28, describe and correct the error in finding the indefinite integral.

27. $\displaystyle\int \dfrac{4x}{2x^2 + 5x - 3}\, dx$

$\displaystyle = \int \left(\dfrac{A}{2x - 1} + \dfrac{B}{x + 3} \right) dx$

$\displaystyle = \dfrac{4}{7} \int \dfrac{1}{2x - 1}\, dx + \dfrac{12}{7} \int \dfrac{1}{x + 3}\, dx$

$\displaystyle = \dfrac{4}{7} \ln|2x - 1| + \dfrac{12}{7} \ln|x + 3| + C$ ✗

28. $\displaystyle\int \dfrac{1}{x^3 - 6x^2 + 9x}\, dx = \int \left(\dfrac{A}{x} + \dfrac{B}{(x - 3)^2} \right) dx$

$\displaystyle = \dfrac{1}{9} \int \dfrac{1}{x}\, dx + \dfrac{1}{3} \int \dfrac{1}{(x - 3)^2}\, dx$

$\displaystyle = \dfrac{1}{9} \ln|x| - \dfrac{1}{3(x - 3)} + C$ ✗

Finding an Indefinite Integral In Exercises 29–34, use substitution and partial fractions to find the indefinite integral.

29. $\displaystyle\int \dfrac{\sec^2 x}{\tan^2 x - 4}\, dx$

30. $\displaystyle\int \dfrac{\sec^2 x}{(\tan x)(\tan x + 1)}\, dx$

31. $\displaystyle\int \dfrac{e^x}{(e^x - 1)(e^x + 4)}\, dx$

32. $\displaystyle\int \dfrac{e^x}{(e^{2x} + 1)(e^x - 1)}\, dx$

33. $\displaystyle\int \dfrac{\sqrt{x}}{x - 4}\, dx$

34. $\displaystyle\int \dfrac{1}{x\left(\sqrt[3]{x} - 2\sqrt[6]{x} + 1 \right)}\, dx$

Verifying a Formula In Exercises 35–38, use the method of partial fractions to verify the integration formula.

35. $\displaystyle\int \dfrac{1}{x(a + bx)}\, dx = \dfrac{1}{a} \ln \left| \dfrac{x}{a + bx} \right| + C$

36. $\displaystyle\int \dfrac{1}{a^2 - x^2}\, dx = \dfrac{1}{2a} \ln \left| \dfrac{a + x}{a - x} \right| + C$

37. $\displaystyle\int \dfrac{x}{(a + bx)^2}\, dx = \dfrac{1}{b^2} \left(\dfrac{a}{a + bx} + \ln|a + bx| \right) + C$

38. $\displaystyle\int \dfrac{1}{x^2(a + bx)}\, dx = -\dfrac{1}{ax} - \dfrac{b}{a^2} \ln \left| \dfrac{x}{a + bx} \right| + C$

EXPLORING CONCEPTS

Implementing Processes In Exercises 39–41, state the method you would use to find the integral. Explain why you chose that method. Do not integrate.

39. $\displaystyle\int \dfrac{x + 1}{x^2 + 2x - 8}\, dx$

40. $\displaystyle\int \dfrac{7x + 4}{x^2 + 2x - 8}\, dx$

41. $\displaystyle\int \dfrac{4}{x^2 + 2x + 5}\, dx$

42. HOW DO YOU SEE IT? Use the graph of f' shown in the figure to answer the following.

(a) Is $f(3) - f(2) > 0$? Explain.

(b) Which is greater, the area under the graph of f' from 1 to 2, or the area under the graph of f' from 3 to 4?

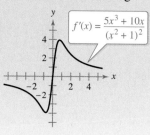

$f'(x) = \dfrac{5x^3 + 10x}{(x^2 + 1)^2}$

Volume In Exercises 43 and 44, use partial fractions to find the volume of the solid generated by revolving the given region about the *x*-axis.

43. $y = \dfrac{15}{9 - x^2}$

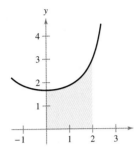

44. $y = \dfrac{7}{16 - x^2}$

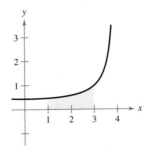

45. Epidemic Model A single infected individual enters a community of n susceptible individuals. Let x be the number of newly infected individuals at time t. The common epidemic model assumes that the disease spreads at a rate proportional to the product of the total number infected and the number not yet infected. So,

$$dx/dt = k(x + 1)(n - x)$$

and you obtain

$$\int \frac{1}{(x + 1)(n - x)}\, dx = \int k\, dt.$$

Solve for x as a function of t.

46. CHEMICAL REACTION

In a chemical reaction, one unit of compound Y and one unit of compound Z are converted into a single unit of compound X. Let x be the amount of compound X formed. The rate of formation of compound X is proportional to the product of the amounts of unconverted compounds Y and Z. So,

$$dx/dt = k(y_0 - x)(z_0 - x)$$

where y_0 and z_0 are the initial amounts of compounds Y and Z. From this equation, you obtain

$$\int \frac{1}{(y_0 - x)(z_0 - x)}\, dx = \int k\, dt.$$

(a) Solve for x as a function of t.

(b) Use the result of part (a) to find x as $t \to \infty$ for (1) $y_0 < z_0$, (2) $y_0 > z_0$, and (3) $y_0 = z_0$.

47. Modeling Data The predicted cost C (in hundreds of thousands of dollars) for a company to remove $p\%$ of a chemical from its wastewater is shown in the table.

p	0	10	20	30	40
C	0	0.7	1.0	1.3	1.7

p	50	60	70	80	90
C	2.0	2.7	3.6	5.5	11.2

A model for the data is given by

$$C = \frac{124p}{(10 + p)(100 - p)}, \quad 0 \le p < 100.$$

Use the model to find the average cost of removing between 75% and 80% of the chemical.

48. Particle Motion The velocity (in inches per second) of a particle moving along a line is

$$v(t) = \frac{2t^2(t^2 - 1)}{(t^2 + 1)^2}$$

where t is the time in seconds. Use partial fractions to find the displacement of the particle on the time interval $0 \le t \le 5$.

49. Using Two Methods Evaluate

$$\int_0^1 \frac{x}{1 + x^4}\, dx$$

in two different ways, one of which is partial fractions.

Calculus AP® – Exam Preparation Questions

50. Multiple Choice $\displaystyle\int_0^1 \frac{x^4(1 - x)^4}{(1 + x^2)^2}\, dx$

(A) $\dfrac{5\pi}{2} - \dfrac{97}{15} - 2 \ln 2$

(B) $3\pi - \dfrac{97}{15} - 2 \ln 2$

(C) $\dfrac{7\pi}{2} - \dfrac{97}{15} - 2 \ln 2$

(D) $5\pi - \dfrac{194}{15} - 4 \ln 2$

51. Multiple Choice $\displaystyle\int \frac{9x}{(3x - 2)(x + 4)}\, dx =$

(A) $\dfrac{3}{7} \ln|3x - 2| + \dfrac{18}{7} \ln|x + 4| + C$

(B) $\dfrac{9}{7} \ln|3x - 2| + \dfrac{18}{7} \ln|x + 4| + C$

(C) $\dfrac{9}{7} \ln|3x - 2| - \dfrac{18}{7} \ln|x + 4| + C$

(D) $\dfrac{3}{7} \ln|3x - 2| - \dfrac{18}{7} \ln|x + 4| + C$

7.6 Integration by Tables and Other Integration Techniques

▶ Find an indefinite integral using a table of integrals.
▶ Find an indefinite integral using reduction formulas.
▶ Find an indefinite integral involving fractional expressions of sine and cosine.

Integration by Tables

So far in this chapter, you have studied several integration techniques that can be used with the basic integration rules. But merely knowing *how* to use the various techniques is not enough. You also need to know *when* to use them. Integration is first and foremost a problem of recognition. That is, you must recognize which rule or technique to apply to obtain an antiderivative. Frequently, a slight alteration of an integrand will require a different integration technique (or produce a function whose antiderivative is not an elementary function), as shown below.

$$\int x \ln x \, dx = \frac{x^2}{2} \ln x - \frac{x^2}{4} + C \qquad \text{Integration by parts}$$

$$\int \frac{\ln x}{x} \, dx = \frac{(\ln x)^2}{2} + C \qquad \text{Power Rule}$$

$$\int \frac{1}{x \ln x} \, dx = \ln|\ln x| + C \qquad \text{Log Rule}$$

$$\int \frac{x}{\ln x} \, dx = ? \qquad \text{Not an elementary function}$$

Many people find tables of integrals to be a valuable supplement to the integration techniques discussed in this chapter. Tables of common integrals can be found in Appendix B. **Integration by tables** is not a "cure-all" for all of the difficulties that can accompany integration—using tables of integrals requires considerable thought and insight and often involves substitution.

Each integration formula in Appendix B can be developed using one or more of the techniques in this chapter. You should try to verify several of the formulas. For instance, Formula 4

$$\int \frac{u}{(a + bu)^2} \, du = \frac{1}{b^2}\left(\frac{a}{a + bu} + \ln|a + bu|\right) + C \qquad \text{Formula 4}$$

can be verified using the method of partial fractions, Formula 19

$$\int \frac{\sqrt{a + bu}}{u} \, du = 2\sqrt{a + bu} + a \int \frac{du}{u\sqrt{a + bu}} \qquad \text{Formula 19}$$

can be verified using integration by parts, and Formula 84

$$\int \frac{1}{1 + e^u} \, du = u - \ln(1 + e^u) + C \qquad \text{Formula 84}$$

can be verified using substitution. Note that the integrals in Appendix B are classified according to the form of the integrand. Several of the forms are listed below.

u^n	$(a + bu)$
$(a + bu + cu^2)$	$\sqrt{a + bu}$
$(a^2 \pm u^2)$	$\sqrt{u^2 \pm a^2}$
$\sqrt{a^2 - u^2}$	Trigonometric functions
Inverse trigonometric functions	Exponential functions
Logarithmic functions	

EXAMPLE 1   Integration by Tables

Find $\displaystyle\int \frac{dx}{x\sqrt{x-1}}$.

Solution   Because the expression inside the radical is linear, you should consider forms involving $\sqrt{a+bu}$.

$$\int \frac{du}{u\sqrt{a+bu}} = \frac{2}{\sqrt{-a}} \arctan \sqrt{\frac{a+bu}{-a}} + C \qquad \text{Formula 17 } (a<0)$$

Let $a = -1$, $b = 1$, and $u = x$. Then $du = dx$, and you can write

$$\int \frac{dx}{x\sqrt{x-1}} = 2 \arctan \sqrt{x-1} + C.$$

EXAMPLE 2   Integration by Tables

See LarsonCalculusforAP.com for an interactive version of this type of example.

Find $\displaystyle\int x\sqrt{x^4-9}\,dx$.

Solution   Because the radical has the form $\sqrt{u^2-a^2}$, you should consider Formula 26.

$$\int \sqrt{u^2-a^2}\,du = \frac{1}{2}\left(u\sqrt{u^2-a^2} - a^2 \ln\left|u + \sqrt{u^2-a^2}\right|\right) + C$$

Let $u = x^2$ and $a = 3$. Then $du = 2x\,dx$, and you have

$$\int x\sqrt{x^4-9}\,dx = \frac{1}{2}\int \sqrt{(x^2)^2 - 3^2}\,(2x)\,dx$$

$$= \frac{1}{4}\left(x^2\sqrt{x^4-9} - 9 \ln\left|x^2 + \sqrt{x^4-9}\right|\right) + C.$$

EXAMPLE 3   Integration by Tables

Evaluate $\displaystyle\int_0^2 \frac{x}{1+e^{-x^2}}\,dx$.

Solution

Of the forms involving e^u, consider the formula

$$\int \frac{du}{1+e^u} = u - \ln(1+e^u) + C. \qquad \text{Formula 84}$$

Let $u = -x^2$. Then $du = -2x\,dx$, and you have

$$\int \frac{x}{1+e^{-x^2}}\,dx = -\frac{1}{2}\int \frac{-2x\,dx}{1+e^{-x^2}}$$

$$= -\frac{1}{2}\left[-x^2 - \ln\left(1+e^{-x^2}\right)\right] + C$$

$$= \frac{1}{2}\left[x^2 + \ln\left(1+e^{-x^2}\right)\right] + C.$$

So, the value of the definite integral is

$$\int_0^2 \frac{x}{1+e^{-x^2}}\,dx = \frac{1}{2}\left[x^2 + \ln(1+e^{-x^2})\right]_0^2 = \frac{1}{2}[4 + \ln(1+e^{-4}) - \ln 2] \approx 1.66.$$

Use a graphing utility to check your answer (see Figure 7.10).

Exploration

Use the tables of integrals in Appendix B and the substitution

$$u = \sqrt{x-1}$$

to find the integral in Example 1. When you do this, you should obtain

$$\int \frac{dx}{x\sqrt{x-1}} = \int \frac{2\,du}{u^2+1}.$$

Does this produce the same result as that obtained in Example 1?

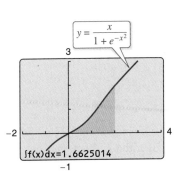

$$y = \frac{x}{1+e^{-x^2}}$$

$\int f(x)\,dx = 1.6625014$

Figure 7.10

Reduction Formulas

Several of the integrals in the integration tables have the form

$$\int f(x)\, dx = g(x) + \int h(x)\, dx.$$

Such integration formulas are called **reduction formulas** because they reduce a given integral to the sum of a function and a simpler integral.

EXAMPLE 4 Using a Reduction Formula

Find $\displaystyle\int x^3 \sin x\, dx$.

Solution

Consider the three formulas listed below.

$$\int u \sin u\, du = \sin u - u \cos u + C \qquad\qquad \text{Formula 52}$$

$$\int u^n \sin u\, du = -u^n \cos u + n \int u^{n-1} \cos u\, du \qquad \text{Formula 54}$$

$$\int u^n \cos u\, du = u^n \sin u - n \int u^{n-1} \sin u\, du \qquad \text{Formula 55}$$

Using Formula 54, Formula 55, and then Formula 52 produces

$$\int x^3 \sin x\, dx = -x^3 \cos x + 3\int x^2 \cos x\, dx$$

$$= -x^3 \cos x + 3\left(x^2 \sin x - 2\int x \sin x\, dx\right)$$

$$= -x^3 \cos x + 3x^2 \sin x + 6x \cos x - 6 \sin x + C.$$

EXAMPLE 5 Using a Reduction Formula

Find $\displaystyle\int \frac{\sqrt{3 - 5x}}{2x}\, dx$.

Solution

Consider the two formulas listed below.

$$\int \frac{du}{u\sqrt{a + bu}} = \frac{1}{\sqrt{a}} \ln\left|\frac{\sqrt{a + bu} - \sqrt{a}}{\sqrt{a + bu} + \sqrt{a}}\right| + C \qquad \text{Formula 17 } (a > 0)$$

$$\int \frac{\sqrt{a + bu}}{u}\, du = 2\sqrt{a + bu} + a\int \frac{du}{u\sqrt{a + bu}} \qquad \text{Formula 19}$$

Using Formula 19, with $a = 3$, $b = -5$, and $u = x$, produces

$$\frac{1}{2}\int \frac{\sqrt{3 - 5x}}{x}\, dx = \frac{1}{2}\left(2\sqrt{3 - 5x} + 3\int \frac{dx}{x\sqrt{3 - 5x}}\right)$$

$$= \sqrt{3 - 5x} + \frac{3}{2}\int \frac{dx}{x\sqrt{3 - 5x}}.$$

Using Formula 17, with $a = 3$, $b = -5$, and $u = x$, produces

$$\int \frac{\sqrt{3 - 5x}}{2x}\, dx = \sqrt{3 - 5x} + \frac{3}{2}\left(\frac{1}{\sqrt{3}} \ln\left|\frac{\sqrt{3 - 5x} - \sqrt{3}}{\sqrt{3 - 5x} + \sqrt{3}}\right|\right) + C$$

$$= \sqrt{3 - 5x} + \frac{\sqrt{3}}{2} \ln\left|\frac{\sqrt{3 - 5x} - \sqrt{3}}{\sqrt{3 - 5x} + \sqrt{3}}\right| + C.$$

Fractional Expressions of Sine and Cosine

EXAMPLE 6 **Integration by Tables**

Find $\displaystyle\int \frac{\sin 2x}{2 + \cos x}\, dx$.

Solution

Substituting $2 \sin x \cos x$ for $\sin 2x$ produces

$$\int \frac{\sin 2x}{2 + \cos x}\, dx = 2\int \frac{\sin x \cos x}{2 + \cos x}\, dx.$$

A check of the forms involving $\sin u$ or $\cos u$ in Appendix B shows that those listed do not apply. So, you can consider forms involving $a + bu$. For example,

$$\int \frac{u\, du}{a + bu} = \frac{1}{b^2}(bu - a\ln|a + bu|) + C. \qquad \text{Formula 3}$$

Let $a = 2$, $b = 1$, and $u = \cos x$. Then $du = -\sin x\, dx$, and you have

$$
\begin{aligned}
2\int \frac{\sin x \cos x}{2 + \cos x}\, dx &= -2\int \frac{(\cos x)(-\sin x\, dx)}{2 + \cos x} \\
&= -2(\cos x - 2\ln|2 + \cos x|) + C \\
&= -2\cos x + 4\ln|2 + \cos x| + C.
\end{aligned}
$$

    Example 6 involves a fractional expression of $\sin x$ and $\cos x$. When you are unable to find an integral of this form in the integration tables, try using the following special substitution to convert the trigonometric expression to a standard rational expression.

Substitution for Fractional Expressions of Sine and Cosine

For integrals involving fractional expressions of sine and cosine, the substitution

$$u = \frac{\sin x}{1 + \cos x} = \tan\frac{x}{2}$$

yields

$$\cos x = \frac{1 - u^2}{1 + u^2}, \quad \sin x = \frac{2u}{1 + u^2}, \quad \text{and} \quad dx = \frac{2\, du}{1 + u^2}.$$

Proof From the substitution for u, it follows that

$$u^2 = \frac{\sin^2 x}{(1 + \cos x)^2} = \frac{1 - \cos^2 x}{(1 + \cos x)^2} = \frac{1 - \cos x}{1 + \cos x}.$$

Solving for $\cos x$ produces

$$\cos x = \frac{1 - u^2}{1 + u^2}.$$

To find $\sin x$, write $u = (\sin x)/(1 + \cos x)$ as

$$\sin x = u(1 + \cos x) = u\left(1 + \frac{1 - u^2}{1 + u^2}\right) = \frac{2u}{1 + u^2}.$$

Finally, to find dx, consider $u = \tan(x/2)$. Then you have $\arctan u = x/2$ and

$$dx = \frac{2\, du}{1 + u^2}.$$

7.6 Exercises

See *CalcChat.com* for tutorial help and worked-out solutions to odd-numbered exercises.

 Integration by Tables In Exercises 1 and 2, use a table of integrals with forms involving $a + bu$ to find the indefinite integral.

1. $\int \dfrac{x^2}{5 + x} \, dx$

2. $\int \dfrac{4}{x^2(3 + 5x)^2} \, dx$

Integration by Tables In Exercises 3 and 4, use a table of integrals with forms involving $\sqrt{a^2 - u^2}$ to find the indefinite integral.

3. $\int \dfrac{1}{x^2\sqrt{1 - x^2}} \, dx$

4. $\int \dfrac{2\sqrt{100 - x^4}}{x} \, dx$

Integration by Tables In Exercises 5–8, use a table of integrals with forms involving the trigonometric functions to find the indefinite integral.

5. $\int \cos^4 3x \, dx$

6. $\int \dfrac{\sin^4 \sqrt{x}}{\sqrt{x}} \, dx$

7. $\int \dfrac{1}{\sqrt{x}\left(1 - \cos\sqrt{x}\right)} \, dx$

8. $\int \dfrac{1}{4 + 4\cot 4x} \, dx$

Integration by Tables In Exercises 9 and 10, use a table of integrals with forms involving e^u to find the indefinite integral.

9. $\int \dfrac{1}{1 + e^{2x}} \, dx$

10. $\int e^{-4x} \sin 3x \, dx$

Integration by Tables In Exercises 11 and 12, use a table of integrals with forms involving $\ln u$ to find the indefinite integral.

11. $\int x^{12} \ln x \, dx$

12. $\int (\ln x)^3 \, dx$

 Using Two Methods In Exercises 13–16, find the indefinite integral (a) using a table of integrals and (b) using the given method.

Integral	Method
13. $\int \ln \dfrac{x}{3} \, dx$	Integration by parts
14. $\int \sin^2 3x \, dx$	Power-reducing formula
15. $\int \dfrac{1}{x^2(x - 1)} \, dx$	Partial fractions
16. $\int \dfrac{dx}{(4 + x^2)^{3/2}}$	Trigonometric substitution

Finding an Indefinite Integral In Exercises 17–38, use a table of integrals to find the indefinite integral.

17. $\int x \operatorname{arccsc}(x^2 + 1) \, dx$

18. $\int \operatorname{arccot}(4x - 5) \, dx$

19. $\int \dfrac{2}{x^3\sqrt{x^4 - 1}} \, dx$

20. $\int \dfrac{1}{x^2 + 4x + 8} \, dx$

21. $\int \dfrac{4x}{(2 - 5x)^2} \, dx$

22. $\int \dfrac{\theta^3}{1 + \sin \theta^4} \, d\theta$

23. $\int e^x \arccos e^x \, dx$

24. $\int \dfrac{e^x}{1 - \tan e^x} \, dx$

25. $\int \dfrac{x}{1 - \sec x^2} \, dx$

26. $\int \dfrac{1}{t[1 + (\ln t)^2]} \, dt$

27. $\int \dfrac{\cos \theta}{3 + 2\sin \theta + \sin^2 \theta} \, d\theta$

28. $\int x^2\sqrt{6 + 16x^2} \, dx$

29. $\int \dfrac{1}{x^2\sqrt{2 + 9x^2}} \, dx$

30. $\int \sqrt{x} \arctan x^{3/2} \, dx$

31. $\int \dfrac{\ln x}{x(3 + 2\ln x)} \, dx$

32. $\int \dfrac{e^x}{(1 - e^{2x})^{3/2}} \, dx$

33. $\int \dfrac{x}{(x^2 - 6x + 10)^2} \, dx$

34. $\int \sqrt{\dfrac{5 - x}{5 + x}} \, dx$

35. $\int \dfrac{x}{\sqrt{x^4 - 6x^2 + 5}} \, dx$

36. $\int \dfrac{\cos x}{\sqrt{\sin^2 x + 1}} \, dx$

37. $\int \dfrac{e^{3x}}{(1 + e^x)^3} \, dx$

38. $\int \cot^4 \theta \, d\theta$

Error Analysis In Exercises 39 and 40, describe and correct the error in finding the indefinite integral.

39. $\int \dfrac{1}{x^2 + 9} = \dfrac{1}{x}\arctan\dfrac{3}{x} + C$ ✗

40. $\int \dfrac{1}{x^2\sqrt{x^2 + 4}} \, dx = \dfrac{\sqrt{x^2 + 4}}{4x} + C$ ✗

 Evaluating a Definite Integral In Exercises 41–48, use a table of integrals to evaluate the definite integral.

41. $\int_0^1 \dfrac{x}{\sqrt{1 + x}} \, dx$

42. $\int_0^1 2x^3 e^{x^2} \, dx$

43. $\int_1^2 x^4 \ln x \, dx$

44. $\int_0^{\pi/2} x \sin 2x \, dx$

45. $\int_{-\pi/2}^{\pi/2} \dfrac{\cos x}{1 + \sin^2 x} \, dx$

46. $\int_0^5 \dfrac{x^2}{(5 + 2x)^2} \, dx$

47. $\int_0^{\pi/2} t^3 \cos t \, dt$

48. $\int_0^3 \sqrt{x^2 + 16} \, dx$

Verifying a Formula In Exercises 49–52, verify the integration formula.

49. $\int \dfrac{1}{(u^2 \pm a^2)^{3/2}} \, du = \dfrac{\pm u}{a^2\sqrt{u^2 \pm a^2}} + C$

50. $\int u^n \cos u \, du = u^n \sin u - n\int u^{n-1} \sin u \, du$

51. $\int \arctan u \, du = u \arctan u - \ln\sqrt{1 + u^2} + C$

52. $\int (\ln u)^n \, du = u(\ln u)^n - n \int (\ln u)^{n-1} \, du$

Finding or Evaluating an Integral **In Exercises 53–60, find or evaluate the integral.**

53. $\int \dfrac{1}{2 - 3\sin\theta} \, d\theta$

54. $\int \dfrac{\sin\theta}{1 + \cos^2\theta} \, d\theta$

55. $\int_{-\pi/4}^{\pi/4} \dfrac{1}{1 + \cos\theta} \, d\theta$

56. $\int_0^{\pi/2} \dfrac{1}{3 - 2\cos\theta} \, d\theta$

57. $\int \dfrac{\sin\theta}{3 - 2\cos\theta} \, d\theta$

58. $\int \dfrac{\cos\theta}{1 + \cos\theta} \, d\theta$

59. $\int \dfrac{\sin\sqrt{\theta}}{\sqrt{\theta}} \, d\theta$

60. $\int \dfrac{4}{\csc\theta - \cot\theta} \, d\theta$

 Area **In Exercises 61 and 62, find the area of the region bounded by the graphs of the equations.**

61. $y = \dfrac{1}{(16 - x^2)^{3/2}}, \quad y = 0, \, x = -2, \, x = 2$

62. $y = \dfrac{x}{\left(1 + \frac{4}{9}x\right)^2}, \quad y = 0, \, x = 10$

EXPLORING CONCEPTS

63. Communication Describe what is meant by a reduction formula. Give an example.

64. Implementing Processes State the method or integration formula you would use to find the antiderivative. Explain. Do not integrate.

(a) $\int \dfrac{e^x}{e^{2x} + 1} \, dx$ (b) $\int \dfrac{e^x}{e^x + 1} \, dx$ (c) $\int xe^{x^2} \, dx$

(d) $\int xe^x \, dx$ (e) $\int e^{2x}\sqrt{e^{2x} + 1} \, dx$

65. Construction The cross section of a concrete beam is bounded by the graphs of the equations

$$x = \dfrac{2}{\sqrt{1 + y^2}}, \quad x = \dfrac{-2}{\sqrt{1 + y^2}}, \quad y = 0, \quad \text{and} \quad y = 3$$

where x and y are measured in feet. The length of the beam is 20 feet (see figure). The concrete weighs 148 pounds per cubic foot. Find the weight of the beam.

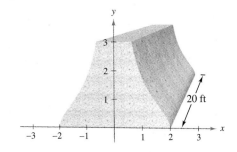

66. 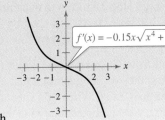 **HOW DO YOU SEE IT?** Use the graph of f' shown in the figure to answer the following.

(a) Approximate the slope of f at $x = -1$. Explain.

(b) Approximate any open intervals on which the graph of f is increasing and any open intervals on which it is decreasing. Explain.

67. Volume Consider the region bounded by the graphs of $y = x\sqrt{16 - x^2}$, $y = 0$, $x = 0$, and $x = 4$. Find the volume of the solid generated by revolving the region about the y-axis.

68. Population A population is growing according to the logistic model

$$N = \dfrac{5000}{1 + e^{4.8 - 1.9t}}$$

where t is the time in days. Find the average population over the interval $[0, 2]$.

Calculus AP® – Exam Preparation Questions

69. Multiple Choice $\displaystyle\int_0^4 \dfrac{x}{\sqrt{3 + 2x}} \, dx =$

(A) $\dfrac{\sqrt{11}}{3} - 2\sqrt{3}$ (B) $\dfrac{\sqrt{11}}{3} + \sqrt{3}$

(C) $\dfrac{14}{3}$ (D) 26

70. Multiple Choice $\displaystyle\int \dfrac{1}{6x^2 - 23x + 7} \, dx =$

(A) $\dfrac{3}{19}\ln|3x - 1| + \dfrac{2}{19}\ln|2x - 7| + C$

(B) $-\dfrac{3}{19}\ln|3x - 1| + \dfrac{2}{19}\ln|2x - 7| + C$

(C) $-\dfrac{1}{19}\ln|3x - 1| + \dfrac{1}{19}\ln|2x - 7| + C$

(D) $-\dfrac{1}{19}\ln|(3x - 1)(2x - 7)| + C$

71. Multiple Choice $\displaystyle\int_0^2 x^2 e^x \, dx =$

(A) $2e^2 - 2$ (B) $2e^2$

(C) $2e^2 + 2$ (D) $6e^2 - 2$

7.7 Indeterminate Forms and L'Hôpital's Rule

▶ Recognize limits that produce indeterminate forms.
▶ Apply L'Hôpital's Rule to evaluate a limit.

Indeterminate Forms

Recall from Chapters 1 and 3 that the forms $0/0$ and ∞/∞ are called *indeterminate* because they do not guarantee that a limit exists, nor do they indicate what the limit is, if one does exist. When you encountered one of these indeterminate forms earlier in the text, you attempted to rewrite the expression by using various algebraic techniques.

Indeterminate Form	Limit	Algebraic Technique
$\dfrac{0}{0}$	$\displaystyle\lim_{x \to -1} \frac{2x^2 - 2}{x + 1} = \lim_{x \to -1} 2(x - 1)$ $= -4$	Divide numerator and denominator by $(x + 1)$.
$\dfrac{\infty}{\infty}$	$\displaystyle\lim_{x \to \infty} \frac{3x^2 - 1}{2x^2 + 1} = \lim_{x \to \infty} \frac{3 - (1/x^2)}{2 + (1/x^2)}$ $= \dfrac{3}{2}$	Divide numerator and denominator by x^2.

Occasionally, you can extend these algebraic techniques to find limits of transcendental functions. For instance, the limit

$$\lim_{x \to 0} \frac{e^{2x} - 1}{e^x - 1}$$

produces the indeterminate form $0/0$. Factoring and then dividing produces

$$\lim_{x \to 0} \frac{e^{2x} - 1}{e^x - 1} = \lim_{x \to 0} \frac{(e^x + 1)(e^x - 1)}{e^x - 1}$$
$$= \lim_{x \to 0} (e^x + 1)$$
$$= 2.$$

Not all indeterminate forms, however, can be evaluated by algebraic manipulation. This is often true when *both* algebraic and transcendental functions are involved. For instance, the limit

$$\lim_{x \to 0} \frac{e^{2x} - 1}{x}$$

produces the indeterminate form $0/0$. Rewriting the expression to obtain

$$\lim_{x \to 0} \left(\frac{e^{2x}}{x} - \frac{1}{x} \right)$$

merely produces another indeterminate form, $\infty - \infty$. Of course, you could use technology to estimate the limit, as shown in the table and in Figure 7.11. From the table and the graph, the limit appears to be 2. (This limit will be verified in Example 1.)

x	-1	-0.1	-0.01	-0.001	0	0.001	0.01	0.1	1
$\dfrac{e^{2x} - 1}{x}$	0.865	1.813	1.980	1.998	?	2.002	2.020	2.214	6.389

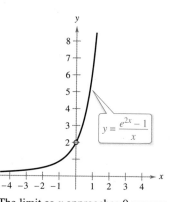

The limit as x approaches 0 appears to be 2.

Figure 7.11

L'Hôpital's Rule

To find the limit illustrated in Figure 7.11, you can use a theorem called **L'Hôpital's Rule,** named after the French mathematician Guillaume L'Hôpital (1661–1704). This theorem states that under certain conditions, the limit of the quotient $f(x)/g(x)$ is determined by the limit of the quotient of the derivatives

$$\frac{f'(x)}{g'(x)}.$$

To prove this theorem, you can use a more general result called the **Extended Mean Value Theorem.**

Theorem 7.3   The Extended Mean Value Theorem

If f and g are differentiable on an open interval (a, b) and continuous on $[a, b]$ such that $g'(x) \neq 0$ for any x in (a, b), then there exists a point c in (a, b) such that

$$\frac{f'(c)}{g'(c)} = \frac{f(b) - f(a)}{g(b) - g(a)}.$$

A proof of this theorem is given in Appendix A.

To see why Theorem 7.3 is called the Extended Mean Value Theorem, consider the special case in which $g(x) = x$. For this case, you obtain the "standard" Mean Value Theorem as presented in Section 3.2.

Theorem 7.4   L'Hôpital's Rule

Let f and g be functions that are differentiable on an open interval (a, b) containing c, except possibly at c itself. Assume that $g'(x) \neq 0$ for all x in (a, b), except possibly at c itself. If the limit of $f(x)/g(x)$ as x approaches c produces the indeterminate form $0/0$, then

$$\lim_{x \to c} \frac{f(x)}{g(x)} = \lim_{x \to c} \frac{f'(x)}{g'(x)}$$

provided the limit on the right exists (or is infinite). This result also applies when the limit of $f(x)/g(x)$ as x approaches c produces any one of the indeterminate forms ∞/∞, $(-\infty)/\infty$, $\infty/(-\infty)$, or $(-\infty)/(-\infty)$.

A proof of this theorem is given in Appendix A.

> **Insight**
>
> Indeterminate forms and L'Hôpital's Rule are tested on both versions of the AP® Exam. Note that only two indeterminate forms, $0/0$ and ∞/∞, will be assessed on the exam.

People occasionally use L'Hôpital's Rule incorrectly by applying the Quotient Rule to $f(x)/g(x)$. Be sure you see that the rule involves

$$\frac{f'(x)}{g'(x)}$$

not the derivative of $f(x)/g(x)$.

L'Hôpital's Rule can also be applied to one-sided limits. For instance, if the limit of $f(x)/g(x)$ as x approaches c *from the right* produces the indeterminate form $0/0$, then

$$\lim_{x \to c^+} \frac{f(x)}{g(x)} = \lim_{x \to c^+} \frac{f'(x)}{g'(x)}$$

provided the limit exists (or is infinite).

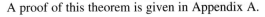

EXAMPLE 1 Indeterminate Form 0/0

Evaluate $\lim\limits_{x \to 0} \dfrac{e^{2x} - 1}{x}$.

Solution Because direct substitution results in the indeterminate form 0/0

$$\lim_{x \to 0} \frac{e^{2x} - 1}{x} \quad \begin{array}{l} \nearrow \ \lim\limits_{x \to 0} (e^{2x} - 1) = 0 \\[2ex] \searrow \ \lim\limits_{x \to 0} x = 0 \end{array}$$

you can apply L'Hôpital's Rule, as shown below.

$$\lim_{x \to 0} \frac{e^{2x} - 1}{x} = \lim_{x \to 0} \frac{\dfrac{d}{dx}[e^{2x} - 1]}{\dfrac{d}{dx}[x]} \qquad \text{Apply L'Hôpital's Rule.}$$

$$= \lim_{x \to 0} \frac{2e^{2x}}{1} \qquad \text{Differentiate numerator and denominator.}$$

$$= 2 \qquad \text{Evaluate the limit.}$$

In the solution to Example 1, note that you actually do not know that the first limit is equal to the second limit until you have shown that the second limit exists. In other words, if the second limit had not existed, then it would not have been permissible to apply L'Hôpital's Rule.

Another form of L'Hôpital's Rule states that if the limit of $f(x)/g(x)$ as x approaches ∞ (or $-\infty$) produces the indeterminate form $0/0$ or ∞/∞, then

$$\lim_{x \to \infty} \frac{f(x)}{g(x)} = \lim_{x \to \infty} \frac{f'(x)}{g'(x)}$$

provided the limit on the right exists.

EXAMPLE 2 Indeterminate Form ∞/∞

Evaluate $\lim\limits_{x \to \infty} \dfrac{\ln x}{x}$.

Solution Because direct substitution results in the indeterminate form ∞/∞, you can apply L'Hôpital's Rule to obtain

$$\lim_{x \to \infty} \frac{\ln x}{x} = \lim_{x \to \infty} \frac{\dfrac{d}{dx}[\ln x]}{\dfrac{d}{dx}[x]} \qquad \text{Apply L'Hôpital's Rule.}$$

$$= \lim_{x \to \infty} \frac{1}{x} \qquad \text{Differentiate numerator and denominator.}$$

$$= 0. \qquad \text{Evaluate the limit.}$$

Exploration

Numerical and Graphical Approaches Use a numerical or a graphical approach to approximate each limit.

a. $\lim\limits_{x \to 0} \dfrac{2^{2x} - 1}{x}$

b. $\lim\limits_{x \to 0} \dfrac{3^{2x} - 1}{x}$

c. $\lim\limits_{x \to 0} \dfrac{4^{2x} - 1}{x}$

d. $\lim\limits_{x \to 0} \dfrac{5^{2x} - 1}{x}$

What pattern do you observe? Does an analytic approach have an advantage for determining these limits? If so, explain your reasoning.

Technology

Use a graphing utility to graph $y_1 = \ln x$ and $y_2 = x$ in the same viewing window. Which function grows faster as x approaches ∞? How is this observation related to Example 2?

Occasionally it is necessary to apply L'Hôpital's Rule more than once to remove an indeterminate form, as shown in Example 3.

EXAMPLE 3   Applying L'Hôpital's Rule More than Once

Evaluate $\displaystyle\lim_{x\to-\infty}\frac{x^2}{e^{-x}}$.

Solution

Because direct substitution results in the indeterminate form ∞/∞, you can apply L'Hôpital's Rule.

$$\lim_{x\to-\infty}\frac{x^2}{e^{-x}}=\lim_{x\to-\infty}\frac{\dfrac{d}{dx}[x^2]}{\dfrac{d}{dx}[e^{-x}]}=\lim_{x\to-\infty}\frac{2x}{-e^{-x}}$$

This limit yields the indeterminate form $(-\infty)/(-\infty)$, so you can apply L'Hôpital's Rule again to obtain

$$\lim_{x\to-\infty}\frac{2x}{-e^{-x}}=\lim_{x\to-\infty}\frac{\dfrac{d}{dx}[2x]}{\dfrac{d}{dx}[-e^{-x}]}=\lim_{x\to-\infty}\frac{2}{e^{-x}}=0.$$

In addition to the forms $0/0$ and ∞/∞, there are other indeterminate forms such as $0\cdot\infty$, 1^∞, ∞^0, 0^0, and $\infty-\infty$. For example, consider the following four limits that lead to the indeterminate form $0\cdot\infty$.

$$\underbrace{\lim_{x\to0}\left(\frac{1}{x}\right)(x),}_{\text{Limit is 1.}}\qquad\underbrace{\lim_{x\to0}\left(\frac{2}{x}\right)(x),}_{\text{Limit is 2.}}\qquad\underbrace{\lim_{x\to\infty}\left(\frac{1}{e^x}\right)(x),}_{\text{Limit is 0.}}\qquad\underbrace{\lim_{x\to\infty}\left(\frac{1}{x}\right)(e^x)}_{\text{Limit is }\infty.}$$

Because each limit is different, it is clear that the form $0\cdot\infty$ is indeterminate in the sense that it does not determine the value (or even the existence) of the limit. The remaining examples in this section show methods for evaluating these forms. Basically, you attempt to convert each of these forms to $0/0$ or ∞/∞ so that L'Hôpital's Rule can be applied.

EXAMPLE 4   Indeterminate Form $0\cdot\infty$

Evaluate $\displaystyle\lim_{x\to\infty}e^{-x}\sqrt{x}$.

Algebraic Solution

Because direct substitution produces the indeterminate form $0\cdot\infty$, you should try to rewrite the limit to fit the form $0/0$ or ∞/∞. In this case, you can rewrite the limit to fit the second form.

$$\lim_{x\to\infty}e^{-x}\sqrt{x}=\lim_{x\to\infty}\frac{\sqrt{x}}{e^x}$$

Now, by L'Hôpital's Rule, you have

$$\lim_{x\to\infty}\frac{\sqrt{x}}{e^x}=\lim_{x\to\infty}\frac{1/(2\sqrt{x})}{e^x}\qquad\text{Differentiate numerator and denominator.}$$

$$=\lim_{x\to\infty}\frac{1}{2\sqrt{x}e^x}\qquad\text{Simplify.}$$

$$=0.\qquad\text{Evaluate the limit.}$$

Numerical Solution

Enter $y_1=e^{-x}\sqrt{x}$.

Use the *table* feature (in *ask* mode) to evaluate y_1 for increasing values of x.

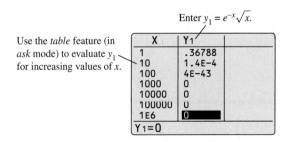

X	Y1
1	.36788
10	1.4E-4
100	4E-43
1000	0
10000	0
100000	0
1E6	0

Y1=0

From the table, it seems reasonable to conclude that

$$\lim_{x\to\infty}e^{-x}\sqrt{x}=0.$$

When rewriting a limit in one of the forms $0/0$ or ∞/∞ does not seem to work, try the other form. For instance, in Example 4, you can write the limit as

$$\lim_{x\to\infty} e^{-x}\sqrt{x} = \lim_{x\to\infty} \frac{e^{-x}}{x^{-1/2}}$$

which yields the indeterminate form $0/0$. As it happens, applying L'Hôpital's Rule to this limit produces

$$\lim_{x\to\infty} \frac{e^{-x}}{x^{-1/2}} = \lim_{x\to\infty} \frac{-e^{-x}}{-1/(2x^{3/2})}$$

which also yields the indeterminate form $0/0$.

The indeterminate forms 1^{∞}, ∞^0, and 0^0 arise from limits of functions that have variable bases and variable exponents. When you previously encountered this type of function, you used logarithmic differentiation to find the derivative. You can use a similar procedure when taking limits, as shown in the next example.

EXAMPLE 5   Indeterminate Form 1^{∞}

Evaluate $\displaystyle\lim_{x\to\infty} \left(1 + \frac{1}{x}\right)^x$.

Solution

Because direct substitution yields the indeterminate form 1^{∞}, you can proceed as follows. To begin, assume that the limit exists and is equal to y.

$$y = \lim_{x\to\infty} \left(1 + \frac{1}{x}\right)^x$$

Taking the natural logarithm of each side produces

$$\ln y = \ln\left[\lim_{x\to\infty} \left(1 + \frac{1}{x}\right)^x\right].$$

Because the natural logarithmic function is continuous, you can write

$$\ln y = \lim_{x\to\infty}\left[x \ln\left(1 + \frac{1}{x}\right)\right] \qquad \text{Indeterminate form } \infty \cdot 0$$

$$= \lim_{x\to\infty}\left(\frac{\ln[1 + (1/x)]}{1/x}\right) \qquad \text{Indeterminate form } 0/0$$

$$= \lim_{x\to\infty}\left(\frac{(-1/x^2)\{1/[1 + (1/x)]\}}{-1/x^2}\right) \qquad \text{L'Hôpital's Rule}$$

$$= \lim_{x\to\infty} \frac{1}{1 + (1/x)}$$

$$= 1.$$

Now, because you have shown that

$$\ln y = 1$$

you can conclude that

$$y = e$$

and obtain

$$\lim_{x\to\infty} \left(1 + \frac{1}{x}\right)^x = e.$$

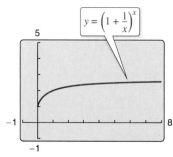

You can use a graphing utility to support this result, as shown at the right.

The limit of $[1 + (1/x)]^x$ as x approaches infinity is e.

L'Hôpital's Rule can also be applied to one-sided limits, as demonstrated in Examples 6 and 7.

EXAMPLE 6   Indeterminate Form 0^0

See LarsonCalculusforAP.com for an interactive version of this type of example.

Evaluate $\lim\limits_{x \to 0^+} (\sin x)^x$.

Solution   Because direct substitution produces the indeterminate form 0^0, you can proceed as shown below. To begin, assume that the limit exists and is equal to y.

$$y = \lim_{x \to 0^+} (\sin x)^x \qquad \text{Indeterminate form } 0^0$$

$$\ln y = \ln \left[\lim_{x \to 0^+} (\sin x)^x \right] \qquad \text{Take natural log of each side.}$$

$$= \lim_{x \to 0^+} \left[\ln(\sin x)^x \right] \qquad \text{Continuity}$$

$$= \lim_{x \to 0^+} \left[x \ln(\sin x) \right] \qquad \text{Indeterminate form } 0 \cdot (-\infty)$$

$$= \lim_{x \to 0^+} \frac{\ln(\sin x)}{1/x} \qquad \text{Indeterminate form } -\infty/\infty$$

$$= \lim_{x \to 0^+} \frac{\cot x}{-1/x^2} \qquad \text{L'Hôpital's Rule}$$

$$= \lim_{x \to 0^+} \frac{-x^2}{\tan x} \qquad \text{Indeterminate form } 0/0$$

$$= \lim_{x \to 0^+} \frac{-2x}{\sec^2 x} \qquad \text{L'Hôpital's Rule}$$

$$= 0$$

Now, because $\ln y = 0$, you can conclude that $y = e^0 = 1$, and it follows that

$$\lim_{x \to 0^+} (\sin x)^x = 1.$$

Technology

When evaluating complicated limits such as the one in Example 6, it is helpful to check the reasonableness of the solution with a graphing utility. For instance, the calculations in the table and the graph in the figure (see below) are consistent with the conclusion that $(\sin x)^x$ approaches 1 as x approaches 0 from the right.

x	1	0.1	0.01	0.001	0.0001	0.00001
$(\sin x)^x$	0.8415	0.7942	0.9550	0.9931	0.9991	0.9999

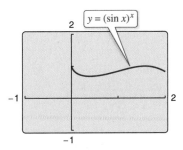

The limit of $(\sin x)^x$ is 1 as x approaches 0 from the right.

Use a graphing utility to estimate the limits $\lim\limits_{x \to 0} (1 - \cos x)^x$ and $\lim\limits_{x \to 0^+} (\tan x)^x$. Then try to verify your estimates analytically.

EXAMPLE 7 Indeterminate Form $\infty - \infty$

Evaluate $\displaystyle\lim_{x \to 1^+} \left(\frac{1}{\ln x} - \frac{1}{x - 1} \right)$.

Solution

Because direct substitution yields the indeterminate form $\infty - \infty$, you should try to rewrite the expression to produce a form to which you can apply L'Hôpital's Rule. In this case, you can combine the two fractions to obtain

$$\lim_{x \to 1^+} \left(\frac{1}{\ln x} - \frac{1}{x - 1} \right) = \lim_{x \to 1^+} \frac{x - 1 - \ln x}{(x - 1) \ln x}.$$

Now, because direct substitution produces the indeterminate form $0/0$, you can apply L'Hôpital's Rule to obtain

$$\lim_{x \to 1^+} \frac{x - 1 - \ln x}{(x - 1) \ln x} = \lim_{x \to 1^+} \frac{(d/dx)[x - 1 - \ln x]}{(d/dx)[(x - 1) \ln x]}$$

$$= \lim_{x \to 1^+} \frac{1 - (1/x)}{(x - 1)(1/x) + \ln x}$$

$$= \lim_{x \to 1^+} \frac{x - 1}{x - 1 + x \ln x}.$$

This limit also yields the indeterminate form $0/0$, so you can apply L'Hôpital's Rule again to obtain

$$\lim_{x \to 1^+} \frac{x - 1}{x - 1 + x \ln x} = \lim_{x \to 1^+} \frac{1}{1 + x(1/x) + \ln x} = \frac{1}{2}.$$

Use a graphing utility to check the reasonableness of this solution by estimating the original limit (see Figure 7.12).

X	Y₁
2	.4427
1.5	.4663
1.25	.48142
1.1	.49206
1.01	.49917
1.001	.49992
1.0001	.49999

Y₁=.499991667

Use the *table* feature in *ask* mode to evaluate $y_1 = 1/(\ln x) - 1/(x - 1)$ as x gets closer to 1 from the right.
Figure 7.12

The forms $0/0$, ∞/∞, $\infty - \infty$, $0 \cdot \infty$, 0^0, 1^∞, and ∞^0 have been identified as *indeterminate*. There are similar forms that you should recognize as "determinate."

$\infty + \infty \to \infty$	Limit is positive infinity.
$-\infty - \infty \to -\infty$	Limit is negative infinity.
$0^\infty \to 0$	Limit is zero.
$0^{-\infty} \to \infty$	Limit is positive infinity.

As a final comment, remember that L'Hôpital's Rule can be applied only to quotients leading to the indeterminate forms $0/0$ and ∞/∞. For instance, the application of L'Hôpital's Rule shown below is *incorrect*.

$$\lim_{x \to 0} \frac{e^x}{x} \overset{?}{=} \lim_{x \to 0} \frac{e^x}{1} = 1 \qquad \text{Incorrect use of L'Hôpital's Rule}$$

The reason this application is incorrect is that, even though the limit of the denominator is 0, the limit of the numerator is 1, which means that the hypotheses of L'Hôpital's Rule have not been satisfied.

> **Justification**
>
> You are asked to verify that 0^∞ and $0^{-\infty}$ are "determinate" in Exercises 107 and 108, respectively.

> **Exploration**
>
> In each of the examples presented in this section, L'Hôpital's Rule is used to find a limit that exists. It can also be used to conclude that a limit is infinite. For instance, try using L'Hôpital's Rule to show that $\displaystyle\lim_{x \to \infty} e^x/x = \infty$.

7.7   Exercises

See *CalcChat.com* for tutorial help and worked-out solutions to odd-numbered exercises.

Numerical and Graphical Analysis   In Exercises 1–4, complete the table and use the result to estimate the limit. Use a graphing utility to graph the function to support your result.

1. $\lim\limits_{x \to 0} \dfrac{\sin 4x}{\sin 3x}$

x	-0.1	-0.01	-0.001	0.001	0.01	0.1
$f(x)$						

2. $\lim\limits_{x \to 0} \dfrac{1 - e^x}{x}$

x	-0.1	-0.01	-0.001	0.001	0.01	0.1
$f(x)$						

3. $\lim\limits_{x \to \infty} x^5 e^{-x/100}$

x	1	10	10^2	10^3	10^4	10^5
$f(x)$						

4. $\lim\limits_{x \to \infty} \dfrac{6x}{\sqrt{3x^2 - 2x}}$

x	1	10	10^2	10^3	10^4	10^5
$f(x)$						

 Using Two Methods   In Exercises 5–12, evaluate the limit (a) using techniques from Chapter 1 and (b) using L'Hôpital's Rule.

5. $\lim\limits_{x \to 4} \dfrac{3(x - 4)}{x^2 - 16}$

6. $\lim\limits_{x \to -4} \dfrac{2x^2 + 13x + 20}{x + 4}$

7. $\lim\limits_{x \to 6} \dfrac{\sqrt{x + 10} - 4}{x - 6}$

8. $\lim\limits_{x \to -1} \dfrac{1 - \sqrt{x + 2}}{x + 1}$

9. $\lim\limits_{x \to 0} \dfrac{2 - 2\cos x}{6x}$

10. $\lim\limits_{x \to 0} \dfrac{\sin 6x}{4x}$

11. $\lim\limits_{x \to \infty} \dfrac{5x^2 - 3x + 1}{3x^2 - 5}$

12. $\lim\limits_{x \to \infty} \dfrac{x^4 - 3}{1 - 5x^2}$

 Evaluating a Limit   In Exercises 13–44, evaluate the limit, using L'Hôpital's Rule if necessary.

13. $\lim\limits_{x \to 0} \dfrac{\sqrt{25 - x^2} - 5}{x}$

14. $\lim\limits_{x \to 5^-} \dfrac{\sqrt{25 - x^2}}{x - 5}$

15. $\lim\limits_{x \to 0^+} \dfrac{e^x - (1 + x)}{x^3}$

16. $\lim\limits_{x \to 1} \dfrac{\ln x^a}{x^b - 1}, \ a, b \neq 0$

17. $\lim\limits_{x \to 1} \dfrac{x^{11} + x^{3/2} - 2}{x^2 - 1}$

18. $\lim\limits_{x \to 1} \dfrac{x^a - 1}{x^b - 1}, \ a, b \neq 0$

19. $\lim\limits_{x \to 0} \dfrac{\sin 3x}{\sin 5x}$

20. $\lim\limits_{x \to 0} \dfrac{\sin ax}{\sin bx}, \ a, b \neq 0$

21. $\lim\limits_{x \to \infty} \dfrac{7x^3 - 2x + 1}{6x^3 + 1}$

22. $\lim\limits_{x \to \infty} \dfrac{8 - x}{x^3}$

23. $\lim\limits_{x \to 4} \dfrac{\sqrt{x} - 2}{4 - x}$

24. $\lim\limits_{x \to 4} \dfrac{\sqrt{x^5} - 8x}{x - 2\sqrt{x}}$

25. $\lim\limits_{x \to \infty} \dfrac{x^2 + 4x + 7}{x - 6}$

26. $\lim\limits_{x \to \infty} \dfrac{x^3}{x + 2}$

27. $\lim\limits_{x \to \infty} \dfrac{x^3}{e^{x/2}}$

28. $\lim\limits_{x \to \infty} \dfrac{x^a}{e^x}, \ a > 0$

29. $\lim\limits_{x \to \infty} \dfrac{x}{\sqrt{x^2 + 1}}$

30. $\lim\limits_{x \to \infty} \dfrac{x^2}{\sqrt{x^2 + 1}}$

31. $\lim\limits_{x \to -\infty} \dfrac{7x - 1}{\sqrt{x^2 + 2}}$

32. $\lim\limits_{x \to -\infty} \dfrac{3 - x^2}{\sqrt{x^2 + 9}}$

33. $\lim\limits_{x \to \infty} \dfrac{\cos x}{x}$

34. $\lim\limits_{x \to \infty} \dfrac{\sin x}{x - \pi}$

35. $\lim\limits_{x \to \infty} \dfrac{\ln x}{x^2}$

36. $\lim\limits_{x \to \infty} \dfrac{\ln x^4}{x^3}$

37. $\lim\limits_{x \to \infty} \dfrac{e^x}{x^4}$

38. $\lim\limits_{x \to \infty} \dfrac{e^{x-2}}{x^a}, \ a > 0$

39. $\lim\limits_{x \to 0} \dfrac{\sin 5x}{\tan 9x}$

40. $\lim\limits_{x \to 1} \dfrac{\ln x}{\sin \pi x}$

41. $\lim\limits_{x \to (\pi/2)^-} (\cos x) \ln\left(\dfrac{\pi}{2} - x\right)$

42. $\lim\limits_{x \to 0^+} (\sin x) \ln x$

43. $\lim\limits_{x \to \infty} \dfrac{\int_1^x \ln(e^{4t - 1})\, dt}{x}$

44. $\lim\limits_{x \to 1^+} \dfrac{\int_1^x \cos \theta \, d\theta}{x - 1}$

 Evaluating a Limit   In Exercises 45–62, (a) describe the type of indeterminate form (if any) that is obtained by direct substitution. (b) Evaluate the limit, using L'Hôpital's Rule if necessary. (c) Use a graphing utility to graph the function and verify the result in part (b).

45. $\lim\limits_{x \to \infty} x \ln x$

46. $\lim\limits_{x \to 0^+} x^3 \cot x$

47. $\lim\limits_{x \to \infty} \left(x \sin \dfrac{1}{x}\right)$

48. $\lim\limits_{x \to \infty} \left(x \tan \dfrac{1}{x}\right)$

49. $\lim\limits_{x \to 0^+} x^{1/x}$

50. $\lim\limits_{x \to 0^+} \left(1 + \dfrac{1}{x}\right)^x$

51. $\lim\limits_{x \to \infty} x^{1/x}$

52. $\lim\limits_{x \to 0^+} (e^x + x)^{2/x}$

53. $\lim\limits_{x \to 0^+} (1 + x)^{1/x}$

54. $\lim\limits_{x \to \infty} (1 + x)^{1/x}$

55. $\lim\limits_{x \to 0^+} [3(x)^{x/2}]$

56. $\lim\limits_{x \to 4^+} [3(x - 4)]^{x - 4}$

57. $\lim\limits_{x \to 1^+} (\ln x)^{x - 1}$

58. $\lim\limits_{x \to 0^+} \left[\cos\left(\dfrac{\pi}{2} - x\right)\right]^x$

59. $\lim\limits_{x \to 4} \left(\dfrac{x - 2}{x - 4} - \dfrac{16}{x^2 - 16}\right)$

60. $\lim\limits_{x \to 1} \left(\dfrac{x + 1}{x - 1} - \dfrac{4x}{x^2 - 1}\right)$

61. $\lim\limits_{x \to 1^+} \left(\dfrac{3}{\ln x} - \dfrac{2}{x - 1}\right)$

62. $\lim\limits_{x \to 0^+} \left(\dfrac{10}{x} - \dfrac{3}{x^2}\right)$

EXPLORING CONCEPTS

63. Finding Functions Find differentiable functions f and g that satisfy the specified condition such that

$$\lim_{x \to 5} f(x) = 0 \quad \text{and} \quad \lim_{x \to 5} g(x) = 0.$$

Explain how you obtained your answers. (*Note:* There are many correct answers.)

(a) $\displaystyle\lim_{x \to 5} \frac{f(x)}{g(x)} = 10$ 　　(b) $\displaystyle\lim_{x \to 5} \frac{f(x)}{g(x)} = 0$

(c) $\displaystyle\lim_{x \to 5} \frac{f(x)}{g(x)} = \infty$

64. Finding Functions Find differentiable functions f and g such that

$$\lim_{x \to \infty} f(x) = \lim_{x \to \infty} g(x) = \infty$$

and

$$\lim_{x \to \infty} [f(x) - g(x)] = 25.$$

Explain how you obtained your answers. (*Note:* There are many correct answers.)

65. Justifying Determine which of the following limits can be evaluated using L'Hôpital's Rule. Explain your reasoning. Do not evaluate the limit.

(a) $\displaystyle\lim_{x \to 2} \frac{x - 2}{x^3 - x - 6}$ 　　(b) $\displaystyle\lim_{x \to 0} \frac{x^2 - 4x}{2x - 1}$

(c) $\displaystyle\lim_{x \to \infty} \frac{x^3}{e^x}$ 　　(d) $\displaystyle\lim_{x \to 3} \frac{e^{x^2} - e^9}{x - 3}$

(e) $\displaystyle\lim_{x \to 1} \frac{\cos \pi x}{\ln x}$ 　　(f) $\displaystyle\lim_{x \to 1} \frac{1 + x(\ln x - 1)}{(x - 1)\ln x}$

66. HOW DO YOU SEE IT? Use the graph of f to find the limit.

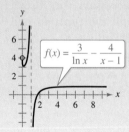

$$f(x) = \frac{3}{\ln x} - \frac{4}{x - 1}$$

(a) $\displaystyle\lim_{x \to 1^-} f(x)$ 　　(b) $\displaystyle\lim_{x \to 1^+} f(x)$ 　　(c) $\displaystyle\lim_{x \to 1} f(x)$

67. Numerical Analysis Complete the table to show that x eventually "overpowers" $(\ln x)^4$.

x	10	10^2	10^4	10^6	10^8	10^{10}
$\dfrac{(\ln x)^4}{x}$						

68. Numerical Analysis Complete the table to show that e^x eventually "overpowers" x^5.

x	1	5	10	20	30	40	50	100
$\dfrac{e^x}{x^5}$								

Connecting Representations In Exercises 69–74, use L'Hôpital's Rule to determine the comparative rates of increase of the functions $f(x) = x^m$, $g(x) = e^{nx}$, and $h(x) = (\ln x)^n$, where $n > 0$, $m > 0$, and $x \to \infty$.

69. $\displaystyle\lim_{x \to \infty} \frac{x^2}{e^{5x}}$ 　　**70.** $\displaystyle\lim_{x \to \infty} \frac{x^3}{e^{2x}}$

71. $\displaystyle\lim_{x \to \infty} \frac{(\ln x)^3}{x}$ 　　**72.** $\displaystyle\lim_{x \to \infty} \frac{(\ln x)^2}{x^3}$

73. $\displaystyle\lim_{x \to \infty} \frac{(\ln x)^n}{x^m}$ 　　**74.** $\displaystyle\lim_{x \to \infty} \frac{x^m}{e^{nx}}$

Asymptotes and Relative Extrema In Exercises 75–78, find any asymptotes and relative extrema that may exist and use a graphing utility to graph the function.

75. $y = x^{1/x}, \quad x > 0$

76. $y = x^x, \quad x > 0$

77. $y = 2xe^{-x}$

78. $y = \dfrac{\ln x}{x}$

Error Analysis In Exercises 79 and 80, L'Hôpital's Rule is used incorrectly. Describe and correct the error in finding the limit.

79. $\displaystyle\lim_{x \to \infty} \frac{e^{-x}}{1 + e^{-x}} = \lim_{x \to \infty} \frac{-e^{-x}}{-e^{-x}}$

$$= \lim_{x \to \infty} 1$$

$$= 1 \qquad ✗$$

80. $\displaystyle\lim_{x \to \infty} x \cos \frac{1}{x} = \lim_{x \to \infty} \frac{\cos(1/x)}{1/x}$

$$= \lim_{x \to \infty} \frac{[-\sin(1/x)](1/x^2)}{-1/x^2}$$

$$= \lim_{x \to \infty} \sin \frac{1}{x}$$

$$= 0 \qquad ✗$$

Connecting Representations In Exercises 81 and 82, (a) explain why L'Hôpital's Rule cannot be used to find the limit, (b) find the limit analytically, and (c) use a graphing utility to graph the function and approximate the limit from the graph. Compare the result with that in part (b).

81. $\displaystyle\lim_{x \to \infty} \frac{x}{\sqrt{x^2 + 1}}$ 　　**82.** $\displaystyle\lim_{x \to (\pi/2)^-} \frac{\tan x}{\sec x}$

Connecting Representations   In Exercises 83 and 84, graph $f(x)/g(x)$ and $f'(x)/g'(x)$ near $x = 0$. What do you notice about these ratios as $x \to 0$? How does this illustrate L'Hôpital's Rule?

83. $f(x) = \sin 3x$, $g(x) = \sin 4x$

84. $f(x) = e^{3x} - 1$, $g(x) = x$

85. Velocity in a Resisting Medium   The velocity v of an object falling through a resisting medium such as air or water is given by

$$v = \frac{32}{k}\left(1 - e^{-kt} + \frac{v_0 k e^{-kt}}{32}\right)$$

where v_0 is the initial velocity, t is the time in seconds, and k is the resistance constant of the medium. Use L'Hôpital's Rule to find the formula for the velocity of a falling body in a vacuum by fixing v_0 and t and letting k approach zero. (Assume that the downward direction is positive.)

86. Electric Circuit   The diagram shows a simple electric circuit consisting of a power source, a resistor, and an inductor. If voltage V is first applied at time $t = 0$, then the current I flowing through the circuit at time t is given by

$$I = \frac{V}{R}(1 - e^{-Rt/L})$$

where L is the inductance and R is the resistance. Use L'Hôpital's Rule to find the formula for the currents by fixing V and L and letting R approach 0 from the right.

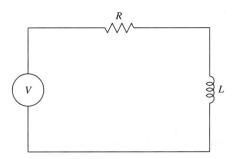

87. The Gamma Function   The Gamma Function $\Gamma(n)$ is defined in terms of the integral of the function given by $f(x) = x^{n-1}e^{-x}$, $n > 0$. Show that for any fixed value of n, the limit of $f(x)$ as x approaches infinity is zero.

88. Compound Interest   The formula for the amount A in a savings account compounded n times per year for t years at an interest rate r and an initial deposit of P is given by

$$A = P\left(1 + \frac{r}{n}\right)^{nt}.$$

Use L'Hôpital's Rule to show that the limiting formula as the number of compoundings per year approaches infinity is given by $A = Pe^{rt}$.

Justifying   In Exercises 89–92, verify that the Extended Mean Value Theorem can be applied to the functions f and g on the closed interval $[a, b]$. Then find all values c in the open interval (a, b) such that

$$\frac{f'(c)}{g'(c)} = \frac{f(b) - f(a)}{g(b) - g(a)}.$$

	Functions	Interval
89.	$f(x) = x^3$, $g(x) = x^2 + 1$	$[0, 1]$
90.	$f(x) = \dfrac{1}{x}$, $g(x) = x^2 - 4$	$[1, 2]$
91.	$f(x) = \sin x$, $g(x) = \cos x$	$\left[0, \dfrac{\pi}{2}\right]$
92.	$f(x) = \ln x$, $g(x) = x^3$	$[1, 4]$

True or False?   In Exercises 93–98, determine whether the statement is true or false. If it is false, explain why or give an example that shows it is false.

93. A limit of the form $\infty/0$ is indeterminate.

94. A limit of the form $\infty \cdot \infty$ is indeterminate.

95. An indeterminate form does not guarantee the existence of a limit.

96. $\displaystyle\lim_{x \to 0} \frac{x^2 + x + 1}{x} = \lim_{x \to 0} \frac{2x + 1}{1} = 1$

97. If $p(x)$ is a polynomial, then $\displaystyle\lim_{x \to \infty} \frac{p(x)}{e^x} = 0$.

98. If $\displaystyle\lim_{x \to \infty} \frac{f(x)}{g(x)} = 1$, then $\displaystyle\lim_{x \to \infty} [f(x) - g(x)] = 0$.

99. Area   Find the limit, as x approaches 0, of the ratio of the area of the triangle to the total shaded area in the figure.

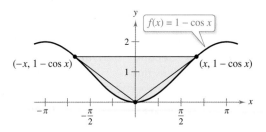

100. Finding a Limit   In Section 1.3, a geometric argument (see figure) was used to prove that

$$\lim_{\theta \to 0} \frac{\sin \theta}{\theta} = 1.$$

(a) Write the area of $\triangle ABD$ in terms of θ.

(b) Write the area of the shaded region in terms of θ.

(c) Write the ratio R of the area of $\triangle ABD$ to that of the shaded region.

(d) Find $\displaystyle\lim_{\theta \to 0} R$.

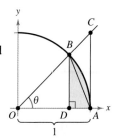

Continuous Function In Exercises 101 and 102, find the value of c that makes the function continuous at $x = 0$.

101. $f(x) = \begin{cases} \dfrac{4x - 2 \sin 2x}{2x^3}, & x \neq 0 \\ c, & x = 0 \end{cases}$

102. $f(x) = \begin{cases} (e^x + x)^{1/x}, & x \neq 0 \\ c, & x = 0 \end{cases}$

103. Finding Values Find the values of a and b such that

$$\lim_{x \to 0} \frac{a - \cos bx}{x^2} = 2.$$

104. Connecting Representations Use a graphing utility to graph

$$f(x) = \frac{x^k - 1}{k}$$

for $k = 1, 0.1,$ and 0.01. Then evaluate the limit

$$\lim_{k \to 0^+} \frac{x^k - 1}{k}.$$

105. Connecting Representations

(a) Let $f'(x)$ be continuous. Show that

$$\lim_{h \to 0} \frac{f(x + h) - f(x - h)}{2h} = f'(x).$$

(b) Explain the result of part (a) graphically.

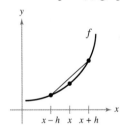

106. Finding a Second Derivative Let $f''(x)$ be continuous. Show that

$$\lim_{h \to 0} \frac{f(x + h) - 2f(x) + f(x - h)}{h^2} = f''(x).$$

107. Proof Prove that if

$$f(x) \geq 0, \quad \lim_{x \to a} f(x) = 0, \quad \text{and} \quad \lim_{x \to a} g(x) = \infty$$

then $\lim_{x \to a} f(x)^{g(x)} = 0.$

108. Proof Prove that if

$$f(x) \geq 0, \quad \lim_{x \to a} f(x) = 0, \quad \text{and} \quad \lim_{x \to a} g(x) = -\infty$$

then $\lim_{x \to a} f(x)^{g(x)} = \infty.$

109. Implementing Processes Use two different methods to find the limit

$$\lim_{x \to \infty} \frac{\ln x^m}{\ln x^n}$$

where $m > 0$, $n > 0$, and $x > 0$.

110. Justifying Show that the indeterminate forms 0^0, ∞^0, and 1^∞ do not always have a value of 1 by evaluating each limit.

(a) $\lim_{x \to 0^+} x^{(\ln 2)/(1 + \ln x)}$

(b) $\lim_{x \to \infty} x^{(\ln 2)/(1 + \ln x)}$

(c) $\lim_{x \to 0} (x + 1)^{(\ln 2)/x}$

111. Connecting Representations Consider the function

$$h(x) = \frac{x + \sin x}{x}.$$

(a) Use a graphing utility to graph the function. Then use the *zoom* and *trace* features to investigate $\lim_{x \to \infty} h(x)$.

(b) Find $\lim_{x \to \infty} h(x)$ analytically by writing

$$h(x) = \frac{x}{x} + \frac{\sin x}{x}.$$

(c) Can you use L'Hôpital's Rule to find $\lim_{x \to \infty} h(x)$? Explain your reasoning.

112. Justifying Let $f(x) = x + x \sin x$ and $g(x) = x^2 - 4$.

(a) Show that $\lim_{x \to \infty} \dfrac{f(x)}{g(x)} = 0.$

(b) Show that $\lim_{x \to \infty} f(x) = \infty$ and $\lim_{x \to \infty} g(x) = \infty.$

(c) Evaluate the limit

$$\lim_{x \to \infty} \frac{f'(x)}{g'(x)}.$$

What do you notice?

(d) Do your answers to parts (a) through (c) contradict L'Hôpital's Rule? Explain your reasoning.

Calculus AP® – Exam Preparation Questions

113. Multiple Choice $\lim_{x \to 0} \dfrac{4e^x - \sin x - 4}{x^2 + 4x}$ is

(A) 0.　　　　　　　(B) $\dfrac{3}{4}$.

(C) 1.　　　　　　　(D) nonexistent.

114. Multiple Choice $\lim_{x \to 0^+} (-x \ln x)$ is

(A) 0.　　　　　　　(B) $\dfrac{1}{2}$.

(C) 1.　　　　　　　(D) nonexistent.

115. Multiple Choice $\lim_{x \to 2} \dfrac{\int_2^x e^{t/2} \, dt}{x^3 - 8}$ is

(A) 0.　　　　　　　(B) $\dfrac{e}{24}$.

(C) $\dfrac{e}{12}$.　　　　　　(D) e.

7.8   Improper Integrals

▶ Evaluate an improper integral that has an infinite limit of integration.
▶ Evaluate an improper integral that has an infinite discontinuity.

Improper Integrals with Infinite Limits of Integration

The definition of a definite integral

$$\int_a^b f(x)\,dx$$

requires that the interval $[a, b]$ be finite. Furthermore, the Fundamental Theorem of Calculus, by which you have been evaluating definite integrals, requires that f be continuous on $[a, b]$. In this section, you will study a procedure for evaluating integrals that do not satisfy these requirements—usually because either one or both of the limits of integration are infinite, or because f has a finite number of infinite discontinuities in the interval $[a, b]$. Integrals that possess either property are **improper integrals.** Note that a function f is said to have an **infinite discontinuity** at c when, *from the right or left,*

$$\lim_{x \to c} f(x) = \infty \quad \text{or} \quad \lim_{x \to c} f(x) = -\infty.$$

To get an idea of how to evaluate an improper integral, consider the integral

$$\int_1^b \frac{dx}{x^2} = -\frac{1}{x}\bigg]_1^b = -\frac{1}{b} + 1 = 1 - \frac{1}{b}$$

which can be interpreted as the area of the shaded region shown in Figure 7.13. Taking the limit as $b \to \infty$ produces

$$\int_1^\infty \frac{dx}{x^2} = \lim_{b \to \infty}\left(\int_1^b \frac{dx}{x^2}\right) = \lim_{b \to \infty}\left(1 - \frac{1}{b}\right) = 1.$$

This improper integral can be interpreted as the area of the *unbounded* region between the graph of $f(x) = 1/x^2$ and the x-axis (to the right of $x = 1$).

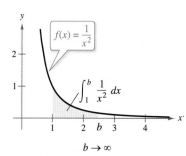

$b \to \infty$

The unbounded region has an area of 1.
Figure 7.13

Definition of Improper Integrals with Infinite Integration Limits

1. If f is continuous on the interval $[a, \infty)$, then

$$\int_a^\infty f(x)\,dx = \lim_{b \to \infty} \int_a^b f(x)\,dx.$$

2. If f is continuous on the interval $(-\infty, b]$, then

$$\int_{-\infty}^b f(x)\,dx = \lim_{a \to -\infty} \int_a^b f(x)\,dx.$$

3. If f is continuous on the interval $(-\infty, \infty)$, then

$$\int_{-\infty}^\infty f(x)\,dx = \int_{-\infty}^c f(x)\,dx + \int_c^\infty f(x)\,dx$$

where c is any real number (see Exercise 93).

In the first two cases, the improper integral **converges** when the limit exists—otherwise, the improper integral **diverges.** In the third case, the improper integral on the left diverges when either of the improper integrals on the right diverges.

Insight

Improper integrals are tested on the AP® Calculus BC Exam.

EXAMPLE 1 An Improper Integral That Diverges

Evaluate $\displaystyle\int_1^\infty \frac{dx}{x}$.

Solution

$$
\begin{aligned}
\int_1^\infty \frac{dx}{x} &= \lim_{b\to\infty} \int_1^b \frac{dx}{x} && \text{Take limit as } b\to\infty. \\
&= \lim_{b\to\infty} \left[\ln x\right]_1^b && \text{Apply Log Rule.} \\
&= \lim_{b\to\infty} (\ln b - 0) && \text{Apply Fundamental Theorem of Calculus.} \\
&= \infty && \text{Evaluate limit.}
\end{aligned}
$$

The limit does not exist. So, you can conclude that the improper integral diverges. See Figure 7.14.

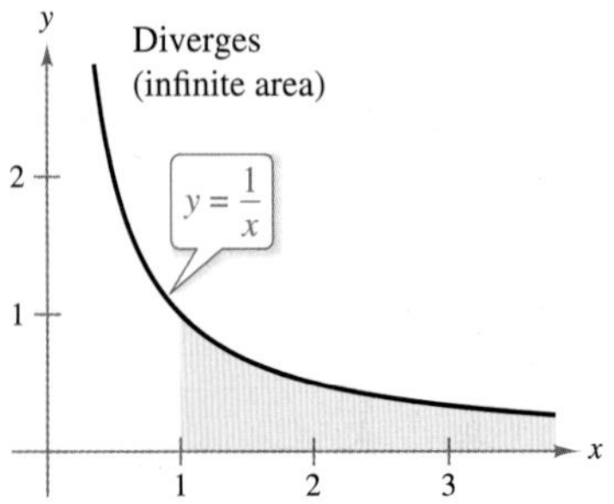

This unbounded region has an infinite area.

Figure 7.14

Try comparing the regions shown in Figures 7.13 and 7.14. They look similar, yet the region in Figure 7.13 has a finite area of 1 and the region in Figure 7.14 has an infinite area.

EXAMPLE 2 Improper Integrals That Converge

Evaluate each improper integral.

a. $\displaystyle\int_0^\infty e^{-x}\, dx$

b. $\displaystyle\int_0^\infty \frac{1}{x^2 + 1}\, dx$

Solution

a.
$$
\begin{aligned}
\int_0^\infty e^{-x}\, dx &= \lim_{b\to\infty} \int_0^b e^{-x}\, dx \\
&= \lim_{b\to\infty} \left[-e^{-x}\right]_0^b \\
&= \lim_{b\to\infty} (-e^{-b} + 1) \\
&= 1
\end{aligned}
$$

See Figure 7.15.

b.
$$
\begin{aligned}
\int_0^\infty \frac{1}{x^2 + 1}\, dx &= \lim_{b\to\infty} \int_0^b \frac{1}{x^2 + 1}\, dx \\
&= \lim_{b\to\infty} \left[\arctan x\right]_0^b \\
&= \lim_{b\to\infty} \arctan b \\
&= \frac{\pi}{2}
\end{aligned}
$$

See Figure 7.16.

Algebra Review

For help on the algebra in Example 2(a), see Example 5 in the *Chapter 7 Algebra Review* on page A49.

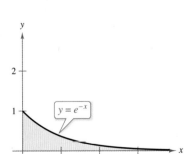

The area of the unbounded region is 1.

Figure 7.15

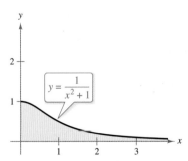

The area of the unbounded region is $\pi/2$.

Figure 7.16

In the next example, note how L'Hôpital's Rule can be used to evaluate an improper integral.

EXAMPLE 3   Using L'Hôpital's Rule with an Improper Integral

Evaluate $\displaystyle\int_{1}^{\infty} (1 - x)e^{-x}\, dx$.

Solution

Use integration by parts, with $dv = e^{-x}\, dx$ and $u = (1 - x)$.

$$\int (1 - x)e^{-x}\, dx = -e^{-x}(1 - x) - \int e^{-x}\, dx$$

$$= -e^{-x} + xe^{-x} + e^{-x} + C$$

$$= xe^{-x} + C$$

Now, apply the definition of an improper integral.

$$\int_{1}^{\infty} (1 - x)e^{-x}\, dx = \lim_{b \to \infty} \left[xe^{-x} \right]_{1}^{b}$$

$$= \lim_{b \to \infty} \left(\frac{b}{e^{b}} - \frac{1}{e} \right)$$

$$= \lim_{b \to \infty} \frac{b}{e^{b}} - \lim_{b \to \infty} \frac{1}{e}$$

For the first limit, use L'Hôpital's Rule.

$$\lim_{b \to \infty} \frac{b}{e^{b}} = \lim_{b \to \infty} \frac{1}{e^{b}} = 0$$

So, you can conclude that

$$\int_{1}^{\infty} (1 - x)e^{-x}\, dx = \lim_{b \to \infty} \frac{b}{e^{b}} - \lim_{b \to \infty} \frac{1}{e}$$

$$= 0 - \frac{1}{e}$$

$$= -\frac{1}{e}. \qquad \text{See Figure 7.17.}$$

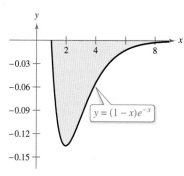

The area of the unbounded region is $|-1/e|$.

Figure 7.17

EXAMPLE 4   Infinite Upper and Lower Limits of Integration

Evaluate $\displaystyle\int_{-\infty}^{\infty} \frac{e^{x}}{1 + e^{2x}}\, dx$.

Solution

Note that the integrand is continuous on $(-\infty, \infty)$. To evaluate the integral, you can break it into two parts, choosing $c = 0$ as a convenient value.

$$\int_{-\infty}^{\infty} \frac{e^{x}}{1 + e^{2x}}\, dx = \int_{-\infty}^{0} \frac{e^{x}}{1 + e^{2x}}\, dx + \int_{0}^{\infty} \frac{e^{x}}{1 + e^{2x}}\, dx$$

$$= \lim_{a \to -\infty} \left[\arctan e^{x} \right]_{a}^{0} + \lim_{b \to \infty} \left[\arctan e^{x} \right]_{0}^{b}$$

$$= \lim_{a \to -\infty} \left(\frac{\pi}{4} - \arctan e^{a} \right) + \lim_{b \to \infty} \left(\arctan e^{b} - \frac{\pi}{4} \right)$$

$$= \frac{\pi}{4} - 0 + \frac{\pi}{2} - \frac{\pi}{4}$$

$$= \frac{\pi}{2} \qquad \text{See Figure 7.18.}$$

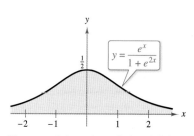

The area of the unbounded region is $\pi/2$.

Figure 7.18

Improper Integrals with Infinite Discontinuities

The second basic type of improper integral is one that has an infinite discontinuity *at or between* the limits of integration.

Definition of Improper Integrals with Infinite Discontinuities

1. If f is continuous on the interval $[a, b)$ and has an infinite discontinuity at b, then
$$\int_a^b f(x)\, dx = \lim_{c \to b^-} \int_a^c f(x)\, dx.$$

2. If f is continuous on the interval $(a, b]$ and has an infinite discontinuity at a, then
$$\int_a^b f(x)\, dx = \lim_{c \to a^+} \int_c^b f(x)\, dx.$$

3. If f is continuous on the interval $[a, b]$, except for some c in (a, b) at which f has an infinite discontinuity, then
$$\int_a^b f(x)\, dx = \int_a^c f(x)\, dx + \int_c^b f(x)\, dx.$$

In the first two cases, the improper integral **converges** when the limit exists—otherwise, the improper integral **diverges**. In the third case, the improper integral on the left diverges when either of the improper integrals on the right diverges.

EXAMPLE 5   An Improper Integral with an Infinite Discontinuity

Evaluate $\displaystyle\int_0^1 \frac{dx}{\sqrt[3]{x}}$.

Solution

The integrand has an infinite discontinuity at $x = 0$, as shown in Figure 7.19. You can evaluate this integral as shown below.

$$\int_0^1 x^{-1/3}\, dx = \lim_{b \to 0^+} \left[\frac{x^{2/3}}{2/3} \right]_b^1 = \lim_{b \to 0^+} \frac{3}{2}(1 - b^{2/3}) = \frac{3}{2}$$

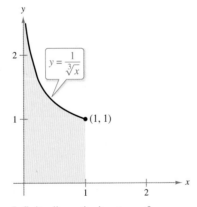

$$y = \frac{1}{\sqrt[3]{x}}$$

$(1, 1)$

Infinite discontinuity at $x = 0$
Figure 7.19

EXAMPLE 6   An Improper Integral That Diverges

Evaluate $\displaystyle\int_0^2 \frac{dx}{x^3}$.

Solution

Because the integrand has an infinite discontinuity at $x = 0$, you can write

$$\int_0^2 \frac{dx}{x^3} = \lim_{b \to 0^+} \left[-\frac{1}{2x^2} \right]_b^2$$

$$= \lim_{b \to 0^+} \left(-\frac{1}{8} + \frac{1}{2b^2} \right)$$

$$= \infty.$$

So, you can conclude that the improper integral diverges.

EXAMPLE 7   An Improper Integral with an Interior Discontinuity

Evaluate $\displaystyle\int_{-1}^2 \frac{dx}{x^3}$.

Solution

This integral is improper because the integrand has an infinite discontinuity at the interior point $x = 0$, as shown in Figure 7.20. So, you can write

$$\int_{-1}^2 \frac{dx}{x^3} = \int_{-1}^0 \frac{dx}{x^3} + \int_0^2 \frac{dx}{x^3}.$$

From Example 6, you know that the second integral diverges. So, the original improper integral also diverges.

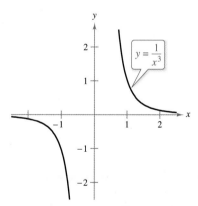

The improper integral $\displaystyle\int_{-1}^2 \frac{dx}{x^3}$ diverges.

Figure 7.20

Remember to check for infinite discontinuities at interior points as well as at endpoints when determining whether an integral is improper. For instance, if you had not recognized that the integral in Example 7 was improper, you would have obtained the *incorrect* result

$$\int_{-1}^2 \frac{dx}{x^3} \overset{?}{=} \left. \frac{-1}{2x^2} \right]_{-1}^2 = -\frac{1}{8} + \frac{1}{2} = \frac{3}{8}. \qquad \text{Incorrect evaluation}$$

The integral in the next example is improper for *two* reasons. One limit of integration is infinite, and the integrand has an infinite discontinuity at the other limit of integration.

EXAMPLE 8 A Doubly Improper Integral

See LarsonCalculusforAP.com for an interactive version of this type of example.

Evaluate $\displaystyle\int_0^\infty \frac{dx}{\sqrt{x}(x+1)}$.

Solution

To evaluate this integral, split it at a convenient point (say, $x = 1$) and write

$$\int_0^\infty \frac{dx}{\sqrt{x}(x+1)} = \int_0^1 \frac{dx}{\sqrt{x}(x+1)} + \int_1^\infty \frac{dx}{\sqrt{x}(x+1)}$$

$$= \lim_{b\to0^+}\left[2\arctan\sqrt{x}\,\right]_b^1 + \lim_{c\to\infty}\left[2\arctan\sqrt{x}\,\right]_1^c$$

$$= \lim_{b\to0^+}\left(2\arctan 1 - 2\arctan\sqrt{b}\right) + \lim_{c\to\infty}\left(2\arctan\sqrt{c} - 2\arctan 1\right)$$

$$= 2\left(\frac{\pi}{4}\right) - 0 + 2\left(\frac{\pi}{2}\right) - 2\left(\frac{\pi}{4}\right)$$

$$= \pi.$$

See Figure 7.21.

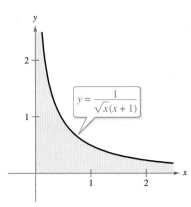

The area of the unbounded region is π.

Figure 7.21

EXAMPLE 9 An Application Involving Arc Length

Use the formula for arc length to show that the circumference of the circle $x^2 + y^2 = 1$ is 2π.

Solution

To simplify the work, consider the quarter circle given by $y = \sqrt{1 - x^2}$, where $0 \le x \le 1$. The function y is differentiable for any x in this interval except $x = 1$. Therefore, the arc length of the quarter circle is given by the improper integral

$$s = \int_0^1 \sqrt{1 + (y')^2}\, dx$$

$$= \int_0^1 \sqrt{1 + \left(\frac{-x}{\sqrt{1-x^2}}\right)^2}\, dx$$

$$= \int_0^1 \frac{dx}{\sqrt{1-x^2}}.$$

This integral is improper because it has an infinite discontinuity at $x = 1$. So, you can write

$$s = \int_0^1 \frac{dx}{\sqrt{1-x^2}}$$

$$= \lim_{b\to1^-}\left[\arcsin x\right]_0^b$$

$$= \lim_{b\to1^-}(\arcsin b - \arcsin 0)$$

$$= \frac{\pi}{2} - 0$$

$$= \frac{\pi}{2}.$$

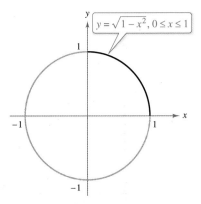

The circumference of the circle is 2π.

Figure 7.22

Finally, multiplying by 4, you can conclude that the circumference of the circle is $4s = 2\pi$, as shown in Figure 7.22.

This section concludes with a useful theorem describing the convergence or divergence of a common type of improper integral. The proof of this theorem is left as an exercise (see Exercise 49).

Theorem 7.5   A Special Type of Improper Integral

$$\int_1^\infty \frac{dx}{x^p} = \begin{cases} \dfrac{1}{p-1}, & p > 1 \\ \text{diverges}, & p \le 1 \end{cases}$$

EXAMPLE 10   An Application Involving a Solid of Revolution

The solid formed by revolving (about the x-axis) the *unbounded* region lying between the graph of $f(x) = 1/x$ and the x-axis $(x \ge 1)$ is called **Gabriel's Horn.** (See Figure 7.23.) Show that this solid has a finite volume and an infinite surface area.

Solution

Using the disk method and Theorem 7.5, you can determine the volume to be

$$V = \pi \int_1^\infty \left(\frac{1}{x}\right)^2 dx \qquad \text{Theorem 7.5, } p = 2 > 1$$

$$= \pi \left(\frac{1}{2-1}\right)$$

$$= \pi.$$

The surface area is given by

$$S = 2\pi \int_1^\infty f(x)\sqrt{1 + [f'(x)]^2}\, dx = 2\pi \int_1^\infty \frac{1}{x}\sqrt{1 + \frac{1}{x^4}}\, dx.$$

Because

$$\sqrt{1 + \frac{1}{x^4}} > 1$$

on the interval $[1, \infty)$, and the improper integral

$$\int_1^\infty \frac{1}{x}\, dx$$

diverges, you can conclude that the improper integral

$$\int_1^\infty \frac{1}{x}\sqrt{1 + \frac{1}{x^4}}\, dx$$

also diverges. (See Exercise 52.) So, the surface area is infinite.

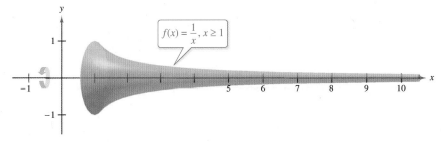

Gabriel's Horn has a finite volume and an infinite surface area.

Figure 7.23

7.8   Exercises

See *CalcChat.com* for tutorial help and worked-out solutions to odd-numbered exercises.

Determining Whether an Integral Is Improper In Exercises 1–8, decide whether the integral is improper. Explain your reasoning.

1. $\int_{-\infty}^{0} e^x \, dx$

2. $\int_{1}^{\infty} \ln \sqrt{x} \, dx$

3. $\int_{-5}^{0} \frac{5-x}{5+x} \, dx$

4. $\int_{0}^{1} \frac{x-1}{\sqrt{x+1}} \, dx$

5. $\int_{0}^{3} \frac{x-2}{x^2-x-2} \, dx$

6. $\int_{-2}^{2} \frac{e^{-x}}{x^2-4} \, dx$

7. $\int_{0}^{\pi} \sin x \, dx$

8. $\int_{-\pi/2}^{0} \tan x \, dx$

Evaluating an Improper Integral In Exercises 9–12, explain why the integral is improper and determine whether it diverges or converges. Evaluate the integral if it converges.

9. $\int_{0}^{4} \frac{1}{\sqrt{x}} \, dx$

10. $\int_{3}^{4} \frac{1}{(x-3)^{3/2}} \, dx$

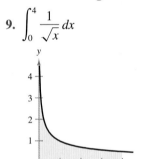

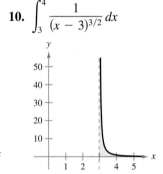

11. $\int_{0}^{2} \frac{1}{(x-1)^2} \, dx$

12. $\int_{-\infty}^{0} e^{3x} \, dx$

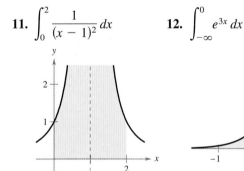

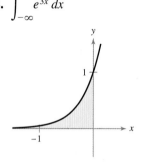

Error Analysis In Exercises 13–16, explain why the evaluation of the integral is *incorrect*. Use the integration capabilities of a graphing utility to attempt to evaluate the integral. Determine whether the utility gives the correct answer.

13. $\int_{-1}^{1} \frac{1}{x^2} \, dx = -2$ ✗

14. $\int_{0}^{1} \frac{1}{x^3} \, dx = -\frac{1}{2}$ ✗

15. $\int_{0}^{\infty} e^{-x} \, dx = 0$ ✗

16. $\int_{0}^{\pi} \sec x \, dx = 0$ ✗

Evaluating an Improper Integral In Exercises 17–32, determine whether the improper integral diverges or converges. Evaluate the integral if it converges.

17. $\int_{1}^{\infty} \frac{1}{x^3} \, dx$

18. $\int_{1}^{\infty} \frac{1}{x^4} \, dx$

19. $\int_{-\infty}^{-1} \frac{1}{2\sqrt[3]{x}} \, dx$

20. $\int_{1}^{\infty} \frac{4}{\sqrt[4]{x}} \, dx$

21. $\int_{0}^{\infty} e^{x/3} \, dx$

22. $\int_{-\infty}^{0} xe^{-4x} \, dx$

23. $\int_{0}^{\infty} x^2 e^{-x} \, dx$

24. $\int_{0}^{\infty} e^{-x} \cos x \, dx$

25. $\int_{4}^{\infty} \frac{1}{x(\ln x)^3} \, dx$

26. $\int_{1}^{\infty} \frac{\ln x}{x} \, dx$

27. $\int_{0}^{\infty} \frac{x^3}{(x^2+1)^2} \, dx$

28. $\int_{-\infty}^{\infty} \frac{4}{16+x^2} \, dx$

29. $\int_{-\infty}^{\infty} \frac{1}{e^x + e^{-x}} \, dx$

30. $\int_{0}^{\infty} \frac{e^x}{1+e^x} \, dx$

31. $\int_{0}^{\infty} \cos \pi x \, dx$

32. $\int_{0}^{\infty} \sin \frac{x}{2} \, dx$

Evaluating an Improper Integral In Exercises 33–48, determine whether the improper integral diverges or converges. Evaluate the integral if it converges, and check your results with the results obtained by using the integration capabilities of a graphing utility.

33. $\int_{0}^{1} \frac{1}{x^2} \, dx$

34. $\int_{0}^{5} \frac{10}{x} \, dx$

35. $\int_{0}^{4} \frac{x}{x^2-4} \, dx$

36. $\int_{0}^{2} \frac{1}{\sqrt[3]{x-1}} \, dx$

37. $\int_{0}^{1} x \ln x \, dx$

38. $\int_{0}^{e} \ln x^2 \, dx$

39. $\int_{0}^{\pi/2} \tan \theta \, d\theta$

40. $\int_{0}^{\pi/2} \sec \theta \, d\theta$

41. $\int_{2}^{4} \frac{2}{x\sqrt{x^2-4}} \, dx$

42. $\int_{3}^{6} \frac{6}{\sqrt{36-x^2}} \, dx$

43. $\int_{3}^{5} \frac{1}{\sqrt{x^2-9}} \, dx$

44. $\int_{0}^{5} \frac{1}{25-x^2} \, dx$

45. $\int_{4}^{\infty} \frac{\sqrt{x^2-16}}{x^2} \, dx$

46. $\int_{3}^{\infty} \frac{1}{x\sqrt{x^2-9}} \, dx$

47. $\int_{0}^{\infty} \frac{4}{\sqrt{x}(x+6)} \, dx$

48. $\int_{1}^{\infty} \frac{1}{x \ln x} \, dx$

Finding Values In Exercises 49 and 50, determine all values of *p* for which the improper integral converges.

49. $\int_{1}^{\infty} \frac{1}{x^p} \, dx$

50. $\int_{0}^{1} \frac{1}{x^p} \, dx$

51. Justifying Use mathematical induction to verify that the following integral converges for any positive integer n.

$$\int_0^\infty x^n e^{-x}\, dx$$

52. Comparison Test for Improper Integrals In some cases, it is impossible to find the exact value of an improper integral, but it is important to determine whether the integral converges or diverges. Suppose the functions f and g are continuous and $0 \le g(x) \le f(x)$ on the interval $[a, \infty)$. It can be shown that if $\int_a^\infty f(x)\, dx$ converges, then $\int_a^\infty g(x)\, dx$ also converges, and if $\int_a^\infty g(x)\, dx$ diverges, then $\int_a^\infty f(x)\, dx$ also diverges. This is called the Comparison Test for improper integrals.

(a) Use the Comparison Test to determine whether $\int_1^\infty e^{-x^2}\, dx$ converges or diverges. (*Hint:* Use the fact that $e^{-x^2} \le e^{-x}$ for $x \ge 1$.)

(b) Use the Comparison Test to determine whether

$$\int_1^\infty \frac{1}{x^5 + 1}\, dx$$

converges or diverges. (*Hint:* Use the fact that

$$\frac{1}{x^5 + 1} \le \frac{1}{x^5}$$

for $x \ge 1$.)

Convergence or Divergence In Exercises 53–62, use the results of Exercises 49–52 to determine whether the improper integral converges or diverges.

53. $\int_0^1 \dfrac{1}{x^5}\, dx$

54. $\int_0^1 \dfrac{1}{\sqrt[5]{x}}\, dx$

55. $\int_1^\infty \dfrac{1}{x^5}\, dx$

56. $\int_0^\infty x^4 e^{-x}\, dx$

57. $\int_1^\infty \dfrac{1}{x^2 + 5}\, dx$

58. $\int_2^\infty \dfrac{1}{\sqrt{x - 1}}\, dx$

59. $\int_2^\infty \dfrac{1}{\sqrt[3]{x(x - 1)}}\, dx$

60. $\int_1^\infty \dfrac{1}{\sqrt{x}(x + 1)}\, dx$

61. $\int_0^\infty \dfrac{x^3}{e^x + x}\, dx$

62. $\int_1^\infty \dfrac{1 - \sin x}{x^2}\, dx$

EXPLORING CONCEPTS

63. Communication and Notation If $\lim\limits_{b \to \infty} \int_1^b f(x)\, dx = a$, where a is a real number, does the improper integral $\int_1^\infty f(x)\, dx$ converge or diverge?

64. Implementing Processes Consider the integral

$$\int_0^3 \frac{10}{x^2 - 2x}\, dx.$$

To determine the convergence or divergence of the integral, how many improper integrals must be analyzed? What must be true of each of these integrals if the given integral converges?

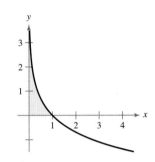

Area In Exercises 65–68, find the area of the unbounded shaded region.

65. $y = -\dfrac{7}{(x - 1)^3}$,

$-\infty < x \le -1$

66. $y = -\ln x$

67. **Witch of Agnesi:**

$y = \dfrac{1}{x^2 + 1}$

68. **Witch of Agnesi:**

$y = \dfrac{8}{x^2 + 4}$

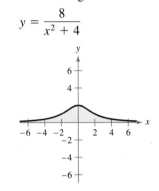

Area and Volume In Exercises 69 and 70, consider the region satisfying the inequalities. If possible, find (a) the area of the region, (b) the volume of the solid generated by revolving the region about the x-axis, and (c) the volume of the solid generated by revolving the region about the y-axis.

69. $y \le e^{-x}$, $y \ge 0$, $x \ge 0$

70. $y \le \dfrac{1}{x^2}$, $y \ge 0$, $x \ge 1$

71. Arc Length Sketch the graph of the hypocycloid of four cusps $x^{2/3} + y^{2/3} = 9$ and find its perimeter.

72. Arc Length Find the arc length of the graph of $y = \sqrt{16 - x^2}$ over the interval $[0, 4]$.

73. Volume Find the volume of the solid generated by revolving the region bounded by the graph of f about the x-axis.

$$f(x) = \begin{cases} x \ln x, & 0 < x \le 2 \\ 0, & x = 0 \end{cases}$$

74. Volume Find the volume of the solid generated by revolving the unbounded region lying between $y = -\ln x$ and the y-axis $(y \ge 0)$ about the x-axis.

Probability A nonnegative function f is called a *probability density function* if $\int_{-\infty}^{\infty} f(t)\, dt = 1$. The probability that x lies between a and b is given by $P(a \le x \le b) = \int_a^b f(t)\, dt$. The expected value of x is given by $E(x) = \int_{-\infty}^{\infty} t f(t)\, dt$. In Exercises 75 and 76, (a) show that the nonnegative function is a probability density function, (b) find $P(0 \le x \le 4)$, and (c) find $E(x)$.

75. $f(t) = \begin{cases} \frac{1}{7} e^{-t/7}, & t \ge 0 \\ 0, & t < 0 \end{cases}$ **76.** $f(t) = \begin{cases} \frac{2}{5} e^{-2t/5}, & t \ge 0 \\ 0, & t < 0 \end{cases}$

Capitalized Cost In Exercises 77 and 78, find the capitalized cost C of an asset (a) for $n = 5$ years, (b) for $n = 10$ years, and (c) forever. The capitalized cost is given by

$$C = C_0 + \int_0^n c(t) e^{-rt}\, dt$$

where C_0 is the original investment, t is the time in years, r is the annual interest rate compounded continuously, and $c(t)$ is the annual cost of maintenance.

77. $C_0 = \$200{,}000$ **78.** $C_0 = \$200{,}000$

     $c(t) = \$10{,}000$ $c(t) = \$10{,}000(1 + 0.08t)$

     $r = 0.04$ $r = 0.04$

79. Electromagnetic Theory The magnetic potential P at a point on the axis of a circular coil is given by

$$P = \frac{2\pi NIr}{k} \int_c^{\infty} \frac{1}{(r^2 + x^2)^{3/2}}\, dx$$

where N, I, r, k, and c are constants. Find P.

80. Gravitational Force A "semi-infinite" uniform rod occupies the nonnegative x-axis. The rod has a linear density δ, which means that a segment of length dx has a mass of $\delta\, dx$. A particle of mass M is located at the point $(-a, 0)$. The gravitational force F that the rod exerts on the mass is given by

$$F = \int_0^{\infty} \frac{GM\delta}{(a + x)^2}\, dx$$

where G is the gravitational constant. Find F.

True or False? In Exercises 81–84, determine whether the statement is true or false. If it is false, explain why or give an example that shows it is false.

81. If f is continuous on $[0, \infty)$ and $\lim_{x \to \infty} f(x) = 0$, then $\int_0^{\infty} f(x)\, dx$ converges.

82. If f is continuous on $[0, \infty)$ and $\int_0^{\infty} f(x)\, dx$ diverges, then $\lim_{x \to \infty} f(x) \ne 0$.

83. If f' is continuous on $[0, \infty)$ and $\lim_{x \to \infty} f(x) = 0$, then $\int_0^{\infty} f'(x)\, dx = -f(0)$.

84. The Comparison Test described in Exercise 52 and Theorem 7.5 imply that $\int_1^{\infty} 1/\left(x^2 - \frac{1}{2}\right) dx$ converges.

85. Justifying

(a) Show that $\int_{-\infty}^{\infty} \sin x\, dx$ diverges.

(b) Show that $\lim_{a \to \infty} \int_{-a}^{a} \sin x\, dx = 0$.

(c) What do parts (a) and (b) show about the definition of improper integrals?

86. Making an Integral Improper For each integral, find a nonnegative real number b that makes the integral improper. Explain your reasoning.

(a) $\int_0^b \frac{1}{x^2 - 9}\, dx$ (b) $\int_0^b \frac{1}{\sqrt{4 - x}}\, dx$

(c) $\int_0^b \frac{x}{x^2 - 7x + 12}\, dx$ (d) $\int_b^{10} \ln x\, dx$

(e) $\int_0^b \tan 2x\, dx$ (f) $\int_0^b \frac{\cos x}{1 - \sin x}\, dx$

Laplace Transforms Let $f(t)$ be a function defined for all positive values of t. The Laplace Transform of $f(t)$ is defined by

$$F(s) = \int_0^{\infty} e^{-st} f(t)\, dt$$

when the improper integral exists. Laplace Transforms are used to solve differential equations. In Exercises 87–92, find the Laplace Transform of the function.

87. $f(t) = 1$ **88.** $f(t) = t$

89. $f(t) = t^2$ **90.** $f(t) = e^{at}$

91. $f(t) = \cos at$ **92.** $f(t) = \sin at$

93. Justifying Let $\int_{-\infty}^{\infty} f(x)\, dx$ be convergent and let a and b be real numbers where $a \ne b$. Show that

$$\int_{-\infty}^{a} f(x)\, dx + \int_a^{\infty} f(x)\, dx = \int_{-\infty}^{b} f(x)\, dx + \int_b^{\infty} f(x)\, dx.$$

94. Connecting Representations Consider the integral

$$\int_0^{\pi/2} \frac{4}{1 + (\tan x)^n}\, dx$$

where n is a positive integer.

(a) Is the integral improper? Explain.

(b) Use a graphing utility to graph the integrand for $n = 2, 4, 8,$ and 12.

(c) Use the graphs to approximate the integral as $n \to \infty$.

(d) Use a computer algebra system to evaluate the integral for the values of n in part (b). Make a conjecture about the value of the integral for any positive integer n. Compare your results with your answer in part (c).

95. NORMAL PROBABILITY

The mean height of American men between 20 and 29 years old is 69 inches, and the standard deviation is 3 inches. A 20- to 29-year-old man is chosen at random from the population. The probability that he is 6 feet tall or taller is

$$P(72 \leq x < \infty) = \int_{72}^{\infty} \frac{1}{3\sqrt{2\pi}} e^{-(x-69)^2/18} \, dx.$$

(Source: National Center for Health Statistics)

(a) Use a graphing utility to graph the integrand and estimate that the area between the x-axis and the integrand is approximately 1.

(b) Use a graphing utility to approximate $P(72 \leq x < \infty)$.

(c) Approximate $0.5 - P(69 \leq x \leq 72)$ using a graphing utility. Use the graph in part (a) to explain why this result is the same as the answer in part (b).

96. HOW DO YOU SEE IT?   The graph shows the probability density function for the gas mileage of a model of car that has a mean fuel efficiency of 26 miles per gallon and a standard deviation of 2.4 miles per gallon.

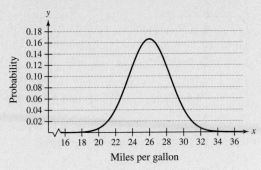

(a) Which is greater, the probability of choosing a car at random that gets between 26 and 28 miles per gallon or the probability of choosing a car at random that gets between 22 and 24 miles per gallon?

(b) Which is greater, the probability of choosing a car at random that gets between 20 and 22 miles per gallon or the probability of choosing a car at random that gets at least 30 miles per gallon?

97. The Gamma Function   The Gamma Function $\Gamma(n)$ is defined by $\Gamma(n) = \int_0^{\infty} x^{n-1}e^{-x} \, dx, \ n > 0.$

(a) Find $\Gamma(1)$, $\Gamma(2)$, and $\Gamma(3)$.

(b) Use integration by parts to show that $\Gamma(n+1) = n\Gamma(n)$.

(c) Write $\Gamma(n)$ using factorial notation where n is a positive integer.

98. Proof   Prove that $I_n = \left(\dfrac{n-1}{n+2}\right)I_{n-1}$, where

$$I_n = \int_0^{\infty} \frac{x^{2n-1}}{(x^2+1)^{n+3}} \, dx, \quad n \geq 1.$$

Then evaluate each integral.

(a) $\displaystyle\int_0^{\infty} \frac{x}{(x^2+1)^4} \, dx$ (b) $\displaystyle\int_0^{\infty} \frac{x^3}{(x^2+1)^5} \, dx$

(c) $\displaystyle\int_0^{\infty} \frac{x^5}{(x^2+1)^6} \, dx$

99. Finding a Value   For what value of c does the integral

$$\int_0^{\infty} \left(\frac{1}{\sqrt{x^2+1}} - \frac{c}{x+1}\right) dx$$

converge? Evaluate the integral for this value of c.

100. Finding a Value   For what value of c does the integral

$$\int_1^{\infty} \left(\frac{cx}{x^2+2} - \frac{1}{3x}\right) dx$$

converge? Evaluate the integral for this value of c.

Calculus AP® – Exam Preparation Questions

101. Multiple Choice   For what values of p does

$$\int_1^{\infty} \frac{1}{x^{p-1}} \, dx$$

converge?

(A) $p \leq 2$ (B) $p > 1$

(C) $p \geq 2$ (D) $p > 2$

102. Multiple Choice $\displaystyle\int_{-\infty}^{\infty} 3xe^{-4x^2} \, dx$ is

(A) $-\frac{3}{4}$.   (B) 0.   (C) $\frac{3}{4}$.   (D) divergent.

103. Multiple Choice   Which integral(s) shown below diverges?

I. $\displaystyle\int_0^4 \frac{dx}{(3-x)^2}$ II. $\displaystyle\int_2^{\infty} \frac{x}{(4+x^2)^2} \, dx$

III. $\displaystyle\int_0^2 \frac{2}{\sqrt{4-x^2}} \, dx$

(A) None   (B) I only

(C) I and II only   (D) I, II, and III

Finding or Evaluating an Integral In Exercises 1–8, use the basic integration rules to find or evaluate the integral.

1. $\displaystyle\int 3x\sqrt{x^2+9}\,dx$

2. $\displaystyle\int x^2 e^{x^3+2}\,dx$

3. $\displaystyle\int \csc^2\left(\frac{x+6}{3}\right)dx$

4. $\displaystyle\int \frac{x}{\sqrt[3]{4-x^2}}\,dx$

5. $\displaystyle\int_1^e \frac{\ln 2x}{x}\,dx$

6. $\displaystyle\int_{3/2}^2 2x\sqrt{2x-3}\,dx$

7. $\displaystyle\int \frac{100}{\sqrt{100-x^2}}\,dx$

8. $\displaystyle\int \frac{2x}{x-3}\,dx$

Using Integration by Parts In Exercises 9–16, use integration by parts to find the indefinite integral.

9. $\displaystyle\int x^2 e^{4x}\,dx$

10. $\displaystyle\int xe^{5-x}\,dx$

11. $\displaystyle\int e^{2x}\sin 3x\,dx$

12. $\displaystyle\int x\sqrt{x-1}\,dx$

13. $\displaystyle\int x^2\cos 2x\,dx$

14. $\displaystyle\int \ln\sqrt{x^2-4}\,dx$

15. $\displaystyle\int x\arcsin 2x\,dx$

16. $\displaystyle\int \arctan 2x\,dx$

Finding a Trigonometric Integral In Exercises 17–26, find the indefinite integral.

17. $\displaystyle\int \sin^6 x\cos x\,dx$

18. $\displaystyle\int \sin^2 x\cos^3 x\,dx$

19. $\displaystyle\int \cos^3(\pi x-1)\,dx$

20. $\displaystyle\int \sin^2\frac{\pi x}{2}\,dx$

21. $\displaystyle\int \sec^4\frac{x}{2}\,dx$

22. $\displaystyle\int \tan\theta\sec^4\theta\,d\theta$

23. $\displaystyle\int x\tan^4 x^2\,dx$

24. $\displaystyle\int \frac{\tan^3 x}{\sec^4 x}\,dx$

25. $\displaystyle\int \frac{1}{1-\sin\theta}\,d\theta$

26. $\displaystyle\int (\cos 2\theta)(\sin\theta+\cos\theta)^2\,d\theta$

Area In Exercises 27 and 28, find the area of the shaded region using any method.

27. $y=\sin^4 x$

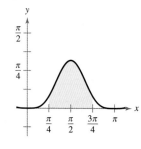

28. $y=\sin 3x\cos 2x$

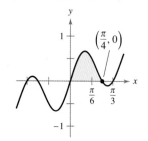

Using Trigonometric Substitution In Exercises 29–34, use trigonometric substitution to find or evaluate the integral.

29. $\displaystyle\int \frac{-12}{x^2\sqrt{4-x^2}}\,dx$

30. $\displaystyle\int \frac{\sqrt{x^2-9}}{x}\,dx$

31. $\displaystyle\int \frac{x^3}{\sqrt{169+x^2}}\,dx$

32. $\displaystyle\int \sqrt{25-9x^2}\,dx$

33. $\displaystyle\int_0^1 \frac{6x^3}{\sqrt{16+x^2}}\,dx$

34. $\displaystyle\int_3^4 x^3\sqrt{x^2-9}\,dx$

Using Different Methods In Exercises 35 and 36, find the indefinite integral using each method.

35. $\displaystyle\int \frac{x^3}{\sqrt{4+x^2}}\,dx$

   (a) Trigonometric substitution

   (b) Substitution: $u^2=4+x^2$

   (c) Integration by parts: $dv=\dfrac{x}{\sqrt{4+x^2}}\,dx$

36. $\displaystyle\int x\sqrt{4+x}\,dx$

   (a) Trigonometric substitution

   (b) Substitution: $u^2=4+x$

   (c) Substitution: $u=4+x$

   (d) Integration by parts: $dv=\sqrt{4+x}\,dx$

Using Partial Fractions In Exercises 37–42, use partial fractions to find the indefinite integral.

37. $\displaystyle\int \frac{x-8}{x^2-x-6}\,dx$

38. $\displaystyle\int \frac{5x-2}{x^2-x}\,dx$

39. $\displaystyle\int \frac{x^2}{x^2-2x+1}\,dx$

40. $\displaystyle\int \frac{x^3+4}{x^2-4x}\,dx$

41. $\displaystyle\int \frac{4e^x}{(e^{2x}-1)(e^x+3)}\,dx$

42. $\displaystyle\int \frac{\sec^2\theta}{(\tan\theta)(\tan\theta-1)}\,d\theta$

Integration by Tables In Exercises 43–48, use a table of integrals to find or evaluate the integral.

43. $\displaystyle\int \frac{x}{(4+5x)^2}\,dx$

44. $\displaystyle\int \frac{x^2}{\sqrt{4+5x}}\,dx$

45. $\displaystyle\int_0^{\sqrt{\pi/2}} \frac{x}{1+\sin x^2}\,dx$

46. $\displaystyle\int_0^1 \frac{x}{1+e^{x^2}}\,dx$

47. $\displaystyle\int \frac{x}{x^2+4x+8}\,dx$

48. $\displaystyle\int \frac{1}{1+\sec 3x}\,dx$

49. **Justifying** Verify the reduction formula

$$\int \cot^n x\,dx = -\frac{1}{n-1}\cot^{n-1}x - \int \cot^{n-2}x\,dx.$$

50. **Justifying** Verify the reduction formula

$$\int \tan^n x\,dx = \frac{1}{n-1}\tan^{n-1}x - \int \tan^{n-2}x\,dx.$$

Finding an Indefinite Integral In Exercises 51–58, find the indefinite integral using any method.

51. $\displaystyle\int \theta \sin \theta \cos \theta \, d\theta$

52. $\displaystyle\int \frac{\csc \sqrt{2x}}{\sqrt{x}} \, dx$

53. $\displaystyle\int \frac{x^{1/4}}{1 + x^{1/2}} \, dx$

54. $\displaystyle\int \sqrt{1 + \sqrt{x}} \, dx$

55. $\displaystyle\int \sqrt{1 + \cos x} \, dx$

56. $\displaystyle\int \frac{3x^3 + 4x}{(x^2 + 1)^2} \, dx$

57. $\displaystyle\int (\cos x)[\ln(\sin x)] \, dx$

58. $\displaystyle\int (\sin \theta + \cos \theta)^2 \, d\theta$

Differential Equation In Exercises 59–62, find the general solution of the differential equation using any method.

59. $\dfrac{dy}{dx} = \dfrac{25}{x^2 - 25}$

60. $\dfrac{dy}{dx} = \dfrac{\sqrt{4 - x^2}}{2x}$

61. $y' = \ln(x^2 + x)$

62. $y' = \sqrt{1 - \cos \theta}$

Evaluating a Definite Integral In Exercises 63–68, evaluate the definite integral using any method. Use a graphing utility to verify your result.

63. $\displaystyle\int_{2}^{\sqrt{5}} x(x^2 - 4)^{3/2} \, dx$

64. $\displaystyle\int_{0}^{1} \frac{x}{(x - 2)(x - 4)} \, dx$

65. $\displaystyle\int_{1}^{4} \frac{\ln x}{x} \, dx$

66. $\displaystyle\int_{0}^{2} xe^{3x} \, dx$

67. $\displaystyle\int_{2}^{\pi} (x^2 - 4) \sin x \, dx$

68. $\displaystyle\int_{0}^{5} \frac{x}{\sqrt{4 + x}} \, dx$

Area In Exercises 69 and 70, find the area of the region.

69. $y = x\sqrt{4 - x}$

70. $y = \dfrac{1}{25 - x^2}$

Arc Length In Exercises 71 and 72, approximate to two decimal places the arc length of the curve over the given interval.

71. $y = \sin x, \ [0, \pi]$

72. $y = \sin^2 x, \ [0, \pi]$

Evaluating a Limit In Exercises 73–80, use L'Hôpital's Rule to evaluate the limit.

73. $\displaystyle\lim_{x \to 1} \frac{(\ln x)^2}{x - 1}$

74. $\displaystyle\lim_{x \to 0} \frac{\sin \pi x}{\sin 5\pi x}$

75. $\displaystyle\lim_{x \to \infty} \frac{e^{2x}}{x^2}$

76. $\displaystyle\lim_{x \to \infty} xe^{-x^2}$

77. $\displaystyle\lim_{x \to \infty} (\ln x)^{2/x}$

78. $\displaystyle\lim_{x \to 1^+} (x - 1)^{\ln x}$

79. $\displaystyle\lim_{n \to \infty} 1000\left(1 + \frac{0.09}{n}\right)^n$

80. $\displaystyle\lim_{x \to 1^+} \left(\frac{2}{\ln x} - \frac{2}{x - 1}\right)$

Evaluating an Improper Integral In Exercises 81–88, determine whether the improper integral diverges or converges. Evaluate the integral if it converges.

81. $\displaystyle\int_{0}^{16} \frac{1}{\sqrt[4]{x}} \, dx$

82. $\displaystyle\int_{0}^{2} \frac{7}{x - 2} \, dx$

83. $\displaystyle\int_{1}^{\infty} x^2 \ln x \, dx$

84. $\displaystyle\int_{0}^{\infty} \frac{e^{-1/x}}{x^2} \, dx$

85. $\displaystyle\int_{1}^{\infty} \frac{\ln x}{x^2} \, dx$

86. $\displaystyle\int_{1}^{\infty} \frac{1}{\sqrt[4]{x}} \, dx$

87. $\displaystyle\int_{2}^{\infty} \frac{1}{x\sqrt{x^2 - 4}} \, dx$

88. $\displaystyle\int_{0}^{\infty} \frac{2}{\sqrt{x}(x + 4)} \, dx$

89. Present Value The board of directors of a corporation is calculating the price to pay for a business that is forecast to yield a continuous flow of profit of $500,000 per year. The money will earn a nominal rate of 5% per year compounded continuously. The present value of the business for t_0 years is

$$\text{Present value} = \int_{0}^{t_0} 500,000e^{-0.05t} \, dt.$$

(a) Find the present value of the business for 20 years.

(b) Find the present value of the business in perpetuity (forever).

90. Volume Find the volume of the solid generated by revolving the region satisfying the inequalities $y \le xe^{-x}, \ y \ge 0$, and $x \ge 0$ about the x-axis.

91. Probability The average lengths (from beak to tail) of different species of warblers in the eastern United States are approximately normally distributed with a mean of 13.18 centimeters and a standard deviation of 1.30 centimeters (see figure). The probability that a randomly selected warbler has a length between a and b centimeters is

$$P(a \le x \le b) = \frac{1}{1.30\sqrt{2\pi}} \int_{a}^{b} e^{-(x - 13.18)^2/3.38} \, dx.$$

Use a graphing utility to approximate the probability that a randomly selected warbler has a length of (a) 13 centimeters or greater and (b) 15 centimeters or greater. (*Source: Peterson's Field Guide: Eastern Birds*)

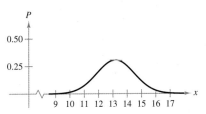

What You Need to Know

- Be ready to recognize various forms of antiderivatives on the AP® Exam.
- When showing your work on the AP® Exam, it is important to use proper notation in each of your steps. For example, when evaluating a limit using L'Hôpital's Rule, use the limit notation for each step, not just the first and last steps of your solution.
- It is important for you to continue working on recognition when working with integrals. For example, recognizing that an integral is improper is just as important as the integration itself.

Practice Questions

Section 1, Part A, Multiple Choice, No Technology

1. $\int (\sin x)e^{2+\cos x}\, dx =$

(A) $-e^{2+\cos x} + C$

(B) $e^{2+\cos x} + C$

(C) $(\cos x)e^{2+\cos x} + C$

(D) $e^{-\sin x} + C$

2. $\int \dfrac{1}{\sqrt{x^2 + 12x}}\, dx =$

(A) $\ln\left|x + 6 - \sqrt{x^2 + 12x}\right| + C$

(B) $\ln\left|x + 6 - \sqrt{x^2 - 12x}\right| + C$

(C) $\ln\left|x + 6 + \sqrt{x^2 - 12x}\right| + C$

(D) $\ln\left|x + 6 + \sqrt{x^2 + 12x}\right| + C$

3. $\displaystyle\lim_{x\to 1} \dfrac{5e^{1-x} - \ln x - 5}{x^2 - 1}$ is

(A) -3.

(B) 4.

(C) 5.

(D) nonexistent.

4. The table below gives values of f, f', g, and g' for selected values of x.

x	1	2
$f(x)$	3	2
$f'(x)$	-2	1
$g(x)$	-1	3
$g'(x)$	1	-3

If $\displaystyle\int_1^2 f'(x)g(x)\, dx = 3$, then $\displaystyle\int_1^2 f(x)g'(x)\, dx =$

(A) -9.

(B) -4.

(C) -3.

(D) 6.

5. $\displaystyle\int_0^3 \dfrac{1}{x^2 - 9x + 20}\, dx =$

(A) $\ln\dfrac{8}{5}$

(B) $\ln 2$

(C) $\ln\dfrac{5}{2}$

(D) $\dfrac{\ln 8}{\ln 5}$

6. $\displaystyle\int_0^\pi \cos^3 \dfrac{x}{2}\, dx =$

(A) $\dfrac{4}{3}$

(B) $\dfrac{5}{3}$

(C) $\dfrac{3\sqrt{3}}{4}$

(D) $\dfrac{11}{12}$

7. $\displaystyle\int_0^\infty xe^{-x/3}\, dx$ is

(A) 0.

(B) 3.

(C) 9.

(D) divergent.

8. $\displaystyle\lim_{x\to\pi} \dfrac{\cos 2x - x\sin x - 1}{\pi^3 - x^3}$ is

(A) $-\dfrac{1}{3\pi}$.

(B) $-\dfrac{1}{3\pi^2}$.

(C) $\dfrac{1}{3\pi}$.

(D) nonexistent.

9. If $f'(x) = \sec^2 x$ and $g'(x) = 4$ for all x, and if $f(0) = g(0) = 0$, then

$\displaystyle\lim_{x\to 0} \dfrac{f(x)}{g(x)}$

is

(A) 0.

(B) $\dfrac{1}{4}$.

(C) 4.

(D) nonexistent.

10. $\displaystyle\int_1^\infty \dfrac{dx}{x^{5/2}}$ is

(A) 0.

(B) $\dfrac{2}{5}$.

(C) $\dfrac{2}{3}$.

(D) divergent.

11. Given the region A bounded by the graphs of $y = \sqrt{36 - 4x^2}/x$ $x = 2$, $y = 0$, and $x = 3$, what is the volume of the solid generated when the region A is revolved about the y-axis?

(A) 16.76

(B) 19.46

(C) 33.51

(D) 38.92

12. (a) Find the area of the region R in the first quadrant bounded by the function $y = x \sin x$, the x-axis, and the vertical line $x = \pi$ using integration by parts.

(b) Find the area of the region S in the first quadrant bounded by the function $y = x \sin x$, the line $y = -2x + 5$, and the y-axis.

(c) The vertical line $x = k$ divides S into two regions of equal area. Write, but do not solve, an equation involving one or more integrals whose solution gives the value of k.

13. A particle moves along the x-axis at a velocity of

$$v(t) = te^{-t/3} - \frac{1}{2}, \quad t \geq 0.$$

At time $t = 0$, the particle is at position $x = 2$.

(a) Use integration by parts to find the position of the particle when $t = 2$.

(b) Write, but do not evaluate, an expression involving one or more integrals which gives the total distance traveled by the particle from $t = 0$ to $t = 2$.

(c) Find the acceleration of the particle at time t. Is the speed of the particle increasing or decreasing when $t = 3$? Explain your answer.

14. Let f be a function defined for $x > 1$, with $f(e) = 4$ and

$$f'(x) = \frac{1}{x(\ln x)^3}.$$

(a) Write an equation for the line tangent to the graph of f at the point $(e, 4)$.

(b) Is the graph of f concave upward or concave downward on the interval $1 < x < 5$? Give a reason for your answer.

(c) Use antidifferentiation to find $f(x)$.

15. Let a function f be defined by

$$f(x) = \begin{cases} \tan^2(x - 1) + \dfrac{1}{4}, & x \leq 1 \\ \dfrac{\sqrt{x} - 1}{x^2 - 1}, & x > 1 \end{cases}.$$

(a) Show that f is continuous at $x = 1$.

(b) For $x \neq 1$, express $f'(x)$ as a piecewise-defined function.

(c) Find the average value of f on the interval $[0, 4]$.

16. Consider the differential equation

$$\frac{dT}{dR} = \frac{1}{2R(5 - R)}.$$

(a) Given that $T = 0$ when $R = 3$, find T as a function of R.

(b) Find the R-values of all inflection points of the graph of T.

17. Consider the function $g(x) = xe^{-x}$.

(a) Find all horizontal asymptotes of the graph of g. Show the work that leads to your answer.

(b) Find the maximum value of $g(x)$. Justify your answer.

(c) Consider the region A bounded by the graph of $y = g(x)$, the x-axis, the vertical line $x = 1$, and unbounded on the right. Find the area of A or show that the area is infinite.

18. Let g be a function such that

$$g'(x) = (x - 2)^{-2}.$$

(a) Determine whether $\int_0^3 g'(x)\, dx$ converges or diverges. Show the work that leads to your answer.

(b) Explain why $\int_0^3 g'(x)\, dx$ is *not* equivalent to $g(3) - g(0)$.

(c) Evaluate $\int_4^\infty g'(x)\, dx$.

19. Consider the differential equation

$$dy/dx = y^2(4x + 1).$$

Let $y = f(x)$ be the particular solution of the differential equation with initial condition $f(0) = -2$.

(a) Find

$$\lim_{x \to 0} \frac{f(x) + 2}{\tan x}.$$

Show the work that leads to your answer.

(b) Use Euler's Method, starting at $x = 0$ with two steps of equal size, to approximate $f\left(\frac{1}{2}\right)$.

(c) Find $y = f(x)$.

7   Performance Task

Work

The concept of work is important to scientists and engineers for determining the energy needed to perform various jobs. For instance, it is useful to know the amount of work done when a crane lifts a steel girder, when a spring is compressed, when a rocket is propelled into the air, or when a truck pulls a load along a highway.

In general, **work** is done by a force when it moves an object. If an object is moved a distance D in the direction of an applied constant force F, then the work W done by the force is defined as

$$W = FD.$$ Work done by a constant force

A **force** can be thought of as a *push* or a *pull*; a force changes the state of rest or state of motion of a body. For gravitational forces on Earth, it is common to use units of measure corresponding to the weight of an object. In the U.S. measurement system, work is typically expressed in foot-pounds (ft-lb), inch-pounds, or foot-tons. In the International System of Units (SI), the basic unit of force is the **newton**—the force required to produce an acceleration of 1 meter per second per second on a mass of 1 kilogram. In this system, work is typically expressed in newton-meters, also called joules.

When the force is *constant*, you do not need calculus to determine the work done. When a *variable* force is applied to an object, calculus is needed to determine the work done, because the amount of force changes as the object changes position. So, if an object is moved along a straight line by a continuously varying force $F(x)$, then the work W done by the force as the object is moved from $x = a$ to $x = b$ is given by

$$W = \int_a^b F(x)\, dx.$$ Work done by a variable force

Exercises

1. **Lifting an Object**   Determine the work done in lifting a 50-pound object 4 feet. Did you have to use calculus to determine the work done? Why or why not?

2. **Hooke's Law**   The force F required to compress or stretch a spring (within its elastic limits) is proportional to the distance d that the spring is compressed or stretched from its original length. That is, $F = kd$, where the constant of proportionality k (the spring constant) depends on the specific nature of the spring. A force of 750 pounds compresses a spring 3 inches from its natural length of 15 inches (see figure). Find the work done in compressing the spring an additional 3 inches.

In Exercises 3 and 4, use the following information. The weight of a body is inversely proportional to the square of its distance from the center of Earth, so the force $F(x)$ exerted by gravity is $F(x) = C/x^2$, where C is the constant of proportionality.

3. **Sending a Space Module into Orbit**   A space module weighs 15 metric tons on the surface of Earth. How much work is done in propelling the module to a height of 800 miles above Earth, as shown in the figure? (Use 4000 miles as the radius of Earth. Do not consider the effect of air resistance or the weight of the propellant.)

4. **Sending a Space Module into Space**   Consider propelling the 15-metric-ton space module in Exercise 3 an unlimited distance from Earth.

    (a) Does it require an infinite amount of work to do so? Justify your answer.

    (b) How far has the space module traveled when half the total work has occurred?

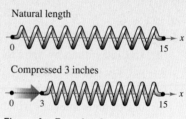

Natural length

Compressed 3 inches

Figure for Exercise 2

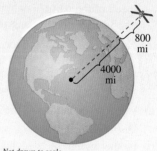

Not drawn to scale

Figure for Exercise 3

8 Infinite Series

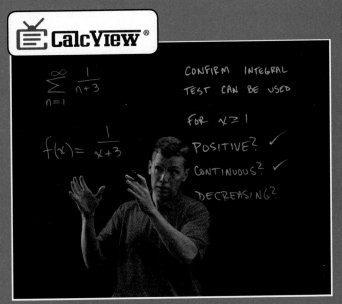

CalcView®

$$\sum_{n=1}^{\infty} \frac{1}{n+3}$$

$$f(x) = \frac{1}{x+3}$$

CONFIRM INTEGRAL TEST CAN BE USED

FOR $x \geq 1$

POSITIVE? ✓

CONTINUOUS? ✓

DECREASING?

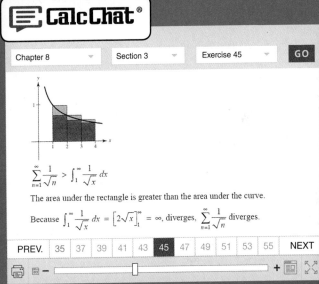

CalcChat®

| Chapter 8 ▾ | Section 3 ▾ | Exercise 45 ▾ | GO |

$$\sum_{n=1}^{\infty} \frac{1}{\sqrt{n}} > \int_{1}^{\infty} \frac{1}{\sqrt{x}}\, dx$$

The area under the rectangle is greater than the area under the curve.

Because $\int_{1}^{\infty} \frac{1}{\sqrt{x}}\, dx = \left[2\sqrt{x}\right]_{1}^{\infty} = \infty$, diverges, $\sum_{n=1}^{\infty} \frac{1}{\sqrt{n}}$ diverges.

| PREV. | 35 | 37 | 39 | 41 | 43 | **45** | 47 | 49 | 51 | 53 | 55 | NEXT |

8.1 Inflation *(Exercise 80, p. 544)*

8.2 Multiplier Effect *(Exercise 73, p. 552)*

8.1 Sequences

▶ Write the terms of a sequence.
▶ Determine whether a sequence converges or diverges.
▶ Write a formula for the nth term of a sequence.
▶ Use properties of monotonic sequences and bounded sequences.

Sequences

In mathematics, the word "sequence" is used in much the same way as it is in ordinary English. Saying that a collection of objects or events is *in sequence* usually means that the collection is ordered in such a way that it has an identified first member, second member, third member, and so on.

Mathematically, a **sequence** is defined as a function whose domain is the set of positive integers. Although a sequence is a function, it is common to represent sequences by subscript notation rather than by the standard function notation. For instance, in the sequence

$$
\begin{array}{ccccccc}
1, & 2, & 3, & 4, & \ldots, & n, & \ldots \\
\downarrow & \downarrow & \downarrow & \downarrow & \downarrow & \downarrow & \downarrow \\
a_1, & a_2, & a_3, & a_4, & \ldots, & a_n, & \ldots
\end{array}
$$
Sequence

1 is mapped onto a_1, 2 is mapped onto a_2, and so on. The numbers

$$a_1, a_2, a_3, \ldots, a_n, \ldots$$

are the **terms** of the sequence. The number a_n is the **nth term** of the sequence, and the entire sequence is denoted by $\{a_n\}$. Occasionally, it is convenient to begin a sequence with a_0, so that the terms of the sequence become $a_0, a_1, a_2, a_3, \ldots, a_n, \ldots$ and the domain is the set of nonnegative integers.

EXAMPLE 1 Writing the Terms of a Sequence

a. The terms of the sequence $\{a_n\} = \{3 + (-1)^n\}$ are

$$3 + (-1)^1, \ 3 + (-1)^2, \ 3 + (-1)^3, \ 3 + (-1)^4, \ldots$$
$$2, \qquad 4, \qquad 2, \qquad 4, \qquad \ldots.$$

b. The terms of the sequence $\{b_n\} = \left\{\dfrac{n}{1 - 2n}\right\}$ are

$$\frac{1}{1 - 2 \cdot 1}, \ \frac{2}{1 - 2 \cdot 2}, \ \frac{3}{1 - 2 \cdot 3}, \ \frac{4}{1 - 2 \cdot 4}, \ \cdots$$
$$-1, \qquad -\frac{2}{3}, \qquad -\frac{3}{5}, \qquad -\frac{4}{7}, \qquad \ldots.$$

c. The terms of the sequence $\{c_n\} = \left\{\dfrac{n^2}{2^n - 1}\right\}$ are

$$\frac{1^2}{2^1 - 1}, \ \frac{2^2}{2^2 - 1}, \ \frac{3^2}{2^3 - 1}, \ \frac{4^2}{2^4 - 1}, \ \cdots$$
$$\frac{1}{1}, \qquad \frac{4}{3}, \qquad \frac{9}{7}, \qquad \frac{16}{15}, \qquad \ldots.$$

d. The terms of the **recursively defined** sequence $\{d_n\}$, where $d_1 = 25$ and $d_{n+1} = d_n - 5$, are

$$25, \quad 25 - 5 = 20, \quad 20 - 5 = 15, \quad 15 - 5 = 10, \ldots. \qquad ■$$

Exploration

Finding Patterns Describe a pattern for each of the sequences listed below. Then use your description to write a formula for the nth term of each sequence. As n increases, do the terms appear to be approaching a limit? Explain your reasoning.

a. $1, \dfrac{1}{2}, \dfrac{1}{4}, \dfrac{1}{8}, \dfrac{1}{16}, \cdots$

b. $1, \dfrac{1}{2}, \dfrac{1}{6}, \dfrac{1}{24}, \dfrac{1}{120}, \cdots$

c. $10, \dfrac{10}{3}, \dfrac{10}{6}, \dfrac{10}{10}, \dfrac{10}{15}, \cdots$

d. $\dfrac{1}{4}, \dfrac{4}{9}, \dfrac{9}{16}, \dfrac{16}{25}, \dfrac{25}{36}, \cdots$

e. $\dfrac{3}{7}, \dfrac{5}{10}, \dfrac{7}{13}, \dfrac{9}{16}, \dfrac{11}{19}, \cdots$

Remark

Some sequences are defined recursively. To define a sequence recursively, you need to be given one or more of the first few terms. All other terms of the sequence are then defined using previous terms, as shown in Example 1(d).

Limit of a Sequence

The primary focus of this chapter concerns sequences whose terms approach limiting values. Such sequences are said to **converge.** For instance, the sequence $\{1/2^n\}$

$$\frac{1}{2}, \frac{1}{4}, \frac{1}{8}, \frac{1}{16}, \frac{1}{32}, \ldots$$

converges to 0, as indicated in the next definition.

Definition of the Limit of a Sequence

Let L be a real number. The **limit** of a sequence $\{a_n\}$ is L, written as

$$\lim_{n \to \infty} a_n = L$$

if for each $\varepsilon > 0$, there exists $M > 0$ such that $|a_n - L| < \varepsilon$ whenever $n > M$. If the limit L of a sequence exists, then the sequence **converges** to L. If the limit of a sequence does not exist, then the sequence **diverges.**

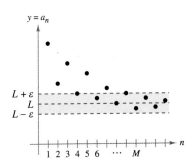

For $n > M$, the terms of the sequence all lie within ε units of L.

Figure 8.1

Graphically, this definition says that eventually (for $n > M$ and $\varepsilon > 0$), the terms of a sequence that converges to L will lie within the band between the lines $y = L + \varepsilon$ and $y = L - \varepsilon$, as shown in Figure 8.1.

If a sequence $\{a_n\}$ agrees with a function f at every positive integer, and if $f(x)$ approaches a limit L as $x \to \infty$, then the sequence must converge to the same limit L.

Theorem 8.1   Limit of a Sequence

Let L be a real number. Let f be a function of a real variable such that

$$\lim_{x \to \infty} f(x) = L.$$

If $\{a_n\}$ is a sequence such that $f(n) = a_n$ for every positive integer n, then

$$\lim_{n \to \infty} a_n = L.$$

> **Remark**
>
> The converse of Theorem 8.1 is not true (see Exercise 87).

EXAMPLE 2   Finding the Limit of a Sequence

Find the limit of the sequence whose nth term is $a_n = \left(1 + \dfrac{1}{n}\right)^n$.

Solution

In Section 7.7, Example 5, you learned that

$$\lim_{x \to \infty} \left(1 + \frac{1}{x}\right)^x = e.$$

So, you can apply Theorem 8.1 to conclude that

$$\lim_{n \to \infty} a_n = \lim_{n \to \infty} \left(1 + \frac{1}{n}\right)^n = e. \qquad \blacksquare$$

There are different ways in which a sequence can fail to have a limit. One way is that the terms of the sequence increase without bound or decrease without bound. These cases are written symbolically, as shown below.

Terms increase without bound: $\lim\limits_{n \to \infty} a_n = \infty$

Terms decrease without bound: $\lim\limits_{n \to \infty} a_n = -\infty$

The properties of limits of sequences listed in the next theorem parallel those given for limits of functions of a real variable in Section 1.3.

Theorem 8.2 **Properties of Limits of Sequences**

Let $\lim\limits_{n\to\infty} a_n = L$ and $\lim\limits_{n\to\infty} b_n = K$.

1. **Scalar multiple:** $\lim\limits_{n\to\infty} (ca_n) = cL$, c is any real number.

2. **Sum or difference:** $\lim\limits_{n\to\infty} (a_n \pm b_n) = L \pm K$

3. **Product:** $\lim\limits_{n\to\infty} (a_n b_n) = LK$

4. **Quotient:** $\lim\limits_{n\to\infty} \dfrac{a_n}{b_n} = \dfrac{L}{K}$, $b_n \neq 0$ and $K \neq 0$

EXAMPLE 3 **Determining Convergence or Divergence**

See LarsonCalculusforAP.com for an interactive version of this type of example.

a. Because the sequence $\{a_n\} = \{3 + (-1)^n\}$ has terms

$$2, 4, 2, 4, \ldots \qquad \text{See Example 1(a).}$$

that alternate between 2 and 4, the limit

$$\lim_{n\to\infty} a_n$$

does not exist. So, the sequence diverges.

b. For $\{b_n\} = \left\{ \dfrac{n}{1 - 2n} \right\}$, divide the numerator and denominator by n to obtain

$$\lim_{n\to\infty} \frac{n}{1 - 2n} = \lim_{n\to\infty} \frac{1}{(1/n) - 2} = -\frac{1}{2} \qquad \text{See Example 1(b).}$$

which implies that the sequence converges to $-\frac{1}{2}$.

EXAMPLE 4 **Using L'Hôpital's Rule to Determine Convergence**

Show that the sequence whose nth term is

$$a_n = \frac{n^2}{2^n - 1}$$

converges.

Algebraic Solution

Consider the function of a real variable

$$f(x) = \frac{x^2}{2^x - 1}.$$

Applying L'Hôpital's Rule twice produces

$$\lim_{x\to\infty} \frac{x^2}{2^x - 1} = \lim_{x\to\infty} \frac{2x}{(\ln 2)2^x} = \lim_{x\to\infty} \frac{2}{(\ln 2)^2 2^x} = 0.$$

Because $f(n) = a_n$ for every positive integer n, you can apply Theorem 8.1 to conclude that

$$\lim_{n\to\infty} \frac{n^2}{2^n - 1} = 0. \qquad \text{See Example 1(c).}$$

So, the sequence converges to 0.

Numerical Solution

In *sequence* mode, enter $u_n = \dfrac{n^2}{2^n - 1}$.

Use the *table* feature (in *ask* mode) to evaluate u_n for increasing values of n.

n	$u(n)$	
1	1	
5	.80645	
10	.09775	
25	1.9E-5	
50	2E-12	
100	8E-27	
200	2E-56	

$u(n)=2.48921\text{E-}56$

From the table, it seems reasonable to conclude that the sequence converges to 0.

The symbol $n!$ (read "n factorial") is used to simplify some of the formulas developed in this chapter. Let n be a positive integer; then **n factorial** is defined as

$$n! = 1 \cdot 2 \cdot 3 \cdot 4 \cdots (n-1) \cdot n.$$

As a special case, **zero factorial** is defined as $0! = 1$. From this definition, you can see that $1! = 1$, $2! = 1 \cdot 2 = 2$, $3! = 1 \cdot 2 \cdot 3 = 6$, and so on. Factorials follow the same conventions for order of operations as exponents. That is, just as $2x^3$ and $(2x)^3$ imply different orders of operations, $2n!$ and $(2n)!$ imply the orders

$$2n! = 2(n!) = 2(1 \cdot 2 \cdot 3 \cdot 4 \cdots n)$$

and

$$(2n)! = 1 \cdot 2 \cdot 3 \cdot 4 \cdots n \cdot (n+1) \cdots 2n$$

respectively.

Another useful limit theorem that can be rewritten for sequences is the Squeeze Theorem from Section 1.3.

Theorem 8.3   Squeeze Theorem for Sequences

If $\lim\limits_{n \to \infty} a_n = L = \lim\limits_{n \to \infty} b_n$ and there exists an integer N such that $a_n \leq c_n \leq b_n$ for all $n > N$, then $\lim\limits_{n \to \infty} c_n = L$.

EXAMPLE 5   Using the Squeeze Theorem

Show that the sequence $\{c_n\} = \left\{ (-1)^n \dfrac{1}{n!} \right\}$ converges, and find its limit.

Solution

To apply the Squeeze Theorem, you must find two convergent sequences that can be related to $\{c_n\}$. Two possibilities are $a_n = -1/2^n$ and $b_n = 1/2^n$, both of which converge to 0. By comparing the term $n!$ with 2^n, you can see that

$$n! = 1 \cdot 2 \cdot 3 \cdot 4 \cdot 5 \cdot 6 \cdots n = 24 \cdot \underbrace{5 \cdot 6 \cdots n}_{n-4 \text{ factors}} \qquad (n \geq 4)$$

and

$$2^n = 2 \cdot 2 \cdot 2 \cdot 2 \cdot 2 \cdot 2 \cdots 2 = 16 \cdot \underbrace{2 \cdot 2 \cdots 2}_{n-4 \text{ factors}}. \qquad (n \geq 4)$$

This implies that for $n \geq 4$, $2^n < n!$, and you have

$$-\frac{1}{2^n} \leq (-1)^n \frac{1}{n!} \leq \frac{1}{2^n}, \quad n \geq 4$$

as shown in Figure 8.2. So, by the Squeeze Theorem, it follows that

$$\lim_{n \to \infty} (-1)^n \frac{1}{n!} = 0. \qquad \blacksquare$$

Example 5 suggests something about the rate at which $n!$ increases as $n \to \infty$. As Figure 8.2 suggests, both $1/2^n$ and $1/n!$ approach 0 as $n \to \infty$. Yet $1/n!$ approaches 0 so much faster than $1/2^n$ does that

$$\lim_{n \to \infty} \frac{1/n!}{1/2^n} = \lim_{n \to \infty} \frac{2^n}{n!} = 0.$$

In fact, it can be shown that for any fixed number k, $\lim\limits_{n \to \infty} (k^n/n!) = 0$. This means that *the factorial function grows faster than any exponential function.*

Algebra Review

For help in simplifying factorial expressions, see Example 1 in the *Chapter 8 Algebra Review* on page A50.

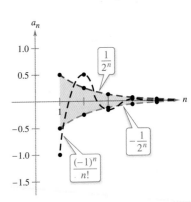

For $n \geq 4$, $(-1)^n/n!$ is squeezed between $-1/2^n$ and $1/2^n$.

Figure 8.2

In Example 5, the sequence $\{c_n\}$ has both positive and negative terms. For this sequence, it happens that the sequence of absolute values, $\{|c_n|\}$, also converges to 0. You can show this by the Squeeze Theorem using the inequality

$$0 \le \frac{1}{n!} \le \frac{1}{2^n}, \quad n \ge 4.$$

In such cases, it is often convenient to consider the sequence of absolute values—and then apply Theorem 8.4, which states that if the absolute value sequence converges to 0, then the original signed sequence also converges to 0.

Theorem 8.4 Absolute Value Theorem

For the sequence $\{a_n\}$, if

$$\lim_{n \to \infty} |a_n| = 0 \quad \text{then} \quad \lim_{n \to \infty} a_n = 0.$$

Proof   Consider the two sequences $\{|a_n|\}$ and $\{-|a_n|\}$. Because both of these sequences converge to 0 and

$$-|a_n| \le a_n \le |a_n|$$

you can use the Squeeze Theorem to conclude that $\{a_n\}$ converges to 0.   ∎

Pattern Recognition for Sequences

Sometimes the terms of a sequence are generated by some rule that does not explicitly identify the nth term of the sequence. In such cases, you may be required to discover a *pattern* in the sequence and to describe the nth term. Once the nth term has been specified, you can investigate the convergence or divergence of the sequence.

EXAMPLE 6   Finding the nth Term of a Sequence

Find a sequence $\{a_n\}$ whose first five terms are

$$\frac{2}{1}, \frac{4}{3}, \frac{8}{5}, \frac{16}{7}, \frac{32}{9}, \ldots$$

and then determine whether the sequence you have chosen converges or diverges.

Solution

First, note that the numerators are successive powers of 2, and the denominators form the sequence of positive odd integers. By comparing a_n with n, you have the following pattern.

$$\frac{2^1}{1}, \frac{2^2}{3}, \frac{2^3}{5}, \frac{2^4}{7}, \frac{2^5}{9}, \ldots, \frac{2^n}{2n-1}, \ldots$$

Consider the function of a real variable $f(x) = 2^x/(2x - 1)$. Applying L'Hôpital's Rule produces

$$\lim_{x \to \infty} \frac{2^x}{2x - 1} = \lim_{x \to \infty} \frac{2^x(\ln 2)}{2} = \infty.$$

So, you can conclude that

$$\lim_{n \to \infty} \frac{2^n}{2n - 1} = \infty$$

and the sequence diverges.

Without a specific rule for generating the terms of a sequence or some knowledge of the context in which the terms of the sequence are obtained, it is not possible to determine the convergence or divergence of the sequence merely from its first several terms. For instance, although the first three terms of the following four sequences are identical, the first two sequences converge to 0, the third sequence converges to $\frac{1}{9}$, and the fourth sequence diverges.

$$\{a_n\} : \frac{1}{2}, \frac{1}{4}, \frac{1}{8}, \frac{1}{16}, \cdot\cdot\cdot , \frac{1}{2^n}, \cdot\cdot\cdot$$

$$\{b_n\} : \frac{1}{2}, \frac{1}{4}, \frac{1}{8}, \frac{1}{15}, \cdot\cdot\cdot , \frac{6}{(n+1)(n^2-n+6)}, \cdot\cdot\cdot$$

$$\{c_n\} : \frac{1}{2}, \frac{1}{4}, \frac{1}{8}, \frac{7}{62}, \cdot\cdot\cdot , \frac{n^2-3n+3}{9n^2-25n+18}, \cdot\cdot\cdot$$

$$\{d_n\} : \frac{1}{2}, \frac{1}{4}, \frac{1}{8}, 0, \cdot\cdot\cdot , \frac{-n(n+1)(n-4)}{6(n^2+3n-2)}, \cdot\cdot\cdot$$

The process of determining an nth term from the pattern observed in the first several terms of a sequence is an example of *inductive reasoning*.

EXAMPLE 7   Finding the nth Term of a Sequence

Determine the nth term for a sequence whose first five terms are

$$-\frac{2}{1}, \frac{8}{2}, -\frac{26}{6}, \frac{80}{24}, -\frac{242}{120}, \cdot\cdot\cdot$$

and then decide whether the sequence converges or diverges.

Solution

Note that the numerators are 1 less than 3^n.

$$3^1 - 1 = 2 \quad 3^2 - 1 = 8 \quad 3^3 - 1 = 26 \quad 3^4 - 1 = 80 \quad 3^5 - 1 = 242$$

So, you can reason that the numerators are given by the rule $3^n - 1$. Factoring the denominators produces

$$1 = 1$$
$$2 = 1 \cdot 2$$
$$6 = 1 \cdot 2 \cdot 3$$
$$24 = 1 \cdot 2 \cdot 3 \cdot 4$$

and

$$120 = 1 \cdot 2 \cdot 3 \cdot 4 \cdot 5.$$

This suggests that the denominators are represented by $n!$. Finally, because the signs alternate, you can write the nth term as

$$a_n = (-1)^n \left(\frac{3^n - 1}{n!} \right).$$

From the discussion about the growth of $n!$ on the bottom of page 537, it follows that

$$\lim_{n \to \infty} |a_n| = \lim_{n \to \infty} \frac{3^n - 1}{n!} = 0.$$

Applying Theorem 8.4, you can conclude that

$$\lim_{n \to \infty} a_n = 0.$$

So, the sequence $\{a_n\}$ converges to 0.

Monotonic Sequences and Bounded Sequences

So far, you have determined the convergence of a sequence by finding its limit. Even when you cannot determine the limit of a particular sequence, it still may be useful to know whether the sequence converges. Theorem 8.5 (on the next page) provides a test for convergence of sequences without determining the limit. First, some preliminary definitions are given.

Definition of Monotonic Sequence

A sequence $\{a_n\}$ is **monotonic** when its terms are nondecreasing

$$a_1 \le a_2 \le a_3 \le \cdots \le a_n \le \cdots$$

or when its terms are nonincreasing

$$a_1 \ge a_2 \ge a_3 \ge \cdots \ge a_n \ge \cdots.$$

EXAMPLE 8   **Determining Whether a Sequence Is Monotonic**

Determine whether each sequence having the given nth term is monotonic.

a. $a_n = 3 + (-1)^n$ **b.** $b_n = \dfrac{2n}{1+n}$ **c.** $c_n = \dfrac{n^2}{2^n - 1}$

Solution

a. This sequence alternates between 2 and 4. So, it is not monotonic. [See Figure 8.3(a).]

b. This sequence is monotonic because each successive term is greater than its predecessor. To see this, compare the terms b_n and b_{n+1}. [Note that, because n is positive, you can multiply each side of the inequality by $(1 + n)$ and $(2 + n)$ without reversing the inequality sign.]

$$b_n = \frac{2n}{1+n} \overset{?}{<} \frac{2(n+1)}{1 + (n+1)} = b_{n+1}$$

$$2n(2 + n) \overset{?}{<} (1 + n)(2n + 2)$$

$$4n + 2n^2 \overset{?}{<} 2 + 4n + 2n^2$$

$$0 < 2$$

Starting with the final inequality, which is valid, you can reverse the steps to conclude that the original inequality is also valid. [See Figure 8.3(b).]

c. This sequence is not monotonic because the second term is greater than the first and third terms. [See Figure 8.3(c).]

$$c_2 = \frac{4}{3} > 1 = c_1 \quad \text{and} \quad c_2 = \frac{4}{3} > \frac{9}{7} = c_3$$

(Note that when you drop the first term, the remaining sequence $c_2, c_3, c_4, \ldots$ is monotonic.)   ∎

In Example 8(b), another way to see that the sequence is monotonic is to argue that the derivative of the corresponding differentiable function

$$f(x) = \frac{2x}{1+x}$$

is positive for all x. This implies that f is increasing, which in turn implies that $\{b_n\}$ is increasing.

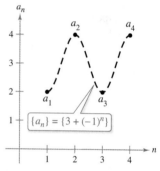

(a) Not monotonic

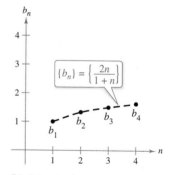

(b) Monotonic

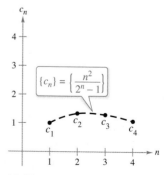

(c) Not monotonic

Figure 8.3

Definition of Bounded Sequence

1. A sequence $\{a_n\}$ is **bounded above** when there is a real number M such that $a_n \le M$ for all n. The number M is called an **upper bound** of the sequence.
2. A sequence $\{a_n\}$ is **bounded below** when there is a real number N such that $N \le a_n$ for all n. The number N is called a **lower bound** of the sequence.
3. A sequence $\{a_n\}$ is **bounded** when it is bounded above and bounded below.

Note that all three sequences in Example 8 (and shown in Figure 8.3) are bounded. To see this, note that

$$2 \le a_n \le 4, \quad 1 \le b_n \le 2, \quad \text{and} \quad 0 \le c_n \le \frac{4}{3}.$$

One important property of the real numbers is that they are **complete.** Informally, this means that there are no holes or gaps on the real number line. (The set of rational numbers does not have the completeness property.) The completeness axiom for real numbers can be used to conclude that if a sequence has an upper bound, then it must have a **least upper bound** (an upper bound that is less than all other upper bounds for the sequence). For example, the least upper bound of the sequence $\{a_n\} = \{n/(n + 1)\}$,

$$\frac{1}{2}, \frac{2}{3}, \frac{3}{4}, \frac{4}{5}, \ldots, \frac{n}{n + 1}, \ldots$$

is 1. The completeness axiom is used in the proof of Theorem 8.5.

Theorem 8.5   Bounded Monotonic Sequences

If a sequence $\{a_n\}$ is bounded and monotonic, then it converges.

Proof   Assume that the sequence is nondecreasing, as shown in Figure 8.4. For the sake of simplicity, also assume that each term in the sequence is positive. Because the sequence is bounded, there must exist an upper bound M such that

$$a_1 \le a_2 \le a_3 \le \cdots \le a_n \le \cdots \le M.$$

From the completeness axiom, it follows that there is a least upper bound L such that

$$a_1 \le a_2 \le a_3 \le \cdots \le a_n \le \cdots \le L.$$

For $\varepsilon > 0$, it follows that $L - \varepsilon < L$, and therefore $L - \varepsilon$ cannot be an upper bound for the sequence. Consequently, at least one term of $\{a_n\}$ is greater than $L - \varepsilon$. That is, $L - \varepsilon < a_N$ for some positive integer N. Because the terms of $\{a_n\}$ are nondecreasing, it follows that $a_N \le a_n$ for $n > N$. You now know that $L - \varepsilon < a_N \le a_n \le L < L + \varepsilon$, for every $n > N$. It follows that $|a_n - L| < \varepsilon$ for $n > N$, which by definition means that $\{a_n\}$ converges to L. The proof for a nonincreasing sequence is similar (see Exercise 93). ∎

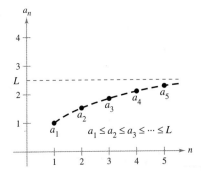

Every bounded, nondecreasing sequence converges.

Figure 8.4

EXAMPLE 9   **Bounded and Monotonic Sequences**

a. The sequence $\{a_n\} = \{1/n\}$ is both bounded and monotonic, and so, by Theorem 8.5, it must converge.

b. The divergent sequence $\{b_n\} = \{n^2/(n + 1)\}$ is monotonic but not bounded. (It is bounded below.)

c. The divergent sequence $\{c_n\} = \{(-1)^n\}$ is bounded but not monotonic.

8.1   Exercises

See *CalcChat.com* for tutorial help and worked-out solutions to odd-numbered exercises.

Writing Terms of a Sequence   In Exercises 1–10, write the first five terms of the sequence.

1. $\{a_n\} = \{4n - 3\}$

2. $\{a_n\} = \{20 - 6n\}$

3. $\{a_n\} = \{(-3)^n\}$

4. $\{a\}_n = \left\{\left(\frac{5}{2}\right)^n\right\}$

5. $\{a_n\} = \left\{\sin\frac{n\pi}{2}\right\}$

6. $\{a_n\} = \{n \cos n\pi\}$

7. $\{a_n\} = \left\{(-1)^{n+1}\left(\frac{2}{n}\right)\right\}$

8. $\{a_n\} = \left\{\frac{(-1)^n}{\sqrt{2n-1}}\right\}$

9. $a_1 = 3, \; a_{k+1} = 2(a_k - 1)$

10. $a_1 = 6, \; a_{k+1} = \frac{1}{3}a_k^2$

Matching   In Exercises 11–14, match the sequence with the given nth term with its graph. [The graphs are labeled (a), (b), (c), and (d).]

(a)

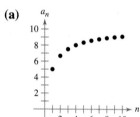

(b)

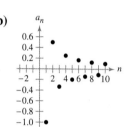

(c)

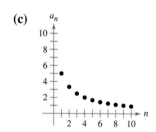

(d)

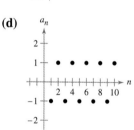

11. $a_n = \dfrac{10}{n+1}$

12. $a_n = \dfrac{10n}{n+1}$

13. $a_n = (-1)^n$

14. $a_n = \dfrac{(-1)^n}{n}$

Writing Terms   In Exercises 15–18, write the next two apparent terms of the sequence. Describe the pattern you used to find these terms.

15. $11, 8, 5, 2, \ldots$

16. $8, 13, 18, 23, 28, \ldots$

17. $5, 10, 20, 40, \ldots$

18. $6, -2, \frac{2}{3}, -\frac{2}{9}, \ldots$

Simplifying Factorials   In Exercises 19–22, simplify the ratio of factorials.

19. $\dfrac{(n+1)!}{n!}$

20. $\dfrac{n!}{(n+2)!}$

21. $\dfrac{(2n-1)!}{(2n+1)!}$

22. $\dfrac{(2n+2)!}{(2n)!}$

Finding the Limit of a Sequence   In Exercises 23–28, find the limit (if possible) of the sequence with the given nth term.

23. $a_n = \dfrac{n+1}{n}$

24. $a_n = 6 + \dfrac{2}{n^2}$

25. $a_n = \dfrac{2n}{\sqrt{n^2+1}}$

26. $a_n = \dfrac{n^2}{(1-n)(2n+4)}$

27. $a_n = \cos\dfrac{2}{n}$

28. $a_n = \dfrac{\sin 3n}{n}$

Error Analysis   In Exercises 29 and 30, describe and correct the error in finding the limit of the sequence whose nth term is $a_n = (n+4)/e^n$.

29. $\displaystyle\lim_{n\to\infty}\frac{n+4}{e^n} = \lim_{n\to\infty}\frac{(n+4)/n}{e^{n/n}} = \lim_{n\to\infty}\frac{1}{e^1} = \frac{1}{e}$

30. $\displaystyle\lim_{x\to\infty}\frac{x+4}{e^x} = \lim_{x\to\infty}\frac{\frac{d}{dx}[x+4]}{\frac{d}{dx}[e^x]} = \lim_{x\to\infty}\frac{1}{e^x} = \infty$

The sequence diverges.

Finding the Limit of a Sequence   In Exercises 31–34, use a graphing utility to graph the first 10 terms of the sequence with the given nth term. Use the graph to make an inference about the convergence or divergence of the sequence. Verify your inference analytically and, if the sequence converges, find its limit.

31. $a_n = \dfrac{4n+1}{n}$

32. $a_n = \dfrac{2n^{3/2}}{2n-1}$

33. $a_n = \sin n\pi/2$

34. $a_n = 2 - 4^{-n}$

Determining Convergence or Divergence   In Exercises 35–50, determine the convergence or divergence of the sequence with the given nth term. If the sequence converges, find its limit.

35. $a_n = \dfrac{5}{n+2}$

36. $a_n = 8 + \dfrac{5}{n}$

37. $a_n = (-1)^n\left(\dfrac{n}{n+1}\right)$

38. $a_n = \dfrac{1+(-1)^n}{n^2}$

39. $a_n = \dfrac{10n^2+3n+7}{2n^2-6}$

40. $a_n = \dfrac{\sqrt[3]{n}}{\sqrt[3]{n}+1}$

41. $a_n = \dfrac{\ln n^3}{2n}$

42. $a_n = \dfrac{\sqrt{n}}{\ln n}$

43. $a_n = \dfrac{(n+1)!}{n!}$

44. $a_n = \dfrac{(n-2)!}{n!}$

45. $a_n = \dfrac{n^p}{e^n}, \; p > 0$

46. $a_n = n\sin\dfrac{1}{n}$

47. $a_n = 2^{1/n}$

48. $a_n = -5^n(-3)^{-n}$

49. $a_n = \dfrac{\sin n}{n}$

50. $a_n = \dfrac{\cos \pi n}{n^2}$

Finding the nth Term of a Sequence In Exercises 51–58, write an expression for the *n*th term of the sequence. Then use this expression to determine whether the sequence converges or diverges. (There is more than one correct answer.)

51. 2, 8, 14, 20, . . .   **52.** 1, −6, 36, −216, . . .
53. $1, -\frac{1}{4}, \frac{1}{9}, -\frac{1}{16}, \ldots$ **54.** −2, 1, 6, 13, 22, . . .
55. $\frac{2}{3}, \frac{3}{4}, \frac{4}{5}, \frac{5}{6}, \ldots$
56. $\frac{1}{2 \cdot 3}, \frac{2}{3 \cdot 4}, \frac{3}{4 \cdot 5}, \frac{4}{5 \cdot 6}, \ldots$
57. $1, \frac{1}{2}, \frac{1}{6}, \frac{1}{24}, \frac{1}{120}, \ldots$
58. 2, 24, 720, 40,320, 3,628,800, . . .

 Finding Monotonic and Bounded Sequences In Exercises 59–66, determine whether the sequence with the given *n*th term is monotonic and whether it is bounded. Use a graphing utility to confirm your results.

59. $a_n = 4 - \dfrac{1}{n}$ **60.** $a_n = \dfrac{3n}{n + 2}$

61. $a_n = ne^{-n/2}$ **62.** $a_n = \left(-\dfrac{2}{3}\right)^n$

63. $a_n = \left(\dfrac{2}{3}\right)^n$ **64.** $a_n = \left(\dfrac{3}{2}\right)^n$

65. $a_n = n \sin \dfrac{n\pi}{6}$ **66.** $a_n = \dfrac{\cos n}{n}$

Justifying In Exercises 67–70, (a) use Theorem 8.5 to show that the sequence with the given *n*th term converges, and (b) use a graphing utility to graph the first 10 terms of the sequence and find its limit.

67. $a_n = 7 + \dfrac{1}{n}$ **68.** $a_n = 5 - \dfrac{2}{n}$

69. $a_n = \dfrac{1}{3}\left(1 - \dfrac{1}{3^n}\right)$ **70.** $a_n = 2 + \dfrac{1}{5^n}$

71. COMPOUND INTEREST

Consider the sequence $\{A_n\}$ whose *n*th term is given by

$$A_n = P\left(1 + \frac{r}{12}\right)^n$$

where *P* is the principal, A_n is the account balance after *n* months, and *r* is the interest rate compounded annually.

(a) Is $\{A_n\}$ a convergent sequence? Explain.

(b) Find the first 10 terms of the sequence when *P* = $10,000 and *r* = 0.055.

72. Compound Interest A deposit of $100 is made in an account at the beginning of each month at an annual interest rate of 3% compounded monthly. The balance in the account after *n* months is $A_n = 100(401)(1.0025^n - 1)$.

(a) Compute the first six terms of the sequence $\{A_n\}$.

(b) Find the balance in the account after 5 years by computing the 60th term of the sequence.

(c) Find the balance in the account after 20 years by computing the 240th term of the sequence.

73. Communicating Let $\{a_n\}$ be an increasing sequence such that $2 \le a_n \le 4$. Explain why $\{a_n\}$ has a limit. What can you conclude about the limit?

74. Communicating Let $\{a_n\}$ be a monotonic sequence such that $a_n \le 1$. Discuss the convergence of $\{a_n\}$. When $\{a_n\}$ converges, what can you conclude about its limit?

EXPLORING CONCEPTS

Writing a Sequence In Exercises 75–77, give an example of a sequence satisfying the condition or explain why no such sequence exists. (Examples are not unique.)

75. A monotonically increasing sequence that converges to 10

76. A monotonically increasing bounded sequence that does not converge

77. A sequence that converges to two different numbers

 78. HOW DO YOU SEE IT? The graphs of two sequences are shown in the figures. Which graph or graphs represent the sequence that (a) converges, (b) is not bounded, and (c) is monotonic? Explain.

(i) 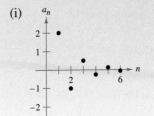   (ii)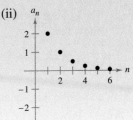

79. Government Expenditures A government program that currently costs taxpayers $4.5 billion per year is cut back by 20 percent per year.

(a) Write an expression for the amount budgeted for this program after *n* years.

(b) Compute the budgets for the first 4 years.

(c) Determine the convergence or divergence of the sequence of reduced budgets. If the sequence converges, find its limit.

80. INFLATION

When the rate of inflation is $4\frac{1}{2}\%$ per year and the average price of a car is currently $30,000, the average price after n years is $P_n = \$30{,}000(1.045)^n$. Compute the average prices for the next 5 years. Does the sequence of prices converge? Explain.

True or False? In Exercises 81–84, determine whether the statement is true or false. If it is false, explain why or give an example that shows it is false.

81. If $\{a_n\}$ converges and $\{b_n\}$ converges to 0, then $\{a_n/b_n\}$ must diverge.

82. If $\{a_n\}$ converges, then $\lim\limits_{n\to\infty} (a_n - a_{n+1}) = 0$.

83. If $\{a_n\}$ converges, then $\{a_n/n\}$ converges to 0.

84. If $\{a_n\}$ diverges and $\{b_n\}$ diverges, then $\{a_n + b_n\}$ must diverge.

85. Fibonacci Sequence In a study of the progeny of rabbits, Fibonacci (ca. 1170–ca. 1240) encountered the sequence now bearing his name. The sequence is defined recursively as $a_{n+2} = a_n + a_{n+1}$, where $a_1 = 1$ and $a_2 = 1$.

(a) Write the first 12 terms of the sequence.

(b) Write the first 10 terms of the sequence defined by $b_n = a_{n+1}/a_n$, where $n \geq 1$.

(c) Using the definition in part (b), show that

$$b_n = 1 + \frac{1}{b_{n-1}}.$$

(d) The **golden ratio** ρ can be defined by $\lim\limits_{n\to\infty} b_n = \rho$. Show that

$$\rho = 1 + \frac{1}{\rho}$$

and solve this equation for ρ.

86. Proof Prove that if $\{s_n\}$ converges to L and $L > 0$, then there exists a number N such that $s_n > 0$ for $n > N$.

87. Justifying Show that the converse of Theorem 8.1 is not true. [*Hint:* Find a function $f(x)$ such that $f(n) = a_n$ converges, but $\lim\limits_{x\to\infty} f(x)$ does not exist.]

88. Implementing Processes Consider the sequence $\{a_n\}$, where $a_1 = \sqrt{k}$, $a_{n+1} = \sqrt{k + a_n}$, and $k > 0$.

(a) Show that $\{a_n\}$ is increasing and bounded.

(b) Prove that $\lim\limits_{n\to\infty} a_n$ exists.

(c) Find $\lim\limits_{n\to\infty} a_n$.

89. Squeeze Theorem

(a) Show that $\int_1^n \ln x \, dx < \ln(n!)$ for $n \geq 2$.

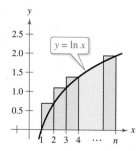

(b) Draw a graph similar to the one above that shows $\ln(n!) < \int_1^{n+1} \ln x \, dx$.

(c) Use the results of parts (a) and (b) to show that

$$\frac{n^n}{e^{n-1}} < n! < \frac{(n+1)^{n+1}}{e^n}, \quad \text{for} \quad n > 1.$$

(d) Use the Squeeze Theorem for Sequences and the result of part (c) to show that $\lim\limits_{n\to\infty} \left(\sqrt[n]{n!}/n\right) = 1/e$.

(e) Test the result of part (d) for $n = 20, 50,$ and 100.

90. Proof Prove, using the definition of the limit of a sequence, that $\lim\limits_{n\to\infty} (1/n^3) = 0$.

91. Proof Prove, using the definition of the limit of a sequence, that $\lim\limits_{n\to\infty} r^n = 0$ for $-1 < r < 1$.

92. Writing a Sequence Find a divergent sequence $\{a_n\}$ such that $\{a_{2n}\}$ converges.

93. Proof Prove Theorem 8.5 for a nonincreasing sequence.

Calculus AP® – Exam Preparation Questions

94. Multiple Choice What is the limit of the sequence $\{a_n\} = \{\sqrt[n]{n}\}$?

(A) 0   (B) 1

(C) e

(D) The sequence diverges.

95. Multiple Choice Which of the following sequences does *not* converge to 0?

I. $\{a_n\} = \left\{\dfrac{e^n + 2}{e^{2n} - 1}\right\}$ II. $\{a_n\} = \left\{\dfrac{\ln n}{n^{5/3}}\right\}$

III. $\{a_n\} = \left\{\dfrac{2 + 7n^2}{n + n^2}\right\}$

(A) None   (B) I and II only

(C) II and III only   (D) III only

96. Multiple Choice Which of the following sequences is bounded and monotonic?

(A) $\{a_n\} = \left\{n^2 + \dfrac{1}{n}\right\}$ (B) $\{a_n\} = \left\{\dfrac{e^n}{n}\right\}$

(C) $\{a_n\} = \left\{\dfrac{n^2 + 1}{n^3 + 1}\right\}$ (D) $\{a_n\} = \left\{\cos\dfrac{n\pi}{2}\right\}$

8.2 Series and Convergence

▶ Understand the definition of a convergent infinite series.
▶ Use properties of infinite geometric series.
▶ Use the nth-Term Test for Divergence of an infinite series.

Infinite Series

One important application of infinite sequences is in representing "infinite summations." Informally, if $\{a_n\}$ is an infinite sequence, then

$$\sum_{n=1}^{\infty} a_n = a_1 + a_2 + a_3 + \cdots + a_n + \cdots \qquad \text{Infinite Series}$$

is an **infinite series** (or simply a **series**). The numbers a_1, a_2, a_3, and so on are the **terms** of the series. For some series, it is convenient to begin the index at $n = 0$ (or some other integer). As a typesetting convention, it is common to represent an infinite series as $\Sigma\, a_n$. In such cases, the starting value for the index must be taken from the context of the statement.

To find the sum of an infinite series, consider the **sequence of partial sums** listed below.

$$S_1 = a_1$$
$$S_2 = a_1 + a_2$$
$$S_3 = a_1 + a_2 + a_3$$
$$S_4 = a_1 + a_2 + a_3 + a_4$$
$$S_5 = a_1 + a_2 + a_3 + a_4 + a_5$$
$$\vdots$$
$$S_n = a_1 + a_2 + a_3 + a_4 + a_5 + \cdots + a_n$$

If this sequence of partial sums converges, then the series is said to converge and has the sum indicated in the next definition.

> ### Communication and Notation
>
> As you study this chapter, it is important to distinguish between an infinite series and a sequence. A sequence is an ordered collection of numbers
>
> $$a_1, a_2, a_3, \ldots, a_n, \ldots$$
>
> whereas a series is an infinite sum of terms from a sequence
>
> $$a_1 + a_2 + a_3 + \cdots + a_n + \cdots.$$

Definitions of Convergent and Divergent Series

For the infinite series $\displaystyle\sum_{n=1}^{\infty} a_n$, the **$n$th partial sum** is

$$S_n = a_1 + a_2 + \cdots + a_n.$$

If the sequence of partial sums $\{S_n\}$ converges to S, then the series $\displaystyle\sum_{n=1}^{\infty} a_n$ **converges**. The limit S is called the **sum of the series.**

$$S = a_1 + a_2 + \cdots + a_n + \cdots \qquad S = \sum_{n=1}^{\infty} a_n$$

If $\{S_n\}$ diverges, then the series **diverges.**

As you study this chapter, you will see that there are two basic questions involving infinite series.

- Does a series converge or does it diverge?
- When a series converges, what is its sum?

These questions are not always easy to answer, especially the second one.

EXAMPLE 1 Convergent and Divergent Series

a. The series

$$\sum_{n=1}^{\infty} \frac{1}{2^n} = \frac{1}{2} + \frac{1}{4} + \frac{1}{8} + \frac{1}{16} + \cdots$$

has the partial sums listed below.

$$S_1 = \frac{1}{2}$$

$$S_2 = \frac{1}{2} + \frac{1}{4} = \frac{3}{4}$$

$$S_3 = \frac{1}{2} + \frac{1}{4} + \frac{1}{8} = \frac{7}{8}$$

$$\vdots$$

$$S_n = \frac{1}{2} + \frac{1}{4} + \frac{1}{8} + \cdots + \frac{1}{2^n} = \frac{2^n - 1}{2^n}$$

Because

$$\lim_{n \to \infty} \frac{2^n - 1}{2^n} = 1$$

it follows that the series converges and its sum is 1. (You can also determine the partial sums of the series geometrically, as shown in Figure 8.6.)

b. The nth partial sum of the series

$$\sum_{n=1}^{\infty} \left(\frac{1}{n} - \frac{1}{n+1} \right) = \left(1 - \frac{1}{2} \right) + \left(\frac{1}{2} - \frac{1}{3} \right) + \left(\frac{1}{3} - \frac{1}{4} \right) + \cdots$$

is

$$S_n = 1 - \frac{1}{n+1}.$$

Because the limit of S_n is 1, the series converges and its sum is 1.

c. The series

$$\sum_{n=1}^{\infty} 1 = 1 + 1 + 1 + 1 + \cdots$$

diverges because $S_n = n$ and the sequence of partial sums diverges.

The series in Example 1(b) is a **telescoping series** of the form

$$(b_1 - b_2) + (b_2 - b_3) + (b_3 - b_4) + (b_4 - b_5) + \cdots. \qquad \text{Telescoping series}$$

Note that b_2 is canceled by the second term, b_3 is canceled by the third term, and so on. Because the nth partial sum of this series is

$$S_n = b_1 - b_{n+1}$$

it follows that a telescoping series will converge if and only if b_n approaches a finite number as $n \to \infty$. Moreover, if the series converges, then its sum is

$$S = b_1 - \lim_{n \to \infty} b_{n+1}.$$

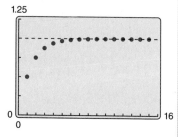

Technology

Figure 8.5 shows the first 15 partial sums of the infinite series in Example 1(a). Notice how the values appear to approach the line $y = 1$.

Figure 8.5

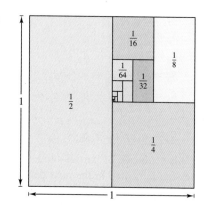

You can determine the partial sums of the series in Example 1(a) geometrically using this figure.

Figure 8.6

EXAMPLE 2   Writing a Series in Telescoping Form

Find the sum of the series $\displaystyle\sum_{n=1}^{\infty} \frac{2}{4n^2 - 1}$.

Solution

Using partial fractions, you can write

$$a_n = \frac{2}{4n^2 - 1} = \frac{2}{(2n-1)(2n+1)} = \frac{1}{2n-1} - \frac{1}{2n+1}.$$

From this telescoping form, you can see that the nth partial sum is

$$S_n = \left(\frac{1}{1} - \frac{1}{3}\right) + \left(\frac{1}{3} - \frac{1}{5}\right) + \cdots + \left(\frac{1}{2n-1} - \frac{1}{2n+1}\right) = 1 - \frac{1}{2n+1}.$$

So, the series converges and its sum is 1. That is,

$$\sum_{n=1}^{\infty} \frac{2}{4n^2 - 1} = \lim_{n \to \infty} S_n = \lim_{n \to \infty}\left(1 - \frac{1}{2n+1}\right) = 1.$$

Geometric Series

The series in Example 1(a) is a **geometric series.** In general, the series

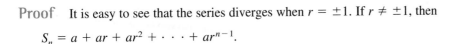

$$\sum_{n=0}^{\infty} ar^n = a + ar + ar^2 + \cdots + ar^n + \cdots, \quad a \neq 0 \qquad \text{Geometric series}$$

is a **geometric series** with ratio r, $r \neq 0$.

Theorem 8.6   Convergence of a Geometric Series

A geometric series with ratio r diverges when $|r| \geq 1$. If $|r| < 1$, then the series converges to the sum

$$\sum_{n=0}^{\infty} ar^n = \frac{a}{1-r}, \quad |r| < 1.$$

Proof   It is easy to see that the series diverges when $r = \pm 1$. If $r \neq \pm 1$, then

$$S_n = a + ar + ar^2 + \cdots + ar^{n-1}.$$

Multiplication by r yields

$$rS_n = ar + ar^2 + ar^3 + \cdots + ar^n.$$

Subtracting the second equation from the first produces $S_n - rS_n = a - ar^n$. Therefore, $S_n(1 - r) = a(1 - r^n)$, and the nth partial sum is

$$S_n = \frac{a}{1-r}(1 - r^n).$$

When $|r| < 1$, it follows that $r^n \to 0$ as $n \to \infty$, and you obtain

$$\lim_{n \to \infty} S_n = \lim_{n \to \infty}\left[\frac{a}{1-r}(1 - r^n)\right] = \frac{a}{1-r}\left[\lim_{n \to \infty}(1 - r^n)\right] = \frac{a}{1-r}$$

which means that the series *converges* and its sum is $a/(1 - r)$. It is left to you to show that the series diverges when $|r| > 1$.

Algebra Review

For help on the algebra in Example 2, see Example 2(a) in the *Chapter 8 Algebra Review* on page A51.

Exploration

In "Proof Without Words," by Benjamin G. Klein and Irl C. Bivens, the authors present the diagram below. Explain why the second statement after the diagram is valid. How is this result related to Theorem 8.6?

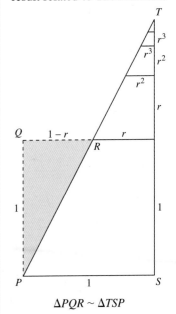

$$\Delta PQR \sim \Delta TSP$$

$$1 + r + r^2 + r^3 + \cdots = \frac{1}{1-r}$$

Exercise taken from "Proof Without Words" by Benjamin G. Klein and Irl C. Bivens, *Mathematics Magazine*, 61, No. 4, October 1988, p. 219, by permission of the authors.

EXAMPLE 3 Convergent and Divergent Geometric Series

Determine the convergence or divergence of each series.

a. $\displaystyle\sum_{n=0}^{\infty} \frac{3}{2^n} = \sum_{n=0}^{\infty} 3\left(\frac{1}{2}\right)^n = 3(1) + 3\left(\frac{1}{2}\right) + 3\left(\frac{1}{2}\right)^2 + \cdots$

b. $\displaystyle\sum_{n=0}^{\infty} \left(\frac{3}{2}\right)^n = 1 + \frac{3}{2} + \frac{9}{4} + \frac{27}{8} + \cdots$

Algebraic Solution

a. This geometric series has a ratio of $r = \frac{1}{2}$ with $a = 3$. Because $|r| < 1$, the series converges and its sum is

$$S = \frac{a}{1-r} = \frac{3}{1-(1/2)} = 6.$$

b. This geometric series has a ratio of $r = \frac{3}{2}$. Because $|r| \geq 1$, the series diverges.

Numerical Solution

a. The partial sums in the table suggest that the series converges to $S = 6$.

n	10	50	100	500
S_n	5.997	6.000	6.000	6.000

b. The partial sums in the table suggest that the series diverges.

n	10	50	100	500
S_n	170.995	1.913×10^9	1.220×10^{18}	3.332×10^{88}

The formula for the sum of a geometric series can be used to write a repeating decimal as the ratio of two integers, as demonstrated in the next example.

EXAMPLE 4 A Geometric Series for a Repeating Decimal

See LarsonCalculusforAP.com for an interactive version of this type of example.

Use a geometric series to write $0.\overline{08}$ as the ratio of two integers.

Solution

For the repeating decimal $0.\overline{08}$, you can write

$$0.080808\ldots = \frac{8}{10^2} + \frac{8}{10^4} + \frac{8}{10^6} + \frac{8}{10^8} + \cdots = \sum_{n=0}^{\infty} \left(\frac{8}{10^2}\right)\left(\frac{1}{10^2}\right)^n.$$

For this series, you have $a = 8/10^2$ and $r = 1/10^2$. So,

$$0.080808\ldots = \frac{a}{1-r} = \frac{8/10^2}{1-(1/10^2)} = \frac{8}{99}.$$

Try dividing 8 by 99 on a calculator to see that it produces $0.\overline{08}$.

The convergence of a series is not affected by the removal of a finite number of terms from the beginning of the series. For instance, the geometric series

$$\sum_{n=4}^{\infty} \left(\frac{1}{2}\right)^n \quad \text{and} \quad \sum_{n=0}^{\infty} \left(\frac{1}{2}\right)^n$$

both converge. Furthermore, because the sum of the second series is

$$\frac{a}{1-r} = \frac{1}{1-(1/2)} = 2$$

you can conclude that the sum of the first series is

$$S = 2 - \left[\left(\frac{1}{2}\right)^0 + \left(\frac{1}{2}\right)^1 + \left(\frac{1}{2}\right)^2 + \left(\frac{1}{2}\right)^3\right] = 2 - \frac{15}{8} = \frac{1}{8}.$$

Communication and Notation

In words, Theorem 8.6 states that "the sum of a convergent geometric series is the first term of the series divided by the difference of 1 and the ratio r." So, for the series

$$\sum_{n=4}^{\infty} \left(\frac{1}{2}\right)^n$$

another way to find the sum is to note that the first term is $(1/2)^4$, $r = 1/2$, and thus

$$S = \frac{(1/2)^4}{1-(1/2)} = \frac{1}{8}.$$

The properties in the next theorem are direct consequences of the corresponding properties of limits of sequences.

Theorem 8.7 Properties of Infinite Series

Let $\Sigma \, a_n$ and $\Sigma \, b_n$ be convergent series, and let A, B, and c be real numbers. If $\Sigma \, a_n = A$ and $\Sigma \, b_n = B$, then the following series converge to the indicated sums.

1. $\displaystyle\sum_{n=1}^{\infty} ca_n = cA$ **2.** $\displaystyle\sum_{n=1}^{\infty} (a_n + b_n) = A + B$

3. $\displaystyle\sum_{n=1}^{\infty} (a_n - b_n) = A - B$

---

nth-Term Test for Divergence

The next theorem states that when a series converges, the limit of its nth term must be 0.

Theorem 8.8 Limit of the nth Term of a Convergent Series

If $\displaystyle\sum_{n=1}^{\infty} a_n$ converges, then $\displaystyle\lim_{n\to\infty} a_n = 0$.

Proof Assume that

$$\sum_{n=1}^{\infty} a_n = \lim_{n\to\infty} S_n = L.$$

Then, because $S_n = S_{n-1} + a_n$ and

$$\lim_{n\to\infty} S_n = \lim_{n\to\infty} S_{n-1} = L$$

it follows that

$$
\begin{aligned}
L &= \lim_{n\to\infty} S_n \\
&= \lim_{n\to\infty} (S_{n-1} + a_n) \\
&= \lim_{n\to\infty} S_{n-1} + \lim_{n\to\infty} a_n \\
&= L + \lim_{n\to\infty} a_n
\end{aligned}
$$

which implies that $\{a_n\}$ converges to 0.

> **Communication and Notation** Be sure you see that the converse of Theorem 8.8 is generally not true. That is, if the sequence $\{a_n\}$ converges to 0, then the series $\Sigma \, a_n$ may either converge or diverge.

The contrapositive of Theorem 8.8 provides a useful test for *divergence*. This **nth-Term Test for Divergence** (also known as the **Divergence Test**) states that if the limit of the nth term of a series does *not* converge to 0, then the series must diverge.

Insight

The Geometric Series and nth-Term Tests are commonly covered on the AP® Calculus BC Exam.

Theorem 8.9 nth-Term Test for Divergence

If $\displaystyle\lim_{n\to\infty} a_n \neq 0$, then $\displaystyle\sum_{n=1}^{\infty} a_n$ diverges.

EXAMPLE 5 Using the *n*th-Term Test for Divergence

a. For the series $\displaystyle\sum_{n=0}^{\infty} 2^n$, you have

$$\lim_{n\to\infty} 2^n = \infty.$$

So, the limit of the *n*th term is not 0, and the series diverges.

b. For the series $\displaystyle\sum_{n=1}^{\infty} \frac{n!}{2n! + 1}$, you have

$$\lim_{n\to\infty} \frac{n!}{2n! + 1} = \lim_{n\to\infty} \frac{1}{2 + (1/n!)} = \frac{1}{2}.$$

So, the limit of the *n*th term is not 0, and the series diverges.

c. For the series $\displaystyle\sum_{n=1}^{\infty} \frac{1}{n}$, you have

$$\lim_{n\to\infty} \frac{1}{n} = 0.$$

Because the limit of the *n*th term is 0, the *n*th-Term Test for Divergence does *not* apply and you can draw no conclusions about convergence or divergence. (In the next section, you will see that this particular series diverges.)

EXAMPLE 6 Bouncing Ball Problem

A ball is dropped from a height of 6 feet and begins bouncing, as shown in Figure 8.7. The height of each bounce is three-fourths the height of the previous bounce. Find the total vertical distance traveled by the ball.

Solution

When the ball hits the ground for the first time, it has traveled a distance of $D_1 = 6$ feet. For subsequent bounces, let D_i be the distance traveled up and down. For example, D_2 and D_3 are

$$D_2 = \underbrace{6\left(\frac{3}{4}\right)}_{\text{Up}} + \underbrace{6\left(\frac{3}{4}\right)}_{\text{Down}} = 12\left(\frac{3}{4}\right)$$

and

$$D_3 = \underbrace{6\left(\frac{3}{4}\right)\left(\frac{3}{4}\right)}_{\text{Up}} + \underbrace{6\left(\frac{3}{4}\right)\left(\frac{3}{4}\right)}_{\text{Down}} = 12\left(\frac{3}{4}\right)^2.$$

By continuing this process, it can be determined that the total vertical distance is

$$D = 6 + 12\left(\frac{3}{4}\right) + 12\left(\frac{3}{4}\right)^2 + 12\left(\frac{3}{4}\right)^3 + \cdots$$

$$= 6 + 12 \sum_{n=0}^{\infty} \left(\frac{3}{4}\right)^{n+1}$$

$$= 6 + 12\left(\frac{3}{4}\right) \sum_{n=0}^{\infty} \left(\frac{3}{4}\right)^{n}$$

$$= 6 + 9\left[\frac{1}{1 - (3/4)}\right]$$

$$= 6 + 9(4)$$

$$= 42 \text{ feet.}$$

> **Remark**
>
> The series in Example 5(c) will play an important role in this chapter.
>
> $$\sum_{n=1}^{\infty} \frac{1}{n} = 1 + \frac{1}{2} + \frac{1}{3} + \cdots$$
>
> In the next section, you will see that this series diverges even though the *n*th term approaches 0 as *n* approaches ∞.

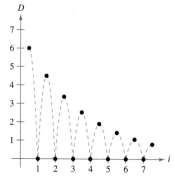

The height of each bounce is three-fourths the height of the preceding bounce.

Figure 8.7

8.2 Exercises

Finding Partial Sums In Exercises 1–6, find the sequence of partial sums $S_1, S_2, S_3, S_4,$ and S_5.

1. $1 + \frac{1}{4} + \frac{1}{9} + \frac{1}{16} + \frac{1}{25} + \cdots$

2. $\frac{1}{2 \cdot 3} + \frac{2}{3 \cdot 4} + \frac{3}{4 \cdot 5} + \frac{4}{5 \cdot 6} + \frac{5}{6 \cdot 7} + \cdots$

3. $3 - \frac{9}{2} + \frac{27}{4} - \frac{81}{8} + \frac{243}{16} - \cdots$

4. $\frac{1}{2} + \frac{1}{4} + \frac{1}{6} + \frac{1}{8} + \frac{1}{10} + \cdots$

5. $\displaystyle\sum_{n=1}^{\infty} \frac{3}{2^{n-1}}$

6. $\displaystyle\sum_{n=1}^{\infty} \frac{(-1)^{n+1}}{n!}$

Verifying Divergence In Exercises 7–14, verify that the infinite series diverges.

7. $\displaystyle\sum_{n=0}^{\infty} 5\left(\frac{5}{2}\right)^n$

8. $\displaystyle\sum_{n=0}^{\infty} \frac{1}{2}(-3)^n$

9. $\displaystyle\sum_{n=1}^{\infty} \frac{n}{n+1}$

10. $\displaystyle\sum_{n=1}^{\infty} \frac{n}{2n+3}$

11. $\displaystyle\sum_{n=0}^{\infty} \frac{n^3}{n^3 - n^2}$

12. $\displaystyle\sum_{n=0}^{\infty} \frac{2n}{\sqrt{n^2 + 1}}$

13. $\displaystyle\sum_{n=1}^{\infty} \frac{4^n + 3}{4^{n+1}}$

14. $\displaystyle\sum_{n=1}^{\infty} \frac{n!}{2^n}$

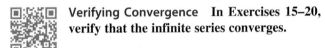

Verifying Convergence In Exercises 15–20, verify that the infinite series converges.

15. $\displaystyle\sum_{n=0}^{\infty} \left(\frac{5}{6}\right)^n$

16. $\displaystyle\sum_{n=1}^{\infty} 2\left(-\frac{1}{2}\right)^n$

17. $\displaystyle\sum_{n=0}^{\infty} (0.9)^n$

18. $\displaystyle\sum_{n=0}^{\infty} (-0.2)^n$

19. $\displaystyle\sum_{n=1}^{\infty} \frac{1}{n(n+1)}$ (*Hint:* Use partial fractions.)

20. $\displaystyle\sum_{n=1}^{\infty} \frac{1}{n(n+2)}$ (*Hint:* Use partial fractions.)

Connecting Representations In Exercises 21–24, (a) find the sum of the series, (b) use a graphing utility to find the indicated partial sum S_n and complete the table, (c) use a graphing utility to graph the first 10 terms of the sequence of partial sums and a horizontal line representing the sum, and (d) explain the relationship between the magnitudes of the terms of the series and the rate at which the sequence of partial sums approaches the sum of the series.

n	5	10	20	50	100
S_n					

21. $\displaystyle\sum_{n=1}^{\infty} \frac{6}{n(n+3)}$

22. $\displaystyle\sum_{n=1}^{\infty} \frac{4}{n(n+4)}$

23. $\displaystyle\sum_{n=1}^{\infty} 2(0.9)^{n-1}$

24. $\displaystyle\sum_{n=1}^{\infty} 10\left(-\frac{1}{4}\right)^{n-1}$

Finding the Sum of a Convergent Series In Exercises 25–34, find the sum of the convergent series.

25. $\displaystyle\sum_{n=0}^{\infty} 4\left(\frac{2}{3}\right)^n$

26. $\displaystyle\sum_{n=0}^{\infty} \left(-\frac{1}{8}\right)^n$

27. $\displaystyle\sum_{n=1}^{\infty} \frac{4}{n(n+2)}$

28. $\displaystyle\sum_{n=1}^{\infty} \frac{1}{(2n+1)(2n+3)}$

29. $8 + 6 + \frac{9}{2} + \frac{27}{8} + \cdots$

30. $9 - 3 + 1 - \frac{1}{3} + \cdots$

31. $\displaystyle\sum_{n=0}^{\infty} \left(\frac{1}{2^n} - \frac{1}{3^n}\right)$

32. $\displaystyle\sum_{n=0}^{\infty} [(0.2)^n + (0.6)^n]$

33. $\displaystyle\sum_{n=1}^{\infty} (\sin 1)^n$

34. $\displaystyle\sum_{n=1}^{\infty} \frac{1}{9n^2 + 3n - 2}$

Error Analysis In Exercises 35 and 36, describe and correct the error in finding the sum of the convergent series.

35. $\displaystyle\sum_{n=0}^{\infty} \left(-\frac{3}{4}\right)^n = \frac{1}{1 - (3/4)} = \frac{1}{1/4} = 4$ ✗

36. $\displaystyle\sum_{n=0}^{\infty} \frac{3}{5^n} = \frac{1}{1 - (3/5)} = \frac{1}{2/5} = \frac{5}{2}$ ✗

Using a Geometric Series In Exercises 37–40, (a) write the repeating decimal as a geometric series, and (b) write the sum of the series as the ratio of two integers.

37. $0.\overline{4}$

38. $0.\overline{45}$

39. $0.\overline{02}$

40. $0.\overline{068}$

Convergent and Divergent Series In Exercises 41–54, determine the convergence or divergence of the series. If the series converges, find its sum.

41. $\displaystyle\sum_{n=0}^{\infty} (1.075)^n$

42. $\displaystyle\sum_{n=0}^{\infty} \frac{3^n}{1000}$

43. $\displaystyle\sum_{n=1}^{\infty} \frac{n+1}{2n-1}$

44. $\displaystyle\sum_{n=1}^{\infty} \frac{4n+1}{3n-1}$

45. $\displaystyle\sum_{n=1}^{\infty} \left(\frac{1}{n} - \frac{1}{n+2}\right)$

46. $\displaystyle\sum_{n=1}^{\infty} \left(\frac{1}{n+1} - \frac{1}{n+2}\right)$

47. $\displaystyle\sum_{n=1}^{\infty} \frac{3^n}{n^3}$

48. $\displaystyle\sum_{n=0}^{\infty} \frac{5}{4^n}$

49. $\displaystyle\sum_{n=2}^{\infty} \frac{n}{\ln n}$

50. $\displaystyle\sum_{n=1}^{\infty} \ln \frac{1}{n}$

51. $\displaystyle\sum_{n=1}^{\infty} \left(1 + \frac{k}{n}\right)^n$

52. $\displaystyle\sum_{n=1}^{\infty} e^{-n}$

53. $\displaystyle\sum_{n=1}^{\infty} \arctan n$

54. $\displaystyle\sum_{n=1}^{\infty} \ln\left(\frac{n+1}{n}\right)$

EXPLORING CONCEPTS

55. Communication and Notation Describe the difference between

$$\lim_{n \to \infty} a_n = 5 \quad \text{and} \quad \sum_{n=1}^{\infty} a_n = 5.$$

56. Using Divergent Series Find two divergent series $\Sigma\, a_n$ and $\Sigma\, b_n$ such that $\Sigma(a_n + b_n)$ converges.

57. Communication and Notation Explain any differences among the following series.

(a) $\displaystyle\sum_{n=1}^{\infty} a_n$ (b) $\displaystyle\sum_{k=1}^{\infty} a_k$ (c) $\displaystyle\sum_{n=1}^{\infty} a_k$

58. Convergence or Divergence of a Modified Series

(a) You delete a finite number of terms from a divergent series. Will the new series still diverge? Explain your reasoning.

(b) You add a finite number of terms to a convergent series. Will the new series still converge? Explain your reasoning.

Finding Intervals of Convergence   In Exercises 59–64, **find all values of x for which the series converges. For these values, write the sum of the series as a function of x.**

59. $\displaystyle\sum_{n=1}^{\infty} (4x)^n$ **60.** $\displaystyle\sum_{n=0}^{\infty} \left(\frac{3}{x}\right)^n$

61. $\displaystyle\sum_{n=1}^{\infty} (x-1)^n$ **62.** $\displaystyle\sum_{n=0}^{\infty} 5\left(\frac{x-2}{3}\right)^n$

63. $\displaystyle\sum_{n=0}^{\infty} (-1)^n x^n$ **64.** $\displaystyle\sum_{n=0}^{\infty} (-1)^n x^{2n}$

Connecting Representations   In Exercises 65 and 66, **(a) find the common ratio of the geometric series, (b) write the function that gives the sum of the series, and (c) use a graphing utility to graph the function and the partial sums S_3 and S_5. What do you notice?**

65. $1 + x + x^2 + x^3 + \cdots$

66. $1 - \dfrac{x}{2} + \dfrac{x^2}{4} - \dfrac{x^3}{8} + \cdots$

Communicating   In Exercises 67 and 68, **use a graphing utility to determine the first term that is less than 0.0001 in each of the convergent series. Note that the answers are very different. Explain how this will affect the rate at which the series converges.**

67. $\displaystyle\sum_{n=1}^{\infty} \frac{1}{n(n+1)}, \ \sum_{n=1}^{\infty} \left(\frac{1}{8}\right)^n$ **68.** $\displaystyle\sum_{n=1}^{\infty} \frac{1}{2^n}, \ \sum_{n=1}^{\infty} (0.01)^n$

69. Marketing A manufacturer estimates the annual sales of a new product to be 8000 units. Each year, 5% of the units that have been sold will become inoperative. So, 8000 units will be in use after 1 year, $[8000 + 0.95(8000)]$ units will be in use after 2 years, and so on. How many units will be in use after n years?

70. Depreciation A company buys a machine for $475,000 that depreciates at a rate of 30% per year. Find a formula for the value of the machine after n years. What is its value after 5 years?

71. Modeling Data The annual profits a_n (in millions of dollars) for Fiserv, Inc. from 2009 through 2018 are shown in the table, where n represents the year, with $n = 9$ corresponding to 2009. *(Source: Fiserv, Inc.)*

n	9	10	11	12	13
a_n	550	614	661	706	795

n	14	15	16	17	18
a_n	852	921	993	1103	1281

(a) Use the regression capabilities of a graphing utility to find an exponential model $y = ab^x$ for the data.

(b) Write a geometric series that corresponds to the model in part (a). Does this series converge? Explain.

(c) Use a partial sum of the series in part (b) to approximate the total profits for the 10-year period. Then find the actual total profits for the 10-year period. Compare the results.

72. Present Value The winner of a $2,000,000 sweepstakes will be paid $100,000 per year for 20 years. The money earns 6% interest per year. The present value of the winnings is $\displaystyle\sum_{n=1}^{20} 100{,}000\left(\frac{1}{1.06}\right)^n$. Compute the present value and interpret its meaning. [*Hint:* The formula for the nth partial sum of a geometric series is

$$\sum_{i=0}^{n-1} ar^i = \frac{a(1-r^n)}{1-r}.]$$

73. MULTIPLIER EFFECT

The total annual spending by tourists in a resort city is $500 million. Approximately 75% of that revenue is again spent in the resort city, and of that amount approximately 75% is again spent in the same city, and so on. Write the geometric series that gives the total amount of spending generated by the $500 million and find the sum of the series.

74. Multiplier Effect Repeat Exercise 73 when the percent of the revenue that is spent again in the city decreases to 60%.

75. Distance A ball is dropped from a height of 16 feet. Each time it drops h feet, it rebounds $0.81h$ feet. Find the total distance traveled by the ball.

76. Time The ball in Exercise 75 takes the following times for each fall.

$$s_1 = -16t^2 + 16, \qquad s_1 = 0 \text{ when } t = 1$$

$$s_2 = -16t^2 + 16(0.81), \qquad s_2 = 0 \text{ when } t = 0.9$$

$$s_3 = -16t^2 + 16(0.81)^2, \qquad s_3 = 0 \text{ when } t = (0.9)^2$$

$$s_4 = -16t^2 + 16(0.81)^3, \qquad s_4 = 0 \text{ when } t = (0.9)^3$$

$$\vdots \qquad\qquad \vdots$$

$$s_n = -16t^2 + 16(0.81)^{n-1}, \quad s_n = 0 \text{ when } t = (0.9)^{n-1}$$

Beginning with s_2, the ball takes the same amount of time to bounce up as it does to fall, and so the total time elapsed before it comes to rest is given by

$$t = 1 + 2 \sum_{n=1}^{\infty} (0.9)^n.$$

Find this total time.

77. Area The sides of a square are 16 inches in length. A new square is formed by connecting the midpoints of the sides of the original square, and two of the triangles outside the second square are shaded (see figure). Determine the area of the shaded regions (a) when this process is continued five more times, and (b) when this pattern of shading is continued infinitely.

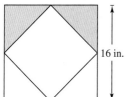
Figure for 77

Figure for 78

78. Length A right triangle XYZ is shown above, where $|XY| = z$ and $\angle X = \theta$. Line segments are continually drawn to be perpendicular to the triangle, as shown in the figure.

(a) Find the total length of the perpendicular line segments $|Yy_1| + |x_1y_1| + |x_1y_2| + \cdots$ in terms of z and θ.

(b) Find the total length of the perpendicular line segments when $z = 1$ and $\theta = \pi/6$.

Probability In Exercises 79 and 80, the random variable n represents the number of units of a product sold per day in a store. The probability distribution of n is given by $P(n)$. Find the probability that two units are sold in a given day $[P(2)]$ and show that $P(0) + P(1) + P(2) + P(3) + \cdots = 1$.

79. $P(n) = \frac{1}{2}\left(\frac{1}{2}\right)^n$ **80.** $P(n) = \frac{1}{3}\left(\frac{2}{3}\right)^n$

81. Probability A fair coin is tossed repeatedly. The probability that the first head occurs on the nth toss is given by $P(n) = \left(\frac{1}{2}\right)^n$, where $n \geq 1$.

(a) Show that $\displaystyle\sum_{n=1}^{\infty} \left(\frac{1}{2}\right)^n = 1$.

(b) The expected number of tosses required until the first head occurs in the experiment is given by

$$\sum_{n=1}^{\infty} n\left(\frac{1}{2}\right)^n.$$

Is this series geometric?

(c) Use a computer algebra system to find the sum in part (b).

82. Probability In an experiment, three people toss a fair coin one at a time until one of them tosses a head. Determine, for each person, the probability that he or she tosses the first head.

True or False? In Exercises 83–87, determine whether the statement is true or false. If it is false, explain why or give an example that shows it is false.

83. If $\displaystyle\lim_{n \to \infty} a_n = 0$, then $\displaystyle\sum_{n=1}^{\infty} a_n$ must converge.

84. If $\displaystyle\sum_{n=1}^{\infty} a_n = L$, then $\displaystyle\sum_{n=0}^{\infty} a_n = L + a_0$.

85. If $|r| < 1$, then $\displaystyle\sum_{n=1}^{\infty} ar^n = \frac{a}{1-r}$.

86. $0.75 = 0.749999 \ldots$

87. Every decimal with a repeating pattern of digits is a rational number.

88. HOW DO YOU SEE IT? The figure below represents an informal way of showing that

$$\sum_{n=1}^{\infty} \frac{1}{n^2} < 2.$$

Explain how the figure implies this conclusion.

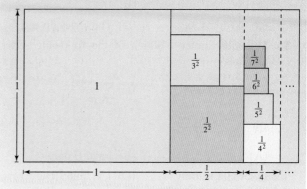

For more on this exercise, see the article "Convergence with Pictures" by P.J. Rippon in *American Mathematical Monthly*.

89. Fibonacci Sequence The Fibonacci sequence is defined recursively by $a_{n+2} = a_n + a_{n+1}$, where $a_1 = 1$ and $a_2 = 1$.

(a) Show that $\dfrac{1}{a_{n+1}a_{n+3}} = \dfrac{1}{a_{n+1}a_{n+2}} - \dfrac{1}{a_{n+2}a_{n+3}}$.

(b) Show that $\displaystyle\sum_{n=0}^{\infty} \dfrac{1}{a_{n+1}a_{n+3}} = 1$.

90. Proof Given two infinite series $\Sigma\, a_n$ and $\Sigma\, b_n$ such that $\Sigma\, a_n$ converges and $\Sigma\, b_n$ diverges, prove that $\Sigma(a_n + b_n)$ diverges.

91. Remainder Let $\Sigma\, a_n$ be a convergent series, and let

$$R_N = a_{N+1} + a_{N+2} + \cdots$$

be the remainder of the series after the first N terms. Prove that $\lim\limits_{N\to\infty} R_N = 0$.

92. Proof Prove that

$$\frac{1}{r} + \frac{1}{r^2} + \frac{1}{r^3} + \cdots = \frac{1}{r-1}$$

for $|r| > 1$.

Calculus AP® – Exam Preparation Questions

93. Multiple Choice For what values of k does the series $\displaystyle\sum_{n=1}^{\infty} \left(\frac{11}{2k^2 + 3}\right)^n$ converge?

(A) $k \le -2$ and $k \ge 2$

(B) $k < -2$ and $k > 2$ only

(C) $k > 2$ only   (D) $k \ge 2$ only

94. Multiple Choice What is the value of $\displaystyle\sum_{n=0}^{\infty} \left(\frac{\pi}{e}\right)^n$?

(A) $\dfrac{e}{e - \pi}$ (B) $\dfrac{e - \pi}{e}$

(C) $\dfrac{\pi}{e}$ (D) The series diverges.

95. Multiple Choice What is the value of $\displaystyle\sum_{n=1}^{\infty} \frac{4^{n+1}}{5^n}$?

(A) 5   (B) 16

(C) 20   (D) The series diverges.

96. Multiple Choice Which of the following series diverges?

I. $\displaystyle\sum_{n=1}^{\infty} \frac{2e^n}{2e^n - 3}$ II. $\displaystyle\sum_{n=1}^{\infty} \frac{4n^3}{n^3 - 4}$

III. $\displaystyle\sum_{n=0}^{\infty} \left(\frac{\cos 2\pi}{\pi}\right)^n$

(A) I only   (B) I and II only

(C) I and III only   (D) I, II, and III

SECTION PROJECT

Cantor's Disappearing Table

The following procedure shows how to make a table disappear by removing only half of the table!

(a) Original table has a length of L.

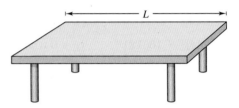

(b) Remove $\frac{1}{4}$ of the table centered at the midpoint. Each remaining piece has a length that is less than $\frac{1}{2}L$.

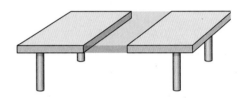

(c) Remove $\frac{1}{8}$ of the table by taking sections of length $\frac{1}{16}L$ from the centers of each of the two remaining pieces. Now, you have removed $\frac{1}{4} + \frac{1}{8}$ of the table. Each remaining piece has a length that is less than $\frac{1}{4}L$.

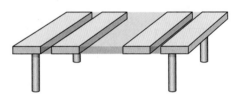

(d) Remove $\frac{1}{16}$ of the table by taking sections of length $\frac{1}{64}L$ from the centers of each of the four remaining pieces. Now, you have removed $\frac{1}{4} + \frac{1}{8} + \frac{1}{16}$ of the table. Each remaining piece has a length that is less than $\frac{1}{8}L$.

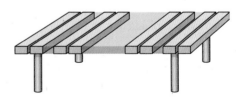

Will continuing this process cause the table to disappear, even though you have only removed half of the table? Why?

For more on this project, see the article "Cantor's Disappearing Table" by Larry E. Knop in *The College Mathematics Journal*.

8.3   The Integral Test and *p*-Series

▶ Use the Integral Test to determine whether an infinite series converges or diverges.
▶ Use properties of *p*-series and harmonic series.

The Integral Test

In this and the next section, you will study several convergence tests that apply to series with *positive* terms.

Theorem 8.10   The Integral Test

If f is positive, continuous, and decreasing for $x \geq 1$ and $a_n = f(n)$, then

$$\sum_{n=1}^{\infty} a_n \quad \text{and} \quad \int_{1}^{\infty} f(x)\, dx$$

either both converge or both diverge.

Insight

The Integral Test is covered on the AP® Calculus BC Exam.

Proof   Begin by partitioning the interval $[1, n]$ into $(n - 1)$ unit intervals, as shown in Figure 8.8. The total areas of the inscribed rectangles and the circumscribed rectangles are

$$\sum_{i=2}^{n} f(i) = f(2) + f(3) + \cdots + f(n) \qquad \text{Inscribed area}$$

and

$$\sum_{i=1}^{n-1} f(i) = f(1) + f(2) + \cdots + f(n-1). \qquad \text{Circumscribed area}$$

The exact area under the graph of f from $x = 1$ to $x = n$ lies between the inscribed and circumscribed areas.

$$\sum_{i=2}^{n} f(i) \leq \int_{1}^{n} f(x)\, dx \leq \sum_{i=1}^{n-1} f(i)$$

Using the *n*th partial sum

$$S_n = f(1) + f(2) + \cdots + f(n)$$

you can write this inequality as

$$S_n - f(1) \leq \int_{1}^{n} f(x)\, dx \leq S_{n-1}.$$

Now, assuming that $\int_{1}^{\infty} f(x)\, dx$ converges to L, it follows that for $n \geq 1$

$$S_n - f(1) \leq L \quad \Longrightarrow \quad S_n \leq L + f(1).$$

Consequently, $\{S_n\}$ is bounded and monotonic, and by Theorem 8.5 it converges. So, $\Sigma\, a_n$ converges. For the other direction of the proof, assume that the improper integral diverges. Then $\int_{1}^{n} f(x)\, dx$ approaches infinity as $n \to \infty$, and the inequality $S_{n-1} \geq \int_{1}^{n} f(x)\, dx$ implies that $\{S_n\}$ diverges. So, $\Sigma\, a_n$ diverges. ■

Remember that the convergence or divergence of $\Sigma\, a_n$ is not affected by deleting the first N terms. Similarly, when the conditions for the Integral Test are satisfied for all $x \geq N > 1$, you can simply use the integral $\int_{N}^{\infty} f(x)\, dx$ to test for convergence or divergence. (This is illustrated in Example 4.)

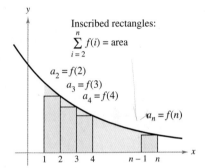

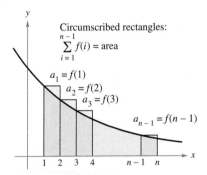

Figure 8.8

EXAMPLE 1 Using the Integral Test

Apply the Integral Test to the series $\displaystyle\sum_{n=1}^{\infty} \frac{n}{n^2 + 1}$.

Solution

The function $f(x) = x/(x^2 + 1)$ is positive and continuous for $x \geq 1$. To determine whether f is decreasing, find the derivative.

$$f'(x) = \frac{(x^2 + 1)(1) - x(2x)}{(x^2 + 1)^2} = \frac{-x^2 + 1}{(x^2 + 1)^2}$$

So, $f'(x) < 0$ for $x > 1$ and it follows that f satisfies the conditions for the Integral Test. You can integrate to obtain

$$\int_1^{\infty} \frac{x}{x^2 + 1}\, dx = \frac{1}{2}\int_1^{\infty} \frac{2x}{x^2 + 1}\, dx \qquad \text{Multiply and divide by 2.}$$

$$= \frac{1}{2}\lim_{b\to\infty} \int_1^b \frac{2x}{x^2 + 1}\, dx \qquad \text{Definition of improper integral}$$

$$= \frac{1}{2}\lim_{b\to\infty} \left[\ln(x^2 + 1)\right]_1^b \qquad \text{Apply Log Rule.}$$

$$= \frac{1}{2}\lim_{b\to\infty} \left[\ln(b^2 + 1) - \ln 2\right] \qquad \text{Apply Fundamental Theorem of Calculus.}$$

$$= \infty. \qquad \text{Evaluate limit.}$$

The integral *diverges*, so the series *diverges*.

> ### Justification
>
> Before applying the Integral Test, be sure to check that the function is positive, continuous, and decreasing for $x \geq 1$. When the function fails to satisfy any one of these conditions, you cannot apply the Integral Test.

EXAMPLE 2 Using the Integral Test

See LarsonCalculusforAP.com for an interactive version of this type of example.

Apply the Integral Test to the series $\displaystyle\sum_{n=1}^{\infty} \frac{1}{n^2 + 1}$.

Solution

Because $f(x) = 1/(x^2 + 1)$ satisfies the conditions for the Integral Test (check this), you can integrate to obtain

$$\int_1^{\infty} \frac{1}{x^2 + 1}\, dx = \lim_{b\to\infty} \int_1^b \frac{1}{x^2 + 1}\, dx \qquad \text{Definition of improper integral}$$

$$= \lim_{b\to\infty} \left[\arctan x\right]_1^b \qquad \text{Apply Arctan Rule.}$$

$$= \lim_{b\to\infty} (\arctan b - \arctan 1) \qquad \text{Apply Fundamental Theorem of Calculus.}$$

$$= \frac{\pi}{2} - \frac{\pi}{4} \qquad \text{Evaluate limit.}$$

$$= \frac{\pi}{4}. \qquad \text{Simplify.}$$

The integral *converges*, so the series *converges*. (See Figure 8.9.)

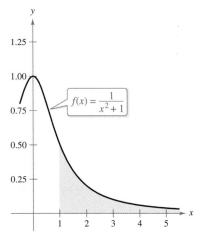

Because the improper integral converges, the infinite series also converges.

Figure 8.9

In Example 2, the fact that the improper integral converges to $\pi/4$ does not imply that the infinite series converges to $\pi/4$. To approximate the sum of the series, you can use the inequality

$$\sum_{n=1}^{N} \frac{1}{n^2 + 1} \leq \sum_{n=1}^{\infty} \frac{1}{n^2 + 1} \leq \sum_{n=1}^{N} \frac{1}{n^2 + 1} + \int_N^{\infty} \frac{1}{x^2 + 1}\, dx.$$

(See Exercise 54.) The larger the value of N, the better the approximation. For instance, using $N = 200$ produces $1.072 \leq \Sigma\, 1/(n^2 + 1) \leq 1.077$.

p-Series and Harmonic Series

In the remainder of this section, you will investigate a second type of series that has a simple arithmetic test for convergence or divergence. A series of the form

$$\sum_{n=1}^{\infty} \frac{1}{n^p} = \frac{1}{1^p} + \frac{1}{2^p} + \frac{1}{3^p} + \cdots \qquad \text{\textit{p}-series}$$

is a ***p*-series,** where *p* is a positive constant. For $p = 1$, the series

$$\sum_{n=1}^{\infty} \frac{1}{n} = 1 + \frac{1}{2} + \frac{1}{3} + \cdots \qquad \text{Harmonic series}$$

is the **harmonic** series. A **general harmonic series** is of the form

$$\sum_{n=1}^{\infty} \frac{1}{an + b}.$$

In music, strings of the same material, diameter, and tension, and whose lengths form a harmonic series, produce harmonic tones.

The Integral Test is convenient for establishing the convergence or divergence of *p*-series. This is shown in the proof of Theorem 8.11.

> **Theorem 8.11   Convergence of *p*-Series**
>
> The *p*-series
>
> $$\sum_{n=1}^{\infty} \frac{1}{n^p} = \frac{1}{1^p} + \frac{1}{2^p} + \frac{1}{3^p} + \frac{1}{4^p} + \cdots$$
>
> converges for $p > 1$, and diverges for $0 < p \le 1$.

Proof   The proof follows from the Integral Test and from Theorem 7.5, which states that

$$\int_1^{\infty} \frac{1}{x^p}\, dx$$

converges for $p > 1$ and diverges for $0 < p \le 1$.

EXAMPLE 3   Convergent and Divergent *p*-Series

Discuss the convergence or divergence of (a) the harmonic series and (b) the *p*-series with $p = 2$.

Solution

a. From Theorem 8.11, it follows that the harmonic series

$$\sum_{n=1}^{\infty} \frac{1}{n} = \frac{1}{1} + \frac{1}{2} + \frac{1}{3} + \cdots \qquad p = 1$$

diverges.

b. From Theorem 8.11, it follows that the *p*-series

$$\sum_{n=1}^{\infty} \frac{1}{n^2} = \frac{1}{1^2} + \frac{1}{2^2} + \frac{1}{3^2} + \cdots \qquad p = 2$$

converges.

The sum of the series in Example 3(b) can be shown to be $\pi^2/6$. (This was proved by Leonhard Euler, but the proof is too difficult to present here.) Be sure you see that the Integral Test does not tell you that the sum of the series is equal to the value of the integral. For instance, the sum of the series in Example 3(b) is

$$\sum_{n=1}^{\infty} \frac{1}{n^2} = \frac{\pi^2}{6} \approx 1.645$$

whereas the value of the corresponding improper integral is

$$\int_1^{\infty} \frac{1}{x^2}\,dx = 1.$$

EXAMPLE 4   Testing a Series for Convergence

Determine whether the series $\displaystyle\sum_{n=2}^{\infty} \frac{1}{n \ln n}$ converges or diverges.

Solution

This series is similar to the divergent harmonic series. If its terms were greater than those of the harmonic series, you would expect it to diverge. However, because its terms are less than those of the harmonic series, you are not sure what to expect. The function

$$f(x) = \frac{1}{x \ln x}$$

is positive and continuous for $x \geq 2$. To determine whether f is decreasing, first rewrite f as

$$f(x) = (x \ln x)^{-1} \qquad \text{Rewrite using negative exponent.}$$

and then find its derivative.

$$f'(x) = (-1)(x \ln x)^{-2}(1 + \ln x) = -\frac{1 + \ln x}{x^2(\ln x)^2}$$

So, $f'(x) < 0$ for $x > 2$ and it follows that f satisfies the conditions for the Integral Test.

$$
\begin{aligned}
\int_2^{\infty} \frac{1}{x \ln x}\,dx &= \int_2^{\infty} \frac{1/x}{\ln x}\,dx && \text{Rewrite integrand.} \\
&= \lim_{b \to \infty} \int_2^b \frac{1/x}{\ln x}\,dx && \text{Definition of improper integral} \\
&= \lim_{b \to \infty} \Big[\ln(\ln x) \Big]_2^b && \text{Apply Log Rule.} \\
&= \lim_{b \to \infty} \big[\ln(\ln b) - \ln(\ln 2) \big] && \text{Apply Fundamental Theorem of Calculus.} \\
&= \infty && \text{Evaluate limit.}
\end{aligned}
$$

The series diverges. ■

Note that the infinite series in Example 4 diverges very slowly. For instance, as shown in the table, the sum of the first 10 terms is approximately 1.6878196, whereas the sum of the first 100 terms is just slightly greater: 2.3250871. In fact, the sum of the first 10,000 terms is approximately 3.0150217. You can see that although the infinite series "adds up to infinity," it does so very slowly.

n	11	101	1001	10,001	100,001
S_n	1.6878	2.3251	2.7275	3.0150	3.2382

8.3 Exercises

See *CalcChat.com* for tutorial help and worked-out solutions to odd-numbered exercises.

 Using the Integral Test In Exercises 1–22, confirm that the Integral Test can be applied to the series. Then use the Integral Test to determine the convergence or divergence of the series.

1. $\displaystyle\sum_{n=1}^{\infty} \frac{1}{n+3}$

2. $\displaystyle\sum_{n=1}^{\infty} \frac{2}{3n+5}$

3. $\displaystyle\sum_{n=1}^{\infty} \frac{1}{2^n}$

4. $\displaystyle\sum_{n=1}^{\infty} 3^{-n}$

5. $\displaystyle\sum_{n=1}^{\infty} e^{-n}$

6. $\displaystyle\sum_{n=1}^{\infty} ne^{-n/2}$

7. $\dfrac{1}{2} + \dfrac{1}{6} + \dfrac{1}{12} + \dfrac{1}{20} + \dfrac{1}{30} + \cdots$

8. $\dfrac{1}{3} + \dfrac{1}{5} + \dfrac{1}{7} + \dfrac{1}{9} + \dfrac{1}{11} + \cdots$

9. $\dfrac{\ln 2}{2} + \dfrac{\ln 3}{3} + \dfrac{\ln 4}{4} + \dfrac{\ln 5}{5} + \dfrac{\ln 6}{6} + \cdots$

10. $\dfrac{\ln 2}{\sqrt{2}} + \dfrac{\ln 3}{\sqrt{3}} + \dfrac{\ln 4}{\sqrt{4}} + \dfrac{\ln 5}{\sqrt{5}} + \dfrac{\ln 6}{\sqrt{6}} + \cdots$

11. $\ln 2 + \ln \dfrac{3}{2} + \ln \dfrac{4}{3} + \ln \dfrac{5}{4} + \ln \dfrac{6}{5} + \cdots$

12. $\dfrac{1}{4} + \dfrac{2}{7} + \dfrac{3}{12} + \dfrac{4}{19} + \dfrac{5}{28} + \cdots$

13. $\displaystyle\sum_{n=1}^{\infty} \frac{\arctan n}{n^2+1}$

14. $\displaystyle\sum_{n=2}^{\infty} \frac{\ln n}{n^3}$

15. $\displaystyle\sum_{n=1}^{\infty} \frac{\ln n}{n^2}$

16. $\displaystyle\sum_{n=2}^{\infty} \frac{1}{n\sqrt{\ln n}}$

17. $\displaystyle\sum_{n=1}^{\infty} \frac{1}{(2n+3)^3}$

18. $\displaystyle\sum_{n=1}^{\infty} \frac{n+2}{n+1}$

19. $\displaystyle\sum_{n=1}^{\infty} \frac{4n}{2n^2+1}$

20. $\displaystyle\sum_{n=1}^{\infty} \frac{1}{\sqrt[3]{n+9}}$

21. $\displaystyle\sum_{n=1}^{\infty} \frac{n}{n^4+1}$

22. $\displaystyle\sum_{n=1}^{\infty} \frac{n}{n^4+2n^2+1}$

Using the Integral Test In Exercises 23 and 24, use the Integral Test to determine the convergence or divergence of the series, where *k* is a positive integer.

23. $\displaystyle\sum_{n=1}^{\infty} \frac{n^{k-1}}{n^k+c}$

24. $\displaystyle\sum_{n=1}^{\infty} n^k e^{-n}$

 Justifying In Exercises 25–28, explain why the Integral Test does not apply to the series.

25. $\displaystyle\sum_{n=1}^{\infty} \frac{(-1)^n}{n}$

26. $\displaystyle\sum_{n=1}^{\infty} e^{-n} \cos n$

27. $\displaystyle\sum_{n=1}^{\infty} \frac{2+\sin n}{n}$

28. $\displaystyle\sum_{n=1}^{\infty} \left(\frac{\sin n}{n}\right)^2$

 Using the Integral Test In Exercises 29–32, use the Integral Test to determine the convergence or divergence of the *p*-series.

29. $\displaystyle\sum_{n=1}^{\infty} \frac{1}{n^7}$

30. $\displaystyle\sum_{n=1}^{\infty} \frac{1}{n^{1.001}}$

31. $\displaystyle\sum_{n=1}^{\infty} \frac{1}{n^{4/5}}$

32. $\displaystyle\sum_{n=1}^{\infty} \frac{1}{n^{\ln 2}}$

Using a *p*-Series In Exercises 33–38, use Theorem 8.11 to determine the convergence or divergence of the *p*-series.

33. $\displaystyle\sum_{n=1}^{\infty} \frac{1}{\sqrt[5]{n}}$

34. $\displaystyle\sum_{n=1}^{\infty} \frac{3}{n^{5/3}}$

35. $1 + \dfrac{1}{2\sqrt{2}} + \dfrac{1}{3\sqrt{3}} + \dfrac{1}{4\sqrt{4}} + \dfrac{1}{5\sqrt{5}} + \cdots$

36. $1 + \dfrac{1}{\sqrt[3]{4}} + \dfrac{1}{\sqrt[3]{9}} + \dfrac{1}{\sqrt[3]{16}} + \dfrac{1}{\sqrt[3]{25}} + \cdots$

37. $\displaystyle\sum_{n=1}^{\infty} \frac{1}{n^{1.03}}$

38. $\displaystyle\sum_{n=1}^{\infty} \frac{1}{n^\pi}$

Error Analysis In Exercises 39 and 40, describe and correct the error in determining the convergence or divergence of the series.

39. $\displaystyle\sum_{n=1}^{\infty} \frac{1}{\sqrt[5]{n^3}}$

From Theorem 8.11, the *p*-series converges because $p = 3 > 1$. ✗

40. $\dfrac{1}{10,000} + \dfrac{1}{10,001} + \dfrac{1}{10,002} + \cdots$

The series converges because the terms are very small and approach 0 rapidly. ✗

 41. Numerical and Graphical Analysis Use a graphing utility to find the partial sum S_n when $n = 5, 10, 20, 50,$ and 100. Then use a graphing utility to graph the first 10 terms of the sequence of partial sums. Compare the rates at which the sequences of partial sums approach the sum of the series.

(a) $\displaystyle\sum_{n=1}^{\infty} 3\left(\frac{1}{5}\right)^{n-1} = \frac{15}{4}$ (b) $\displaystyle\sum_{n=1}^{\infty} \frac{1}{n^2} = \frac{\pi^2}{6}$

 42. Justifying Because the harmonic series diverges, it follows that for any positive real number *M*, there exists a positive integer *N* such that the partial sum

$$\sum_{n=1}^{N} \frac{1}{n} > M.$$

(a) Use a graphing utility to find the value of *N* when $M = 2, 4, 6,$ and 8.

(b) As the real number *M* increases in equal increments, does the number *N* increase in equal increments? Explain.

EXPLORING CONCEPTS

43. Communicating State the Integral Test and give an example of its use.

44. Communicating Define a *p*-series and state the requirements for its convergence.

45. Using a Series Use a graph to show that the inequality is true. What can you conclude about the convergence or divergence of the series? Explain.

(a) $\displaystyle\sum_{n=1}^{\infty} \frac{1}{\sqrt{n}} > \int_{1}^{\infty} \frac{1}{\sqrt{x}}\, dx$

(b) $\displaystyle\sum_{n=2}^{\infty} \frac{1}{n^2} < \int_{1}^{\infty} \frac{1}{x^2}\, dx$

46. HOW DO YOU SEE IT? The graphs show the sequences of partial sums of the *p*-series

$$\sum_{n=1}^{\infty} \frac{1}{n^{0.4}} \quad \text{and} \quad \sum_{n=1}^{\infty} \frac{1}{n^{1.5}}.$$

Using Theorem 8.11, the first series diverges and the second series converges. Explain how the graphs show this.

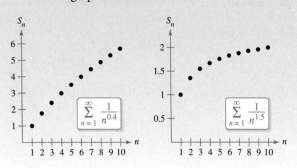

Finding Values In Exercises 47–52, find the positive values of *p* for which the series converges.

47. $\displaystyle\sum_{n=2}^{\infty} \frac{1}{n(\ln n)^p}$

48. $\displaystyle\sum_{n=2}^{\infty} \frac{\ln n}{n^p}$

49. $\displaystyle\sum_{n=1}^{\infty} \frac{n}{(1 + n^2)^p}$

50. $\displaystyle\sum_{n=1}^{\infty} n(1 + n^2)^p$

51. $\displaystyle\sum_{n=1}^{\infty} \left(\frac{5}{n}\right)^{-p+3}$

52. $\displaystyle\sum_{n=3}^{\infty} \frac{1}{(n \ln n)[\ln(\ln n)]^p}$

53. Proof Let *f* be a positive, continuous, and decreasing function for $x \geq 1$, and $a_n = f(n)$. Prove that if the series

$$\sum_{n=1}^{\infty} a_n$$

converges to *S*, then the remainder $R_N = S - S_N$ is bounded by

$$0 \leq R_N \leq \int_{N}^{\infty} f(x)\, dx.$$

54. Using a Remainder Show that the result of Exercise 53 can be written as

$$\sum_{n=1}^{N} a_n \leq \sum_{n=1}^{\infty} a_n \leq \sum_{n=1}^{N} a_n + \int_{N}^{\infty} f(x)\, dx.$$

Approximating a Sum In Exercises 55–58, use the result of Exercise 53 to approximate the sum of the convergent series using the indicated number of terms. Include an estimate of the maximum error for your approximation.

55. $\displaystyle\sum_{n=1}^{\infty} \frac{1}{n^2 + 1}$, eight terms

56. $\displaystyle\sum_{n=1}^{\infty} \frac{1}{(n + 1)[\ln(n + 1)]^3}$, ten terms

57. $\displaystyle\sum_{n=1}^{\infty} ne^{-n^2}$, four terms   **58.** $\displaystyle\sum_{n=1}^{\infty} e^{-2n}$, five terms

Finding a Value In Exercises 59–62, use the result of Exercise 53 to find *N* such that $R_N \leq 0.001$ for the convergent series.

59. $\displaystyle\sum_{n=1}^{\infty} \frac{1}{n^4}$

60. $\displaystyle\sum_{n=2}^{\infty} \frac{1}{n(\ln n)^4}$

61. $\displaystyle\sum_{n=1}^{\infty} e^{-n/2}$

62. $\displaystyle\sum_{n=1}^{\infty} \frac{1}{n^2 + 1}$

63. Comparing Series

(a) Show that $\displaystyle\sum_{n=2}^{\infty} \frac{1}{n^{1.1}}$ converges and $\displaystyle\sum_{n=2}^{\infty} \frac{1}{n \ln n}$ diverges.

(b) Compare the first five terms of each series in part (a).

(c) Find $n > 3$ such that $\dfrac{1}{n^{1.1}} < \dfrac{1}{n \ln n}$.

64. Using a *p*-Series Ten terms are used to approximate a convergent *p*-series. Therefore, the remainder is a function of *p* and

$$0 \leq R_{10}(p) \leq \int_{10}^{\infty} \frac{1}{x^p}\, dx, \quad p > 1.$$

(a) Perform the integration in the inequality.

(b) Use a graphing utility to represent the inequality graphically.

(c) Identify any asymptotes of the remainder function and interpret their meaning.

65. Riemann Zeta Function The Riemann zeta function for real numbers is defined for all *x* for which the series

$$\zeta(x) = \sum_{n=1}^{\infty} n^{-x}$$

converges. Find the domain of the function.

66. Using a Series Consider the series $\displaystyle\sum_{n=2}^{\infty} x^{\ln n}$.

(a) Determine the convergence or divergence of the series for $x = 1$ and $x = 1/e$.

(b) Find the positive values of *x* for which the series converges.

Implementing Processes In Exercises 67–78, determine the convergence or divergence of the series.

67. $\displaystyle\sum_{n=1}^{\infty} \frac{1}{3n-2}$

68. $\displaystyle\sum_{n=2}^{\infty} \frac{1}{n\sqrt{n^2-1}}$

69. $\displaystyle\sum_{n=1}^{\infty} \frac{1}{n\sqrt[4]{n}}$

70. $3\displaystyle\sum_{n=1}^{\infty} \frac{1}{n^{0.95}}$

71. $\displaystyle\sum_{n=0}^{\infty} \left(\frac{2}{3}\right)^n$

72. $\displaystyle\sum_{n=0}^{\infty} (1.042)^n$

73. $\displaystyle\sum_{n=1}^{\infty} \frac{n}{\sqrt{3n^2+3}}$

74. $\displaystyle\sum_{n=1}^{\infty} \left(\frac{1}{n^2} - \frac{1}{n^3}\right)$

75. $\displaystyle\sum_{n=1}^{\infty} \left(1+\frac{1}{n}\right)^n$

76. $\displaystyle\sum_{n=4}^{\infty} \ln\frac{n}{2}$

77. $\displaystyle\sum_{n=1}^{\infty} \frac{n}{(1+n^2)^{1/5}}$

78. $\displaystyle\sum_{n=1}^{\infty} \frac{n^3}{(1+n^2)^3}$

Calculus AP® – Exam Preparation Questions

In Exercises 79 and 80, let f be a positive, continuous, and decreasing function for $x \geq 1$, such that $a_n = f(n)$.

79. Multiple Choice If $\displaystyle\sum_{n=1}^{\infty} a_n$ converges to L, which of the following must be true?

(A) $\displaystyle\int_1^{\infty} f(x)\,dx$ converges.

(B) $\displaystyle\int_1^{\infty} f(x)\,dx$ diverges.

(C) $\displaystyle\int_1^{\infty} f(x)\,dx = L$

(D) $\displaystyle\lim_{n\to\infty} a_n = L$

80. Multiple Choice Which of the following orders the quantities from least to greatest?

(A) $\displaystyle\sum_{n=1}^{6} a_n,\ \sum_{n=2}^{7} a_n,\ \int_1^7 f(x)\,dx$

(B) $\displaystyle\sum_{n=1}^{6} a_n,\ \int_1^7 f(x)\,dx,\ \sum_{n=2}^{7} a_n$

(C) $\displaystyle\sum_{n=2}^{7} a_n,\ \int_1^7 f(x)\,dx,\ \sum_{n=1}^{6} a_n$

(D) $\displaystyle\int_1^7 f(x)\,dx,\ \sum_{n=2}^{7} a_n,\ \sum_{n=1}^{6} a_n$

81. Multiple Choice For what value of k will the three series below converge?

$\displaystyle\sum_{n=0}^{\infty} \left(\frac{3}{8-k}\right)^n \quad \sum_{n=1}^{\infty} \frac{1}{\sqrt[k]{n^4}} \quad \sum_{n=1}^{\infty} \left(\frac{k}{12}\right)^n$

(A) 4   (B) 5

(C) 7   (D) None of these

SECTION PROJECT

The Harmonic Series

The harmonic series

$$\sum_{n=1}^{\infty} \frac{1}{n} = 1 + \frac{1}{2} + \frac{1}{3} + \frac{1}{4} + \cdots + \frac{1}{n} + \cdots$$

is one of the most important series in this chapter. Even though its terms tend to zero as n increases,

$$\lim_{n\to\infty} \frac{1}{n} = 0$$

the harmonic series diverges. In other words, even though the terms are getting smaller and smaller, the sum "adds up to infinity."

(a) One way to show that the harmonic series diverges is attributed to James Bernoulli. He grouped the terms of the harmonic series as follows.

$$1 + \underbrace{\frac{1}{2}}_{} + \underbrace{\frac{1}{3} + \frac{1}{4}}_{>\frac{1}{2}} + \underbrace{\frac{1}{5} + \cdots + \frac{1}{8}}_{>\frac{1}{2}} + \underbrace{\frac{1}{9} + \cdots + \frac{1}{16}}_{>\frac{1}{2}}$$

$$+ \underbrace{\frac{1}{17} + \cdots + \frac{1}{32}}_{>\frac{1}{2}} + \cdots$$

Write a short paragraph explaining how you can use this grouping to show that the harmonic series diverges.

(b) Use the proof of the Integral Test, Theorem 8.10, to show that

$$\ln(n+1) \leq 1 + \frac{1}{2} + \frac{1}{3} + \frac{1}{4} + \cdots + \frac{1}{n} \leq 1 + \ln n.$$

(c) Use part (b) to determine how many terms M you would need so that

$$\sum_{n=1}^{M} \frac{1}{n} > 50.$$

(d) Show that the sum of the first million terms of the harmonic series is less than 15.

(e) Show that the following inequalities are valid.

$$\ln\frac{21}{10} \leq \frac{1}{10} + \frac{1}{11} + \cdots + \frac{1}{20} \leq \ln\frac{20}{9}$$

$$\ln\frac{201}{100} \leq \frac{1}{100} + \frac{1}{101} + \cdots + \frac{1}{200} \leq \ln\frac{200}{99}$$

(f) Use the inequalities in part (e) to find the limit

$$\lim_{m\to\infty} \sum_{n=m}^{2m} \frac{1}{n}.$$

▶ Use the Direct Comparison Test to determine whether a series converges or diverges.
▶ Use the Limit Comparison Test to determine whether a series converges or diverges.

Direct Comparison Test

For the convergence tests developed so far, the terms of the series have to be fairly simple and the series must have special characteristics in order for the convergence tests to be applied. A slight deviation from these special characteristics can make a test inapplicable. For example, in the pairs listed below, the second series cannot be tested by the same convergence test as the first series, even though it is similar to the first.

1. $\displaystyle\sum_{n=0}^{\infty} \frac{1}{2^n}$ is geometric, but $\displaystyle\sum_{n=0}^{\infty} \frac{n}{2^n}$ is not.

2. $\displaystyle\sum_{n=1}^{\infty} \frac{1}{n^3}$ is a p-series, but $\displaystyle\sum_{n=1}^{\infty} \frac{1}{n^3 + 1}$ is not.

3. $a_n = \dfrac{n}{(n^2 + 3)^2}$ is easily integrated, but $b_n = \dfrac{n^2}{(n^2 + 3)^2}$ is not.

In this section, you will study two additional tests for positive-term series. These two tests greatly expand the variety of series you are able to test for convergence or divergence. They allow you to *compare* a series having complicated terms with a simpler series whose convergence or divergence is known.

> **Theorem 8.12   Direct Comparison Test**
>
> Let $0 < a_n \le b_n$ for all n.
>
> 1. If $\displaystyle\sum_{n=1}^{\infty} b_n$ converges, then $\displaystyle\sum_{n=1}^{\infty} a_n$ converges.
>
> 2. If $\displaystyle\sum_{n=1}^{\infty} a_n$ diverges, then $\displaystyle\sum_{n=1}^{\infty} b_n$ diverges.

Proof   To prove the first property, let $L = \displaystyle\sum_{n=1}^{\infty} b_n$ and let

$$S_n = a_1 + a_2 + \cdots + a_n.$$

Because $0 < a_n \le b_n$, the sequence

$$S_1, S_2, S_3, \ldots$$

is nondecreasing and bounded above by L; so, it must converge. Because

$$\lim_{n \to \infty} S_n = \sum_{n=1}^{\infty} a_n$$

it follows that $\displaystyle\sum_{n=1}^{\infty} a_n$ converges. The second property is logically equivalent to the first.

Note that the Direct Comparison Test is inconclusive when term-by-term comparison reveals a series that is *less* than a divergent series (see Example 2). Likewise, the test is inconclusive when term-by-term comparison reveals a series that is *greater* than a convergent series.

Justification

As stated, the Direct Comparison Test requires that $0 < a_n \le b_n$ for all n. Because the convergence of a series is not dependent on its first several terms, you could modify the test to require only that $0 < a_n \le b_n$ for all n greater than some integer N.

Both parts of the Direct Comparison Test require that $0 < a_n \le b_n$. An informal way of visualizing the Direct Comparison Test is shown in Figure 8.10. Let the "larger" series b_n be represented by the truck and let the "smaller" series a_n be represented by the van. In Figure 8.10(a), the truck can fit under the bridge, so the smaller van will also fit. In Figure 8.10(b), the van cannot fit under the second bridge, so the larger truck will not fit either.

(a) The truck fits under the bridge, so the smaller van will also fit.

EXAMPLE 1   Using the Direct Comparison Test

Determine the convergence or divergence of

$$\sum_{n=1}^{\infty} \frac{1}{2 + 3^n}.$$

Solution

This series resembles

$$\sum_{n=1}^{\infty} \frac{1}{3^n}. \qquad \text{Convergent geometric series}$$

Term-by-term comparison yields

$$a_n = \frac{1}{2 + 3^n} < \frac{1}{3^n} = b_n, \ n \ge 1.$$

So, by the Direct Comparison Test, the series converges.

(b) The van does not fit under the bridge, so the larger truck will not fit.

Figure 8.10

EXAMPLE 2   Using the Direct Comparison Test

See LarsonCalculusforAP.com for an interactive version of this type of example.

Determine the convergence or divergence of

$$\sum_{n=1}^{\infty} \frac{1}{2 + \sqrt{n}}.$$

Solution

This series resembles

$$\sum_{n=1}^{\infty} \frac{1}{n^{1/2}}. \qquad \text{Divergent } p\text{-series}$$

Term-by-term comparison yields

$$\frac{1}{2 + \sqrt{n}} \le \frac{1}{\sqrt{n}}, \ n \ge 1$$

which *does not* meet the requirements for divergence. (Remember that when term-by-term comparison reveals a series that is *less* than a divergent series, the Direct Comparison Test tells you nothing.) Still expecting the series to diverge, you can compare the series with

$$\sum_{n=1}^{\infty} \frac{1}{n}. \qquad \text{Divergent harmonic series}$$

In this case, term-by-term comparison yields

$$a_n = \frac{1}{n} \le \frac{1}{2 + \sqrt{n}} = b_n, \ n \ge 4$$

and, by the Direct Comparison Test, the given series diverges. To verify the last inequality, try showing that $2 + \sqrt{n} \le n$ whenever $n \ge 4$.

Limit Comparison Test

Sometimes a series closely resembles a p-series or a geometric series, yet you cannot establish the term-by-term comparison necessary to apply the Direct Comparison Test. Under these circumstances, you may be able to apply a second comparison test, called the **Limit Comparison Test.**

Theorem 8.13 **Limit Comparison Test**

If $a_n > 0$, $b_n > 0$, and

$$\lim_{n \to \infty} \frac{a_n}{b_n} = L$$

where L is *finite and positive*, then

$$\sum_{n=1}^{\infty} a_n \quad \text{and} \quad \sum_{n=1}^{\infty} b_n$$

either both converge or both diverge.

Justification

As with the Direct Comparison Test, the Limit Comparison Test could be modified to require only that a_n and b_n be positive for all n greater than some integer N.

Proof Because $a_n > 0$, $b_n > 0$, and

$$\lim_{n \to \infty} \frac{a_n}{b_n} = L$$

there exists $N > 0$ such that

$$0 < \frac{a_n}{b_n} < L + 1, \text{ for } n \ge N.$$

This implies that

$$0 < a_n < (L + 1)b_n.$$

So, by the Direct Comparison Test, the convergence of $\Sigma\, b_n$ implies the convergence of $\Sigma\, a_n$. Similarly, the fact that

$$\lim_{n \to \infty} \frac{b_n}{a_n} = \frac{1}{L}$$

can be used to show that the convergence of $\Sigma\, a_n$ implies the convergence of $\Sigma\, b_n$. ∎

Insight

The Limit Comparison Test is covered on the AP® Calculus BC Exam.

EXAMPLE 3 **Using the Limit Comparison Test**

Show that the general harmonic series below diverges.

$$\sum_{n=1}^{\infty} \frac{1}{an + b}, \quad a > 0, \ b > 0$$

Solution

By comparison with

$$\sum_{n=1}^{\infty} \frac{1}{n} \qquad \text{Divergent harmonic series}$$

you have

$$\lim_{n \to \infty} \frac{1/(an + b)}{1/n} = \lim_{n \to \infty} \frac{n}{an + b} = \frac{1}{a}.$$

Because this limit is greater than 0, you can conclude from the Limit Comparison Test that the series diverges. ∎

Justification

When using the Limit Comparison Test, it does not matter which series is assigned as a_n or b_n. For instance, try doing Example 3 with $a_n = 1/n$ and $b_n = 1/(an + b)$. Do you come to the same conclusion as the one in the example?

The Limit Comparison Test works well for comparing a "messy" algebraic series with a p-series. In choosing an appropriate p-series, you must choose one with an nth term of the same magnitude as the nth term of the given series.

Given Series	*Comparison Series*	*Conclusion*
$\displaystyle\sum_{n=1}^{\infty} \frac{1}{3n^2 - 4n + 5}$	$\displaystyle\sum_{n=1}^{\infty} \frac{1}{n^2}$	Both series converge.
$\displaystyle\sum_{n=1}^{\infty} \frac{1}{\sqrt{3n - 2}}$	$\displaystyle\sum_{n=1}^{\infty} \frac{1}{\sqrt{n}}$	Both series diverge.
$\displaystyle\sum_{n=1}^{\infty} \frac{n^2 - 10}{4n^5 + n^3}$	$\displaystyle\sum_{n=1}^{\infty} \frac{n^2}{n^5} = \sum_{n=1}^{\infty} \frac{1}{n^3}$	Both series converge.

In other words, when choosing a series for comparison, you can disregard all but the *highest powers of n* in both the numerator and the denominator.

EXAMPLE 4   Using the Limit Comparison Test

Determine the convergence or divergence of

$$\sum_{n=1}^{\infty} \frac{\sqrt{n}}{n^2 + 1}.$$

Solution

Disregarding all but the highest powers of n in the numerator and the denominator, you can compare the series with

$$\sum_{n=1}^{\infty} \frac{\sqrt{n}}{n^2} = \sum_{n=1}^{\infty} \frac{1}{n^{3/2}}. \qquad \text{Convergent } p\text{-series}$$

Because

$$\lim_{n \to \infty} \frac{a_n}{b_n} = \lim_{n \to \infty} \left(\frac{\sqrt{n}}{n^2 + 1} \right) \left(\frac{n^{3/2}}{1} \right)$$

$$= \lim_{n \to \infty} \frac{n^2}{n^2 + 1}$$

$$= 1$$

you can conclude by the Limit Comparison Test that the series converges.

EXAMPLE 5   Using the Limit Comparison Test

Determine the convergence or divergence of $\displaystyle\sum_{n=1}^{\infty} \frac{n2^n}{4n^3 + 1}.$

Solution

A reasonable comparison would be with the series

$$\sum_{n=1}^{\infty} \frac{2^n}{n^2}. \qquad \text{Divergent series}$$

Note that this series diverges by the nth-Term Test. From the limit

$$\lim_{n \to \infty} \frac{a_n}{b_n} = \lim_{n \to \infty} \left(\frac{n2^n}{4n^3 + 1} \right) \left(\frac{n^2}{2^n} \right)$$

$$= \lim_{n \to \infty} \frac{n^3}{4n^3 + 1}$$

$$= \frac{1}{4}$$

you can conclude by the Limit Comparison Test that the series diverges.

Justification

When finding limits at $\pm\infty$ of rational functions, recall from Section 1.6 that if the degree of the numerator is equal to the degree of the denominator, then the limit of the rational function is the ratio of the leading coefficients.

8.4 Exercises

See *CalcChat.com* for tutorial help and worked-out solutions to odd-numbered exercises.

1. Graphical Analysis The figures show the graphs of the first 10 terms of each series, and the graphs of the first 10 terms of the sequence of partial sums of each series.

$$\sum_{n=1}^{\infty} \frac{6}{n^{3/2}}, \quad \sum_{n=1}^{\infty} \frac{6}{n^{3/2} + 3}, \quad \text{and} \quad \sum_{n=1}^{\infty} \frac{6}{n\sqrt{n^2 + 0.5}}$$

(a) Identify the series in each figure. Which series is a *p*-series? Does it converge or diverge?

(b) How do the magnitudes of the terms of the *p*-series compare with the magnitudes of the terms of the other two series? What conclusion can you draw about the convergence or divergence of the series?

(c) Explain the relationship between the magnitudes of the terms of the series and the magnitudes of the partial sums.

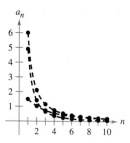

Graphs of terms   Graphs of partial sums

2. Graphical Analysis The figures show the graphs of the first 10 terms of each series, and the graphs of the first 10 terms of the sequence of partial sums of each series.

$$\sum_{n=1}^{\infty} \frac{2}{\sqrt{n}}, \quad \sum_{n=1}^{\infty} \frac{2}{\sqrt{n} - 0.5}, \quad \text{and} \quad \sum_{n=1}^{\infty} \frac{4}{\sqrt{n} + 0.5}$$

(a) Identify the series in each figure. Which series is a *p*-series? Does it converge or diverge?

(b) How do the magnitudes of the terms of the *p*-series compare with the magnitudes of the terms of the other two series? What conclusion can you draw about the convergence or divergence of the series?

(c) Explain the relationship between the magnitudes of the terms of the series and the magnitudes of the partial sums.

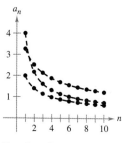 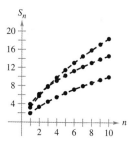

Graphs of terms   Graphs of partial sums

 Using the Direct Comparison Test In Exercises 3–14, use the Direct Comparison Test to determine the convergence or divergence of the series.

3. $\displaystyle\sum_{n=1}^{\infty} \frac{1}{2n - 1}$

4. $\displaystyle\sum_{n=1}^{\infty} \frac{1}{3n^2 + 2}$

5. $\displaystyle\sum_{n=1}^{\infty} \frac{1}{2(4)^n - 1}$

6. $\displaystyle\sum_{n=0}^{\infty} \left(\frac{5 + n}{4}\right)^n$

7. $\displaystyle\sum_{n=2}^{\infty} \frac{2}{\sqrt{n} - 1}$

8. $\displaystyle\sum_{n=0}^{\infty} \frac{4^n}{5^n + 3}$

9. $\displaystyle\sum_{n=2}^{\infty} \frac{\ln n}{n + 1}$

10. $\displaystyle\sum_{n=2}^{\infty} \frac{e^n - 7}{10n + 1}$

11. $\displaystyle\sum_{n=0}^{\infty} \frac{1}{n!}$

12. $\displaystyle\sum_{n=1}^{\infty} \frac{1}{4\sqrt[3]{n} - 1}$

13. $\displaystyle\sum_{n=1}^{\infty} \frac{2^n \cos^2 n}{3^n}$

14. $\displaystyle\sum_{n=0}^{\infty} e^{-n^2}$

 Using the Limit Comparison Test In Exercises 15–24, use the Limit Comparison Test to determine the convergence or divergence of the series.

15. $\displaystyle\sum_{n=1}^{\infty} \frac{n}{n^2 + 1}$

16. $\displaystyle\sum_{n=0}^{\infty} \frac{1}{\sqrt{n^2 + 1}}$

17. $\displaystyle\sum_{n=0}^{\infty} \frac{3^n - 1}{5^n}$

18. $\displaystyle\sum_{n=1}^{\infty} \frac{1 + 6^n}{1 - 4^n}$

19. $\displaystyle\sum_{n=1}^{\infty} \frac{2n^2 - 1}{3n^5 + 2n + 1}$

20. $\displaystyle\sum_{n=1}^{\infty} \frac{1}{n^2(n + 3)}$

21. $\displaystyle\sum_{n=1}^{\infty} \frac{1}{n\sqrt{n^2 + 1}}$

22. $\displaystyle\sum_{n=1}^{\infty} \frac{n}{(n + 1)2^{n-1}}$

23. $\displaystyle\sum_{n=1}^{\infty} \frac{n^{k-1}}{n^k + 1}, \; k > 2$

24. $\displaystyle\sum_{n=1}^{\infty} \sin \frac{1}{n}$

Implementing Processes In Exercises 25–32, test for convergence or divergence, using each test at least once. Identify which test was used.

(a) **nth-Term Test**   (b) **Geometric Series Test**

(c) **p-Series Test**   (d) **Telescoping Series Test**

(e) **Integral Test**   (f) **Direct Comparison Test**

(g) **Limit Comparison Test**

25. $\displaystyle\sum_{n=1}^{\infty} \frac{\sqrt[3]{n}}{n}$

26. $\displaystyle\sum_{n=0}^{\infty} 5\left(-\frac{4}{3}\right)^n$

27. $\displaystyle\sum_{n=1}^{\infty} \frac{1}{5^n + 1}$

28. $\displaystyle\sum_{n=2}^{\infty} \frac{1}{n^3 - 8}$

29. $\displaystyle\sum_{n=1}^{\infty} \frac{2n}{3n - 2}$

30. $\displaystyle\sum_{n=1}^{\infty} \left(\frac{1}{n + 1} - \frac{1}{n + 2}\right)$

31. $\displaystyle\sum_{n=1}^{\infty} \frac{n}{(n^2 + 1)^2}$

32. $\displaystyle\sum_{n=1}^{\infty} \frac{3}{n(n + 3)}$

Error Analysis In Exercises 33 and 34, describe and correct the error in choosing the series that should be used with the Limit Comparison Test.

33. For $\sum_{n=1}^{\infty} \frac{\sqrt{n}}{2n^2 + 6}$, compare with $\sum_{n=1}^{\infty} \frac{1}{n}$. ✗

34. For $\sum_{n=1}^{\infty} \frac{n4^n}{3n^4 - 2}$, compare with $\sum_{n=1}^{\infty} \frac{1}{n^3}$. ✗

35. Using the Limit Comparison Test Use the Limit Comparison Test with the harmonic series to show that the series $\sum a_n$ (where $0 < a_n$) diverges when $\lim_{n \to \infty} na_n$ is finite and nonzero.

36. Proof Prove that, if $P(n)$ and $Q(n)$ are polynomials of degree j and k, respectively, then the series

$$\sum_{n=1}^{\infty} \frac{P(n)}{Q(n)}$$

converges if $j < k - 1$ and diverges if $j \geq k - 1$.

Determining Convergence or Divergence In Exercises 37–40, use the polynomial test given in Exercise 36 to determine whether the series converges or diverges.

37. $\sum_{n=1}^{\infty} \frac{n}{6 + n^5}$

38. $\sum_{n=1}^{\infty} \frac{n^2}{n^3 + 1}$

39. $\frac{1}{2} + \frac{2}{5} + \frac{3}{10} + \frac{4}{17} + \frac{5}{26} + \cdots$

40. $\frac{1}{3} + \frac{1}{8} + \frac{1}{15} + \frac{1}{24} + \frac{1}{35} + \cdots$

Verifying Divergence In Exercises 41 and 42, use the divergence test given in Exercise 35 to show that the series diverges.

41. $\sum_{n=1}^{\infty} \frac{n^4}{5n^5 + n}$

42. $\sum_{n=1}^{\infty} \frac{9n^2 - 1}{n^2 + 3n^3}$

Determining Convergence or Divergence In Exercises 43–46, determine the convergence or divergence of the series.

43. $\frac{1}{200} + \frac{1}{400} + \frac{1}{600} + \frac{1}{800} + \cdots$

44. $\frac{1}{200} + \frac{1}{210} + \frac{1}{220} + \frac{1}{230} + \cdots$

45. $\frac{1}{201} + \frac{1}{204} + \frac{1}{209} + \frac{1}{216} + \cdots$

46. $\frac{1}{201} + \frac{1}{208} + \frac{1}{227} + \frac{1}{264} + \cdots$

EXPLORING CONCEPTS ————————————

47. Limit Comparison Test Can you use the Limit Comparison Test to determine the limit of a series? Explain why or why not.

48. Justifying Suppose you want to show that the series $a_n = \sum_{n=2}^{\infty} \frac{1}{(n^2 - 1)}$ converges by comparing it with the p-series $b_n = \sum_{n=2}^{\infty} \frac{1}{n^2}$. Should you use the Direct Comparison Test or the Limit Comparison Test? Explain.

EXPLORING CONCEPTS (continued)

49. Communicating Review the results of Exercises 43–46. Explain why careful analysis is required to determine the convergence or divergence of a series and why only considering the magnitudes of the terms of a series could be misleading.

50. Comparing Series It appears that the terms of the series

$$\frac{1}{1000} + \frac{1}{1001} + \frac{1}{1002} + \frac{1}{1003} + \cdots$$

are less than the corresponding terms of the convergent series

$$1 + \frac{1}{4} + \frac{1}{9} + \frac{1}{16} + \cdots.$$

If the statement above is correct, then the first series converges. Is this correct? Why or why not? Make a statement about how the divergence or convergence of a series is affected by the inclusion or exclusion of the first finite number of terms.

 **51. Using a Series** Consider the series $\sum_{n=1}^{\infty} \frac{1}{(2n - 1)^2}$.

(a) Verify that the series converges.

(b) Use a graphing utility to complete the table.

n	5	10	20	50	100
S_n					

(c) The sum of the series is $\pi^2/8$. Find the sum of the series

$$\sum_{n=3}^{\infty} \frac{1}{(2n - 1)^2}.$$

(d) Use a graphing utility to find the sum of the series

$$\sum_{n=10}^{\infty} \frac{1}{(2n - 1)^2}.$$

52. HOW DO YOU SEE IT? The figure shows the first 20 terms of two series, $\sum c_n$ and $\sum d_n$. If $\sum c_n$ converges, can you conclude that $\sum d_n$ converges? Explain why or why not.

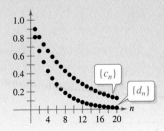

True or False?   **In Exercises 53–58, determine whether the statement is true or false. If it is false, explain why or give an example that shows it is false.**

53. If $0 < a_n \le b_n$ and $\displaystyle\sum_{n=1}^{\infty} a_n$ converges, then $\displaystyle\sum_{n=1}^{\infty} b_n$ must diverge.

54. If $0 < a_{n+10} \le b_n$ and $\displaystyle\sum_{n=1}^{\infty} b_n$ converges, then $\displaystyle\sum_{n=1}^{\infty} a_n$ must converge.

55. If $0 < a_n \le b_n$ and $\displaystyle\sum_{n=1}^{\infty} b_n$ converges, then $\displaystyle\sum_{n=1}^{\infty} (a_n + b_n)$ must converge.

56. If $0 < a_n \le b_n$ and $\displaystyle\sum_{n=1}^{\infty} b_n$ diverges, then $\displaystyle\sum_{n=1}^{\infty} a_n$ must diverge.

57. If $a_n + b_n \le c_n$ and $\displaystyle\sum_{n=1}^{\infty} c_n$ converges, then the series

$$\sum_{n=1}^{\infty} a_n \quad \text{and} \quad \sum_{n=1}^{\infty} b_n$$

both must converge. (Assume that the terms of all three series are positive.)

58. If $a_n \le b_n + c_n$ and $\displaystyle\sum_{n=1}^{\infty} a_n$ diverges, then the series

$$\sum_{n=1}^{\infty} b_n \quad \text{and} \quad \sum_{n=1}^{\infty} c_n$$

both must diverge. (Assume that the terms of all three series are positive.)

59. Proof   Prove that if the nonnegative series

$$\sum_{n=1}^{\infty} a_n \quad \text{and} \quad \sum_{n=1}^{\infty} b_n$$

converge, then so does the series $\displaystyle\sum_{n=1}^{\infty} a_n b_n$.

60. Proof   Use the result of Exercise 59 to prove that if the nonnegative series $\displaystyle\sum_{n=1}^{\infty} a_n$ converges, then so does the series $\displaystyle\sum_{n=1}^{\infty} a_n^2$.

61. Finding Series   Find two series that demonstrate the result of Exercise 59.

62. Finding Series   Find two series that demonstrate the result of Exercise 60.

63. Proof   Suppose that $\Sigma\, a_n$ and $\Sigma\, b_n$ are series with positive terms. Prove that if

$$\lim_{n\to\infty} \frac{a_n}{b_n} = 0$$

and $\Sigma\, b_n$ converges, then $\Sigma\, a_n$ also converges.

64. Proof   Suppose that $\Sigma\, a_n$ and $\Sigma\, b_n$ are series with positive terms. Prove that if

$$\lim_{n\to\infty} \frac{a_n}{b_n} = \infty$$

and $\Sigma\, b_n$ diverges, then $\Sigma\, a_n$ also diverges.

65. Verifying Convergence   Use the result of Exercise 63 to show that each series converges.

(a) $\displaystyle\sum_{n=1}^{\infty} \frac{1}{(n+1)^3}$ (b) $\displaystyle\sum_{n=1}^{\infty} \frac{1}{\sqrt{n}\,\pi^n}$

66. Verifying Divergence   Use the result of Exercise 64 to show that each series diverges.

(a) $\displaystyle\sum_{n=1}^{\infty} \frac{\ln n}{n}$ (b) $\displaystyle\sum_{n=2}^{\infty} \frac{1}{\ln n}$

67. Proof   Suppose that $\Sigma\, a_n$ is a series with positive terms. Prove that if $\Sigma\, a_n$ converges, then $\Sigma \sin a_n$ also converges.

68. Proof   Prove that the series

$$\sum_{n=1}^{\infty} \frac{1}{1 + 2 + 3 + \cdots + n}$$

converges.

69. Comparing Series   Show that

$$\sum_{n=1}^{\infty} \frac{\ln n}{n\sqrt{n}}$$

converges by comparison with $\displaystyle\sum_{n=1}^{\infty} \frac{1}{n^{5/4}}$.

Calculus AP® – Exam Preparation Questions

70. Multiple Choice   Determine the convergence or divergence of the series

$$\sum_{n=1}^{\infty} \frac{\sqrt{n+4}}{n\sqrt{n+3}}$$

using the Direct Comparison Test.

(A) Diverges by comparison with $\displaystyle\sum_{n=1}^{\infty} \frac{1}{n}$

(B) Converges by comparison with $\displaystyle\sum_{n=1}^{\infty} \frac{1}{n}$

(C) Converges by comparison with $\displaystyle\sum_{n=1}^{\infty} \frac{1}{n^{3/2}}$

(D) Converges by comparison with $\displaystyle\sum_{n=1}^{\infty} \frac{1}{n^2}$

71. Multiple Choice   Which of the following series diverges?

I. $\displaystyle\sum_{n=1}^{\infty} \sin \frac{1}{n^2}$

II. $\displaystyle\sum_{n=1}^{\infty} \frac{3^n}{4^n - 1}$

III. $\displaystyle\sum_{n=1}^{\infty} \frac{n + \sqrt{n}}{\sqrt{n^3 + 3n^2}}$

(A) None

(B) III only

(C) I and III only

(D) II and III only

8.5   Alternating Series

▶ Use the Alternating Series Test to determine whether an infinite series converges.
▶ Use the Alternating Series Remainder to approximate the sum of an alternating series.
▶ Classify a convergent series as absolutely or conditionally convergent.
▶ Rearrange an infinite series to obtain a different sum.

Alternating Series

So far, most series you have dealt with have had positive terms. In this section and the next section, you will study series that contain both positive and negative terms. The simplest such series is an **alternating series,** whose terms alternate in sign. For example, the geometric series

$$\sum_{n=0}^{\infty} \left(-\frac{1}{2}\right)^n = \sum_{n=0}^{\infty} (-1)^n \frac{1}{2^n}$$

$$= 1 - \frac{1}{2} + \frac{1}{4} - \frac{1}{8} + \frac{1}{16} - \cdots$$

is an *alternating geometric series* with $r = -\frac{1}{2}$. Alternating series occur in two ways: either the odd terms are negative or the even terms are negative.

Theorem 8.14   Alternating Series Test

Let $a_n > 0$. The alternating series

$$\sum_{n=1}^{\infty} (-1)^n a_n \quad \text{and} \quad \sum_{n=1}^{\infty} (-1)^{n+1} a_n$$

converge when the two conditions listed below are met.

1. $\lim_{n \to \infty} a_n = 0$ **2.** $a_{n+1} \le a_n$, for all n

---

Proof   Consider the alternating series

$$\sum_{n=1}^{\infty} (-1)^{n+1} a_n.$$

For this series, the partial sum (where $2n$ is even)

$$S_{2n} = (a_1 - a_2) + (a_3 - a_4) + (a_5 - a_6) + \cdots + (a_{2n-1} - a_{2n})$$

has all nonnegative terms, and therefore $\{S_{2n}\}$ is a nondecreasing sequence. But you can also write

$$S_{2n} = a_1 - (a_2 - a_3) - (a_4 - a_5) - \cdots - (a_{2n-2} - a_{2n-1}) - a_{2n}$$

which implies that $S_{2n} \le a_1$ for every integer n. So, $\{S_{2n}\}$ is a bounded, nondecreasing sequence that converges to some value L. Because $S_{2n-1} - a_{2n} = S_{2n}$ and $a_{2n} \to 0$, you have

$$\lim_{n \to \infty} S_{2n-1} = \lim_{n \to \infty} S_{2n} + \lim_{n \to \infty} a_{2n} = L + \lim_{n \to \infty} a_{2n} = L.$$

Because both S_{2n} and S_{2n-1} converge to the same limit L, it follows that $\{S_n\}$ also converges to L. Consequently, the given alternating series converges. A similar proof can be made for

$$\sum_{n=1}^{\infty} (-1)^n a_n.$$

Justification

The second condition in the Alternating Series Test can be modified to require only that $0 < a_{n+1} \le a_n$ for all n greater than some integer N.

EXAMPLE 1 Using the Alternating Series Test

Determine the convergence or divergence of

$$\sum_{n=1}^{\infty} (-1)^{n+1}\frac{1}{n}.$$

Solution

Note that $\lim_{n\to\infty} a_n = \lim_{n\to\infty} (1/n) = 0$. So, the first condition of Theorem 8.14 is satisfied. Also note that the second condition of Theorem 8.14 is satisfied because

$$a_{n+1} = \frac{1}{n+1} \le \frac{1}{n} = a_n$$

for all n. So, applying the Alternating Series Test, you can conclude that the series converges.

Connecting Representations

The series in Example 1 is called the *alternating harmonic series*. More is said about this series in Example 8.

EXAMPLE 2 Using the Alternating Series Test

Determine the convergence or divergence of

$$\sum_{n=1}^{\infty} \frac{n}{(-2)^{n-1}}.$$

Solution

To apply the Alternating Series Test, note that, for $n \ge 1$,

$$\frac{1}{2} \le \frac{n}{n+1}$$

$$\frac{2^{n-1}}{2^n} \le \frac{n}{n+1}$$

$$(n+1)2^{n-1} \le n2^n$$

$$\frac{n+1}{2^n} \le \frac{n}{2^{n-1}}.$$

So, $a_{n+1} = (n+1)/2^n \le n/2^{n-1} = a_n$ for all n. Furthermore, by L'Hôpital's Rule,

$$\lim_{x\to\infty} \frac{x}{2^{x-1}} = \lim_{x\to\infty} \frac{1}{2^{x-1}(\ln 2)} = 0 \implies \lim_{n\to\infty} \frac{n}{2^{n-1}} = 0.$$

Therefore, by the Alternating Series Test, the series converges.

EXAMPLE 3 When the Alternating Series Test Does Not Apply

a. The alternating series

$$\sum_{n=1}^{\infty} \frac{(-1)^{n+1}(n+1)}{n} = \frac{2}{1} - \frac{3}{2} + \frac{4}{3} - \frac{5}{4} + \frac{6}{5} - \cdots$$

passes the second condition of the Alternating Series Test because $a_{n+1} \le a_n$ for all n. You cannot apply the Alternating Series Test, however, because the series does not pass the first condition. In fact, the series diverges.

b. The alternating series

$$\frac{2}{1} - \frac{1}{1} + \frac{2}{2} - \frac{1}{2} + \frac{2}{3} - \frac{1}{3} + \frac{2}{4} - \frac{1}{4} + \cdots$$

passes the first condition because a_n approaches 0 as $n\to\infty$. You cannot apply the Alternating Series Test, however, because the series does not pass the second condition. To conclude that the series diverges, you can argue that S_{2N} equals the Nth partial sum of the divergent harmonic series. This implies that the sequence of partial sums diverges. So, the series diverges.

Implementing Processes

In Example 3(a), remember that whenever a series does not pass the first condition of the Alternating Series Test, you can use the nth-Term Test for Divergence to conclude that the series diverges.

Alternating Series Remainder

For a convergent alternating series, the partial sum S_N can be a useful approximation for the sum S of the series. The error involved in using $S \approx S_N$ is the remainder $R_N = S - S_N$.

Theorem 8.15   Alternating Series Remainder

If a convergent alternating series satisfies the condition $a_{n+1} \le a_n$, then the absolute value of the remainder R_N involved in approximating the sum S by S_N is less than (or equal to) the first neglected term. That is,

$$|S - S_N| = |R_N| \le a_{N+1}.$$

A proof of this theorem is given in Appendix A.

EXAMPLE 4   Approximating the Sum of an Alternating Series

See LarsonCalculusforAP.com for an interactive version of this type of example.

Approximate the sum of the series by its first six terms.

$$\sum_{n=1}^{\infty} (-1)^{n+1}\left(\frac{1}{n!}\right) = \frac{1}{1!} - \frac{1}{2!} + \frac{1}{3!} - \frac{1}{4!} + \frac{1}{5!} - \frac{1}{6!} + \cdots$$

Solution

The series converges by the Alternating Series Test because

$$\frac{1}{(n+1)!} \le \frac{1}{n!} \quad \text{and} \quad \lim_{n \to \infty} \frac{1}{n!} = 0.$$

The sum of the first six terms is

$$S_6 = 1 - \frac{1}{2} + \frac{1}{6} - \frac{1}{24} + \frac{1}{120} - \frac{1}{720} = \frac{91}{144} \approx 0.63194$$

and, by the Alternating Series Remainder, you have

$$|S - S_6| = |R_6| \le a_7 = \frac{1}{5040} \approx 0.0002.$$

So, the sum S lies between $0.63194 - 0.0002$ and $0.63194 + 0.0002$, and you have $0.63174 \le S \le 0.63214$.

Technology

Later, using the techniques in Section 8.10, you will be able to show that the series in Example 4 converges to

$$\frac{e-1}{e} \approx 0.63212.$$

(See Section 8.10, Exercise 52.) For now, try using a graphing utility to obtain an approximation of the sum of the series. How many terms do you need to obtain an approximation that is within 0.00001 of the actual sum?

EXAMPLE 5   Finding the Number of Terms

Determine the number of terms required to approximate the sum of the series with an error of less than 0.001.

$$\sum_{n=1}^{\infty} \frac{(-1)^{n+1}}{n^4}$$

Solution   By Theorem 8.15, you know that

$$|R_N| \le a_{N+1} = \frac{1}{(N+1)^4}.$$

For an error of less than 0.001, N must satisfy the inequality $1/(N+1)^4 < 0.001$.

$$\frac{1}{(N+1)^4} < 0.001 \implies (N+1)^4 > 1000 \implies N > \sqrt[4]{1000} - 1 \approx 4.6$$

So, you will need at least 5 terms. Using 5 terms, the sum is $S \approx S_5 \approx 0.94754$, which has an error of less than 0.001.

Absolute and Conditional Convergence

Occasionally, a series may have both positive and negative terms and not be an alternating series. For instance, the series

$$\sum_{n=1}^{\infty} \frac{\sin n}{n^2} = \frac{\sin 1}{1} + \frac{\sin 2}{4} + \frac{\sin 3}{9} + \cdots$$

has both positive and negative terms, yet it is not an alternating series. One way to obtain some information about the convergence of this series is to investigate the convergence of the series

$$\sum_{n=1}^{\infty} \left| \frac{\sin n}{n^2} \right|.$$

By direct comparison, you have $|\sin n| \le 1$ for all n, so

$$\left| \frac{\sin n}{n^2} \right| \le \frac{1}{n^2}, \quad n \ge 1.$$

Therefore, by the Direct Comparison Test, the series $\sum |(\sin n)/n^2|$ converges. The next theorem tells you that the original series also converges.

Theorem 8.16 Absolute Convergence

If the series $\sum |a_n|$ converges, then the series $\sum a_n$ also converges.

Proof   Because $0 \le a_n + |a_n| \le 2|a_n|$ for all n, the series

$$\sum_{n=1}^{\infty} (a_n + |a_n|)$$

converges by comparison with the convergent series

$$\sum_{n=1}^{\infty} 2|a_n|.$$

Furthermore, because $a_n = (a_n + |a_n|) - |a_n|$, you can write

$$\sum_{n=1}^{\infty} a_n = \sum_{n=1}^{\infty} (a_n + |a_n|) - \sum_{n=1}^{\infty} |a_n|$$

where both series on the right converge. So, it follows that $\sum a_n$ converges.

The converse of Theorem 8.16 is not true. For instance, the **alternating harmonic series**

$$\sum_{n=1}^{\infty} \frac{(-1)^{n+1}}{n} = \frac{1}{1} - \frac{1}{2} + \frac{1}{3} - \frac{1}{4} + \cdots$$

converges by the Alternating Series Test. Yet the harmonic series diverges. This type of convergence is called **conditional.**

Definitions of Absolute and Conditional Convergence

1. The series $\sum a_n$ is **absolutely convergent** when $\sum |a_n|$ converges.
2. The series $\sum a_n$ is **conditionally convergent** when $\sum a_n$ converges but $\sum |a_n|$ diverges.

Insight

Determining whether a series is absolutely convergent, conditionally convergent, or divergent is tested on the AP® Calculus BC Exam.

EXAMPLE 6   Absolute and Conditional Convergence

Determine whether each of the series is convergent or divergent. Classify any convergent series as absolutely or conditionally convergent.

a. $\displaystyle\sum_{n=0}^{\infty} \frac{(-1)^n n!}{2^n} = \frac{0!}{2^0} - \frac{1!}{2^1} + \frac{2!}{2^2} - \frac{3!}{2^3} + \cdots$

b. $\displaystyle\sum_{n=1}^{\infty} \frac{(-1)^n}{\sqrt{n}} = -\frac{1}{\sqrt{1}} + \frac{1}{\sqrt{2}} - \frac{1}{\sqrt{3}} + \frac{1}{\sqrt{4}} - \cdots$

Solution

a. This is an alternating series, but the Alternating Series Test does not apply because the limit of the nth term is not zero. By the nth-Term Test for Divergence, however, you can conclude that this series diverges.

b. This series can be shown to be convergent by the Alternating Series Test. Moreover, because the p-series

$$\sum_{n=1}^{\infty} \left|\frac{(-1)^n}{\sqrt{n}}\right| = \frac{1}{\sqrt{1}} + \frac{1}{\sqrt{2}} + \frac{1}{\sqrt{3}} + \frac{1}{\sqrt{4}} + \cdots$$

diverges, the given series is *conditionally* convergent.

EXAMPLE 7   Absolute and Conditional Convergence

Determine whether each of the series is convergent or divergent. Classify any convergent series as absolutely or conditionally convergent.

a. $\displaystyle\sum_{n=1}^{\infty} \frac{(-1)^{n(n+1)/2}}{3^n} = -\frac{1}{3} - \frac{1}{9} + \frac{1}{27} + \frac{1}{81} - \cdots$

b. $\displaystyle\sum_{n=1}^{\infty} \frac{(-1)^n}{\ln(n+1)} = -\frac{1}{\ln 2} + \frac{1}{\ln 3} - \frac{1}{\ln 4} + \frac{1}{\ln 5} - \cdots$

Solution

a. This is *not* an alternating series (the signs change in pairs). However, note that

$$\sum_{n=1}^{\infty} \left|\frac{(-1)^{n(n+1)/2}}{3^n}\right| = \sum_{n=1}^{\infty} \frac{1}{3^n}$$

is a convergent geometric series, with $r = 1/3$. Consequently, by Theorem 8.16, you can conclude that the given series is *absolutely* convergent (and therefore convergent).

b. In this case, the Alternating Series Test indicates that the series converges. However, the series

$$\sum_{n=1}^{\infty} \left|\frac{(-1)^n}{\ln(n+1)}\right| = \frac{1}{\ln 2} + \frac{1}{\ln 3} + \frac{1}{\ln 4} + \cdots$$

diverges by direct comparison with the terms of the harmonic series. Therefore, the given series is *conditionally* convergent.

Exploration

In Example 7(b), verify that the series

$$\sum_{n=1}^{\infty} \left|\frac{(-1)^n}{\ln(n+1)}\right| = \frac{1}{\ln 2} + \frac{1}{\ln 3} + \frac{1}{\ln 4} + \cdots$$

diverges by showing the direct comparison of the terms of this series with the terms of the harmonic series.

Rearrangement of Series

A finite sum such as

$$1 + 3 - 2 + 5 - 4$$

can be rearranged without changing the value of the sum. This is not necessarily true of an infinite series—it depends on whether the series is absolutely convergent or conditionally convergent.

1. If a series is *absolutely convergent,* then its terms can be rearranged in any order without changing the sum of the series.

2. If a series is *conditionally convergent,* then its terms can be rearranged to give a different sum.

The second case is illustrated in Example 8.

EXAMPLE 8   **Rearrangement of a Series**

The alternating harmonic series converges to ln 2. That is,

$$\sum_{n=1}^{\infty} (-1)^{n+1} \frac{1}{n} = \frac{1}{1} - \frac{1}{2} + \frac{1}{3} - \frac{1}{4} + \cdots = \ln 2. \qquad \text{See Exercise 49, Section 8.10.}$$

Rearrange the terms of the series to produce a different sum.

Solution

Consider the rearrangement below.

$$1 - \frac{1}{2} - \frac{1}{4} + \frac{1}{3} - \frac{1}{6} - \frac{1}{8} + \frac{1}{5} - \frac{1}{10} - \frac{1}{12} + \frac{1}{7} - \frac{1}{14} - \cdots$$

$$= \left(1 - \frac{1}{2}\right) - \frac{1}{4} + \left(\frac{1}{3} - \frac{1}{6}\right) - \frac{1}{8} + \left(\frac{1}{5} - \frac{1}{10}\right) - \frac{1}{12} + \left(\frac{1}{7} - \frac{1}{14}\right) - \cdots$$

$$= \frac{1}{2} - \frac{1}{4} + \frac{1}{6} - \frac{1}{8} + \frac{1}{10} - \frac{1}{12} + \frac{1}{14} - \cdots$$

$$= \frac{1}{2}\left(1 - \frac{1}{2} + \frac{1}{3} - \frac{1}{4} + \frac{1}{5} - \frac{1}{6} + \frac{1}{7} - \cdots\right)$$

$$= \frac{1}{2}(\ln 2)$$

By rearranging the terms, you obtain a sum that is half the original sum.

Exploration

In Example 8, you learned that the alternating harmonic series

$$\sum_{n=1}^{\infty} (-1)^{n+1} \frac{1}{n} = 1 - \frac{1}{2} + \frac{1}{3} - \frac{1}{4} + \frac{1}{5} - \frac{1}{6} + \cdots$$

converges to ln 2 ≈ 0.693. Rearrangement of the terms of the series produces a different sum, $\frac{1}{2} \ln 2 \approx 0.347$.

In this exploration, you will rearrange the terms of the alternating harmonic series in such a way that two positive terms follow each negative term. That is,

$$1 - \frac{1}{2} + \frac{1}{3} + \frac{1}{5} - \frac{1}{4} + \frac{1}{7} + \frac{1}{9} - \frac{1}{6} + \frac{1}{11} + \cdots.$$

Now calculate the partial sums S_4, S_7, S_{10}, S_{13}, S_{16}, and S_{19}. Then estimate the sum of this series to three decimal places.

8.5 Exercises

Connecting Representations   In Exercises 1–4, explore the Alternating Series Remainder.

(a) Use a graphing utility to find the indicated partial sum S_n and complete the table.

n	1	2	3	4	5	6	7	8	9	10
S_n										

(b) Use a graphing utility to graph the first 10 terms of the sequence of partial sums and a horizontal line representing the sum.

(c) What pattern exists between the plot of the successive points in part (b) relative to the horizontal line representing the sum of the series? Do the distances between the successive points and the horizontal line increase or decrease?

(d) Discuss the relationship between the answers in part (c) and the Alternating Series Remainder as given in Theorem 8.15.

1. $\displaystyle\sum_{n=1}^{\infty} \frac{(-1)^{n-1}}{2n-1} = \frac{\pi}{4}$

2. $\displaystyle\sum_{n=1}^{\infty} \frac{(-1)^{n-1}}{(n-1)!} = \frac{1}{e}$

3. $\displaystyle\sum_{n=1}^{\infty} \frac{(-1)^{n-1}}{n^2} = \frac{\pi^2}{12}$

4. $\displaystyle\sum_{n=1}^{\infty} \frac{(-1)^{n-1}}{(2n-1)!} = \sin 1$

 Determining Convergence or Divergence In Exercises 5–26, determine the convergence or divergence of the series.

5. $\displaystyle\sum_{n=1}^{\infty} \frac{(-1)^{n+1}}{n+1}$

6. $\displaystyle\sum_{n=1}^{\infty} \frac{(-1)^{n+1} n}{3n+2}$

7. $\displaystyle\sum_{n=1}^{\infty} \frac{(-1)^n}{3^n}$

8. $\displaystyle\sum_{n=1}^{\infty} \frac{(-1)^n}{e^n}$

9. $\displaystyle\sum_{n=1}^{\infty} \frac{(-1)^n (5n-1)}{4n+1}$

10. $\displaystyle\sum_{n=1}^{\infty} \frac{(-1)^{n+1} n}{n^2+5}$

11. $\displaystyle\sum_{n=1}^{\infty} \frac{(-1)^n n}{\ln(n+1)}$

12. $\displaystyle\sum_{n=1}^{\infty} \frac{(-1)^n}{\ln(2n+1)}$

13. $\displaystyle\sum_{n=1}^{\infty} \frac{(-1)^n}{\sqrt{n}}$

14. $\displaystyle\sum_{n=1}^{\infty} \frac{(-1)^{n+1} n^2}{n^2+4}$

15. $\displaystyle\sum_{n=1}^{\infty} \frac{(-1)^{n+1}(n+1)}{\ln(n+1)}$

16. $\displaystyle\sum_{n=1}^{\infty} \frac{(-1)^{n+1} \ln(n+1)}{n+1}$

17. $\displaystyle\sum_{n=1}^{\infty} \sin \frac{(2n-1)\pi}{2}$

18. $\displaystyle\sum_{n=2}^{\infty} \frac{\cos \pi n}{\ln n}$

19. $\displaystyle\sum_{n=0}^{\infty} \frac{(-1)^n}{n!}$

20. $\displaystyle\sum_{n=2}^{\infty} \frac{(-1)^n \cos \pi n}{\ln n}$

21. $\displaystyle\sum_{n=1}^{\infty} \frac{(-1)^{n+1} \sqrt{n}}{n+2}$

22. $\displaystyle\sum_{n=1}^{\infty} \frac{(-1)^{n+1} \sqrt{n}}{\sqrt[3]{n}}$

23. $\displaystyle\sum_{n=1}^{\infty} \frac{(-1)^{n+1} n!}{1 \cdot 3 \cdot 5 \cdots (2n-1)}$

24. $\displaystyle\sum_{n=1}^{\infty} (-1)^{n+1} \frac{1 \cdot 3 \cdot 5 \cdots (2n-1)}{1 \cdot 4 \cdot 7 \cdots (3n-2)}$

25. $\displaystyle\sum_{n=1}^{\infty} \frac{2(-1)^{n+1}}{e^n - e^{-n}}$

26. $\displaystyle\sum_{n=1}^{\infty} \frac{2(-1)^{n+1}}{e^n + e^{-n}}$

 Approximating the Sum of an Alternating Series In Exercises 27–30, use Theorem 8.15 to approximate the sum of the series by using the first six terms.

27. $\displaystyle\sum_{n=0}^{\infty} \frac{(-1)^n 5}{n!}$

28. $\displaystyle\sum_{n=2}^{\infty} \frac{(-1)^n 2}{\ln n}$

29. $\displaystyle\sum_{n=1}^{\infty} \frac{(-1)^{n+1} 2}{n^3}$

30. $\displaystyle\sum_{n=1}^{\infty} \frac{(-1)^{n+1} n}{3^n}$

 Finding the Number of Terms In Exercises 31–36, use Theorem 8.15 to determine the number of terms required to approximate the sum of the series with an error of less than 0.001.

31. $\displaystyle\sum_{n=1}^{\infty} \frac{(-1)^{n+1}}{n^3}$

32. $\displaystyle\sum_{n=1}^{\infty} \frac{(-1)^{n+1} 2}{n^3}$

33. $\displaystyle\sum_{n=1}^{\infty} \frac{(-1)^{n+1}}{2n^3 - 1}$

34. $\displaystyle\sum_{n=1}^{\infty} \frac{(-1)^{n+1}}{n^5}$

35. $\displaystyle\sum_{n=0}^{\infty} \frac{(-1)^n}{n!}$

36. $\displaystyle\sum_{n=0}^{\infty} \frac{(-1)^n}{(2n)!}$

 Determining Absolute and Conditional Convergence In Exercises 37–54, determine whether the series converges absolutely or conditionally, or diverges.

37. $\displaystyle\sum_{n=1}^{\infty} \frac{(-1)^n}{2^n}$

38. $\displaystyle\sum_{n=1}^{\infty} \frac{(-1)^{n+1}}{n^2}$

39. $\displaystyle\sum_{n=1}^{\infty} \frac{(-1)^n}{n!}$

40. $\displaystyle\sum_{n=1}^{\infty} \frac{(-1)^{n+1}}{n+3}$

41. $\displaystyle\sum_{n=1}^{\infty} \frac{(-1)^{n+1}}{\sqrt{n}}$

42. $\displaystyle\sum_{n=1}^{\infty} \frac{(-1)^{n+1}}{n\sqrt{n}}$

43. $\displaystyle\sum_{n=1}^{\infty} \frac{(-1)^{n+1} n^2}{2 \ln(n+1)}$

44. $\displaystyle\sum_{n=1}^{\infty} \frac{(-1)^{n+1} n}{5n+1}$

45. $\displaystyle\sum_{n=2}^{\infty} \frac{(-1)^n}{n \ln n}$

46. $\displaystyle\sum_{n=0}^{\infty} (-1)^n e^{-n^2}$

47. $\displaystyle\sum_{n=2}^{\infty} \frac{(-1)^n n}{n^3 - 5}$

48. $\displaystyle\sum_{n=1}^{\infty} \frac{(-1)^{n+1}}{n^{4/3}}$

49. $\displaystyle\sum_{n=0}^{\infty} \frac{(-1)^n}{(2n+1)!}$

50. $\displaystyle\sum_{n=0}^{\infty} \frac{(-1)^n}{\sqrt{n+4}}$

51. $\displaystyle\sum_{n=0}^{\infty} \frac{\cos n\pi}{n+1}$

52. $\displaystyle\sum_{n=1}^{\infty} \frac{(-1)^{n+1} \arctan n}{e^n}$

53. $\displaystyle\sum_{n=1}^{\infty} \frac{\cos(n\pi/3)}{n^2}$

54. $\displaystyle\sum_{n=1}^{\infty} \frac{\sin[(2n-1)\pi/2]}{n}$

EXPLORING CONCEPTS

55. Alternating Series Determine whether S_{50} is an underestimate or an overestimate of the sum of the alternating series below. Explain.

$$\sum_{n=1}^{\infty} \frac{(-1)^n}{n}$$

56. Alternating Series Give an example of convergent alternating series $\Sigma\, a_n$ and $\Sigma\, b_n$ such that $\Sigma\, a_n b_n$ diverges.

57. Alternating Series Remainder Give the remainder after N terms of a convergent alternating series.

58. Communicating In your own words, describe the difference between absolute and conditional convergence of an alternating series.

59. Justifying Do you agree with the following statements? Why or why not?

(a) If both $\Sigma\, a_n$ and $\Sigma\, (-a_n)$ converge, then $\Sigma\, |a_n|$ converges.

(b) If $\Sigma\, a_n$ diverges, then $\Sigma\, |a_n|$ diverges.

---

60. **HOW DO YOU SEE IT?** The graphs of the sequences of partial sums of two series are shown in the figures. Which graph represents the partial sums of an alternating series? Explain.

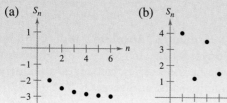

(a) S_n

(b) S_n

Finding Values In Exercises 61 and 62, find the values of p for which the series converges.

61. $\displaystyle\sum_{n=1}^{\infty} (-1)^n \left(\frac{1}{n^p}\right)$

62. $\displaystyle\sum_{n=1}^{\infty} (-1)^n \left(\frac{1}{n+p}\right)$

63. Proof Prove that if $\Sigma\, |a_n|$ converges, then $\Sigma\, a_n^2$ converges. Is the converse true? If not, give an example that shows it is false.

64. Finding a Series Use the result of Exercise 61 to give an example of an alternating p-series that converges, but whose corresponding p-series diverges.

65. Finding a Series Give an example of a series that demonstrates the statement you proved in Exercise 63.

66. Finding Values Find all values of x for which the series $\Sigma\, (x^n/n)$ (a) converges absolutely and (b) converges conditionally.

Using a Series In Exercises 67 and 68, use the given series. (a) Does the series meet the conditions of Theorem 8.14? Explain why or why not. (b) Does the series converge? If so, what is the sum?

67. $\dfrac{1}{2} - \dfrac{1}{3} + \dfrac{1}{4} - \dfrac{1}{9} + \dfrac{1}{8} - \dfrac{1}{27} + \cdots + \dfrac{1}{2^n} - \dfrac{1}{3^n} + \cdots$

68. $\displaystyle\sum_{n=1}^{\infty} (-1)^{n+1} a_n, \quad a_n = \begin{cases} \dfrac{1}{\sqrt{n}}, & \text{if } n \text{ is odd} \\[2mm] \dfrac{1}{n^3}, & \text{if } n \text{ is even} \end{cases}$

Implementing Processes In Exercises 69–78, determine the convergence or divergence of the series and identify the test used.

69. $\displaystyle\sum_{n=1}^{\infty} \frac{8}{\sqrt[3]{n}}$

70. $\displaystyle\sum_{n=1}^{\infty} \frac{3n+5}{n^3 + 2n^2 + 4}$

71. $\displaystyle\sum_{n=1}^{\infty} \frac{3^n}{n^2}$

72. $\displaystyle\sum_{n=1}^{\infty} \frac{1}{4^n - 5}$

73. $\displaystyle\sum_{n=1}^{\infty} \left(\frac{9}{8}\right)^n$

74. $\displaystyle\sum_{n=1}^{\infty} \frac{2n^2}{(n+1)^2}$

75. $\displaystyle\sum_{n=1}^{\infty} 100 e^{-n/2}$

76. $\displaystyle\sum_{n=0}^{\infty} \frac{(-1)^n}{n+4}$

77. $\displaystyle\sum_{n=1}^{\infty} \frac{(-1)^{n+1}\, 4}{3n^2 - 1}$

78. $\displaystyle\sum_{n=2}^{\infty} \frac{\ln n}{n}$

79. Error Analysis Describe the error in the following argument, that $0 = 1$.

$0 = 0 + 0 + 0 + \cdots$

$= (1 - 1) + (1 - 1) + (1 - 1) + \cdots$

$= 1 + (-1 + 1) + (-1 + 1) + \cdots$

$= 1 + 0 + 0 + \cdots$

$= 1$ ✗

Calculus AP® – Exam Preparation Questions

80. Multiple Choice For what value of k will both

$$\sum_{n=1}^{\infty} \frac{(-1)^{kn}}{n} \quad \text{and} \quad \sum_{n=1}^{\infty} \left(\frac{6}{k}\right)^n$$

diverge?

(A) 3 (B) 4 (C) 5 (D) 8

81. Multiple Choice Which of the following statements about the series below is true?

$$\sum_{n=1}^{\infty} \frac{(-1)^{n+1}}{1 + \sqrt{n^5}}$$

(A) The series converges absolutely.

(B) The series converges conditionally.

(C) The series converges, but neither conditionally nor absolutely.

(D) The series diverges.

8.6 The Ratio and Root Tests

- ▶ Use the Ratio Test to determine whether a series converges or diverges.
- ▶ Use the Root Test to determine whether a series converges or diverges.
- ▶ Review the tests for convergence and divergence of an infinite series.

The Ratio Test

This section begins with a test for absolute convergence—the **Ratio Test.**

> **Theorem 8.17 Ratio Test**
>
> Let $\Sigma\, a_n$ be a series with nonzero terms.
>
> 1. The series $\Sigma\, a_n$ converges absolutely when $\displaystyle \lim_{n\to\infty} \left| \frac{a_{n+1}}{a_n} \right| < 1$.
>
> 2. The series $\Sigma\, a_n$ diverges when $\displaystyle \lim_{n\to\infty} \left| \frac{a_{n+1}}{a_n} \right| > 1$ or $\displaystyle \lim_{n\to\infty} \left| \frac{a_{n+1}}{a_n} \right| = \infty$.
>
> 3. The Ratio Test is inconclusive when $\displaystyle \lim_{n\to\infty} \left| \frac{a_{n+1}}{a_n} \right| = 1$.

Remark

The Ratio Test is always inconclusive for any p-series.

Proof To prove Property 1, assume that

$$\lim_{n\to\infty} \left| \frac{a_{n+1}}{a_n} \right| = r < 1$$

and choose R such that $0 \le r < R < 1$. By the definition of the limit of a sequence, there exists some $N > 0$ such that $|a_{n+1}/a_n| < R$ for all $n > N$. Therefore, you can write the following inequalities.

$$|a_{N+1}| < |a_N|R$$
$$|a_{N+2}| < |a_{N+1}|R < |a_N|R^2$$
$$|a_{N+3}| < |a_{N+2}|R < |a_{N+1}|R^2 < |a_N|R^3$$
$$\vdots$$

The geometric series

$$\sum_{n=1}^{\infty} |a_N|R^n = |a_N|R + |a_N|R^2 + \cdots + |a_N|R^n + \cdots$$

converges, and so, by the Direct Comparison Test, the series

$$\sum_{n=1}^{\infty} |a_{N+n}| = |a_{N+1}| + |a_{N+2}| + \cdots + |a_{N+n}| + \cdots$$

also converges. This, in turn, implies that the series $\Sigma\, |a_n|$ converges, because discarding a finite number of terms ($n = N - 1$) does not affect convergence. Consequently, by Theorem 8.16, the series $\Sigma\, a_n$ converges absolutely. The proof of Property 2 is similar and is left as an exercise. (See Exercise 95.) ∎

The fact that the Ratio Test is inconclusive when $|a_{n+1}/a_n| \to 1$ can be seen by comparing the two series $\Sigma\, (1/n)$ and $\Sigma\, (1/n^2)$. The first series diverges and the second one converges, but in both cases

$$\lim_{n\to\infty} \left| \frac{a_{n+1}}{a_n} \right| = 1.$$

Although the Ratio Test is not a cure for all ills related to testing for convergence, it is particularly useful for series that *converge rapidly*. Series involving factorials or exponentials are frequently of this type.

EXAMPLE 1   Using the Ratio Test

Determine the convergence or divergence of

$$\sum_{n=0}^{\infty} \frac{2^n}{n!}.$$

Algebraic Solution

Because

$$a_n = \frac{2^n}{n!}$$

you can write the following.

$$\lim_{n \to \infty} \left| \frac{a_{n+1}}{a_n} \right| = \lim_{n \to \infty} \left[\frac{2^{n+1}}{(n+1)!} \div \frac{2^n}{n!} \right]$$

$$= \lim_{n \to \infty} \left[\frac{2^{n+1}}{(n+1)!} \cdot \frac{n!}{2^n} \right]$$

$$= \lim_{n \to \infty} \frac{2}{n+1}$$

$$= 0 < 1$$

The series converges because the limit of $|a_{n+1}/a_n|$ is less than 1.

Graphical Solution

Recall from Section 8.1 that the factorial function grows faster than any exponential function. So, you expect this series to converge. The figure shows the first 15 partial sums of the series.

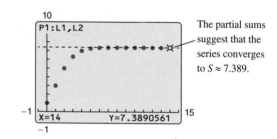

The partial sums suggest that the series converges to $S \approx 7.389$.

EXAMPLE 2   Using the Ratio Test

Determine whether each series converges or diverges.

a. $\sum_{n=0}^{\infty} \frac{n^2\, 2^{n+1}}{3^n}$ **b.** $\sum_{n=1}^{\infty} \frac{n^n}{n!}$

Solution

a. This series converges because the limit of $|a_{n+1}/a_n|$ is less than 1.

$$\lim_{n \to \infty} \left| \frac{a_{n+1}}{a_n} \right| = \lim_{n \to \infty} \left[(n+1)^2 \left(\frac{2^{n+2}}{3^{n+1}} \right) \left(\frac{3^n}{n^2\, 2^{n+1}} \right) \right]$$

$$= \lim_{n \to \infty} \frac{2(n+1)^2}{3n^2}$$

$$= \frac{2}{3} < 1$$

b. This series diverges because the limit of $|a_{n+1}/a_n|$ is greater than 1.

$$\lim_{n \to \infty} \left| \frac{a_{n+1}}{a_n} \right| = \lim_{n \to \infty} \left[\frac{(n+1)^{n+1}}{(n+1)!} \left(\frac{n!}{n^n} \right) \right]$$

$$= \lim_{n \to \infty} \left[\frac{(n+1)^{n+1}}{(n+1)} \left(\frac{1}{n^n} \right) \right]$$

$$= \lim_{n \to \infty} \frac{(n+1)^n}{n^n}$$

$$= \lim_{n \to \infty} \left(1 + \frac{1}{n} \right)^n$$

$$= e > 1$$

> **Algebra Review**
>
> For help in simplifying factorial expressions, see Example 1 in the *Chapter 8 Algebra Review* on page A50.

EXAMPLE 3   A Failure of the Ratio Test

See LarsonCalculusforAP.com for an interactive version of this type of example.

Determine the convergence or divergence of

$$\sum_{n=1}^{\infty} (-1)^n \frac{\sqrt{n}}{n+1}.$$

Solution   The limit of $|a_{n+1}/a_n|$ is equal to 1.

$$\lim_{n\to\infty} \left| \frac{a_{n+1}}{a_n} \right| = \lim_{n\to\infty} \left[\left(\frac{\sqrt{n+1}}{n+2} \right) \left(\frac{n+1}{\sqrt{n}} \right) \right]$$

$$= \lim_{n\to\infty} \left[\sqrt{\frac{n+1}{n}} \left(\frac{n+1}{n+2} \right) \right]$$

$$= \sqrt{1}(1)$$

$$= 1$$

So, the Ratio Test is inconclusive. To determine whether the series converges, you need to try a different test. In this case, you can apply the Alternating Series Test. To show that $a_{n+1} \le a_n$, let

$$f(x) = \frac{\sqrt{x}}{x+1}.$$

Then the derivative is

$$f'(x) = \frac{-x+1}{2\sqrt{x}(x+1)^2}.$$

Because the derivative is negative for $x > 1$, you know that f is a decreasing function. Also, by L'Hôpital's Rule,

$$\lim_{x\to\infty} \frac{\sqrt{x}}{x+1} = \lim_{x\to\infty} \frac{1/(2\sqrt{x})}{1}$$

$$= \lim_{x\to\infty} \frac{1}{2\sqrt{x}}$$

$$= 0.$$

Therefore, by the Alternating Series Test, the series converges.

The series in Example 3 is *conditionally convergent*. This follows from the fact that the series

$$\sum_{n=1}^{\infty} |a_n|$$

diverges $\left(\text{by the Limit Comparison Test with } \Sigma \, 1/\sqrt{n}\right)$, but the series

$$\sum_{n=1}^{\infty} a_n$$

converges.

Technology

A graphing utility can reinforce the conclusion that the series in Example 3 converges *conditionally*. By adding the first 100 terms of the series, you obtain a sum of about -0.2. (The sum of the first 100 terms of the series $\Sigma \, |a_n|$ is about 16.9.)

The Root Test

The next test for convergence or divergence of series works especially well for series involving nth powers. The proof of this theorem is similar to the proof given for the Ratio Test, and is left as an exercise (see Exercise 96).

Theorem 8.18 Root Test

1. The series $\Sigma \, a_n$ converges absolutely when

$$\lim_{n \to \infty} \sqrt[n]{|a_n|} < 1.$$

2. The series $\Sigma \, a_n$ diverges when

$$\lim_{n \to \infty} \sqrt[n]{|a_n|} > 1 \quad \text{or} \quad \lim_{n \to \infty} \sqrt[n]{|a_n|} = \infty.$$

3. The Root Test is inconclusive when

$$\lim_{n \to \infty} \sqrt[n]{|a_n|} = 1.$$

Insight

The Root Test is not covered on the AP® Calculus Exam.

Remark

The Root Test is always inconclusive for any p-series.

EXAMPLE 4 Using the Root Test

Determine the convergence or divergence of

$$\sum_{n=1}^{\infty} \frac{e^{2n}}{n^n}.$$

Algebraic Solution

You can apply the Root Test as follows.

$$\lim_{n \to \infty} \sqrt[n]{|a_n|} = \lim_{n \to \infty} \sqrt[n]{\frac{e^{2n}}{n^n}}$$

$$= \lim_{n \to \infty} \frac{e^{2n/n}}{n^{n/n}}$$

$$= \lim_{n \to \infty} \frac{e^2}{n}$$

$$= 0 < 1$$

Because this limit is less than 1, you can conclude that the series converges absolutely (and therefore converges).

Numerical Solution

The partial sums in the table suggest that the series converges to $S \approx 60.386$.

n	10	50	100	500
S_n	60.370	60.386	60.386	60.386

To see the usefulness of the Root Test for the series in Example 4, try applying the Ratio Test to that series. When you do this, you obtain the following.

$$\lim_{n \to \infty} \left| \frac{a_{n+1}}{a_n} \right| = \lim_{n \to \infty} \left[\frac{e^{2(n+1)}}{(n+1)^{n+1}} \div \frac{e^{2n}}{n^n} \right]$$

$$= \lim_{n \to \infty} \left[\frac{e^{2(n+1)}}{(n+1)^{n+1}} \cdot \frac{n^n}{e^{2n}} \right]$$

$$= \lim_{n \to \infty} e^2 \frac{n^n}{(n+1)^{n+1}}$$

$$= \lim_{n \to \infty} e^2 \left(\frac{n}{n+1} \right)^n \left(\frac{1}{n+1} \right)$$

$$= 0$$

Note that this limit is not as easily evaluated as the limit obtained by the Root Test in Example 4.

Strategies for Testing Series

You have now studied 10 tests for determining the convergence or divergence of an infinite series. (See the summary in the table on the next page.) Skill in choosing and applying the various tests will come only with practice. Below is a set of guidelines for choosing an appropriate test.

Guidelines for Testing a Series for Convergence or Divergence

1. Does the nth term approach 0? If not, the series diverges.
2. Is the series one of the special types—geometric, p-series, telescoping, or alternating?
3. Can the Integral Test, the Root Test, or the Ratio Test be applied?
4. Can the series be compared favorably to one of the special types?

In some instances, more than one test is applicable. However, your objective should be to learn to choose the most efficient test.

EXAMPLE 5   Applying the Strategies for Testing Series

Determine the convergence or divergence of each series.

a. $\displaystyle\sum_{n=1}^{\infty} \frac{n+1}{3n+1}$

b. $\displaystyle\sum_{n=1}^{\infty} \left(\frac{\pi}{6}\right)^n$

c. $\displaystyle\sum_{n=1}^{\infty} ne^{-n^2}$

d. $\displaystyle\sum_{n=1}^{\infty} \frac{1}{3n+1}$

e. $\displaystyle\sum_{n=1}^{\infty} (-1)^n \frac{3}{4n+1}$

f. $\displaystyle\sum_{n=1}^{\infty} \frac{n!}{10^n}$

g. $\displaystyle\sum_{n=1}^{\infty} \left(\frac{n+1}{2n+1}\right)^n$

Solution

a. For this series, the limit of the nth term is not 0 $\left(a_n \to \frac{1}{3}\text{ as }n \to \infty\right)$. So, by the nth-Term Test, the series diverges.

b. This series is geometric. Moreover, because the ratio of the terms

$$r = \frac{\pi}{6}$$

is less than 1 in absolute value, you can conclude that the series converges.

c. Because the function

$$f(x) = xe^{-x^2}$$

is easily integrated, you can use the Integral Test to conclude that the series converges.

d. The nth term of this series can be compared to the nth term of the harmonic series. After using the Limit Comparison Test, you can conclude that the series diverges.

e. This is an alternating series whose nth term approaches 0. Because $a_{n+1} \leq a_n$, you can use the Alternating Series Test to conclude that the series converges.

f. The nth term of this series involves a factorial, which indicates that the Ratio Test may work well. After applying the Ratio Test, you can conclude that the series diverges.

g. The nth term of this series involves a variable that is raised to the nth power, which indicates that the Root Test may work well. After applying the Root Test, you can conclude that the series converges.

Summary of Tests for Series

Test	Series	Condition(s) of Convergence	Condition(s) of Divergence	Comment
nth-Term	$\displaystyle\sum_{n=1}^{\infty} a_n$		$\displaystyle\lim_{n\to\infty} a_n \neq 0$	This test cannot be used to show convergence.
Geometric Series $(r \neq 0)$	$\displaystyle\sum_{n=0}^{\infty} ar^n$	$\lvert r \rvert < 1$	$\lvert r \rvert \geq 1$	Sum: $S = \dfrac{a}{1-r}$
Telescoping Series	$\displaystyle\sum_{n=1}^{\infty} (b_n - b_{n+1})$	$\displaystyle\lim_{n\to\infty} b_n = L$		Sum: $S = b_1 - L$
p-Series	$\displaystyle\sum_{n=1}^{\infty} \dfrac{1}{n^p}$	$p > 1$	$0 < p \leq 1$	
Alternating Series $(a_n > 0)$	$\displaystyle\sum_{n=1}^{\infty} (-1)^{n-1} a_n$	$a_{n+1} \leq a_n$ and $\displaystyle\lim_{n\to\infty} a_n = 0$		Remainder: $\lvert R_N \rvert \leq a_{N+1}$
Integral (f is continuous, positive, and decreasing)	$\displaystyle\sum_{n=1}^{\infty} a_n,$ $a_n = f(n) \geq 0$	$\displaystyle\int_1^{\infty} f(x)\,dx$ converges	$\displaystyle\int_1^{\infty} f(x)\,dx$ diverges	Remainder: $0 < R_N < \displaystyle\int_N^{\infty} f(x)\,dx$
Root	$\displaystyle\sum_{n=1}^{\infty} a_n$	$\displaystyle\lim_{n\to\infty} \sqrt[n]{\lvert a_n \rvert} < 1$	$\displaystyle\lim_{n\to\infty} \sqrt[n]{\lvert a_n \rvert} > 1$ or $= \infty$	Test is inconclusive when $\displaystyle\lim_{n\to\infty} \sqrt[n]{\lvert a_n \rvert} = 1$.
Ratio	$\displaystyle\sum_{n=1}^{\infty} a_n$	$\displaystyle\lim_{n\to\infty} \left\lvert \dfrac{a_{n+1}}{a_n} \right\rvert < 1$	$\displaystyle\lim_{n\to\infty} \left\lvert \dfrac{a_{n+1}}{a_n} \right\rvert > 1$ or $= \infty$	Test is inconclusive when $\displaystyle\lim_{n\to\infty} \left\lvert \dfrac{a_{n+1}}{a_n} \right\rvert = 1$.
Direct Comparison $(a_n, b_n > 0)$	$\displaystyle\sum_{n=1}^{\infty} a_n$	$0 < a_n \leq b_n$ and $\displaystyle\sum_{n=1}^{\infty} b_n$ converges	$0 < b_n \leq a_n$ and $\displaystyle\sum_{n=1}^{\infty} b_n$ diverges	
Limit Comparison $(a_n, b_n > 0)$	$\displaystyle\sum_{n=1}^{\infty} a_n$	$\displaystyle\lim_{n\to\infty} \dfrac{a_n}{b_n} = L > 0$ and $\displaystyle\sum_{n=1}^{\infty} b_n$ converges	$\displaystyle\lim_{n\to\infty} \dfrac{a_n}{b_n} = L > 0$ and $\displaystyle\sum_{n=1}^{\infty} b_n$ diverges	

8.6   Exercises

See *CalcChat.com* for tutorial help and worked-out solutions to odd-numbered exercises.

Verifying a Formula   In Exercises 1–4, verify the formula.

1. $\dfrac{n5^{n+2}}{5^{n+1}} = 5n$

2. $\dfrac{(n+1)4^n}{n4^{n+1}} = \dfrac{n+1}{4n}$

3. $\dfrac{(n+1)!}{(n-2)!} = (n+1)(n)(n-1)$

4. $\dfrac{(2k-2)!}{(2k)!} = \dfrac{1}{(2k)(2k-1)}$

Connecting Representations   In Exercises 5–10, match the series with the graph of its sequence of partial sums. [The graphs are labeled (a), (b), (c), (d), (e), and (f).]

(a)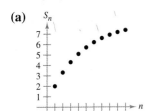

(b)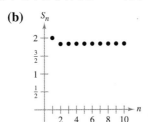

(c)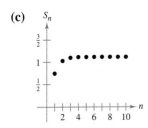

(d)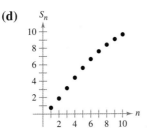

(e)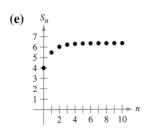

(f)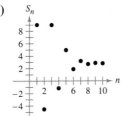

5. $\displaystyle\sum_{n=1}^{\infty} n\left(\dfrac{3}{4}\right)^n$

6. $\displaystyle\sum_{n=1}^{\infty} \left(\dfrac{3}{4}\right)^n\left(\dfrac{1}{n!}\right)$

7. $\displaystyle\sum_{n=1}^{\infty} \dfrac{(-3)^{n+1}}{n!}$

8. $\displaystyle\sum_{n=1}^{\infty} \dfrac{(-1)^{n-1}4}{(2n)!}$

9. $\displaystyle\sum_{n=1}^{\infty} \left(\dfrac{4n}{5n-3}\right)^n$

10. $\displaystyle\sum_{n=0}^{\infty} 4e^{-n}$

 Using the Ratio Test   In Exercises 11–34, use the Ratio Test to determine the convergence or divergence of the series.

11. $\displaystyle\sum_{n=1}^{\infty} \dfrac{1}{6^n}$

12. $\displaystyle\sum_{n=1}^{\infty} \dfrac{3}{n!}$

13. $\displaystyle\sum_{n=0}^{\infty} \dfrac{n!}{5^n}$

14. $\displaystyle\sum_{n=1}^{\infty} \dfrac{4^n}{n!}$

15. $\displaystyle\sum_{n=1}^{\infty} n\left(\dfrac{4}{3}\right)^n$

16. $\displaystyle\sum_{n=1}^{\infty} n\left(\dfrac{4}{5}\right)^n$

17. $\displaystyle\sum_{n=1}^{\infty} \dfrac{9^n}{n^5}$

18. $\displaystyle\sum_{n=1}^{\infty} \dfrac{n+1}{4^n}$

19. $\displaystyle\sum_{n=1}^{\infty} \dfrac{n^3}{3^n}$

20. $\displaystyle\sum_{n=1}^{\infty} \dfrac{(-1)^{n+1}(n+2)}{n(n+1)}$

21. $\displaystyle\sum_{n=1}^{\infty} \dfrac{(-1)^n 5^n}{n!}$

22. $\displaystyle\sum_{n=1}^{\infty} \dfrac{(-1)^{n-1}(3/2)^n}{n^2}$

23. $\displaystyle\sum_{n=1}^{\infty} \dfrac{n^2}{(n+1)(n^2+2)}$

24. $\displaystyle\sum_{n=1}^{\infty} \dfrac{n!}{n^n}$

25. $\displaystyle\sum_{n=0}^{\infty} \dfrac{e^n}{n!}$

26. $\displaystyle\sum_{n=1}^{\infty} \dfrac{e^{-2n}}{n}$

27. $\displaystyle\sum_{n=0}^{\infty} \dfrac{6^n}{(n+1)^n}$

28. $\displaystyle\sum_{n=0}^{\infty} \dfrac{4^n}{2^n+1}$

29. $\displaystyle\sum_{n=1}^{\infty} \dfrac{(2n)!}{n^5}$

30. $\displaystyle\sum_{n=0}^{\infty} \dfrac{(n!)^2}{(3n)!}$

31. $\displaystyle\sum_{n=0}^{\infty} \dfrac{(-1)^n 2^{4n}}{(2n+1)!}$

32. $\displaystyle\sum_{n=1}^{\infty} \dfrac{(-1)^n 3^n}{n2^n}$

33. $\displaystyle\sum_{n=0}^{\infty} \dfrac{(-1)^{n+1}n!}{1\cdot 3\cdot 5\cdots(2n+1)}$

34. $\displaystyle\sum_{n=1}^{\infty} \dfrac{(-1)^n[2\cdot 4\cdot 6\cdots(2n)]}{2\cdot 5\cdot 8\cdots(3n-1)}$

 Using the Root Test   In Exercises 35–48, use the Root Test to determine the convergence or divergence of the series.

35. $\displaystyle\sum_{n=1}^{\infty} \left(\dfrac{n}{2n+1}\right)^n$

36. $\displaystyle\sum_{n=1}^{\infty} \dfrac{1}{n^n}$

37. $\displaystyle\sum_{n=1}^{\infty} \left(\dfrac{3n+2}{n+3}\right)^n$

38. $\displaystyle\sum_{n=1}^{\infty} \left(\dfrac{n-2}{5n+1}\right)^n$

39. $\displaystyle\sum_{n=2}^{\infty} \dfrac{(-1)^n}{(\ln n)^n}$

40. $\displaystyle\sum_{n=1}^{\infty} \left(\dfrac{-3n}{2n+1}\right)^{3n}$

41. $\displaystyle\sum_{n=1}^{\infty} \left(2\sqrt[n]{n}+1\right)^n$

42. $\displaystyle\sum_{n=0}^{\infty} e^{-3n}$

43. $\displaystyle\sum_{n=1}^{\infty} \dfrac{n}{3^n}$

44. $\displaystyle\sum_{n=1}^{\infty} \left(\dfrac{n}{500}\right)^n$

45. $\displaystyle\sum_{n=1}^{\infty} \left(\dfrac{1}{n}-\dfrac{1}{n^2}\right)^n$

46. $\displaystyle\sum_{n=1}^{\infty} \left(\dfrac{\ln n}{n}\right)^n$

47. $\displaystyle\sum_{n=2}^{\infty} \dfrac{n}{(\ln n)^n}$

48. $\displaystyle\sum_{n=1}^{\infty} \dfrac{(n!)^n}{(n^n)^2}$

Applying the Strategies for Testing a Series In Exercises 49–64, determine the convergence or divergence of the series using any appropriate test from this chapter. Identify the test used.

49. $\sum_{n=1}^{\infty} \frac{(-1)^{n+1} 5}{n}$

50. $\sum_{n=1}^{\infty} \frac{100}{n}$

51. $\sum_{n=1}^{\infty} \frac{3}{n\sqrt{n}}$

52. $\sum_{n=1}^{\infty} \left(\frac{2\pi}{3}\right)^n$

53. $\sum_{n=1}^{\infty} \frac{5n}{2n-1}$

54. $\sum_{n=1}^{\infty} \frac{n}{2n^2+1}$

55. $\sum_{n=1}^{\infty} \frac{(-1)^n 3^{n-2}}{2^n}$

56. $\sum_{n=1}^{\infty} \frac{10}{3\sqrt{n^3}}$

57. $\sum_{n=1}^{\infty} \frac{10n+3}{n2^n}$

58. $\sum_{n=1}^{\infty} \frac{2^n}{4n^2-1}$

59. $\sum_{n=1}^{\infty} \frac{\cos n}{3^n}$

60. $\sum_{n=2}^{\infty} \frac{(-1)^n}{n \ln n}$

61. $\sum_{n=1}^{\infty} \frac{\ln n}{n^2}$

62. $\sum_{n=1}^{\infty} \frac{(-1)^n 3^{n-1}}{n!}$

63. $\sum_{n=1}^{\infty} \frac{(-3)^n}{3 \cdot 5 \cdot 7 \cdots (2n+1)}$

64. $\sum_{n=1}^{\infty} \frac{3 \cdot 5 \cdot 7 \cdots (2n+1)}{18^n (2n-1) n!}$

Connecting Representations In Exercises 65–68, identify the two series that are the same.

65. (a) $\sum_{n=1}^{\infty} \frac{n5^n}{n!}$

(b) $\sum_{n=0}^{\infty} \frac{n5^n}{(n+1)!}$

(c) $\sum_{n=0}^{\infty} \frac{(n+1)5^{n+1}}{(n+1)!}$

66. (a) $\sum_{n=4}^{\infty} n\left(\frac{3}{4}\right)^n$

(b) $\sum_{n=0}^{\infty} (n+1)\left(\frac{3}{4}\right)^n$

(c) $\sum_{n=1}^{\infty} n\left(\frac{3}{4}\right)^{n-1}$

67. (a) $\sum_{n=0}^{\infty} \frac{(-1)^n}{(2n+1)!}$

(b) $\sum_{n=1}^{\infty} \frac{(-1)^{n-1}}{(2n-1)!}$

(c) $\sum_{n=1}^{\infty} \frac{(-1)^{n-1}}{(2n+1)!}$

68. (a) $\sum_{n=2}^{\infty} \frac{(-1)^n}{(n-1)2^{n-1}}$

(b) $\sum_{n=1}^{\infty} \frac{(-1)^{n+1}}{n2^n}$

(c) $\sum_{n=0}^{\infty} \frac{(-1)^{n+1}}{(n+1)2^n}$

Writing an Equivalent Series In Exercises 69 and 70, write an equivalent series with the index of summation beginning at $n = 0$.

69. $\sum_{n=1}^{\infty} \frac{n}{7^n}$

70. $\sum_{n=2}^{\infty} \frac{3^{n+1}}{(n-2)!}$

Finding the Number of Terms In Exercises 71 and 72, (a) determine the number of terms required to approximate the sum of the series with an error less than 0.0001, and (b) use a graphing utility to approximate the sum of the series with an error less than 0.0001.

71. $\sum_{k=1}^{\infty} \frac{(-3)^k}{2^k k!}$

72. $\sum_{k=0}^{\infty} \frac{(-3)^k}{1 \cdot 3 \cdot 5 \cdots (2k+1)}$

Using a Recursively Defined Series In Exercises 73–78, the terms of a series $\sum_{n=1}^{\infty} a_n$ are defined recursively. Determine the convergence or divergence of the series. Explain your reasoning.

73. $a_1 = \frac{1}{2}, \ a_{n+1} = \frac{4n-1}{3n+2} a_n$

74. $a_1 = 2, \ a_{n+1} = \frac{2n+1}{5n-4} a_n$

75. $a_1 = 1, \ a_{n+1} = \frac{\sin n + 1}{\sqrt{n}} a_n$

76. $a_1 = \frac{1}{5}, \ a_{n+1} = \frac{\cos n + 1}{n} a_n$

77. $a_1 = \frac{1}{3}, \ a_{n+1} = \left(1 + \frac{1}{n}\right) a_n$

78. $a_1 = \frac{1}{4}, \ a_{n+1} = \sqrt[n]{a_n}$

Implementing Processes In Exercises 79–82, use the Ratio Test or the Root Test to determine the convergence or divergence of the series.

79. $1 + \frac{1 \cdot 2}{1 \cdot 3} + \frac{1 \cdot 2 \cdot 3}{1 \cdot 3 \cdot 5} + \frac{1 \cdot 2 \cdot 3 \cdot 4}{1 \cdot 3 \cdot 5 \cdot 7} + \cdots$

80. $1 + \frac{2}{3} + \frac{3}{3^2} + \frac{4}{3^3} + \frac{5}{3^4} + \frac{6}{3^5} + \cdots$

81. $\frac{1}{(\ln 3)^3} + \frac{1}{(\ln 4)^4} + \frac{1}{(\ln 5)^5} + \frac{1}{(\ln 6)^6} + \cdots$

82. $1 + \frac{1 \cdot 3}{3!} + \frac{1 \cdot 3 \cdot 5}{5!} + \frac{1 \cdot 3 \cdot 5 \cdot 7}{7!} + \cdots$

Finding Values In Exercises 83–88, find the values of x for which the series converges.

83. $\sum_{n=0}^{\infty} 2\left(\frac{x}{3}\right)^n$

84. $\sum_{n=0}^{\infty} \left(\frac{x-3}{5}\right)^n$

85. $\sum_{n=1}^{\infty} \frac{(-1)^n (x+1)^n}{n}$

86. $\sum_{n=0}^{\infty} 3(x-4)^n$

87. $\sum_{n=0}^{\infty} n!\left(\frac{x}{2}\right)^n$

88. $\sum_{n=0}^{\infty} \frac{(x+1)^n}{n!}$

Connecting Representations In Exercises 89 and 90, (a) use the ratio test to verify that the series converges, (b) use a graphing utility to find the indicated partial sums S_n to complete the table, (c) use a graphing utility to graph the first 10 terms of the sequence of partial sums and (d) use the table to estimate the sum of the series.

n	5	10	15	20	25	30
S_n						

89. $\sum_{n=1}^{\infty} n^3 \left(\frac{1}{2}\right)^n$

90. $\sum_{n=1}^{\infty} \frac{n^2+1}{n!}$

EXPLORING CONCEPTS

91. Communicating   Use the results of Exercises 89 and 90 to explain how the magnitudes of the terms of a series tend to affect the rate at which the sequence of partial sums approaches the sum of the series.

92. Think About It   What can you conclude about the convergence or divergence of $\Sigma\, a_n$ for each of the following conditions? Explain your reasoning.

(a) $\lim\limits_{n\to\infty} \left| \dfrac{a_{n+1}}{a_n} \right| = 0$ (b) $\lim\limits_{n\to\infty} \left| \dfrac{a_{n+1}}{a_n} \right| = 1$

(c) $\lim\limits_{n\to\infty} \left| \dfrac{a_{n+1}}{a_n} \right| = \dfrac{3}{2}$ (d) $\lim\limits_{n\to\infty} \sqrt[n]{|a_n|} = 2$

(e) $\lim\limits_{n\to\infty} \sqrt[n]{|a_n|} = 1$ (f) $\lim\limits_{n\to\infty} \sqrt[n]{|a_n|} = e$

93. Think About It   What can you conclude about the convergence or divergence of $\Sigma\, a_n$ using the Ratio Test when a_n is a rational function of n? Explain.

94. HOW DO YOU SEE IT?   The graphs show the sequences of partial sums of the series

$$\sum_{n=1}^{\infty} \frac{2^n}{n} \quad \text{and} \quad \sum_{n=1}^{\infty} \frac{n}{3^n}.$$

Based on the figures, what can you determine about

$$\lim_{n\to\infty} \left| \frac{a_{n+1}}{a_n} \right|$$

for each series?

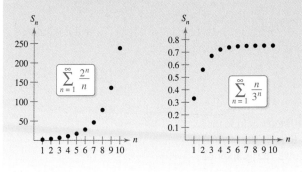

95. Proof   Prove Property 2 of Theorem 8.17.

96. Proof   Prove Theorem 8.18. *(Hint for Property 1:* If the limit equals $r < 1$, choose a real number R such that $r < R < 1$. By the definitions of the limit, there exists some $N > 0$ such that $\sqrt[n]{|a_n|} < R$ for all $n > N$.)

Justifying   In Exercises 97–100, verify that the Ratio Test is inconclusive for the *p*-series.

97. $\displaystyle\sum_{n=1}^{\infty} \frac{1}{n^{3/2}}$ **98.** $\displaystyle\sum_{n=1}^{\infty} \frac{1}{n^{1/2}}$

99. $\displaystyle\sum_{n=1}^{\infty} \frac{1}{n^4}$ **100.** $\displaystyle\sum_{n=1}^{\infty} \frac{1}{n^p}$

101. Justifying   Show that the Root Test is inconclusive for the *p*-series

$$\sum_{n=1}^{\infty} \frac{1}{n^p}.$$

102. Justifying   Show that the Ratio Test and the Root Test are both inconclusive for the logarithmic *p*-series

$$\sum_{n=2}^{\infty} \frac{1}{n(\ln n)^p}.$$

103. Testing for Different Values   Determine the convergence or divergence of the series

$$\sum_{n=1}^{\infty} \frac{(n!)^2}{(xn)!}$$

when (a) $x = 1$, (b) $x = 2$, (c) $x = 3$, and (d) x is a positive integer.

104. Using Absolute Convergence   Show that if

$$\sum_{n=1}^{\infty} a_n$$

is absolutely convergent, then

$$\left| \sum_{n=1}^{\infty} a_n \right| \le \sum_{n=1}^{\infty} |a_n|.$$

Calculus AP® – Exam Preparation Questions

105. Multiple Choice   Consider the series

$$\sum_{n=1}^{\infty} \frac{9^n}{(n+1)!}.$$

If the Ratio Test is applied to the series, which of the following limits results, implying that the series converges?

(A) $\lim\limits_{n\to\infty} \dfrac{9^n}{(n+1)!}$ (B) $\lim\limits_{n\to\infty} \dfrac{9}{n+2}$

(C) $\lim\limits_{n\to\infty} \dfrac{(n+1)!}{9^n}$ (D) $\lim\limits_{n\to\infty} \dfrac{n+2}{9}$

106. Multiple Choice   Which of the following series diverge?

I. $\displaystyle\sum_{n=1}^{\infty} \frac{5}{n}$

II. $\displaystyle\sum_{n=1}^{\infty} \frac{n6^n}{n!}$

III. $\displaystyle\sum_{n=1}^{\infty} \frac{(-1)^{n+1}8}{n}$

(A) I only   (B) I and II only

(C) II and III only   (D) I, II, and III

8.7 Taylor Polynomials and Approximations

▶ Find polynomial approximations of elementary functions and compare them with the elementary functions.
▶ Find Taylor and Maclaurin polynomial approximations of elementary functions.
▶ Use the remainder of a Taylor polynomial.

Polynomial Approximations of Elementary Functions

The goal of this section is to show how polynomial functions can be used as approximations for other elementary functions. To find a polynomial function P that approximates another function f, begin by choosing a number c in the domain of f at which f and P have the same value. That is,

$P(c) = f(c)$.   Graphs of f and P pass through $(c, f(c))$.

The approximating polynomial is said to be **expanded about** c or **centered at** c. Geometrically, the requirement that $P(c) = f(c)$ means that the graph of P passes through the point $(c, f(c))$. Of course, there are many polynomials whose graphs pass through the point $(c, f(c))$. Your task is to find a polynomial whose graph resembles the graph of f near this point. One way to do this is to impose the additional requirement that the slope of the polynomial function be the same as the slope of the graph of f at the point $(c, f(c))$.

$P'(c) = f'(c)$ Graphs of f and P have the same slope at $(c, f(c))$.

With these two requirements, you can obtain a simple linear approximation of f, as shown in Figure 8.11.

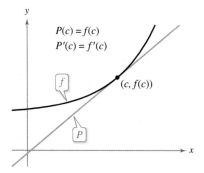

Near $(c, f(c))$, the graph of P can be used to approximate the graph of f.
Figure 8.11

EXAMPLE 1   First-Degree Polynomial Approximation of $f(x) = e^x$

For the function $f(x) = e^x$, find a first-degree polynomial function $P_1(x) = a_0 + a_1 x$ whose value and slope agree with the value and slope of f at $x = 0$.

Solution

Because $f(x) = e^x$ and $f'(x) = e^x$, the value and the slope of f at $x = 0$ are

$f(0) = e^0 = 1$ Value of f at $x = 0$

and

$f'(0) = e^0 = 1$.   Slope of f at $x = 0$

Because $P_1(x) = a_0 + a_1 x$, you can use the condition that $P_1(0) = f(0)$ to conclude that $a_0 = 1$. Moreover, because $P_1'(x) = a_1$, you can use the condition that $P_1'(0) = f'(0)$ to conclude that $a_1 = 1$. Therefore, $P_1(x) = 1 + x$. The figure shows the graphs of $P_1(x) = 1 + x$ and $f(x) = e^x$.

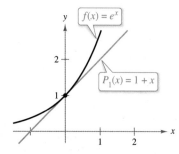

P_1 is the first-degree polynomial approximation of $f(x) = e^x$.

In Figure 8.12, you can see that, at points near $(0, 1)$, the graph of the first-degree polynomial function

$$P_1(x) = 1 + x \qquad \text{1st-degree approximation}$$

is reasonably close to the graph of $f(x) = e^x$. As you move away from $(0, 1)$, however, the graphs move farther and farther from each other and the accuracy of the approximation decreases. To improve the approximation, you can impose yet another requirement—that the values of the second derivatives of P and f agree when $x = 0$. The polynomial, P_2, of least degree that satisfies all three requirements $P_2(0) = f(0)$, $P_2'(0) = f'(0)$, and $P_2''(0) = f''(0)$ can be shown to be

$$P_2(x) = 1 + x + \frac{1}{2}x^2. \qquad \text{2nd-degree approximation}$$

Moreover, in Figure 8.12, you can see that P_2 is a better approximation of f than P_1. By requiring that the values of $P_n(x)$ and its first n derivatives match those of $f(x) = e^x$ at $x = 0$, you obtain the nth-degree approximation shown below.

$$P_n(x) = 1 + x + \frac{1}{2}x^2 + \frac{1}{3!}x^3 + \cdots + \frac{1}{n!}x^n \qquad \text{nth-degree approximation}$$

$$\approx e^x$$

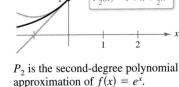

P_2 is the second-degree polynomial approximation of $f(x) = e^x$.

Figure 8.12

EXAMPLE 2   Third-Degree Polynomial Approximation of $f(x) = e^x$

Construct a table comparing the values of the polynomial

$$P_3(x) = 1 + x + \frac{1}{2}x^2 + \frac{1}{3!}x^3 \qquad \text{3rd-degree approximation}$$

with $f(x) = e^x$ for several values of x near 0.

Solution   Use a graphing utility to obtain the results shown in the table. Note that for $x = 0$, the two functions have the same value, but that as x moves farther away from 0, the accuracy of the approximating polynomial $P_3(x)$ decreases.

x	-1	-0.2	-0.1	0	0.1	0.2	1
e^x	0.3679	0.81873	0.904837	1	1.105171	1.22140	2.7183
$P_3(x)$	0.3333	0.81867	0.904833	1	1.105167	1.22133	2.6667

Technology

A graphing utility can be used to compare the graph of the approximating polynomial with the graph of the function f. For instance, in Figure 8.13, the graph of

$$P_3(x) = 1 + x + \tfrac{1}{2}x^2 + \tfrac{1}{6}x^3 \qquad \text{3rd-degree approximation}$$

is compared with the graph of $f(x) = e^x$. Use a graphing utility to compare the graphs of

$$P_4(x) = 1 + x + \tfrac{1}{2}x^2 + \tfrac{1}{6}x^3 + \tfrac{1}{24}x^4 \qquad \text{4th-degree approximation}$$

$$P_5(x) = 1 + x + \tfrac{1}{2}x^2 + \tfrac{1}{6}x^3 + \tfrac{1}{24}x^4 + \tfrac{1}{120}x^5 \qquad \text{5th-degree approximation}$$

and

$$P_6(x) = 1 + x + \tfrac{1}{2}x^2 + \tfrac{1}{6}x^3 + \tfrac{1}{24}x^4 + \tfrac{1}{120}x^5 + \tfrac{1}{720}x^6 \qquad \text{6th-degree approximation}$$

with the graph of f. What do you notice?

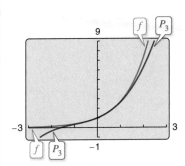

P_3 is the third-degree polynomial approximation of $f(x) = e^x$.

Figure 8.13

Taylor and Maclaurin Polynomials

The polynomial approximation of

$$f(x) = e^x$$

in Example 2 is expanded about $c = 0$. For expansions about an arbitrary value of c, it is convenient to write the polynomial in the form

$$P_n(x) = a_0 + a_1(x - c) + a_2(x - c)^2 + a_3(x - c)^3 + \cdots + a_n(x - c)^n.$$

In this form, repeated differentiation produces

$$P_n'(x) = a_1 + 2a_2(x - c) + 3a_3(x - c)^2 + \cdots + na_n(x - c)^{n-1}$$
$$P_n''(x) = 2a_2 + 2(3a_3)(x - c) + \cdots + n(n - 1)a_n(x - c)^{n-2}$$
$$P_n'''(x) = 2(3a_3) + \cdots + n(n - 1)(n - 2)a_n(x - c)^{n-3}$$
$$\vdots$$
$$P_n^{(n)}(x) = n(n - 1)(n - 2) \cdots (2)(1)a_n.$$

Letting $x = c$, you then obtain

$$P_n(c) = a_0, \quad P_n'(c) = a_1, \quad P_n''(c) = 2a_2, \quad \ldots, \quad P_n^{(n)}(c) = n!a_n$$

and because the values of f and its first n derivatives must agree with the values of P_n and its first n derivatives at $x = c$, it follows that

$$f(c) = a_0, \quad f'(c) = a_1, \quad \frac{f''(c)}{2!} = a_2, \quad \ldots, \quad \frac{f^{(n)}(c)}{n!} = a_n.$$

With these coefficients, you can obtain the following definition of **Taylor polynomials,** named after the English mathematician Brook Taylor (1685–1731), and **Maclaurin polynomials,** named after the Scottish mathematician Colin Maclaurin (1698–1746).

Definitions of *n*th Taylor Polynomial and *n*th Maclaurin Polynomial

If f has n derivatives at c, then the polynomial

$$P_n(x) = f(c) + f'(c)(x - c) + \frac{f''(c)}{2!}(x - c)^2 + \cdots + \frac{f^{(n)}(c)}{n!}(x - c)^n$$

is called the **nth Taylor polynomial for f at c.** If $c = 0$, then

$$P_n(x) = f(0) + f'(0)x + \frac{f''(0)}{2!}x^2 + \frac{f'''(0)}{3!}x^3 + \cdots + \frac{f^{(n)}(0)}{n!}x^n$$

is also called the **nth Maclaurin polynomial for f.**

Connecting Representations

Maclaurin polynomials are special types of Taylor polynomials for which $c = 0$.

EXAMPLE 3 A Maclaurin Polynomial for $f(x) = e^x$

Find the nth Maclaurin polynomial for

$$f(x) = e^x.$$

Solution

From the discussion on the preceding page, the nth Maclaurin polynomial for

$$f(x) = e^x$$

is

$$P_n(x) = 1 + x + \frac{1}{2!}x^2 + \frac{1}{3!}x^3 + \cdots + \frac{1}{n!}x^n.$$

EXAMPLE 4   **Finding Taylor Polynomials for ln x**

Find the Taylor polynomials P_0, P_1, P_2, P_3, and P_4 for $f(x) = \ln x$, centered at $c = 1$.

Solution

Expanding about $c = 1$ yields the following.

$$f(x) = \ln x \qquad\qquad f(1) = \ln 1 = 0$$

$$f'(x) = \frac{1}{x} \qquad\qquad f'(1) = \frac{1}{1} = 1$$

$$f''(x) = -\frac{1}{x^2} \qquad\qquad f''(1) = -\frac{1}{1^2} = -1$$

$$f'''(x) = \frac{2!}{x^3} \qquad\qquad f'''(1) = \frac{2!}{1^3} = 2$$

$$f^{(4)}(x) = -\frac{3!}{x^4} \qquad\qquad f^{(4)}(1) = -\frac{3!}{1^4} = -6$$

Therefore, the Taylor polynomials are as follows.

$$P_0(x) = f(1) = 0$$

$$P_1(x) = f(1) + f'(1)(x - 1) = (x - 1)$$

$$P_2(x) = f(1) + f'(1)(x - 1) + \frac{f''(1)}{2!}(x - 1)^2$$

$$= (x - 1) - \frac{1}{2}(x - 1)^2$$

$$P_3(x) = f(1) + f'(1)(x - 1) + \frac{f''(1)}{2!}(x - 1)^2 + \frac{f'''(1)}{3!}(x - 1)^3$$

$$= (x - 1) - \frac{1}{2}(x - 1)^2 + \frac{1}{3}(x - 1)^3$$

$$P_4(x) = f(1) + f'(1)(x - 1) + \frac{f''(1)}{2!}(x - 1)^2 + \frac{f'''(1)}{3!}(x - 1)^3 + \frac{f^{(4)}(1)}{4!}(x - 1)^4$$

$$= (x - 1) - \frac{1}{2}(x - 1)^2 + \frac{1}{3}(x - 1)^3 - \frac{1}{4}(x - 1)^4$$

Figure 8.14 compares the graphs of P_1, P_2, P_3, and P_4 with the graph of $f(x) = \ln x$. Note that near $x = 1$, the graphs are nearly indistinguishable. For instance,

$$P_4(1.1) \approx 0.0953083$$

and

$$\ln(1.1) \approx 0.0953102.$$

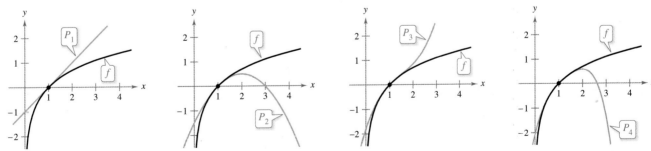

As n increases, the graph of P_n becomes a better and better approximation of the graph of $f(x) = \ln x$ near $x = 1$.
Figure 8.14

EXAMPLE 5 Finding Maclaurin Polynomials for cos *x*

Find the Maclaurin polynomials P_0, P_2, P_4, and P_6 for $f(x) = \cos x$. Use $P_6(x)$ to approximate the value of $\cos(0.1)$.

Solution

Expanding about $c = 0$ yields the following.

$$f(x) = \cos x \qquad\qquad f(0) = \cos 0 = 1$$
$$f'(x) = -\sin x \qquad\qquad f'(0) = -\sin 0 = 0$$
$$f''(x) = -\cos x \qquad\qquad f''(0) = -\cos 0 = -1$$
$$f'''(x) = \sin x \qquad\qquad f'''(0) = \sin 0 = 0$$

Through repeated differentiation, you can see that the pattern $1, 0, -1, 0$ continues, and you obtain the Maclaurin polynomials

$$P_0(x) = 1, \quad P_2(x) = 1 - \frac{1}{2!}x^2, \quad P_4(x) = 1 - \frac{1}{2!}x^2 + \frac{1}{4!}x^4,$$

and

$$P_6(x) = 1 - \frac{1}{2!}x^2 + \frac{1}{4!}x^4 - \frac{1}{6!}x^6.$$

To nine decimal places, $P_6(0.1) \approx 0.995004165$ is the same as $\cos(0.1)$. Figure 8.15 compares the graphs of $f(x) = \cos x$ and P_6. ■

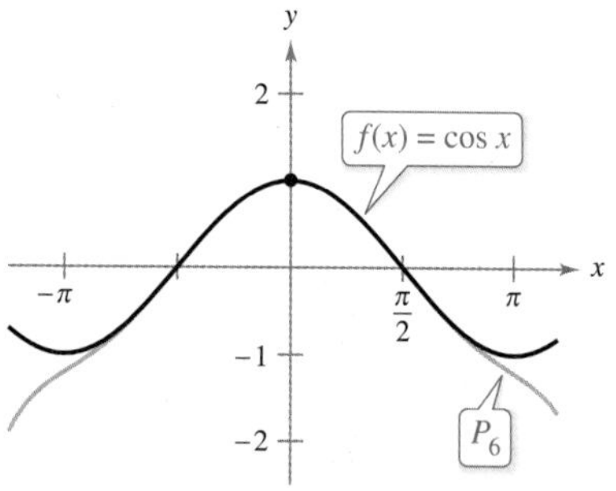

Near $(0, 1)$, the graph of P_6 can be used to approximate the graph of $f(x) = \cos x$.

Figure 8.15

Note in Example 5 that the Maclaurin polynomials for $\cos x$ have only even powers of x. Similarly, the Maclaurin polynomials for $\sin x$ have only odd powers of x (see Exercise 13). This is not generally true of the Taylor polynomials for $\sin x$ and $\cos x$ expanded about $c \neq 0$, as shown in the next example.

EXAMPLE 6 Finding a Taylor Polynomial for sin *x*

See LarsonCalculusforAP.com for an interactive version of this type of example.

Find the third Taylor polynomial for $f(x) = \sin x$, expanded about $c = \pi/6$.

Solution

Expanding about $c = \pi/6$ yields the following.

$$f(x) = \sin x \qquad\qquad f\left(\frac{\pi}{6}\right) = \sin\frac{\pi}{6} = \frac{1}{2}$$

$$f'(x) = \cos x \qquad\qquad f'\left(\frac{\pi}{6}\right) = \cos\frac{\pi}{6} = \frac{\sqrt{3}}{2}$$

$$f''(x) = -\sin x \qquad\qquad f''\left(\frac{\pi}{6}\right) = -\sin\frac{\pi}{6} = -\frac{1}{2}$$

$$f'''(x) = -\cos x \qquad\qquad f'''\left(\frac{\pi}{6}\right) = -\cos\frac{\pi}{6} = -\frac{\sqrt{3}}{2}$$

So, the third Taylor polynomial for $f(x) = \sin x$, expanded about $c = \pi/6$, is

$$P_3(x) = f\left(\frac{\pi}{6}\right) + f'\left(\frac{\pi}{6}\right)\left(x - \frac{\pi}{6}\right) + \frac{f''\left(\frac{\pi}{6}\right)}{2!}\left(x - \frac{\pi}{6}\right)^2 + \frac{f'''\left(\frac{\pi}{6}\right)}{3!}\left(x - \frac{\pi}{6}\right)^3$$

$$= \frac{1}{2} + \frac{\sqrt{3}}{2}\left(x - \frac{\pi}{6}\right) - \frac{1}{2(2!)}\left(x - \frac{\pi}{6}\right)^2 - \frac{\sqrt{3}}{2(3!)}\left(x - \frac{\pi}{6}\right)^3.$$

Figure 8.16 compares the graphs of $f(x) = \sin x$ and P_3. ■

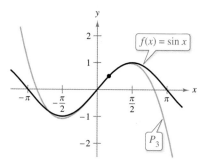

Near $(\pi/6, 1/2)$, the graph of P_3 can be used to approximate the graph of $f(x) = \sin x$.

Figure 8.16

Taylor polynomials and Maclaurin polynomials can be used to approximate the value of a function at a specific point. For instance, to approximate the value of $\ln(1.1)$, you can use Taylor polynomials for $f(x) = \ln x$ expanded about $c = 1$, as shown in Example 4, or you can use Maclaurin polynomials, as shown in Example 7.

EXAMPLE 7   Approximation Using Maclaurin Polynomials

Use a fourth Maclaurin polynomial to approximate the value of $\ln(1.1)$.

Solution

Because 1.1 is closer to 1 than to 0, you should consider Maclaurin polynomials for the function $g(x) = \ln(1 + x)$.

$$g(x) = \ln(1 + x) \qquad\qquad g(0) = \ln(1 + 0) = 0$$
$$g'(x) = (1 + x)^{-1} \qquad\qquad g'(0) = (1 + 0)^{-1} = 1$$
$$g''(x) = -(1 + x)^{-2} \qquad\qquad g''(0) = -(1 + 0)^{-2} = -1$$
$$g'''(x) = 2(1 + x)^{-3} \qquad\qquad g'''(0) = 2(1 + 0)^{-3} = 2$$
$$g^{(4)}(x) = -6(1 + x)^{-4} \qquad\qquad g^{(4)}(0) = -6(1 + 0)^{-4} = -6$$

Note that you obtain the same coefficients as in Example 4. Therefore, the fourth Maclaurin polynomial for $g(x) = \ln(1 + x)$ is

$$P_4(x) = g(0) + g'(0)x + \frac{g''(0)}{2!}x^2 + \frac{g'''(0)}{3!}x^3 + \frac{g^{(4)}(0)}{4!}x^4$$

$$= x - \frac{1}{2}x^2 + \frac{1}{3}x^3 - \frac{1}{4}x^4.$$

Consequently,

$$\ln(1.1) = \ln(1 + 0.1) \approx P_4(0.1) \approx 0.0953083.$$

> **Exploration**
>
> Check to see that the fourth Taylor polynomial (from Example 4), evaluated at $x = 1.1$, yields the same result as the fourth Maclaurin polynomial in Example 7.

The table below illustrates the accuracy of the Maclaurin polynomial approximation of the calculator value of $\ln(1.1)$. You can see that as n increases, $P_n(0.1)$ approaches $\ln(1.1) \approx 0.0953102$.

Maclaurin Polynomial Approximations of ln(1 + x) for x = 0.1

n	1	2	3	4
$P_n(0.1)$	0.1000000	0.0950000	0.0953333	0.0953083

On the other hand, the table below illustrates that as you move away from the expansion point $c = 0$, the accuracy of the approximation decreases.

Fourth Maclaurin Polynomial Approximations of ln(1 + x)

x	0	0.1	0.5	0.75	1.0
$\ln(1 + x)$	0	0.0953102	0.4054651	0.5596158	0.6931472
$P_4(x)$	0	0.0953083	0.4010417	0.5302734	0.5833333

These two tables illustrate two very important points about the accuracy of Taylor (or Maclaurin) polynomials for use in approximations.

1. The approximation is usually better for higher-degree Taylor (or Maclaurin) polynomials than for those of lower degree.

2. The approximation is usually better at x-values close to c than at x-values far from c.

Remainder of a Taylor Polynomial

An approximation technique is of little value without some idea of its accuracy. To measure the accuracy of approximating a function value $f(x)$ by the Taylor polynomial $P_n(x)$, you can use the concept of a **remainder** $R_n(x)$, defined as follows.

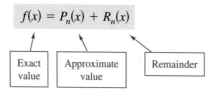

$$f(x) = P_n(x) + R_n(x)$$

| Exact value | Approximate value | Remainder |

So, $R_n(x) = f(x) - P_n(x)$. The absolute value of $R_n(x)$ is called the **error** associated with the approximation. That is,

$$\text{Error} = |R_n(x)| = |f(x) - P_n(x)|.$$

The next theorem gives a general procedure for estimating the remainder associated with a Taylor polynomial. This important theorem is called **Taylor's Theorem,** and the remainder given in the theorem is called the **Lagrange form of the remainder.**

Theorem 8.19   Taylor's Theorem

If a function f is differentiable through order $n + 1$ in an interval I containing c, then, for each x in I, there exists z between x and c such that

$$f(x) = f(c) + f'(c)(x - c) + \frac{f''(c)}{2!}(x - c)^2 + \cdots + \frac{f^{(n)}(c)}{n!}(x - c)^n + R_n(x)$$

where

$$R_n(x) = \frac{f^{(n+1)}(z)}{(n + 1)!}(x - c)^{n+1}.$$

A proof of this theorem is given in Appendix A.

One useful consequence of Taylor's Theorem is that

$$|R_n(x)| \le \frac{|x - c|^{n+1}}{(n + 1)!} \max |f^{(n+1)}(z)|$$

where $\max |f^{(n+1)}(z)|$ is the maximum value of $f^{(n+1)}(z)$ between x and c.

For $n = 0$, Taylor's Theorem states that if f is differentiable in an interval I containing c, then, for each x in I, there exists z between x and c such that

$$f(x) = f(c) + f'(z)(x - c)$$

or

$$f'(z) = \frac{f(x) - f(c)}{x - c}.$$

Do you recognize this special case of Taylor's Theorem? (It is the Mean Value Theorem.)

When applying Taylor's Theorem, you should not expect to be able to find the exact value of z. (If you could do this, an approximation would not be necessary.) Rather, you are trying to find bounds for $f^{(n+1)}(z)$ from which you are able to tell how large the remainder $R_n(x)$ is.

EXAMPLE 8   Determining the Accuracy of an Approximation

The third Maclaurin polynomial for $\sin x$ is

$$P_3(x) = x - \frac{x^3}{3!}.$$

Use Taylor's Theorem to approximate $\sin(0.1)$ by $P_3(0.1)$ and determine the accuracy of the approximation.

Solution

Using Taylor's Theorem, you have

$$\sin x = x - \frac{x^3}{3!} + R_3(x) = x - \frac{x^3}{3!} + \frac{f^{(4)}(z)}{4!}x^4$$

where $0 < z < 0.1$. Therefore,

$$\sin(0.1) \approx 0.1 - \frac{(0.1)^3}{3!} \approx 0.1 - 0.000167 = 0.099833.$$

Because $f^{(4)}(z) = \sin z$, it follows that the error $|R_3(0.1)|$ can be bounded as follows.

$$0 < R_3(0.1) = \frac{\sin z}{4!}(0.1)^4 < \frac{0.0001}{4!} \approx 0.000004$$

This implies that

$$0.099833 < \sin(0.1) \approx 0.099833 + R_3(0.1) < 0.099833 + 0.000004$$

or

$$0.099833 < \sin(0.1) < 0.099837.$$

Remark

Note that when you use a calculator,

$$\sin(0.1) \approx 0.0998334.$$

EXAMPLE 9   Approximating a Value to a Desired Accuracy

Determine the degree of the Taylor polynomial $P_n(x)$ expanded about $c = 1$ that should be used to approximate $\ln(1.2)$ so that the error is less than 0.001.

Solution

Following the pattern of Example 4, you can see that the $(n + 1)$st derivative of $f(x) = \ln x$ is

$$f^{(n+1)}(x) = (-1)^n \frac{n!}{x^{n+1}}.$$

Using Taylor's Theorem, you know that the error $|R_n(1.2)|$ is

$$|R_n(1.2)| = \left| \frac{f^{(n+1)}(z)}{(n+1)!}(1.2 - 1)^{n+1} \right|$$

$$= \frac{n!}{z^{n+1}}\left[\frac{1}{(n+1)!} \right](0.2)^{n+1}$$

$$= \frac{(0.2)^{n+1}}{z^{n+1}(n+1)}$$

where $1 < z < 1.2$. In this interval, $(0.2)^{n+1}/[z^{n+1}(n+1)]$ is less than $(0.2)^{n+1}/(n+1)$. So, you are seeking a value of n such that

$$\frac{(0.2)^{n+1}}{(n+1)} < 0.001 \quad \Longrightarrow \quad 1000 < (n+1)5^{n+1}.$$

By trial and error, you can determine that the least value of n that satisfies this inequality is $n = 3$. So, you would need the third Taylor polynomial to achieve the desired accuracy in approximating $\ln(1.2)$.

Remark

Note that when you use a calculator,

$$P_3(1.2) \approx 0.1827$$

and

$$\ln(1.2) \approx 0.1823.$$

8.7　Exercises

Connecting Representations　In Exercises 1–4, match the Taylor polynomial approximation of the function $f(x) = e^{-x^2/2}$ with its graph. [The graphs are labeled (a), (b), (c), and (d).]

(a)
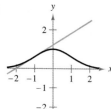

(b)
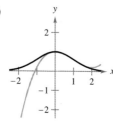

(c)
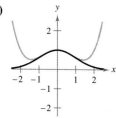

(d)
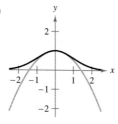

1. $g(x) = -\dfrac{1}{2}x^2 + 1$

2. $g(x) = \dfrac{1}{8}x^4 - \dfrac{1}{2}x^2 + 1$

3. $g(x) = e^{-1/2}[(x + 1) + 1]$

4. $g(x) = e^{-1/2}\left[\dfrac{1}{3}(x - 1)^3 - (x - 1) + 1\right]$

 **Finding a First-Degree Polynomial Approximation**　In Exercises 5–8, find a first-degree polynomial function P_1 whose value and slope agree with the value and slope of f at $x = c$. Use a graphing utility to graph f and P_1.

5. $f(x) = \dfrac{4}{\sqrt{x}}, \quad c = 4$

6. $f(x) = \dfrac{6}{\sqrt[3]{x}}, \quad c = 8$

7. $f(x) = \sec x, \quad c = \dfrac{\pi}{6}$

8. $f(x) = \tan x, \quad c = \dfrac{\pi}{4}$

9. Conjecture　Consider the function $f(x) = \cos x$ and its Maclaurin polynomials P_2, P_4, and P_6 (see Example 5).

(a) Use a graphing utility to graph f and the indicated polynomial approximations.

(b) Evaluate and compare the values of $f^{(n)}(0)$ and $P_n^{(n)}(0)$ for $n = 2, 4$, and 6.

(c) Use the results in part (b) to make a conjecture about $f^{(n)}(0)$ and $P_n^{(n)}(0)$.

10. Conjecture　Consider the function $f(x) = x^3 e^{2x}$.

(a) Find the Maclaurin polynomials P_4, P_5, and P_6 for f.

(b) Use a graphing utility to graph f, P_4, P_5, and P_6.

(c) Evaluate and compare the values of $f^{(n)}(0)$ and $P_n^{(n)}(0)$ for $n = 4, 5$, and 6.

(d) Use the results in part (c) to make a conjecture about $f^{(n)}(0)$ and $P_n^{(n)}(0)$.

 Finding a Maclaurin Polynomial　In Exercises 11–20, find the nth Maclaurin polynomial for the function.

11. $f(x) = e^{4x}, \quad n = 4$　　**12.** $f(x) = e^{-x/2}, \quad n = 4$

13. $f(x) = \sin x, \quad n = 5$　　**14.** $f(x) = \cos \pi x, \quad n = 4$

15. $f(x) = xe^x, \quad n = 4$　　**16.** $f(x) = x^2 e^{-x}, \quad n = 4$

17. $f(x) = \dfrac{1}{1 - x}, \quad n = 5$　　**18.** $f(x) = \dfrac{x}{x + 1}, \quad n = 4$

19. $f(x) = \sec x, \quad n = 2$　　**20.** $f(x) = \tan x, \quad n = 3$

 Finding a Taylor Polynomial　In Exercises 21–26, find the nth Taylor polynomial for $f(x)$, centered at c.

21. $f(x) = \dfrac{2}{x}, \quad n = 3, \quad c = 1$

22. $f(x) = \dfrac{1}{x^2}, \quad n = 4, \quad c = -2$

23. $f(x) = \sqrt{x}, \quad n = 3, \quad c = 4$

24. $f(x) = \sqrt[3]{x}, \quad n = 3, \quad c = 8$

25. $f(x) = \ln x, \quad n = 4, \quad c = 2$

26. $f(x) = x^2 \cos x, \quad n = 2, \quad c = \pi$

Error Analysis　In Exercises 27 and 28, describe and correct the error in finding the nth Taylor polynomial for $f(x)$, centered at c.

27. $f(x) = \tan \pi x, \quad n = 3, \quad c = 1$

$f(x) = \tan \pi x$ 　　　　　　　　$f(1) = 0$

$f'(x) = \pi \sec^2 \pi x$ 　　　　　$f'(1) = \pi$

$f''(x) = 2\pi^2 \sec^2 \pi x \tan \pi x$ 　$f''(1) = 0$

$f'''(x) = 2\pi^3(2 \sec^2 \pi x \tan^2 \pi x + \sec^4 \pi x)$ 　$f'''(1) = 2\pi^3$

$P_3(x) = \pi(x - 1) + \dfrac{2\pi^3}{3}(x - 1)^3$ ✗

28. $f(x) = xe^{2x}, \quad n = 2, \quad c = 1$

$f(x) = xe^{2x}$ 　　　　　$f(1) = e^2$

$f'(x) = e^{2x}(2x + 1)$ 　$f'(1) = 3e^2$

$f''(x) = 4e^{2x}(x + 1)$ 　$f''(1) = 8e^2$

$P_2(x) = e^2 + 3e^2 x + 4e^2 x^2$

Identifying Maclaurin Polynomials In Exercises 29–32, the graph of $y = f(x)$ is shown with four of its Maclaurin polynomials. Identify the Maclaurin polynomials and use a graphing utility to confirm your results.

29. 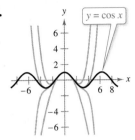 $y = \cos x$

30. 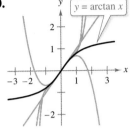 $y = \arctan x$

31. 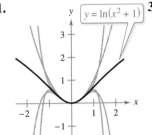 $y = \ln(x^2 + 1)$

32. $y = 4xe^{(-x^2/4)}$

33. Connecting Representations

(a) Use the Maclaurin polynomials P_1, P_3, and P_5 for $f(x) = \sin x$ to complete the table.

x	0	0.25	0.50	0.75	1
$\sin x$	0	0.2474	0.4794	0.6816	0.8415
$P_1(x)$					
$P_3(x)$					
$P_5(x)$					

(b) Use a graphing utility to graph $f(x) = \sin x$ and the Maclaurin polynomials in part (a).

(c) Describe the change in accuracy of a polynomial approximation as the distance from the point where the polynomial is centered increases.

34. Connecting Representations

(a) Use the Taylor polynomials P_1, P_2, and P_4 for $f(x) = e^x$, centered at $c = 1$, to complete the table.

x	1	1.25	1.50	1.75	2
e^x	e	3.4903	4.4817	5.7546	7.3891
$P_1(x)$					
$P_2(x)$					
$P_4(x)$					

(b) Use a graphing utility to graph $f(x) = e^x$ and the Taylor polynomials in part (a).

(c) Describe the change in accuracy of polynomial approximations as the degree increases.

Numerical and Graphical Approximations In Exercises 35 and 36, (a) find the Maclaurin polynomial P_3 for f, (b) complete the table, and (c) sketch the graphs of f and P_3 on the same set of coordinate axes.

x	-0.75	-0.50	-0.25	0	0.25	0.50	0.75
$f(x)$							
$P_3(x)$							

35. $f(x) = \arcsin x$
36. $f(x) = \arctan x$

Approximating a Function Value In Exercises 37–40, approximate the function at the given value of x, using the polynomial found in the indicated exercise.

37. $f(x) = e^{4x}$, $x = \dfrac{1}{4}$, Exercise 11

38. $f(x) = x^2 e^{-x}$, $x = \dfrac{1}{5}$, Exercise 16

39. $f(x) = \ln x$, $x = 2.1$, Exercise 25

40. $f(x) = x^2 \cos x$, $x = \dfrac{7\pi}{8}$, Exercise 26

Using Taylor's Theorem In Exercises 41–44, use Taylor's Theorem to obtain an upper bound for the error of the approximation. Then calculate the exact value of the error.

41. $\cos(0.3) \approx 1 - \dfrac{(0.3)^2}{2!} + \dfrac{(0.3)^4}{4!}$

42. $e \approx 1 + 1 + \dfrac{1^2}{2!} + \dfrac{1^3}{3!} + \dfrac{1^4}{4!} + \dfrac{1^5}{5!}$

43. $\arcsin(0.4) \approx 0.4 + \dfrac{(0.4)^3}{2 \cdot 3}$

44. $\arctan(0.4) \approx 0.4 - \dfrac{(0.4)^3}{3}$

Finding a Degree In Exercises 45–50, determine the degree of the Maclaurin polynomial required for the error in the approximation of the function at the indicated value of x to be less than 0.001.

45. $f(x) = \sin x$, approximate $f(0.3)$
46. $f(x) = \cos x$, approximate $f(0.1)$
47. $f(x) = e^x$, approximate $f(0.6)$
48. $f(x) = \ln x$, approximate $f(1.25)$
49. $f(x) = \dfrac{1}{x - 2}$, approximate $f(0.15)$
50. $f(x) = \dfrac{1}{x + 1}$, approximate $f(0.2)$

Finding Values   In Exercises 51 and 52, determine the values of x for which the function can be replaced by the Taylor polynomial if the error cannot exceed 0.001.

51. $f(x) = e^x \approx 1 + x + \dfrac{x^2}{2!} + \dfrac{x^3}{3!}, \quad x < 0$

52. $f(x) = \sin x \approx x - \dfrac{x^3}{3!}$

EXPLORING CONCEPTS

53. Communicating   An elementary function is approximated by a polynomial. In your own words, describe what is meant by saying that the polynomial is *expanded about c* or *centered at c*.

54. Accuracy of a Taylor Polynomial   Describe the accuracy of the nth-degree Taylor polynomial of f centered at c as the distance between c and x increases.

55. Maclaurin Polynomials   Find the fourth Maclaurin polynomials for $f(x) = e^x$ and $g(x) = e^{2x}$. Explain how you can use the fourth Maclaurin polynomial for f to find the fourth Maclaurin polynomial for g.

56. **HOW DO YOU SEE IT?**   The figure shows the graphs of the first-, second-, and third-degree polynomial approximations P_1, P_2, and P_3 of a function f. Label the graphs of P_1, P_2, and P_3. To print an enlarged copy of the graph, go to *MathGraphs.com*.

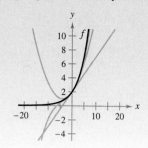

57. Probability   The function $p(x) = \dfrac{1}{\sqrt{2\pi}} e^{-x^2/2}$ is referred to as the standard normal distribution in probability and statistics. The probability that x is between a and b is

$$P(a \le x \le b) = \frac{1}{\sqrt{2\pi}} \int_a^b e^{-x^2/2}\, dx.$$

(a) Find the sixth-degree Maclaurin polynomial for p.

(b) Use the result from part (a) to approximate $P(-1.1 \le x \le 0.9)$.

(c) Using a computer algebra system, approximate $P(-1.1 \le x \le 0.9)$. Is the result from part (b) a good approximation of $P(-1.1 \le x \le 0.9)$? Explain.

58. Differentiating Maclaurin Polynomials

(a) Differentiate the Maclaurin polynomial of degree 5 for $f(x) = \sin x$ and compare the result with the Maclaurin polynomial of degree 4 for $g(x) = \cos x$.

(b) Differentiate the Maclaurin polynomial of degree 6 for $f(x) = \cos x$ and compare the result with the Maclaurin polynomial of degree 5 for $g(x) = \sin x$.

(c) Differentiate the Maclaurin polynomial of degree 4 for $f(x) = e^x$. Describe the relationship between the two polynomials.

59. Graphical Reasoning   The figure shows the graphs of the function $f(x) = \sin(\pi x/4)$ and the second-degree Taylor polynomial $P_2(x) = 1 - (\pi^2/32)(x - 2)^2$ centered at $x = 2$.

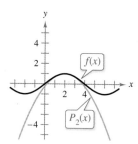

(a) Use the symmetry of the graph of f to write the second-degree Taylor polynomial $Q_2(x)$ for f centered at $x = -2$.

(b) Use a horizontal translation of the result in part (a) to find the second-degree Taylor polynomial $R_2(x)$ for f centered at $x = 6$.

(c) Is it possible to use a horizontal translation of the result in part (a) to write a second-degree Taylor polynomial for f centered at $x = 4$? Explain.

60. Proof   Prove that if f is an odd function, then its nth Maclaurin polynomial contains only terms with odd powers of x.

61. Proof   Consider a function f with continuous first and second derivatives at $x = c$. Prove that if f has a relative maximum at $x = c$, then the second Taylor polynomial centered at $x = c$ also has a relative maximum at $x = c$.

Calculus AP® – Exam Preparation Questions

62. Multiple Choice   Let $f(x) = x^2 \sin x$. The first three nonzero terms of the Maclaurin polynomial for f' are

(A) $x^3 - \frac{1}{6}x^5 + \frac{1}{120}x^7$.   (B) $2x^2 - \frac{1}{3}x^4 + \frac{1}{60}x^6$.

(C) $x^2 - \frac{1}{2}x^4 + \frac{1}{24}x^6$.   (D) $3x^2 - \frac{5}{6}x^4 + \frac{7}{120}x^6$.

63. Multiple Choice   The third Taylor polynomial for a function f centered at $c = 5$ is

$$P_3(x) = 1 - \tfrac{1}{5}(x - 5) + \tfrac{1}{25}(x - 5)^2 - \tfrac{1}{125}(x - 5)^3.$$

What is the value of $f''(5)$?

(A) $\frac{1}{25}$ (B) $\frac{2}{25}$ (C) $\frac{1}{50}$ (D) $\frac{1}{2}$

8.8   Power Series

▶ Understand the definition of a power series.
▶ Find the radius and interval of convergence of a power series.
▶ Determine the endpoint convergence of a power series.
▶ Differentiate and integrate a power series.

Power Series

In Section 8.7, you were introduced to the concept of approximating functions by Taylor polynomials. For instance, the function $f(x) = e^x$ can be *approximated* by its third-degree Maclaurin polynomial

$$e^x \approx 1 + x + \frac{x^2}{2!} + \frac{x^3}{3!}.$$

In that section, you saw that the higher the degree of the approximating polynomial, the better the approximation becomes.

In this and the next two sections, you will see that several important types of functions, including $f(x) = e^x$, can be represented *exactly* by an infinite series called a **power series.** For example, the power series representation for e^x is

$$e^x = 1 + x + \frac{x^2}{2!} + \frac{x^3}{3!} + \cdots + \frac{x^n}{n!} + \cdots.$$

For each real number x, it can be shown that the infinite series on the right converges to the number e^x. Before doing this, however, some preliminary results dealing with power series will be discussed—beginning with the next definition.

Definition of Power Series

If x is a variable, then an infinite series of the form

$$\sum_{n=0}^{\infty} a_n x^n = a_0 + a_1 x + a_2 x^2 + a_3 x^3 + \cdots + a_n x^n + \cdots$$

is called a **power series.** More generally, an infinite series of the form

$$\sum_{n=0}^{\infty} a_n(x - c)^n = a_0 + a_1(x - c) + a_2(x - c)^2 + \cdots + a_n(x - c)^n + \cdots$$

is called a **power series centered at c,** where c is a constant.

EXAMPLE 1   Power Series

a. The following power series is centered at 0.

$$\sum_{n=0}^{\infty} \frac{x^n}{n!} = 1 + x + \frac{x^2}{2} + \frac{x^3}{3!} + \cdots$$

b. The following power series is centered at -1.

$$\sum_{n=0}^{\infty} (-1)^n(x + 1)^n = 1 - (x + 1) + (x + 1)^2 - (x + 1)^3 + \cdots$$

c. The following power series is centered at 1.

$$\sum_{n=1}^{\infty} \frac{1}{n}(x - 1)^n = (x - 1) + \frac{1}{2}(x - 1)^2 + \frac{1}{3}(x - 1)^3 + \cdots$$

Exploration

Graphical Reasoning   Use a graphing utility to approximate the graph of each power series near $x = 0$. (Use the first several terms of each series.) Each series represents a well-known function. What is the function?

a. $\displaystyle\sum_{n=0}^{\infty} \frac{(-1)^n x^n}{n!}$

b. $\displaystyle\sum_{n=0}^{\infty} \frac{(-1)^n x^{2n}}{(2n)!}$

c. $\displaystyle\sum_{n=0}^{\infty} \frac{(-1)^n x^{2n+1}}{(2n + 1)!}$

d. $\displaystyle\sum_{n=0}^{\infty} \frac{(-1)^n x^{2n+1}}{2n + 1}$

e. $\displaystyle\sum_{n=0}^{\infty} \frac{2^n x^n}{n!}$

Justification

To simplify the notation for power series, assume that $(x - c)^0 = 1$, even when $x = c$.

Radius and Interval of Convergence

A power series in x can be viewed as a function of x

$$f(x) = \sum_{n=0}^{\infty} a_n(x - c)^n$$

where the *domain of* f is the set of all x for which the power series converges. Determination of the domain of a power series is the primary concern in this section. Of course, every power series converges at its center c because

$$f(c) = \sum_{n=0}^{\infty} a_n(c - c)^n$$

$$= a_0(1) + 0 + 0 + \cdots + 0 + \cdots$$

$$= a_0.$$

So, c always lies in the domain of f. Theorem 8.20 (see below) states that the domain of a power series can take three basic forms: a single point, an interval centered at c, or the entire real number line, as shown in Figure 8.17.

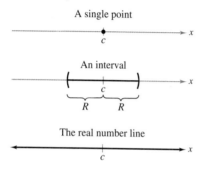

The domain of a power series has only three basic forms: a single point, an interval centered at c, or the entire real number line.

Figure 8.17

Theorem 8.20 **Convergence of a Power Series**

For a power series centered at c, precisely one of the following is true.

1. The series converges only at c.

2. There exists a real number $R > 0$ such that the series converges absolutely for

$$|x - c| < R$$

and diverges for

$$|x - c| > R.$$

3. The series converges absolutely for all x.

The number R is the **radius of convergence** of the power series. If the series converges only at c, then the radius of convergence is $R = 0$. If the series converges for all x, then the radius of convergence is $R = \infty$. The set of all values of x for which the power series converges is the **interval of convergence** of the power series.

A proof of this theorem is given in Appendix A.

To determine the radius of convergence of a power series, use the Ratio Test, as demonstrated in Examples 2, 3, and 4.

EXAMPLE 2   Finding the Radius of Convergence

Find the radius of convergence of $\displaystyle\sum_{n=0}^{\infty} n!x^n$.

Solution

For $x = 0$, you obtain

$$f(0) = \sum_{n=0}^{\infty} n!0^n = 1 + 0 + 0 + \cdots = 1.$$

For any fixed value of x such that $|x| > 0$, let $u_n = n!x^n$. Then

$$\lim_{n\to\infty} \left| \frac{u_{n+1}}{u_n} \right| = \lim_{n\to\infty} \left| \frac{(n+1)!x^{n+1}}{n!x^n} \right|$$

$$= |x| \lim_{n\to\infty} (n+1)$$

$$= \infty.$$

Therefore, by the Ratio Test, the series diverges for $|x| > 0$ and converges only at its center, 0. So, the radius of convergence is $R = 0$.

EXAMPLE 3   Finding the Radius of Convergence

Find the radius of convergence of $\displaystyle\sum_{n=0}^{\infty} 3(x-2)^n$.

Solution

For $x \neq 2$, let $u_n = 3(x-2)^n$. Then

$$\lim_{n\to\infty} \left| \frac{u_{n+1}}{u_n} \right| = \lim_{n\to\infty} \left| \frac{3(x-2)^{n+1}}{3(x-2)^n} \right|$$

$$= \lim_{n\to\infty} |x-2|$$

$$= |x-2|.$$

By the Ratio Test, the series converges for $|x-2| < 1$ and diverges for $|x-2| > 1$. Therefore, the radius of convergence of the series is $R = 1$.

EXAMPLE 4   Finding the Radius of Convergence

Find the radius of convergence of $\displaystyle\sum_{n=0}^{\infty} \frac{(-1)^n x^{2n+1}}{(2n+1)!}$.

Solution

Let $u_n = (-1)^n x^{2n+1}/(2n+1)!$. Then

$$\lim_{n\to\infty} \left| \frac{u_{n+1}}{u_n} \right| = \lim_{n\to\infty} \left| \frac{\dfrac{(-1)^{n+1} x^{2n+3}}{(2n+3)!}}{\dfrac{(-1)^n x^{2n+1}}{(2n+1)!}} \right|$$

$$= \lim_{n\to\infty} \frac{x^2}{(2n+3)(2n+2)}.$$

For any *fixed* value of x, this limit is 0. So, by the Ratio Test, the series converges for all x. Therefore, the radius of convergence is $R = \infty$.

Endpoint Convergence

Note that for a power series whose radius of convergence is a finite number R, Theorem 8.20 says nothing about the convergence at the *endpoints* of the interval of convergence. Each endpoint must be tested separately for convergence or divergence. As a result, the interval of convergence of a power series can take any one of the six forms shown in Figure 8.18.

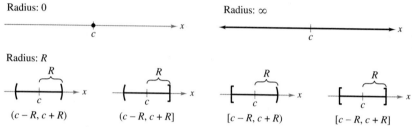

Intervals of convergence
Figure 8.18

EXAMPLE 5 **Finding the Interval of Convergence**

See LarsonCalculusforAP.com for an interactive version of this type of example.

Find the interval of convergence of

$$\sum_{n=1}^{\infty} \frac{x^n}{n}.$$

Solution

Letting $u_n = x^n/n$ produces

$$\lim_{n\to\infty} \left| \frac{u_n + 1}{u_n} \right| = \lim_{n\to\infty} \left| \frac{\dfrac{x^{n+1}}{(n+1)}}{\dfrac{x^n}{n}} \right|$$

$$= \lim_{n\to\infty} \left| \frac{nx}{n+1} \right|$$

$$= |x|.$$

So, by the Ratio Test, the radius of convergence is $R = 1$. Moreover, because the series is centered at 0, it converges in the interval $(-1, 1)$. This interval, however, is not necessarily the *interval of convergence*. To determine this, you must test for convergence at each endpoint. When $x = 1$, you obtain the *divergent* harmonic series

$$\sum_{n=1}^{\infty} \frac{1}{n} = \frac{1}{1} + \frac{1}{2} + \frac{1}{3} + \cdots.$$ 　　Diverges when $x = 1$.

When $x = -1$, you obtain the *convergent* alternating harmonic series

$$\sum_{n=1}^{\infty} \frac{(-1)^n}{n} = -1 + \frac{1}{2} - \frac{1}{3} + \frac{1}{4} - \cdots.$$ 　　Converges when $x = -1$.

So, the interval of convergence for the series is $[-1, 1)$, as shown in Figure 8.19.

Interval: $[-1, 1)$
Radius: $R = 1$

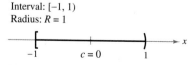

Figure 8.19

EXAMPLE 6   Finding the Interval of Convergence

Find the interval of convergence of $\displaystyle\sum_{n=0}^{\infty} \frac{(-1)^n(x+1)^n}{2^n}$.

Solution

Letting $u_n = (-1)^n(x+1)^n/2^n$ produces

$$\lim_{n\to\infty} \left|\frac{u_{n+1}}{u_n}\right| = \lim_{n\to\infty} \left|\frac{\dfrac{(-1)^{n+1}(x+1)^{n+1}}{2^{n+1}}}{\dfrac{(-1)^n(x+1)^n}{2^n}}\right|$$

$$= \lim_{n\to\infty} \left|\frac{x+1}{2}\right|$$

$$= \left|\frac{x+1}{2}\right|.$$

By the Ratio Test, the series converges for

$$\left|\frac{x+1}{2}\right| < 1$$

or $|x+1| < 2$. So, the radius of convergence is $R = 2$. Because the series is centered at $x = -1$, it will converge in the interval $(-3, 1)$. Furthermore, at the endpoints, you have

$$\sum_{n=0}^{\infty} \frac{(-1)^n(-2)^n}{2^n} = \sum_{n=0}^{\infty} \frac{2^n}{2^n} = \sum_{n=0}^{\infty} 1 \qquad \text{Diverges when } x = -3.$$

and

$$\sum_{n=0}^{\infty} \frac{(-1)^n(2)^n}{2^n} = \sum_{n=0}^{\infty} (-1)^n \qquad \text{Diverges when } x = 1.$$

both of which diverge. So, the interval of convergence is $(-3, 1)$, as shown in Figure 8.20.

Interval: $(-3, 1)$
Radius: $R = 2$

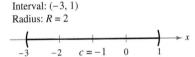

Figure 8.20

EXAMPLE 7   Finding the Interval of Convergence

Find the interval of convergence of $\displaystyle\sum_{n=1}^{\infty} \frac{x^n}{n^2}$.

Solution

Letting $u_n = x^n/n^2$ produces

$$\lim_{n\to\infty} \left|\frac{u_{n+1}}{u_n}\right| = \lim_{n\to\infty} \left|\frac{x^{n+1}/(n+1)^2}{x^n/n^2}\right|$$

$$= \lim_{n\to\infty} \left|\frac{n^2 x}{(n+1)^2}\right|$$

$$= |x|.$$

So, the radius of convergence is $R = 1$. Because the series is centered at $x = 0$, it converges in the interval $(-1, 1)$. When $x = 1$, you obtain the convergent p-series

$$\sum_{n=1}^{\infty} \frac{1}{n^2} = \frac{1}{1^2} + \frac{1}{2^2} + \frac{1}{3^2} + \frac{1}{4^2} + \cdots. \qquad \text{Converges when } x = 1.$$

When $x = -1$, you obtain the convergent alternating series

$$\sum_{n=1}^{\infty} \frac{(-1)^n}{n^2} = -\frac{1}{1^2} + \frac{1}{2^2} - \frac{1}{3^2} + \frac{1}{4^2} - \cdots. \qquad \text{Converges when } x = -1.$$

Therefore, the interval of convergence is $[-1, 1]$, as shown in Figure 8.21.

Interval: $[-1, 1]$
Radius: $R = 1$

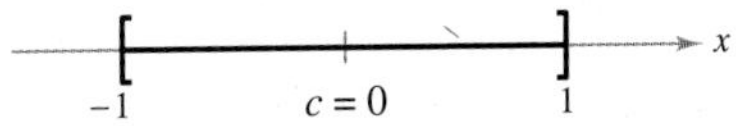

Figure 8.21

Differentiation and Integration of Power Series

Power series representation of functions has played an important role in the development of calculus. In fact, much of Newton's work with differentiation and integration was done in the context of power series—especially his work with complicated algebraic functions and transcendental functions. Euler, Lagrange, Leibniz, and the Bernoullis all used power series extensively in calculus.

Once you have defined a function with a power series, it is natural to wonder how you can determine the characteristics of the function. Is it continuous? Differentiable? Theorem 8.21, which is stated without proof, answers these questions.

Theorem 8.21   Properties of Functions Defined by Power Series

If the function

$$f(x) = \sum_{n=0}^{\infty} a_n(x - c)^n$$
$$= a_0 + a_1(x - c) + a_2(x - c)^2 + a_3(x - c)^3 + \cdots$$

has a radius of convergence of $R > 0$, then, on the interval

$$(c - R, c + R)$$

f is differentiable (and therefore continuous). Moreover, the derivative and antiderivative of f are as follows.

1. $f'(x) = \displaystyle\sum_{n=1}^{\infty} na_n(x - c)^{n-1}$
$$= a_1 + 2a_2(x - c) + 3a_3(x - c)^2 + \cdots$$

2. $\displaystyle\int f(x)\, dx = C + \sum_{n=0}^{\infty} a_n \frac{(x - c)^{n+1}}{n + 1}$
$$= C + a_0(x - c) + a_1\frac{(x - c)^2}{2} + a_2\frac{(x - c)^3}{3} + \cdots$$

The *radius of convergence* of the series obtained by differentiating or integrating a power series is the same as that of the original power series. The *interval of convergence*, however, may differ as a result of the behavior at the endpoints.

Theorem 8.21 states that, in many ways, a function defined by a power series behaves like a polynomial. It is continuous in its interval of convergence, and both its derivative and its antiderivative can be determined by differentiating and integrating each term of the power series. For instance, the derivative of the power series

$$f(x) = \sum_{n=0}^{\infty} \frac{x^n}{n!}$$
$$= 1 + x + \frac{x^2}{2} + \frac{x^3}{3!} + \frac{x^4}{4!} + \cdots$$

is

$$f'(x) = 1 + (2)\frac{x}{2} + (3)\frac{x^2}{3!} + (4)\frac{x^3}{4!} + \cdots$$
$$= 1 + x + \frac{x^2}{2} + \frac{x^3}{3!} + \frac{x^4}{4!} + \cdots$$
$$= f(x).$$

Notice that $f'(x) = f(x)$. Do you recognize this function?

EXAMPLE 8   Intervals of Convergence for $f(x)$, $f'(x)$, and $\int f(x)\,dx$

Consider the function

$$f(x) = \sum_{n=1}^{\infty} \frac{x^n}{n} = x + \frac{x^2}{2} + \frac{x^3}{3} + \cdots.$$

Find the interval of convergence for each of the following.

a. $\int f(x)\,dx$ **b.** $f(x)$ **c.** $f'(x)$

Solution

By Theorem 8.21, you have

$$f'(x) = \sum_{n=1}^{\infty} x^{n-1}$$

$$= 1 + x + x^2 + x^3 + \cdots$$

and

$$\int f(x)\,dx = C + \sum_{n=1}^{\infty} \frac{x^{n+1}}{n(n+1)}$$

$$= C + \frac{x^2}{1 \cdot 2} + \frac{x^3}{2 \cdot 3} + \frac{x^4}{3 \cdot 4} + \cdots.$$

By the Ratio Test, you can show that each series has a radius of convergence of $R = 1$. Considering the interval $(-1, 1)$, you have the following.

a. For $\int f(x)\,dx$, the series

$$\sum_{n=1}^{\infty} \frac{x^{n+1}}{n(n+1)} \qquad \text{Interval of convergence: } [-1, 1]$$

converges for $x = \pm 1$, and its interval of convergence is $[-1, 1]$. See Figure 8.22(a).

b. For $f(x)$, the series

$$\sum_{n=1}^{\infty} \frac{x^n}{n} \qquad \text{Interval of convergence: } [-1, 1)$$

converges for $x = -1$ and diverges for $x = 1$. So, its interval of convergence is $[-1, 1)$. See Figure 8.22(b).

c. For $f'(x)$, the series

$$\sum_{n=1}^{\infty} x^{n-1} \qquad \text{Interval of convergence: } (-1, 1)$$

diverges for $x = \pm 1$, and its interval of convergence is $(-1, 1)$. See Figure 8.22(c).

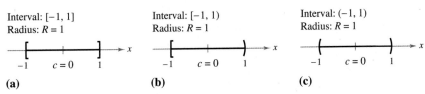

Interval: $[-1, 1]$
Radius: $R = 1$

(a)

Interval: $[-1, 1)$
Radius: $R = 1$

(b)

Interval: $(-1, 1)$
Radius: $R = 1$

(c)

Figure 8.22

From Example 8, it appears that of the three series, the one for the derivative, $f'(x)$, is the least likely to converge at the endpoints. In fact, it can be shown that if the series for $f'(x)$ converges at the endpoints

$$x = c \pm R$$

then the series for $f(x)$ will also converge there.

8.8 Exercises

See *CalcChat.com* for tutorial help and worked-out solutions to odd-numbered exercises.

Finding the Center of a Power Series In Exercises 1–4, state where the power series is centered.

1. $\displaystyle\sum_{n=0}^{\infty} \left(\frac{x}{4}\right)^n$

2. $\displaystyle\sum_{n=1}^{\infty} \frac{(-1)^n(2n-1)}{2^n n!} x^n$

3. $\displaystyle\sum_{n=1}^{\infty} \frac{(-1)^{n+1}(x+5)^n}{(2n)!}$

4. $\displaystyle\sum_{n=1}^{\infty} \frac{(x-2)^n}{n^2(n+1)}$

Finding the Radius of Convergence In Exercises 5–12, find the radius of convergence of the power series.

5. $\displaystyle\sum_{n=0}^{\infty} (-1)^n \frac{x^n}{n+1}$

6. $\displaystyle\sum_{n=0}^{\infty} (3x)^n$

7. $\displaystyle\sum_{n=1}^{\infty} \frac{(4x)^n}{n^2}$

8. $\displaystyle\sum_{n=0}^{\infty} \frac{(-1)^n x^n}{5^n}$

9. $\displaystyle\sum_{n=0}^{\infty} (-1)^n (n+1)! x^n$

10. $\displaystyle\sum_{n=1}^{\infty} \frac{(-2x)^n}{(3n-1)!}$

11. $\displaystyle\sum_{n=0}^{\infty} \frac{x^{2n}}{(2n)!}$

12. $\displaystyle\sum_{n=0}^{\infty} \frac{(2n)! x^{2n}}{n!}$

Finding the Interval of Convergence In Exercises 13–36, find the interval of convergence of the power series. (Be sure to include a check for convergence at the endpoints of the interval.)

13. $\displaystyle\sum_{n=0}^{\infty} \left(\frac{x}{4}\right)^n$

14. $\displaystyle\sum_{n=0}^{\infty} (2x)^n$

15. $\displaystyle\sum_{n=1}^{\infty} \frac{(-1)^n x^n}{n}$

16. $\displaystyle\sum_{n=0}^{\infty} (-1)^{n+1}(n+1)x^n$

17. $\displaystyle\sum_{n=0}^{\infty} \frac{x^{5n}}{n!}$

18. $\displaystyle\sum_{n=0}^{\infty} \frac{(3x)^n}{(2n)!}$

19. $\displaystyle\sum_{n=0}^{\infty} (2n)! \left(\frac{x}{3}\right)^{2n}$

20. $\displaystyle\sum_{n=0}^{\infty} \frac{(-3x)^n}{(n+1)(n+2)}$

21. $\displaystyle\sum_{n=1}^{\infty} \frac{(-1)^{n+1}(x+1)^n}{6^n}$

22. $\displaystyle\sum_{n=0}^{\infty} \frac{(-1)^n n!(x-5)^n}{3^n}$

23. $\displaystyle\sum_{n=1}^{\infty} \frac{(-1)^{n+1}(x-4)^n}{n9^n}$

24. $\displaystyle\sum_{n=0}^{\infty} \frac{(x-3)^{n+1}}{(n+1)4^{n+1}}$

25. $\displaystyle\sum_{n=0}^{\infty} \frac{(-1)^{n+1}(x-1)^{n+1}}{n+1}$

26. $\displaystyle\sum_{n=1}^{\infty} \frac{(-1)^{n+1}(x-2)^n}{n2^n}$

27. $\displaystyle\sum_{n=1}^{\infty} \frac{(x+3)^{n-1}}{n^2 3^{n-1}}$

28. $\displaystyle\sum_{n=0}^{\infty} \frac{(-1)^n x^{2n+1}}{2n+1}$

29. $\displaystyle\sum_{n=1}^{\infty} \frac{n}{n+1}(-2x)^{n-1}$

30. $\displaystyle\sum_{n=0}^{\infty} \frac{(-1)^n x^{2n}}{n!}$

31. $\displaystyle\sum_{n=0}^{\infty} \frac{x^{3n+1}}{(3n+1)!}$

32. $\displaystyle\sum_{n=1}^{\infty} \frac{n!(x+5)^n}{(2n)!}$

33. $\displaystyle\sum_{n=1}^{\infty} \frac{2 \cdot 3 \cdot 4 \cdots (n+1)x^n}{n!}$

34. $\displaystyle\sum_{n=1}^{\infty} \left[\frac{2 \cdot 4 \cdot 6 \cdots 2n}{3 \cdot 5 \cdot 7 \cdots (2n+1)}\right] x^{2n+1}$

35. $\displaystyle\sum_{n=1}^{\infty} \frac{(-1)^{n+1} 3 \cdot 7 \cdot 11 \cdots (4n-1)(x-3)^n}{4^n}$

36. $\displaystyle\sum_{n=1}^{\infty} \frac{n!(x+1)^n}{1 \cdot 3 \cdot 5 \cdots (2n-1)}$

Finding the Radius of Convergence In Exercises 37 and 38, find the radius of convergence of the power series, where $c > 0$ and k is a positive integer.

37. $\displaystyle\sum_{n=1}^{\infty} \frac{(x-c)^{n-1}}{c^{n-1}}$

38. $\displaystyle\sum_{n=0}^{\infty} \frac{(n!)^k x^n}{(kn)!}$

Finding the Interval of Convergence In Exercises 39–42, find the interval of convergence of the power series, where $c > 0$ and k is a positive integer. (Be sure to include a check for convergence at the endpoints of the interval.)

39. $\displaystyle\sum_{n=0}^{\infty} \left(\frac{x}{k}\right)^n$

40. $\displaystyle\sum_{n=1}^{\infty} \frac{(-1)^{n+1}(x-c)^n}{nc^n}$

41. $\displaystyle\sum_{n=1}^{\infty} \frac{k(k+1)(k+2) \cdots (k+n-1)x^n}{n!}$

42. $\displaystyle\sum_{n=1}^{\infty} \frac{n!(x-c)^n}{1 \cdot 3 \cdot 5 \cdots (2n-1)}$

Finding Derivatives and Antiderivatives In Exercises 43–46, find (a) $f'(x)$, (b) $f''(x)$, and (c) $\int f(x)\,dx$.

43. $\displaystyle f(x) = \sum_{n=0}^{\infty} (4x)^n$

44. $\displaystyle f(x) = \sum_{n=0}^{\infty} \frac{(-1)^n x^{n+1}}{n!}$

45. $\displaystyle f(x) = \sum_{n=1}^{\infty} \frac{(-1)^{n+1}(x-3)^{n+1}}{n3^n}$

46. $\displaystyle f(x) = \sum_{n=1}^{\infty} \frac{(x+10)^n}{n(n+1)(n+2)}$

Finding Intervals of Convergence In Exercises 47–50, find the intervals of convergence of (a) $f(x)$, (b) $f'(x)$, (c) $f''(x)$, and (d) $\int f(x)\,dx$. (Be sure to include a check for convergence at the endpoints of the intervals.)

47. $\displaystyle f(x) = \sum_{n=0}^{\infty} \left(\frac{x}{3}\right)^n$

48. $\displaystyle f(x) = \sum_{n=1}^{\infty} \frac{(-1)^{n+1}(x-5)^n}{n5^n}$

49. $\displaystyle f(x) = \sum_{n=0}^{\infty} \frac{(-1)^{n+1}(x-1)^{n+1}}{n+1}$

50. $\displaystyle f(x) = \sum_{n=1}^{\infty} \frac{(-1)^{n+1}(x-2)^n}{n}$

EXPLORING CONCEPTS

51. Communicating Compare the radius of convergence and the interval of convergence of a power series.

52. Implementing Processes Explain how to write an equivalent power series by changing the lower bound of summation. Write a power series equivalent to $\sum_{n=0}^{\infty} (-1)^{n+1}(n+1)x^n$ with lower bound $n=1$.

53. Domain of a Power Series Describe the three basic forms of the domain of a power series.

54. Communicating Describe how to differentiate and integrate a power series with a radius of convergence R. Will the series resulting from the operations of differentiation and integration have a different radius of convergence? Explain.

55. Justifying Give examples that show that the convergence of a power series at an endpoint of its interval of convergence may be either conditional or absolute. Explain your reasoning.

Writing a Power Series In Exercises 56 and 57, write a power series that has the indicated interval of convergence. Explain your reasoning.

56. $(-3, 3)$ **57.** $[-3, 7]$

58. HOW DO YOU SEE IT? Match the graph of the first 10 terms of the sequence of partial sums of the series

$$g(x) = \sum_{n=0}^{\infty} \left(\frac{x}{3}\right)^n$$

with the indicated value of the function. [The graphs are labeled (i), (ii), (iii), and (iv).] Explain how you made your choice.

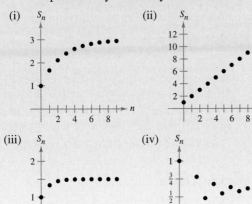

(a) $g(1)$ (b) $g(2)$ (c) $g(3)$ (d) $g(-2)$

59. Using Power Series Let

$$f(x) = \sum_{n=0}^{\infty} \frac{(-1)^n x^{2n+1}}{(2n+1)!} \quad \text{and} \quad g(x) = \sum_{n=0}^{\infty} \frac{(-1)^n x^{2n}}{(2n)!}.$$

(a) Find the intervals of convergence of f and g.

(b) Show that $f'(x) = g(x)$ and $g'(x) = -f(x)$.

(c) Identify the functions f and g.

60. Using a Power Series Let $f(x) = \sum_{n=0}^{\infty} \frac{x^n}{n!}$.

(a) Find the interval of convergence of f.

(b) Show that $f'(x) = f(x)$ and $f(0) = 1$.

(c) Identify the function f.

 Differential Equation In Exercises 61–66, show that the function represented by the power series is a solution of the differential equation.

61. $y = \sum_{n=0}^{\infty} \frac{(-1)^n x^{2n+1}}{(2n+1)!}, \quad y'' + y = 0$

62. $y = \sum_{n=0}^{\infty} \frac{(-1)^n x^{2n}}{(2n)!}, \quad y'' + y = 0$

63. $y = \sum_{n=0}^{\infty} \frac{x^{2n+1}}{(2n+1)!}, \quad y'' - y = 0$

64. $y = \sum_{n=0}^{\infty} \frac{x^{2n}}{(2n)!}, \quad y'' - y = 0$

65. $y = \sum_{n=0}^{\infty} \frac{x^{2n}}{2^n n!}, \quad y'' - xy' - y = 0$

66. $y = 1 + \sum_{n=1}^{\infty} \frac{(-1)^n x^{4n}}{2^{2n} n! \cdot 3 \cdot 7 \cdot 11 \cdots (4n-1)},$
$y'' + x^2 y = 0$

67. Bessel Function The Bessel function of order 0 is

$$J_0(x) = \sum_{k=0}^{\infty} \frac{(-1)^k x^{2k}}{2^{2k}(k!)^2}.$$

(a) Show that the series converges for all x.

(b) Show that the series is a solution of the differential equation $x^2 J_0'' + x J_0' + x^2 J_0 = 0$.

(c) Use a graphing utility to graph the polynomial composed of the first four terms of J_0.

(d) Approximate $\int_0^1 J_0 \, dx$ accurate to two decimal places.

68. Bessel Function The Bessel function of order 1 is

$$J_1(x) = x \sum_{k=0}^{\infty} \frac{(-1)^k x^{2k}}{2^{2k+1} k!(k+1)!}.$$

(a) Show that the series converges for all x.

(b) Show that the series is a solution of the differential equation $x^2 J_1'' + x J_1' + (x^2 - 1)J_1 = 0$.

(c) Use a graphing utility to graph the polynomial composed of the first four terms of J_1.

(d) Use J_0 from Exercise 67 to show that $J_0'(x) = -J_1(x)$.

69. Investigation The interval of convergence of the geometric series $\sum\limits_{n=0}^{\infty} \left(\dfrac{x}{4}\right)^n$ is $(-4, 4)$.

(a) Find the sum of the series when $x = \frac{5}{2}$. Use a graphing utility to graph the first six terms of the sequence of partial sums and the horizontal line representing the sum of the series.

(b) Repeat part (a) for $x = -\frac{5}{2}$.

(c) Write a short paragraph comparing the rates of convergence of the partial sums with the sums of the series in parts (a) and (b). How do the plots of the partial sums differ as they converge toward the sum of the series?

(d) Given any positive real number M, there exists a positive integer N such that the partial sum

$$\sum_{n=0}^{N} \left(\frac{5}{4}\right)^n > M.$$

Use a graphing utility to complete the table.

M	10	100	1000	10,000
N				

70. Investigation The interval of convergence of the series $\sum\limits_{n=0}^{\infty} (3x)^n$ is $\left(-\frac{1}{3}, \frac{1}{3}\right)$.

(a) Find the sum of the series when $x = \frac{1}{6}$. Use a graphing utility to graph the first six terms of the sequence of partial sums and the horizontal line representing the sum of the series.

(b) Repeat part (a) for $x = -\frac{1}{6}$.

(c) Write a short paragraph comparing the rates of convergence of the partial sums with the sums of the series in parts (a) and (b). How do the plots of the partial sums differ as they converge toward the sum of the series?

(d) Given any positive real number M, there exists a positive integer N such that the partial sum

$$\sum_{n=0}^{N} \left(3 \cdot \frac{2}{3}\right)^n > M.$$

Use a graphing utility to complete the table.

M	10	100	1000	10,000
N				

True or False? In Exercises 71–74, determine whether the statement is true or false. If it is false, explain why or give an example that shows it is false.

71. If the power series $\sum\limits_{n=1}^{\infty} a_n x^n$ converges for $x = 2$, then it also converges for $x = -2$.

72. It is possible to find a power series whose interval of convergence is $[0, \infty)$.

73. If the interval of convergence for

$$\sum_{n=0}^{\infty} a_n x^n$$

is $(-1, 1)$, then the interval of convergence for

$$\sum_{n=0}^{\infty} a_n (x - 1)^n$$

is $(0, 2)$.

74. If $f(x) = \sum\limits_{n=0}^{\infty} a_n x^n$ converges for $|x| < 2$, then

$$\int_0^1 f(x) \, dx = \sum_{n=0}^{\infty} \frac{a_n}{n + 1}.$$

75. Proof Prove that the power series

$$\sum_{n=0}^{\infty} \frac{(n + p)!}{n!(n + q)!} x^n$$

has a radius of convergence of $R = \infty$ when p and q are positive integers.

76. Proof Prove that if the power series $\sum\limits_{n=0}^{\infty} c_n x^n$ has a radius of convergence of R, then $\sum\limits_{n=0}^{\infty} c_n x^{2n}$ has a radius of convergence of $\sqrt{R}$.

77. Proof For $n > 0$, let $R > 0$ and $c_n > 0$. Prove that if the interval of convergence of the series

$$\sum_{n=0}^{\infty} c_n (x - x_0)^n$$

is $[x_0 - R, x_0 + R)$, then the series converges conditionally at $x = x_0 - R$.

Calculus AP® – Exam Preparation Questions

78. Multiple Choice The radius of convergence for the power series

$$\sum_{n=1}^{\infty} \frac{(x - 4)^{2n}}{n}$$

is equal to 1. What is the interval of convergence?

(A) $-1 < x < 1$ (B) $-1 \le x < 1$

(C) $3 < x < 5$ (D) $3 \le x < 5$

79. Multiple Choice Which of the following series converges for all real numbers x?

(A) $\sum\limits_{n=1}^{\infty} \dfrac{x^{3n}}{n}$

(B) $\sum\limits_{n=1}^{\infty} \dfrac{x^{3n}}{\sqrt[3]{n}}$

(C) $\sum\limits_{n=1}^{\infty} \dfrac{e^{3n} x^{3n}}{n!}$

(D) $\sum\limits_{n=1}^{\infty} \dfrac{n! x^{3n}}{e^{3n}}$

8.9   Representation of Functions by Power Series

▶ Find a geometric power series that represents a function.
▶ Construct a power series using series operations.

Geometric Power Series

In this section and the next, you will study several techniques for finding a power series that represents a function. Consider the function

$$f(x) = \frac{1}{1 - x}.$$

The form of f closely resembles the sum of a geometric series

$$\sum_{n=0}^{\infty} ar^n = \frac{a}{1 - r}, \quad |r| < 1.$$

In other words, when $a = 1$ and $r = x$, a power series representation for $1/(1 - x)$, centered at 0, is

$$\frac{1}{1 - x} = \sum_{n=0}^{\infty} ar^n$$

$$= \sum_{n=0}^{\infty} x^n$$

$$= 1 + x + x^2 + x^3 + \cdots, \quad |x| < 1.$$

Of course, this series represents $f(x) = 1/(1 - x)$ only on the interval $(-1, 1)$, whereas f is defined for all $x \neq 1$, as shown in Figure 8.23. To represent f in another interval, you must develop a different series. For instance, to obtain the power series centered at -1, you could write

$$\frac{1}{1 - x} = \frac{1}{2 - (x + 1)} = \frac{1/2}{1 - [(x + 1)/2]} = \frac{a}{1 - r}$$

which implies that $a = \frac{1}{2}$ and $r = (x + 1)/2$. So, for $|x + 1| < 2$, you have

$$\frac{1}{1 - x} = \sum_{n=0}^{\infty} \left(\frac{1}{2}\right)\left(\frac{x + 1}{2}\right)^n$$

$$= \frac{1}{2}\left[1 + \frac{(x + 1)}{2} + \frac{(x + 1)^2}{4} + \frac{(x + 1)^3}{8} + \cdots\right], \quad |x + 1| < 2$$

which converges on the interval $(-3, 1)$.

> ### Justification
> A geometric series converges when $|r| < 1$. So, a geometric power series centered at c with $r = x - c$ converges when $|x - c| < 1$.

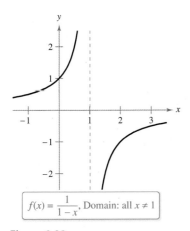

$f(x) = \dfrac{1}{1-x}$, Domain: all $x \neq 1$

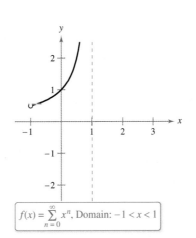

$f(x) = \displaystyle\sum_{n=0}^{\infty} x^n$, Domain: $-1 < x < 1$

Figure 8.23

EXAMPLE 1 Finding a Geometric Power Series Centered at 0

Find a power series for $f(x) = \dfrac{4}{x+2}$, centered at 0.

Solution

Writing $f(x)$ in the form $a/(1-r)$ produces

$$\frac{4}{2+x} = \frac{2}{1-(-x/2)} = \frac{a}{1-r}$$

which implies that $a = 2$ and

$$r = -\frac{x}{2}.$$

So, the power series for $f(x)$ is

$$\frac{4}{x+2} = \sum_{n=0}^{\infty} ar^n$$

$$= \sum_{n=0}^{\infty} 2\left(-\frac{x}{2}\right)^n$$

$$= 2\left(1 - \frac{x}{2} + \frac{x^2}{4} - \frac{x^3}{8} + \cdots\right).$$

This power series converges when

$$\left|-\frac{x}{2}\right| < 1$$

which implies that the interval of convergence is $(-2, 2)$. ■

Another way to determine a power series for a rational function such as the one in Example 1 is to use long division. For instance, by dividing $2 + x$ into 4, you obtain the result shown at the right.

Long Division

$$
\begin{array}{r}
2 - \ x + \tfrac{1}{2}x^2 - \tfrac{1}{4}x^3 + \cdots \\
2 + x\overline{\smash{)}4 } \\
\underline{4 + 2x} \\
-2x \\
\underline{-2x - \ x^2} \\
x^2 \\
x^2 + \tfrac{1}{2}x^3 \\
\underline{-\tfrac{1}{2}x^3} \\
-\tfrac{1}{2}x^3 - \tfrac{1}{4}x^4
\end{array}
$$

EXAMPLE 2 Finding a Geometric Power Series Centered at 1

Find a power series for $f(x) = \dfrac{1}{x}$, centered at 1.

Solution

Writing $f(x)$ in the form $a/(1-r)$ produces

$$\frac{1}{x} = \frac{1}{1-(-x+1)} = \frac{a}{1-r}$$

which implies that $a = 1$ and $r = 1 - x = -(x - 1)$. So, the power series for $f(x)$ is

$$\frac{1}{x} = \sum_{n=0}^{\infty} ar^n$$

$$= \sum_{n=0}^{\infty} [-(x-1)]^n$$

$$= \sum_{n=0}^{\infty} (-1)^n(x-1)^n$$

$$= 1 - (x-1) + (x-1)^2 - (x-1)^3 + \cdots.$$

This power series converges when

$$|x - 1| < 1$$

which implies that the interval of convergence is $(0, 2)$. ■

Operations with Power Series

The versatility of geometric power series will be shown later in this section, following a discussion of power series operations. These operations, used with differentiation and integration, provide a means of developing power series for a variety of elementary functions. (For simplicity, the operations are stated for a series centered at 0.)

Operations with Power Series

Let $f(x) = \displaystyle\sum_{n=0}^{\infty} a_n x^n$ and $g(x) = \displaystyle\sum_{n=0}^{\infty} b_n x^n$.

1. $f(kx) = \displaystyle\sum_{n=0}^{\infty} a_n k^n x^n$

2. $f(x^N) = \displaystyle\sum_{n=0}^{\infty} a_n x^{nN}$

3. $f(x) \pm g(x) = \displaystyle\sum_{n=0}^{\infty} (a_n \pm b_n) x^n$

The operations described above can change the interval of convergence for the resulting series. For example, in the addition shown below, the interval of convergence for the sum is the *intersection* of the intervals of convergence of the two original series.

$$\underbrace{\sum_{n=0}^{\infty} x^n}_{(-1,1)} + \underbrace{\sum_{n=0}^{\infty} \left(\frac{x}{2}\right)^n}_{(-2,2)} = \underbrace{\sum_{n=0}^{\infty} \left(1 + \frac{1}{2^n}\right) x^n}_{(-1,1)}$$

$$(-1,1) \;\cap\; (-2,2) \;=\; (-1,1)$$

EXAMPLE 3   Adding Two Power Series

Find a power series for

$$f(x) = \frac{3x - 1}{x^2 - 1}$$

centered at 0.

Solution

Using partial fractions, you can write $f(x)$ as

$$\frac{3x - 1}{x^2 - 1} = \frac{2}{x + 1} + \frac{1}{x - 1}.$$

By adding the two geometric power series

$$\frac{2}{x + 1} = \frac{2}{1 - (-x)} = \sum_{n=0}^{\infty} 2(-1)^n x^n, \quad |x| < 1$$

and

$$\frac{1}{x - 1} = \frac{-1}{1 - x} = -\sum_{n=0}^{\infty} x^n, \quad |x| < 1$$

you obtain the power series shown below.

$$\frac{3x - 1}{x^2 - 1} = \sum_{n=0}^{\infty} [2(-1)^n - 1] x^n$$

$$= 1 - 3x + x^2 - 3x^3 + x^4 - \cdots$$

The interval of convergence for this power series is $(-1, 1)$.

Algebra Review

For help on the algebra in Example 3, see Example 2(b) in the *Chapter 8 Algebra Review* on page A51.

EXAMPLE 4   Finding a Power Series by Integration

Find a power series for $f(x) = \ln x$, centered at 1.

Solution

From Example 2, you know that

$$\frac{1}{x} = \sum_{n=0}^{\infty} (-1)^n (x - 1)^n. \qquad \text{Interval of convergence: } (0, 2)$$

Integrating this series produces

$$\ln x = \int \frac{1}{x}\, dx + C$$

$$= C + \sum_{n=0}^{\infty} (-1)^n \frac{(x - 1)^{n+1}}{n + 1}.$$

By letting $x = 1$, you can conclude that $C = 0$. Therefore,

$$\ln x = \sum_{n=0}^{\infty} (-1)^n \frac{(x - 1)^{n+1}}{n + 1}$$

$$= \frac{(x - 1)}{1} - \frac{(x - 1)^2}{2} + \frac{(x - 1)^3}{3} - \frac{(x - 1)^4}{4} + \cdots . \qquad \begin{array}{l}\text{Interval of}\\ \text{convergence: } (0, 2]\end{array}$$

Note that the series converges at $x = 2$. This is consistent with the observation in the preceding section that integration of a power series may alter the convergence at the endpoints of the interval of convergence.

In Section 8.7, Example 4, the fourth-degree Taylor polynomial (centered at $c = 1$) for the natural logarithmic function

$$\ln x \approx (x - 1) - \frac{(x - 1)^2}{2} + \frac{(x - 1)^3}{3} - \frac{(x - 1)^4}{4}$$

was used to approximate $\ln(1.1)$.

$$\ln(1.1) \approx (0.1) - \tfrac{1}{2}(0.1)^2 + \tfrac{1}{3}(0.1)^3 - \tfrac{1}{4}(0.1)^4 \approx 0.0953083$$

You now know from Example 4 in this section that this polynomial represents the first four terms of the power series for $\ln x$. Moreover, using the Alternating Series Remainder, you can determine that the error in this approximation is less than

$$|R_4| \leq |a_5| = \tfrac{1}{5}(0.1)^5 = 0.000002.$$

During the seventeenth and eighteenth centuries, mathematical tables for logarithms and values of other transcendental functions were computed in this manner. Such numerical techniques are far from outdated, because it is precisely by such means that many modern calculating devices are programmed to evaluate transcendental functions.

Exploration

In Example 8 of Section 8.5, you saw that $\ln 2 = 1 - \tfrac{1}{2} + \tfrac{1}{3} - \tfrac{1}{4} + \cdots$. Now you can see why this is true by substituting $x = 2$ into

$$\ln x = \frac{(x - 1)}{1} - \frac{(x - 1)^2}{2} + \frac{(x - 1)^3}{3} - \frac{(x - 1)^4}{4} + \cdots .$$

How would you approximate $\ln(1.5)$? Can this series be used to evaluate $\ln 3$? Why or why not?

EXAMPLE 5 Finding a Power Series by Integration

See LarsonCalculusforAP.com for an interactive version of this type of example.

Find a power series for $g(x) = \arctan x$, centered at 0.

Solution

Because $D_x[\arctan x] = 1/(1 + x^2)$, you can use the series

$$f(x) = \frac{1}{1 + x} = \sum_{n=0}^{\infty} (-1)^n x^n.$$ Interval of convergence: $(-1, 1)$

Substituting x^2 for x produces

$$f(x^2) = \frac{1}{1 + x^2} = \sum_{n=0}^{\infty} (-1)^n x^{2n}.$$

Finally, by integrating, you obtain

$$\arctan x = \int \frac{1}{1 + x^2} \, dx + C$$

$$= C + \sum_{n=0}^{\infty} (-1)^n \frac{x^{2n+1}}{2n + 1}$$

$$= \sum_{n=0}^{\infty} (-1)^n \frac{x^{2n+1}}{2n + 1}$$ Let $x = 0$, then $C = 0$.

$$= x - \frac{x^3}{3} + \frac{x^5}{5} - \frac{x^7}{7} + \cdots.$$ Interval of convergence: $(-1, 1)$ ∎

It can be shown that the power series developed for $\arctan x$ in Example 5 also converges (to $\arctan x$) for $x = \pm 1$. For instance, when $x = 1$, you can write

$$\arctan 1 = 1 - \frac{1}{3} + \frac{1}{5} - \frac{1}{7} + \cdots$$

$$= \frac{\pi}{4}.$$

However, this series (developed by James Gregory in 1671) is not a practical way of approximating π because it converges so slowly that hundreds of terms have to be used to obtain reasonable accuracy. Example 6 shows how to use *two* different arctangent series to obtain a very good approximation of π using only a few terms. This approximation was developed by John Machin in 1706.

EXAMPLE 6 Approximating π with a Series

Use the trigonometric identity

$$4 \arctan \frac{1}{5} - \arctan \frac{1}{239} = \frac{\pi}{4}$$

to approximate π. [See Exercise 44(b).]

Solution

By using only five terms from each of the series for $\arctan(1/5)$ and $\arctan(1/239)$, you obtain

$$4\left(4 \arctan \frac{1}{5} - \arctan \frac{1}{239}\right) \approx 3.1415927$$

which agrees with the exact value of π with an error of less than 0.0000001.   ∎

8.9   Exercises

See *CalcChat.com* for tutorial help and worked-out solutions to odd-numbered exercises.

Finding a Geometric Power Series In Exercises 1–4, find a geometric power series for the function, centered at 0, (a) by the technique shown in Examples 1 and 2, and (b) by long division.

1. $f(x) = \dfrac{1}{4 - x}$

2. $f(x) = \dfrac{1}{3 + x}$

3. $f(x) = \dfrac{3}{4 + x}$

4. $f(x) = \dfrac{2}{5 - x}$

Error Analysis In Exercises 5 and 6, correct the error in stating the power series centered at 0 for $f(x)$.

5. $f(x) = \dfrac{1}{1 - (x/2)} = \displaystyle\sum_{n=0}^{\infty} \dfrac{1}{2} x^n$ ✗

6. $f(x) = \dfrac{2}{1 - (-x)} = \displaystyle\sum_{n=0}^{\infty} 2^n (-1)^n x^n$ ✗

Finding a Power Series In Exercises 7–18, find a power series for the function, centered at c, and determine the interval of convergence.

7. $f(x) = \dfrac{1}{6 - x}, \quad c = 1$

8. $f(x) = \dfrac{2}{6 - x}, \quad c = -2$

9. $f(x) = \dfrac{1}{1 - 3x}, \quad c = 0$

10. $h(x) = \dfrac{1}{1 - 4x}, \quad c = 0$

11. $f(x) = \dfrac{3}{2x - 1}, \quad c = 2$

12. $g(x) = \dfrac{5}{2x - 3}, \quad c = -3$

13. $f(x) = \dfrac{4}{3x + 2}, \quad c = 3$

14. $f(x) = \dfrac{2}{5x + 4}, \quad c = -1$

15. $g(x) = \dfrac{4x}{x^2 + 2x - 3}, \quad c = 0$

16. $g(x) = \dfrac{3x - 8}{3x^2 + 5x - 2}, \quad c = 0$

17. $f(x) = \dfrac{2}{1 - x^2}, \quad c = 0$

18. $f(x) = \dfrac{5}{4 - x^2}, \quad c = 0$

Using a Power Series In Exercises 19–28, find a power series for the function, centered at 0, and determine the interval of convergence by using the power series

$$\dfrac{1}{1 + x} = \sum_{n=0}^{\infty} (-1)^n x^n, \quad |x| < 1.$$

19. $h(x) = \dfrac{-2}{x^2 - 1} = \dfrac{1}{1 + x} + \dfrac{1}{1 - x}$

20. $h(x) = \dfrac{x}{x^2 - 1} = \dfrac{1}{2(1 + x)} - \dfrac{1}{2(1 - x)}$

21. $f(x) = -\dfrac{1}{(x + 1)^2} = \dfrac{d}{dx}\left[\dfrac{1}{x + 1}\right]$

22. $f(x) = \dfrac{2}{(x + 1)^3} = \dfrac{d^2}{dx^2}\left[\dfrac{1}{x + 1}\right]$

23. $f(x) = \ln(x + 1) = \displaystyle\int \dfrac{1}{x + 1}\, dx$

24. $f(x) = \ln(1 - x^2) = \displaystyle\int \dfrac{1}{1 + x}\, dx - \int \dfrac{1}{1 - x}\, dx$

25. $g(x) = \dfrac{1}{x^2 + 1}$

26. $f(x) = \ln(x^2 + 1)$

27. $h(x) = \dfrac{1}{4x^2 + 1}$

28. $f(x) = \arctan 2x$

Connecting Representations In Exercises 29 and 30, let

$$S_n = x - \dfrac{x^2}{2} + \dfrac{x^3}{3} - \dfrac{x^4}{4} + \cdots \pm \dfrac{x^n}{n}.$$

Use a graphing utility to confirm the inequality graphically. Then complete the table to confirm the inequality numerically.

x	0.0	0.2	0.4	0.6	0.8	1.0
S_n						
$\ln(x + 1)$						
S_{n+1}						

29. $S_2 \le \ln(x + 1) \le S_3$

30. $S_4 \le \ln(x + 1) \le S_5$

Implementing Processes In Exercises 31 and 32, (a) use a graphing utility to graph several partial sums of the series, (b) find the sum of the series and its radius of convergence, (c) use a graphing utility and 50 terms of the series to approximate the sum when $x = 0.5$, and (d) determine what the approximation represents and how good the approximation is.

31. $\displaystyle\sum_{n=1}^{\infty} \dfrac{(-1)^{n+1}(x - 1)^n}{n}$

32. $\displaystyle\sum_{n=0}^{\infty} \dfrac{(-1)^n x^{2n+1}}{(2n + 1)!}$

Approximating a Value In Exercises 33–36, use the power series for $f(x) = \arctan x$ to approximate the value using $R_N \le 0.001$.

33. $\arctan \dfrac{1}{4}$

34. $\displaystyle\int_0^{3/4} \arctan x^2\, dx$

35. $\displaystyle\int_0^{1/2} \dfrac{\arctan x^2}{x}\, dx$

36. $\displaystyle\int_0^{1/2} x^2 \arctan x\, dx$

Using a Power Series In Exercises 37–40, find a power series for the function, centered at 0, and determine the interval of convergence by using the power series

$$\dfrac{1}{1 - x} = \sum_{n=0}^{\infty} x^n, \quad |x| < 1.$$

37. $f(x) = \dfrac{1}{(1 - x)^2}$

38. $f(x) = \dfrac{x}{(1 - x)^2}$

39. $f(x) = \dfrac{1 + x}{(1 - x)^2}$ **40.** $f(x) = \dfrac{x(1 + x)}{(1 - x)^2}$

41. Probability   A fair coin is tossed repeatedly. The probability that the first head occurs on the nth toss is $P(n) = \left(\frac{1}{2}\right)^n$. When this game is repeated many times, the average number of tosses $E(n)$ required until the first head occurs is the *expected value of n*, where

$$E(n) = \sum_{n=1}^{\infty} n P(n).$$

Use the results of Exercises 37–40 to find $E(n)$. Is the answer what you expected? Why or why not?

42. Finding the Sum of a Series   Use the results of Exercises 37–40 to find the sum of each series.

(a) $\dfrac{1}{3} \displaystyle\sum_{n=1}^{\infty} n\left(\dfrac{2}{3}\right)^n$ (b) $\dfrac{1}{10} \displaystyle\sum_{n=1}^{\infty} n\left(\dfrac{9}{10}\right)^n$

43. Proof   Prove that

$$\arctan x + \arctan y = \arctan \frac{x + y}{1 - xy}$$

for $xy \neq 1$ provided the value of the left side of the equation is between $-\pi/2$ and $\pi/2$.

44. Justifying   Use the result of Exercise 43 to verify each identity.

(a) $\arctan \dfrac{120}{119} - \arctan \dfrac{1}{239} = \dfrac{\pi}{4}$

(b) $4 \arctan \dfrac{1}{5} - \arctan \dfrac{1}{239} = \dfrac{\pi}{4}$

[*Hint:* Use Exercise 43 twice to find $4 \arctan \frac{1}{5}$. Then use part (a).]

Approximating Pi   **In Exercises 45 and 46, (a) use the result of Exercise 43 to verify the given identity and (b) use the identity and the series for the arctangent to approximate π by using four terms of each series.**

45. $2 \arctan \dfrac{1}{2} - \arctan \dfrac{1}{7} = \dfrac{\pi}{4}$

46. $\arctan \dfrac{1}{2} + \arctan \dfrac{1}{3} = \dfrac{\pi}{4}$

Finding the Sum of a Series   **In Exercises 47–52, find the sum of the convergent series by using a well-known function. Identify the function and explain how you obtained the sum.**

47. $\displaystyle\sum_{n=1}^{\infty} (-1)^{n+1} \dfrac{1}{2^n n}$ **48.** $\displaystyle\sum_{n=1}^{\infty} (-1)^{n+1} \dfrac{1}{3^n n}$

49. $\displaystyle\sum_{n=1}^{\infty} (-1)^{n+1} \dfrac{2^n}{5^n n}$ **50.** $\displaystyle\sum_{n=0}^{\infty} (-1)^n \dfrac{1}{2n + 1}$

51. $\displaystyle\sum_{n=0}^{\infty} (-1)^n \dfrac{1}{2^{2n+1}(2n + 1)}$

52. $\displaystyle\sum_{n=1}^{\infty} (-1)^{n+1} \dfrac{1}{3^{2n-1}(2n - 1)}$

EXPLORING CONCEPTS

 53. Comparing Rates of Convergence   One of the series in Exercises 47–52 converges to its sum at a much lower rate than the other five series. Which is it? Explain why this series converges so slowly. Use a graphing utility to illustrate the rate of convergence.

54. Radius of Convergence   The radius of convergence of the power series $\displaystyle\sum_{n=0}^{\infty} a_n x^n$ is 3. What is the radius of convergence of the series $\displaystyle\sum_{n=1}^{\infty} n a_n x^{n-1}$? Explain.

55. Convergence of a Power Series   The power series $\displaystyle\sum_{n=0}^{\infty} a_n x^n$ converges for $|x + 1| < 4$. What can you conclude about the series $\displaystyle\sum_{n=0}^{\infty} a_n \dfrac{x^{n+1}}{n + 1}$? Explain.

56. HOW DO YOU SEE IT?   The figure on the left shows the graph of a function. The figure on the right shows the graph of a power series representation of the function

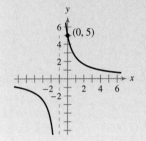 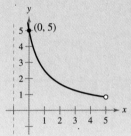

(a) Identify the function.

(b) What are the center and interval of convergence of the power series?

Calculus AP® – Exam Preparation Questions

57. Free Response   A function f is defined by the power series

$$f(x) = \frac{1}{5} + \frac{2}{5^2}x + \frac{3}{5^3}x^2 + \cdots + \frac{n + 1}{5^{n+1}}x^n + \cdots$$

for all real numbers x for which the power series converges.

(a) Find the interval of convergence for the power series.

(b) Find $\displaystyle\lim_{x \to 0} \dfrac{f(x) - 1/5}{x}$.

(c) Write the first three nonzero terms and the general term for a series that represents $\int_0^1 f(x)\, dx$.

(d) Find the sum of the series from part (c).

8.10 Taylor and Maclaurin Series

▶ Find a Taylor or Maclaurin series for a function.
▶ Find a binomial series.
▶ Use a basic list of Taylor series to find other Taylor series.

Taylor Series and Maclaurin Series

In Section 8.9, you derived power series for several functions using geometric series with term-by-term differentiation or integration. In this section, you will study a *general* procedure for deriving the power series for a function that has derivatives of all orders. The next theorem gives the form that *every* convergent power series must take.

Theorem 8.22   The Form of a Convergent Power Series

If f is represented by a power series

$$f(x) = \sum_{n=0}^{\infty} a_n(x - c)^n$$

for all x in an open interval I containing c, then

$$a_n = \frac{f^{(n)}(c)}{n!}$$

and

$$f(x) = f(c) + f'(c)(x - c) + \frac{f''(c)}{2!}(x - c)^2 + \cdots + \frac{f^{(n)}(c)}{n!}(x - c)^n + \cdots.$$

Communication and Notation

Be sure you understand Theorem 8.22. The theorem says that, *if a power series converges to $f(x)$, then the series must be a Taylor series.* The theorem does *not* say that every series formed with the Taylor coefficients $a_n = f^{(n)}(c)/n!$ will converge to $f(x)$.

Proof   Consider a power series $\Sigma \, a_n(x - c)^n$ that has a radius of convergence R. Then, by Theorem 8.21, you know that the nth derivative of f exists for $|x - c| < R$, and by successive differentiation you obtain the following.

$$f^{(0)}(x) = a_0 + a_1(x - c) + a_2(x - c)^2 + a_3(x - c)^3 + a_4(x - c)^4 + \cdots$$
$$f^{(1)}(x) = a_1 + 2a_2(x - c) + 3a_3(x - c)^2 + 4a_4(x - c)^3 + \cdots$$
$$f^{(2)}(x) = 2a_2 + 3!a_3(x - c) + 4 \cdot 3a_4(x - c)^2 + \cdots$$
$$f^{(3)}(x) = 3!a_3 + 4!a_4(x - c) + \cdots$$
$$\vdots$$
$$f^{(n)}(x) = n!a_n + (n + 1)!a_{n+1}(x - c) + \cdots$$

Evaluating each of these derivatives at $x = c$ yields

$$f^{(0)}(c) = 0!a$$
$$f^{(1)}(c) = 1!a_1$$
$$f^{(2)}(c) = 2!a_2$$
$$f^{(3)}(c) = 3!a_3$$

and, in general, $f^{(n)}(c) = n!a_n$. By solving for a_n, you find that the coefficients of the power series representation of $f(x)$ are

$$a_n = \frac{f^{(n)}(c)}{n!}.$$ ∎

Notice that the coefficients of the power series in Theorem 8.22 are precisely the coefficients of the Taylor polynomials for f at c as defined in Section 8.7. For this reason, the series is called the **Taylor series** for f at c.

Definition of Taylor and Maclaurin Series

If a function f has derivatives of all orders at $x = c$, then the series

$$\sum_{n=0}^{\infty} \frac{f^{(n)}(c)}{n!}(x - c)^n = f(c) + f'(c)(x - c) + \cdots + \frac{f^{(n)}(c)}{n!}(x - c)^n + \cdots$$

is called the **Taylor series for f at c.** Moreover, if $c = 0$ then the series is the **Maclaurin series for f.**

When you know the pattern for the coefficients of the Taylor polynomials for a function, you can extend the pattern to form the corresponding Taylor series. For instance, in Example 4 in Section 8.7, you found the fourth Taylor polynomial for $\ln x$, centered at 1, to be

$$P_4(x) = (x - 1) - \frac{1}{2}(x - 1)^2 + \frac{1}{3}(x - 1)^3 - \frac{1}{4}(x - 1)^4.$$

From this pattern, you can obtain the Taylor series for $\ln x$ centered at $c = 1$,

$$(x - 1) - \frac{1}{2}(x - 1)^2 + \cdots + \frac{(-1)^{n+1}}{n}(x - 1)^n + \cdots.$$

> **Connecting Representations**
>
> Note that the fourth Taylor polynomial for $\ln x$ is the fourth partial sum of the Taylor series for $\ln x$.

EXAMPLE 1   Forming a Power Series

Use the function

$$f(x) = \sin x$$

to form the Maclaurin series

$$\sum_{n=0}^{\infty} \frac{f^{(n)}(0)}{n!}x^n = f(0) + f'(0)x + \frac{f''(0)}{2!}x^2 + \frac{f'''(0)}{3!}x^3 + \frac{f^{(4)}(0)}{4!}x^4 + \cdots$$

and determine the interval of convergence.

Solution

Taking successive derivatives of f yields

$$
\begin{aligned}
f(x) &= \sin x & f(0) &= \sin 0 = 0 \\
f'(x) &= \cos x & f'(0) &= \cos 0 = 1 \\
f''(x) &= -\sin x & f''(0) &= -\sin 0 = 0 \\
f'''(x) &= -\cos x & f'''(0) &= -\cos 0 = -1 \\
f^{(4)}(x) &= \sin x & f^{(4)}(0) &= \sin 0 = 0 \\
f^{(5)}(x) &= \cos x & f^{(5)}(0) &= \cos 0 = 1
\end{aligned}
$$

and so on. The pattern repeats after the third derivative. So, the power series is as follows.

$$\sum_{n=0}^{\infty} \frac{f^{(n)}(0)}{n!}x^n = f(0) + f'(0)x + \frac{f''(0)}{2!}x^2 + \frac{f'''(0)}{3!}x^3 + \frac{f^{(4)}(0)}{4!}x^4 + \cdots$$

$$= 0 + (1)x + \frac{0}{2!}x^2 + \frac{(-1)}{3!}x^3 + \frac{0}{4!}x^4 + \frac{1}{5!}x^5 + \frac{0}{6!}x^6 + \frac{(-1)}{7!}x^7 + \cdots$$

$$= x - \frac{x^3}{3!} + \frac{x^5}{5!} - \frac{x^7}{7!} + \cdots$$

$$= \sum_{n=0}^{\infty} \frac{(-1)^n x^{2n+1}}{(2n + 1)!}$$

By the Ratio Test, you can conclude that this series converges for all x. ∎

Notice that in Example 1, you cannot conclude that the power series converges to $\sin x$ for all x. You can simply conclude that the power series converges to some function, but you are not sure what function it is. This is a subtle, but important, point in dealing with Taylor or Maclaurin series. To persuade yourself that the series

$$f(c) + f'(c)(x - c) + \frac{f''(c)}{2!}(x - c)^2 + \ldots + \frac{f^{(n)}(c)}{n!}(x - c)^n + \cdots$$

might converge to a function other than f, remember that the derivatives are being evaluated at a single point. It can easily happen that another function will agree with the values of $f^{(n)}(x)$ when $x = c$ and disagree at other x-values. For instance, the power series (centered at 0) for the function f shown in Figure 8.24 is the same series as in Example 1. You know that the series converges for all x, and yet it obviously cannot converge to both $f(x)$ and $\sin x$ for all x.

Let f have derivatives of all orders in an open interval I centered at c. The Taylor series for f may fail to converge for some x in I. Or, even when it is convergent, it may fail to have $f(x)$ as its sum. Nevertheless, Theorem 8.19 tells us that for each n,

$$f(x) = f(c) + f'(c)(x - c) + \frac{f''(c)}{2!}(x - c)^2 + \cdots + \frac{f^{(n)}(c)}{n!}(x - c)^n + R_n(x)$$

where

$$R_n(x) = \frac{f^{(n+1)}(z)}{(n + 1)!}(x - c)^{n+1}.$$

Note that in this remainder formula, the particular value of z that makes the remainder formula true depends on the values of x and n. If $R_n \to 0$, then the next theorem tells us that the Taylor series for f actually converges to $f(x)$ for all x in I.

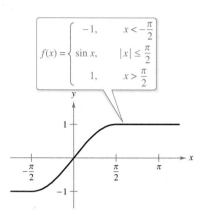

$$f(x) = \begin{cases} -1, & x < -\dfrac{\pi}{2} \\ \sin x, & |x| \le \dfrac{\pi}{2} \\ 1, & x > \dfrac{\pi}{2} \end{cases}$$

Figure 8.24

Theorem 8.23   Convergence of Taylor Series

If $\lim\limits_{n \to \infty} R_n = 0$ for all x in the interval I, then the Taylor series for f converges and equals $f(x)$,

$$f(x) = \sum_{n=0}^{\infty} \frac{f^{(n)}(c)}{n!}(x - c)^n.$$

Proof For a Taylor series, the nth partial sum coincides with the nth Taylor polynomial. That is, $S_n(x) = P_n(x)$. Moreover, because

$$P_n(x) = f(x) - R_n(x)$$

it follows that

$$\begin{aligned} \lim_{n \to \infty} S_n(x) &= \lim_{n \to \infty} P_n(x) \\ &= \lim_{n \to \infty} [f(x) - R_n(x)] \\ &= f(x) - \lim_{n \to \infty} R_n(x). \end{aligned}$$

So, for a given x, the Taylor series (the sequence of partial sums) converges to $f(x)$ if and only if $R_n(x) \to 0$ as $n \to \infty$. ∎

Stated another way, Theorem 8.23 says that a power series formed with Taylor coefficients

$$a_n = \frac{f^{(n)}(c)}{n!}$$

converges to the function from which it was derived at precisely those values for which the remainder approaches 0 as $n \to \infty$.

In Example 1, you derived the power series from the sine function and you also concluded that the series converges to some function on the entire real number line. In Example 2, you will see that the series actually converges to $\sin x$. The key observation is that although the value of z is not known, it is possible to obtain an upper bound for

$$\left| f^{(n+1)}(z) \right|.$$

EXAMPLE 2   A Convergent Maclaurin Series

Show that the Maclaurin series for

$$f(x) = \sin x$$

converges to $\sin x$ for all x.

Solution

Using the result in Example 1, you need to show that

$$\sin x = x - \frac{x^3}{3!} + \frac{x^5}{5!} - \frac{x^7}{7!} + \cdots + \frac{(-1)^n x^{2n+1}}{(2n+1)!} + \cdots$$

is true for all x. Because

$$f^{(n+1)}(x) = \pm \sin x$$

or

$$f^{(n+1)}(x) = \pm \cos x$$

you know that $\left| f^{(n+1)}(z) \right| \leq 1$ for every real number z. Therefore, for any fixed x, you can apply Taylor's Theorem (Theorem 8.19) to conclude that

$$0 \leq |R_n(x)| = \left| \frac{f^{(n+1)}(z)}{(n+1)!} x^{n+1} \right| \leq \frac{|x|^{n+1}}{(n+1)!}.$$

From the discussion in Section 8.1 regarding the relative rates of convergence of exponential and factorial sequences, it follows that for a fixed x

$$\lim_{n \to \infty} \frac{|x|^{n+1}}{(n+1)!} = 0.$$

Finally, by the Squeeze Theorem, it follows that for all x, $R_n(x) \to 0$ as $n \to \infty$. So, by Theorem 8.23, the Maclaurin series for $\sin x$ converges to $\sin x$ for all x.

Figure 8.25 visually illustrates the convergence of the Maclaurin series for $\sin x$ by comparing the graphs of the Maclaurin polynomials P_1, P_3, P_5, and P_7 with the graph of the sine function. Notice that as the degree of the polynomial increases, its graph more closely resembles that of the sine function.

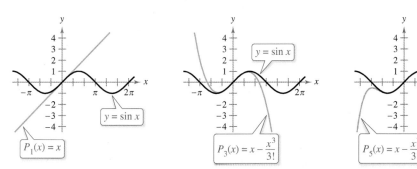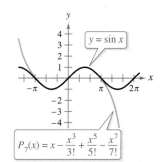

As n increases, the graph of P_n more closely resembles the sine function.
Figure 8.25

The guidelines for finding a Taylor series for f at c are summarized below.

Guidelines for Finding a Taylor Series

1. Differentiate f with respect to x several times and evaluate each derivative at c.

$$f(c), f'(c), f''(c), f'''(c), \cdots, f^{(n)}(c), \cdots$$

Try to recognize a pattern in these numbers.

2. Use the sequence developed in the first step to form the Taylor coefficients $a_n = f^{(n)}(c)/n!$, and determine the interval of convergence for the resulting power series

$$f(c) + f'(c)(x - c) + \frac{f''(c)}{2!}(x - c)^2 + \cdots + \frac{f^{(n)}(c)}{n!}(x - c)^n + \cdots.$$

3. Within this interval of convergence, determine whether the series converges to $f(x)$.

Implementing Processes

When you have difficulty recognizing a pattern, remember that you can use Theorem 8.22 to find the Taylor series. Also, you can try using the coefficients of a known Taylor or Maclaurin series, as shown in Example 3.

The direct determination of Taylor or Maclaurin coefficients using successive differentiation can be difficult, and the next example illustrates a shortcut for finding the coefficients indirectly—using the coefficients of a known Taylor or Maclaurin series.

EXAMPLE 3   Maclaurin Series for a Composite Function

Find the Maclaurin series for

$$f(x) = \sin x^2.$$

Solution

To find the coefficients for this Maclaurin series directly, you must calculate successive derivatives of $f(x) = \sin x^2$. By calculating just the first two,

$$f'(x) = 2x \cos x^2$$

and

$$f''(x) = -4x^2 \sin x^2 + 2 \cos x^2$$

you can see that this task would be quite cumbersome. Fortunately, there is an alternative. First, consider the Maclaurin series for $\sin x$ found in Example 1.

$$g(x) = \sin x$$

$$= x - \frac{x^3}{3!} + \frac{x^5}{5!} - \frac{x^7}{7!} + \cdots$$

Now, because $\sin x^2 = g(x^2)$, you can substitute x^2 for x in the series for $\sin x$ to obtain

$$\sin x^2 = g(x^2)$$

$$= x^2 - \frac{x^6}{3!} + \frac{x^{10}}{5!} - \frac{x^{14}}{7!} + \cdots.$$

Be sure to understand the point illustrated in Example 3. Because direct computation of Taylor or Maclaurin coefficients can be tedious, the most practical way to find a Taylor or Maclaurin series is to develop power series for a *basic list* of elementary functions. From this list, you can determine power series for other functions by the operations of addition, subtraction, multiplication, division, differentiation, integration, and composition with known power series.

Binomial Series

Before presenting the basic list for elementary functions, you will develop one more series—for a function of the form $f(x) = (1 + x)^k$. This produces the **binomial series**.

> **Insight**
>
> The binomial series is not covered on the AP® Calculus Exam.

EXAMPLE 4   Binomial Series

Find the Maclaurin series for $f(x) = (1 + x)^k$ and determine its radius of convergence. Assume that k is not a positive integer and $k \neq 0$.

Solution

By successive differentiation, you have

$$f(x) = (1 + x)^k \qquad\qquad f(0) = 1$$
$$f'(x) = k(1 + x)^{k-1} \qquad\qquad f'(0) = k$$
$$f''(x) = k(k - 1)(1 + x)^{k-2} \qquad\qquad f''(0) = k(k - 1)$$
$$f'''(x) = k(k - 1)(k - 2)(1 + x)^{k-3} \qquad f'''(0) = k(k - 1)(k - 2)$$
$$\vdots \qquad\qquad\qquad\qquad\qquad \vdots$$
$$f^{(n)}(x) = k \cdots (k - n + 1)(1 + x)^{k-n} \qquad f^{(n)}(0) = k(k - 1) \cdots (k - n + 1)$$

which produces the series

$$1 + kx + \frac{k(k - 1)x^2}{2} + \cdots + \frac{k(k - 1) \cdots (k - n + 1)x^n}{n!} + \cdots .$$

By the Ratio Test, you can conclude that the radius of convergence is $R = 1$. So, the series converges to some function in the interval $(-1, 1)$. ∎

Note that Example 4 shows that the Taylor series for $(1 + x)^k$ converges to some function in the interval $(-1, 1)$. However, the example does not show that the series actually converges to $(1 + x)^k$. To do this, you could show that the remainder $R_n(x)$ converges to 0, as illustrated in Example 2. You now have enough information to find a binomial series for a function, as shown in the next example.

EXAMPLE 5   Finding a Binomial Series

Find the power series for $f(x) = \sqrt[3]{1 + x}$.

Solution

Using the binomial series

$$(1 + x)^k = 1 + kx + \frac{k(k - 1)x^2}{2!} + \frac{k(k - 1)(k - 2)x^3}{3!} + \cdots$$

let $k = \frac{1}{3}$ and write

$$(1 + x)^{1/3} = 1 + \frac{x}{3} - \frac{2x^2}{3^2 2!} + \frac{2 \cdot 5x^3}{3^3 3!} - \frac{2 \cdot 5 \cdot 8x^4}{3^4 4!} + \cdots . \qquad ∎$$

Technology

Use a graphing utility to confirm the result in Example 5. When you graph the functions

$$f(x) = (1 + x)^{1/3} \quad \text{and} \quad P_4(x) = 1 + \frac{x}{3} - \frac{x^2}{9} + \frac{5x^3}{81} - \frac{10x^4}{243}$$

in the same viewing window, you should obtain the result shown in Figure 8.26.

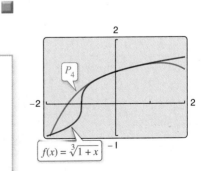

Figure 8.26

Deriving Taylor Series from a Basic List

The list below provides the power series for several elementary functions with the corresponding intervals of convergence.

Power Series for Elementary Functions

Function	Interval of Convergence
$\dfrac{1}{x} = 1 - (x - 1) + (x - 1)^2 - (x - 1)^3 + (x - 1)^4 - \cdots + (-1)^n(x - 1)^n + \cdots$	$0 < x < 2$
$\dfrac{1}{1 - x} = 1 + x + x^2 + x^3 + x^4 + x^5 + \cdots + x^n + \cdots$	$-1 < x < 1$
$\dfrac{1}{1 + x} = 1 - x + x^2 - x^3 + x^4 - x^5 + \cdots + (-1)^n x^n + \cdots$	$-1 < x < 1$
$\ln x = (x - 1) - \dfrac{(x - 1)^2}{2} + \dfrac{(x - 1)^3}{3} - \dfrac{(x - 1)^4}{4} + \cdots + \dfrac{(-1)^{n-1}(x - 1)^n}{n} + \cdots$	$0 < x \le 2$
$e^x = 1 + x + \dfrac{x^2}{2!} + \dfrac{x^3}{3!} + \dfrac{x^4}{4!} + \dfrac{x^5}{5!} + \cdots + \dfrac{x^n}{n!} + \cdots$	$-\infty < x < \infty$
$\sin x = x - \dfrac{x^3}{3!} + \dfrac{x^5}{5!} - \dfrac{x^7}{7!} + \dfrac{x^9}{9!} - \cdots + \dfrac{(-1)^n x^{2n+1}}{(2n + 1)!} + \cdots$	$-\infty < x < \infty$
$\cos x = 1 - \dfrac{x^2}{2!} + \dfrac{x^4}{4!} - \dfrac{x^6}{6!} + \dfrac{x^8}{8!} - \cdots + \dfrac{(-1)^n x^{2n}}{(2n)!} + \cdots$	$-\infty < x < \infty$
$\arctan x = x - \dfrac{x^3}{3} + \dfrac{x^5}{5} - \dfrac{x^7}{7} + \dfrac{x^9}{9} - \cdots + \dfrac{(-1)^n x^{2n+1}}{2n + 1} + \cdots$	$-1 \le x \le 1$
$\arcsin x = x + \dfrac{x^3}{2 \cdot 3} + \dfrac{1 \cdot 3 x^5}{2 \cdot 4 \cdot 5} + \dfrac{1 \cdot 3 \cdot 5 x^7}{2 \cdot 4 \cdot 6 \cdot 7} + \cdots + \dfrac{(2n)! x^{2n+1}}{(2^n n!)^2 (2n + 1)} + \cdots$	$-1 \le x \le 1$
$(1 + x)^k = 1 + kx + \dfrac{k(k - 1)x^2}{2!} + \dfrac{k(k - 1)(k - 2)x^3}{3!} + \cdots$ $\quad + \dfrac{k(k - 1) \cdots (k - n + 1)x^n}{n!} + \cdots$	$-1 < x < 1^*$

*The convergence at $x = \pm 1$ depends on the value of k.

Note that the binomial series is valid for noninteger values of k. Also, when k is a positive integer, the binomial series reduces to a simple binomial expansion.

EXAMPLE 6 Deriving a Power Series from a Basic List

Find the power series for

$$f(x) = \cos \sqrt{x}.$$

Solution

Using the power series

$$\cos x = 1 - \frac{x^2}{2!} + \frac{x^4}{4!} - \frac{x^6}{6!} + \frac{x^8}{8!} - \cdots$$

you can replace x by $\sqrt{x}$ to obtain the series

$$\cos \sqrt{x} = 1 - \frac{x}{2!} + \frac{x^2}{4!} - \frac{x^3}{6!} + \frac{x^4}{8!} - \cdots.$$

This series converges for all x in the domain of $\cos \sqrt{x}$—that is, for $x \ge 0$.

Power series can be multiplied and divided like polynomials. After finding the first few terms of the product (or quotient), you may be able to recognize a pattern.

EXAMPLE 7   Multiplication of Power Series

Find the first three nonzero terms in the Maclaurin series $e^x \arctan x$.

Solution

Using the Maclaurin series for e^x and $\arctan x$, you have

$$e^x \arctan x = \left(1 + x + \frac{x^2}{2!} + \frac{x^3}{3!} + \frac{x^4}{4!} + \cdots\right)\left(x - \frac{x^3}{3} + \frac{x^5}{5} - \cdots\right).$$

Multiply these expressions and collect like terms as you would in multiplying polynomials.

$$
\begin{array}{l}
1 + x + \dfrac{1}{2}x^2 + \dfrac{1}{6}x^3 + \dfrac{1}{24}x^4 + \cdots \\[2mm]
\qquad x \qquad\qquad - \dfrac{1}{3}x^3 \qquad\qquad + \dfrac{1}{5}x^5 - \cdots \\[1mm]
\hline
x + \ x^2 + \dfrac{1}{2}x^3 + \dfrac{1}{6}x^4 + \dfrac{1}{24}x^5 + \cdots \\[2mm]
\qquad\qquad\quad - \dfrac{1}{3}x^3 - \dfrac{1}{3}x^4 - \dfrac{1}{6}x^5 - \cdots \\[2mm]
\qquad\qquad\qquad\qquad\qquad\quad + \dfrac{1}{5}x^5 + \cdots \\[1mm]
\hline
x + \ x^2 + \dfrac{1}{6}x^3 - \dfrac{1}{6}x^4 + \dfrac{3}{40}x^5 + \cdots
\end{array}
$$

So, $e^x \arctan x = x + x^2 + \frac{1}{6}x^3 + \cdots$.

EXAMPLE 8   Division of Power Series

Find the first three nonzero terms in the Maclaurin series $\tan x$.

Solution

Using the Maclaurin series for $\sin x$ and $\cos x$, you have

$$\tan x = \frac{\sin x}{\cos x} = \frac{x - \dfrac{x^3}{3!} + \dfrac{x^5}{5!} - \cdots}{1 - \dfrac{x^2}{2!} + \dfrac{x^4}{4!} - \cdots}.$$

Divide using long division.

$$
\begin{array}{r}
x + \dfrac{1}{3}x^3 + \dfrac{2}{15}x^5 + \cdots \\[1mm]
1 - \dfrac{1}{2}x^2 + \dfrac{1}{24}x^4 - \cdots \ \overline{\smash{\big)}\ x - \dfrac{1}{6}x^3 + \dfrac{1}{120}x^5 - \cdots} \\[1mm]
\underline{x - \dfrac{1}{2}x^3 + \dfrac{1}{24}x^5 - \cdots} \\[1mm]
\dfrac{1}{3}x^3 - \dfrac{1}{30}x^5 + \cdots \\[1mm]
\underline{\dfrac{1}{3}x^3 - \dfrac{1}{6}x^5 + \cdots} \\[1mm]
\dfrac{2}{15}x^5 + \cdots
\end{array}
$$

So, $\tan x = x + \frac{1}{3}x^3 + \frac{2}{15}x^5 + \cdots$.

> **Insight**
>
> You should know the power series for $\sin x$, $\cos x$, e^x, and $1/(1 + x)$ for the AP® Calculus BC Exam.

EXAMPLE 9 A Power Series for $\sin^2 x$

Find the power series for

$$f(x) = \sin^2 x.$$

Solution

Consider rewriting $\sin^2 x$ as

$$\sin^2 x = \frac{1 - \cos 2x}{2} = \frac{1}{2} - \frac{1}{2}\cos 2x.$$

Now, use the series for $\cos x$.

$$\cos x = 1 - \frac{x^2}{2!} + \frac{x^4}{4!} - \frac{x^6}{6!} + \frac{x^8}{8!} - \cdots$$

$$\cos 2x = 1 - \frac{2^2}{2!}x^2 + \frac{2^4}{4!}x^4 - \frac{2^6}{6!}x^6 + \frac{2^8}{8!}x^8 - \cdots$$

$$-\frac{1}{2}\cos 2x = -\frac{1}{2} + \frac{2}{2!}x^2 - \frac{2^3}{4!}x^4 + \frac{2^5}{6!}x^6 - \frac{2^7}{8!}x^8 + \cdots$$

$$\frac{1}{2} - \frac{1}{2}\cos 2x = \frac{1}{2} - \frac{1}{2} + \frac{2}{2!}x^2 - \frac{2^3}{4!}x^4 + \frac{2^5}{6!}x^6 - \frac{2^7}{8!}x^8 + \cdots$$

So, the series for $f(x) = \sin^2 x$ is

$$\sin^2 x = \frac{2}{2!}x^2 - \frac{2^3}{4!}x^4 + \frac{2^5}{6!}x^6 - \frac{2^7}{8!}x^8 + \cdots.$$

This series converges for $-\infty < x < \infty$.

As mentioned in the preceding section, power series can be used to obtain tables of values of transcendental functions. They are also useful for estimating the values of definite integrals for which antiderivatives cannot be found. The next example demonstrates this use.

EXAMPLE 10 Power Series Approximation of a Definite Integral

See LarsonCalculusforAP.com for an interactive version of this type of example.

Use a power series to approximate

$$\int_0^1 e^{-x^2}\, dx$$

with an error of less than 0.01.

Solution

Replacing x with $-x^2$ in the series for e^x produces the following.

$$e^{-x^2} = 1 - x^2 + \frac{x^4}{2!} - \frac{x^6}{3!} + \frac{x^8}{4!} - \cdots$$

$$\int_0^1 e^{-x^2}\, dx = \left[x - \frac{x^3}{3} + \frac{x^5}{5 \cdot 2!} - \frac{x^7}{7 \cdot 3!} + \frac{x^9}{9 \cdot 4!} - \cdots \right]_0^1$$

$$= 1 - \frac{1}{3} + \frac{1}{10} - \frac{1}{42} + \frac{1}{216} - \cdots$$

Summing the first four terms, you have

$$\int_0^1 e^{-x^2}\, dx \approx 0.74$$

which, by the Alternating Series Test, has an error of less than $\frac{1}{216} \approx 0.005$.

8.10 Exercises

See *CalcChat.com* for tutorial help and worked-out solutions to odd-numbered exercises.

 Finding a Taylor Series In Exercises 1–12, use the definition of Taylor series to find the Taylor series, centered at c, for the function.

1. $f(x) = e^{2x}, \quad c = 0$ **2.** $f(x) = e^{-4x}, \quad c = 0$

3. $f(x) = \cos x, \quad c = \dfrac{\pi}{4}$ **4.** $f(x) = \sin x, \quad c = \dfrac{\pi}{2}$

5. $f(x) = \dfrac{1}{x}, \quad c = 1$ **6.** $f(x) = \dfrac{1}{1 - x}, \quad c = 5$

7. $f(x) = \ln x, \quad c = 1$ **8.** $f(x) = e^x, \quad c = 1$

9. $f(x) = \sin 3x, \quad c = 0$

10. $f(x) = \ln(x^2 + 1), \quad c = 0$

11. $f(x) = \sec x, \quad c = 0$ (first three nonzero terms)

12. $f(x) = \tan x, \quad c = 0$ (first three nonzero terms)

 Proof In Exercises 13 and 14, prove that the Maclaurin series for the function converges to the function for all x.

13. $f(x) = \cos x$ **14.** $f(x) = e^{-2x}$

 Using a Binomial Series In Exercises 15–20, use the binomial series to find the Maclaurin series for the function.

15. $f(x) = \dfrac{1}{(1 + x)^4}$ **16.** $f(x) = \dfrac{1}{\sqrt[3]{1 + x^2}}$

17. $f(x) = \dfrac{1}{\sqrt{1 - x^2}}$ **18.** $f(x) = \dfrac{1}{(2 + x)^3}$

19. $f(x) = \sqrt[4]{1 + x}$ **20.** $f(x) = \sqrt{1 + x^7}$

 Finding a Maclaurin Series In Exercises 21–32, find the Maclaurin series for the function. Use the list of power series for elementary functions on page 620.

21. $f(x) = e^{x^2/2}$ **22.** $g(x) = e^{-x/3}$

23. $f(x) = \ln(1 + x)^2$ **24.** $f(x) = \ln(1 + x^3)$

25. $g(x) = \sin 5x$ **26.** $f(x) = \sin \pi x$

27. $g(x) = \arctan 5x$ **28.** $f(x) = \arcsin \pi x$

29. $f(x) = \cos x^{3/2}$ **30.** $g(x) = 2 \sin x^3$

31. $f(x) = 3 + 4e^{x^3}$ **32.** $f(x) = \cos^2 x$

Error Analysis In Exercises 33 and 34, describe and correct the error in finding the Maclaurin series for the functions $f(x) = e^{-7x}$ and $g(x) = \cos x^4$. Use the list of power series for elementary functions on page 620.

33. $e^{-7x} = \displaystyle\sum_{n=0}^{\infty} \dfrac{-7x^n}{n!}$ ✗

34. $\cos x^4 = \displaystyle\sum_{n=0}^{\infty} \dfrac{(-1)^n (x^4)^{2n}}{(2n)!} = \displaystyle\sum_{n=0}^{\infty} \dfrac{(-1)^n x^{2n+4}}{(2n)!}$ ✗

 Finding a Maclaurin Series In Exercises 35–38, find the Maclaurin series for the function.

35. $f(x) = x \sin x$ **36.** $h(x) = x \cos x$

37. $g(x) = \begin{cases} \dfrac{\sin x}{x}, & x \neq 0 \\ 1, & x = 0 \end{cases}$ **38.** $f(x) = \begin{cases} \dfrac{\arcsin x}{x}, & x \neq 0 \\ 1, & x = 0 \end{cases}$

Verifying In Exercises 39 and 40, use a power series and the fact that $i^2 = -1$ to verify the formula.

39. $g(x) = \dfrac{1}{2i}(e^{ix} - e^{-ix}) = \sin x$

40. $g(x) = \dfrac{1}{2}(e^{ix} + e^{-ix}) = \cos x$

 Finding Terms of a Maclaurin Series In Exercises 41–46, find the first four nonzero terms of the Maclaurin series for the function by multiplying or dividing the appropriate power series. Use the list of power series for elementary functions on page 620. Use a graphing utility to graph the function and its corresponding polynomial approximation.

41. $f(x) = e^x \sin x$ **42.** $g(x) = e^x \cos x$

43. $h(x) = (\cos x) \ln(1 + x)$

44. $f(x) = e^x \ln(1 + x)$

45. $g(x) = \dfrac{\sin x}{1 + x}$ **46.** $f(x) = \dfrac{e^x}{1 + x}$

Finding a Maclaurin Series In Exercises 47 and 48, find a Maclaurin series for $f(x)$.

47. $f(x) = \displaystyle\int_0^x (e^{-t^2} - 1) \, dt$

48. $f(x) = \displaystyle\int_0^x \sqrt{1 + t^5} \, dt$

Verifying In Exercises 49–52, verify the sum. Then use a graphing utility to approximate the sum with an error of less than 0.0001.

49. $\displaystyle\sum_{n=1}^{\infty} (-1)^{n+1} \dfrac{1}{n} = \ln 2$

50. $\displaystyle\sum_{n=0}^{\infty} (-1)^n \left[\dfrac{1}{(2n+1)!} \right] = \sin 1$

51. $\displaystyle\sum_{n=0}^{\infty} \dfrac{2^n}{n!} = e^2$

52. $\displaystyle\sum_{n=1}^{\infty} (-1)^{n-1} \left(\dfrac{1}{n!} \right) = \dfrac{e-1}{e}$

Finding a Limit In Exercises 53–56, use the series representation of the function f to find $\lim\limits_{x \to 0} f(x)$, if it exists.

53. $f(x) = \dfrac{1 - \cos x}{x}$

54. $f(x) = \dfrac{2 \sin x}{x}$

55. $f(x) = \dfrac{e^x - 1}{x}$

56. $f(x) = \dfrac{\ln(x + 1)}{x}$

 Approximating an Integral In Exercises 57–64, use a power series to approximate the value of the integral with an error of less than 0.0001. (In Exercises 59 and 61, assume that the integrand is defined as 1 when $x = 0$.)

57. $\displaystyle\int_0^1 e^{-x^2/3} \, dx$

58. $\displaystyle\int_0^{1/4} x \ln(x + 1) \, dx$

59. $\displaystyle\int_0^1 \frac{\sin x}{x} \, dx$

60. $\displaystyle\int_0^1 \cos x^2 \, dx$

61. $\displaystyle\int_0^{1/2} \frac{\arctan x}{x} \, dx$

62. $\displaystyle\int_0^{1/2} \arctan x^2 \, dx$

63. $\displaystyle\int_{0.1}^{0.3} \sqrt{1 + x^3} \, dx$

64. $\displaystyle\int_0^{0.2} \sqrt{1 + x^2} \, dx$

Area In Exercises 65 and 66, use a power series to approximate the area of the region with an error of less than 0.0001. Use a graphing utility to verify the result.

65. $\displaystyle\int_0^{\pi/2} \sqrt{x} \cos x \, dx$

66. $\displaystyle\int_{0.5}^1 \cos \sqrt{x} \, dx$

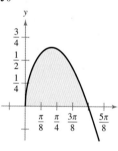

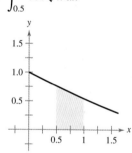

Probability In Exercises 67 and 68, approximate the normal probability with an error of less than 0.0001, where the probability is given by

$$P(a < x < b) = \frac{1}{\sqrt{2\pi}} \int_a^b e^{-x^2/2} \, dx.$$

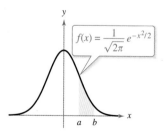

$$f(x) = \frac{1}{\sqrt{2\pi}} e^{-x^2/2}$$

67. $P(0 < x < 1)$

68. $P(1 < x < 2)$

EXPLORING CONCEPTS

69. Implementing Processes Describe three ways to find the Maclaurin series for $\cos^2 x$. Show that each method produces the same first three terms.

70. Implementing Processes Explain how to use the power series for $f(x) = \arctan x$ to find the Maclaurin series for

$$g(x) = \frac{1}{1 + x^2}.$$

What is another way to find the Maclaurin series for g using a power series for an elementary function?

71. Finding a Function Which function has the Maclaurin series

$$\sum_{n=0}^{\infty} \frac{(-1)^n (x + 3)^{2n+1}}{2^2(2n + 1)!}?$$

Explain your reasoning.

72. HOW DO YOU SEE IT? Identify the function represented by each power series and match the function with its graph. [The graphs are labeled (i) and (ii).]

(i)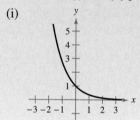

(ii)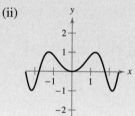

(a) $\displaystyle\sum_{n=0}^{\infty} \frac{(-1)^n x^{4n+2}}{(2n + 1)!}$

(b) $\displaystyle\sum_{n=0}^{\infty} \frac{(-1)^n x^n}{n!}$

73. Projectile Motion A projectile fired from the ground follows the trajectory given by

$$y = \left(\tan \theta - \frac{g}{kv_0 \cos \theta}\right)x - \frac{g}{k^2} \ln\left(1 - \frac{kx}{v_0 \cos \theta}\right)$$

where v_0 is the initial speed, θ is the angle of projection, g is the acceleration due to gravity, and k is the drag factor caused by air resistance. Using the power series representation

$$\ln(1 + x) = x - \frac{x^2}{2} + \frac{x^3}{3} - \frac{x^4}{4} + \cdots, \quad -1 < x < 1$$

verify that the trajectory can be rewritten as

$$y = (\tan \theta)x + \frac{gx^2}{2v_0^2 \cos^2 \theta} + \frac{kgx^3}{3v_0^3 \cos^3 \theta} + \frac{k^2 g x^4}{4v_0^4 \cos^4 \theta} + \cdots.$$

74. PROJECTILE MOTION

Use the result of Exercise 73 to determine the series for the path of a projectile launched from ground level at an angle of $\theta = 60°$, with an initial speed of $v_0 = 64$ feet per second and a drag factor of $k = \frac{1}{16}$.

75. Connecting Representations Consider the function

$$f(x) = \begin{cases} e^{-1/x^2}, & x \neq 0 \\ 0, & x = 0 \end{cases}.$$

(a) Sketch a graph of the function.

(b) Use the alternative form of the definition of the derivative (Section 2.1) and L'Hôpital's Rule to show that $f'(0) = 0$. [By continuing this process, it can be shown that $f^{(n)}(0) = 0$ for $n > 1$.]

(c) Using the result in part (b), find the Maclaurin series for f. Does the series converge to f?

76. Connecting Representations

(a) Find the power series centered at 0 for the function $f(x) = [\ln(x^2 + 1)]/x^2$.

(b) Use a graphing utility to graph f and the eighth-degree Taylor polynomial $P_8(x)$ for f.

(c) Use a graphing utility to complete the table, where

$$F(x) = \int_0^x \frac{\ln(t^2 + 1)}{t^2}\, dt \text{ and } G(x) = \int_0^x P_8(t)\, dt.$$

x	0.25	0.50	0.75	1.00	1.50	2.00
$F(x)$						
$G(x)$						

(d) Describe the relationship between the graphs of f and P_8, and the results given in the table in part (c).

Evaluating a Binomial Coefficient In Exercises 77–80, evaluate the binomial coefficient using the formula

$$\binom{k}{n} = \frac{k(k-1)(k-2)(k-3)\cdots(k-n+1)}{n!}$$

where k is a real number, n is a positive integer, and

$$\binom{k}{0} = 1.$$

77. $\binom{8}{3}$

78. $\binom{-12}{3}$

79. $\binom{-0.25}{6}$

80. $\binom{2/5}{2}$

81. Writing a Power Series Write the power series for $(1 + x)^k$ in terms of binomial coefficients.

82. Finding a Maclaurin Series Find the Maclaurin series for

$$f(x) = \ln\frac{1 + x}{1 - x}$$

and determine its radius of convergence. Use the first four terms of the series to approximate ln 3.

83. Proof Prove that e is irrational. [*Hint:* Assume that $e = p/q$ is rational (p and q are integers) and consider

$$e = 1 + 1 + \frac{1}{2!} + \cdots + \frac{1}{n!} + \cdots.]$$

84. Using Fibonacci Numbers Show that the Maclaurin series for the function $g(x) = x/(1 - x - x^2)$ is

$$\sum_{n=1}^{\infty} F_n x^n$$

where F_n is the nth Fibonacci number with $F_1 = F_2 = 1$ and $F_n = F_{n-2} + F_{n-1}$, for $n \geq 3$.

(*Hint:* Write

$$\frac{x}{1 - x - x^2} = a_0 + a_1 x + a_2 x^2 + \cdots$$

and multiply each side of this equation by $1 - x - x^2$.)

Calculus AP® – Exam Preparation Questions

85. Multiple Choice Which expression below represents the first five terms of the Maclaurin approximation of the area of the region bounded by the graph of $f(x) = e^{3x^2}$ and the x-axis from $x = 0$ to $x = 1$?

(A) $1 + 1 + \frac{9}{10} + \frac{9}{14} + \frac{3}{8}$

(B) $1 + 1 + \frac{9}{2} + \frac{9}{2} + \frac{3}{8}$

(C) $1 + 3 + \frac{9}{2} + \frac{9}{2} + \frac{27}{8}$

(D) $1 + 3 + \frac{3}{2} + \frac{1}{2} + \frac{1}{8}$

86. Multiple Choice Which of the following is the Maclaurin series for $f(x) = x\cos 2x$?

(A) $\displaystyle\sum_{n=0}^{\infty} \frac{(-1)^n 2x^{2n}}{(2n)!}$

(B) $\displaystyle\sum_{n=0}^{\infty} \frac{(-1)^n 2^{2n} x^{2n}}{(2n)!}$

(C) $\displaystyle\sum_{n=0}^{\infty} \frac{(-1)^n 2^{2n} x^{2n+1}}{(2n)!}$

(D) $\displaystyle\sum_{n=0}^{\infty} \frac{(-1)^n 2x^{2n+1}}{(2n)!}$

87. Multiple Choice The Maclaurin series for a function f is given by

$$x + \frac{x^3}{3!} + \frac{x^5}{5!} + \frac{x^7}{7!} + \cdots + \frac{x^{2n+1}}{(2n+1)!} + \cdots.$$

Which of the following is an expression for $f(x)$?

(A) $\sin x$

(B) $\frac{1}{2}(e^x - e^{-x})$

(C) $-\sin x$

(D) $e^x - e^{-x}$

8   Review Exercises

See *CalcChat.com* for tutorial help and worked-out solutions to odd-numbered exercises.

Finding the Limit of a Sequence   In Exercises 1 and 2, use a graphing utility to graph the first 10 terms of the sequence with the given nth term. Use the graph to make an inference about the convergence or divergence of the sequence. Verify your inference analytically and, if the sequence converges, find its limit.

1. $a_n = \dfrac{5n + 2}{n}$

2. $a_n = \sin\dfrac{n\pi}{2}$

Determining Convergence or Divergence   In Exercises 3–10, determine the convergence or divergence of the sequence with the given nth term. If the sequence converges, find its limit.

3. $a_n = 2 + \left(\dfrac{4}{3}\right)^n$

4. $a_n = \dfrac{n^2 - n}{3n^2 + 6}$

5. $a_n = \dfrac{n^3 + 1}{n^2}$

6. $a_n = \dfrac{1}{\sqrt{n}}$

7. $a_n = \dfrac{(-1)^n n}{n^2 + 1}$

8. $a_n = \dfrac{n}{\ln n}$

9. $a_n = \sqrt{n + 1} - \sqrt{n}$

10. $a_n = \dfrac{\sin\sqrt{n}}{\sqrt{n}}$

Finding the Sum of a Convergent Series   In Exercises 11–14, find the sum of the convergent series.

11. $\displaystyle\sum_{n=0}^{\infty} \left(-\dfrac{1}{6}\right)^n$

12. $\displaystyle\sum_{n=0}^{\infty} \dfrac{3^{n+2}}{7^n}$

13. $\displaystyle\sum_{n=1}^{\infty} [(0.6)^n + (0.8)^n]$

14. $\displaystyle\sum_{n=0}^{\infty} \left[\left(\dfrac{2}{3}\right)^n - \dfrac{1}{(n+1)(n+2)}\right]$

Using a Geometric Series   In Exercises 15 and 16, (a) write the repeating decimal as a geometric series, and (b) write the sum of the series as the ratio of two integers.

15. $0.0\overline{7}$

16. $0.\overline{89}$

Using a Geometric Series or the nth-Term Test   In Exercises 17–20, use a geometric series or the nth-Term Test to determine the convergence or divergence of the series.

17. $\displaystyle\sum_{n=0}^{\infty} (1.67)^n$

18. $\displaystyle\sum_{n=0}^{\infty} (0.36)^n$

19. $\displaystyle\sum_{n=2}^{\infty} \dfrac{(-1)^n n}{\ln n}$

20. $\displaystyle\sum_{n=0}^{\infty} \dfrac{2n + 1}{3n + 2}$

21. Distance   A ball is dropped from a height of 8 meters. Each time it drops h meters, it rebounds $0.7h$ meters. Find the total distance traveled by the ball.

22. Salary   You go to work at a company that pays $0.01 for the first day, $0.02 for the second day, $0.04 for the third day, and so on. If the daily wage keeps doubling, what would your total income be for working (a) 29 days, (b) 30 days, and (c) 31 days?

Using the Integral Test or a p-Series   In Exercises 23–28, use the Integral Test or a p-series to determine the convergence or divergence of the series.

23. $\displaystyle\sum_{n=1}^{\infty} \dfrac{2}{6n + 1}$

24. $\displaystyle\sum_{n=1}^{\infty} \dfrac{1}{\sqrt[4]{n^3}}$

25. $\displaystyle\sum_{n=1}^{\infty} \dfrac{1}{n^{5/2}}$

26. $\displaystyle\sum_{n=1}^{\infty} \dfrac{1}{5^n}$

27. $\displaystyle\sum_{n=1}^{\infty} \left(\dfrac{1}{n^2} - \dfrac{1}{n}\right)$

28. $\displaystyle\sum_{n=1}^{\infty} \dfrac{\ln n}{n^4}$

Using the Direct Comparison Test or the Limit Comparison Test   In Exercises 29–34, use the Direct Comparison Test or the Limit Comparison Test to determine the convergence or divergence of the series.

29. $\displaystyle\sum_{n=2}^{\infty} \dfrac{1}{\sqrt[3]{n} - 1}$

30. $\displaystyle\sum_{n=1}^{\infty} \dfrac{\sin^2 n}{3^n}$

31. $\displaystyle\sum_{n=1}^{\infty} \dfrac{n}{\sqrt{n^3 + 3n}}$

32. $\displaystyle\sum_{n=1}^{\infty} \dfrac{n + 1}{n(n + 2)}$

33. $\displaystyle\sum_{n=1}^{\infty} \dfrac{1 \cdot 3 \cdot 5 \cdots (2n - 1)}{2 \cdot 4 \cdot 6 \cdots (2n)}$

34. $\displaystyle\sum_{n=1}^{\infty} \dfrac{1}{3^n - 5}$

Using the Alternating Series Test   In Exercises 35–40, use the Alternating Series Test, if applicable, to determine the convergence or divergence of the series. If the series converges, determine whether it converges absolutely or conditionally.

35. $\displaystyle\sum_{n=1}^{\infty} \dfrac{(-1)^n}{n^5}$

36. $\displaystyle\sum_{n=1}^{\infty} \dfrac{(-1)^n(n + 1)}{n^2 + 1}$

37. $\displaystyle\sum_{n=1}^{\infty} \dfrac{(-1)^n \sqrt{n}}{n + 1}$

38. $\displaystyle\sum_{n=1}^{\infty} \dfrac{(-1)^{n+1} n^2}{n!}$

39. $\displaystyle\sum_{n=4}^{\infty} \dfrac{(-1)^n n}{n - 3}$

40. $\displaystyle\sum_{n=2}^{\infty} \dfrac{(-1)^n \ln n^3}{n}$

Using the Ratio Test or the Root Test   In Exercises 41–46, use the Ratio Test or the Root Test to determine the convergence or divergence of the series.

41. $\displaystyle\sum_{n=1}^{\infty} \left(\dfrac{3n - 1}{2n + 5}\right)^n$

42. $\displaystyle\sum_{n=1}^{\infty} \left(\dfrac{4n}{7n - 1}\right)^n$

43. $\displaystyle\sum_{n=1}^{\infty} \dfrac{n}{e^{n^2}}$

44. $\displaystyle\sum_{n=1}^{\infty} \dfrac{n!}{e^n}$

45. $\displaystyle\sum_{n=1}^{\infty} \dfrac{2^n}{n^3}$

46. $\displaystyle\sum_{n=1}^{\infty} \dfrac{5 \cdot 10 \cdot 15 \cdots (5n)}{3 \cdot 6 \cdot 9 \cdots (3n)}$

Connecting Representations In Exercises 47 and 48, (a) verify that the series converges, (b) use a graphing utility to find the indicated partial sums S_n to complete the table, (c) use a graphing utility to graph the first 10 terms of the sequence of partial sums, and (d) use the table to estimate the sum of the series.

n	5	10	15	20	25
S_n					

47. $\displaystyle\sum_{n=1}^{\infty} n\left(\frac{3}{5}\right)^n$

48. $\displaystyle\sum_{n=1}^{\infty} \frac{(-1)^{n-1}n}{n^3 + 5}$

Finding a Maclaurin Polynomial In Exercises 49 and 50, find the nth Maclaurin polynomial for the function.

49. $f(x) = e^{x/3}, \ n = 4$ **50.** $f(x) = \sin \pi x, \ n = 3$

Finding a Taylor Polynomial In Exercises 51 and 52, find the third-degree Taylor polynomial for $f(x)$, centered at c.

51. $f(x) = e^{-3x}, \ c = 0$ **52.** $f(x) = \tan x, \ c = -\pi/4$

Finding a Degree In Exercises 53 and 54, determine the degree of the Maclaurin polynomial required for the error in the approximation of the function at the indicated value of x to be less than 0.001.

53. $f(x) = \cos x$, approximate $f(0.75)$

54. $f(x) = e^x$, approximate $f(-0.25)$

Finding the Interval of Convergence In Exercises 55–60, find the interval of convergence of the power series. (Be sure to include a check for convergence at the endpoints of the interval.)

55. $\displaystyle\sum_{n=0}^{\infty} \left(\frac{3x}{4}\right)^n$

56. $\displaystyle\sum_{n=0}^{\infty} \frac{(-2x)^{n+1}}{n!}$

57. $\displaystyle\sum_{n=0}^{\infty} \frac{(-1)^n(x-2)^n}{(n+1)^2}$

58. $\displaystyle\sum_{n=1}^{\infty} \frac{3^n(x-2)^n}{n}$

59. $\displaystyle\sum_{n=0}^{\infty} n!(x-2)^n$

60. $\displaystyle\sum_{n=0}^{\infty} \frac{(x-2)^n}{2^n}$

Finding Intervals of Convergence In Exercises 61 and 62, find the intervals of convergence of (a) $f(x)$, (b) $f'(x)$, (c) $f''(x)$, and (d) $\int f(x)\,dx$. (Be sure to include a check for convergence at the endpoints of the intervals.)

61. $f(x) = \displaystyle\sum_{n=0}^{\infty} \left(\frac{x}{5}\right)^n$

62. $f(x) = \displaystyle\sum_{n=1}^{\infty} \frac{(-1)^{n+1}(x-4)^n}{n}$

Finding a Geometric Power Series In Exercises 63 and 64, find a geometric power series for the function, centered at 0.

63. $g(x) = \dfrac{2}{3-x}$

64. $h(x) = \dfrac{3}{2+x}$

Finding a Power Series In Exercises 65 and 66, find a power series for the function, centered at c, and determine the interval of convergence.

65. $f(x) = \dfrac{6}{4-x}, \quad c = 1$ **66.** $f(x) = \dfrac{1}{3-2x}, \quad c = 0$

Finding the Sum of a Series In Exercises 67–72, find the sum of the convergent series by using a well-known function. Identify the function and explain how you obtained the sum.

67. $\displaystyle\sum_{n=1}^{\infty} (-1)^{n+1} \frac{1}{4^n n}$

68. $\displaystyle\sum_{n=1}^{\infty} (-1)^{n+1} \frac{1}{5^n n}$

69. $\displaystyle\sum_{n=0}^{\infty} \frac{1}{2^n n!}$

70. $\displaystyle\sum_{n=0}^{\infty} \frac{2^n}{3^n n!}$

71. $\displaystyle\sum_{n=0}^{\infty} (-1)^n \frac{2^{2n}}{3^{2n}(2n)!}$

72. $\displaystyle\sum_{n=0}^{\infty} (-1)^n \frac{1}{3^{2n+1}(2n+1)!}$

Finding a Taylor Series In Exercises 73–78, use the definition of Taylor series to find the Taylor series, centered at c, for the function.

73. $f(x) = \sin x, \quad c = \dfrac{3\pi}{4}$ **74.** $f(x) = 3^x, \quad c = 0$

75. $f(x) = \dfrac{1}{x}, \quad c = -1$ **76.** $f(x) = \sqrt{x}, \quad c = 4$

77. $g(x) = \sqrt[5]{1+x}, \quad c = 0$

78. $h(x) = \dfrac{1}{(1+x)^3}, \quad c = 0$

79. Forming Maclaurin Series Determine the first four terms of the Maclaurin series for e^{2x}

(a) by using the definition of the Maclaurin series and the formula for the coefficient of the nth term, $a_n = f^{(n)}(0)/n!$.

(b) by replacing x by $2x$ in the series for e^x.

(c) by multiplying the series for e^x by itself, because $e^{2x} = e^x \cdot e^x$.

80. Forming Maclaurin Series Determine the first four terms of the Maclaurin series for $\sin 2x$

(a) by using the definition of the Maclaurin series and the formula for the coefficient of the nth term, $a_n = f^{(n)}(0)/n!$.

(b) by replacing x by $2x$ in the series for $\sin 2x$.

(c) by multiplying 2 by the series for $\sin x$ by the series for $\cos x$, because $\sin 2x = 2 \sin x \cos x$.

Finding a Maclaurin Series In Exercises 81 and 82, find the Maclaurin series for the function. Use the list of power series for elementary functions on page 620.

81. $f(x) = e^{6x}$ **82.** $f(x) = \cos 3x$

AP® Exam Practice Questions

See *LarsonCalculusforAP.com* for worked-out solutions to these questions.

What You Need to Know

- The *p*-Series Test, the Direct Comparison Test, and the Limit Comparison Test are covered most often on the multiple-choice section of the AP® Calculus BC Exam.

- The Ratio Test is commonly covered on the AP® Calculus BC Exam, primarily on the free-response section.

- Finding the radius and interval of convergence of a power series is commonly tested on the AP® Calculus BC Exam.

- When finding an interval of convergence of a power series, be sure to test for convergence at each endpoint.

- You should be able to perform algebraic manipulations of power series, including differentiation, integration, and composition.

- When finding Maclaurin and Taylor polynomials, you do not have to simplify coefficients.

- Be prepared to answer questions involving the Lagrange form of the remainder (or error bound) for Taylor polynomials and the Alternating Series Remainder (or error bound) for alternating series.

- The AP® Calculus BC Exam frequently assesses your ability to manipulate a known series.

Practice Questions

Section 1, Part A, Multiple Choice, No Technology

1. Which of the following series diverges?

   I. $\displaystyle\sum_{n=1}^{\infty} \frac{3}{\sqrt[3]{n}}$ II. $\displaystyle\sum_{n=1}^{\infty} \left(\frac{e}{\sin 2}\right)^n$ III. $\displaystyle\sum_{n=1}^{\infty} \frac{5}{(n+1)!}$

   (A) I only
   (B) II only
   (C) I and II only
   (D) I, II, and III

2. Which of the following describes the series $\displaystyle\sum_{n=1}^{\infty} \frac{(-1)^n n^3}{4^n}$?

   I. converges

   II. converges absolutely

   III. converges conditionally

   (A) I only
   (B) I and II only
   (C) I and III only
   (D) I, II, and III

3. What is the sum of the series

   $1 + \ln 3 + \dfrac{(\ln 3)^2}{2!} + \cdots + \dfrac{(\ln 3)^n}{n!} + \cdots?$

   (A) $\ln 3$
   (B) e^3
   (C) 3
   (D) The series diverges.

4. For what values of p does the series

   $\displaystyle\sum_{n=2}^{\infty} \frac{5(n+3)}{(n-1)^p}$

   converge?

   (A) $p > 0$
   (B) $p > 1$
   (C) $p > 2$
   (D) The series diverges for all values of p.

5. The Maclaurin series for $\cos x$ is

   $\displaystyle\sum_{n=0}^{\infty} (-1)^n \frac{x^{2n}}{(2n)!}.$

   Which of the following is the power series for $x^2 \cos x^2$?

   (A) $1 - \dfrac{x^4}{2!} + \dfrac{x^8}{4!} - \dfrac{x^{12}}{6!} + \dfrac{x^{16}}{8!} - \cdots$

   (B) $x^2 - \dfrac{x^4}{2!} + \dfrac{x^6}{4!} - \dfrac{x^8}{6!} + \dfrac{x^{10}}{8!} - \cdots$

   (C) $x^2 - \dfrac{x^6}{2!} + \dfrac{x^{10}}{4!} - \dfrac{x^{14}}{6!} + \dfrac{x^{18}}{8!} - \cdots$

   (D) $2x - \dfrac{4x^3}{2!} + \dfrac{6x^5}{4!} - \dfrac{8x^7}{6!} + \dfrac{10x^9}{8!} - \cdots$

Section 1, Part B, Multiple Choice, Technology Permitted

6. What is the minimum number of terms required to approximate the sum of the series

   $\displaystyle\sum_{n=1}^{\infty} \frac{(-1)^{n+1}}{3n^3 + 1}$

   with an error of less than 0.001?

   (A) 5   (B) 6   (C) 7   (D) 10

7. At what x-value does the graph of the function represented by

   $1 - x + x^2 - x^3 + \cdots + (-1)^n x^n + \cdots$

   intersect the graph of $y = x^2$?

   (A) None
   (B) -0.703
   (C) 0.755
   (D) 1

Section 2, Part A, Free Response, Technology Permitted

8. Let g be a function having derivatives of all orders for all x. Selected values of g and its first four derivatives are listed in the table. The function g and its first four derivatives are increasing on the interval $2 \leq x \leq 4$.

x	$g(x)$	$g'(x)$	$g''(x)$	$g'''(x)$	$g^{(4)}(x)$
2	17	22	20	14	5
3	50	$\dfrac{160}{3}$	$\dfrac{141}{4}$	21	$\dfrac{151}{8}$
4	232	$\dfrac{604}{3}$	$\dfrac{2703}{16}$	152	$\dfrac{1123}{8}$

(a) Write the first-degree Taylor polynomial P_1 for g at $x = 3$ and use it to approximate $g(3.1)$. Is this approximation greater than or less than $g(3.1)$? Explain.

(b) Write the third-degree Taylor polynomial P_3 for g at $x = 3$ and use it to approximate $g(3.1)$.

(c) Use the Lagrange error bound to show that

$$|g(3.1) - P_3(3.1)| < 0.0006.$$

Section 2, Part B, Free Response, No Technology

9. Let $f(x) = xe^{-x}$.

(a) Write the first four nonzero terms and the general term of the Taylor series for f at $x = 0$.

(b) Find $\displaystyle\lim_{x \to 0} \frac{f(x) - x + x^2}{x^3}$.

(c) Write the first four nonzero terms and the general term of the Taylor series for

$$g(x) = \int_0^x t e^{-t}\, dt$$

at $x = 0$. Use the first three terms to approximate $g\left(\frac{1}{5}\right)$.

(d) Evaluated at $x = \frac{1}{5}$, the Taylor series for g is an alternating decreasing series with individual terms that decrease in absolute value to zero. Show that your approximation in part (c) must differ from $g\left(\frac{1}{5}\right)$ by less than $\frac{1}{90,000}$.

10. Let $f(x) = \cos x^2$.

(a) Find the first four terms and the general term of the Maclaurin series for f.

(b) Determine the radius of convergence for this series.

(c) Use the first three terms of the Maclaurin series for f to approximate $\cos 1$. Show that the approximation is accurate to within $\frac{1}{500}$.

11. For all real numbers x, the function f is defined by the power series

$$f(x) = \sum_{n=0}^{\infty} \frac{(-1)^n x^{2n}}{n!} = 1 - x^2 + \frac{x^4}{2!} - \frac{x^6}{3!} + \frac{x^8}{4!} - \frac{x^{10}}{5!} + \cdots.$$

(a) Find $f'(0)$ and $f''(0)$. Determine whether f has a local maximum, a local minimum, or neither at $x = 0$. Give a reason for your answer.

(b) To approximate $f(1)$ with an error less than 0.1, can you use the expression $\frac{1}{2!} - \frac{1}{3!}$? Explain.

(c) Show that $y = f(x)$ is a solution of the differential equation $y' + 2xy = 0$.

12. The function f is defined by the power series

$$f(x) = (x - 1) - \frac{(x-1)^2}{2} + \frac{(x-1)^3}{3} - \frac{(x-1)^4}{4} + \cdots$$
$$= \sum_{n=1}^{\infty} \frac{(-1)^{n-1}(x-1)^n}{n}$$

for all real numbers x for which the series converges.

(a) Determine the interval of convergence for f. Justify your answer.

(b) Given $g(x) = f'(x)$, find the first three terms and the general term of the power series for g.

(c) Find a rational function that is identical to g over its interval of convergence.

(d) Let $h(x) = f(x^3 + 1)$. Find h'.

13. The function g is thrice-differentiable with $g(2) = 3$ and $g''(2) = 20$. On the interval $[2, 2.4]$, g' is an increasing function. Select values of g' are given in the table below.

x	2	2.1	2.2	2.3	2.4
$g'(x)$	4	5	7	8	10.5

(a) Write an equation for the line tangent to g at $x = 2$. Use this to approximate $g(2.4)$. Is this approximation greater than or less than $g(2.4)$? Explain.

(b) Use a midpoint Riemann sum with two subintervals of equal length to approximate

$$\int_2^{2.4} g'(x)\, dx.$$

Use your approximation to estimate $g(2.4)$.

(c) Use Euler's Method with two steps of equal size to estimate $g(2.4)$.

(d) Write the second-degree Taylor polynomial for g at $x = 2$ and use it to approximate $g(2.4)$. Given that $g'''(x) \leq 6$ for $2 \leq x \leq 2.4$, show that your approximation is correct to within one-tenth.

Koch Snowflake: Infinite Perimeter?

Clouds, biological growth, and coastlines are examples of real-life phenomena that seem too complex to be described using typical mathematical functions. By developing *fractal* geometry, Benoit Mandelbrot (1924–2010) found a way to describe real-life phenomena using a new mathematical construct. Mandelbrot first used the word fractal in 1975 to describe any geometric object whose detail is not lost as it is magnified. Being "endlessly magnifiable" means that you can zoom in on any portion of the fractal and it will be identical to the original fractal.

One of the "classic" fractals is the Koch snowflake, named after the Swedish mathematician Helge von Koch (1870–1924). It is sometimes classified as a "coastline curve" because of the way a coastline appears increasingly more complex with magnification. To describe the Koch snowflake, Mandelbrot coined the term *teragon*, which translates literally from the Greek words for "monster curve."

The construction of the Koch snowflake begins with an equilateral triangle whose sides are one unit long. In the first iteration, a triangle with sides one-third unit long is added in the center of each side of the original triangle. In the second iteration, a triangle with sides one-ninth unit long is added in the center of each side of the first iteration. Successive iterations continue this process indefinitely. The first four stages are shown below.

After developing some of the first computer graphics programs, Benoit Mandelbrot was able to share some of the most beautiful fractals with the world and create a growing interest in fractal geometry.

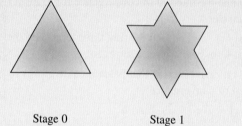  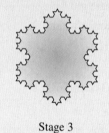

| Stage 0 | Stage 1 | Stage 2 | Stage 3 |

Exercises

1. Numerical Analysis Use the iteration for the Koch snowflake described above to complete the table.

Stage	0	1	2	3	4	5	$\cdots$	n
Sides	3							
Area	$\dfrac{\sqrt{3}}{4}$							
Perimeter	3							

2. Area What will happen to the area of the snowflake as n approaches infinity? Justify your answer.

3. Perimeter What will happen to the perimeter of the snowflake as n approaches infinity? Justify your answer.

4. Making a Conclusion Based on the results of Exercises 1–3, is it possible for a closed and bounded region in the plane to have a finite area and an infinite perimeter?

9 Parametric Equations, Polar Coordinates, and Vectors

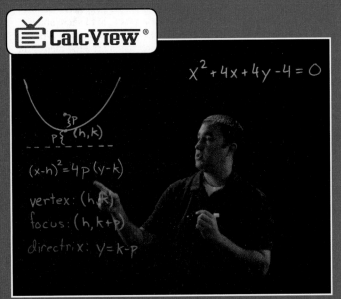

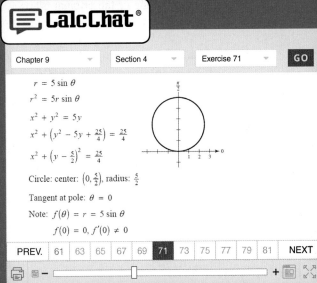

$$r = 5 \sin \theta$$
$$r^2 = 5r \sin \theta$$
$$x^2 + y^2 = 5y$$
$$x^2 + \left(y^2 - 5y + \frac{25}{4}\right) = \frac{25}{4}$$
$$x^2 + \left(y - \frac{5}{2}\right)^2 = \frac{25}{4}$$

Circle: center: $\left(0, \frac{5}{2}\right)$, radius: $\frac{5}{2}$

Tangent at pole: $\theta = 0$

Note: $f(\theta) = r = 5 \sin \theta$
$$f(0) = 0, f'(0) \neq 0$$

9.1 Architecture (*Exercise 67, p. 643*)

9.6 Navigation (*Exercise 79, p. 688*)

9.1 Conics and Calculus

▶ Understand the definition of a conic section.
▶ Analyze and write equations of parabolas using properties of parabolas.
▶ Analyze and write equations of ellipses using properties of ellipses.
▶ Analyze and write equations of hyperbolas using properties of hyperbolas.

Conic Sections

Each **conic section** (or simply **conic**) can be described as the intersection of a plane and a double-napped cone. Notice in Figure 9.1 that for the four basic conics, the intersecting plane does not pass through the vertex of the cone. When the plane passes through the vertex, the resulting figure is a **degenerate conic,** as shown in Figure 9.2.

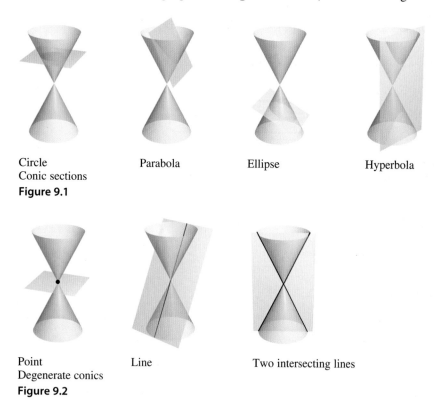

Circle
Conic sections
Figure 9.1

Parabola

Ellipse

Hyperbola

Point
Degenerate conics
Figure 9.2

Line

Two intersecting lines

There are several ways to study conics. You could begin as the Greeks did, by defining the conics in terms of the intersections of planes and cones, or you could define them algebraically in terms of the general second-degree equation

$$Ax^2 + Bxy + Cy^2 + Dx + Ey + F = 0.$$ General second-degree equation

However, a third approach, in which each of the conics is defined as a **locus** (collection) of points satisfying a certain geometric property, works best. For example, a circle can be defined as the collection of all points (x, y) that are equidistant from a fixed point (h, k). This locus definition easily produces the standard equation of a circle

$$(x - h)^2 + (y - k)^2 = r^2.$$ Standard equation of a circle

For information about rotating second-degree equations in two variables, see Appendix E.

Parabolas

A **parabola** is the set of all points (x, y) that are equidistant from a fixed line, the **directrix,** and a fixed point, the **focus,** not on the line. The midpoint between the focus and the directrix is the **vertex,** and the line passing through the focus and the vertex is the **axis** of the parabola. Note in Figure 9.3 that a parabola is symmetric with respect to its axis.

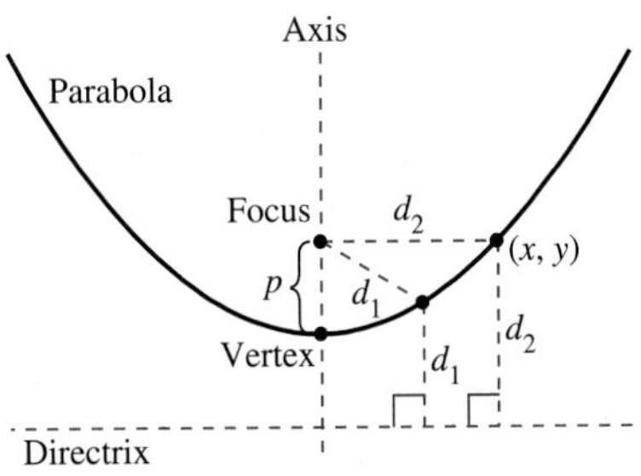

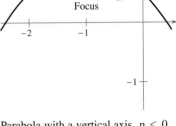

Figure 9.3

Theorem 9.1   Standard Equation of a Parabola

The **standard form** of the equation of a parabola with vertex (h, k) and directrix $y = k - p$ is

$$(x - h)^2 = 4p(y - k). \qquad \text{Vertical axis}$$

For directrix $x = h - p$, the equation is

$$(y - k)^2 = 4p(x - h). \qquad \text{Horizontal axis}$$

The focus lies on the axis p units (*directed distance*) from the vertex. The coordinates of the focus are as follows.

$$(h, k + p) \qquad \text{Vertical axis}$$

$$(h + p, k) \qquad \text{Horizontal axis}$$

EXAMPLE 1   Finding the Focus of a Parabola

Find the focus of the parabola

$$y = \frac{1}{2} - x - \frac{1}{2}x^2.$$

Solution

To find the focus, convert to standard form by completing the square.

$$y = \frac{1}{2} - x - \frac{1}{2}x^2 \qquad \text{Write original equation.}$$

$$2y = 1 - 2x - x^2 \qquad \text{Multiply each side by 2.}$$

$$2y = 1 - (x^2 + 2x) \qquad \text{Group terms.}$$

$$2y = 2 - (x^2 + 2x + 1) \qquad \text{Add and subtract 1 on right side.}$$

$$x^2 + 2x + 1 = -2y + 2$$

$$(x + 1)^2 = -2(y - 1) \qquad \text{Write in standard form.}$$

Comparing this equation with $(x - h)^2 = 4p(y - k)$, you can conclude that

$$h = -1, \quad k = 1, \quad \text{and} \quad p = -\frac{1}{2}.$$

Because p is negative, the parabola opens downward, as shown in Figure 9.4. So, the focus of the parabola is p units from the vertex, or

$$(h, k + p) = \left(-1, \frac{1}{2}\right). \qquad \text{Focus}$$

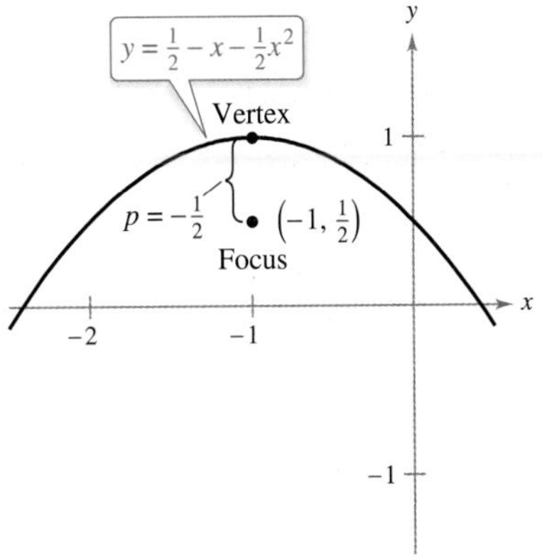

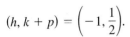

Parabola with a vertical axis, $p < 0$
Figure 9.4

A line segment that passes through the focus of a parabola and has endpoints on the parabola is called a **focal chord.** The specific focal chord perpendicular to the axis of the parabola is the **latus rectum.** The next example shows how to determine the length of the latus rectum and the length of the corresponding intercepted arc.

EXAMPLE 2   Focal Chord Length and Arc Length

See LarsonCalculusforAP.com for an interactive version of this type of example.

Find the length of the latus rectum of the parabola

$$x^2 = 4py.$$

Then find the length of the parabolic arc intercepted by the latus rectum.

Solution

Because the latus rectum passes through the focus $(0, p)$ and is perpendicular to the y-axis, the coordinates of its endpoints are

$$(-x, p) \quad \text{and} \quad (x, p).$$

Substituting p for y in the equation of the parabola produces

$$x^2 = 4p(p) \implies x = \pm 2p.$$

So, the endpoints of the latus rectum are $(-2p, p)$ and $(2p, p)$, and you can conclude that its length is $4p$, as shown in Figure 9.5. In contrast, the length of the intercepted arc is

$$
\begin{aligned}
s &= \int_{-2p}^{2p} \sqrt{1 + (y')^2}\, dx && \text{Use arc length formula.} \\
&= 2 \int_{0}^{2p} \sqrt{1 + \left(\frac{x}{2p}\right)^2}\, dx && y = \frac{x^2}{4p} \implies y' = \frac{x}{2p} \\
&= \frac{1}{p} \int_{0}^{2p} \sqrt{4p^2 + x^2}\, dx && \text{Simplify.} \\
&= \frac{1}{2p} \left[x\sqrt{4p^2 + x^2} + 4p^2 \ln\left|x + \sqrt{4p^2 + x^2}\right| \right]_{0}^{2p} && \text{Theorem 7.2} \\
&= \frac{1}{2p} \left[2p\sqrt{8p^2} + 4p^2 \ln\left(2p + \sqrt{8p^2}\right) - 4p^2 \ln(2p) \right] \\
&= 2p\left[\sqrt{2} + \ln\left(1 + \sqrt{2}\right) \right] \\
&\approx 4.59p.
\end{aligned}
$$

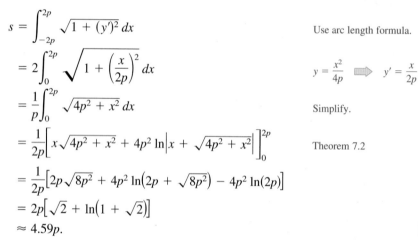

Length of latus rectum: $4p$
Figure 9.5

One widely used property of a parabola is its reflective property. In physics, a surface is called **reflective** when the tangent line at any point on the surface makes equal angles with an incoming ray and the resulting outgoing ray. The angle corresponding to the incoming ray is the **angle of incidence,** and the angle corresponding to the outgoing ray is the **angle of reflection.** One example of a reflective surface is a flat mirror.

Another type of reflective surface is that formed by revolving a parabola about its axis. The resulting surface has the property that all incoming rays parallel to the axis are directed through the focus of the parabola. This is the principle behind the design of the parabolic mirrors used in reflecting telescopes. Conversely, all light rays emanating from the focus of a parabolic reflector used in a flashlight are parallel, as shown in Figure 9.6.

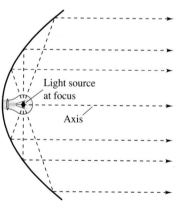

Parabolic reflector: Light is reflected in parallel rays.
Figure 9.6

Theorem 9.2   Reflective Property of a Parabola

Let P be a point on a parabola. The tangent line to the parabola at point P makes equal angles with the following two lines.

1. The line passing through P and the focus

2. The line passing through P parallel to the axis of the parabola

Ellipses

More than a thousand years after the close of the Alexandrian period of Greek mathematics, Western civilization finally began a Renaissance of mathematical and scientific discovery. One of the principal figures in this rebirth was the Polish astronomer Nicolaus Copernicus (1473–1543). In his work *On the Revolutions of the Heavenly Spheres*, Copernicus claimed that all of the planets, including Earth, revolved about the sun in circular orbits. Although some of Copernicus's claims were invalid, the controversy set off by his heliocentric theory motivated astronomers to search for a mathematical model to explain the observed movements of the sun and planets. The first to find an accurate model was the German astronomer Johannes Kepler (1571–1630). Kepler discovered that the planets move about the sun in elliptical orbits, with the sun not as the center but as a focal point of the orbit.

The use of ellipses to explain the movements of the planets is only one of many practical and aesthetic uses. As with parabolas, you will begin your study of this second type of conic by defining it as a locus of points. Now, however, *two* focal points are used rather than one.

An **ellipse** is the set of all points (x, y) the sum of whose distances from two distinct fixed points called **foci** is constant. (See Figure 9.7.) The line through the foci intersects the ellipse at two points, called the **vertices.** The chord joining the vertices is the **major axis,** and its midpoint is the **center** of the ellipse. The chord perpendicular to the major axis at the center is the **minor axis** of the ellipse. (See Figure 9.8.)

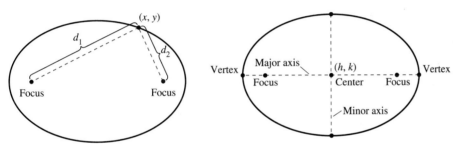

$d_1 + d_2$ is constant.
Figure 9.7

Figure 9.8

Theorem 9.3   Standard Equation of an Ellipse

The **standard form** of the equation of an ellipse with center (h, k) and major and minor axes of lengths $2a$ and $2b$, respectively, where $a > b$, is

$$\frac{(x - h)^2}{a^2} + \frac{(y - k)^2}{b^2} = 1 \qquad \text{Major axis is horizontal.}$$

or

$$\frac{(x - h)^2}{b^2} + \frac{(y - k)^2}{a^2} = 1. \qquad \text{Major axis is vertical.}$$

The foci lie on the major axis, c units from the center, with

$$c^2 = a^2 - b^2.$$

You can visualize the definition of an ellipse by imagining two thumbtacks placed at the foci, as shown in Figure 9.9. If the ends of a fixed length of string are fastened to the thumbtacks and the string is drawn taut with a pencil, then the path traced by the pencil will be an ellipse.

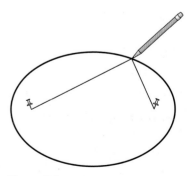

Figure 9.9

EXAMPLE 3 Analyzing an Ellipse

Find the center, vertices, and foci of the ellipse

$$4x^2 + y^2 - 8x + 4y - 8 = 0. \qquad \text{General second-degree equation}$$

Solution

Complete the square to write the original equation in standard form.

$$4x^2 + y^2 - 8x + 4y - 8 = 0 \qquad \text{Write original equation.}$$

$$4x^2 - 8x + y^2 + 4y = 8$$

$$4(x^2 - 2x + 1) + (y^2 + 4y + 4) = 8 + 4 + 4$$

$$4(x - 1)^2 + (y + 2)^2 = 16$$

$$\frac{(x - 1)^2}{4} + \frac{(y + 2)^2}{16} = 1 \qquad \text{Write in standard form.}$$

So, the major axis is parallel to the y-axis, where $h = 1$, $k = -2$, $a = 4$, $b = 2$, and $c = \sqrt{16 - 4} = 2\sqrt{3}$. So, you obtain the following.

Center: $(1, -2)$ $\qquad\qquad (h, k)$

Vertices: $(1, -6)$ and $(1, 2)$ $\qquad (h, k \pm a)$

Foci: $\left(1, -2 - 2\sqrt{3}\right)$ and $\left(1, -2 + 2\sqrt{3}\right)$ $\qquad (h, k \pm c)$

The graph of the ellipse is shown in Figure 9.10.

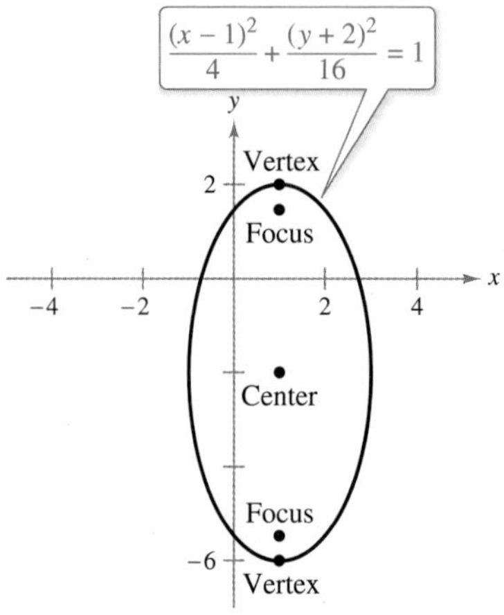

Ellipse with a vertical major axis
Figure 9.10

In Example 3, the constant term in the general second-degree equation is $F = -8$. For a constant term greater than or equal to 8, you would obtain one of the degenerate cases listed below.

1. $F = 8$, single point, $(1, -2)$: $\dfrac{(x - 1)^2}{4} + \dfrac{(y + 2)^2}{16} = 0$

2. $F > 8$, no solution points: $\dfrac{(x - 1)^2}{4} + \dfrac{(y + 2)^2}{16} < 0$

EXAMPLE 4 The Orbit of the Moon

The moon orbits Earth in an elliptical path with the center of Earth at one focus, as shown in Figure 9.11. The major and minor axes of the orbit have lengths of 768,800 kilometers and 767,641 kilometers, respectively. Find the greatest and least distances (the apogee and perigee) from Earth's center to the moon's center.

Solution

Begin by solving for a and b.

$$2a = 768,800 \qquad\qquad \text{Length of major axis}$$

$$a = 384,400 \qquad\qquad \text{Solve for } a.$$

$$2b = 767,641 \qquad\qquad \text{Length of minor axis}$$

$$b = 383,820.5 \qquad\qquad \text{Solve for } b.$$

Now, using these values, you can solve for c as follows.

$$c = \sqrt{a^2 - b^2} \approx 21,099$$

The greatest distance between the center of Earth and the center of the moon is

$$a + c \approx 405,499 \text{ kilometers}$$

and the least distance is

$$a - c \approx 363,301 \text{ kilometers}.$$

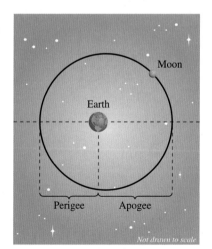

Figure 9.11

Theorem 9.2 presented a reflective property of parabolas. Ellipses have a similar reflective property. You are asked to prove the next theorem in Exercise 76.

Theorem 9.4   Reflective Property of an Ellipse

Let P be a point on an ellipse. The tangent line to the ellipse at point P makes equal angles with the lines through P and the foci.

One of the reasons that astronomers had difficulty detecting that the orbits of the planets are ellipses is that the foci of the planetary orbits are relatively close to the center of the sun, making the orbits nearly circular. To measure the ovalness of an ellipse, you can use the concept of **eccentricity.**

Definition of Eccentricity of an Ellipse

The **eccentricity** e of an ellipse is given by the ratio $e = \dfrac{c}{a}$.

To see how this ratio is used to describe the shape of an ellipse, note that because the foci of an ellipse are located along the major axis between the vertices and the center, it follows that $0 < c < a$. For an ellipse that is nearly circular, the foci are close to the center and the ratio c/a is close to 0, and for an elongated ellipse, the foci are close to the vertices and the ratio c/a is close to 1, as shown in Figure 9.12. Note that

$0 < e < 1$ The eccentricity e of an ellipse is between 0 and 1.

for every ellipse.

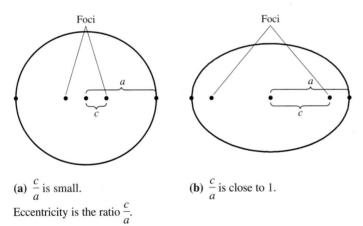

(a) $\dfrac{c}{a}$ is small.   **(b)** $\dfrac{c}{a}$ is close to 1.

Eccentricity is the ratio $\dfrac{c}{a}$.

Figure 9.12

The orbit of the moon has an eccentricity of $e \approx 0.0549$, and the eccentricities of the eight planetary orbits are listed below.

Mercury: $e \approx 0.2056$	Jupiter: $e \approx 0.0489$
Venus: $e \approx 0.0067$	Saturn: $e \approx 0.0565$
Earth: $e \approx 0.0167$	Uranus: $e \approx 0.0457$
Mars: $e \approx 0.0935$	Neptune: $e \approx 0.0113$

Recall from Section 7.4, Example 7, that you used integration to show that the area of an ellipse is $A = \pi ab$. It is not so simple, however, to find the *circumference* of an ellipse. The next example shows how to use eccentricity to set up an "elliptic integral" for the circumference of an ellipse.

EXAMPLE 5   Finding the Circumference of an Ellipse

See LarsonCalculusforAP.com for an interactive version of this type of example.

Show that the circumference of the ellipse $(x^2/a^2) + (y^2/b^2) = 1$ is

$$4a \int_0^{\pi/2} \sqrt{1 - e^2 \sin^2 \theta} \, d\theta. \qquad e = \frac{c}{a}$$

Solution

Because the ellipse is symmetric with respect to both the *x*-axis and the *y*-axis, you know that its circumference *C* is four times the arc length of

$$y = \frac{b}{a} \sqrt{a^2 - x^2}$$

in the first quadrant. The function *y* is differentiable for all *x* in the interval $[0, a]$ except at $x = a$. So, the circumference is given by the improper integral

$$C = \lim_{d \to a^-} 4 \int_0^d \sqrt{1 + (y')^2} \, dx = 4 \int_0^a \sqrt{1 + (y')^2} \, dx = 4 \int_0^a \sqrt{1 + \frac{b^2 x^2}{a^2(a^2 - x^2)}} \, dx.$$

Using the trigonometric substitution $x = a \sin \theta$, you obtain

$$C = 4 \int_0^{\pi/2} \sqrt{1 + \frac{b^2 \sin^2 \theta}{a^2 \cos^2 \theta}} (a \cos \theta) \, d\theta$$

$$= 4 \int_0^{\pi/2} \sqrt{a^2 \cos^2 \theta + b^2 \sin^2 \theta} \, d\theta$$

$$= 4 \int_0^{\pi/2} \sqrt{a^2(1 - \sin^2 \theta) + b^2 \sin^2 \theta} \, d\theta$$

$$= 4 \int_0^{\pi/2} \sqrt{a^2 - (a^2 - b^2)\sin^2 \theta} \, d\theta.$$

Because $e^2 = c^2/a^2 = (a^2 - b^2)/a^2$, you can rewrite this integral as

$$C = 4a \int_0^{\pi/2} \sqrt{1 - e^2 \sin^2 \theta} \, d\theta.$$

> **Algebra Review**
>
> For help on the algebra in Example 5, see Example 1 in the *Chapter 9 Algebra Review* on page A52.

A great deal of time has been devoted to the study of elliptic integrals. Such integrals generally do not have elementary antiderivatives. To find the circumference of an ellipse, you must usually resort to an approximation technique.

EXAMPLE 6   Approximating the Value of an Elliptical Integral

Use the elliptic integral in Example 5 to approximate the circumference of the ellipse

$$\frac{x^2}{25} + \frac{y^2}{16} = 1.$$

Solution

Because $e^2 = c^2/a^2 = (a^2 - b^2)/a^2 = 9/25$, you have

$$C = (4)(5) \int_0^{\pi/2} \sqrt{1 - \frac{9 \sin^2 \theta}{25}} \, d\theta.$$

Applying the Trapezoidal Rule with $n = 4$ produces

$$C \approx 20 \left(\frac{\pi}{16}\right) [1 + 2(0.9733) + 2(0.9055) + 2(0.8323) + 0.8] \approx 28.36.$$

So, the ellipse has a circumference of about 28.36 units, as shown in Figure 9.13.

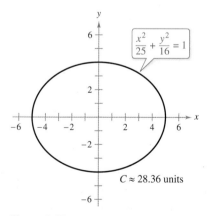

$C \approx 28.36$ units

Figure 9.13

Hyperbolas

The definition of a hyperbola is similar to that of an ellipse. For an ellipse, the *sum* of the distances between the foci and a point on the ellipse is fixed, whereas for a hyperbola, the absolute value of the *difference* between these distances is fixed.

A **hyperbola** is the set of all points (x, y) for which the absolute value of the difference between the distances from two distinct fixed points called **foci** is constant. (See Figure 9.14.) The line through the two foci intersects a hyperbola at two points called the **vertices.** The line segment connecting the vertices is the **transverse axis,** and the midpoint of the transverse axis is the **center** of the hyperbola. One distinguishing feature of a hyperbola is that its graph has two separate *branches*.

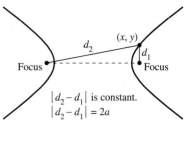

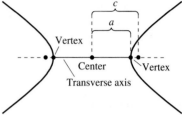

Figure 9.14

Theorem 9.5 Standard Equation of a Hyperbola

The **standard form** of the equation of a hyperbola with center at (h, k) is

$$\frac{(x - h)^2}{a^2} - \frac{(y - k)^2}{b^2} = 1 \qquad \text{Transverse axis is horizontal.}$$

or

$$\frac{(y - k)^2}{a^2} - \frac{(x - h)^2}{b^2} = 1. \qquad \text{Transverse axis is vertical.}$$

The vertices are a units from the center, and the foci are c units from the center, where $c^2 = a^2 + b^2$.

Note that the constants a, b, and c do not have the same relationship for hyperbolas as they do for ellipses. For hyperbolas, $c^2 = a^2 + b^2$, but for ellipses, $c^2 = a^2 - b^2$.

An important aid in sketching the graph of a hyperbola is the determination of its **asymptotes,** as shown in Figure 9.15. Each hyperbola has two asymptotes that intersect at the center of the hyperbola. The asymptotes pass through the vertices of a rectangle of dimensions $2a$ by $2b$ with its center at (h, k). The line segment of length $2b$ joining

$$(h, k + b)$$

and

$$(h, k - b)$$

is referred to as the **conjugate axis** of the hyperbola.

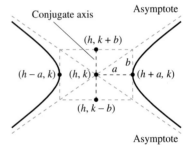

Figure 9.15

Theorem 9.6 Asymptotes of a Hyperbola

For a *horizontal* transverse axis, the equations of the asymptotes are

$$y = k + \frac{b}{a}(x - h) \quad \text{and} \quad y = k - \frac{b}{a}(x - h).$$

For a *vertical* transverse axis, the equations of the asymptotes are

$$y = k + \frac{a}{b}(x - h) \quad \text{and} \quad y = k - \frac{a}{b}(x - h).$$

In Figure 9.15, you can see that the asymptotes coincide with the diagonals of the rectangle with dimensions $2a$ and $2b$, centered at (h, k). This provides you with a quick means of sketching the asymptotes, which in turn aids in sketching the hyperbola.

EXAMPLE 7 Using Asymptotes to Sketch a Hyperbola

See LarsonCalculusforAP.com for an interactive version of this type of example.

Sketch the graph of the hyperbola

$$4x^2 - y^2 = 16.$$

Solution

Begin by rewriting the equation in standard form.

$$\frac{x^2}{4} - \frac{y^2}{16} = 1$$

The transverse axis is horizontal and the vertices occur at $(-2, 0)$ and $(2, 0)$. The ends of the conjugate axis occur at $(0, -4)$ and $(0, 4)$. Using these four points, you can sketch the rectangle shown in Figure 9.16(a). By drawing the asymptotes through the corners of this rectangle, you can complete the sketch as shown in Figure 9.16(b).

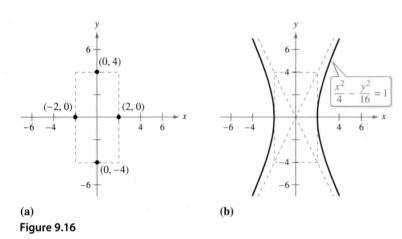

(a)   **(b)**

Figure 9.16

Technology

You can use a graphing utility to verify the graph obtained in Example 7 by solving the original equation for y and graphing the following equations.

$$y_1 = \sqrt{4x^2 - 16}$$
$$y_2 = -\sqrt{4x^2 - 16}$$

Definition of Eccentricity of a Hyperbola

The **eccentricity** e of a hyperbola is given by the ratio

$$e = \frac{c}{a}.$$

As with an ellipse, the **eccentricity** of a hyperbola is $e = c/a$. Because $c > a$ for hyperbolas, it follows that $e > 1$ for hyperbolas. If the eccentricity is large, then the branches of the hyperbola are nearly flat. If the eccentricity is close to 1, then the branches of the hyperbola are more pointed, as shown in Figure 9.17.

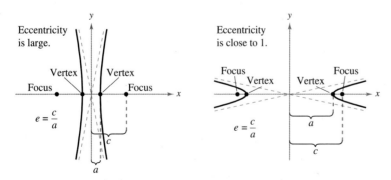

Figure 9.17

The application in Example 8 was developed during World War II. It shows how the properties of hyperbolas can be used in radar and other detection systems.

EXAMPLE 8   A Hyperbolic Detection System

Two microphones, 1 mile apart, record an explosion. Microphone A receives the sound 2 seconds before microphone B. Where was the explosion?

Solution

Assuming that sound travels at 1100 feet per second, you know that the explosion took place 2200 feet farther from B than from A, as shown in Figure 9.18. The locus of all points that are 2200 feet closer to A than to B is one branch of the hyperbola

$$\frac{x^2}{a^2} - \frac{y^2}{b^2} = 1$$

where

$$c = \frac{1 \text{ mile}}{2} = \frac{5280 \text{ feet}}{2} = 2640 \text{ feet}$$

and

$$a = \frac{2200 \text{ feet}}{2} = 1100 \text{ feet}.$$

Because $c^2 = a^2 + b^2$, it follows that

$$b^2 = c^2 - a^2$$
$$= (2640)^2 - (1100)^2$$
$$= 5,759,600$$

and you can conclude that the explosion occurred somewhere on the right branch of the hyperbola

$$\frac{x^2}{1,210,000} - \frac{y^2}{5,759,600} = 1.$$ ■

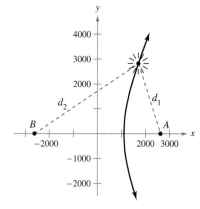

$2c = 5280$
$d_2 - d_1 = 2a = 2200$
Figure 9.18

In Example 8, you were able to determine only the hyperbola on which the explosion occurred, but not the exact location of the explosion. If, however, you had received the sound at a third position C, then two other hyperbolas would be determined. The exact location of the explosion would be the point at which these three hyperbolas intersect.

Another interesting application of conics involves the orbits of comets in our solar system. Comets can have elliptical, parabolic, or hyperbolic orbits. The center of the sun is a focus of each orbit, and each orbit has a vertex at the point at which the comet is closest to the sun, as shown in Figure 9.19. Undoubtedly, many comets with parabolic or hyperbolic orbits have not been identified—such comets pass through our solar system only once. Only comets with elliptical orbits, such as Halley's comet, remain in our solar system.

The type of orbit for a comet can be determined as follows.

1. Ellipse: $v < \sqrt{2GM/p}$
2. Parabola: $v = \sqrt{2GM/p}$
3. Hyperbola: $v > \sqrt{2GM/p}$

In each of the above, p is the distance between one vertex and one focus of the comet's orbit (in meters), v is the velocity of the comet at the vertex (in meters per second), $M \approx 1.989 \times 10^{30}$ kilograms is the mass of the sun, and $G \approx 6.67 \times 10^{-11}$ cubic meter per kilogram-second squared is the gravitational constant.

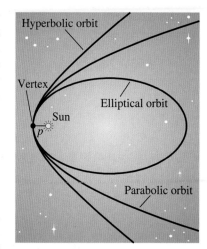

Figure 9.19

Matching In Exercises 1–4, match the equation with its graph. [The graphs are labeled (a), (b), (c), and (d).]

(a)

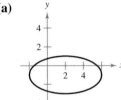

(b)

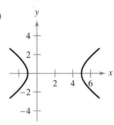

(c)

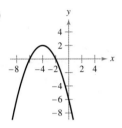

(d)

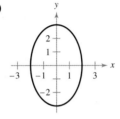

1. $(x + 4)^2 = -2(y - 2)$ **2.** $\dfrac{(x - 2)^2}{16} + \dfrac{(y + 1)^2}{4} = 1$

3. $\dfrac{x^2}{4} + \dfrac{y^2}{9} = 1$ **4.** $\dfrac{(x - 2)^2}{9} - \dfrac{y^2}{4} = 1$

 Sketching a Parabola In Exercises 5–10, find the vertex, focus, and directrix of the parabola, and sketch its graph.

5. $y^2 = -8x$ **6.** $x^2 + 6y = 0$

7. $(x + 5) + (y - 3)^2 = 0$

8. $(x - 6)^2 - 2(y + 7) = 0$

9. $x^2 + 4x + 4y - 4 = 0$ **10.** $x^2 - 2x - 4y - 7 = 0$

 Finding the Standard Equation of a Parabola In Exercises 11–18, find the standard form of the equation of the parabola.

11. Vertex: $(5, 4)$ **12.** Vertex: $(-3, -1)$
Focus: $(3, 4)$ Focus: $(-3, 1)$

13. Vertex: $(0, 5)$ **14.** Focus: $(2, 2)$
Directrix: $y = -3$ Directrix: $x = -2$

15. Vertex: $(0, 4)$ **16.** Vertex: $(2, 4)$
Points on the parabola: Points on the parabola:
$(-2, 0), (2, 0)$ $(0, 0), (4, 0)$

17. Axis is parallel to y-axis; graph passes through $(0, 3)$, $(3, 4)$, and $(4, 11)$.

18. Directrix: $y = -2$; endpoints of latus rectum are $(0, 2)$ and $(8, 2)$.

Finding Arc Length In Exercises 19–22, find the length of the arc of the parabola between the two points.

19. $x^2 = 4y$; $(-2, 1), (2, 1)$ **20.** $x^2 = 8y$; $(-4, 2), (4, 2)$

21. $x^2 = 2y$; $(0, 0), (4, 8)$ **22.** $x^2 = y$; $(-1, 1), (3, 9)$

 Sketching an Ellipse In Exercises 23–28, find the center, foci, vertices, and eccentricity of the ellipse, and sketch its graph.

23. $16x^2 + y^2 = 16$ **24.** $3x^2 + 7y^2 = 63$

25. $\dfrac{(x - 3)^2}{16} + \dfrac{(y - 1)^2}{25} = 1$

26. $(x + 4)^2 + \dfrac{(y + 6)^2}{1/4} = 1$

27. $9x^2 + 4y^2 + 36x - 24y + 36 = 0$

28. $x^2 + 10y^2 - 6x + 20y + 18 = 0$

 Finding the Standard Equation of an Ellipse In Exercises 29–34, find the standard form of the equation of the ellipse.

29. Center: $(0, 0)$ **30.** Vertices: $(0, 3), (8, 3)$
Focus: $(5, 0)$ Eccentricity: $\frac{3}{4}$
Vertex: $(6, 0)$

31. Vertices: $(3, 1), (3, 9)$ **32.** Foci: $(0, \pm 9)$
Minor axis length: 6   Major axis length: 22

33. Center: $(0, 0)$
Major axis: horizontal
Points on the ellipse: $(3, 1), (4, 0)$

34. Center: $(1, 2)$
Major axis: vertical
Points on the ellipse: $(1, 6), (3, 2)$

35. **Error Analysis** Describe and correct the error in writing the equation of the ellipse $3(x - 2)^2 + (y + 1)^2 = 9$ in standard form.

$$\frac{3(x - 2)^2 + (y + 1)^2}{3} = \frac{9}{3}$$

$$(x - 2)^2 + \frac{(y + 1)^2}{3} = 3 \quad ✗$$

36. **Error Analysis** Describe and correct the error in finding the focus of the parabola given by $x^2 = -12y$.

$$x^2 = -12y = -4(3)y$$

So, $h = 0$, $k = 0$, and $p = 3$. The focus is $(0, 3)$. ✗

 Finding Circumference In Exercises 37 and 38, use the elliptic integral in Example 5 to approximate the circumference of the ellipse using (a) the Trapezoidal Rule with $n = 4$ and (b) the integration capabilities of a graphing utility.

37. $\dfrac{x^2}{9} + \dfrac{y^2}{4} = 1$ **38.** $\dfrac{x^2}{36} + \dfrac{y^2}{9} = 1$

Sketching a Hyperbola **In Exercises 39–44, find the center, foci, vertices, and eccentricity of the hyperbola, and sketch its graph using asymptotes as an aid.**

39. $\dfrac{x^2}{25} - \dfrac{y^2}{16} = 1$

40. $\dfrac{(y+3)^2}{225} - \dfrac{(x-5)^2}{64} = 1$

41. $9x^2 - y^2 - 36x - 6y + 18 = 0$

42. $y^2 - 16x^2 + 64x - 208 = 0$

43. $4x^2 - 3y^2 + 8x + 6y - 11 = 0$

44. $9x^2 - 4y^2 + 54x + 8y + 78 = 0$

Finding the Standard Equation of a Hyperbola **In Exercises 45–52, find the standard form of the equation of the hyperbola.**

45. Vertices: $(\pm 1, 0)$
Asymptotes: $y = \pm 5x$

46. Vertices: $(0, \pm 4)$
Asymptotes: $y = \pm 2x$

47. Vertices: $(2, \pm 3)$
Point on graph: $(0, 5)$

48. Vertices: $(2, \pm 3)$
Foci: $(2, \pm 5)$

49. Center: $(0, 0)$
Vertex: $(0, 2)$
Focus: $(0, 4)$

50. Center: $(0, 0)$
Vertex: $(6, 0)$
Focus: $(10, 0)$

51. Vertices: $(0, 2), (6, 2)$
Asymptotes: $y = \frac{2}{3}x$
$y = 4 - \frac{2}{3}x$

52. Focus: $(20, 0)$
Asymptotes: $y = \pm \frac{3}{4}x$

Finding Equations of Tangent Lines and Normal Lines **In Exercises 53 and 54, find equations for (a) the tangent lines and (b) the normal lines to the hyperbola for the given value of x. (The *normal line* at a point is perpendicular to the tangent line at the point.)**

53. $\dfrac{x^2}{9} - y^2 = 1$, $x = 6$

54. $\dfrac{y^2}{4} - \dfrac{x^2}{2} = 1$, $x = 4$

Classifying the Graph of an Equation **In Exercises 55–62, classify the graph of the equation as a circle, a parabola, an ellipse, or a hyperbola.**

55. $x^2 + 4y^2 - 6x + 16y + 21 = 0$

56. $4x^2 - y^2 - 4x - 3 = 0$

57. $25x^2 - 10x - 200y - 119 = 0$

58. $y^2 - 4y = x + 5$

59. $9x^2 + 9y^2 - 36x + 6y + 34 = 0$

60. $2x(x - y) = y(3 - y - 2x)$

61. $3(x - 1)^2 = 6 + 2(y + 1)^2$

62. $9(x + 3)^2 = 36 - 4(y - 2)^2$

63. Solar Collector A solar collector for heating water is constructed with a sheet of stainless steel that is formed into the shape of a parabola (see figure). The water will flow through a pipe that is located at the focus of the parabola. At what distance from the vertex is the pipe?

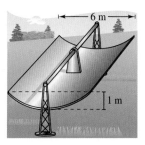
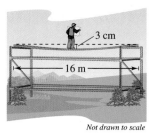

Not drawn to scale

Figure for 63   Figure for 64

64. Beam Deflection A simply supported beam that is 16 meters long has a load concentrated at the center (see figure). The deflection of the beam at its center is 3 centimeters. Assume that the shape of the deflected beam is parabolic. (a) Find an equation of the parabola. (Assume that the origin is at the center of the beam.) (b) How far from the center of the beam is the deflection 1 centimeter?

65. Proof

(a) Prove that any two distinct tangent lines to a parabola intersect.

(b) Demonstrate the result of part (a) by finding the point of intersection of the tangent lines to the parabola $x^2 - 4x - 4y = 0$ at the points $(0, 0)$ and $(6, 3)$.

66. Proof

(a) Prove that if any two tangent lines to a parabola intersect at right angles, then their point of intersection must lie on the directrix.

(b) Demonstrate the result of part (a) by showing that the tangent lines to the parabola $x^2 - 4x - 4y + 8 = 0$ at the points $(-2, 5)$ and $\left(3, \frac{5}{4}\right)$ intersect at right angles, and that their point of intersection lies on the directrix.

67. ARCHITECTURE

A church window is bounded above by a parabola and below by the arc of a circle (see figure). Find the surface area of the window.

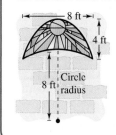

68. Bridge Design A cable of a suspension bridge is suspended (in the shape of a parabola) between two towers that are 120 meters apart and 20 meters above the roadway (see figure). The cable touches the roadway midway between the towers. Find an equation for the shape of the cable. Then find the length of the cable.

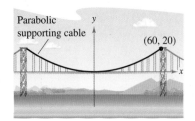

69. Orbit of Earth Earth moves in an elliptical orbit with the sun at one of the foci. The length of half of the major axis is 149,600,000 kilometers, and the eccentricity is 0.0167. Find the minimum distance (*perihelion*) and the maximum distance (*aphelion*) of Earth from the sun.

70. HALLEY'S COMET

Halley's comet has an elliptical orbit with the sun at one focus. Its maximum distance from the sun is approximately 35.25 AU (1 astronomical unit is approximately 92.956×10^6 miles), and its minimum distance is approximately 0.59 AU. Find the eccentricity of the orbit.

71. Satellite Orbit The *apogee* (the point in orbit farthest from Earth) and the *perigee* (the point in orbit closest to Earth) of an elliptical orbit of an Earth satellite are given by A and P. Show that the eccentricity of the orbit is

$$e = \frac{A - P}{A + P}.$$

72. Explorer 1 On January 31, 1958, the United States launched the research satellite Explorer 1. Its low and high points above the surface of Earth were 220 miles and 1563 miles. Find the eccentricity of its elliptical orbit. (Use 3960 miles as the radius of Earth.)

Area, Volume, and Surface Area In Exercises 73 and 74, (a) find the area of the region bounded by the ellipse. Then find the volume and surface area of (b) the prolate spheroid generated by revolving the region about its major axis and (c) the oblate spheroid generated by revolving the region about its minor axis.

73. $\dfrac{x^2}{4} + \dfrac{y^2}{1} = 1$ **74.** $\dfrac{x^2}{16} + \dfrac{y^2}{9} = 1$

75. Geometry The area of the ellipse in the figure is twice the area of the circle. What is the length of the major axis?

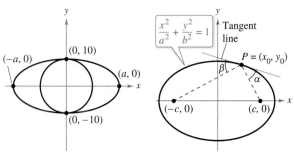

Figure for 75   Figure for 76

76. Proof Prove Theorem 9.4 by showing that the tangent line to an ellipse at a point P makes equal angles with lines through P and the foci (see figure). [*Hint:* (1) Find the slope of the tangent line at P, (2) find the slopes of the lines through P and each focus, and (3) use the formula for the tangent of the angle between two lines, which is $\tan \theta = |(m_1 - m_2)/(1 + m_1 m_2)|$, where θ is the angle between the two lines, and m_1 and m_2 are the slopes of two lines.]

77. Navigation LORAN (long distance radio navigation) for aircraft and ships uses synchronized pulses transmitted by widely separated transmitting stations. These pulses travel at the speed of light (186,000 miles per second). The difference in the times of arrival of these pulses at an aircraft or ship is constant on a hyperbola having the transmitting stations as foci. Assume that two stations, 300 miles apart, are positioned on a rectangular coordinate system at $(-150, 0)$ and $(150, 0)$ and that a ship is traveling on a path with coordinates $(x, 75)$. (See figure.) Find the x-coordinate of the position of the ship if the time difference between the pulses from the transmitting stations is 1000 microseconds (0.001 second).

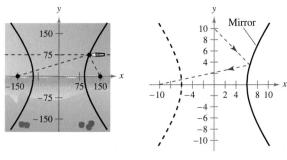

Figure for 77   Figure for 78

78. Hyperbolic Mirror A hyperbolic mirror (used in some telescopes) has the property that a light ray directed at the focus will be reflected to the other focus. The mirror in the figure has the equation $(x^2/36) - (y^2/64) = 1$. At which point on the mirror will light from the point $(0, 10)$ be reflected to the other focus?

EXPLORING CONCEPTS

79. Connecting Representations Sketch the graphs of $x^2 = 4py$ for $p = \frac{1}{4}, \frac{1}{2}, 1, \frac{3}{2}$, and 2 on the same coordinate axes. Discuss the change in the graphs as p increases.

80. Justifying

(a) Show that the equation of an ellipse can be written as

$$\frac{(x-h)^2}{a^2} + \frac{(y-k)^2}{a^2(1-e^2)} = 1.$$

(b) Use a graphing utility to graph the ellipse

$$\frac{(x-2)^2}{4} + \frac{(y-3)^2}{4(1-e^2)} = 1$$

for $e = 0.95$, $e = 0.75$, $e = 0.5$, and $e = 0.25$.

(c) Use the results of part (b) to make a conjecture about the change in the shape of the ellipse as e approaches 0.

81. Justifying Let C be the circumference of the ellipse

$$\frac{x^2}{a^2} + \frac{y^2}{b^2} = 1, \quad b < a.$$

Explain why $2\pi b < C < 2\pi a$. Use a graph to support your explanation.

82. Justifying Consider a hyperbola centered at the origin with a horizontal transverse axis. Use the definition of a hyperbola to derive its standard form

$$\frac{x^2}{a^2} - \frac{y^2}{b^2} = 1.$$

83. Connecting Representations Consider the equation $9x^2 + 4y^2 - 36x - 24y - 36 = 0$.

(a) Classify the graph of the equation as a circle, a parabola, an ellipse, or a hyperbola.

(b) Change the $4y^2$-term in the equation to $-4y^2$. Classify the graph of the new equation.

(c) Describe one way you could change the original equation so that its graph is a parabola.

---

84. HOW DO YOU SEE IT? In parts (a)–(d), describe in words how a plane could intersect with the double-napped cone to form the conic section (see figure).

(a) Circle

(b) Ellipse

(c) Parabola

(d) Hyperbola

True or False? In Exercises 85–90, determine whether the statement is true or false. If it is false, explain why or give an example that shows it is false.

85. It is possible for a parabola to intersect its directrix.

86. The point on a parabola closest to its focus is its vertex.

87. If C is the circumference of the ellipse

$$\frac{x^2}{a^2} + \frac{y^2}{b^2} = 1, \quad b < a$$

then $2\pi b \le C \le 2\pi a$.

88. If $D \ne 0$ or $E \ne 0$, then the graph of $y^2 - x^2 + Dx + Ey = 0$ is a hyperbola.

89. If the asymptotes of the hyperbola $(x^2/a^2) - (y^2/b^2) = 1$ intersect at right angles, then $a = b$.

90. Every tangent line to a hyperbola intersects the hyperbola only at the point of tangency.

91. Finding an Equation of a Hyperbola Find an equation of the hyperbola such that for any point on the hyperbola, the difference between its distances from the points $(2, 2)$ and $(10, 2)$ is 6.

92. Particle Motion Consider a particle traveling clockwise on the elliptical path

$$\frac{x^2}{100} + \frac{y^2}{25} = 1.$$

The particle leaves the orbit at the point $(-8, 3)$ and travels in a straight line tangent to the ellipse. At what point will the particle cross the y-axis?

93. Proof Prove that the graph of the equation

$$Ax^2 + Cy^2 + Dx + Ey + F = 0$$

is one of the following (except in degenerate cases).

Conic	Condition
(a) Circle	$A = C$
(b) Parabola	$A = 0$ or $C = 0$ (but not both)
(c) Ellipse	$AC > 0$
(d) Hyperbola	$AC < 0$

Calculus AP® – Exam Preparation Questions

94. Multiple Choice What is the slope of the line tangent to $(x^2/4) - (y^2/12) = 1$ at $(4, 6)$?

(A) -2 (B) $-\frac{1}{2}$ (C) $\frac{1}{2}$ (D) 2

95. Multiple Choice Which of the following integrals gives the length of the graph $x^2 = 20y$ between $x = a$ and $x = b$ where $0 < a < b$?

(A) $\displaystyle\int_a^b \sqrt{1 + \frac{1}{100}x^2}\, dx$ (B) $\displaystyle\int_a^b \sqrt{1 + 4x^2}\, dx$

(C) $\displaystyle\int_a^b \sqrt{1 + \frac{1}{10}x}\, dx$ (D) $\displaystyle\int_a^b \sqrt{1 + \frac{1}{10}x^2}\, dx$

9.2 Plane Curves and Parametric Equations

▶ Sketch the graph of a curve given by a set of parametric equations.
▶ Eliminate the parameter in a set of parametric equations.
▶ Find a set of parametric equations to represent a curve.

Plane Curves and Parametric Equations

Until now, you have been representing a graph by a single equation involving *two* variables. In this section, you will study situations in which *three* variables are used to represent a curve in the plane.

Consider the path followed by an object that is propelled into the air at an angle of 45°. For an initial velocity of 48 feet per second, the object travels the parabolic path given by

$$y = -\frac{x^2}{72} + x \qquad \text{Rectangular equation}$$

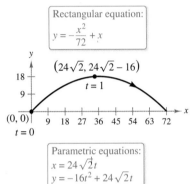

Rectangular equation:
$$y = -\frac{x^2}{72} + x$$

$(24\sqrt{2}, 24\sqrt{2} - 16)$

$t = 1$

$(0, 0)$
$t = 0$

Parametric equations:
$x = 24\sqrt{2}t$
$y = -16t^2 + 24\sqrt{2}t$

Curvilinear motion: two variables for position, one variable for time

as shown in the figure. This equation, however, does not tell the whole story. Although it does tell you *where* the object has been, it does not tell you *when* the object was at a given point (x, y). To determine this time, you can introduce a third variable t, called a **parameter.** By writing both x and y as functions of t, you obtain the **parametric equations**

$$x = 24\sqrt{2}t \qquad \text{Parametric equation for } x$$

and

$$y = -16t^2 + 24\sqrt{2}t. \qquad \text{Parametric equation for } y$$

From this set of equations, you can determine that at time $t = 0$, the object is at the point $(0, 0)$. Similarly, at time $t = 1$, the object is at the point $(24\sqrt{2}, 24\sqrt{2} - 16)$, and so on.

For this particular motion problem, x and y are continuous functions of t, and the resulting path is called a **plane curve.**

Definition of a Plane Curve

If f and g are continuous functions of t on an interval I, then the equations

$$x = f(t) \quad \text{and} \quad y = g(t)$$

are **parametric equations** and t is the **parameter.** The set of points (x, y) obtained as t varies over the interval I is the **graph** of the parametric equations. Taken together, the parametric equations and the graph are a **plane curve,** denoted by C.

▶ **Communication and Notation**   At times, it is important to distinguish between a graph (the set of points) and a curve (the points together with their defining parametric equations). When it is important, the distinction will be explicit. When it is not important, C will be used to represent either the graph or the curve.

When sketching a curve represented by a set of parametric equations, you can plot points in the xy-plane. Each set of coordinates (x, y) is determined from a value chosen for the parameter t. By plotting the resulting points in order of increasing values of t, the curve is traced out in a specific direction. This is called the **orientation** of the curve.

EXAMPLE 1   Sketching a Curve

Sketch the curve described by the parametric equations

$$x = f(t) = t^2 - 4$$

and

$$y = g(t) = \frac{t}{2}$$

where $-2 \le t \le 3$.

Solution

For values of t on the given interval, the parametric equations yield the points (x, y) shown in the table.

t	-2	-1	0	1	2	3
x	0	-3	-4	-3	0	5
y	-1	$-\frac{1}{2}$	0	$\frac{1}{2}$	1	$\frac{3}{2}$

By plotting these points in order of increasing values of t and using the continuity of f and g, you obtain the curve C shown in Figure 9.20. Note that the arrows on the curve indicate its orientation as t increases from -2 to 3.

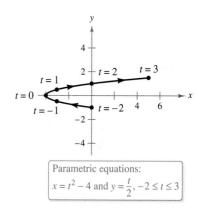

Parametric equations:
$x = t^2 - 4$ and $y = \frac{t}{2}$, $-2 \le t \le 3$

Figure 9.20

According to the Vertical Line Test, the graph shown in Figure 9.20 does not define y as a function of x. This points out one benefit of parametric equations—they can be used to represent graphs that are more general than graphs of functions.

It often happens that two different sets of parametric equations have the same graph. For instance, the set of parametric equations

$$x = 4t^2 - 4 \quad \text{and} \quad y = t, \quad -1 \le t \le \frac{3}{2}$$

has the same graph as the set given in Example 1. (See Figure 9.21.) However, comparing the values of t in Figures 9.20 and 9.21, you can see that the second graph is traced out more *rapidly* (considering t as time) than the first graph. So, in applications, different parametric representations can be used to represent various *speeds* at which objects travel along a given path.

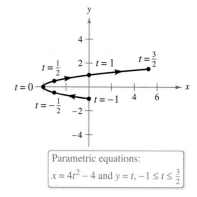

Parametric equations:
$x = 4t^2 - 4$ and $y = t$, $-1 \le t \le \frac{3}{2}$

Figure 9.21

Technology

Most graphing utilities have a *parametric* graphing mode. If you have access to such a utility, use it to confirm the graphs shown in Figures 9.20 and 9.21. Does the curve given by the parametric equations

$$x = 4t^2 - 8t \quad \text{and} \quad y = 1 - t, \quad -\frac{1}{2} \le t \le 2$$

represent the same graph as that shown in Figures 9.20 and 9.21? What do you notice about the *orientation* of this curve?

Eliminating the Parameter

Finding a rectangular equation that represents the graph of a set of parametric equations is called **eliminating the parameter.** For instance, you can eliminate the parameter from the set of parametric equations in Example 1 as follows.

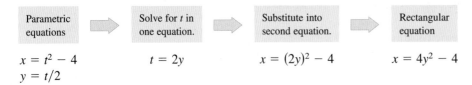

Parametric equations	$\Rightarrow$	Solve for t in one equation.	$\Rightarrow$	Substitute into second equation.	$\Rightarrow$	Rectangular equation
$x = t^2 - 4$		$t = 2y$		$x = (2y)^2 - 4$		$x = 4y^2 - 4$
$y = t/2$						

Once you have eliminated the parameter, you can recognize that the equation $x = 4y^2 - 4$ represents a parabola with a horizontal axis and vertex at $(-4, 0)$, as shown in Figure 9.20.

The range of x and y implied by the parametric equations may be altered by the change to rectangular form. In such instances, the domain of the rectangular equation must be adjusted so that its graph matches the graph of the parametric equations. Such a situation is demonstrated in the next example.

EXAMPLE 2 Adjusting the Domain

Sketch the curve represented by the equations

$$x = \frac{1}{\sqrt{t + 1}} \quad \text{and} \quad y = \frac{t}{t + 1}, \quad t > -1$$

by eliminating the parameter and adjusting the domain of the resulting rectangular equation.

Solution

Begin by solving one of the parametric equations for t. For instance, you can solve the first equation for t as follows.

$$x = \frac{1}{\sqrt{t + 1}} \qquad \text{Parametric equation for } x$$

$$x^2 = \frac{1}{t + 1} \qquad \text{Square each side.}$$

$$t + 1 = \frac{1}{x^2}$$

$$t = \frac{1}{x^2} - 1$$

$$t = \frac{1 - x^2}{x^2} \qquad \text{Solve for } t.$$

Now, substituting into the parametric equation for y produces

$$y = \frac{t}{t + 1} \qquad \text{Parametric equation for } y$$

$$y = \frac{(1 - x^2)/x^2}{[(1 - x^2)/x^2] + 1} \qquad \text{Substitute } (1 - x^2)/x^2 \text{ for } t.$$

$$y = 1 - x^2. \qquad \text{Simplify.}$$

The rectangular equation, $y = 1 - x^2$, is defined for all values of x, but from the parametric equation for x, you can see that the curve is defined only when $t > -1$. This implies that you should restrict the domain of x to positive values, as shown in Figure 9.22.

Algebra Review

For help on the algebra in Example 2, see Example 2 in the *Chapter 9 Algebra Review* on page A52.

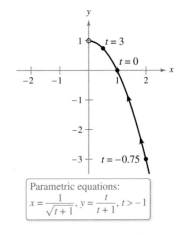

Parametric equations:
$x = \dfrac{1}{\sqrt{t + 1}}, y = \dfrac{t}{t + 1}, t > -1$

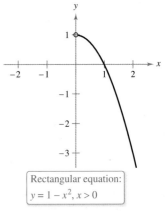

Rectangular equation:
$y = 1 - x^2, x > 0$

Figure 9.22

It is not necessary for the parameter in a set of parametric equations to represent time. The next example uses an *angle* as the parameter.

EXAMPLE 3   Using Trigonometry to Eliminate a Parameter

See LarsonCalculusforAP.com for an interactive version of this type of example.

Sketch the curve represented by

$$x = 3 \cos \theta \quad \text{and} \quad y = 4 \sin \theta, \quad 0 \le \theta \le 2\pi$$

by eliminating the parameter and finding the corresponding rectangular equation.

Solution

Begin by solving for $\cos \theta$ and $\sin \theta$ in the given equations.

$$\cos \theta = \frac{x}{3} \qquad \text{Solve for } \cos \theta.$$

and

$$\sin \theta = \frac{y}{4} \qquad \text{Solve for } \sin \theta.$$

Next, make use of the identity

$$\sin^2 \theta + \cos^2 \theta = 1$$

to form an equation involving only x and y.

$$\cos^2 \theta + \sin^2 \theta = 1 \qquad \text{Trigonometric identity}$$

$$\left(\frac{x}{3}\right)^2 + \left(\frac{y}{4}\right)^2 = 1 \qquad \text{Substitute.}$$

$$\frac{x^2}{9} + \frac{y^2}{16} = 1 \qquad \text{Rectangular equation}$$

From this rectangular equation, you can see that the graph is an ellipse centered at $(0, 0)$, with vertices at $(0, 4)$ and $(0, -4)$ and minor axis of length $2b = 6$, as shown in Figure 9.23. Note that the ellipse is traced out *counterclockwise* as θ varies from 0 to 2π.

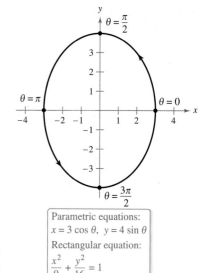

Parametric equations:
$x = 3 \cos \theta, \ y = 4 \sin \theta$
Rectangular equation:
$\dfrac{x^2}{9} + \dfrac{y^2}{16} = 1$

Figure 9.23

Using the technique shown in Example 3, you can conclude that the graph of the parametric equations

$$x = h + a \cos \theta \quad \text{and} \quad y = k + b \sin \theta, \quad 0 \le \theta \le 2\pi$$

is the ellipse (traced counterclockwise) given by

$$\frac{(x - h)^2}{a^2} + \frac{(y - k)^2}{b^2} = 1.$$

The graph of the parametric equations

$$x = h + a \sin \theta \quad \text{and} \quad y = k + b \cos \theta, \quad 0 \le \theta \le 2\pi$$

is also the ellipse (traced clockwise) given by

$$\frac{(x - h)^2}{a^2} + \frac{(y - k)^2}{b^2} = 1.$$

In Examples 2 and 3, it is important to realize that eliminating the parameter is primarily an *aid to curve sketching*. When the parametric equations represent the path of a moving object, the graph alone is not sufficient to describe the motion of the object. You still need the parametric equations to tell you the *position, direction,* and *speed* at a given time.

Finding Parametric Equations

The first three examples in this section illustrate techniques for sketching the graph represented by a set of parametric equations. You will now investigate the reverse problem. How can you determine a set of parametric equations for a given graph or a given physical description? From the discussion following Example 1, you know that such a representation is not unique. This is demonstrated further in the next example, which finds two different parametric representations for a given graph.

EXAMPLE 4 Finding Parametric Equations for a Given Graph

Find a set of parametric equations that represents the graph of $y = 1 - x^2$, using each of the following parameters.

a. $t = x$ **b.** The slope $m = dy/dx$ at the point (x, y)

Solution

a. Letting $x = t$ produces the parametric equations

$$x = t \quad \text{and} \quad y = 1 - x^2 = 1 - t^2.$$

b. To write x and y in terms of the parameter m, you can proceed as follows.

$$m = \frac{dy}{dx}$$

$$m = -2x \qquad \text{Differentiate } y = 1 - x^2.$$

$$x = -\frac{m}{2} \qquad \text{Solve for } x.$$

This produces a parametric equation for x. To obtain a parametric equation for y, substitute $-m/2$ for x in the original equation.

$$y = 1 - x^2 \qquad \text{Write original rectangular equation.}$$

$$y = 1 - \left(-\frac{m}{2}\right)^2 \qquad \text{Substitute } -m/2 \text{ for } x.$$

$$y = 1 - \frac{m^2}{4} \qquad \text{Simplify.}$$

So, the parametric equations are

$$x = -\frac{m}{2} \quad \text{and} \quad y = 1 - \frac{m^2}{4}.$$

In Figure 9.24, note that the resulting curve has a right-to-left orientation as determined by the increasing values of slope m. For part (a), the curve would have the opposite orientation.

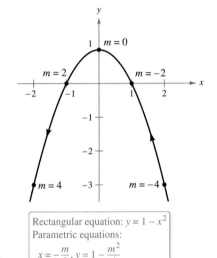

Rectangular equation: $y = 1 - x^2$
Parametric equations:
$$x = -\frac{m}{2},\ y = 1 - \frac{m^2}{4}$$

Figure 9.24

Technology

To be efficient at using a graphing utility, it is important that you develop skill in representing a graph by a set of parametric equations. The reason for this is that many graphing utilities have only three graphing modes—(1) functions, (2) parametric equations, and (3) polar equations. Most graphing utilities are not programmed to graph a general equation. For instance, suppose you want to graph the hyperbola $x^2 - y^2 = 1$. To graph the hyperbola in *function* mode, you need two equations, $y = \sqrt{x^2 - 1}$ and $y = -\sqrt{x^2 - 1}$. In *parametric* mode, you can represent the graph by $x = \sec t$ and $y = \tan t$.

EXAMPLE 5   Parametric Equations for a Cycloid

Determine the curve traced by a point P on the circumference of a circle of radius a rolling along a straight line in a plane. Such a curve is called a **cycloid.** (Assume that P starts at the origin and the circle rolls along the x-axis.)

Solution   Let the parameter θ be the measure of the circle's rotation, and let the point $P = (x, y)$ begin at the origin. When $\theta = 0$, P is at the origin. When $\theta = \pi$, P is at a maximum point $(\pi a, 2a)$. When $\theta = 2\pi$, P is back on the x-axis at $(2\pi a, 0)$. From Figure 9.25, you can see that $\angle APC = 180° - \theta$. So,

$$\sin \theta = \sin(180° - \theta) = \sin(\angle APC) = \frac{AC}{a} = \frac{BD}{a}$$

$$\cos \theta = -\cos(180° - \theta) = -\cos(\angle APC) = \frac{AP}{-a}$$

which implies that $AP = -a \cos \theta$ and $BD = a \sin \theta$. The circle rolls along the x-axis, so you know that $OD = \overset{\frown}{PD} = a\theta$. Also, because $BA = DC = a$, you have

$$x = OD - BD = a\theta - a \sin \theta$$

$$y = BA + AP = a - a \cos \theta.$$

So, the parametric equations are $x = a(\theta - \sin \theta)$ and $y = a(1 - \cos \theta)$.

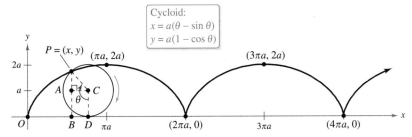

Cycloid:
$x = a(\theta - \sin \theta)$
$y = a(1 - \cos \theta)$

Figure 9.25

Technology

Some graphing utilities allow you to simulate the motion of an object that is moving in the plane or in space. If you have access to such a utility, use it to trace out the path of the cycloid shown in Figure 9.25.

The cycloid in Figure 9.25 has sharp corners called **cusps** at the values $x = 2n\pi a$. Notice that the derivatives $x'(\theta)$ and $y'(\theta)$ are both zero at the points for which $\theta = 2n\pi$.

$$x(\theta) = a(\theta - \sin \theta) \qquad y(\theta) = a(1 - \cos \theta)$$
$$x'(\theta) = a - a \cos \theta \qquad y'(\theta) = a \sin \theta$$
$$x'(2n\pi) = 0 \qquad y'(2n\pi) = 0$$

Between these points, the cycloid is called **smooth.**

Definition of a Smooth Curve

A curve C represented by $x = f(t)$ and $y = g(t)$ on an interval I is called **smooth** when f' and g' are continuous on I and not simultaneously 0, except possibly at the endpoints of I. The curve C is called **piecewise smooth** when it is smooth on each subinterval of some partition of I.

9.2 Exercises

See *CalcChat.com* for tutorial help and worked-out solutions to odd-numbered exercises.

Using Parametric Equations In Exercises 1–18, sketch the curve represented by the parametric equations (indicate the orientation of the curve), and write the corresponding rectangular equation by eliminating the parameter.

1. $x = 2t - 3$, $y = 3t + 1$
2. $x = 5 - 4t$, $y = 2 + 5t$
3. $x = t + 1$, $y = t^2$
4. $x = 2t^2$, $y = t^3 + 1$
5. $x = t^3 - t$, $y = 4t$
6. $x = t^2 + t$, $y = t^2 - t$
7. $x = \sqrt{t}$, $y = t - 5$
8. $x = \sqrt[4]{t}$, $y = 8 - t$
9. $x = t - 3$, $y = \dfrac{t}{t - 3}$
10. $x = 1 + \dfrac{1}{t}$, $y = t - 1$
11. $x = 2t$, $y = |t - 2|$
12. $x = |t - 1|$, $y = t + 2$
13. $x = e^t$, $y = e^{3t} + 1$
14. $x = e^{-t}$, $y = e^{2t} - 1$
15. $x = \sec \theta$, $y = \cos \theta$, $0 \le \theta < \pi/2$, $\pi/2 < \theta \le \pi$
16. $x = \tan^2 \theta$, $y = \sec^2 \theta$
17. $x = 8 \cos \theta$, $y = 8 \sin \theta$
18. $x = 3 \cos \theta$, $y = 7 \sin \theta$

Error Analysis In Exercises 19 and 20, describe and correct the error in eliminating the parameter and writing the corresponding equation.

19. $x = t + 3$, $y = 7 - 2t$

$t = x - 3$
$y = 7 - 2(x - 3)$
$= 7 - 2x - 6$
$= 1 - 2x$ ✗

20. $x = \sqrt{\dfrac{t}{3}}$, $y = t^3$

$t = 3x^2$
$y = (3x^2)^3$
$= 27x^6$ ✗

Using Parametric Equations In Exercises 21–28, use a graphing utility to graph the curve represented by the parametric equations (indicate the orientation of the curve). Eliminate the parameter and write the corresponding rectangular equation.

21. $x = 4 + 2 \cos \theta$
    $y = -1 + \sin \theta$
22. $x = \cos \theta$
    $y = 2 \sin 2\theta$
23. $x = 6 \sec \theta$
    $y = 4 \tan \theta$
24. $x = -2 + 3 \cos \theta$
    $y = -5 + 3 \sin \theta$
25. $x = 4 \sec \theta$, $y = 3 \tan \theta$
26. $x = \cos^3 \theta$, $y = \sin^3 \theta$
27. $x = t^3$, $y = 3 \ln t$
28. $x = \ln 2t$, $y = t^2$

Comparing Plane Curves In Exercises 29–32, determine any differences between the curves of the parametric equations. Are the graphs the same? Are the orientations the same? Are the curves smooth? Explain.

29. (a) $x = t$, $y = t^2$
    (b) $x = -t$, $y = t^2$
30. (a) $x = t + 1$, $y = t^3$
    (b) $x = -t + 1$, $y = (-t)^3$
31. (a) $x = t$, $y = 2t + 1$
    (b) $x = \cos \theta$, $y = 2 \cos \theta + 1$
    (c) $x = e^{-t}$, $y = 2e^{-t} + 1$
    (d) $x = e^t$, $y = 2e^t + 1$
32. (a) $x = 2 \cos \theta$
        $y = 2 \sin \theta$
    (b) $x = \sqrt{4t^2 - 1}/|t|$
        $y = 1/t$
    (c) $x = \sqrt{t}$
        $y = \sqrt{4 - t}$
    (d) $x = -\sqrt{4 - e^{2t}}$
        $y = e^t$

Eliminating a Parameter In Exercises 33–36, eliminate the parameter and obtain the standard form of the rectangular equation.

33. Line through (x_1, y_1) and (x_2, y_2):
    $x = x_1 + t(x_2 - x_1)$, $y = y_1 + t(y_2 - y_1)$
34. Circle: $x = h + r \cos \theta$, $y = k + r \sin \theta$
35. Ellipse: $x = h + a \cos \theta$, $y = k + b \sin \theta$
36. Hyperbola: $x = h + a \sec \theta$, $y = k + b \tan \theta$

Writing a Set of Parametric Equations In Exercises 37–44, use the results of Exercises 33–36 to find a set of parametric equations for the line or conic.

37. Line: passes through $(0, 0)$ and $(4, -7)$
38. Line: passes through $(-3, 1)$ and $(1, 9)$
39. Circle: center: $(1, 1)$; radius: 2
40. Circle: center: $\left(-\dfrac{1}{2}, -4\right)$; radius: $\dfrac{5}{3}$
41. Ellipse: vertices: $(-3, 0), (7, 0)$; foci: $(-1, 0), (5, 0)$
42. Ellipse: vertices: $(-1, 6), (-1, -10)$;
    foci: $(-1, 4), (-1, -8)$
43. Hyperbola: vertices: $(0, \pm 2)$; foci: $\left(0, \pm \sqrt{5}\right)$
44. Hyperbola: vertices: $(-3, 1), (1, 1)$;
    foci: $(-4, 1), (2, 1)$

Finding Parametric Equations In Exercises 45–48, find two different sets of parametric equations for the rectangular equation.

45. $y = 6x - 5$

46. $y = \dfrac{4}{x - 1}$

47. $y = x^3$

48. $y = x^2$

Finding Parametric Equations In Exercises 49–52, find a set of parametric equations for the rectangular equation that satisfies the given condition.

49. $y = 2x - 5$, $t = 0$ at the point $(3, 1)$

50. $y = 4x + 1$, $t = -1$ at the point $(-2, -7)$

51. $y = x^2$, $t = 4$ at the point $(4, 16)$

52. $y = 4 - x^2$, $t = 1$ at the point $(1, 3)$

Graphing a Plane Curve In Exercises 53–60, use a graphing utility to graph the curve represented by the parametric equations. Indicate the orientation of the curve. Identify any points at which the curve is not smooth.

53. Cycloid: $x = 2(\theta - \sin \theta)$, $y = 2(1 - \cos \theta)$

54. Cycloid: $x = \theta + \sin \theta$, $y = 1 - \cos \theta$

55. Prolate cycloid: $x = \theta - \frac{3}{2} \sin \theta$, $y = 1 - \frac{3}{2} \cos \theta$

56. Prolate cycloid: $x = 2\theta - 4 \sin \theta$, $y = 2 - 4 \cos \theta$

57. Hypocycloid: $x = 3 \cos^3 \theta$, $y = 3 \sin^3 \theta$

58. Curtate cycloid: $x = \theta - 0.75 \sin \theta$, $y = 1 - 0.75 \cos \theta$

59. Witch of Agnesi: $x = 7 \cot \theta$, $y = 7 \sin^2 \theta$

60. Folium of Descartes: $x = \dfrac{3t}{1 + t^3}$, $y = \dfrac{3t^2}{1 + t^3}$

EXPLORING CONCEPTS

61. Orientation Describe the orientation of the parametric equations $x = t^2$ and $y = t^4$ for $-1 \le t \le 1$.

62. Justifying Make a conjecture about the change in the graph of parametric equations when the sign of the parameter is changed. Explain your reasoning using examples to support your conjecture.

63. Justifying The following sets of parametric equations have the same graph. Does this contradict your conjecture from Exercise 62? Explain.

$x = \cos \theta$, $y = \sin^2 \theta$, $0 < \theta < \pi$

$x = \cos(-\theta)$, $y = \sin^2(-\theta)$, $0 < \theta < \pi$

64. Communicating Explain the process of sketching a plane curve given by parametric equations. What is meant by the orientation of the curve?

65. Connecting Representation How can two sets of parametric equations represent the same graph but different curves?

66. HOW DO YOU SEE IT? Which set of parametric equations is shown in the graph below? Explain your reasoning.

(a) $x = t$
    $y = t^2$

(b) $x = t^2$
    $y = t$

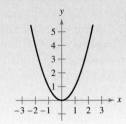

Connecting Representation In Exercises 67–70, match the set of parametric equations with its graph. [The graphs are labeled (a), (b), (c), and (d).] Explain your reasoning.

(a)
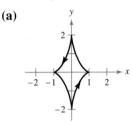

(b)
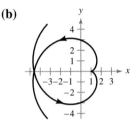

(c)
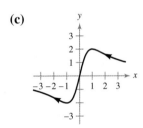

(d)
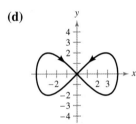

67. Lissajous curve: $x = 4 \cos \theta$, $y = 2 \sin 2\theta$

68. Evolute of ellipse: $x = \cos^3 \theta$, $y = 2 \sin^3 \theta$

69. Involute of circle: $x = \cos \theta + \theta \sin \theta$, $y = \sin \theta - \theta \cos \theta$

70. Serpentine curve: $x = \cot \theta$, $y = 4 \sin \theta \cos \theta$

71. Curtate Cycloid A wheel of radius a rolls along a line without slipping. The curve traced by a point P that is b units from the center $(b < a)$ is called a **curtate cycloid** (see figure). Use the angle θ to find a set of parametric equations for this curve.

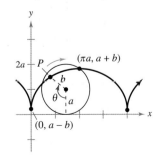

Figure for 71   Figure for 72

72. Epicycloid A circle of radius 1 rolls around the outside of a circle of radius 2 without slipping. The curve traced by a point on the circumference of the smaller circle is called an epicycloid (see figure on previous page). Use the angle θ to find a set of parametric equations for this curve.

True or False? **In Exercises 73–75, determine whether the statement is true or false. If it is false, explain why or give an example that shows it is false.**

73. The graph of the parametric equations $x = t^2$ and $y = t^2$ is the line $y = x$.

74. If y is a function of t and x is a function of t, then y is a function of x.

75. The curve represented by the parametric equations $x = t$ and $y = \cos t$ can be written as an equation of the form $y = f(x)$.

76. Particle Motion The path of a particle moving on a plane is a curve represented by the parametric equations $x = 3 \cos 3\theta$ and $y = 5 \sin 3\theta$.

(a) Describe the curve represented by the parametric equations.

(b) How does this curve change when cosine and sine are interchanged?

(c) Compare this curve to the path of a second particle represented by the parametric equations $x = 2 + 3 \cos 3\theta$ and $y = -6 + 5 \sin 3\theta$.

Projectile Motion **In Exercises 77 and 78, consider a projectile launched at a height h feet above the ground and at an angle θ with the horizontal. When the initial velocity is v_0 feet per second, the path of the projectile is modeled by the parametric equations $x = (v_0 \cos \theta)t$ and $y = h + (v_0 \sin \theta)t - 16t^2$.**

77. The center field fence in a ballpark is 10 feet high and 400 feet from home plate. The ball is hit 3 feet above the ground. It leaves the bat at an angle of θ degrees with the horizontal at a speed of 100 miles per hour (see figure).

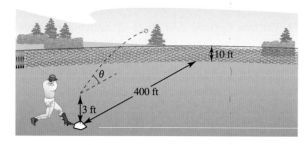

(a) Write a set of parametric equations for the path of the ball.

(b) Use a graphing utility to graph the path of the ball when $\theta = 15°$. Is the hit a home run?

(c) Use a graphing utility to graph the path of the ball when $\theta = 23°$. Is the hit a home run?

(d) Find the minimum angle at which the ball must leave the bat in order for the hit to be a home run.

78. A rectangular equation for the path of a projectile is $y = 5 + x - 0.005x^2$.

(a) Eliminate the parameter t from the parametric equations for the path of a projectile to show that the rectangular equation is

$$y = -\frac{16 \sec^2 \theta}{v_0^2}x^2 + (\tan \theta)x + h.$$

(b) Use the result of part (a) to find h, v_0, and θ. Write the parametric equations of the path.

(c) Use a graphing utility to graph the rectangular equation for the path of the projectile. Confirm your answer in part (b) by sketching the curve represented by the parametric equations.

(d) Use a graphing utility to approximate the maximum height of the projectile and its range.

Calculus AP® – Exam Preparation Questions

79. Multiple Choice In the xy-plane, the graph of the parametric equations $x = 4t - 3$ and $y = 8t$ is a line segment with a slope of

(A) -2.   (B) $\frac{1}{2}$.

(C) 2.   (D) 4.

80. Multiple Choice A particle moves along the x-axis so that any time $t \geq 0$, its velocity is given by $v(t) = \sin 4t$. The position of the particle at time $t = \pi/4$ is $x = 1$. What is the position of the particle at time $t = 0$?

(A) 3 (B) $\frac{3}{2}$

(C) $\frac{1}{2}$ (D) -1

81. Multiple Choice Let h be a differentiable function and let f be the function defined by

$$f(x) = h(x^3 - 9x).$$

Which of the following is equal to $f'(4)$?

(A) $39h'(28)$

(B) $h'(28)$

(C) $h'(39)$

(D) $39h'(39)$

82. Free Response The derivative of a function f is given by $f'(x) = (x - 2)e^x$ for $x > 0$, and $f(1) = 5$.

(a) The function f has a critical point at $x = 2$. At this point, does f have a relative minimum, a relative maximum, or neither? Justify your answer.

(b) On what intervals, if any, is the graph of f both decreasing and concave upward? Explain.

(c) Find the value of $f(2)$.

9.3 Parametric Equations and Calculus

▶ Find the slope of a tangent line to a curve given by a set of parametric equations.
▶ Find the arc length of a curve given by a set of parametric equations.

Slope and Tangent Lines

Now that you can represent a graph in the plane by a set of parametric equations, it is natural to ask how to use calculus to study plane curves. Consider the projectile represented by the parametric equations

$$x = 24\sqrt{2}t \quad \text{and} \quad y = -16t^2 + 24\sqrt{2}t$$

as shown in Figure 9.26. From the discussion at the beginning of Section 9.2, you know that these equations enable you to locate the position of the projectile at a given time. You also know that the object is initially projected at an angle of 45°, or a slope of $m = \tan 45° = 1$. But how can you find the slope at some other time t? The next theorem answers this question by giving a formula for the slope of the tangent line as a function of t.

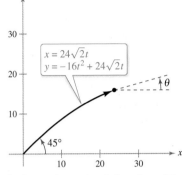

At time t, the angle of elevation of the projectile is θ.

Figure 9.26

Theorem 9.7 Parametric Form of the Derivative

If a smooth curve C is given by the equations

$$x = f(t) \quad \text{and} \quad y = g(t)$$

then the slope of C at (x, y) is

$$\frac{dy}{dx} = \frac{dy/dt}{dx/dt}, \quad \frac{dx}{dt} \neq 0.$$

Proof In Figure 9.27, consider $\Delta t > 0$ and let

$$\Delta y = g(t + \Delta t) - g(t)$$

and

$$\Delta x = f(t + \Delta t) - f(t).$$

Because $\Delta x \to 0$ as $\Delta t \to 0$, you can write

$$\frac{dy}{dx} = \lim_{\Delta x \to 0} \frac{\Delta y}{\Delta x}$$

$$= \lim_{\Delta t \to 0} \frac{g(t + \Delta t) - g(t)}{f(t + \Delta t) - f(t)}.$$

Dividing both the numerator and denominator by Δt, you can use the differentiability of f and g to conclude that

$$\frac{dy}{dx} = \lim_{\Delta t \to 0} \frac{[g(t + \Delta t) - g(t)]/\Delta t}{[f(t + \Delta t) - f(t)]/\Delta t}$$

$$= \frac{\displaystyle \lim_{\Delta t \to 0} \frac{g(t + \Delta t) - g(t)}{\Delta t}}{\displaystyle \lim_{\Delta t \to 0} \frac{f(t + \Delta t) - f(t)}{\Delta t}}$$

$$= \frac{g'(t)}{f'(t)}$$

$$= \frac{dy/dt}{dx/dt}.$$

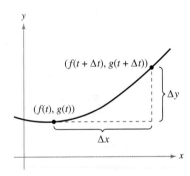

The slope of the secant line through the points $(f(t), g(t))$ and $(f(t + \Delta t), g(t + \Delta t))$ is $\Delta y/\Delta x$.

Figure 9.27

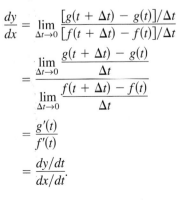

EXAMPLE 1 Differentiation and Parametric Form

Find dy/dx for the curve given by $x = \sin t$ and $y = \cos t$.

Solution

$$\frac{dy}{dx} = \frac{dy/dt}{dx/dt}$$

$$= \frac{-\sin t}{\cos t}$$

$$= -\tan t$$

> **Exploration**
>
> The curve traced out in Example 1 is a circle. Use the formula
>
> $$\frac{dy}{dx} = -\tan t$$
>
> to find the slopes at the points $(1, 0)$ and $(0, 1)$.

Because dy/dx is a function of t, you can use Theorem 9.7 repeatedly to find *higher-order* derivatives. For instance,

$$\frac{d^2y}{dx^2} = \frac{d}{dx}\left[\frac{dy}{dx}\right] = \frac{\frac{d}{dt}\left[\frac{dy}{dx}\right]}{dx/dt} \qquad \text{Second derivative}$$

$$\frac{d^3y}{dx^3} = \frac{d}{dx}\left[\frac{d^2y}{dx^2}\right] = \frac{\frac{d}{dt}\left[\frac{d^2y}{dx^2}\right]}{dx/dt}. \qquad \text{Third derivative}$$

EXAMPLE 2 Finding Slope and Concavity

For the curve given by

$$x = \sqrt{t} \quad \text{and} \quad y = \frac{1}{4}(t^2 - 4), \quad t \geq 0$$

find the slope and concavity at the point $(2, 3)$.

Solution

Because

$$\frac{dy}{dx} = \frac{dy/dt}{dx/dt} = \frac{(1/2)t}{(1/2)t^{-1/2}} = t^{3/2} \qquad \text{Parametric form of first derivative}$$

you can find the second derivative to be

$$\frac{d^2y}{dx^2} = \frac{\frac{d}{dt}\left[\frac{dy}{dx}\right]}{dx/dt} = \frac{\frac{d}{dt}[t^{3/2}]}{dx/dt} = \frac{(3/2)t^{1/2}}{(1/2)t^{-1/2}} = 3t. \qquad \text{Parametric form of second derivative}$$

At $(x, y) = (2, 3)$, it follows that $t = 4$, and the slope is

$$\frac{dy}{dx} = (4)^{3/2} = 8.$$

Moreover, when $t = 4$, the second derivative is

$$\frac{d^2y}{dx^2} = 3(4) = 12 > 0$$

and you can conclude that the graph is concave upward at $(2, 3)$, as shown in Figure 9.28.

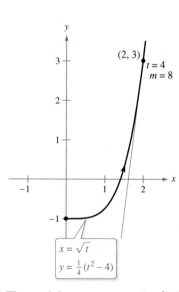

The graph is concave upward at $(2, 3)$ when $t = 4$.

Figure 9.28

Because the parametric equations $x = f(t)$ and $y = g(t)$ need not define y as a function of x, it is possible for a plane curve to loop around and cross itself. At such points, the curve may have more than one tangent line, as shown in the next example.

EXAMPLE 3 A Curve with Two Tangent Lines at a Point

See LarsonCalculusforAP.com for an interactive version of this type of example.

The **prolate cycloid** given by $x = 2t - \pi \sin t$ and $y = 2 - \pi \cos t$ crosses itself at the point $(0, 2)$, as shown in Figure 9.29. Find the equations of both tangent lines at this point.

Solution

Because $x = 0$ and $y = 2$ when $t = \pm \pi/2$, and

$$\frac{dy}{dx} = \frac{dy/dt}{dx/dt} = \frac{\pi \sin t}{2 - \pi \cos t}$$

you have $dy/dx = -\pi/2$ when $t = -\pi/2$ and $dy/dx = \pi/2$ when $t = \pi/2$. So, the two tangent lines at $(0, 2)$ are

$$y - 2 = -\frac{\pi}{2}x \qquad \text{Tangent line when } t = -\frac{\pi}{2}$$

and

$$y - 2 = \frac{\pi}{2}x. \qquad \text{Tangent line when } t = \frac{\pi}{2}$$

If $dy/dt = 0$ and $dx/dt \neq 0$ when $t = t_0$, then the curve represented by $x = f(t)$ and $y = g(t)$ has a horizontal tangent at $(f(t_0), g(t_0))$. For instance, in Example 3, the given curve has a horizontal tangent at the point $(0, 2 - \pi)$ (when $t = 0$). Similarly, if $dx/dt = 0$ and $dy/dt \neq 0$ when $t = t_0$, then the curve represented by $x = f(t)$ and $y = g(t)$ has a vertical tangent at $(f(t_0), g(t_0))$. If dy/dt and dx/dt are *simultaneously* 0, then no conclusion can be drawn about tangent lines.

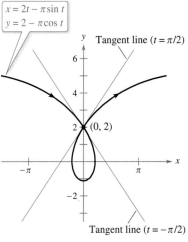

$x = 2t - \pi \sin t$
$y = 2 - \pi \cos t$

Tangent line ($t = \pi/2$)

$(0, 2)$

Tangent line ($t = -\pi/2$)

This prolate cycloid has two tangent lines at the point $(0, 2)$.
Figure 9.29

Algebra Review

For help on the algebra in Example 3, see Example 3 in the *Chapter 9 Algebra Review* on page A53.

Arc Length

You have seen how parametric equations can be used to describe the path of a particle moving in the plane. You will now develop a formula for determining the *distance* traveled by the particle along its path.

Recall from Section 6.4 that the formula for the arc length of a curve C given by $y = h(x)$ over the interval $[x_0, x_1]$ is

$$s = \int_{x_0}^{x_1} \sqrt{1 + [h'(x)]^2}\, dx$$

$$= \int_{x_0}^{x_1} \sqrt{1 + \left(\frac{dy}{dx}\right)^2}\, dx.$$

If C is represented by the parametric equations $x = f(t)$ and $y = g(t)$, $a \leq t \leq b$, and if $dx/dt = f'(t) > 0$, then

$$s = \int_{x_0}^{x_1} \sqrt{1 + \left(\frac{dy}{dx}\right)^2}\, dx$$

$$= \int_{x_0}^{x_1} \sqrt{1 + \left(\frac{dy/dt}{dx/dt}\right)^2}\, dx$$

$$= \int_{a}^{b} \sqrt{\frac{(dx/dt)^2 + (dy/dt)^2}{(dx/dt)^2}}\, \frac{dx}{dt}\, dt$$

$$= \int_{a}^{b} \sqrt{\left(\frac{dx}{dt}\right)^2 + \left(\frac{dy}{dt}\right)^2}\, dt$$

$$= \int_{a}^{b} \sqrt{[f'(t)]^2 + [g'(t)]^2}\, dt.$$

Theorem 9.8 **Arc Length in Parametric Form**

If a smooth curve C is given by $x = f(t)$ and $y = g(t)$ such that C does not intersect itself on the interval $a \le t \le b$ (except possibly at the endpoints), then the arc length of C over the interval is given by

$$s = \int_a^b \sqrt{\left(\frac{dx}{dt}\right)^2 + \left(\frac{dy}{dt}\right)^2}\, dt = \int_a^b \sqrt{[f'(t)]^2 + [g'(t)]^2}\, dt.$$

Insight

On the AP® Exam, the arc length of a curve given in parametric form is frequently interpreted as the total distance traveled by a particle.

▶ **Justification** When applying the arc length formula to a curve, be sure that the curve is traced out only once on the interval of integration. For instance, the circle given by $x = \cos t$ and $y = \sin t$ is traced out once on the interval $0 \le t \le 2\pi$ but is traced out twice on the interval $0 \le t \le 4\pi$.

In the preceding section, you saw that if a circle rolls along a line, then a point on its circumference will trace a path called a cycloid. If the circle rolls around the circumference of another circle, then the path of the point is an **epicycloid.** The next example shows how to find the arc length of an epicycloid.

EXAMPLE 4 **Finding Arc Length**

A circle of radius 1 inch rolls around the circumference of a larger circle of radius 4 inches, as shown in Figure 9.30. The epicycloid traced by a point on the circumference of the smaller circle is given by $x = 5 \cos t - \cos 5t$ and $y = 5 \sin t - \sin 5t$. Find the distance traveled by the point in one complete trip about the larger circle.

Solution

Before applying Theorem 9.8, note in Figure 9.30 that the curve has sharp points when $t = 0$ and $t = \pi/2$. Between these two points, dx/dt and dy/dt are not simultaneously 0. So, the portion of the curve generated from $t = 0$ to $t = \pi/2$ is smooth. To find the total distance traveled by the point, you can find the arc length of that portion lying in the first quadrant and multiply by 4.

$$s = 4 \int_0^{\pi/2} \sqrt{\left(\frac{dx}{dt}\right)^2 + \left(\frac{dy}{dt}\right)^2}\, dt \qquad \text{Parametric form for arc length}$$

$$= 4 \int_0^{\pi/2} \sqrt{(-5 \sin t + 5 \sin 5t)^2 + (5 \cos t - 5 \cos 5t)^2}\, dt$$

$$= 20 \int_0^{\pi/2} \sqrt{2 - 2 \sin t \sin 5t - 2 \cos t \cos 5t}\, dt$$

$$= 20 \int_0^{\pi/2} \sqrt{2 - 2 \cos 4t}\, dt \qquad \text{Difference formula for cosine}$$

$$= 20 \int_0^{\pi/2} \sqrt{4 \sin^2 2t}\, dt \qquad \text{Double-angle formula}$$

$$= 40 \int_0^{\pi/2} \sin 2t\, dt$$

$$= -20 \left[\cos 2t \right]_0^{\pi/2}$$

$$= 40 \text{ inches}$$

For the epicycloid shown in Figure 9.30, an arc length of 40 inches seems about right because the circumference of a circle of radius 6 inches is $2\pi r = 12\pi \approx 37.7$ inches. ■

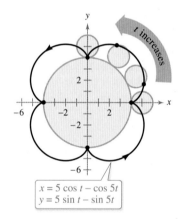

$$x = 5 \cos t - \cos 5t$$
$$y = 5 \sin t - \sin 5t$$

An epicycloid is traced by a point on the smaller circle as it rolls around the larger circle.

Figure 9.30

9.3 Exercises

 Finding a Derivative In Exercises 1–4, find dy/dx.

1. $x = t^2$, $y = 7 - 6t$ **2.** $x = t^3$, $y = \sqrt{t} + 3$

3. $x = \cos^2 2\theta$, $y = \sin 2\theta$ **4.** $x = e^{1/\theta}$, $y = \ln \theta$

 Finding Slope and Concavity In Exercises 5–14, find dy/dx and d^2y/dx^2, and find the slope and concavity (if possible) at the given value of the parameter.

Parametric Equations	Parameter
5. $x = 6t$, $y = 1 - 3t$	$t = 0$
6. $x = \sqrt{t}$, $y = 3t - 1$	$t = 1$
7. $x = \sqrt{t - 1}$, $y = 2t^2$	$t = 5$
8. $x = t^2 + 5t + 4$, $y = 4t$	$t = 0$
9. $x = 4 \cos \theta$, $y = 4 \sin \theta$	$\theta = \pi/4$
10. $x = \cos \theta$, $y = 3 \sin \theta$	$\theta = 0$
11. $x = 2 + \sec \theta$, $y = 1 + 2 \tan \theta$	$\theta = \pi/6$
12. $x = 1 + \csc t$, $y = 3 + \sec t$	$\theta = 3\pi/4$
13. $x = \cos^3 \theta$, $y = \sin^3 \theta$	$\theta = \pi/4$
14. $x = \theta - \sin \theta$, $y = 1 - \cos \theta$	$\theta = \pi$

15. Error Analysis Describe and correct the error in finding dy/dx for the curve given by $x = t^2$ and $y = 2t^3 - 5$.

$$\frac{dy}{dx} = \frac{dy/dt}{dx/dt} = \frac{2t}{6t^2} = \frac{1}{3t} \quad \text{✗}$$

16. Error Analysis Describe and correct the error in finding d^2y/dx^2 for the curve given by $x = \sin \theta$ and $y = \tan \theta$.

$$\frac{dy}{dx} = \frac{dy/d\theta}{dx/d\theta} = \frac{\sec^2 \theta}{\cos \theta} = \sec^3 \theta$$

$$\frac{d^2y}{dx^2} = \frac{\dfrac{d}{d\theta}\left(\dfrac{dy}{d\theta}\right)}{\dfrac{d}{d\theta}\left(\dfrac{dx}{d\theta}\right)} = \frac{2 \sec^2 \theta \tan \theta}{-\sin \theta} = -2 \sec^3 \theta \quad \text{✗}$$

 Finding Equations of Tangent Lines In Exercises 17–20, find an equation of the tangent line at each given point on the curve.

17. $x = 2 \cot \theta$, $y = 2 \sin^2 \theta$,

$$\left(-\frac{2}{\sqrt{3}}, \frac{3}{2}\right), \ (0, 2), \ \left(2\sqrt{3}, \frac{1}{2}\right)$$

18. $x = 2 - 3 \cos \theta$, $y = 3 + 2 \sin \theta$,

$$(-1, 3), \ (2, 5), \ \left(2 + 3\sqrt{3}/2, 2\right)$$

19. $x = t^2 - 4$, $y = t^2 - 2t$, $(0, 0)$, $(-3, -1)$, $(-3, 3)$

20. $x = t^4 + 2$, $y = t^3 + t$, $(2, 0)$, $(3, -2)$, $(18, 10)$

 Finding an Equation of a Tangent Line In Exercises 21–24, (a) use a graphing utility to graph the curve represented by the parametric equations, (b) use a graphing utility to find dx/dt, dy/dt, and dy/dx at the given value of the parameter, (c) find an equation of the tangent line to the curve at the given value of the parameter, and (d) use a graphing utility to graph the curve and the tangent line from part (c).

Parametric Equations	Parameter
21. $x = 6t$, $y = t^2 + 4$	$t = 1$
22. $x = t - 2$, $y = \dfrac{1}{t} + 3$	$t = 1$
23. $x = t^2 - t + 2$, $y = t^3 - 3t$	$t = -1$
24. $x = 3t - t^2$, $y = 2t^{3/2}$	$t = \frac{1}{4}$

 Finding Equations of Tangent Lines In Exercises 25–28, find the equations of the tangent lines at the point where the curve crosses itself.

25. $x = 2 \sin 2t$, $y = 3 \sin t$

26. $x = 2 - \pi \cos t$, $y = 2t - \pi \sin t$

27. $x = t^2 - t$, $y = t^3 - 3t - 1$

28. $x = t^3 - 6t$, $y = t^2$

Horizontal and Vertical Tangency In Exercises 29–40, find all points (if any) of horizontal and vertical tangency to the portion of the curve shown.

29. Involute of a circle:

$x = \cos \theta + \theta \sin \theta$

$y = \sin \theta - \theta \cos \theta$

30. $x = 2\theta$

$y = 2(1 - \cos \theta)$

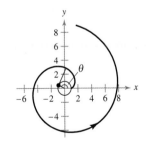

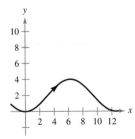

31. $x = 6 - t$, $y = t^3$ **32.** $x = 2t - 5$, $y = 3t^2 + t$

33. $x = 2 + t^4$, $y = t^2 - 4t + 1$

34. $x = t^2 - t + 2$, $y = t^3 - 3t$

35. $x = 3 \cos \theta$, $y = 3 \sin \theta$

36. $x = \cos \theta$, $y = 2 \sin 2\theta$

37. $x = 5 + 3 \cos \theta$, $y = -2 + \sin \theta$

38. $x = 4 \cos^2 \theta$, $y = 2 \sin \theta$

39. $x = \sec \theta$, $y = \tan \theta$ **40.** $x = \cos^2 \theta$, $y = \cos \theta$

Determining Concavity In Exercises 41–46, determine the open *t*-intervals on which the curve is concave downward or concave upward.

41. $x = 3t^2$, $y = t^3 - t$ **42.** $x = 2 - t^2$, $y = t^2 + t^3$

43. $x = 2t + \ln t$, $y = 2t - \ln t$

44. $x = t^2$, $y = \ln t$

45. $x = \sin t$, $y = \cos t$, $0 < t < \pi$

46. $x = 4 \cos t$, $y = 2 \sin t$, $0 < t < 2\pi$

Arc Length In Exercises 47–52, find the arc length of the curve on the given interval.

Parametric Equations	Interval
47. $x = 3t + 7$, $y = 2t^{3/2}$	$0 \le t \le 3$
48. $x = 6t^2$, $y = 2t^3$	$1 \le t \le 4$
49. $x = e^{-t} \cos t$, $y = e^{-t} \sin t$	$0 \le t \le \dfrac{\pi}{2}$
50. $x = \arcsin t$, $y = \ln \sqrt{1 - t^2}$	$0 \le t \le \dfrac{1}{2}$
51. $x = \sqrt{t}$, $y = 3t - 1$	$0 \le t \le 1$
52. $x = t$, $y = \dfrac{t^5}{10} + \dfrac{1}{6t^3}$	$1 \le t \le 2$

Arc Length In Exercises 53–56, find the arc length of the curve on the interval $[0, 2\pi]$.

53. Hypocycloid perimeter: $x = a \cos^3 \theta$, $y = a \sin^3 \theta$

54. Circle circumference: $x = a \cos \theta$, $y = a \sin \theta$

55. Cycloid arch: $x = a(\theta - \sin \theta)$, $y = a(1 - \cos \theta)$

56. Involute of a circle:

$x = \cos \theta + \theta \sin \theta$, $y = \sin \theta - \theta \cos \theta$

57. Path of a Projectile The path of a projectile is modeled by the parametric equations $x = (90 \cos 30°)t$ and $y = (90 \sin 30°)t - 16t^2$, where x and y are measured in feet.

(a) Use a graphing utility to graph the path of the projectile.

(b) Use a graphing utility to approximate the range of the projectile.

(c) Use the integration capabilities of a graphing utility to approximate the arc length of the path. Compare this result with the range of the projectile.

58. Path of a Projectile When the projectile in Exercise 57 is launched at an angle θ with the horizontal, its parametric equations are

$x = (90 \cos \theta)t$ and $y = (90 \sin \theta)t - 16t^2$.

Use a graphing utility to find the angle that maximizes the range of the projectile. What angle maximizes the arc length of the trajectory?

59. Folium of Descartes Consider the parametric equations

$$x = \frac{4t}{1 + t^3} \quad \text{and} \quad y = \frac{4t^2}{1 + t^3}.$$

(a) Use a graphing utility to graph the curve represented by the parametric equations and find the points of horizontal tangency to the curve.

(b) Use the integration capabilities of a graphing utility to approximate the arc length of the closed loop. (*Hint:* Use symmetry and integrate over the interval $0 \le t \le 1$.)

60. Witch of Agnesi Consider the parametric equations $x = 4 \cot \theta$ and $y = 4 \sin^2 \theta$, where $-\pi/2 \le \theta \le \pi/2$.

(a) Use a graphing utility to graph the curve represented by the parametric equations and find the points of horizontal tangency to the curve.

(b) Use the integration capabilities of a graphing utility to approximate the arc length over the interval $\pi/4 \le \theta \le \pi/2$.

61. Connecting Representations

(a) Use a graphing utility to graph each set of parametric equations.

$x = t - \sin t$, $y = 1 - \cos t$, $0 \le t \le 2\pi$

$x = 2t - \sin 2t$, $y = 1 - \cos 2t$, $0 \le t \le \pi$

(b) Compare the graphs of the two sets of parametric equations in part (a). When the curve represents the motion of a particle and t is time, what can you infer about the average speeds of the particle on the paths represented by the two sets of parametric equations?

(c) Without graphing the curve, determine the time required for a particle to traverse the same path as in parts (a) and (b) when the path is modeled by

$x = \frac{1}{2}t - \sin \frac{1}{2}t$ and $y = 1 - \cos \frac{1}{2}t$.

62. Communicating

(a) Each set of parametric equations represents the motion of a particle. Use a graphing utility to graph each set.

First Particle: $x = 3 \cos t$, $y = 4 \sin t$, $0 \le t \le 2\pi$

Second Particle: $x = 4 \sin t$, $y = 3 \cos t$, $0 \le t \le 2\pi$

(b) Determine the number of points of intersection.

(c) Will the particles ever be at the same place at the same time? If so, identify the point(s).

(d) Explain what happens when the motion of the second particle is represented by

$x = 2 + 3 \sin t$, $y = 2 - 4 \cos t$, $0 \le t \le 2\pi$.

EXPLORING CONCEPTS

63. Notation The curve given by $x = f(t)$ and $y = g(t)$ is nonvertical when it passes through the point $(f(t_1), g(t_1))$. Write a formula in terms of t_1 for the equation of the tangent line.

EXPLORING CONCEPTS (continued)

64. Mental Math Mentally determine dy/dx for each set of parametric equations.

(a) $x = t,\ y = 3$ (b) $x = t,\ y = 6t - 5$

65. Communicating Explain how to find the arc length of the smooth curve given by $x = f(t)$ and $y = g(t)$ on the interval $[a, b]$.

66. HOW DO YOU SEE IT? Using the graph of f, determine whether dy/dt is positive or negative given that dx/dt is (a) negative and (b) positive. Explain your reasoning.

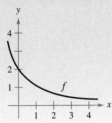

67. Sketching a Graph Find a set of parametric equations $x = f(t)$ and $y = g(t)$ such that $dy/dx < 0$ and $d^2y/dx^2 < 0$ for all real numbers t. Then sketch a graph of the curve.

68. Integration by Substitution Use integration by substitution to show that if y is a continuous function of x on the interval $a \le x \le b$, where $x = f(t)$ and $y = g(t)$, then

$$\int_a^b y\, dx = \int_{t_1}^{t_2} g(t)f'(t)\, dt$$

where $f(t_1) = a$, $f(t_2) = b$, and both g and f' are continuous on $[t_1, t_2]$.

Area In Exercises 69 and 70, find the area of the region. (Use the result of Exercise 68.)

69. $x = 2 \sin^2 \theta$
$y = 2 \sin^2 \theta \tan \theta$
$0 \le \theta < \dfrac{\pi}{2}$

70. $x = 2 \cot \theta$
$y = 2 \sin^2 \theta$
$0 < \theta < \pi$

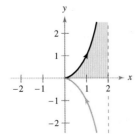

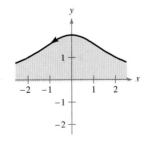

Connecting Representations In Exercises 71–76, use a computer algebra system and the result of Exercise 68 to match the closed curve with its area. (These exercises were based on "The Surveyor's Area Formula" by Bart Braden, *College Mathematics Journal*, September 1986, pp. 335–337, by permission of the author.)

(a) $\frac{8}{3}ab$ (b) $\frac{3}{8}\pi a^2$ (c) $2\pi a^2$

(d) πab (e) $2\pi ab$ (f) $6\pi a^2$

71. Ellipse: $(0 \le t \le 2\pi)$
$x = b \cos t$
$y = a \sin t$

72. Astroid: $(0 \le t \le 2\pi)$
$x = a \cos^3 t$
$y = a \sin^3 t$

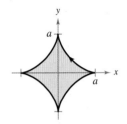

73. Cardioid: $(0 \le t \le 2\pi)$
$x = 2a \cos t - a \cos 2t$
$y = 2a \sin t - a \sin 2t$

74. Deltoid: $(0 \le t \le 2\pi)$
$x = 2a \cos t + a \cos 2t$
$y = 2a \sin t - a \sin 2t$

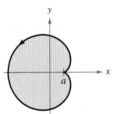

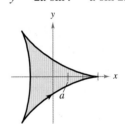

75. Hourglass:
$(0 \le t \le 2\pi)$
$x = a \sin 2t$
$y = b \sin t$

76. Teardrop:
$(0 \le t \le 2\pi)$
$x = 2a \cos t - a \sin 2t$
$y = b \sin t$

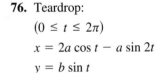

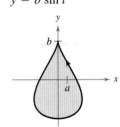

Particle Motion In Exercises 77–80, use the result of Exercise 68 to find the displacement of the particle that travels along the given path over the given interval.

77. $x = 9t,\ y = t^2,\ 1 \le t \le 4$

78. $x = t^3 - 1,\ y = t,\ 0 \le t \le 3$

79. $x = t,\ y = \sin t,\ 0 \le t \le \pi$

80. $x = 2(t - \sin t),\ y = 2(1 - \cos t),\ 0 \le t \le 2\pi$

81. Cycloid Use the parametric equations

$$x = a(\theta - \sin \theta) \quad \text{and} \quad y = a(1 - \cos \theta)$$

where $a > 0$ to answer the following.

(a) Find dy/dx and d^2y/dx^2.

(b) Find the equation of the tangent line at the point where $\theta = \pi/6$.

(c) Find all points (if any) of horizontal tangency.

(d) Determine where the curve is concave upward or concave downward.

(e) Find the length of one arc of the curve.

82. Implementing Processes Use the parametric equations

$$x = t^2\sqrt{3} \quad \text{and} \quad y = 3t - \frac{1}{3}t^3, \quad -3 \le t \le 3$$

to answer the following.

(a) Use a graphing utility to graph the curve.

(b) Find dy/dx and d^2y/dx^2.

(c) Find the equation of the tangent line at the point $\left(\sqrt{3}, \frac{8}{3}\right)$.

(d) Find the length of the curve.

83. Involute of a Circle The involute of a circle is described by the endpoint P of a string that is held taut as it is unwound from a spool that does not turn (see figure). Show that a parametric representation of the involute is

$$x = r(\cos \theta + \theta \sin \theta) \quad \text{and} \quad y = r(\sin \theta - \theta \cos \theta).$$

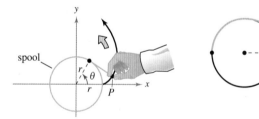

spool	
Figure for 83	Figure for 84

84. Involute of a Circle The figure shows a piece of string tied to a circle with a radius of one unit. The string is just long enough to reach the opposite side of the circle. Find the area that is covered when the string is unwound counterclockwise.

True or False? In Exercises 85–87, determine whether the statement is true or false. If it is false, explain why or give an example that shows it is false.

85. The curve given by $x = f(t)$ and $y = g(t)$ has the same arc length on $[a, b]$ as the curve given by $x = g(t)$ and $y = f(t)$.

86. If $x = f(t)$ and $y = g(t)$, then

$$\frac{d^2y}{dx^2} = \frac{g''(t)}{f''(t)}.$$

87. The curve given by $x = t^3$ and $y = t^2$ has a horizontal tangent at the origin because $dy/dt = 0$ when $t = 0$.

88. Implementing Processes

(a) Use a graphing utility to graph the curve given by

$$x = \frac{1 - t^2}{1 + t^2} \quad \text{and} \quad y = \frac{2t}{1 + t^2}$$

where $-20 \le t \le 20$.

(b) Describe the graph and confirm your result analytically.

(c) Discuss the speed at which the curve is traced as t increases from -20 to 20.

Calculus AP® – Exam Preparation Questions

89. Multiple Choice If $x = 2t^4$ and $y = (4t + 1)^2$, then $dy/dx =$

(A) $\dfrac{1}{t^2} + \dfrac{1}{4t^3}.$

(B) $\dfrac{4}{t^2} + \dfrac{1}{t^3}.$

(C) $\dfrac{t^3}{4t + 1}.$

(D) $\dfrac{t^2}{4} + t^3.$

90. Multiple Choice The length of the curve given by $x = \sin 3t$ and $y = \cos 2t$ from $t = 0$ to $t = \pi$ is represented by

(A) $\displaystyle\int_0^\pi \sqrt{9 \sin^2 3t + 4 \cos^2 2t}\, dt.$

(B) $\displaystyle\int_0^\pi \sqrt{9 \cos^2 3t + 4 \sin^2 2t}\, dt.$

(C) $\displaystyle\int_0^\pi \sqrt{3 \sin 3t + 2 \cos 2t}\, dt.$

(D) $\displaystyle\int_0^\pi \sqrt{3 \cos 3t - 2 \sin 2t}\, dt.$

91. Free Response At time $t \ge 0$, the position of the particle moving along a curve in the xy-plane is $(x(t), y(t))$, where

$$\frac{dx}{dt} = 2t - 5 \cos t \quad \text{and} \quad \frac{dy}{dt} = -\sin t.$$

At time $t = 4$, the particle is at the point $(-1, 3)$.

(a) Write an equation for the tangent line to the path of the particle at time $t = 4$.

(b) Find the time t when the tangent line to the path of the particle is vertical. Is the direction of the motion of the particle up or down at that moment? Explain your reasoning.

(c) Find the y-coordinate of the position of the particle at time $t = 0$.

(d) Find the total distance traveled by the particle on the interval $0 \le t \le 4$.

9.4 Polar Coordinates and Polar Graphs

▶ Understand the polar coordinate system.
▶ Rewrite rectangular coordinates and equations in polar form and vice versa.
▶ Sketch the graph of an equation given in polar form.
▶ Find the slope of a tangent line to a polar graph.
▶ Identify several types of special polar graphs.

Polar Coordinates

So far, you have been representing graphs as collections of points (x, y) on the rectangular coordinate system. The corresponding equations for these graphs have been in either rectangular or parametric form. In this section, you will study a coordinate system called the **polar coordinate system.**

To form the polar coordinate system in the plane, fix a point O, called the **pole** (or **origin**), and construct from O an initial ray called the **polar axis,** as shown in Figure 9.31. Then each point P in the plane can be assigned **polar coordinates** (r, θ), as follows.

r = *directed distance* from O to P

θ = *directed angle*, counterclockwise from polar axis to segment $\overline{OP}$

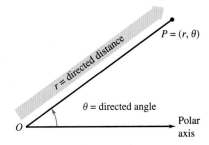

Polar coordinates
Figure 9.31

Figure 9.32 shows three points on the polar coordinate system. Notice that in this system, it is convenient to locate points with respect to a grid of concentric circles intersected by **radial lines** through the pole.

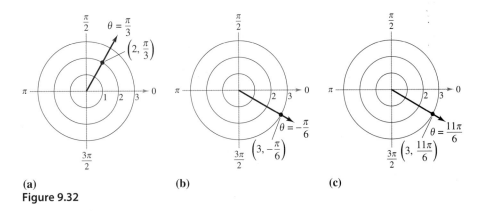

(a)   (b)   (c)
Figure 9.32

With rectangular coordinates, each point (x, y) has a unique representation. This is not true with polar coordinates. For instance, the coordinates

$$(r, \theta) \quad \text{and} \quad (r, 2\pi + \theta)$$

represent the same point. [See parts (b) and (c) in Figure 9.32.] Also, because r is a *directed distance,* the coordinates

$$(r, \theta) \quad \text{and} \quad (-r, \theta + \pi)$$

represent the same point. In general, the point (r, θ) can be written as

$$(r, \theta) = (r, \theta + 2n\pi)$$

or

$$(r, \theta) = (-r, \theta + (2n + 1)\pi)$$

where n is any integer. Moreover, the pole is represented by $(0, \theta)$, where θ is any angle.

Coordinate Conversion

To establish the relationship between polar and rectangular coordinates, let the polar axis coincide with the positive x-axis and the pole with the origin, as shown in Figure 9.33. Because (x, y) lies on a circle of radius r, it follows that

$$r^2 = x^2 + y^2.$$

Moreover, for $r > 0$, the definitions of the trigonometric functions imply that

$$\tan \theta = \frac{y}{x}, \quad \cos \theta = \frac{x}{r}, \quad \text{and} \quad \sin \theta = \frac{y}{r}.$$

You can show that the same relationships hold for $r < 0$.

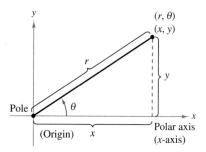

Relating polar and rectangular coordinates
Figure 9.33

Theorem 9.9   Coordinate Conversion

The polar coordinates (r, θ) of a point are related to the rectangular coordinates (x, y) of the point as follows.

Polar-to-Rectangular	*Rectangular-to-Polar*
$x = r \cos \theta$	$\tan \theta = \dfrac{y}{x}$
$y = r \sin \theta$	$r^2 = x^2 + y^2$

EXAMPLE 1   Polar-to-Rectangular Conversion

a. For the point $(r, \theta) = (2, \pi)$,

$$x = r \cos \theta = 2 \cos \pi = -2 \quad \text{and} \quad y = r \sin \theta = 2 \sin \pi = 0.$$

So, the rectangular coordinates are $(x, y) = (-2, 0)$.

b. For the point $(r, \theta) = \left(\sqrt{3}, \pi/6\right)$,

$$x = \sqrt{3} \cos \frac{\pi}{6} = \frac{3}{2} \quad \text{and} \quad y = \sqrt{3} \sin \frac{\pi}{6} = \frac{\sqrt{3}}{2}.$$

So, the rectangular coordinates are $(x, y) = \left(3/2, \sqrt{3}/2\right)$.

See Figure 9.34.

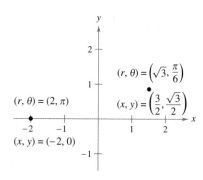

To convert from polar to rectangular coordinates, let $x = r \cos \theta$ and $y = r \sin \theta$.
Figure 9.34

EXAMPLE 2   Rectangular-to-Polar Conversion

a. For the second-quadrant point $(x, y) = (-1, 1)$,

$$\tan \theta = \frac{y}{x} = -1 \quad \Longrightarrow \quad \theta = \frac{3\pi}{4}.$$

Because θ was chosen to be in the same quadrant as (x, y), use a positive value of r.

$$r = \sqrt{x^2 + y^2} = \sqrt{(-1)^2 + (1)^2} = \sqrt{2}$$

This implies that *one* set of polar coordinates is $(r, \theta) = \left(\sqrt{2}, 3\pi/4\right)$.

b. Because the point $(x, y) = (0, 2)$ lies on the positive y-axis, choose $\theta = \pi/2$ and $r = 2$, and one set of polar coordinates is $(r, \theta) = (2, \pi/2)$.

See Figure 9.35.

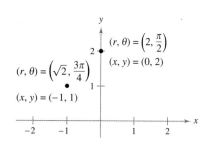

To convert from rectangular to polar coordinates, let $\tan \theta = y/x$ and $r = \sqrt{x^2 + y^2}$.
Figure 9.35

Note that you can also use Theorem 9.9 to convert a polar equation to a rectangular equation (and vice versa), as shown in Example 3.

Polar Graphs

One way to sketch the graph of a polar equation is to convert to rectangular coordinates and then sketch the graph of the rectangular equation.

EXAMPLE 3   Graphing Polar Equations

Describe the graph of each polar equation. Confirm each description by converting to a rectangular equation.

a. $r = 2$ **b.** $\theta = \dfrac{\pi}{3}$ **c.** $r = \sec \theta$

Solution

a. The graph of the polar equation $r = 2$ consists of all points that are two units from the pole. So, this graph is a circle centered at the origin with a radius of 2. [See Figure 9.36(a).] You can confirm this by using the relationship $r^2 = x^2 + y^2$ to obtain the rectangular equation

$$x^2 + y^2 = 2^2. \qquad \text{Rectangular equation}$$

b. The graph of the polar equation $\theta = \pi/3$ consists of all points on the line that makes an angle of $\pi/3$ with the positive x-axis. [See Figure 9.36(b).] You can confirm this by using the relationship $\tan \theta = y/x$ to obtain the rectangular equation

$$y = \sqrt{3}x. \qquad \text{Rectangular equation}$$

c. The graph of the polar equation $r = \sec \theta$ is not evident by simple inspection, so you can begin by converting to rectangular form using the relationship $r \cos \theta = x$.

$$r = \sec \theta \qquad \text{Polar equation}$$
$$r \cos \theta = 1$$
$$x = 1 \qquad \text{Rectangular equation}$$

From the rectangular equation, you can see that the graph is a vertical line. [See Figure 9.36(c).] ■

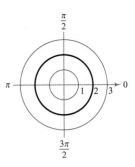

(a) Circle: $r = 2$

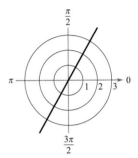

(b) Radial line: $\theta = \dfrac{\pi}{3}$

(c) Vertical line: $r = \sec \theta$

Figure 9.36

Technology

Sketching the graphs of complicated polar equations *by hand* can be tedious. With technology, however, the task is not difficult. Use a graphing utility in *polar* mode to graph the equations in the exercise set. If your graphing utility does not have a *polar* mode, but does have a *parametric* mode, you can graph $r = f(\theta)$ by writing the equation as

$$x = f(\theta) \cos \theta \quad \text{and} \quad y = f(\theta) \sin \theta.$$

For instance, the graph of $r = \frac{1}{2}\theta$ shown in the figure at the right was produced with a graphing utility in parametric mode. This equation was graphed using the parametric equations

$$x = \frac{1}{2}\theta \cos \theta \quad \text{and} \quad y = \frac{1}{2}\theta \sin \theta$$

with the values of θ varying from -4π to 4π. This curve is of the form

$$r = a\theta$$

and is called a **spiral of Archimedes.**

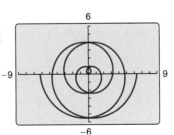

Spiral of Archimedes

EXAMPLE 4 Sketching a Polar Graph

See LarsonCalculusforAP.com for an interactive version of this type of example.

Sketch the graph of $r = 2 \cos 3\theta$.

Solution

Begin by writing the polar equation in parametric form.

$$x = 2 \cos 3\theta \cos \theta \quad \text{and} \quad y = 2 \cos 3\theta \sin \theta$$

After some experimentation, you will find that the entire curve, which is called a **rose curve,** can be sketched by letting θ vary from 0 to π, as shown in Figure 9.37. If you try duplicating this graph with a graphing utility, you will find that by letting θ vary from 0 to 2π, you will actually trace the entire curve *twice.*

> **Connecting Representations**
>
> One way to sketch the graph of $r = 2 \cos 3\theta$ by hand is to make a table of values.
>
> | θ | 0 | $\dfrac{\pi}{6}$ | $\dfrac{\pi}{3}$ | $\dfrac{\pi}{2}$ | $\dfrac{2\pi}{3}$ |
> |---|---|---|---|---|---|
> | r | 2 | 0 | -2 | 0 | 2 |
>
> By extending the table and plotting the points, you will obtain the curve shown in Example 4.

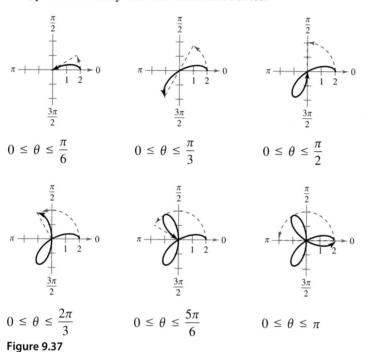

$$0 \le \theta \le \frac{\pi}{6} \qquad 0 \le \theta \le \frac{\pi}{3} \qquad 0 \le \theta \le \frac{\pi}{2}$$

$$0 \le \theta \le \frac{2\pi}{3} \qquad 0 \le \theta \le \frac{5\pi}{6} \qquad 0 \le \theta \le \pi$$

Figure 9.37

Use a graphing utility to experiment with other rose curves. Note that rose curves are of the form

$$r = a \cos n\theta \quad \text{or} \quad r = a \sin n\theta.$$

For instance, Figure 9.38 shows the graphs of two other rose curves.

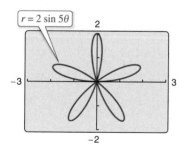

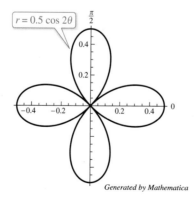

Generated by Mathematica

Rose curves
Figure 9.38

Slope and Tangent Lines

To find the slope of a tangent line to a polar graph, consider a differentiable function given by $r = f(\theta)$. To find the slope in polar form, use the parametric equations

$$x = r \cos \theta = f(\theta) \cos \theta \quad \text{and} \quad y = r \sin \theta = f(\theta) \sin \theta.$$

Using the parametric form of dy/dx given in Theorem 9.7, you have

$$\frac{dy}{dx} = \frac{dy/d\theta}{dx/d\theta} = \frac{f(\theta) \cos \theta + f'(\theta) \sin \theta}{-f(\theta) \sin \theta + f'(\theta) \cos \theta}$$

which establishes the next theorem.

Theorem 9.10   Slope in Polar Form

If f is a differentiable function of θ, then the *slope* of the tangent line to the graph of $r = f(\theta)$ at the point (r, θ) is

$$\frac{dy}{dx} = \frac{dy/d\theta}{dx/d\theta} = \frac{f(\theta) \cos \theta + f'(\theta) \sin \theta}{-f(\theta) \sin \theta + f'(\theta) \cos \theta}$$

provided that $dx/d\theta \neq 0$ at (r, θ). (See Figure 9.39.)

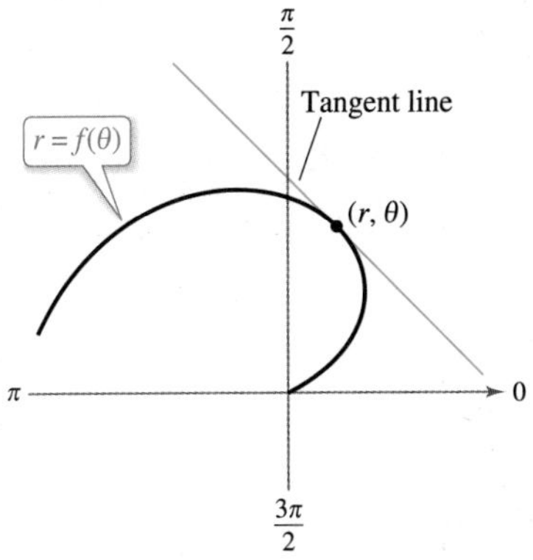

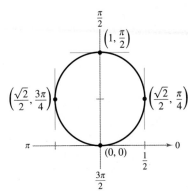

Tangent line to polar curve
Figure 9.39

From Theorem 9.10, you can make the following observations.

1. Solutions of $\dfrac{dy}{d\theta} = 0$ yield horizontal tangents, provided that $\dfrac{dx}{d\theta} \neq 0$.

2. Solutions of $\dfrac{dx}{d\theta} = 0$ yield vertical tangents, provided that $\dfrac{dy}{d\theta} \neq 0$.

If $dy/d\theta$ and $dx/d\theta$ are *simultaneously* 0, then no conclusion can be drawn about tangent lines.

EXAMPLE 5   Finding Horizontal and Vertical Tangent Lines

Find the horizontal and vertical tangent lines of $r = \sin \theta$, where $0 \leq \theta < \pi$.

Solution

Begin by writing the equation in parametric form.

$$x = r \cos \theta = \sin \theta \cos \theta \quad \text{and} \quad y = r \sin \theta = \sin \theta \sin \theta = \sin^2 \theta$$

Next, differentiate x and y with respect to θ and set each derivative equal to 0.

$$\frac{dx}{d\theta} = \cos^2 \theta - \sin^2 \theta = \cos 2\theta = 0 \quad \Longrightarrow \quad \theta = \frac{\pi}{4}, \frac{3\pi}{4}$$

$$\frac{dy}{d\theta} = 2 \sin \theta \cos \theta = \sin 2\theta = 0 \quad \Longrightarrow \quad \theta = 0, \frac{\pi}{2}$$

So, the graph has vertical tangent lines at

$$\left(\frac{\sqrt{2}}{2}, \frac{\pi}{4} \right) \quad \text{and} \quad \left(\frac{\sqrt{2}}{2}, \frac{3\pi}{4} \right)$$

and it has horizontal tangent lines at

$$(0, 0) \quad \text{and} \quad \left(1, \frac{\pi}{2} \right)$$

as shown in Figure 9.40.

Horizontal and vertical tangent lines of $r = \sin \theta$
Figure 9.40

EXAMPLE 6   Finding Horizontal and Vertical Tangent Lines

Find the horizontal and vertical tangent lines to the graph of $r = 2(1 - \cos \theta)$, where $0 \le \theta < 2\pi$.

Solution   Let $y = r \sin \theta$ and then differentiate with respect to θ.

$y = r \sin \theta$	Parametric equations for y
$\quad = 2(1 - \cos \theta) \sin \theta$	Substitute for r.
$\dfrac{dy}{d\theta} = 2[(1 - \cos \theta)(\cos \theta) + (\sin \theta)(\sin \theta)]$	Take derivative for y with respect to θ.
$\quad = 2(\cos \theta - \cos^2 \theta + \sin^2 \theta)$	Multiply.
$\quad = 2(\cos \theta - \cos^2 \theta + 1 - \cos^2 \theta)$	Pythagorean identity
$\quad = -2(2 \cos^2 \theta - \cos \theta - 1)$	Combine like terms and factor out -1.
$\quad = -2(2 \cos \theta + 1)(\cos \theta - 1)$	Factor.

Setting $dy/d\theta$ equal to 0, you can see that $\cos \theta = -\frac{1}{2}$ and $\cos \theta = 1$. So, $dy/d\theta = 0$ when $\theta = 2\pi/3$, $4\pi/3$, and 0. Similarly, using $x = r \cos \theta$, you have

$x = r \cos \theta$	Parametric equations for x
$\quad = 2(1 - \cos \theta) \cos \theta$	Substitute for r.
$\quad = 2 \cos \theta - 2 \cos^2 \theta$	Multiply.
$\dfrac{dx}{d\theta} = -2 \sin \theta + 4 \cos \theta \sin \theta$	Take derivative of x with respect to θ.
$\quad = (2 \sin \theta)(2 \cos \theta - 1).$	Factor.

Setting $dx/d\theta$ equal to 0, you can see that $\sin \theta = 0$ and $\cos \theta = \frac{1}{2}$. So, you can conclude that $dx/d\theta = 0$ when $\theta = 0$, π, $\pi/3$, and $5\pi/3$. From these results, and from the graph shown in Figure 9.41, you can conclude that the graph has horizontal tangents at $(3, 2\pi/3)$ and $(3, 4\pi/3)$, and has vertical tangents at $(1, \pi/3)$, $(1, 5\pi/3)$, and $(4, \pi)$. This graph is called a **cardioid**. Note that both derivatives ($dy/d\theta$ and $dx/d\theta$) are 0 when $\theta = 0$. Using this information alone, you do not know whether the graph has a horizontal or vertical tangent line at the pole. From Figure 9.41, however, you can see that the graph has a cusp at the pole.

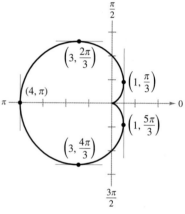

Horizontal and vertical tangent lines of $r = 2(1 - \cos \theta)$
Figure 9.41

Theorem 9.10 has an important consequence. If the graph of $r = f(\theta)$ passes through the pole when $\theta = \alpha$ and $f'(\alpha) \ne 0$, then the formula for dy/dx simplifies as follows.

$$\frac{dy}{dx} = \frac{f'(\alpha) \sin \alpha + f(\alpha) \cos \alpha}{f'(\alpha) \cos \alpha - f(\alpha) \sin \alpha} = \frac{f'(\alpha) \sin \alpha + 0}{f'(\alpha) \cos \alpha - 0} = \frac{\sin \alpha}{\cos \alpha} = \tan \alpha$$

So, the line $\theta = \alpha$ is tangent to the graph at the pole, $(0, \alpha)$.

Theorem 9.11   Tangent Lines at the Pole

If $f(\alpha) = 0$ and $f'(\alpha) \ne 0$, then the line $\theta = \alpha$ is tangent at the pole to the graph of $r = f(\theta)$.

Theorem 9.11 is useful because it states that the zeros of $r = f(\theta)$ can be used to find the tangent lines at the pole. Note that because a polar curve can cross the pole more than once, it can have more than one tangent line at the pole. For example, the rose curve $f(\theta) = 2 \cos 3\theta$ has three tangent lines at the pole, as shown in Figure 9.42. For this curve, $f(\theta) = 2 \cos 3\theta$ is 0 when θ is $\pi/6$, $\pi/2$, and $5\pi/6$. Moreover, the derivative $f'(\theta) = -6 \sin 3\theta$ is not 0 for these values of θ.

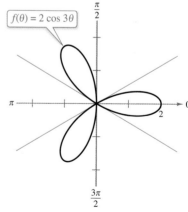

$f(\theta) = 2 \cos 3\theta$

This rose curve has three tangent lines ($\theta = \pi/6$, $\theta = \pi/2$, and $\theta = 5\pi/6$) at the pole.
Figure 9.42

Special Polar Graphs

Several important types of graphs have equations that are simpler in polar form than in rectangular form. For example, the polar equation of a circle having a radius of a and centered at the origin is simply $r = a$. Several other types of graphs that have simpler equations in polar form are shown below.

Limaçons

$r = a \pm b \cos \theta$

$r = a \pm b \sin \theta$

$(a > 0, b > 0)$

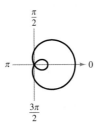

$\dfrac{a}{b} < 1$	$\dfrac{a}{b} = 1$	$1 < \dfrac{a}{b} < 2$	$\dfrac{a}{b} \geq 2$
Limaçon with inner loop	Cardioid (heart-shaped)	Dimpled limaçon	Convex limaçon

Rose Curves

n petals when n is odd

$2n$ petals when n is even

$(n \geq 2)$

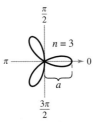

$r = a \cos n\theta$	$r = a \cos n\theta$	$r = a \sin n\theta$	$r = a \sin n\theta$
Rose curve	Rose curve	Rose curve	Rose curve

Circles and Lemniscates

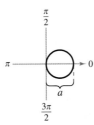

$r = a \cos \theta$	$r = a \sin \theta$	$r^2 = a^2 \sin 2\theta$	$r^2 = a^2 \cos 2\theta$
Circle	Circle	Lemniscate	Lemniscate

Technology

The rose curves described above are of the form $r = a \cos n\theta$ or $r = a \sin n\theta$, where n is a positive integer that is greater than or equal to 2. Use a graphing utility to graph

$r = a \cos n\theta$ or $r = a \sin n\theta$

for some noninteger values of n. Are these graphs also rose curves? For example, try sketching the graph of

$r = \cos \dfrac{2}{3}\theta, \quad 0 \leq \theta \leq 6\pi.$

9.4 Exercises

See *CalcChat.com* for tutorial help and worked-out solutions to odd-numbered exercises.

Polar-to-Rectangular Conversion In Exercises 1–10, the polar coordinates of a point are given. Plot the point and find the corresponding rectangular coordinates for the point.

1. $\left(8, \dfrac{\pi}{2}\right)$ **2.** $\left(-2, \dfrac{5\pi}{3}\right)$

3. $\left(-4, -\dfrac{3\pi}{4}\right)$ **4.** $\left(0, -\dfrac{7\pi}{6}\right)$

5. $\left(7, \dfrac{5\pi}{4}\right)$ **6.** $\left(-2, \dfrac{11\pi}{6}\right)$

7. $\left(\sqrt{2}, 2.36\right)$ **8.** $(-3, -1.57)$

9. $(-8, 7.85)$ **10.** $(1.75, -4.5)$

Rectangular-to-Polar Conversion In Exercises 11–20, the rectangular coordinates of a point are given. Plot the point and find *two* sets of polar coordinates for the point for $0 \le \theta < 2\pi$.

11. $(3, 0)$ **12.** $(0, -7.5)$

13. $(-3, 4)$ **14.** $(2, -6)$

15. $\left(-8, -2\sqrt{2}\right)$ **16.** $\left(3, -\sqrt{3}\right)$

17. $\left(\sqrt{7}, -\sqrt{7}\right)$ **18.** $\left(-2\sqrt{2}, -2\sqrt{2}\right)$

19. $(4, 5)$ **20.** $(1, 8)$

Error Analysis In Exercises 21 and 22, describe and correct the error in converting between rectangular and polar coordinates.

21. $(x, y) = \left(-3\sqrt{2}/2, 3\sqrt{2}/2\right)$

$\tan\theta = \dfrac{-3\sqrt{2}/2}{3\sqrt{2}/2} = -1 \Rightarrow \theta = -\dfrac{\pi}{4}$

$r = \sqrt{\left(-3\sqrt{2}/2\right)^2 + \left(3\sqrt{2}/2\right)^2} = 3$

$(r, \theta) = (3, -\pi/4)$

22. $(r, \theta) = (2, -\pi/6)$

$x = r\sin\theta = 2\sin(-\pi/6) = -1$

$y = r\cos\theta = 2\cos(-\pi/6) = \sqrt{3}$

$(x, y) = \left(-1, \sqrt{3}\right)$

Rectangular-to-Polar Conversion In Exercises 23–32, convert the rectangular equation to polar form and sketch its graph.

23. $x^2 + y^2 = 9$ **24.** $x^2 - y^2 = 9$

25. $x^2 + y^2 = a^2$ **26.** $x^2 + y^2 - 2ax = 0$

27. $y = 8$ **28.** $x = 12$

29. $3x - y + 2 = 0$ **30.** $xy = 4$

31. $y^2 = 9x$

32. $(x^2 + y^2)^2 - 5(4x^2 - y^2) = 0$

Polar-to-Rectangular Conversion In Exercises 33–42, convert the polar equation to rectangular form and sketch its graph.

33. $r = 4$ **34.** $r = -2$

35. $r = 3\sin\theta$ **36.** $r = 5\cos\theta$

37. $r^2 = \cot\theta$ **38.** $\theta = 5\pi/6$

39. $r = 3\sec\theta$ **40.** $r = -4\csc\theta$

41. $r = \sec\theta\tan\theta$ **42.** $r = \cot\theta\csc\theta$

Graphing a Polar Equation In Exercises 43–52, use a graphing utility to graph the polar equation. Find an interval for θ over which the graph is traced *only once*.

43. $r = 2 - 5\cos\theta$ **44.** $r = 3(1 - 4\cos\theta)$

45. $r = -4 + \sin\theta$ **46.** $r = 4 + 3\cos\theta$

47. $r = \dfrac{2}{1 + \cos\theta}$ **48.** $r = \dfrac{1}{4 - 3\sin\theta}$

49. $r = 5\cos\dfrac{3\theta}{4}$ **50.** $r = 3\sin\dfrac{5\theta}{2}$

51. $r^2 = 4\sin 2\theta$ **52.** $r^2 = 1/\theta$

53. Verifying a Polar Equation Convert the equation $r = 2(h\cos\theta + k\sin\theta)$ to rectangular form and verify that it is the equation of a circle. Find the radius and the rectangular coordinates of the center of the circle.

54. **HOW DO YOU SEE IT?** Identify each special polar graph and write its equation.

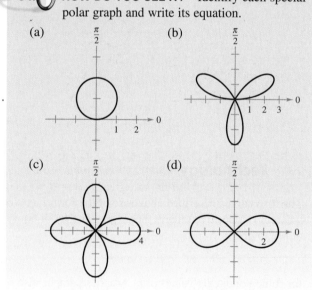

(a)   (b)   (c)   (d)

55. Sketching a Graph Sketch the graph of $r = 4\sin\theta$ over each interval.

(a) $0 \le \theta \le \dfrac{\pi}{2}$ (b) $\dfrac{\pi}{2} \le \theta \le \pi$ (c) $-\dfrac{\pi}{2} \le \theta \le \dfrac{\pi}{2}$

56. Distance Formula

(a) Verify that the Distance Formula for the distance between the two points (r_1, θ_1) and (r_2, θ_2) in polar coordinates is

$$d = \sqrt{r_1^2 + r_2^2 - 2r_1 r_2 \cos(\theta_1 - \theta_2)}.$$

(b) Describe the positions of the points relative to each other for $\theta_1 = \theta_2$. Simplify the Distance Formula for this case. Is the simplification what you expected? Explain.

(c) Simplify the Distance Formula for $\theta_1 - \theta_2 = 90°$. Is the simplification what you expected? Explain.

(d) Choose two points on the polar coordinate system and find the distance between them. Then choose different polar representations of the same two points and apply the Distance Formula again. Discuss the result.

Distance Formula   In Exercises 57–60, use the result of Exercise 56 to find the distance between the two points in polar coordinates.

57. $\left(1, \dfrac{5\pi}{6}\right)$, $\left(4, \dfrac{\pi}{3}\right)$ **58.** $\left(8, \dfrac{7\pi}{4}\right)$, $(5, \pi)$

59. $(2, 0.5)$, $(7, 1.2)$ **60.** $(4, 2.5)$, $(12, 1)$

 Finding Slopes of Tangent Lines In Exercises 61 and 62, find dy/dx and the slopes of the tangent lines shown on the graph of the polar equation.

61. $r = 2 + 3 \sin \theta$ **62.** $r = 2(1 - \sin \theta)$

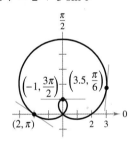 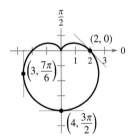

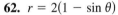 **Finding Slopes of Tangent Lines   In Exercises 63–66, use a graphing utility to (a) graph the polar equation, (b) draw the tangent line at the given value of θ, and (c) find dy/dx at the given value of θ. (Hint: Let the increment between the values of θ equal $\pi/24$.)**

63. $r = 3(1 - \cos \theta)$, $\theta = \dfrac{\pi}{2}$

64. $r = 3 - 2 \cos \theta$, $\theta = 0$

65. $r = 3 \sin \theta$, $\theta = \dfrac{\pi}{3}$ **66.** $r = 4$, $\theta = \dfrac{\pi}{4}$

Horizontal Tangency   In Exercises 67 and 68, find the points of horizontal tangency to the polar curve.

67. $r = 2 \csc \theta + 3$ **68.** $r = a \sin \theta \cos^2 \theta$

 Horizontal and Vertical Tangency In Exercises 69 and 70, find the points of horizontal and vertical tangency to the polar curve.

69. $r = 1 - \sin \theta$ **70.** $r = a \sin \theta$

 Tangent Lines at the Pole In Exercises 71–78, sketch a graph of the polar equation and find the tangent lines at the pole.

71. $r = 5 \sin \theta$ **72.** $r = 5 \cos \theta$

73. $r = 2(1 - \sin \theta)$ **74.** $r = 3(1 - \cos \theta)$

75. $r = 4 \cos 3\theta$ **76.** $r = -\sin 5\theta$

77. $r = 3 \sin 2\theta$ **78.** $r = 3 \cos 2\theta$

Sketching a Polar Graph   In Exercises 79–90, sketch a graph of the polar equation.

79. $r = 8$ **80.** $r = 1$

81. $r = 4(1 + \cos \theta)$ **82.** $r = 1 + \sin \theta$

83. $r = -9 + 6 \cos \theta$ **84.** $r = 5 - 4 \sin \theta$

85. $r = -2 \csc \theta$ **86.** $r = \dfrac{6}{2 \sin \theta - 3 \cos \theta}$

87. $r = 7\theta$ **88.** $r = 1/\theta$

89. $r^2 = 4 \cos 2\theta$ **90.** $r^2 = 4 \sin \theta$

EXPLORING CONCEPTS ——————

91. Communicating Describe the differences between the rectangular coordinate system and the polar coordinate system.

92. Communicating Describe how to test whether a polar graph is symmetric about (a) the x-axis and (b) the y-axis.

93. Tangent Lines How are the slopes of tangent lines determined in polar coordinates? What are tangent lines at the pole and how are they determined?

——————————————————

94. Connecting Representations Use a graphing utility to graph the polar equation $r = 6[1 + \cos(\theta - \phi)]$ for (a) $\phi = 0$, (b) $\phi = \pi/4$, and (c) $\phi = \pi/2$. Use the graphs to describe the effect of the angle ϕ. Write the equation as a function of $\sin \theta$ for part (c).

95. Justifying Verify that if the curve whose polar equation is $r = f(\theta)$ is rotated about the pole through an angle ϕ, then an equation for the rotated curve is $r = f(\theta - \phi)$.

96. Justifying The polar form of an equation of a curve is $r = f(\sin \theta)$. Show that the form becomes

(a) $r = f(-\cos \theta)$ if the curve is rotated counterclockwise $\pi/2$ radians about the pole.

(b) $r = f(-\sin \theta)$ if the curve is rotated counterclockwise π radians about the pole.

(c) $r = f(\cos \theta)$ if the curve is rotated counterclockwise $3\pi/2$ radians about the pole.

Rotated Curve   In Exercises 97 and 98, use the results of Exercises 95 and 96.

97. Write an equation for the limaçon $r = 2 - \sin \theta$ after it has been rotated counterclockwise by an angle of (a) $\theta = \pi/4$, (b) $\theta = r/2$, (c) $\theta = \pi$, and (d) $\theta = 3\pi/2$. Use a graphing utility to graph each rotated limaçon.

98. Prove that the tangent of the angle ψ $(0 \le \psi \le \pi/2)$ between the radial line and the tangent line at the point (r, θ) on the graph of $r = f(\theta)$ (see figure) is given by

$$\tan \psi = \left| \frac{r}{dr/d\theta} \right|.$$

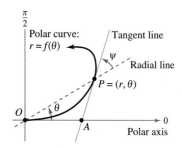

Finding an Angle   In Exercises 99–102, use the result of Exercise 98 to find the angle ψ between the radial and tangent lines to the graph for the indicated value of θ. Use a graphing utility to graph the polar equation, the radial line, and the tangent line for the indicated value of θ.

99. $r = 2(1 - \cos \theta)$, $\theta = \pi$ **100.** $r = 4 \sin 2\theta$, $\theta = \dfrac{\pi}{6}$

101. $r = \dfrac{6}{1 - \cos \theta}$, $\theta = \dfrac{2\pi}{3}$ **102.** $r = 5$, $\theta = \dfrac{\pi}{6}$

True or False?   In Exercises 103 and 104, determine whether the statement is true or false. If it is false, explain why or give an example that shows it is false.

103. If (r_1, θ_1) and (r_2, θ_2) represent the same point on the polar coordinate system, then $|r_1| = |r_2|$.

104. If (r, θ_1) and (r, θ_2) represent the same point on the polar coordinate system, then $\theta_1 = \theta_2 + 2n\pi$ for some integer n.

Calculus AP® – Exam Preparation Questions

105. Free Response   A polar curve is given by $r = 5/(3 - \cos \theta)$.

(a) What is the slope of the tangent line to the curve at $\theta = 3\pi/2$?

(b) What is the rectangular equation of the tangent line at $\theta = 3\pi/2$?

(c) What angle θ corresponds to the point on the curve with an x-coordinate of -1? Justify your answer.

Exam Preparation Questions   (continued)

106. Free Response   The graphs of the polar curves $r = 4$ and $r = 4 - 3 \sin 2\theta$ are shown in the figure for $0 \le \theta \le \pi$.

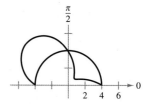

(a) For $r = 4 - 3 \sin 2\theta$, find the value of $dx/d\theta$ at $\theta = \pi/3$.

(b) The distance between the curves changes for $0 < \theta < \pi/2$. Write an expression for the distance D between the curves for $0 < \theta < \pi/2$. Find the rate at which the distance between the curves is changing with respect to θ when $\theta = \pi/6$. Show the work that leads to your answer.

SECTION PROJECT

Cissoid of Diocles

Consider a circle of radius a tangent to the y-axis and the line $x = 2a$. Let O be the origin and let A be the point at which the segment OB intersects the circle, where point B lies on the line $x = 2a$. The **cissoid of Diocles** (shown in the figure) consists of all points P such that P lies on OB and $OP = AB$.

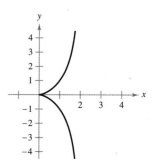

(a) Sketch the cissoid of Diocles when $a = 1$ by first plotting the corresponding circle and vertical line, then using a ruler to plot points P. Compare your graph to the graph above.

(b) Find a polar equation of the cissoid.

(c) Find a set of parametric equations for the cissoid.

(d) Find another set of parametric equations for the cissoid that does not contain trigonometric functions.

(e) Find a rectangular equation of the cissoid.

9.5   Area and Arc Length in Polar Coordinates

▶ Find the area of a region bounded by a polar graph.
▶ Find the points of intersection of two polar graphs.
▶ Find the arc length of a polar graph.

Area of a Polar Region

The development of a formula for the area of a polar region parallels that for the area of a region on the rectangular coordinate system, but uses sectors of a circle instead of rectangles as the basic elements of area. In the figure at the right, note that the area of a circular sector of radius r is $\frac{1}{2}\theta r^2$, provided θ is measured in radians.

The area of a sector of a circle is $A = \frac{1}{2}\theta r^2$.

Consider the function $r = f(\theta)$, where f is continuous and nonnegative on the interval $\alpha \le \theta \le \beta$. The region bounded by the graph of f and the radial lines $\theta = \alpha$ and $\theta = \beta$ is shown in Figure 9.43(a). To find the area of this region, partition the interval $[\alpha, \beta]$ into n equal subintervals

$$\alpha = \theta_0 < \theta_1 < \theta_2 < \cdots < \theta_{n-1} < \theta_n = \beta.$$

Then approximate the area of the region by the sum of the areas of the n sectors, as shown in Figure 9.43(b).

Radius of ith section $= f(\theta_i)$

Central angle of ith sector $= \dfrac{\beta - \alpha}{n} = \Delta\theta$

$$A \approx \sum_{i=1}^{n} \left(\frac{1}{2}\right) \Delta\theta [f(\theta_i)]^2$$

Taking the limit as $n \to \infty$ produces

$$A = \lim_{n \to \infty} \frac{1}{2} \sum_{i=1}^{n} [f(\theta_i)]^2 \Delta\theta$$

$$= \frac{1}{2} \int_{\alpha}^{\beta} [f(\theta)]^2 \, d\theta$$

which leads to the next theorem.

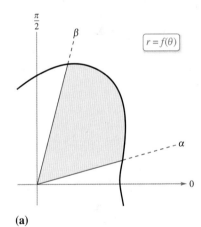

(a)

Theorem 9.12   Area in Polar Coordinates

If f is continuous and nonnegative on the interval $[\alpha, \beta]$ where

$$0 < \beta - \alpha \le 2\pi$$

then the area of the region bounded by the graph of $r = f(\theta)$ between the radial lines $\theta = \alpha$ and $\theta = \beta$ is

$$A = \frac{1}{2} \int_{\alpha}^{\beta} [f(\theta)]^2 \, d\theta$$

$$= \frac{1}{2} \int_{\alpha}^{\beta} r^2 \, d\theta. \qquad 0 < \beta - \alpha \le 2\pi$$

(b)

Figure 9.43

You can use the formula in Theorem 9.12 to find the area of a region bounded by the graph of a continuous *nonpositive* function. The formula is not necessarily valid, however, when f takes on both positive *and* negative values in the interval $[\alpha, \beta]$.

EXAMPLE 1 Finding the Area of a Polar Region

See LarsonCalculusforAP.com for an interactive version of this type of example.

Find the area of one petal of the rose curve $r = 3 \cos 3\theta$.

Solution

In Figure 9.44, you can see that the petal on the right is traced as θ increases from $-\pi/6$ to $\pi/6$. So, the area is

$$A = \frac{1}{2} \int_\alpha^\beta r^2 \, d\theta = \frac{1}{2} \int_{-\pi/6}^{\pi/6} (3 \cos 3\theta)^2 \, d\theta \qquad \text{Use formula for area in polar coordinates.}$$

$$= \frac{9}{2} \int_{-\pi/6}^{\pi/6} \frac{1 + \cos 6\theta}{2} \, d\theta \qquad \text{Power-reducing formula}$$

$$= \frac{9}{4} \left[\theta + \frac{\sin 6\theta}{6} \right]_{-\pi/6}^{\pi/6}$$

$$= \frac{9}{4} \left(\frac{\pi}{6} + \frac{\pi}{6} \right)$$

$$= \frac{3\pi}{4}.$$

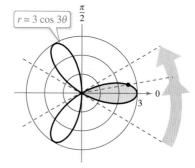

The area of one petal of the rose curve that lies between the radial lines $\theta = -\pi/6$ and $\theta = \pi/6$ is $3\pi/4$.
Figure 9.44

To find the area of the region lying inside all three petals of the rose curve in Example 1, you could *not* simply integrate between 0 and 2π. By doing this, you would obtain $9\pi/2$, which is twice the area of the three petals. The duplication occurs because the rose curve is traced twice as θ increases from 0 to 2π.

EXAMPLE 2 Finding the Area Bounded by a Single Curve

Find the area of the region lying between the inner and outer loops of the limaçon $r = 1 - 2 \sin \theta$.

Solution

In Figure 9.45, note that the inner loop is traced as θ increases from $\pi/6$ to $5\pi/6$. So, the area inside the *inner loop* is

$$A_1 = \frac{1}{2} \int_{\pi/6}^{5\pi/6} (1 - 2 \sin \theta)^2 \, d\theta \qquad \text{Use formula for area in polar coordinates.}$$

$$= \frac{1}{2} \int_{\pi/6}^{5\pi/6} (1 - 4 \sin \theta + 4 \sin^2 \theta) \, d\theta$$

$$= \frac{1}{2} \int_{\pi/6}^{5\pi/6} \left[1 - 4 \sin \theta + 4 \left(\frac{1 - \cos 2\theta}{2} \right) \right] d\theta \qquad \text{Power-reducing formula}$$

$$= \frac{1}{2} \int_{\pi/6}^{5\pi/6} (3 - 4 \sin \theta - 2 \cos 2\theta) \, d\theta \qquad \text{Simplify.}$$

$$= \frac{1}{2} \left[3\theta + 4 \cos \theta - \sin 2\theta \right]_{\pi/6}^{5\pi/6}$$

$$= \frac{1}{2} \left(2\pi - 3\sqrt{3} \right)$$

$$= \pi - \frac{3\sqrt{3}}{2}.$$

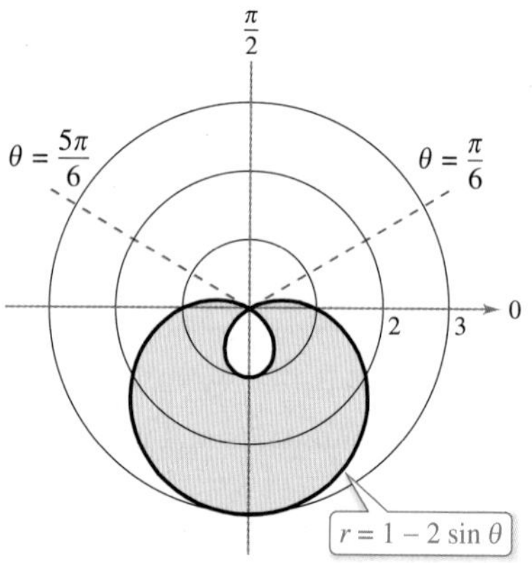

The area between the inner and outer loops is approximately 8.34.
Figure 9.45

In a similar way, you can integrate from $5\pi/6$ to $13\pi/6$ to find that the area of the region lying inside the *outer loop* is $A_2 = 2\pi + \left(3\sqrt{3}/2\right)$. The area of the region lying between the two loops is the difference of A_2 and A_1.

$$A = A_2 - A_1 = \left(2\pi + \frac{3\sqrt{3}}{2} \right) - \left(\pi - \frac{3\sqrt{3}}{2} \right) = \pi + 3\sqrt{3} \approx 8.34$$

Points of Intersection of Polar Graphs

Because a point may be represented in different ways in polar coordinates, care must be taken in determining the points of intersection of two polar graphs. For example, consider the points of intersection of the graphs of

$$r = 1 - 2\cos\theta \quad \text{and} \quad r = 1$$

as shown in Figure 9.46. As with rectangular equations, you can attempt to find the points of intersection by solving the two equations simultaneously, as shown.

$r = 1 - 2\cos\theta$	First equation
$1 = 1 - 2\cos\theta$	Substitute $r = 1$ from 2nd equation into 1st equation.
$\cos\theta = 0$	Simplify.
$\theta = \dfrac{\pi}{2}, \dfrac{3\pi}{2}$	Solve for θ.

The corresponding points of intersection are

$$\left(1, \frac{\pi}{2}\right) \quad \text{and} \quad \left(1, \frac{3\pi}{2}\right).$$

From Figure 9.46, however, you can see that there is a *third* point of intersection that did not show up when the two polar equations were solved simultaneously. (This is one reason why you should sketch a graph when finding the area of a polar region.) The reason the third point was not found is that it does not occur with the same coordinates in the two graphs. On the graph of

$$r = 1$$

the point occurs with coordinates $(1, \pi)$, but on the graph of

$$r = 1 - 2\cos\theta$$

the point occurs with coordinates $(-1, 0)$.

In addition to solving equations simultaneously and sketching a graph, note that because the pole can be represented by $(0, \theta)$, where θ is *any* angle, you should check separately for the pole when finding points of intersection.

You can compare the problem of finding points of intersection of two polar graphs with that of finding collision points of two satellites in intersecting orbits about Earth, as shown in Figure 9.47. The satellites will not collide as long as they reach the points of intersection at different times (θ-values). Collisions will occur only at the points of intersection that are "simultaneous points"—those that are reached at the same time (θ-value).

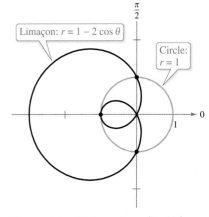

Three points of intersection: $(1, \pi/2)$, $(-1, 0)$, and $(1, 3\pi/2)$

Figure 9.46

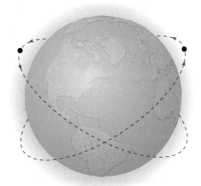

The paths of satellites can cross without causing a collision.

Figure 9.47

EXAMPLE 3 Finding the Area of a Region Between Two Curves

Find the area of the region common to the two regions bounded by the curves

$$r = -6 \cos \theta \qquad \text{Circle}$$

and

$$r = 2 - 2 \cos \theta. \qquad \text{Cardioid}$$

Solution

Because both curves are symmetric with respect to the x-axis, you can work with the upper half-plane, as shown in Figure 9.48. The blue shaded region lies between the circle and the radial line

$$\theta = \frac{2\pi}{3}.$$

Because the circle has coordinates $(0, \pi/2)$ at the pole, you can integrate between $\pi/2$ and $2\pi/3$ to obtain the area of this region. The region that is shaded red is bounded by the radial lines $\theta = 2\pi/3$ and $\theta = \pi$ and the cardioid. So, you can find the area of this second region by integrating between $2\pi/3$ and π. The sum of these two integrals gives the area of the common region lying *above* the radial line $\theta = \pi$.

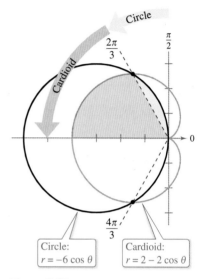

Figure 9.48

$$\overbrace{\phantom{\frac{1}{2} \int_{\pi/2}^{2\pi/3} (-6\cos\theta)^2 d\theta}}^{\substack{\text{Region between circle}\\\text{and radial line } \theta = 2\pi/3}} \quad \overbrace{\phantom{\frac{1}{2} \int_{2\pi/3}^{\pi} (2-2\cos\theta)^2 d\theta}}^{\substack{\text{Region between cardioid and}\\\text{radial lines } \theta = 2\pi/3 \text{ and } \theta = \pi}}$$

$$\frac{A}{2} = \frac{1}{2} \int_{\pi/2}^{2\pi/3} (-6 \cos \theta)^2 \, d\theta + \frac{1}{2} \int_{2\pi/3}^{\pi} (2 - 2 \cos \theta)^2 \, d\theta$$

$$= 18 \int_{\pi/2}^{2\pi/3} \cos^2 \theta \, d\theta + \frac{1}{2} \int_{2\pi/3}^{\pi} (4 - 8 \cos \theta + 4 \cos^2 \theta) \, d\theta$$

$$= 9 \int_{\pi/2}^{2\pi/3} (1 + \cos 2\theta) \, d\theta + \int_{2\pi/3}^{\pi} (3 - 4 \cos \theta + \cos 2\theta) \, d\theta$$

$$= 9 \left[\theta + \frac{\sin 2\theta}{2} \right]_{\pi/2}^{2\pi/3} + \left[3\theta - 4 \sin \theta + \frac{\sin 2\theta}{2} \right]_{2\pi/3}^{\pi}$$

$$= 9 \left(\frac{2\pi}{3} - \frac{\sqrt{3}}{4} - \frac{\pi}{2} \right) + \left(3\pi - 2\pi + 2\sqrt{3} + \frac{\sqrt{3}}{4} \right)$$

$$= \frac{5\pi}{2}$$

Finally, multiplying by 2, you can conclude that the total area is

$$5\pi \approx 15.7. \qquad \text{Area of region inside circle and cardioid}$$

To check the reasonableness of this result, note that the area of the circular region is

$$\pi r^2 = 9\pi. \qquad \text{Area of circle}$$

So, it seems reasonable that the area of the region lying inside the circle and the cardioid is 5π. ∎

To see the benefit of polar coordinates for finding the area in Example 3, consider the integral below, which gives the comparable area in rectangular coordinates.

$$\frac{A}{2} = \int_{-4}^{-3/2} \sqrt{2\sqrt{1 - 2x} - x^2 - 2x + 2} \, dx + \int_{-3/2}^{0} \sqrt{-x^2 - 6x} \, dx$$

Use the integration capabilities of a graphing utility to show that you obtain the same area as that found in Example 3.

Arc Length in Polar Form

The formula for the length of a polar arc can be obtained from the arc length formula for a curve described by parametric equations. (See Exercise 75.)

Theorem 9.13   Arc Length of a Polar Curve

Let f be a function whose derivative is continuous on an interval $\alpha \le \theta \le \beta$. The length of the graph of $r = f(\theta)$ from $\theta = \alpha$ to $\theta = \beta$ is

$$s = \int_{\alpha}^{\beta} \sqrt{[f(\theta)]^2 + [f'(\theta)]^2}\, d\theta = \int_{\alpha}^{\beta} \sqrt{r^2 + \left(\frac{dr}{d\theta}\right)^2}\, d\theta.$$

Justification

When applying the arc length formula to a polar curve, be sure that the curve is traced out only once on the interval of integration. For instance, the rose curve $r = \cos 3\theta$ is traced out once on the interval $0 \le \theta \le \pi$ but is traced out twice on the interval $0 \le \theta \le 2\pi$.

EXAMPLE 4   Finding the Length of a Polar Curve

Find the length of the arc from $\theta = 0$ to $\theta = 2\pi$ for the cardioid

$$r = f(\theta) = 2 - 2\cos\theta$$

as shown in Figure 9.49.

Solution

Because $f'(\theta) = 2\sin\theta$, you can find the arc length as follows.

$$
\begin{aligned}
s &= \int_{\alpha}^{\beta} \sqrt{[f(\theta)]^2 + [f'(\theta)]^2}\, d\theta && \text{Formula for arc length of a polar curve} \\
&= \int_{0}^{2\pi} \sqrt{(2 - 2\cos\theta)^2 + (2\sin\theta)^2}\, d\theta \\
&= 2\sqrt{2} \int_{0}^{2\pi} \sqrt{1 - \cos\theta}\, d\theta && \text{Simplify.} \\
&= 2\sqrt{2} \int_{0}^{2\pi} \sqrt{2\sin^2\frac{\theta}{2}}\, d\theta && \text{Trigonometric identity} \\
&= 4 \int_{0}^{2\pi} \sin\frac{\theta}{2}\, d\theta && \sin\frac{\theta}{2} \ge 0 \text{ for } 0 \le \theta \le 2\pi \\
&= 8\left[-\cos\frac{\theta}{2}\right]_{0}^{2\pi} \\
&= 8(1 + 1) \\
&= 16
\end{aligned}
$$

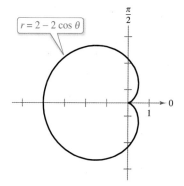

$r = 2 - 2\cos\theta$

Figure 9.49

Using Figure 9.49, you can determine the reasonableness of this answer by comparing it with the circumference of a circle. For example, a circle of radius $\frac{5}{2}$ has a circumference of

$$5\pi \approx 15.7.$$

Note that in the fifth step of the solution, it is legitimate to write

$$\sqrt{2\sin^2\frac{\theta}{2}} = \sqrt{2}\sin\frac{\theta}{2}$$

rather than

$$\sqrt{2\sin^2\frac{\theta}{2}} = \sqrt{2}\left|\sin\frac{\theta}{2}\right|$$

because $\sin(\theta/2) \ge 0$ for $0 \le \theta \le 2\pi$.

Insight

Arc length of a polar curve is not tested on the AP® Exam.

9.5 Exercises

See *CalcChat.com* for tutorial help and worked-out solutions to odd-numbered exercises.

Area of a Polar Region In Exercises 1–4, write an integral that represents the area of the shaded region of the figure. Do not evaluate the integral.

1. $r = 4 \sin \theta$

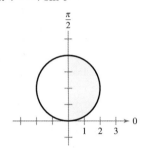

2. $r = \cos 2\theta$

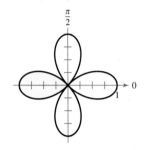

3. $r = 3 - 2 \sin \theta$

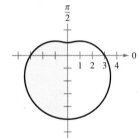

4. $r = 1 - \cos 2\theta$

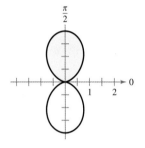

Error Analysis In Exercises 5 and 6, describe and correct the error in writing the integral that represents the area of the region.

5. Interior of $r = \sin \theta$

$$A = \frac{1}{2} \int_0^{2\pi} (\sin \theta)^2 \, d\theta \quad \text{✗}$$

6. One petal of $r = \cos 3\theta$

$$A = \frac{1}{2} \int_{-\pi/3}^{\pi/3} (\cos 3\theta)^2 \, d\theta \quad \text{✗}$$

Finding the Area of a Polar Region In Exercises 7–18, find the area of the region.

7. Interior of $r = 6 \sin \theta$

8. Interior of $r = 3 \cos \theta$

9. One petal of $r = 2 \cos 3\theta$

10. Two petals of $r = 4 \sin 3\theta$

11. Two petals of $r = \sin 2\theta$

12. Three petals of $r = \cos 5\theta$

13. Interior of $r = 6 + 5 \sin \theta$ (below the polar axis)

14. Interior of $r = 2 - \sin \theta$ (above the polar axis)

15. Interior of $r = 4 + \sin \theta$

16. Interior of $r = 1 - \cos \theta$

17. Interior of $r^2 = 4 \cos 2\theta$ **18.** Interior of $r^2 = 6 \sin 2\theta$

Finding the Area of a Polar Region In Exercises 19–26, use a graphing utility to graph the polar equation. Find the area of the given region analytically.

19. Inner loop of $r = 1 + 2 \cos \theta$

20. Inner loop of $r = 2 - 4 \cos \theta$

21. Inner loop of $r = 1 + 2 \sin \theta$

22. Inner loop of $r = 4 - 6 \sin \theta$

23. Between the loops of $r = 1 + 2 \cos \theta$

24. Between the loops of $r = 2(1 + 2 \sin \theta)$

25. Between the loops of $r = 3 - 6 \sin \theta$

26. Between the loops of $r = \frac{1}{2} + \cos \theta$

Finding Points of Intersection In Exercises 27–34, find the points of intersection of the graphs of the equations.

27. $r = 1 + \cos \theta$
$r = 1 - \cos \theta$

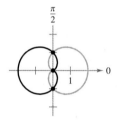

28. $r = 3(1 + \sin \theta)$
$r = 3(1 - \sin \theta)$

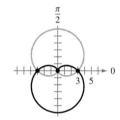

29. $r = 1 + \cos \theta$
$r = 1 - \sin \theta$

30. $r = 2 - 3 \cos \theta$
$r = \cos \theta$

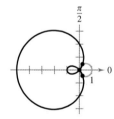

31. $r = 4 - 5 \sin \theta$
$r = 3 \sin \theta$

32. $r = 3 + \sin \theta$
$r = 3 \csc \theta$

33. $r = \dfrac{\theta}{2}, \ r = 2$

34. $\theta = -\dfrac{\pi}{4}, \ r = 2$

Justifying In Exercises 35 and 36, use a graphing utility to graph the polar equations and approximate the points of intersection of the graphs. Watch the graphs as they are traced in the viewing window. Explain why the pole is not a point of intersection obtained by solving the equations simultaneously.

35. $r = \cos \theta$
$r = 2 - 3 \sin \theta$

36. $r = 4 \sin \theta$
$r = 2(1 + \sin \theta)$

Finding the Area of a Polar Region Between Two Curves In Exercises 37–44, use a graphing utility to graph the polar equations. Find the area of the given region analytically.

37. Common interior of $r = 4 \sin 2\theta$ and $r = 2$

38. Common interior of $r = 2(1 + \cos \theta)$ and $r = 2(1 - \cos \theta)$

39. Common interior of $r = 3 - 2 \sin \theta$ and $r = -3 + 2 \sin \theta$

40. Common interior of $r = 5 - 3 \sin \theta$ and $r = 5 - 3 \cos \theta$

41. Common interior of $r = 4 \sin \theta$ and $r = 2$

42. Common interior of $r = 2 \cos \theta$ and $r = 2 \sin \theta$

43. Inside $r = 2 \cos \theta$ and outside $r = 1$

44. Inside $r = 3 \sin \theta$ and outside $r = 1 + \sin \theta$

Finding the Area of a Polar Region Between Two Curves In Exercises 45–48, find the area of the region.

45. Inside $r = a(1 + \cos \theta)$ and outside $r = a \cos \theta$

46. Inside $r = 2a \cos \theta$ and outside $r = a$

47. Common interior of $r = a(1 + \cos \theta)$ and $r = a \sin \theta$

48. Common interior of $r = a \cos \theta$ and $r = a \sin \theta$, where $a > 0$

---

49. ANTENNA RADIATION

The radiation from a transmitting antenna is not uniform in all directions. The region receiving the signal at a given intensity is modeled by $r = a \cos^2 \theta$.

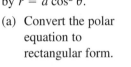

(a) Convert the polar equation to rectangular form.

(b) Use a graphing utility to graph the model for $a = 4$ and $a = 6$.

(c) Find the area of the geographical region between the two curves in part (b).

50. Area The three interlocking circles

$$r = 2a \cos \theta, \quad r = 2a \sin \theta, \quad \text{and} \quad r = a$$

form a region with seven sub-regions. Find the area of each sub-region.

51. Conjecture Find the area of the region enclosed by $r = a \cos n\theta$ for $n = 1, 2, 3, \dots$. Use the results to make a conjecture about the area enclosed by the function when n is even and when n is odd.

52. Area Sketch the strophoid $r = \sec \theta - 2 \cos \theta$, where $-\pi/2 < \theta < \pi/2$. Convert this equation to rectangular coordinates. Find the area enclosed by the loop.

Finding the Arc Length of a Polar Curve In Exercises 53–58, find the length of the curve over the given interval.

53. $r = 8, \ \left[0, \dfrac{\pi}{6}\right]$ **54.** $r = a, \ [0, 2\pi]$

55. $r = 4 \sin \theta, \ [0, \pi]$

56. $r = 2a \cos \theta, \ \left[-\dfrac{\pi}{4}, \dfrac{\pi}{4}\right]$

57. $r = 1 + \sin \theta, \ [0, 2\pi]$

58. $r = 8(1 + \cos \theta), \ \left[0, \dfrac{\pi}{3}\right]$

Finding the Arc Length of a Polar Curve In Exercises 59–64, use a graphing utility to graph the polar equation over the given interval. Use the integration capabilities of the graphing utility to approximate the length of the curve.

59. $r = 2\theta, \ \left[0, \dfrac{\pi}{2}\right]$ **60.** $r = \sec \theta, \ \left[0, \dfrac{\pi}{6}\right]$

61. $r = \dfrac{1}{\theta}, \ [\pi, 2\pi]$ **62.** $r = e^{\theta}, \ \left[0, \dfrac{\pi}{2}\right]$

63. $r = \sin(3 \cos \theta), \ [0, \pi]$

64. $r = 2 \sin(2 \cos \theta), \ [0, \pi]$

EXPLORING CONCEPTS

Implementing Processes In Exercises 65 and 66, (a) sketch the graph of the polar equation, (b) determine the interval that traces the graph only once, (c) find the area of the region bounded by the graph using a geometric formula, and (d) find the area of the region bounded by the graph using integration.

65. $r = 10 \cos \theta$ **66.** $r = 5 \sin \theta$

67. Think About It Let $f(\theta) > 0$ for all θ and let $g(\theta) < 0$ for all θ. Find polar equations $r = f(\theta)$ and $r = g(\theta)$ such that their graphs intersect.

---

68. HOW DO YOU SEE IT? Which graph, traced out only once, has a greater arc length? Explain your reasoning.

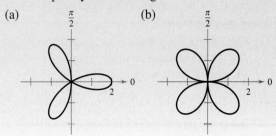

69. Connecting Representations Consider the circle $r = 8 \cos \theta$.

(a) Find the area of the circle.

(b) Complete the table for the areas A of the sectors of the circle between $\theta = 0$ and the values of θ in the table.

θ	0.2	0.4	0.6	0.8	1.0	1.2	1.4
A							

(c) Use the table in part (b) to approximate the values of θ for which the sector of the circle composes $\frac{1}{4}$, $\frac{1}{2}$, and $\frac{3}{4}$ of the total area of the circle.

(d) Use a graphing utility to approximate, to two decimal places, the angles θ for which the sector of the circle composes $\frac{1}{4}$, $\frac{1}{2}$, and $\frac{3}{4}$ of the total area of the circle.

(e) Do the results of part (d) depend on the radius of the circle? Explain.

70. Connecting Representations Consider the circle $r = 3 \sin \theta$.

(a) Find the area of the circle.

(b) Complete the table for the areas A of the sectors of the circle between $\theta = 0$ and the values of θ in the table.

θ	0.2	0.4	0.6	0.8	1.0	1.2	1.4
A							

(c) Use the table in part (b) to approximate the values of θ for which the sector of the circle composes $\frac{1}{8}$, $\frac{1}{4}$, and $\frac{1}{2}$ of the total area of the circle.

(d) Use a graphing utility to approximate, to two decimal places, the angles θ for which the sector of the circle composes $\frac{1}{8}$, $\frac{1}{4}$, and $\frac{1}{2}$ of the total area of the circle.

71. Connecting Representations Find the area of the circle given by $r = \sin \theta + \cos \theta$. Check your result by converting the polar equation to rectangular form, then using the formula for the area of a circle.

72. Spiral of Archimedes The curve represented by the equation $r = a\theta$, where a is a constant, is called the spiral of Archimedes.

(a) Use a graphing utility to graph $r = \theta$, where $\theta \geq 0$. What happens to the graph of $r = a\theta$ as a increases? What happens if $\theta \leq 0$?

(b) Determine the points on the spiral $r = a\theta$ ($a > 0, \theta \geq 0$), where the curve crosses the polar axis.

(c) Find the length of $r = \theta$ over the interval $0 \leq \theta \leq 2\pi$.

(d) Find the area under the curve $r = \theta$ for $0 \leq \theta \leq 2\pi$.

73. Logarithmic Spiral The curve represented by the equation $r = ae^{b\theta}$, where a and b are constants, is called a **logarithmic spiral.** The figure shows the graph of $r = e^{\theta/6}$, $-2\pi \leq \theta \leq 2\pi$. Find the area of the shaded region.

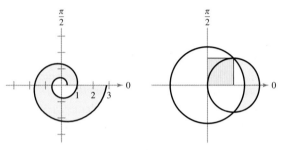

Figure for 73   Figure for 74

74. Area The larger circle in the figure is the graph of $r = 1$. Find the polar equation of the smaller circle such that the shaded regions are equal.

75. Connecting Representations Use the formula for the arc length of a curve in parametric form to derive the formula for the arc length of a polar curve.

Calculus AP® – Exam Preparation Questions

76. Multiple Choice The figure below shows the graphs of the polar curves $r = 5 \cos 2\theta$ and $r = 5$. What is the total area of the shaded regions?

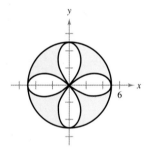

(A) 35.194   (B) 39.270

(C) 41.535   (D) 58.905

77. Multiple Choice Which integral represents the area of the region outside the polar curve $r = 3 + 2 \sin \theta$ and inside the polar curve $r = 2$?

(A) $\dfrac{1}{2}\displaystyle\int_{7\pi/6}^{11\pi/6} [(2)^2 - (3 + 2 \sin \theta)^2]\, d\theta$

(B) $\dfrac{1}{2}\displaystyle\int_{-\pi/6}^{7\pi/6} [(2)^2 - (3 + 2 \sin \theta)^2]\, d\theta$

(C) $\dfrac{1}{2}\displaystyle\int_{7\pi/6}^{11\pi/6} [(3 + 2 \sin \theta)^2 - (2)^2]\, d\theta$

(D) $\dfrac{1}{2}\displaystyle\int_{\pi/6}^{5\pi/6} [(2)^2 - (3 + 2 \sin \theta)^2]\, d\theta$

9.6   Vectors in the Plane

▶ Write the component form of a vector.
▶ Perform vector operations and interpret the results geometrically.

Component Form of a Vector

Many quantities in geometry and physics, such as area, volume, temperature, mass, and time, can be characterized by a single real number that is scaled to appropriate units of measure. These are called **scalar quantities,** and the real number associated with each is called a **scalar.**

Other quantities, such as force, velocity, and acceleration, involve both magnitude and direction and cannot be characterized completely by a single real number. A **directed line segment** is used to represent such a quantity, as shown in Figure 9.50. The directed line segment $\overrightarrow{PQ}$ has **initial point** P and **terminal point** Q, and its **length** (or **magnitude**) is denoted by $\|\overrightarrow{PQ}\|$. Directed line segments that have the same length and direction are **equivalent,** as shown in Figure 9.51. The set of all directed line segments that are equivalent to a given directed line segment $\overrightarrow{PQ}$ is a **vector in the plane** and is denoted by

$$\mathbf{v} = \overrightarrow{PQ}.$$

In typeset material, vectors are usually denoted by lowercase, boldface letters such as **u**, **v**, and **w**. When written by hand, however, vectors are often denoted by letters with arrows above them, such as $\vec{u}$, $\vec{v}$, and $\vec{w}$.

Be sure you understand that a vector represents a *set* of directed line segments (each having the same length and direction). In practice, however, it is common not to distinguish between a vector and one of its representatives.

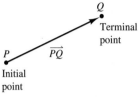
A directed line segment
Figure 9.50

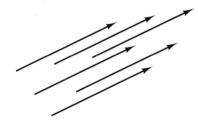
Equivalent directed line segments
Figure 9.51

EXAMPLE 1   Vector Representation: Directed Line Segments

Let **v** be represented by the directed line segment from $(0, 0)$ to $(3, 2)$, and let **u** be represented by the directed line segment from $(1, 2)$ to $(4, 4)$. Show that **v** and **u** are equivalent.

Solution

Let $P(0, 0)$ and $Q(3, 2)$ be the initial and terminal points of **v**, and let $R(1, 2)$ and $S(4, 4)$ be the initial and terminal points of **u**, as shown in Figure 9.52. You can use the Distance Formula to show that $\overrightarrow{PQ}$ and $\overrightarrow{RS}$ have the *same length*.

$$\|\overrightarrow{PQ}\| = \sqrt{(3 - 0)^2 + (2 - 0)^2} = \sqrt{13}$$
$$\|\overrightarrow{RS}\| = \sqrt{(4 - 1)^2 + (4 - 2)^2} = \sqrt{13}$$

Both line segments have the *same direction,* because they both are directed toward the upper right on lines having the same slope.

$$\text{Slope of } \overrightarrow{PQ} = \frac{2 - 0}{3 - 0} = \frac{2}{3}$$

and

$$\text{Slope of } \overrightarrow{RS} = \frac{4 - 2}{4 - 1} = \frac{2}{3}$$

Because $\overrightarrow{PQ}$ and $\overrightarrow{RS}$ have the same length and direction, you can conclude that the two vectors are equivalent. That is, **v** and **u** are equivalent.

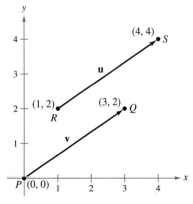
The vectors **u** and **v** are equivalent.
Figure 9.52

The directed line segment whose initial point is the origin is often the most convenient representative of a set of equivalent directed line segments such as those shown in Figure 9.52. This representation of **v** is said to be in **standard position.** A directed line segment whose initial point is the origin can be uniquely represented by the coordinates of its terminal point $Q(v_1, v_2)$, as shown in Figure 9.53. In the next definition, note the difference in the notation between the *component form* of a vector $\mathbf{v} = \langle v_1, v_2 \rangle$ and the *point* (v_1, v_2).

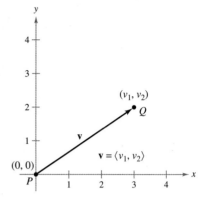

A vector in standard position
Figure 9.53

Definition of Component Form of a Vector in the Plane

If **v** is a vector in the plane whose initial point is the origin and whose terminal point is (v_1, v_2), then the **component form of v** is $\mathbf{v} = \langle v_1, v_2 \rangle$. The coordinates v_1 and v_2 are called the **components of v,** where v_1 is the **horizontal component** and v_2 is the **vertical component.** If both the initial point and the terminal point lie at the origin, then **v** is called the **zero vector** and is denoted by $\mathbf{0} = \langle 0, 0 \rangle$.

This definition implies that two vectors $\mathbf{u} = \langle u_1, u_2 \rangle$ and $\mathbf{v} = \langle v_1, v_2 \rangle$ are **equal** if and only if $u_1 = v_1$ and $u_2 = v_2$.

The procedures listed below can be used to convert directed line segments to component form or vice versa.

1. If $P(p_1, p_2)$ and $Q(q_1, q_2)$ are the initial and terminal points of a directed line segment, then the component form of the vector **v** represented by $\overrightarrow{PQ}$ is

$$\langle v_1, v_2 \rangle = \langle q_1 - p_1, q_2 - p_2 \rangle.$$

Moreover, from the Distance Formula, you can see that the **length** (or **magnitude**) **of v** is

$$\|\mathbf{v}\| = \sqrt{(q_1 - p_1)^2 + (q_2 - p_2)^2} = \sqrt{v_1^2 + v_2^2}. \qquad \text{Length of a vector}$$

2. If $\mathbf{v} = \langle v_1, v_2 \rangle$, then **v** can be represented by the directed line segment, in standard position, from $P(0, 0)$ to $Q(v_1, v_2)$.

The length of **v** is also called the **norm of v.** If $\|\mathbf{v}\| = 1$, then **v** is a **unit vector.** Moreover, $\|\mathbf{v}\| = 0$ if and only if **v** is the zero vector **0.**

EXAMPLE 2   Component Form and Length of a Vector

Find the component form and length of the vector **v** that has initial point $(3, -7)$ and terminal point $(-2, 5)$.

Solution

Let $P(3, -7) = (p_1, p_2)$ and $Q(-2, 5) = (q_1, q_2)$. Then the components of $\mathbf{v} = \langle v_1, v_2 \rangle$ are

$$v_1 = q_1 - p_1 = -2 - 3 = -5$$

and

$$v_2 = q_2 - p_2 = 5 - (-7) = 12.$$

So, as shown in Figure 9.54, $\mathbf{v} = \langle -5, 12 \rangle$, and the length of **v** is

$$\|\mathbf{v}\| = \sqrt{(-5)^2 + 12^2}$$
$$= \sqrt{169}$$
$$= 13.$$

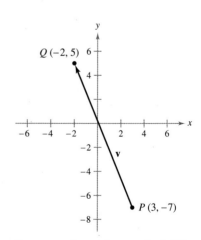

Component form of v: $\mathbf{v} = \langle -5, 12 \rangle$
Figure 9.54

Vector Operations

Definitions of Vector Addition and Scalar Multiplication

Let $\mathbf{u} = \langle u_1, u_2 \rangle$ and $\mathbf{v} = \langle v_1, v_2 \rangle$ be vectors and let c be a scalar.

1. The **vector sum** of $\mathbf{u}$ and $\mathbf{v}$ is the vector

$$\mathbf{u} + \mathbf{v} = \langle u_1 + v_1, u_2 + v_2 \rangle.$$

2. The **scalar multiple** of c and $\mathbf{u}$ is the vector

$$c\mathbf{u} = \langle cu_1, cu_2 \rangle.$$

3. The **negative** of $\mathbf{v}$ is the vector

$$-\mathbf{v} = (-1)\mathbf{v} = \langle -v_1, -v_2 \rangle.$$

4. The **difference** of $\mathbf{u}$ and $\mathbf{v}$ is

$$\mathbf{u} - \mathbf{v} = \mathbf{u} + (-\mathbf{v}) = \langle u_1 - v_1, u_2 - v_2 \rangle.$$

Geometrically, the scalar multiple of a vector $\mathbf{v}$ and a scalar c is the vector that is $|c|$ times as long as $\mathbf{v}$, as shown in Figure 9.55. If c is positive, then $c\mathbf{v}$ has the same direction as $\mathbf{v}$. If c is negative, then $c\mathbf{v}$ has the opposite direction. Whether c is positive or negative, the **length of a scalar multiple** is $\|c\mathbf{v}\| = |c|\|\mathbf{v}\|$.

The sum of two vectors can be represented geometrically by positioning the vectors (without changing their magnitudes or directions) so that the initial point of one coincides with the terminal point of the other, as shown in Figure 9.56. The vector $\mathbf{u} + \mathbf{v}$, called the **resultant vector,** is the diagonal of a parallelogram having $\mathbf{u}$ and $\mathbf{v}$ as its adjacent sides.

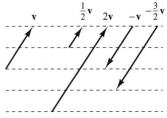

The scalar multiplication of $\mathbf{v}$
Figure 9.55

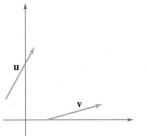
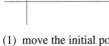
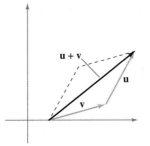

To find $\mathbf{u} + \mathbf{v}$,   (1) move the initial point of $\mathbf{v}$ to the terminal point of $\mathbf{u}$, or   (2) move the initial point of $\mathbf{u}$ to the terminal point of $\mathbf{v}$.

Figure 9.56

Figure 9.57 shows the equivalence of the geometric and algebraic definitions of vector addition and scalar multiplication, and presents (at far right) a geometric interpretation of $\mathbf{u} - \mathbf{v}$.

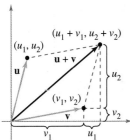
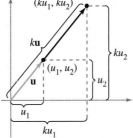
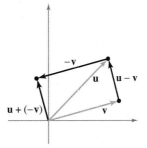

Vector addition   Scalar multiplication   Vector subtraction

Figure 9.57

EXAMPLE 3 Vector Operations

For $\mathbf{v} = \langle -2, 5 \rangle$ and $\mathbf{w} = \langle 3, 4 \rangle$, find each of the vectors.

a. $\frac{1}{2}\mathbf{v}$

b. $\mathbf{w} - \mathbf{v}$

c. $\mathbf{v} + 2\mathbf{w}$

Solution

a. $\frac{1}{2}\mathbf{v} = \langle \frac{1}{2}(-2), \frac{1}{2}(5) \rangle = \langle -1, \frac{5}{2} \rangle$

b. $\mathbf{w} - \mathbf{v} = \langle w_1 - v_1, w_2 - v_2 \rangle = \langle 3 - (-2), 4 - 5 \rangle = \langle 5, -1 \rangle$

c. Using $2\mathbf{w} = \langle 6, 8 \rangle$, you have

$$\begin{aligned} \mathbf{v} + 2\mathbf{w} &= \langle -2, 5 \rangle + \langle 6, 8 \rangle \\ &= \langle -2 + 6, 5 + 8 \rangle \\ &= \langle 4, 13 \rangle. \end{aligned}$$

Vector addition and scalar multiplication share many properties of ordinary arithmetic, as shown in the next theorem.

Theorem 9.14 Properties of Vectors Operations

Let $\mathbf{u}$, $\mathbf{v}$, and $\mathbf{w}$ be vectors in the plane, and let c and d be scalars.

1. $\mathbf{u} + \mathbf{v} = \mathbf{v} + \mathbf{u}$ Commutative Property
2. $(\mathbf{u} + \mathbf{v}) + \mathbf{w} = \mathbf{u} + (\mathbf{v} + \mathbf{w})$ Associative Property
3. $\mathbf{u} + \mathbf{0} = \mathbf{u}$ Additive Identity Property
4. $\mathbf{u} + (-\mathbf{u}) = \mathbf{0}$ Additive Inverse Property
5. $c(d\mathbf{u}) = (cd)\mathbf{u}$
6. $(c + d)\mathbf{u} = c\mathbf{u} + d\mathbf{u}$ Distributive Property
7. $c(\mathbf{u} + \mathbf{v}) = c\mathbf{u} + c\mathbf{v}$ Distributive Property
8. $1(\mathbf{u}) = \mathbf{u}, 0(\mathbf{u}) = \mathbf{0}$

In some applications of vectors, it is useful to find a unit vector that has the same direction as a given vector. If $\mathbf{v}$ is a nonzero vector in the plane, then the vector

$$\mathbf{u} = \frac{\mathbf{v}}{\|\mathbf{v}\|} = \frac{1}{\|\mathbf{v}\|}\mathbf{v} \qquad \text{Unit vector}$$

has length 1 and the same direction as $\mathbf{v}$. The vector $\mathbf{u}$ is called a **unit vector in the direction of v.**

If $\mathbf{u}$ is a unit vector and θ is the angle (measured counterclockwise) from the positive x-axis to $\mathbf{u}$, then the terminal point of $\mathbf{u}$ lies on the unit circle, and you have

$$\mathbf{u} = \langle \cos \theta, \sin \theta \rangle \qquad \text{Unit vector}$$

as shown in Figure 9.58. The angle θ is the **direction angle** of the vector $\mathbf{u}$. For any other nonzero vector $\mathbf{v}$ making an angle θ with the positive x-axis that has the same direction as $\mathbf{u}$, you can write

$$\mathbf{v} = \|\mathbf{v}\|\langle \cos \theta, \sin \theta \rangle.$$

For instance, a vector that has a magnitude of 3 and makes an angle of $30°$ with the positive x-axis can be written as

$$\mathbf{v} = 3\langle \cos 30°, \sin 30° \rangle = \left\langle \frac{3\sqrt{3}}{2}, \frac{3}{2} \right\rangle$$

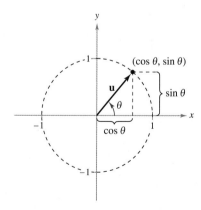

The angle θ from the positive x-axis to the vector $\mathbf{u}$

Figure 9.58

Because $\mathbf{v} = \langle v_1, v_2 \rangle = \|\mathbf{v}\|\langle \cos\theta, \sin\theta \rangle$, it follows that the direction angle θ for $\mathbf{v}$ is determined by

$$\tan\theta = \frac{\sin\theta}{\cos\theta} \qquad \text{Quotient identity}$$

$$= \frac{\|\mathbf{v}\|\sin\theta}{\|\mathbf{v}\|\cos\theta} \qquad \text{Multiply numerator and denominator by } \|\mathbf{v}\|.$$

$$= \frac{v_2}{v_1}. \qquad \text{Simplify.}$$

In surveying and navigation, a **bearing** is a direction that measures the acute angle that a path or line of sight makes with a fixed north-south line. In air navigation, bearings are measured in degrees clockwise from north.

EXAMPLE 4   Finding a Velocity

An airplane is traveling at a fixed altitude with a negligible wind factor. The airplane is traveling at a speed of 500 miles per hour with a bearing of 330°, as shown in Figure 9.59(a). As the airplane reaches a certain point, it encounters wind with a velocity of 70 miles per hour in the direction N 45° E (45° east of north), as shown in Figure 9.59(b). What are the resultant speed and direction of the airplane?

Solution

Using Figure 9.59(a), represent the velocity of the airplane (alone) as

$$\mathbf{v}_1 = 500\langle \cos 120°, \sin 120° \rangle = \langle 500\cos 120°, 500\sin 120° \rangle.$$

The velocity of the wind is represented by the vector

$$\mathbf{v}_2 = 70\langle \cos 45°, \sin 45° \rangle = \langle 70\cos 45°, 70\sin 45° \rangle.$$

The resultant velocity of the airplane (in the wind) is

$$\mathbf{v} = \mathbf{v}_1 + \mathbf{v}_2$$
$$= \langle 500\cos 120°, 500\sin 120° \rangle + \langle 70\cos 45°, 70\sin 45° \rangle$$
$$= \langle 500\cos 120° + 70\cos 45°, 500\sin 120° + 70\sin 45° \rangle$$
$$\approx \langle -200.5, 482.5 \rangle.$$

So, the resultant speed of the airplane is

$$\|\mathbf{v}\| \approx \sqrt{(-200.5)^2 + (482.5)^2}$$
$$\approx 522.5 \text{ miles per hour.}$$

The direction of the airplane is determined from

$$\tan\theta \approx \frac{482.5}{-200.5}.$$

Because the vector $\mathbf{v}$ lies in Quadrant II, the angle θ lies in Quadrant II and its reference angle is

$$\theta' \approx \left| \arctan\left(\frac{482.5}{-200.5}\right) \right| \approx |-67.4°| = 67.4°.$$

It follows that the direction of the airplane is

$$\theta \approx 180° - 67.4° = 112.6°.$$

So, the new speed of the airplane, as altered by the wind, is approximately 522.5 miles per hour in a path that makes an angle of about 112.6° with the positive x-axis, or a bearing of about 337.4°.

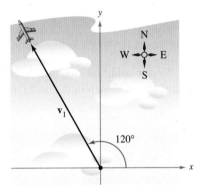

(a) Direction without wind

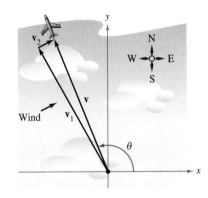

(b) Direction with wind
Figure 9.59

Algebra Review

For help on the algebra in Example 4, see Example 4 in the *Chapter 9 Algebra Review* on page A53.

9.6 Exercises

Equivalent Vectors In Exercises 1–4, find the vectors u and v whose initial and terminal points are given. Show that u and v are equivalent.

	Initial Point	Terminal Point			Initial Point	Terminal Point
1. u:	(3, 2)	(5, 6)	**2. u:**		(−4, 0)	(1, 8)
v:	(1, 4)	(3, 8)	**v:**		(2, −1)	(7, 7)
3. u:	(0, 3)	(6, −2)	**4. u:**		(−4, −1)	(11, −4)
v:	(3, 10)	(9, 5)	**v:**		(10, 13)	(25, 10)

Sketching a Vector In Exercises 5 and 6, (a) find the component form of the vector v and (b) sketch the vector with its initial point at the origin.

5.
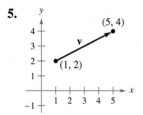

6.
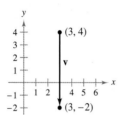

Finding and Using Vectors In Exercises 7–14, the initial and terminal points of a vector v are given. (a) Sketch the given directed line segment, (b) write the vector in component form, and (c) sketch the vector with its initial point at the origin.

	Initial Point	Terminal Point		Initial Point	Terminal Point
7.	(2, 0)	(5, 5)	**8.**	(4, −6)	(3, 6)
9.	(8, 3)	(6, −1)	**10.**	(0, −4)	(−5, −1)
11.	(6, 2)	(6, 6)	**12.**	(7, −1)	(−3, −1)
13.	$\left(\frac{3}{2}, \frac{4}{3}\right)$	$\left(\frac{1}{2}, 3\right)$	**14.**	(0.12, 0.60)	(0.84, 1.25)

Error Analysis In Exercises 15 and 16, describe and correct the error in finding the component form of a vector v with initial point (1, −4) and terminal point (5, 3).

15. $\langle v_1, v_2 \rangle = \langle 1 - 5, -4 - 3 \rangle = \langle -4, -7 \rangle$ ✗

16. $\langle v_1, v_2 \rangle = \langle 5 - 1, 3 - 4 \rangle = \langle 4, -1 \rangle$ ✗

Finding a Magnitude of a Vector In Exercises 17–22, find the magnitude of v.

17. $\mathbf{v} = \langle 4, 0 \rangle$ **18.** $\mathbf{v} = \langle 0, -9 \rangle$

19. $\mathbf{v} = \langle -1, -5 \rangle$ **20.** $\mathbf{v} = \langle 3, 3 \rangle$

21. $\mathbf{v} = \langle 8, 15 \rangle$ **22.** $\mathbf{v} = \langle -24, 7 \rangle$

Sketching Scalar Multiples In Exercises 23 and 24, sketch each scalar multiple of v.

23. $\mathbf{v} = \langle 3, 5 \rangle$
    (a) $2\mathbf{v}$ (b) $-3\mathbf{v}$ (c) $\frac{7}{2}\mathbf{v}$ (d) $\frac{2}{3}\mathbf{v}$

24. $\mathbf{v} = \langle -2, 3 \rangle$
    (a) $4\mathbf{v}$ (b) $-\frac{1}{2}\mathbf{v}$ (c) $0\mathbf{v}$ (d) $-6\mathbf{v}$

Using Vector Operations In Exercises 25 and 26, find (a) $\frac{2}{3}\mathbf{u}$, (b) $3\mathbf{v}$, (c) $\mathbf{v} - \mathbf{u}$, and (d) $2\mathbf{u} + 5\mathbf{v}$.

25. $\mathbf{u} = \langle 4, 9 \rangle$, $\mathbf{v} = \langle 2, -5 \rangle$

26. $\mathbf{u} = \langle -3, -8 \rangle$, $\mathbf{v} = \langle 15, 7 \rangle$

Sketching a Vector In Exercises 27–32, use the figure to sketch a graph of the vector. To print an enlarged copy of the graph, go to *MathGraphs.com.*

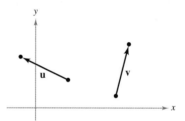

27. $-\mathbf{u}$ **28.** $2\mathbf{u}$

29. $-\mathbf{v}$ **30.** $\frac{1}{2}\mathbf{v}$

31. $\mathbf{u} - \mathbf{v}$ **32.** $\mathbf{u} + 2\mathbf{v}$

Finding a Terminal Point In Exercises 33 and 34, the vector v and its initial point are given. Find the terminal point.

33. $\mathbf{v} = \langle -1, 3 \rangle$; Initial point: (4, 2)

34. $\mathbf{v} = \langle 4, -9 \rangle$; Initial point: (5, 3)

Finding a Unit Vector In Exercises 35–38, find the unit vector in the direction of v and verify that it has length 1.

35. $\mathbf{v} = \langle 3, 12 \rangle$ **36.** $\mathbf{v} = \langle -5, 15 \rangle$

37. $\mathbf{v} = \left\langle \frac{3}{2}, \frac{5}{2} \right\rangle$ **38.** $\mathbf{v} = \langle -6.2, 3.4 \rangle$

Finding Magnitudes In Exercises 39–42, find the following.

(a) $\|\mathbf{u}\|$ (b) $\|\mathbf{v}\|$ (c) $\|\mathbf{u} + \mathbf{v}\|$

(d) $\left\| \dfrac{\mathbf{u}}{\|\mathbf{u}\|} \right\|$ (e) $\left\| \dfrac{\mathbf{v}}{\|\mathbf{v}\|} \right\|$ (f) $\left\| \dfrac{\mathbf{u} + \mathbf{v}}{\|\mathbf{u} + \mathbf{v}\|} \right\|$

39. $\mathbf{u} = \langle 1, -1 \rangle$, $\mathbf{v} = \langle -1, 2 \rangle$

40. $\mathbf{u} = \langle 0, 1 \rangle$, $\mathbf{v} = \langle 3, -3 \rangle$

41. $\mathbf{u} = \left\langle 1, \frac{1}{2} \right\rangle$, $\mathbf{v} = \langle 2, 3 \rangle$

42. $\mathbf{u} = \langle 2, -4 \rangle$, $\mathbf{v} = \langle 5, 5 \rangle$

Finding a Vector In Exercises 43–46, find the vector **v** with the given magnitude and the same direction as **u**.

Magnitude	Direction
43. $\|\mathbf{v}\| = 6$	$\mathbf{u} = \langle 0, 3 \rangle$
44. $\|\mathbf{v}\| = 4$	$\mathbf{u} = \langle 1, 1 \rangle$
45. $\|\mathbf{v}\| = 5$	$\mathbf{u} = \langle -1, 2 \rangle$
46. $\|\mathbf{v}\| = 2$	$\mathbf{u} = \langle \sqrt{3}, 3 \rangle$

Finding a Vector In Exercises 47–50, find the component form of **v** given its magnitude and the angle it makes with the positive x-axis.

47. $\|\mathbf{v}\| = 3, \; \theta = 0°$ **48.** $\|\mathbf{v}\| = 5, \; \theta = 120°$

49. $\|\mathbf{v}\| = 2, \; \theta = 150°$ **50.** $\|\mathbf{v}\| = 4, \; \theta = 3.5°$

Finding a Vector In Exercises 51–54, find the vector **u** + **v** given the lengths of **u** and **v** and the angles that **u** and **v** make with the positive x-axis.

51. $\|\mathbf{u}\| = 1, \; \theta_{\mathbf{u}} = 0°$ **52.** $\|\mathbf{u}\| = 4, \; \theta_{\mathbf{u}} = 0°$
     $\|\mathbf{v}\| = 3, \; \theta_{\mathbf{v}} = 45°$ $\|\mathbf{v}\| = 2, \; \theta_{\mathbf{v}} = 60°$

53. $\|\mathbf{u}\| = 2, \; \theta_{\mathbf{u}} = 4$ **54.** $\|\mathbf{u}\| = 5, \; \theta_{\mathbf{u}} = -0.5$
     $\|\mathbf{v}\| = 1, \; \theta_{\mathbf{v}} = 2$ $\|\mathbf{v}\| = 5, \; \theta_{\mathbf{v}} = 0.5$

EXPLORING CONCEPTS

55. Justifying Consider two forces of equal magnitude acting on a point.

(a) When the magnitude of the resultant is the sum of the magnitudes of the two forces, make a conjecture about the angle between the forces.

(b) When the resultant of the forces is 0, make a conjecture about the angle between the forces.

56. Triangle Consider a triangle with vertices X, Y, and Z. What is $\overrightarrow{XY} + \overrightarrow{YZ} + \overrightarrow{ZX}$? Explain.

Finding Values In Exercises 57–62, find a and b such that $\mathbf{v} = a\mathbf{u} + b\mathbf{w}$, where $\mathbf{u} = \langle 1, 2 \rangle$ and $\mathbf{w} = \langle 1, -1 \rangle$.

57. $\mathbf{v} = \langle 7, 0 \rangle$ **58.** $\mathbf{v} = \langle 0, -8 \rangle$

59. $\mathbf{v} = \langle 4, 5 \rangle$ **60.** $\mathbf{v} = \langle -7, -2 \rangle$

61. $\mathbf{v} = \langle 12, -6 \rangle$ **62.** $\mathbf{v} = \langle -1, -11 \rangle$

Finding Unit Vectors In Exercises 63–68, find a unit vector (a) parallel to and (b) perpendicular to the graph of f at the given point. Then sketch the graph of f and sketch the vectors at the given point.

63. $f(x) = x^2, \; (3, 9)$ **64.** $f(x) = -x^2 + 5, \; (1, 4)$

65. $f(x) = x^3, \; (1, 1)$ **66.** $f(x) = x^3, \; (-2, -8)$

67. $f(x) = \tan x, \; \left(\dfrac{\pi}{4}, 1 \right)$ **68.** $f(x) = \sqrt{25 - x^2}, \; (3, 4)$

Finding a Vector In Exercises 69 and 70, find the vector **v** given the magnitudes of **u** and **u** + **v** and the angles that **u** and **u** + **v** make with the positive x-axis.

69. $\|\mathbf{u}\| = 1, \; \theta = 45°$
     $\|\mathbf{u} + \mathbf{v}\| = \sqrt{2}, \; \theta = 90°$

70. $\|\mathbf{u}\| = 4, \; \theta = 30°$
     $\|\mathbf{u} + \mathbf{v}\| = 6, \; \theta = 120°$

71. Using a Parallelogram Three vertices of a parallelogram are $(1, 2)$, $(3, 1)$, and $(8, 4)$. Find the three possible fourth vertices.

72. **HOW DO YOU SEE IT?** Use the figure to determine whether each statement is true or false. Justify your answer.

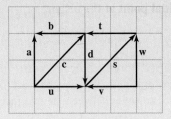

(a) $\mathbf{a} = -\mathbf{d}$ (b) $\mathbf{c} = \mathbf{s}$
(c) $\mathbf{a} + \mathbf{u} = \mathbf{c}$ (d) $\mathbf{v} + \mathbf{w} = -\mathbf{s}$
(e) $\mathbf{a} + \mathbf{d} = 0$ (f) $\mathbf{u} - \mathbf{v} = -2(\mathbf{b} + \mathbf{t})$

Cable Tension In Exercises 73 and 74, determine the tension in each cable supporting the given load.

73.

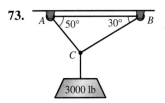

74.

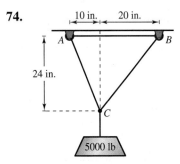

75. Resultant Force Three forces with magnitudes of 75 pounds, 100 pounds, and 125 pounds act on an object at angles of 30°, 45°, and 120°, respectively, with the positive x-axis. Find the direction and magnitude of the resultant force.

76. Resultant Force Three forces with magnitudes of 400 newtons, 280 newtons, and 350 newtons act on an object at angles of $-30°$, $45°$, and $135°$, respectively, with the positive x-axis. Find the direction and magnitude of the resultant force.

77. Resultant Force Forces with magnitudes of 500 pounds and 200 pounds act on a machine part at angles of $30°$ and $-45°$, respectively, with the x-axis (see figure). Find the direction and magnitude of the resultant force.

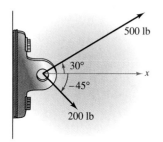

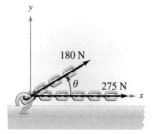

Figure for 77   Figure for 78

 78. Resultant Force Forces with magnitudes of 180 newtons and 275 newtons act on a hook (see figure). The angle between the two forces is θ degrees.

(a) When $\theta = 30°$, find the direction and magnitude of the resultant force.

(b) Write the magnitude M and direction α of the resultant force as functions of θ, where $0° \leq \theta \leq 180°$.

(c) Use a graphing utility to complete the table.

θ	0°	30°	60°	90°	120°	150°	180°
M							
α							

(d) Use a graphing utility to graph the two functions M and α. Explain why one of the functions decreases for increasing values of θ, whereas the other does not.

79. NAVIGATION

A plane flies at a constant groundspeed of 400 miles per hour due east and encounters a 50-mile-per-hour wind from the northwest. Find the airspeed and compass direction that will allow the plane to maintain its groundspeed and eastward direction.

80. Projectile Motion A gun with a muzzle velocity of 1200 feet per second is fired at an angle of $6°$ above the horizontal. Find the vertical and horizontal components of the velocity.

81. Navigation A plane is flying with a bearing of $302°$. Its speed with respect to the air is 900 kilometers per hour. The wind at the plane's altitude is from the southwest at 100 kilometers per hour (see figure). What is the true direction of the plane, and what is its speed with respect to the ground?

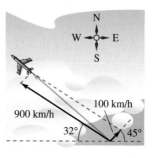

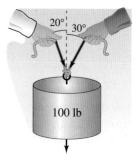

Figure for 81   Figure for 82

82. Shared Load To carry a 100-pound cylindrical weight, two workers lift on the ends of short ropes tied to an eyelet on the top center of the cylinder. One rope makes a $20°$ angle away from the vertical and the other makes a $30°$ angle (see figure).

(a) Find each rope's tension when the resultant force is vertical.

(b) Find the vertical component of each worker's force.

83. Justifying Using vectors, prove that the line segment joining the midpoints of two sides of a triangle is parallel to, and one-half the length of, the third side.

84. Proof Prove that the vector $\mathbf{w} = \|\mathbf{u}\|\mathbf{v} + \|\mathbf{v}\|\mathbf{u}$ bisects the angle between $\mathbf{u}$ and $\mathbf{v}$.

85. Using a Vector Consider the vector $\mathbf{u} = \langle x, y \rangle$. Describe the set of all points (x, y) such that $\|\mathbf{u}\| = 5$.

Calculus AP® – Exam Preparation Questions

86. Multiple Choice A particle moves in the xy-plane with a velocity vector of $\mathbf{v} = \langle -5, 12 \rangle$. What is the magnitude and direction of this velocity?

(A) $\|\mathbf{v}\| = 13$, $\theta \approx 67.4°$

(B) $\|\mathbf{v}\| = 13$, $\theta \approx 112.6°$

(C) $\|\mathbf{v}\| = 13$, $\theta \approx 292.6°$

(D) $\|\mathbf{v}\| = 10.9$, $\theta \approx 112.6°$

87. Multiple Choice A particle moves in the xy-plane from the point $(2, -3)$ to $(4, 1)$. It then moves from $(4, 1)$ to $(-5, 3)$. Which vector represents the total displacement of the particle?

(A) $\langle 2, 4 \rangle$ (B) $\langle -9, 2 \rangle$

(C) $\langle -7, 6 \rangle$ (D) $\langle 7, -6 \rangle$

9.7   Vector-Valued Functions

▶ Analyze and sketch a plane curve given by a vector-valued function.
▶ Extend the concepts of limits and continuity to vector-valued functions.
▶ Differentiate a vector-valued function.
▶ Integrate a vector-valued function.

Plane Curves and Vector-Valued Functions

In Section 9.2, a plane curve was defined as the set of ordered pairs $(f(t), g(t))$ together with their defining parametric equations $x = f(t)$ and $y = g(t)$, where f and g are continuous functions of t on an interval I. Another way to represent a plane curve is with a **vector-valued function.** This type of function maps real numbers to vectors and is of the form

$$\mathbf{r}(t) = \langle f(t), g(t) \rangle \qquad \text{Vector-valued function}$$

where the **component functions** f and g are real-valued functions of the parameter t.

Technically, a curve consists of a collection of points and the defining parametric equations. So, two different curves can have the same graph. For instance, each of the curves $\mathbf{r}(t) = \langle \sin t, \cos t \rangle$ and $\mathbf{r}(t) = \langle \sin t^2, \cos t^2 \rangle$ has the unit circle as its graph, but these equations do not represent the same curve—because the circle is traced out in different ways on the graphs.

Be sure you see the distinction between the vector-valued function $\mathbf{r}$ and the real-valued functions f and g. All are functions of the real variable t, but $\mathbf{r}(t)$ is a vector, whereas $f(t)$ and $g(t)$ are real numbers (for each specific value of t). Real-valued functions are sometimes called **scalar functions** to distinguish them from vector-valued functions.

Vector-valued functions serve dual roles in the representation of curves. By letting the parameter t represent time, you can use a vector-valued function to represent *motion* along a curve. Or, in the more general case, you can use a vector-valued function to *trace the graph* of a curve. In either case, the terminal point of the position vector $\mathbf{r}(t)$ coincides with the point (x, y) on the curve given by the parametric equations, as shown in Figure 9.60. The arrowhead on the curve indicates the curve's orientation by pointing in the direction of increasing values of t.

Unless stated otherwise, the **domain** of a vector-valued function $\mathbf{r}$ is considered to be the intersection of the domains of the component functions f and g. For instance, the domain of $\mathbf{r}(t) = \left\langle \ln t, \sqrt{1 - t} \right\rangle$ is the interval $(0, 1]$.

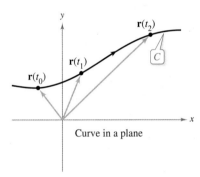

Curve C is traced out by the terminal point of position vector $\mathbf{r}(t)$.
Figure 9.60

EXAMPLE 1   Sketching a Plane Curve

Sketch the plane curve represented by the vector-valued function

$$\mathbf{r}(t) = \langle 2 \cos t, -3 \sin t \rangle, \quad 0 \le t \le 2\pi. \qquad \text{Vector-valued function}$$

Solution

From the position vector $\mathbf{r}(t)$, you can write the parametric equations

$$x = 2 \cos t \quad \text{and} \quad y = -3 \sin t.$$

Solving for $\cos t$ and $\sin t$ and using the identity $\cos^2 t + \sin^2 t = 1$ produces the rectangular equation

$$\frac{x^2}{2^2} + \frac{y^2}{3^2} = 1. \qquad \text{Rectangular equation}$$

The graph of this rectangular equation is the ellipse shown in Figure 9.61. The curve has a *clockwise* orientation. That is, as t increases from 0 to 2π, the position vector $\mathbf{r}(t)$ moves clockwise, and its terminal point traces the ellipse.

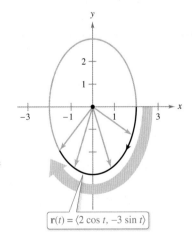

$$\mathbf{r}(t) = \langle 2 \cos t, -3 \sin t \rangle$$

The ellipse is traced clockwise as t increases from 0 to 2π.
Figure 9.61

In Example 1, a vector-valued function was given and you were asked to sketch the corresponding curve. The next example addresses the reverse problem—finding a vector-valued function to represent a given graph. Of course, when the graph is described parametrically, representation by a vector-valued function is straightforward. For instance, to represent the line given by $x = 3 - t$ and $y = 2t$, you can use the vector valued-function

$$\mathbf{r}(t) = \langle 3 - t, 2t \rangle.$$

When a set of parametric equations for the graph is not given, the problem of representing the graph by a vector-valued function boils down to finding a set of parametric equations.

EXAMPLE 2   Representing a Graph: Vector-Valued Function

Represent the parabola $y = x^2 + 1$ by a vector-valued function.

Solution

Although there are many ways to choose the parameter t, a natural choice is to let $x = t$. Then $y = t^2 + 1$ and you have

$$\mathbf{r}(t) = \langle t, t^2 + 1 \rangle. \qquad \text{Vector-valued function}$$

Note in Figure 9.62 the orientation produced by this particular choice of parameter. Had you chosen $x = -t$ as the parameter, the curve would have been oriented in the opposite direction.

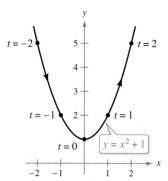

There are many ways to parametrize this graph. One way is to let $x = t$.
Figure 9.62

Limits and Continuity

Many techniques and definitions used in the calculus of real-valued functions can be applied to vector-valued functions. For instance, you can add and subtract vector-valued functions, multiply a vector-valued function by a scalar, take the limit of a vector-valued function, differentiate a vector-valued function, and so on. The basic approach is to capitalize on the linearity of vector operations by extending the definitions on a component-by-component basis. For example, to add two vector-valued functions, you can write

$$\mathbf{r}_1(t) + \mathbf{r}_2(t) = \langle f_1(t), g_1(t) \rangle + \langle f_2(t), g_2(t) \rangle \qquad \text{Sum}$$
$$= \langle f_1(t) + f_2(t), g_1(t) + g_2(t) \rangle.$$

To subtract two vector-valued functions, you can write

$$\mathbf{r}_1(t) - \mathbf{r}_2(t) = \langle f_1(t), g_1(t) \rangle - \langle f_2(t), g_2(t) \rangle \qquad \text{Difference}$$
$$= \langle f_1(t) - f_2(t), g_1(t) - g_2(t) \rangle.$$

Similarly, to multiply a vector-valued function by a scalar, you can write

$$c\mathbf{r}(t) = c\langle f_1(t), g_1(t) \rangle \qquad \text{Scalar multiplication}$$
$$= \langle cf_1(t), cg_1(t) \rangle.$$

To divide a vector-valued function by a scalar, you can write

$$\frac{\mathbf{r}(t)}{c} = \frac{\langle f_1(t), g_1(t) \rangle}{c}, \quad c \neq 0 \qquad \text{Scalar division}$$
$$= \left\langle \frac{f_1(t)}{c}, \frac{g_1(t)}{c} \right\rangle.$$

This component-by-component extension of operations with real-valued functions to vector-valued functions is further illustrated in the definition of the limit of a vector-valued function, as shown on the next page.

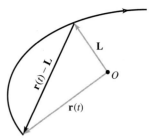

Definition of the Limit of a Vector-Valued Function

If $\mathbf{r}$ is a vector-valued function of the form $\mathbf{r}(t) = \langle f(t), g(t) \rangle$, then

$$\lim_{t \to a} \mathbf{r}(t) = \left\langle \lim_{t \to a} f(t), \lim_{t \to a} g(t) \right\rangle$$

provided f and g have limits as $t \to a$.

If $\mathbf{r}(t)$ approaches the vector $\mathbf{L}$ as $t \to a$, then the length of the vector $\mathbf{r}(t) - \mathbf{L}$ approaches 0. That is,

$$\|\mathbf{r}(t) - \mathbf{L}\| \to 0 \quad \text{as} \quad t \to a.$$

This is illustrated graphically in Figure 9.63. With this definition of the limit of a vector-valued function, you can develop vector versions of most of the limit theorems given in Chapter 1. For example, the limit of the sum of two vector-valued functions is the sum of their individual limits. Also, you can use the orientation of the curve $\mathbf{r}(t)$ to define one-sided limits of vector-valued functions. The next definition extends the notion of continuity to vector-valued functions.

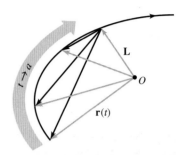

As t approaches a, $\mathbf{r}(t)$ approaches the limit $\mathbf{L}$. For the limit $\mathbf{L}$ to exist, it is not necessary that $\mathbf{r}(a)$ be defined or that $\mathbf{r}(a)$ be equal to $\mathbf{L}$.

Figure 9.63

Definition of Continuity of a Vector-Valued Function

A vector-valued function $\mathbf{r}$ is **continuous at the point** given by $t = a$ when the limit of $\mathbf{r}(t)$ exists as $t \to a$ and

$$\lim_{t \to a} \mathbf{r}(t) = \mathbf{r}(a).$$

A vector-valued function $\mathbf{r}$ is **continuous on an interval** I when it is continuous at every point in the interval.

From this definition, it follows that a vector-valued function is continuous at $t = a$ if and only if each of its component functions is continuous at $t = a$.

EXAMPLE 3   Limits and Continuity

For $\mathbf{r}(t) = \langle t, \sqrt{t + 1} \rangle$, do each of the following.

a. Find $\lim_{t \to -1} \mathbf{r}(t)$.

b. Determine the interval(s) on which the vector-valued function $\mathbf{r}$ is continuous.

Solution

a. As t approaches -1, the limit is

$$\lim_{t \to -1} \mathbf{r}(t) = \left\langle \lim_{t \to -1} f(t), \lim_{t \to -1} g(t) \right\rangle \qquad \text{Definition of limit}$$

$$= \left\langle \lim_{t \to -1} t, \lim_{t \to -1} \sqrt{t + 1} \right\rangle \qquad \text{Substitute for } f \text{ and } g.$$

$$= \left\langle -1, \sqrt{-1 + 1} \right\rangle \qquad \text{Use direct substitution.}$$

$$= \langle -1, 0 \rangle. \qquad \text{Simplify.}$$

Note that $\mathbf{r}(-1) = \langle -1, 0 \rangle$, so $\mathbf{r}$ is continuous at the point given by $t = -1$.

b. The component functions are

$$f(t) = t \quad \text{and} \quad g(t) = \sqrt{t + 1}.$$

The function f is continuous for all real-number values of t. The function g, however, is continuous only for $t \geq -1$. So, $\mathbf{r}$ is continuous on the interval $[-1, \infty)$.

Differentiation of Vector-Valued Functions

The definition of the derivative of a vector-valued function parallels the definition for real-valued functions.

Definition of the Derivative of a Vector-Valued Function

The **derivative of a vector-valued function r** is

$$\mathbf{r}'(t) = \lim_{\Delta t \to 0} \frac{\mathbf{r}(t + \Delta t) - \mathbf{r}(t)}{\Delta t}$$

for all t for which the limit exists. If $\mathbf{r}'(t)$ exists, then **r** is **differentiable at** t. If $\mathbf{r}'(t)$ exists for all t in an open interval I, then **r** is **differentiable on the interval** I. Differentiability of vector-valued functions can be extended to closed intervals by considering one-sided limits.

Communication and Notation

In addition to $\mathbf{r}'(t)$, other notations for the derivative of a vector-valued function are

$$\frac{d}{dt}[\mathbf{r}(t)], \quad \frac{d\mathbf{r}}{dt}, \quad \text{and} \quad D_t[\mathbf{r}(t)].$$

Similar to finding limits of vector-valued functions, differentiation can be done on a *component-by-component basis*. This important result is listed in the next theorem. Note that the derivative of the vector-valued function **r** is itself a vector-valued function.

Theorem 9.15   Differentiation of Vector-Valued Functions

If $\mathbf{r}(t) = \langle f(t), g(t) \rangle$, where f and g are differentiable functions of t, then

$$\mathbf{r}'(t) = \langle f'(t), g'(t) \rangle.$$

EXAMPLE 4   Differentiation of a Vector-Valued Function

See LarsonCalculusforAP.com for an interactive version of this type of example.

For the vector-valued function

$$\mathbf{r}(t) = \langle t, t^2 + 2 \rangle$$

find $\mathbf{r}'(t)$. Then sketch the plane curve represented by $\mathbf{r}(t)$ and the graphs of $\mathbf{r}(1)$ and $\mathbf{r}'(1)$.

Solution

Differentiate on a component-by-component basis to obtain

$$\mathbf{r}'(t) = \langle 1, 2t \rangle. \qquad \text{Derivative}$$

From the position vector $\mathbf{r}(t)$, you can write the parametric equations $x = t$ and $y = t^2 + 2$. The corresponding rectangular equation is $y = x^2 + 2$. When $t = 1$,

$$\mathbf{r}(1) = \langle 1, 3 \rangle$$

and

$$\mathbf{r}'(1) = \langle 1, 2 \rangle.$$

In Figure 9.64, $\mathbf{r}(1)$ is drawn starting at the origin, and $\mathbf{r}'(1)$ is drawn starting at the terminal point of $\mathbf{r}(1)$. You can see from the figure that at $(1, 3)$, the vector $\mathbf{r}'(1)$ is tangent to the curve given by $\mathbf{r}(t)$ and pointing in the direction of increasing t-values.

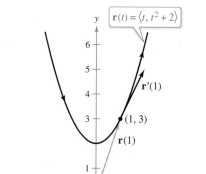

Figure 9.64

Higher-order derivatives of vector-valued functions are obtained by successive differentiation of each component function, as shown in the next example.

EXAMPLE 5 **Higher-Order Differentiation**

Find the second derivative of the vector-valued function $\mathbf{r}(t) = \langle \cos t, 2t^3 \rangle$.

Solution

$\mathbf{r}(t) = \langle \cos t, 2t^3 \rangle$ Write original function.

$\mathbf{r}'(t) = \langle -\sin t, 6t^2 \rangle$ First derivative

$\mathbf{r}''(t) = \langle -\cos t, 12t \rangle$ Second derivative

Most of the differentiation rules in Chapter 2 have counterparts for vector-valued functions, and several of these are listed in the next theorem. (For proofs of these properties, see Exercises 87–90.)

Theorem 9.16 Properties of the Derivative

Let $\mathbf{r}$ and $\mathbf{u}$ be differentiable vector-valued functions of t, let w be a differentiable real-valued function of t, and let c be a scalar.

1. $\dfrac{d}{dt}[c\mathbf{r}(t)] = c\mathbf{r}'(t)$ Constant Multiple Rule

2. $\dfrac{d}{dt}[\mathbf{r}(t) \pm \mathbf{u}(t)] = \mathbf{r}'(t) \pm \mathbf{u}'(t)$ Sum and Difference Rules

3. $\dfrac{d}{dt}[w(t)\mathbf{r}(t)] = w(t)\mathbf{r}'(t) + w'(t)\mathbf{r}(t)$ Product Rule

4. $\dfrac{d}{dt}[\mathbf{r}(w(t))] = \mathbf{r}'(w(t))w'(t)$ Chain Rule

---

EXAMPLE 6 **Using Properties of the Derivative**

Consider the vector-valued functions given by

$$\mathbf{r}(t) = \langle t^3 - 5, 3t \rangle \quad \text{and} \quad \mathbf{u}(t) = \left\langle 4 \sin \frac{t}{2}, 4 \cos \frac{t}{2} \right\rangle.$$

a. Find $\dfrac{d}{dt}[\mathbf{r}(t) + \mathbf{u}(t)]$.

b. Find $\dfrac{d}{dt}[\mathbf{r}(2t)]$.

Solution

a. $\dfrac{d}{dt}[\mathbf{r}(t) + \mathbf{u}(t)] = \mathbf{r}'(t) + \mathbf{u}'(t)$ Sum Rule

$$= \langle 3t^2, 3 \rangle + \left\langle 2 \cos \frac{t}{2}, -2 \sin \frac{t}{2} \right\rangle \quad \text{Differentiate.}$$

$$= \left\langle 3t^2 + 2 \cos \frac{t}{2}, 3 - 2 \sin \frac{t}{2} \right\rangle \quad \text{Add.}$$

b. To use the Chain Rule, note that $\mathbf{r}'(t) = \langle 3t^2, 3 \rangle$.

$$\dfrac{d}{dt}[\mathbf{r}(2t)] = \mathbf{r}'(2t)\dfrac{d}{dt}[2t] \quad \text{Chain Rule}$$

$$= \langle 3(2t)^2, 3 \rangle(2) \quad \text{Substitute and differentiate.}$$

$$= \langle 24t^2, 6 \rangle \quad \text{Simplify.}$$

Integration of Vector-Valued Functions

The next definition is a consequence of the definition of the derivative of a vector-valued function.

Definition of Integration of Vector-Valued Functions

If $\mathbf{r}(t) = \langle f(t), g(t) \rangle$, where f and g are continuous on $[a, b]$, then the **indefinite integral (antiderivative)** of $\mathbf{r}$ is

$$\int \mathbf{r}(t) \, dt = \left\langle \int f(t) \, dt, \int g(t) \, dt \right\rangle$$

and its **definite integral** over the interval $a \le t \le b$ is

$$\int_a^b \mathbf{r}(t) \, dt = \left\langle \int_a^b f(t) \, dt, \int_a^b g(t) \, dt \right\rangle.$$

The antiderivative of a vector-valued function is a family of vector-valued functions all differing by a constant vector $\mathbf{C}$. For instance, if $\mathbf{r}(t) = \langle f(t), g(t) \rangle$, then for the indefinite integral $\int \mathbf{r}(t) \, dt$, you obtain two constants of integration

$$\int f(t) \, dt = F(t) + C_1 \quad \text{and} \quad \int g(t) \, dt = G(t) + C_2$$

where $F'(t) = f(t)$ and $G'(t) = g(t)$. These two *scalar* constants produce one *vector* constant of integration.

$$\int \mathbf{r}(t) \, dt = \langle F(t) + C_1, G(t) + C_2 \rangle = \langle F(t), G(t) \rangle + \langle C_1, C_2 \rangle = \mathbf{R}(t) + \mathbf{C}$$

where $\mathbf{R}'(t) = \mathbf{r}(t)$.

EXAMPLE 7 Integrating Vector-Valued Functions

a. Find $\displaystyle\int \mathbf{r}(t) \, dt$ for $\mathbf{r}(t) = \langle t, 3 \rangle$.

b. Evaluate $\displaystyle\int_0^1 \mathbf{r}(t) \, dt$ for $\mathbf{r}(t) = \langle \sqrt[3]{t}, e^{-t} \rangle$.

Solution

a. Integrating on a component-by-component basis produces

$$\int \mathbf{r}(t) \, dt = \int \langle t, 3 \rangle \, dt$$

$$= \left\langle \frac{t^2}{2}, 3t \right\rangle + \mathbf{C}.$$

b.
$$\int_0^1 \mathbf{r}(t) \, dt = \int_0^1 \langle \sqrt[3]{t}, e^{-t} \rangle \, dt$$

$$= \left\langle \int_0^1 \sqrt[3]{t} \, dt, \int_0^1 e^{-t} \, dt \right\rangle$$

$$= \left\langle \left[\frac{3}{4} t^{4/3} \right]_0^1, \left[-e^{-t} \right]_0^1 \right\rangle$$

$$= \left\langle \frac{3}{4}, 1 - \frac{1}{e} \right\rangle$$

Communication and Notation

In Example 7(a), be sure you understand that $\mathbf{C}$ is a constant *vector*, where $\mathbf{C} = \langle C_1, C_2 \rangle$.

9.7 Exercises

See *CalcChat.com* for tutorial help and worked-out solutions to odd-numbered exercises.

 Finding the Domain   In Exercises 1–6, find the domain of the vector-valued function.

1. $\mathbf{r}(t) = \left\langle \dfrac{1}{t+1}, \dfrac{t}{2} \right\rangle$

2. $\mathbf{r}(t) = \left\langle \sqrt{4-t^2}, t^2 \right\rangle$

3. $\mathbf{r}(t) = \langle \ln t, -e^t \rangle$

4. $\mathbf{r}(t) = \langle \sin t, \cos t \rangle$

5. $\mathbf{r}(t) = \mathbf{F}(t) + \mathbf{G}(t)$, where
$\mathbf{F}(t) = \langle \cos t, \sqrt{t} \rangle$, $\mathbf{G}(t) = \langle \cos t, 0 \rangle$

6. $\mathbf{r}(t) = \mathbf{F}(t) - \mathbf{G}(t)$, where
$\mathbf{F}(t) = \langle 5t, \ln t \rangle$, $\mathbf{G}(t) = \langle -6t, 1 \rangle$

 Evaluating a Function   In Exercises 7 and 8, evaluate (if possible) the vector-valued function at each given value of t.

7. $\mathbf{r}(t) = \left\langle \frac{1}{2}t^2, -t+1 \right\rangle$
  (a) $\mathbf{r}(1)$ (b) $\mathbf{r}(0)$
  (c) $\mathbf{r}(s+1)$ (d) $\mathbf{r}(2+\Delta t) - \mathbf{r}(2)$

8. $\mathbf{r}(t) = \langle \cos t, 2 \sin t \rangle$
  (a) $\mathbf{r}(0)$ (b) $\mathbf{r}(\pi/4)$
  (c) $\mathbf{r}(\theta - \pi)$ (d) $\mathbf{r}(\pi/6 + \Delta t) - \mathbf{r}(\pi/6)$

Connecting Representations   In Exercises 9–12, match the equation with its graph. [The graphs are labeled (a), (b), (c), and (d).]

(a) 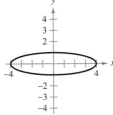 (b)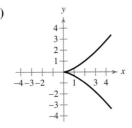

(c) 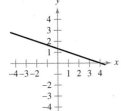 (d)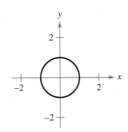

9. $\mathbf{r}(t) = \left\langle 4-t, \dfrac{t}{3} \right\rangle$

10. $\mathbf{r}(t) = \langle 2t^2, -t^3 \rangle$

11. $\mathbf{r}(t) = \langle \cos t, \sin t \rangle$

12. $\mathbf{r}(t) = \langle 4 \cos t, \sin t \rangle$

 Sketching a Plane Curve   In Exercises 13–20, sketch the plane curve represented by the vector-valued function and give the orientation of the curve.

13. $\mathbf{r}(t) = \left\langle \dfrac{t}{4}, t-1 \right\rangle$

14. $\mathbf{r}(t) = \langle 5-t, \sqrt{t} \rangle$

15. $\mathbf{r}(t) = \langle t^3, t^2 \rangle$

16. $\mathbf{r}(t) = \langle t^2+t, t^2-1 \rangle$

17. $\mathbf{r}(\theta) = \langle \cos \theta, 3 \sin \theta \rangle$

18. $\mathbf{r}(t) = \langle 2 \cos t, 2 \sin t \rangle$

19. $\mathbf{r}(\theta) = \langle 3 \sec \theta, 2 \tan \theta \rangle$

20. $\mathbf{r}(t) = \langle 2 \cos^3 t, 2 \sin^3 t \rangle$

 Representing a Graph by a Vector-Valued Function   In Exercises 21–28, represent the plane curve by a vector-valued function. (There are many correct answers.)

21. $y = x+7$ 22. $2x-3y+5=0$

23. $y = (x-2)^2$ 24. $y = 4-x^2$

25. $x^2+y^2=25$ 26. $(x-2)^2+y^2=4$

27. $\dfrac{x^2}{16} - \dfrac{y^2}{4} = 1$ 28. $\dfrac{x^2}{9} + \dfrac{y^2}{81} = 1$

 Finding a Limit   In Exercises 29–34, find the limit (if it exists).

29. $\displaystyle \lim_{t \to \pi} \langle t, \cos t \rangle$

30. $\displaystyle \lim_{t \to 2} \left\langle \dfrac{2}{t^2-1}, \dfrac{1}{t} \right\rangle$

31. $\displaystyle \lim_{t \to \infty} \left\langle 4e^{-t}, \dfrac{3t^2}{t^2+1} \right\rangle$

32. $\displaystyle \lim_{t \to \infty} \left\langle \dfrac{1}{t^2}, \dfrac{6t^3+10}{2t^2-t+5} \right\rangle$

33. $\displaystyle \lim_{t \to 0} \left\langle t^2, \dfrac{1-\cos t}{t} \right\rangle$

34. $\displaystyle \lim_{t \to 0} \left\langle \dfrac{\sin t}{t}, e^t \right\rangle$

 Continuity of a Vector-Valued Function   In Exercises 35–40, determine the interval(s) on which the vector-valued function is continuous.

35. $\mathbf{r}(t) = \left\langle t, \dfrac{1}{t} \right\rangle$ 36. $\mathbf{r}(t) = \langle \sqrt{t}, \arcsin t \rangle$

37. $\mathbf{r}(t) = \langle \sqrt{5-t}, \ln t \rangle$ 38. $\mathbf{r}(t) = \langle 2e^{-t}, \ln(t-1) \rangle$

39. $\mathbf{r}(t) = \langle e^t \sqrt{t}, \tan t \rangle$

40. $\mathbf{r}(t) = \left\langle \dfrac{t+1}{t^2+t}, \sqrt{16-t^2} \right\rangle$

Differentiation of Vector-Valued Functions In Exercises 41–46, find $\mathbf{r}'(t)$, $\mathbf{r}(t_0)$, and $\mathbf{r}'(t_0)$ for the given value of t_0. Then sketch the plane curve represented by $\mathbf{r}(t)$, and sketch the vectors $\mathbf{r}(t_0)$ and $\mathbf{r}'(t_0)$. Position the vectors such that the initial point of $\mathbf{r}(t_0)$ is at the origin and the initial point of $\mathbf{r}'(t_0)$ is at the terminal point of $\mathbf{r}(t_0)$. What is the relationship between $\mathbf{r}'(t_0)$ and the curve?

41. $\mathbf{r}(t) = \langle t^2, t \rangle$, $t_0 = 2$

42. $\mathbf{r}(t) = \langle 1 + t, t^3 \rangle$, $t_0 = 1$

43. $\mathbf{r}(t) = \langle \cos t, \sin t \rangle$, $t_0 = \dfrac{\pi}{2}$

44. $\mathbf{r}(t) = \langle 3 \sin t, 4 \cos t \rangle$, $t_0 = \dfrac{\pi}{2}$

45. $\mathbf{r}(t) = \langle e^t, e^{2t} \rangle$, $t_0 = 0$

46. $\mathbf{r}(t) = \langle e^{-t}, e^t \rangle$, $t_0 = 0$

Finding a Derivative In Exercises 47–52, find $\mathbf{r}'(t)$.

47. $\mathbf{r}(t) = \langle t^3, -3t \rangle$

48. $\mathbf{r}(t) = \left\langle \sqrt{t}, 1 - t^4 \right\rangle$

49. $\mathbf{r}(t) = \left\langle \ln t^3, \sqrt{2t} \right\rangle$

50. $\mathbf{r}(t) = \langle e^t, 4te^t \rangle$

51. $\mathbf{r}(t) = \langle -2 \cos t, t \sin t \rangle$

52. $\mathbf{r}(t) = \langle \sec 2t, \csc 2t \rangle$

Higher-Order Differentiation In Exercises 53–58, find the second derivative of the vector-valued function $\mathbf{r}(t)$.

53. $\mathbf{r}(t) = \left\langle t^3, \frac{1}{2}t^2 \right\rangle$

54. $\mathbf{r}(t) = \langle t^2 + t, t^3 - 3t^2 \rangle$

55. $\mathbf{r}(t) = \langle 4 \cos t, 4 \sin t \rangle$

56. $\mathbf{r}(t) = \langle 8 \cos t, 3 \sin t \rangle$

57. $\mathbf{r}(t) = \left\langle e^{-3t}, \sqrt{t} \right\rangle$

58. $\mathbf{r}(t) = \langle e^{6t}, \ln t \rangle$

Using Properties of the Derivative In Exercises 59–62, use the properties of the derivative to find the following.

(a) $\dfrac{d\mathbf{r}}{dt}$

(b) $\dfrac{d}{dt}[4\mathbf{u}(t)]$

(c) $\dfrac{d}{dt}[\mathbf{r}(t) + \mathbf{u}(t)]$

(d) $\dfrac{d}{dt}[3\mathbf{r}(t) - \mathbf{u}(t)]$

(e) $\dfrac{d}{dt}[(5t)\mathbf{u}(t)]$

(f) $\dfrac{d}{dt}[\mathbf{r}(2t)]$

59. $\mathbf{r}(t) = \langle 3t, t^2 \rangle$, $\mathbf{u}(t) = \langle 4t, t^2 \rangle$

60. $\mathbf{r}(t) = \langle 3 \sin t, 2 \cos t \rangle$, $\mathbf{u}(t) = \langle \sin t, 4 \cos t \rangle$

61. $\mathbf{r}(t) = \langle t, \ln t \rangle$, $\mathbf{u}(t) = \langle e^t, t^3 \rangle$

62. $\mathbf{r}(t) = \langle 2e^{-t}, 5t^2 \rangle$, $\mathbf{u}(t) = \langle \ln t, 2t \rangle$

Finding an Indefinite Integral In Exercises 63–70, find the indefinite integral.

63. $\displaystyle\int \langle 2t, 1 \rangle \, dt$

64. $\displaystyle\int \langle 4t^3, -4\sqrt{t} \rangle \, dt$

65. $\displaystyle\int \left\langle \frac{1}{t}, -t^{3/2} \right\rangle dt$

66. $\displaystyle\int \left\langle \frac{t}{t^2 - 1}, e^{-t} \right\rangle dt$

67. $\displaystyle\int \langle \sqrt[3]{2t + 8}, \sec t \tan t \rangle \, dt$

68. $\displaystyle\int \langle \cos t, 2^t \rangle \, dt$

69. $\displaystyle\int \left\langle \frac{1}{\sqrt{9 + t^2}}, \frac{1}{\sqrt{9 - t^2}} \right\rangle dt$

70. $\displaystyle\int \langle e^{-t} \sin t, e^{-t} \cos t \rangle \, dt$

Evaluating a Definite Integral In Exercises 71–76, evaluate the definite integral.

71. $\displaystyle\int_0^1 \langle 8t, -3 \rangle \, dt$

72. $\displaystyle\int_{-1}^1 \langle t^3, \sqrt[5]{t} \rangle \, dt$

73. $\displaystyle\int_0^{\pi/2} \langle a \cos t, a \sin t \rangle \, dt$

74. $\displaystyle\int_0^{\pi/4} \langle \sec t \tan t, 2 \sin t \cos t \rangle \, dt$

75. $\displaystyle\int_0^2 \langle e^t, -te^t \rangle \, dt$

76. $\displaystyle\int_0^3 \| \langle t, t^2 \rangle \| \, dt$

Finding an Antiderivative In Exercises 77–82, find $\mathbf{r}(t)$ that satisfies the initial condition(s).

77. $\mathbf{r}'(t) = \langle 4e^{2t}, 3e^t \rangle$, $\mathbf{r}(0) = \langle 2, 0 \rangle$

78. $\mathbf{r}'(t) = \langle 3t^2, 6\sqrt{t} \rangle$, $\mathbf{r}(0) = \langle 1, 2 \rangle$

79. $\mathbf{r}'(t) = \langle te^{-t^2}, -e^{-t} \rangle$, $\mathbf{r}(0) = \langle \frac{1}{2}, -1 \rangle$

80. $\mathbf{r}'(t) = \left\langle \dfrac{1}{1 + t^2}, \dfrac{1}{t} \right\rangle$, $\mathbf{r}(1) = \langle 2, 0 \rangle$

81. $\mathbf{r}''(t) = \langle 0, -32 \rangle$, $\mathbf{r}'(0) = \langle 1, 6 \rangle$, $\mathbf{r}(0) = \mathbf{0}$

82. $\mathbf{r}''(t) = \langle -4 \cos t, -3 \sin t \rangle$, $\mathbf{r}'(0) = \langle 0, 3 \rangle$, $\mathbf{r}(0) = \langle 4, 0 \rangle$

EXPLORING CONCEPTS

83. **Justifying** State the definition of continuity of a vector-valued function. Give an example of a vector-valued function that is defined but not continuous at $t = 2$.

84. **Justifying** Suppose $f(t)$ is continuous on all real numbers except $t = 0$ and $g(t)$ is continuous on $(-1, 3]$. On what intervals is $\mathbf{r}(t) = \langle f(t), g(t) \rangle$ continuous?

85. **Communicating** Compare integration of a vector-valued function with integration of a real-valued function.

86. **Communicating** The two components of the derivative of the vector-valued function $\mathbf{u}$ are positive at $t = t_0$. Describe the behavior of $\mathbf{u}$ at $t = t_0$.

Proof In Exercises 87–90, prove the property. In each case, assume **r** and **u** are differentiable vector-valued functions of t, w is a differentiable real-valued function of t, and c is a scalar.

87. $\dfrac{d}{dt}[c\mathbf{r}(t)] = c\mathbf{r}'(t)$

88. $\dfrac{d}{dt}[\mathbf{r}(t) \pm \mathbf{u}(t)] = \mathbf{r}'(t) \pm \mathbf{u}'(t)$

89. $\dfrac{d}{dt}[w(t)\mathbf{r}(t)] = w(t)\mathbf{r}'(t) + w'(t)\mathbf{r}(t)$

90. $\dfrac{d}{dt}[\mathbf{r}(w(t))] = \mathbf{r}'(w(t))w'(t)$

91. Particle Motion A particle moves in the xy-plane along the curve represented by the vector-valued function $\mathbf{r}(t) = \langle t - \sin t, 1 - \cos t \rangle$.

(a) Use a graphing utility to graph **r**. Describe the curve.

(b) Find the minimum and maximum values of $\|\mathbf{r}'\|$ and $\|\mathbf{r}''\|$.

92. Particle Motion A particle moves in the xy-plane along the curve represented by the vector-valued function $\mathbf{r}(t) = \langle 2 \cos t, 3 \sin t \rangle$.

(a) Describe the curve.

(b) Find the minimum and maximum values of $\|\mathbf{r}'\|$ and $\|\mathbf{r}''\|$.

93. Proof Prove that if **r** is a vector-valued function that is continuous at c, then $\|\mathbf{r}\|$ is continuous at c.

94. HOW DO YOU SEE IT? The graph shows a vector-valued function $\mathbf{r}(t)$ for $0 \le t \le 2\pi$ and its derivative $\mathbf{r}'(t)$ for several values of t. For each derivative shown in the graph, determine whether each component is positive or negative.

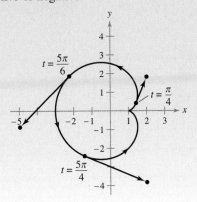

True or False? In Exercises 95–98, determine whether the statement is true or false. If it is false, explain why or give an example that shows it is false.

95. If f and g are first-degree polynomial functions, then the curve given by $x = f(t)$ and $y = g(t)$ is a line.

96. The vector-valued function $\mathbf{r}(t) = \langle t^2 - 2, -t \rangle$ lies on the parabola $x = y^2 - 2$.

97. The definite integral of a vector-valued function is a real number.

98. $\dfrac{d}{dt}[\|\mathbf{r}(t)\|] = \|\mathbf{r}'(t)\|$

Calculus AP® – Exam Preparation Questions

99. Multiple Choice If $\mathbf{r}(t) = \langle 5t^2 - 2t, 3 - \ln t \rangle$, then $-\frac{1}{3}\mathbf{r}'(2) =$

(A) $\left\langle 18, \frac{1}{2} \right\rangle$.

(B) $\left\langle 18, -\frac{1}{2} \right\rangle$.

(C) $\left\langle -6, -\frac{1}{6} \right\rangle$.

(D) $\left\langle -6, \frac{1}{6} \right\rangle$.

100. Multiple Choice If $\mathbf{r}(t) = \langle e^{-4t} + 9, 7 - 4t^3 \rangle$, then $\mathbf{r}''(t) =$

(A) $\langle e^{-4t}, -12t^2 \rangle$. (B) $\langle -4e^{-4t}, -12t^2 \rangle$.

(C) $\langle 16e^{-4t}, -24t \rangle$. (D) $\langle e^{-4t}, -24t \rangle$.

SECTION PROJECT

Witch of Agnesi

In Section 1.6, you studied a famous curve called the **Witch of Agnesi**. In this project, you will take a closer look at this function.

Consider a circle of radius a centered on the y-axis at $(0, a)$. Let A be a point on the horizontal line $y = 2a$, let O be the origin, and let B be the point where the segment OA intersects the circle. A point P is on the Witch of Agnesi when P lies on the horizontal line through B and on the vertical line through A.

(a) Show that the point A is traced out by the vector-valued function $\mathbf{r}_A(\theta) = \langle 2a \cot \theta, 2a \rangle$ for $0 < \theta < \pi$, where θ is the angle that OA makes with the positive x-axis.

(b) Show that the point B is traced out by the vector-valued function

$$\mathbf{r}_B(\theta) = \langle a \sin 2\theta, a(1 - \cos 2\theta) \rangle$$

for $0 < \theta < \pi$.

(c) Combine the results of parts (a) and (b) to find the vector-valued function $\mathbf{r}(\theta)$ for the Witch of Agnesi. Use a graphing utility to graph this curve for $a = 1$.

(d) Describe the limits $\lim\limits_{\theta \to 0^+} \mathbf{r}(\theta)$ and $\lim\limits_{\theta \to \pi^-} \mathbf{r}(\theta)$.

(e) Eliminate the parameter θ and determine the rectangular equation of the Witch of Agnesi. Use a graphing utility to graph this function for $a = 1$ and compare your graph with that obtained in part (c).

9.8 Velcocity and Acceleration

▶ Describe the velocity and acceleration associated with a vector-valued function.

Velocity and Acceleration

You are now ready to combine your study of parametric equations, curves, vectors, and vector-valued functions to form a model for motion along a curve. You will begin by looking at the motion of an object in the plane.

As an object moves along a curve in the plane, the coordinates x and y of its position are each functions of time t. Rather than using the letters f and g to represent these two functions, it is convenient to write $x = x(t)$ and $y = y(t)$. So, the position vector $\mathbf{r}(t)$ takes the form

$$\mathbf{r}(t) = \langle x(t), y(t) \rangle. \qquad \text{Position vector}$$

The beauty of this vector model for representing motion is that you can use the first and second derivatives of the vector-valued function $\mathbf{r}$ to find the object's velocity and acceleration. (Recall from Section 9.6 that velocity and acceleration are both vector quantities having magnitude and direction.) To find the velocity and acceleration vectors at a given time t, consider a point $Q(x(t + \Delta t), y(t + \Delta t))$ that is approaching the point $P(x(t), y(t))$ along the curve C given by $\mathbf{r}(t) = \langle x(t), y(t) \rangle$, as shown in Figure 9.65. As $\Delta t \to 0$, the direction of the vector $\overrightarrow{PQ}$ (denoted by $\Delta \mathbf{r}$) approaches the *direction of motion* at time t.

$$\Delta \mathbf{r} = \mathbf{r}(t + \Delta t) - \mathbf{r}(t)$$

$$\frac{\Delta \mathbf{r}}{\Delta t} = \frac{\mathbf{r}(t + \Delta t) - \mathbf{r}(t)}{\Delta t}$$

$$\lim_{\Delta t \to 0} \frac{\Delta \mathbf{r}}{\Delta t} = \lim_{\Delta t \to 0} \frac{\mathbf{r}(t + \Delta t) - \mathbf{r}(t)}{\Delta t}$$

When this limit exists, it is defined as the **velocity vector** or **tangent vector** to the curve at point P. Note that this is the same limit used to define $\mathbf{r}'(t)$. So, the direction of $\mathbf{r}'(t)$ gives the direction of motion at time t. Moreover, the magnitude of the vector $\mathbf{r}'(t)$

$$\|\mathbf{r}'(t)\| = \|\langle x'(t), y'(t) \rangle\|$$
$$= \sqrt{[x'(t)]^2 + [y'(t)]^2}$$

gives the **speed** of the object at time t.

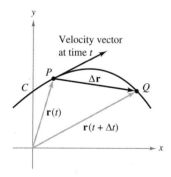
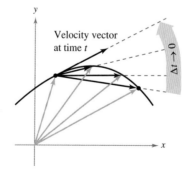

As $\Delta t \to 0$, $\dfrac{\Delta \mathbf{r}}{\Delta t}$ approaches the velocity vector.

Figure 9.65

Similar to how $\mathbf{r}'(t)$ is used to find velocity, you can use $\mathbf{r}''(t)$ to find acceleration, as indicated in the definitions at the top of the next page.

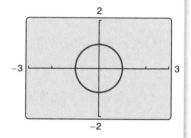

Exploration

Exploring Velocity Consider the circle given by

$$\mathbf{r}(t) = \langle \cos \omega t, \sin \omega t \rangle.$$

(The symbol ω is the Greek letter omega.) Use a graphing utility in *parametric* mode to graph this circle for several values of ω. How does ω affect the velocity of the terminal point as it traces out the curve? For a given value of ω, does the speed appear constant? Does the acceleration appear constant? Explain your reasoning.

Definitions of Velocity and Acceleration

If x and y are twice-differentiable functions of t, and $\mathbf{r}$ is a position vector given by $\mathbf{r}(t) = \langle x(t), y(t) \rangle$, then the velocity vector, acceleration vector, and speed at time t are as follows.

$$\text{Velocity} = \mathbf{v}(t) = \mathbf{r}'(t) = \langle x'(t), y'(t) \rangle$$
$$\text{Acceleration} = \mathbf{a}(t) = \mathbf{r}''(t) = \langle x''(t), y''(t) \rangle$$
$$\text{Speed} = \|\mathbf{v}(t)\| = \|\mathbf{r}'(t)\| = \sqrt{[x'(t)]^2 + [y'(t)]^2}$$

EXAMPLE 1   Velocity and Acceleration Along a Plane Curve

Find the (a) velocity vector, (b) speed, and (c) acceleration vector for the particle that moves along the plane curve C described by

$$\mathbf{r}(t) = \left\langle 2 \sin \frac{t}{2}, 2 \cos \frac{t}{2} \right\rangle. \qquad \text{Position vector}$$

Solution

a. $\mathbf{v}(t) = \mathbf{r}'(t) = \left\langle \cos \frac{t}{2}, -\sin \frac{t}{2} \right\rangle \qquad$ Velocity vector

b. $\|\mathbf{v}(t)\| = \sqrt{\cos^2 \frac{t}{2} + \sin^2 \frac{t}{2}} = 1 \qquad$ Speed

c. $\mathbf{a}(t) = \mathbf{r}''(t) = \left\langle -\frac{1}{2} \sin \frac{t}{2}, -\frac{1}{2} \cos \frac{t}{2} \right\rangle \qquad$ Acceleration vector

Note that the parametric equations for the curve in Example 1 are

$$x = 2 \sin \frac{t}{2} \quad \text{and} \quad y = 2 \cos \frac{t}{2}. \qquad \text{Parametric equations}$$

By eliminating the parameter t, you obtain the rectangular equation

$$x^2 + y^2 = 4. \qquad \text{Rectangular equation}$$

So, the curve is a circle of radius 2 centered at the origin, as shown in Figure 9.66. Because the velocity vector

$$\mathbf{v}(t) = \left\langle \cos \frac{t}{2}, -\sin \frac{t}{2} \right\rangle$$

has a constant magnitude but a changing direction as t increases, the particle moves around the circle at a constant speed.

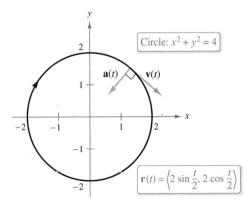

The particle moves around the circle at a constant speed.
Figure 9.66

EXAMPLE 2 Velocity and Acceleration Vectors in the Plane

Sketch the path of an object moving along the plane curve given by

$$\mathbf{r}(t) = \langle t^2 - 4, t \rangle \qquad \text{Position vector}$$

and find the velocity and acceleration vectors when $t = 0$ and $t = 2$.

Solution

Using the parametric equations

$$x = t^2 - 4 \quad \text{and} \quad y = t \qquad \text{Parametric equations}$$

you can determine that the curve is a parabola given by

$$x = y^2 - 4 \qquad \text{Rectangular equation}$$

as shown in Figure 9.67. The velocity vector (at any time) is

$$\mathbf{v}(t) = \mathbf{r}'(t) = \langle 2t, 1 \rangle \qquad \text{Velocity vector}$$

and the acceleration vector (at any time) is

$$\mathbf{a}(t) = \mathbf{r}''(t) = \langle 2, 0 \rangle. \qquad \text{Acceleration vector}$$

When $t = 0$, the velocity and acceleration vectors are

$$\mathbf{v}(0) = \langle 2(0), 1 \rangle = \langle 0, 1 \rangle \quad \text{and} \quad \mathbf{a}(0) = \langle 2, 0 \rangle.$$

When $t = 2$, the velocity and acceleration vectors are

$$\mathbf{v}(2) = \langle 2(2), 1 \rangle = \langle 4, 1 \rangle \quad \text{and} \quad \mathbf{a}(2) = \langle 2, 0 \rangle.$$

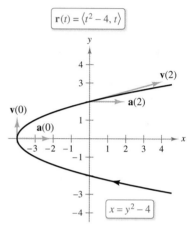

At each point on the curve, the acceleration vector points to the right.

Figure 9.67

As the object moves along the path shown in Figure 9.67, note that the acceleration vector is constant (it has a magnitude of 2 and points to the right). This implies that the speed of the object is decreasing as the object moves toward the vertex of the parabola, and the speed is increasing as the object moves away from the vertex of the parabola. ∎

The type of motion shown in Figure 9.67 is not characteristic of comets that travel on parabolic paths through our solar system. For such comets, the acceleration vector always points to the origin (the sun), which implies that the comet's speed increases as it approaches the vertex of the path and decreases as it moves away from the vertex. (See Figure 9.68.)

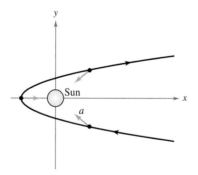

At each point in the comet's orbit, the acceleration vector points toward the sun.

Figure 9.68

Recall from Section 4.5 that you used integration to find the displacement of a particle and the total distance traveled. When the motion of the particle is described using vector-valued functions, use the formulas shown on the next page.

Displacement and Total Distance

Let $\mathbf{v}(t) = \langle x'(t), y'(t) \rangle$ be the velocity of a particle, where $x'(t)$ and $y'(t)$ are continuous on $[a, b]$. The **displacement** of the particle on $[a, b]$ is

$$\int_a^b \mathbf{v}(t) \, dt = \left\langle \int_a^b x'(t) \, dt, \int_a^b y'(t) \, dt \right\rangle$$

and the **total distance traveled** by the particle on $[a, b]$ is

$$\int_a^b \|\mathbf{v}(t)\| \, dt = \int_a^b \sqrt{[x'(t)]^2 + [y'(t)]^2} \, dt.$$

EXAMPLE 3   Finding Displacement and Total Distance

A particle moves in the plane with a velocity of $\mathbf{v}(t) = \langle 2, 4 \rangle$. When $t = 0$, the particle is at the point $(2, 1)$. Find the position of the particle when $t = 2$ and the total distance traveled on the interval $0 \le t \le 2$.

Solution

The displacement of the particle when $t = 2$ is

$$\int_0^2 \mathbf{v}(t) \, dt = \left\langle \int_0^2 2 \, dt, \int_0^2 4 \, dt \right\rangle = \left\langle \Big[2t \Big]_0^2, \Big[4t \Big]_0^2 \right\rangle = \langle 4, 8 \rangle.$$

From $t = 0$ to $t = 2$, the particle has moved 4 units to the right and 8 units up. When $t = 0$, the particle is at $(2, 1)$, so at $t = 2$ the particle is at $(2 + 4, 1 + 8) = (6, 9)$. The total distance traveled on the interval $0 \le t \le 2$ is

$$\int_0^2 \|\mathbf{v}(t)\| \, dt = \int_0^2 \sqrt{2^2 + 4^2} \, dt = \int_0^2 \sqrt{20} \, dt = 2\sqrt{5}\, t \, \Big]_0^2 = 4\sqrt{5} \approx 8.944 \text{ units.} \ \blacksquare$$

So far in this section, you have concentrated on finding the velocity and acceleration by differentiating the position vector. Many practical applications involve the reverse problem—finding the position vector for a given velocity or acceleration. This is demonstrated in the next example.

EXAMPLE 4   Finding a Position Vector by Integration

Find the position vector of the particle in Example 3.

Solution

You are given one *initial condition*. When $t = 0$, the particle is at the point $(2, 1)$. So, you have

$$\mathbf{r}(0) = \langle x(0), y(0) \rangle = \langle 2, 1 \rangle.$$

To find the position vector, integrate $\mathbf{v}$ to produce

$$\mathbf{r}(t) = \int \mathbf{v}(t) \, dt = \left\langle \int 2 \, dt, \int 4 \, dt \right\rangle = \langle 2t, 4t \rangle + \mathbf{C}$$

where $\mathbf{C} = \langle C_1, C_2 \rangle$. Letting $t = 0$ and applying the initial condition $\mathbf{r}(0) = \langle 2, 1 \rangle$, you obtain

$$\mathbf{r}(0) = \langle C_1, C_2 \rangle = \langle 2, 1 \rangle \quad \Longrightarrow \quad C_1 = 2, C_2 = 1.$$

So, the *position* at any time t is

$$\mathbf{r}(t) = \langle 2t + 2, 4t + 1 \rangle. \qquad \text{Position vector}$$

$\blacksquare$

Finding Velocity and Acceleration Along a Plane Curve In Exercises 1–8, the position vector **r** describes the path of an object moving in the plane. (a) Find the velocity vector, speed, and acceleration vector of the object. (b) Evaluate the velocity vector and acceleration vector of the object at the given value of *t*. (c) Sketch a graph of the path, and sketch the velocity and acceleration vectors at the given value of *t*.

1. $\mathbf{r}(t) = \langle 3t, t - 1 \rangle$, $t = 1$
2. $\mathbf{r}(t) = \langle t, -t^2 + 4 \rangle$, $t = 1$
3. $\mathbf{r}(t) = \langle t^2, t \rangle$, $t = 2$ 4. $\mathbf{r}(t) = \langle \frac{2}{5}t^3 + \frac{1}{2}, t \rangle$, $t = 2$
5. $\mathbf{r}(t) = \langle 2 \cos t, 2 \sin t \rangle$, $t = \pi/4$
6. $\mathbf{r}(t) = \langle 3 \cos t, 2 \sin t \rangle$, $t = \pi$
7. $\mathbf{r}(t) = \langle 2t - \sin t, 1 - \cos t \rangle$, $t = 3\pi/2$
8. $\mathbf{r}(t) = \langle e^{-t}, e^t \rangle$, $t = 0$

Finding Displacement, Total Distance, and a Position Vector In Exercises 9–14, the velocity vector **v** and the position of a particle at time $t = 0$ are given. (a) Find the position of the particle when $t = 3$. (b) Find the total distance traveled on the interval $0 \leq t \leq 3$. (c) Find the position vector of the particle.

9. $\mathbf{v}(t) = \langle 3, 1 \rangle$, $(4, 5)$ 10. $\mathbf{v}(t) = \langle 4, 10 \rangle$, $(3, 1)$
11. $\mathbf{v}(t) = \langle 2t, 1 \rangle$, $(4, 1)$
12. $\mathbf{v}(t) = \langle 4t + 9, t/2 \rangle$, $(1, 2)$
13. $\mathbf{v}(t) = \langle 3t^2, 2t \rangle$, $(2, 3)$
14. $\mathbf{v}(t) = \langle 8t - 1, 6t^2 + 1 \rangle$, $(0, 0)$

Finding Velocity and Position Vectors In Exercises 15–18, use the given information to find the velocity and position vectors. Then find the position at time $t = 2$.

15. $\mathbf{a}(t) = \langle 2, 3 \rangle$, $\mathbf{v}(0) = \langle 0, 4 \rangle$, $\mathbf{r}(0) = \langle 0, 0 \rangle$
16. $\mathbf{a}(t) = \langle t, t \rangle$, $\mathbf{v}(0) = \langle 3, 1 \rangle$, $\mathbf{r}(0) = \langle 1, 5 \rangle$
17. $\mathbf{a}(t) = \langle 4t, t^2 \rangle$, $\mathbf{v}(0) = \langle 5, 0 \rangle$, $\mathbf{r}(0) = \langle 4, 2 \rangle$
18. $\mathbf{a}(t) = \langle 3\sqrt{t}, \sin 2t \rangle$, $\mathbf{v}(0) = \langle 0, -1 \rangle$, $\mathbf{r}(0) = \langle 0, 0 \rangle$

19. **Particle Motion** A particle is moving along the curve given by $\mathbf{r}(t) = \langle t, 9 - 6t + t^2 \rangle$ for $0 \leq t \leq 5$.
    (a) Sketch a graph of the path of the particle.
    (b) At what time *t* is the speed of the particle a minimum?
    (c) Find the total distance traveled from $t = 0$ to $t = 5$.

20. **Particle Motion** A particle is moving along the curve given by $\mathbf{r}(t) = \langle 4 - t, 6\sqrt{t} \rangle$ for $0 \leq t \leq 8$.
    (a) Sketch a graph of the path of the particle.
    (b) For what values of *t* is the particle moving to the left?

21. **Particle Motion** A particle is moving along a curve so that its velocity for time $t \geq 0$ is given by

    $$x'(t) = 2e^{-t/4} \quad \text{and} \quad y'(t) = 1 - \frac{5}{t + 1}.$$

    (a) For what values of *t* is the particle moving to the right? For what values of *t* is the particle moving upward?
    (b) Find the position vector and the acceleration vector of the particle for $t \geq 0$. Assume $\mathbf{r}(0) = \langle 0, 0 \rangle$.
    (c) Describe the path of the particle. What happens as *t* approaches ∞? Justify your answer graphically.

22. **Particle Motion** A particle is moving along the curve given by $\mathbf{r}(t) = \langle t^3 - 6t^2, -t^2 + 8t \rangle$ for $t \geq 0$.
    (a) Is the particle moving to the left or to the right at time $t = 2$? Justify your answer.
    (b) Find the velocity of the particle at $t = 2$.
    (c) At what point(s) is the particle at rest? Justify your answer.
    (d) Use a graphing utility to find the total distance traveled from $t = 0$ to $t = 4$.

Error Analysis A particle moves in the plane with a velocity of

$$\mathbf{v}(t) = \left\langle \frac{1}{t + 1}, e^t \right\rangle.$$

When $t = 0$, the particle is at the point $(0, 1)$. In Exercises 23 and 24, describe and correct the error.

23. At $t = 3$, the position of the particle is at

$$\int_0^3 \mathbf{v}(t)\, dt = \left\langle \int_0^3 \frac{1}{t + 1}\, dt, \int_0^3 e^t\, dt \right\rangle$$
$$= \left\langle \left[\ln(t + 1) \right]_0^3, \left[e^t \right]_0^3 \right\rangle$$
$$= \langle \ln 4, e^3 - 1 \rangle. \quad \text{✗}$$

24. The total distance traveled on the interval $0 \leq t \leq 2$ is

$$\int_0^2 \|\mathbf{v}(t)\|\, dt = \int_0^2 \sqrt{\left[-\frac{1}{(t + 1)^2} \right]^2 + (e^t)^2}\, dt$$
$$\approx 6.496. \quad \text{✗}$$

Cycloidal Motion In Exercises 25 and 26, consider the motion of a point (or particle) on the circumference of a rolling circle. As the circle rolls, it generates the cycloid $\mathbf{r}(t) = \langle b(\omega t - \sin \omega t), b(1 - \cos \omega t) \rangle$, where ω is the constant angular velocity of the circle and *b* is the radius of the circle.

25. Find the velocity and acceleration vectors of the particle. Use the results to determine the times at which the speed of the particle will be (a) zero and (b) maximized.

26. Find the maximum speed of a point on the circumference of an automobile tire of radius 1 foot when the automobile is traveling at 60 miles per hour. Compare this speed with the speed of the automobile.

Circular Motion In Exercises 27–30, consider a particle moving on a circular path of radius b described by

$$\mathbf{r}(t) = \langle b \cos \omega t, b \sin \omega t \rangle$$

where $\omega = du/dt$ is the constant angular velocity.

27. Find the velocity vector.

28. (a) Show that the speed of the particle is $b\omega$.

 (b) Use a graphing utility in *parametric* mode to graph the circle for $b = 6$. Try different values of ω. Does the graphing utility draw the circle faster for greater values of ω?

29. Find the acceleration vector and show that its direction is always toward the center of the circle.

30. Show that the magnitude of the acceleration vector is $b\omega^2$.

EXPLORING CONCEPTS ———————————————

31. Communicating Explain how a particle can be accelerating even though its speed is constant.

32. Communicating Consider a particle that is moving along the space curve given by

$$\mathbf{r}_1(t) = t^3\mathbf{i} + (3 - t)\mathbf{j} + 2t^2\mathbf{k}.$$

Write a vector-valued function $\mathbf{r}_2$ for a particle that moves four times as fast as the particle represented by $\mathbf{r}_1$. Explain how you found the function.

33. Circular Motion Consider a particle that moves around a circle. Is the velocity vector of the particle always orthogonal to the acceleration vector of the particle? Explain.

34. HOW DO YOU SEE IT? The graph shows the path of a particle and the velocity and acceleration vectors at times t_1 and t_2. Is the speed increasing or decreasing at times t_1 and t_2? Explain your reasoning.

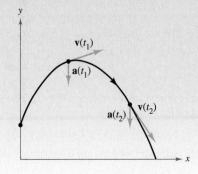

35. Connecting Representations A particle moves on an elliptical path given by the vector-valued function

$$\mathbf{r}(t) = \langle 6 \cos t, 3 \sin t \rangle.$$

(a) Find $\mathbf{v}(t)$, $\|\mathbf{v}(t)\|$, and $\mathbf{a}(t)$.

(b) Find the speed of the particle when $t = 0$, $\pi/4$, $\pi/2$, $2\pi/3$, and π.

(c) Graph the elliptical path and the velocity and acceleration vectors at the values of t given in the table in part (b).

(d) Use the results of parts (b) and (c) to describe the geometric relationship between the velocity and acceleration vectors when the speed of the particle is increasing, and when it is decreasing.

36. Particle Motion Consider a particle moving on an elliptical path described by

$$\mathbf{r}(t) = \langle a \cos \omega t, b \sin \omega t \rangle$$

where $\omega = d\theta/dt$ is the constant angular velocity.

(a) Find the velocity vector. What is the speed of the particle?

(b) Find the acceleration vector and show that its direction is always toward the center of the ellipse.

Calculus AP® – Exam Preparation Questions

37. Multiple Choice A particle moves in the plane with a velocity of $\mathbf{v}(t) = \langle 3t^2, 2t \rangle$. What is the acceleration vector of the particle when $t = 2$?

(A) $\langle 12, 0 \rangle$ (B) $\langle 12, 2 \rangle$

(C) $\langle 8, 4 \rangle$ (D) $4\sqrt{10}$

38. Free Response The graphs of the polar curves $r = 2$ and $r = 3 - 2 \sin \theta$ are shown in the figure.

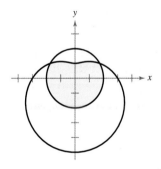

(a) Find the points of intersection of the graphs.

(b) Find the area of the shaded region.

(c) An object moves along the curve $r = 3 - 2 \sin \theta$ so that at time t seconds, $\theta = t^2$. Find the time t in the interval $[1, 2]$ for which the x-coordinate of the object's position is -2.

(d) Find the position vector in terms of t for the object described in part (c). Find the velocity vector at time $t = 1.7$.

9 Review Exercises

Matching In Exercises 1–6, match the equation with its graph. [The graphs are labeled (a), (b), (c), (d), (e), and (f).]

(a)

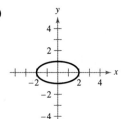

(b)

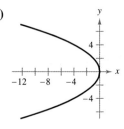

(c)

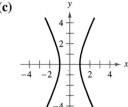

(d)

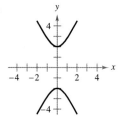

(e)

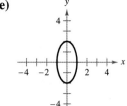

(f)

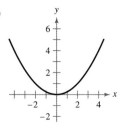

1. $4x^2 + y^2 = 4$
2. $4x^2 - y^2 = 4$
3. $y^2 = -4x$
4. $y^2 - 4x^2 = 4$
5. $x^2 + 4y^2 = 4$
6. $x^2 = 4y$

Identifying a Conic In Exercises 7–14, identify the conic, analyze the equation (center, radius, vertices, foci, eccentricity, directrix, and asymptotes, if possible), and sketch its graph. Use a graphing utility to confirm your results.

7. $16x^2 + 16y^2 - 16x + 24y - 3 = 0$
8. $y^2 - 12y - 8x + 20 = 0$
9. $3x^2 - 2y^2 + 24x + 12y + 24 = 0$
10. $x^2 + y^2 + 4x - 9 = 0$
11. $3x^2 + 2y^2 - 12x + 12y + 29 = 0$
12. $12x^2 - 12y^2 - 12x + 24y - 45 = 0$
13. $x^2 - 6x - 8y + 1 = 0$
14. $9x^2 + 25y^2 + 18x - 100y - 116 = 0$

Finding the Standard Equation of a Parabola In Exercises 15 and 16, find the standard form of the equation of the parabola.

15. Vertex: $(0, 2)$
    Directrix: $x = -3$
16. Vertex: $(2, 6)$
    Focus: $(2, 4)$

Finding the Standard Equation of an Ellipse In Exercises 17–20, find the standard form of the equation of the ellipse.

17. Center: $(0, 1)$
    Focus: $(4, 1)$
    Vertex: $(6, 1)$
18. Center: $(0, 0)$
    Major axis: vertical
    Points on the ellipse:
    $(1, 2), (2, 0)$
19. Vertices: $(3, 1), (3, 7)$
    Eccentricity: $\frac{2}{3}$
20. Foci: $(0, \pm 7)$
    Major axis length: 20

Finding the Standard Equation of a Hyperbola In Exercises 21–24, find the standard form of the equation of the hyperbola.

21. Vertices: $(0, \pm 8)$
    Asymptotes: $y = \pm 2x$
22. Vertices: $(\pm 2, 0)$
    Asymptotes: $y = \pm 32x$
23. Vertices: $(\pm 7, -1)$
    Foci: $(\pm 9, -1)$
24. Center: $(3, 0)$
    Vertex: $(3, 3)$
    Focus: $(3, 6)$

25. **Satellite Antenna** A cross section of a large parabolic antenna is modeled by the graph of

$$y = \frac{x^2}{200}, \quad -100 \le x \le 100.$$

The receiving and transmitting equipment is positioned at the focus.

(a) Find the coordinates of the focus.

(b) Find the surface area of the antenna.

26. **Using an Ellipse** Consider the ellipse $\dfrac{x^2}{25} + \dfrac{y^2}{9} = 1$.

(a) Find the area of the region bounded by the ellipse.

(b) Find the volume of the solid generated by revolving the region about its major axis.

Using Parametric Equations In Exercises 27–34, sketch the curve represented by the parametric equations (indicate the orientation of the curve), and write the corresponding rectangular equation by eliminating the parameter.

27. $x = 1 + 8t, \ y = 3 - 4t$
28. $x = t - 2, \ y = t^2 - 1$
29. $x = \sqrt{t} + 1, \ y = t - 3$
30. $x = e^t - 1, \ y = e^{3t}$
31. $x = 6 \cos \theta, \ y = 6 \sin \theta$
32. $x = 2 + 5 \cos t, \ y = 3 + 2 \sin t$
33. $x = 2 + \sec \theta, \ y = 3 + \tan \theta$
34. $x = 4 \cot^2 t, \ t = 2 \csc^2 t$

Finding Parametric Equations In Exercises 35 and 36, find two different sets of parametric equations for the rectangular equation.

35. $y = 4x + 3$ **36.** $y = x^2 - 2$

37. Rotary Engine The rotary engine was developed by Felix Wankel in the 1950s. It features a rotor that is a modified equilateral triangle. The rotor moves in a chamber that, in two dimensions, is an epitrochoid. Use a graphing utility to graph the chamber modeled by the parametric equations

$$x = \cos 3\theta + 5 \cos \theta \quad \text{and} \quad y = \sin 3\theta + 5 \sin \theta.$$

38. Serpentine Curve Consider the parametric equations $x = 2 \cot \theta$ and $y = 4 \sin \theta \cos \theta, 0 < \theta < \pi$.

(a) Use a graphing utility to graph the curve.

(b) Eliminate the parameter to show that the rectangular equation of the serpentine curve is $(4 + x^2)y = 8x$.

Finding Slope and Concavity In Exercises 39–46, find dy/dx and d^2y/dx^2, and find the slope and concavity (if possible) at the given value of the parameter.

Parametric Equations	*Parameter*
39. $x = \frac{1}{2}t, \quad y = -3t + 1$	$t = -1$
40. $x = t - 6, \quad y = t^2$	$t = 5$
41. $x = 2t^2, \quad y = \sqrt{t} + 1$	$t = 1$
42. $x = \dfrac{1}{t}, \quad y = t^2$	$t = -2$
43. $x = 5 + \cos \theta, \quad y = 3 + 4 \sin \theta$	$\theta = \dfrac{\pi}{6}$
44. $x = 10 \cos \theta, \quad y = 10 \sin \theta$	$\theta = -\dfrac{\pi}{4}$
45. $x = \cos^3 \theta, \quad y = 4 \sin^3 \theta$	$\theta = \dfrac{\pi}{3}$
46. $x = e^t, \quad y = e^{-t}$	$t = 1$

Finding an Equation of a Tangent Line In Exercises 47 and 48, (a) use a graphing utility to graph the curve represented by the parametric equations, (b) use a graphing utility to find dx/dt, dy/dt, and dy/dx at the given value of the parameter, (c) find an equation of the tangent line to the curve at the given value of the parameter, and (d) use a graphing utility to graph the curve and the tangent line from part (c).

Parametric Equations	*Parameter*
47. $x = -t, \quad y = t^3 + 4t^2$	$t = 1$
48. $x = \dfrac{1}{4} \tan t, \quad y = 6 \sin t$	$t = \dfrac{\pi}{3}$

Horizontal and Vertical Tangency In Exercises 49–52, find all points (if any) of horizontal and vertical tangency to the curve. Use a graphing utility to confirm your results.

49. $x = 5 - t, \quad y = 2t^2$

50. $x = t + 2, \quad y = t^3 - 2t$

51. $x = 2 + 2 \sin \theta, \quad y = 1 + \cos \theta$

52. $x = 2 - 2 \cos \theta, \quad y = 2 \sin 2\theta$

Arc Length In Exercises 53 and 54, find the arc length of the curve on the given interval.

53. $x = t^2 + 1, \quad y = 4t^3 + 3, \quad 0 \le t \le 2$

54. $x = 7 \cos \theta, \quad y = 7 \sin \theta, \quad 0 \le \theta \le \pi$

Area In Exercises 55 and 56, find the area of the region.

55. $x = 3 \sin \theta$
$y = 2 \cos \theta$
$-\dfrac{\pi}{2} \le \theta \le \dfrac{\pi}{2}$

56. $x = 2 \cos \theta$
$y = \sin \theta$
$0 \le \theta \le \pi$

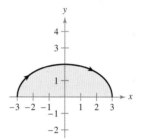   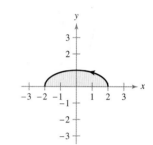

Polar-to-Rectangular Conversion In Exercises 57–60, the polar coordinates of a point are given. Plot the point and find the corresponding rectangular coordinates for the point.

57. $\left(5, \dfrac{3\pi}{2}\right)$ **58.** $\left(-6, \dfrac{5\pi}{6}\right)$

59. $\left(\sqrt{7}, 3.25\right)$ **60.** $(-2, -2.45)$

Rectangular-to-Polar Conversion In Exercises 61–64, the rectangular coordinates of a point are given. Plot the point and find *two* sets of polar coordinates for the point for $0 \le \theta < 2\pi$.

61. $(4, -4)$ **62.** $(0, -7)$

63. $(-1, 3)$ **64.** $\left(-\sqrt{3}, -\sqrt{3}\right)$

Rectangular-to-Polar Conversion In Exercises 65–70, convert the rectangular equation to polar form and sketch its graph.

65. $x^2 + y^2 = 25$ **66.** $x^2 - y^2 = 4$

67. $y = 9$ **68.** $x = 6$

69. $x^2 = 4y$ **70.** $x^2 + y^2 - 4x = 0$

Polar-to-Rectangular Conversion In Exercises 71–76, convert the polar equation to rectangular form and sketch its graph.

71. $r = 6 \cos \theta$ **72.** $r = 10$

73. $r = -5 \sec \theta$ **74.** $r = 3 \csc \theta$

75. $r = -2 \sec \theta \tan \theta$ **76.** $\theta = \dfrac{3\pi}{4}$

Graphing a Polar Equation   In Exercises 77–80, use a graphing utility to graph the polar equation. Find an interval for θ over which the graph is traced *only once*.

77. $r = 3 - 6 \cos \theta$

78. $r = \dfrac{8}{2 + \sin \theta}$

79. $r = 2 \sin \theta \cos^2 \theta$

80. $r^2 = 16 \sin 2\theta$

Horizontal and Vertical Tangency   In Exercises 81 and 82, find the points of horizontal and vertical tangency (if any) to the polar curve.

81. $r = 1 - \cos \theta$ **82.** $r = 3 \tan \theta$

Tangent Lines at the Pole   In Exercises 83 and 84, sketch a graph of the polar equation and find the tangent lines at the pole.

83. $r = 4 \sin 3\theta$ **84.** $r = 3 \cos 4\theta$

Sketching a Polar Graph   In Exercises 85–94, sketch a graph of the polar equation.

85. $r = 6$ **86.** $\theta = \pi/10$

87. $r = -\sec \theta$ **88.** $r = 5 \csc \theta$

89. $r = 4 - 3 \cos \theta$ **90.** $r = 3 + 2 \sin \theta$

91. $r = 4\theta$ **92.** $r = -3 \cos 2\theta$

93. $r^2 = 4 \sin 2\theta$ **94.** $r^2 = 9 \cos 2\theta$

Finding the Area of a Polar Region   In Exercises 95–98, find the area of the region.

95. One petal of $r = 3 \cos 5\theta$

96. Two petals of $r = 2 \sin 6\theta$

97. Interior of $r = 5(1 - \sin \theta)$

98. Interior of $r^2 = 4 \sin 2\theta$

Finding Points of Intersection   In Exercises 99 and 100, find the points of intersection of the graphs of the equations.

99. $r = 1 - \cos \theta$ **100.** $r = 1 + \sin \theta$
     $r = 1 + \sin \theta$ $r = 3 \sin \theta$

Finding the Area of a Polar Region   In Exercises 101–106, use a graphing utility to graph the polar equation. Find the area of the given region analytically.

101. Inner loop of $r = 3 - 6 \cos \theta$

102. Inner loop of $r = 4 + 8 \sin \theta$

103. Between the loops of $r = 3 - 6 \cos \theta$

104. Between the loops of $r = 4 + 8 \sin \theta$

105. Common interior of $r = 5 - 2 \sin \theta$ and
       $r = -5 + 2 \sin \theta$

106. Common interior of $r = 4 \cos \theta$ and $r = 2$

Finding the Arc Length of a Polar Curve   In Exercises 107 and 108, find the length of the curve over the given interval.

107. $r = 5 \cos \theta$, $\left[\dfrac{\pi}{2}, \pi \right]$

108. $r = 3(1 - \cos \theta)$, $[0, \pi]$

Finding and Using Vectors   In Exercises 109 and 110, the initial and terminal points of a vector v are given. (a) Sketch the given directed line segment, (b) write the vector in component form, and (c) sketch the vector with its initial point at the origin.

Initial Point	*Terminal Point*
109. $(2, -4)$	$(-1, 6)$
110. $(-3, 5)$	$(-3, 0)$

Using Vector Operations   In Exercises 111 and 112, find (a) $4\mathbf{u}$, (b) $\frac{1}{2}\mathbf{v}$, (c) $\mathbf{u} - \mathbf{v}$, and (d) $2\mathbf{v} + 5\mathbf{u}$.

111. $\mathbf{u} = \langle 3, -1 \rangle$, $\mathbf{v} = \langle 8, 1 \rangle$

112. $\mathbf{u} = \langle 1, -8 \rangle$, $\mathbf{v} = \langle -3, -4 \rangle$

Finding Magnitudes   In Exercises 113 and 114, find the following.

(a) $\|\mathbf{u}\|$ (b) $\|\mathbf{u} - \mathbf{v}\|$ (c) $\left\| \dfrac{\mathbf{u} + \mathbf{v}}{\|\mathbf{u} + \mathbf{v}\|} \right\|$

113. $\mathbf{u} = \langle 1, -2, \rangle$, $\mathbf{v} = \langle 0, 1 \rangle$

114. $\mathbf{u} = \langle -4, -3 \rangle$, $\mathbf{v} = \langle 2, 2 \rangle$

Finding a Vector   In Exercises 115 and 116, find the component form of v given its magnitude and the angle it makes with the positive x-axis.

115. $\|\mathbf{v}\| = 8$, $\theta = 60°$

116. $\|\mathbf{v}\| = \frac{1}{2}$, $\theta = 225°$

Domain and Continuity   In Exercises 117–120, (a) find the domain of r, and (b) determine the interval(s) on which r is continuous.

117. $\mathbf{r}(t) = \left\langle \sqrt[3]{t}, \dfrac{1}{t} \right\rangle$ **118.** $\mathbf{r}(t) = \left\langle \sqrt{t}, \dfrac{1}{t - 4} \right\rangle$

119. $\mathbf{r}(t) = \langle \ln t, t \rangle$ **120.** $\mathbf{r}(t) = \langle 5t^2, \arccos t \rangle$

Evaluating a Function   In Exercises 121 and 122, evaluate (if possible) the vector-valued function at each given value of t.

121. $\mathbf{r}(t) = \left\langle t^2, -\sqrt{t + 2} \right\rangle$

    (a) $\mathbf{r}(0)$ (b) $\mathbf{r}(-2)$ (c) $\mathbf{r}(c - 1)$

    (d) $\mathbf{r}(1 + \Delta t) - \mathbf{r}(1)$

122. $\mathbf{r}(t) = \langle 3 \cos t, 1 - \sin t \rangle$

    (a) $\mathbf{r}(0)$ (b) $\mathbf{r}\left(\dfrac{\pi}{2} \right)$ (c) $\mathbf{r}(s - \pi)$

    (d) $\mathbf{r}(\pi + \Delta t) - \mathbf{r}(\pi)$

Sketching a Plane Curve In Exercises 123–126, sketch the plane curve represented by the vector-valued function and given the orientation of the curve.

123. $\mathbf{r}(t) = \langle \pi \cos t, \pi \sin t \rangle$ **124.** $\mathbf{r}(t) = \langle t + 2, t^2 - 1 \rangle$
125. $\mathbf{r}(t) = \langle t + 1, 3t - 1 \rangle$ **126.** $\mathbf{r}(t) = \langle 2 \cos t, \sin t \rangle$

Representing a Graph by a Vector-Valued Function In Exercises 127 and 128, represent the plane curve by a vector-valued function. (There are many correct answers.)

127. $3x + 4y - 12 = 0$
128. $\dfrac{y^2}{9} - x^2 = 1$

Finding a Limit In Exercises 129–132, find the limit.

129. $\lim\limits_{t \to 3} \langle 2t, \sqrt{4 - t} \rangle$
130. $\lim\limits_{t \to 1} \langle \ln t, e^t \rangle$
131. $\lim\limits_{t \to \infty} \left\langle \dfrac{1}{3t}, \dfrac{t^3}{2t^3 - 9t + 1} \right\rangle$
132. $\lim\limits_{t \to 0} \left\langle \dfrac{\sin 2t}{t}, e^{-t} \right\rangle$

Finding a Derivative In Exercises 133–136, find $\mathbf{r}'(t)$.

133. $\mathbf{r}(t) = \langle 8 - 9t^2, 3t^{2/3} \rangle$
134. $\mathbf{r}(t) = \langle e^{t^2}, -3t \rangle$
135. $\mathbf{r}(t) = \langle \cos \pi t, 2 \sec t \rangle$
136. $\mathbf{r}(t) = \langle e^t \sin t, \ln 4t \rangle$

Higher-Order Differentiation In Exercises 137–140, find the second derivative of the vector-valued function $\mathbf{r}(t)$.

137. $\mathbf{r}(t) = \langle t^2 + 4t, -3t^2 \rangle$
138. $\mathbf{r}(t) = \langle 5 \cos t, 2 \sin t \rangle$
139. $\mathbf{r}(t) = \langle e^{-8t}, 4t^2 - 7t \rangle$
140. $\mathbf{r}(t) = \langle 2 \ln t, 6\sqrt{t} \rangle$

Using Properties of the Derivative In Exercises 141 and 142, use the properties of the derivative to find the following.

(a) $\dfrac{d\mathbf{r}}{dt}$ (b) $\dfrac{d}{dt}[5\mathbf{u}(t)]$ (c) $\dfrac{d}{dt}[\mathbf{r}(t) + \mathbf{u}(t)]$
(d) $\dfrac{d}{dt}[\mathbf{u}(t) - 2\mathbf{r}(t)]$ (e) $\dfrac{d}{dt}[(3t)\mathbf{r}(t)]$ (f) $\dfrac{d}{dt}[\mathbf{u}(3t)]$

141. $\mathbf{r}(t) = \langle 3t, t - 1 \rangle$, $\mathbf{u}(t) = \langle t, t^2 \rangle$
142. $\mathbf{r}(t) = \langle \sin t, \cos t \rangle$, $\mathbf{u}(t) = \langle 2 \sin t, 3 \cos t \rangle$

Finding an Indefinite Integral In Exercises 143–146, find the indefinite integral.

143. $\displaystyle\int \langle 1, 8t \rangle \, dt$ **144.** $\displaystyle\int \langle \cos t, e^{2t} \rangle \, dt$
145. $\displaystyle\int \left\langle 3\sqrt{t}, \dfrac{2}{t} \right\rangle dt$ **146.** $\displaystyle\int \left\langle \dfrac{t}{\sqrt{t - 1}}, \cot t \right\rangle$

Evaluating a Definite Integral In Exercises 147–150, evaluate the definite integral.

147. $\displaystyle\int_{-2}^{2} \langle 2t^2, -t^3 \rangle \, dt$
148. $\displaystyle\int_{0}^{1} \langle t, \sqrt{t} \rangle \, dt$
149. $\displaystyle\int_{0}^{2} \langle e^{t/2}, -1 \rangle \, dt$
150. $\displaystyle\int_{0}^{\pi/3} \langle 2 \cos t, \sin t \rangle \, dt$

Finding an Antiderivative In Exercises 151 and 152, find $\mathbf{r}(t)$ that satisfies the initial condition.

151. $\mathbf{r}'(t) = \langle 2t, e^t \rangle$, $\mathbf{r}(0) = \langle 1, 3 \rangle$
152. $\mathbf{r}'(t) = \langle \sec t, t^2 \rangle$, $\mathbf{r}(0) = \langle 0, 3 \rangle$

Finding Velocity and Acceleration Vectors Along a Plane Curve In Exercises 153–158, the position vector $\mathbf{r}$ describes the path of an object moving in the plane. (a) Find the velocity vector, speed, and acceleration vector of the object. (b) Evaluate the velocity vector and acceleration vector of the object at the given value of t.

Position Vector	Time
153. $\mathbf{r}(t) = \langle t^2 - 1, t \rangle$	$t = 1$
154. $\mathbf{r}(t) = \langle 4t, t^3 \rangle$	$t = 1$
155. $\mathbf{r}(t) = \langle \sqrt{t}, 5t \rangle$	$t = 4$
156. $\mathbf{r}(t) = \langle \cos^3 t, \sin^3 t \rangle$	$t = \pi$
157. $\mathbf{r}(t) = \langle t, -\tan t \rangle$	$t = 0$
158. $\mathbf{r}(t) = \langle e^t, e^{-t} \rangle$	$t = 0$

Finding Displacement, Total Distance, and a Position Vector In Exercises 159 and 160, the velocity vector $\mathbf{v}$ and the position of a particle at time $t = 0$ are given. (a) Find the position of the particle when $t = 2$. (b) Find the total distance traveled on the interval $0 \le t \le 2$. (c) Find the position vector of the particle.

159. $\mathbf{v}(t) = \langle 4t + 3, 4 \rangle$, $(-2, -3)$
160. $\mathbf{v}(t) = \langle 6t + 1, 3t^2 \rangle$, $(1, 2)$

Finding Velocity and Position Vectors In Exercises 161–164, use the given information to find the velocity and position vectors. Then find the position at time $t = 4$.

161. $\mathbf{a}(t) = \langle 0, 8 \rangle$, $\mathbf{v}(0) = \langle 0, 3 \rangle$, $\mathbf{r}(0) = \langle 1, 5 \rangle$
162. $\mathbf{a}(t) = \langle 1, t \rangle$, $\mathbf{v}(0) = \langle 2, -3 \rangle$, $\mathbf{r}(0) = \langle 0, 1 \rangle$
163. $\mathbf{a}(t) = \langle \cos t, 3 \sin t \rangle$, $\mathbf{v}(0) = \langle 0, -3 \rangle$, $\mathbf{r}(0) = \langle -1, 0 \rangle$
164. $\mathbf{a}(t) = \langle e^{-t}, 1 \rangle$, $\mathbf{v}(0) = \langle 1, 1 \rangle$, $\mathbf{r}(0) = \langle -1, 2 \rangle$

What You Need to Know

- Given a set of parametric equations, you may be asked to find the range of $x(t)$ and $y(t)$. When you are asked to find the value of t for which the rightmost (or leftmost) point occurs, evaluate dx/dt. When you are asked to find the value of t for which the highest (or lowest) point occurs, evaluate dy/dt.
- It is unlikely that you will have to sketch a polar graph, but it may help to make a table to see the direction of the curve, similar to plane curves.
- You should be able to do a complete analysis of motion along a curve when the curve is defined by a vector-valued function.

Practice Questions

Section 1, Part A, Multiple Choice, No Technology

1. At time $t \geq 0$, the position of a particle moving in the xy-plane is given by the parametric equations $x(t) = 2t^3 - 12t^2$ and $y(t) = 20t - \frac{5}{2}t^2$. At which of the following points (x, y) is the particle at rest?

   (A) $(-64, -50)$ (B) $(-64, 40)$

   (C) $(0, 0)$ (D) $(0, 30)$

2. Which expression gives the total area of the region enclosed by the graph of the polar equation $r = \sin^2 \theta$ over the interval $0 \leq \theta \leq 2\pi$?

   (A) $\displaystyle\int_0^\pi \sin^2 \theta \, d\theta$ (B) $\dfrac{1}{2}\displaystyle\int_0^\pi \sin^2 \theta \, d\theta$

   (C) $\displaystyle\int_0^\pi \sin^4 \theta \, d\theta$ (D) $\dfrac{1}{2}\displaystyle\int_0^\pi \sin^4 \theta \, d\theta$

3. What is the slope of the tangent line to the graph of the polar equation $r = \theta$ at the point $\theta = -\pi/2$?

   (A) 0 (B) $\dfrac{2}{\pi}$

   (C) 1 (D) $\dfrac{\pi}{2}$

4. A curve is described by the parametric equations $x = 2t^2 + 3t$ and $y = t^3 + 4t^2$. What is an equation of the tangent line to the curve at $t = 2$?

   (A) $y - 24 = \frac{11}{28}(x - 14)$
   (B) $y - 24 = \frac{28}{11}(x - 14)$
   (C) $y - 14 = \frac{11}{28}(x - 24)$
   (D) $y - 14 = \frac{28}{11}(x - 24)$

5. What is the slope of the tangent line to the graph of the polar equation $r = 3 + 5 \sin \theta$ at $\theta = 0$?

   (A) 0 (B) $\dfrac{3}{5}$

   (C) $\dfrac{5}{3}$ (D) 3

6. A particle moves on a plane curve so that at any time $t > 0$, its x-coordinate is $t^3 - \frac{1}{2}t$ and its y-coordinate is $(3t - 2)^3$. The acceleration vector of the particle at $t = 1$ is

   (A) $\langle 6, 27 \rangle$.   (B) $\langle \frac{5}{2}, 9 \rangle$.

   (C) $\langle 6, 6 \rangle$.   (D) $\langle 6, 54 \rangle$.

Section 1, Part B, Multiple Choice, Technology Permitted

7. The position of a particle moving in the xy-plane at time t is given by the parametric equations $x(t)$ and $y(t)$, where $x'(t) = t \cos t$ and $y'(t) = 2e^{-4t} + 3$. What is the slope of the tangent line to the path of the particle at $t = 4$?

   (A) -2.615 (B) -1.147

   (C) -0.872 (D) 3

Section 2, Part A, Free Response, Technology Permitted

8. A particle moving along a curve in the xy-plane is at position $(x(t), y(t))$ at time t, where

$$\frac{dx}{dt} = e^{-t^2 + 1} - 2$$

and

$$\frac{dy}{dt} = 3\sqrt{25 - t^2}$$

for $0 \leq t \leq 5$. At time $t = 0$, the particle is at $(2, 3)$.

   (a) Find the speed of the object at time $t = 3$.

   (b) Find the total distance traveled by the particle on the interval $0 \leq t \leq 5$.

   (c) Find $y(3)$.

   (d) There is a point corresponding to a value of t in the interval $0 \leq t \leq 5$ at which the tangent line to the curve is vertical. Find the acceleration vector at this point.

9. A particle moving along a curve in the xy-plane is at position $(x(t), y(t))$ for time $t \geq 0$, where

$$\frac{dx}{dt} = \ln[5 + (1 + t)^3]$$

and

$$\frac{dy}{dt} = 4t - 3t^2.$$

At time $t = 0$, the particle is at $(4, 11)$. At time $t = 3$, the object is at point P with y-coordinate 2.

(a) Find the acceleration vector and speed at time $t = 2$.

(b) Find the x-coordinate of P.

(c) Write an equation for the tangent line to the curve at P.

(d) For what values of t, if any, is the particle at rest?

10. Consider the polar equation

$$r = 2\theta + \cos \theta$$

for $0 \leq \theta \leq 2\pi$.

(a) Find the area in the second quadrant enclosed by the coordinate axes and the graph of r.

(b) For $\pi/2 \leq \theta \leq \pi$, there is one point P on the graph of r with y-coordinate 1. Find the angle θ that corresponds to point P. Find the x-coordinate of point P.

(c) A particle is traveling along the graph of r so that its position at time t is $(x(t), y(t))$. Find dx/dt when $\theta = 3\pi/4$ and $d\theta/dt = 3$. Interpret your answer in the context of the problem.

11. On the interval $0 \leq \theta \leq 2\pi$, the graphs of the polar equations

$$r = 3 \quad \text{and} \quad r = 2 + 2 \cos \theta$$

intersect when $\theta = \pi/3$ and $\theta = 5\pi/3$.

(a) Let R be the region enclosed within both $r = 3$ and $r = 2 + 2 \cos \theta$. Find the area of the region R.

(b) A particle moving along the curve given by

$$r = 2 + 2 \cos \theta$$

has position $(x(t), y(t))$ at time t, where $\theta = 0$ when $t = 0$. The particle moves along the curve such that $dr/dt = dr/d\theta$. Find the value of dr/dt at $\theta = \pi/3$. Interpret your answer in terms of the motion of the particle.

(c) For the particle described in part (b), $dx/dt = dx/d\theta$. Find the value of dx/dt at $\theta = \pi/3$. Interpret your answer in terms of the motion of the particle.

Section 2, Part B, Free Response, No Technology

12. Consider the graph of the polar equation $r = 1 - 2 \sin \theta$ for $0 \leq \theta \leq 2\pi$, as shown in the figure.

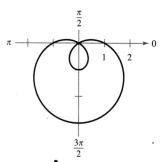

(a) Set up, but do not evaluate, an integral to find the area of the region in the first quadrant bounded by the graph of r and the x-axis.

(b) A particle is traveling along the graph of r so that its position at time t is $(x(t), y(t))$. Write expressions for dx/dt and dy/dt in terms of θ.

(c) Write an equation in terms of x and y of the tangent line to the graph of r at $\theta = \pi$. Show the work that leads to your answer.

13. A particle starts at point A on the positive x-axis at time $t = 0$ and travels along the curve from A to B to C to D, as shown below. The coordinates of the position of the particle at time t are given by $(x(t), y(t))$, where $x(t)$ and $y(t)$ are differentiable functions of time,

$$\frac{dy}{dt} = \frac{-2t^2}{\left(t^3 - \sqrt{27}\right)^{1/3}}$$

and dx/dt is not given.

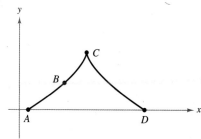

(a) Is dx/dt positive at point B? Is dy/dt positive at point B? Give a reason for each answer.

(b) Find the value of t at which the particle reaches point C. Justify your reasoning.

(c) What is the y-coordinate of point C? Justify your reasoning.

(d) The point $(7, 2)$ lies on the curve. An equation of the tangent line to the curve at this point is $y = -\frac{2}{3}x + \frac{20}{3}$. At this point, $dx/dt \approx 1.837$. Calculate dy/dt. Then find the speed at this point.

9   Performance Task

Projectile Motion

Neglecting air resistance, the path of a projectile launched from an initial height h with initial speed v_0 and angle of elevation θ is described by the vector-valued function

$$\mathbf{r}(t) = \left\langle (v_0 \cos \theta)t, \; h + (v_0 \sin \theta)t - \tfrac{1}{2}gt^2 \right\rangle$$

where g is the acceleration due to gravity.

Exercises

1. **Shot-Put Throw**   A shot is thrown from an initial height of 6 feet with an initial speed of 40 feet per second and an angle of elevation of 35°.

    (a) Find the vector-valued function $\mathbf{r}(t)$ that gives the position of the shot.

    (b) At what time is the shot at its maximum height?

    (c) What is the maximum height of the shot?

    (d) How long is the shot in the air?

    (e) What is the horizontal distance traveled by the shot?

2. **Shot-Put Throw**   A shot is thrown from an initial height of 6 feet with an initial speed of 40 feet per second and an angle of elevation of 45°.

    (a) Find the vector-valued function $\mathbf{r}(t)$ that gives the position of the shot.

    (b) At what time is the shot at its maximum height?

    (c) What is the maximum height of the shot?

    (d) How long is the shot in the air?

    (e) What is the horizontal distance traveled by the shot?

3. **Length of Time in the Air**   Write an equation for the time t when a shot hits the ground when the shot is thrown from an initial height h with initial speed v_0 and angle of elevation θ.

4. **Horizontal Distance Traveled**   Write an equation for the horizontal distance x traveled by a shot thrown from an initial height h with initial speed v_0 and angle of elevation θ.

5. **Shot-Put Throw**   A shot is thrown from an initial height of 6 feet with an initial speed of 40 feet per second and angle of elevation θ.

    (a) Write an equation for the time t when the shot hits the ground in terms of θ.

    (b) Write an equation for the horizontal distance x traveled by the shot in terms of θ.

6. **Graphical Analysis**   Use a graphing utility to graph the equation you wrote in Exercise 5(b). Where does the maximum occur? What does this mean in the context of the problem?

Section 1: Multiple Choice, Part A

A calculator may not be used for Part A.

1. If $g(x) = 2 \cot 3x$, which of the following is equal to $g'\left(\dfrac{\pi}{6}\right)$?

(A) $2 \displaystyle\lim_{h \to 0} \dfrac{\cot\left(\dfrac{\pi}{2} + 3h\right) - \cot\dfrac{\pi}{2}}{h}$

(B) $2 \displaystyle\lim_{h \to 0} \dfrac{\cot\left(\dfrac{\pi}{6} + 3h\right) - \cot\dfrac{\pi}{6}}{h}$

(C) $2 \displaystyle\lim_{h \to 0} \dfrac{\cot\left(\dfrac{\pi}{2} + h\right) - \cot\dfrac{\pi}{2}}{h}$

(D) $\displaystyle\lim_{h \to 0} \dfrac{2 \cot\left(\dfrac{\pi}{2} + 3h\right) - \cot\dfrac{\pi}{2}}{h}$

2. $6 \displaystyle\int_0^1 \dfrac{x + x^3}{1 + x}\, dx =$

(A) 1

(B) $11 - 12 \ln 2$

(C) $11 + 12 \ln 2$

(D) $17 + 12 \ln 2$

3. If $f(x) = \sin(\pi e^{-3x})$, then $f'(0) =$

(A) -3π.   (B) 0.   (C) π.   (D) 3π.

4. The graph of a differentiable function g is shown below. Which of the following is true?

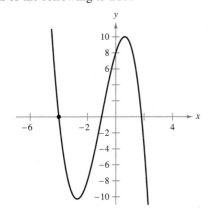

(A) $g(-4) < g'(-4) < g''(-4)$

(B) $g'(-4) < g(-4) < g''(-4)$

(C) $g'(-4) < g''(-4) < g(-4)$

(D) $g''(-4) < g'(-4) < g(-4)$

5. Let f be a function that is continuous on $0 \le x \le 4$ and differentiable on $0 < x < 4$. If $f(0) = 3$ and $f(4) = 27$, then the Mean Value Theorem guarantees that

(A) f is nonlinear on the interval $0 \le x \le 4$.

(B) $f(c) = 12$ for at least one value of c.

(C) $f'(c) = 0$ for at least one value of c.

(D) $f'(c) = 6$ for at least one value of c.

6. Let h be the function defined below. What is the value of $\displaystyle\int_{-1}^2 h(x)\, dx$?

$$h(x) = \begin{cases} e^{3x}, & \text{if } x < 0 \\ \cos\dfrac{x}{5}, & \text{if } x \ge 0 \end{cases}$$

(A) $e^3 - \cos\dfrac{1}{5}$ (B) $\dfrac{e^3 - 1}{3e^3} + 5 \sin 2$

(C) $\dfrac{1 - e^3}{3e^3} + 5 \sin\dfrac{2}{5}$ (D) $\dfrac{e^3 - 1}{3e^3} + 5 \sin\dfrac{2}{5}$

7. If $g(x) = \sqrt[3]{27 - x^3}$, then the derivative of $g(g(x))$ at $x = -8$ is

(A) -8.   (B) -1.   (C) 1.   (D) 8.

8. Let g be the function defined below. For what value of k is g continuous at $x = 0$?

$$g(x) = \begin{cases} 2x \csc 7x, & \text{if } x < 0 \\ k[1 + \ln(x + e^{x+1})], & \text{if } x \ge 0 \end{cases}$$

(A) $-\dfrac{1}{7}$ (B) 0   (C) $\dfrac{1}{7}$ (D) $\dfrac{2}{7}$

9. An equation of the line tangent to the graph of $y = \dfrac{\sqrt{x + 2}}{2x - 6}$ at the point $(2, -1)$ is

(A) $9x + 8y = 7$.   (B) $9x + 8y = 10$.

(C) $9x - 8y = -25$.   (D) $9x - 8y = 26$.

10. $\displaystyle\int \csc^2 x \cos x(1 + \cos x)\, dx =$

(A) $-x - \cot x - \csc x + C$

(B) $-x - \cot x + \csc x + C$

(C) $x + \cot x - \csc x + C$

(D) $x + \cot x + \csc x + C$

11. Let $f(x) = 5 + x - 2x^2 + x^3$. On which interval is the function f both increasing and concave upward?

(A) $x < 0$

(B) $0 < x < \dfrac{1}{3}$

(C) $\dfrac{1}{3} < x < 1$

(D) $x > 1$

12. If $\dfrac{dy}{dt} = \dfrac{y^2}{2t}$, then an equation for y could be

(A) $y = -\dfrac{1}{\ln\sqrt{t} + 2}$.   (B) $y = 2 - \dfrac{1}{\ln\sqrt{t}}$.

(C) $y = 2\sqrt{t}$.   (D) $y = 2e^{1/2t^2}$.

13. Let $f(x) = \ln[(2 - x)^4]$ for all x. Which of the following statements is true?

(A) f is continuous and differentiable at $x = 2$.

(B) f is continuous but not differentiable at $x = 2$.

(C) f is differentiable but not continuous at $x = 2$.

(D) f is not continuous and not differentiable at $x = 2$.

14. A rectangle is inscribed in the region bound by the graph of $f(x) = e^{-0.8x^2}$, the x-axis, and the y-axis, as shown below. For what value of x is the area of the rectangle maximized?

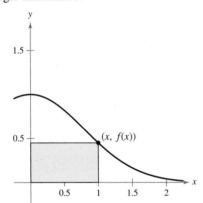

(A) $\dfrac{\sqrt{1.6}}{1.6}$ (B) 1   (C) $\sqrt{1.6}$ (D) $\sqrt{2.6}$

15. If $\dfrac{dy}{dx} = \dfrac{y \ln x^2}{x}$ and $y = 5$ when $x = 1$, then $y =$

(A) $5x$.   (B) $5x^2$.   (C) $5x^{\ln x}$.   (D) $x^{\ln x} + 4$.

16. If $\lim\limits_{x \to 1} f(x) = 4$, then $\lim\limits_{x \to 1} \dfrac{(x^2 + x - 2)f(x)}{x - 1}$ is

(A) 0.   (B) 8.   (C) 12.   (D) nonexistent.

17. If $x^2 - 2y^2 = 2$, what is $\dfrac{d^2y}{dx^2}$ at the point $(2, 1)$?

(A) $-\dfrac{3}{2}$ (B) $-\dfrac{1}{2}$ (C) 0   (D) $\dfrac{1}{2}$

18. Let $g = e^{kx^4}$, where k is a constant. For what value of k does g have a point of inflection at $x = -1$ and $x = 1$?

(A) $-\dfrac{3}{4}$ (B) $-\dfrac{1}{4}$ (C) $\dfrac{1}{4}$ (D) $\dfrac{3}{4}$

19. What is the area of the region bounded by the graphs of $y = 2 - x^2$ and $y = x - 10$?

(A) $\dfrac{73}{6}$ (B) $\dfrac{343}{6}$ (C) $\dfrac{497}{6}$ (D) $\dfrac{503}{6}$

20. If $y = \dfrac{e^{\sqrt{2x}}}{\ln 3x}$, then $\dfrac{dy}{dx} =$

(A) $\dfrac{e^{\sqrt{2x}}(x \ln 3x - 1)}{x \ln^2 3x}$.

(B) $\dfrac{e^{\sqrt{2x}}\left(x \ln 3x - \sqrt{2x}\right)}{x\sqrt{2x} \ln^2 3x}$.

(C) $\dfrac{e^{\sqrt{2x}}\left(x \ln 3x - 2\sqrt{2x}\right)}{2x\sqrt{2x} \ln^2 3x}$.

(D) $\dfrac{e^{\sqrt{2x}}\left(3x \ln 3x - \sqrt{2x}\right)}{3x\sqrt{2x} \ln^2 3x}$.

21. Given the function $p(x) = (x + 2)^2(x - 1)$, at what value of x does p have a relative minimum?

(A) -2 (B) $-\dfrac{1}{2}$ (C) 0   (D) 1

22. Refer to the slope field shown. This slope field could belong to which of the following differential equations?

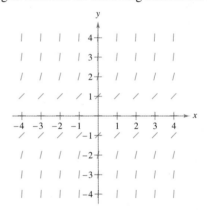

(A) $\dfrac{dy}{dt} = y$ (B) $\dfrac{dy}{dt} = y^2$

(C) $\dfrac{dy}{dt} = t \cdot y$ (D) $\dfrac{dy}{dt} = t \cdot y^2$

23. If $y = \sqrt{1 + e^{\sec x} + \tan x^2}$, then $y' =$

(A) $\sqrt{e^{\sec x} \sec x \tan x + 2x \sec^2 x^2}$.

(B) $\dfrac{1}{2\sqrt{1 + e^{\sec x} + \tan x^2}}$.

(C) $\dfrac{1 + e^{\sec x} + \tan x^2}{2\sqrt{1 + e^{\sec x} + \tan x^2}}$.

(D) $\dfrac{e^{\sec x} \sec x \tan x + 2x \sec^2 x^2}{2\sqrt{1 + e^{\sec x} + \tan x^2}}$.

24. $\lim\limits_{x \to 0} \dfrac{2x - \sin 2x}{3x(1 - \cos x)}$ is

(A) $-\dfrac{2}{3}$.   (B) 0.   (C) $\dfrac{8}{9}$.   (D) nonexistent.

25. $\lim\limits_{x \to \infty} \dfrac{6x^4 + x^2 - 1}{3x^4 + 7x^3 + 2x}$ is

    (A) 0.   (B) 2.   (C) 6.   (D) ∞.

26. Which of the following integrals gives the volume of the solid generated by revolving the region bounded by the graphs of $y = e^x$ and $y = 4 - e^{-x}$ about the x-axis?

    (A) $\pi \displaystyle\int_{\ln(2-\sqrt{3})}^{\ln(2+\sqrt{3})} [(e^x)^2 - (4 - e^{-x})^2] \, dx$

    (B) $2\pi \displaystyle\int_{\ln(2-\sqrt{3})}^{\ln(2+\sqrt{3})} [(e^x)^2 - (4 - e^{-x})^2] \, dx$

    (C) $\pi \displaystyle\int_{\ln(2-\sqrt{3})}^{\ln(2+\sqrt{3})} [(4 - e^{-x})^2 - (e^x)^2] \, dx$

    (D) $2\pi \displaystyle\int_{\ln(2-\sqrt{3})}^{\ln(2+\sqrt{3})} [(4 - e^{-x})^2 - (e^x)^2] \, dx$

27. The Riemann sum

$$\frac{1}{30}\left(\ln\frac{31}{30} + \ln\frac{32}{30} + \ln\frac{33}{30} + \cdots + \ln 3\right)$$

    is an approximation for which integral?

    (A) $\dfrac{1}{30}\displaystyle\int_1^3 \ln\dfrac{x}{30}\, dx$ (B) $\dfrac{1}{30}\displaystyle\int_1^3 \ln x \, dx$

    (C) $\displaystyle\int_1^3 \ln\dfrac{x}{30}\, dx$ (D) $\displaystyle\int_1^3 \ln x \, dx$

28. $\dfrac{d}{dt}\left(\sqrt{t^3}\displaystyle\int_2^t \cot(u + 1)\, du\right) =$

    (A) $\dfrac{3}{2}\sqrt{t}\displaystyle\int_2^t \cot(u + 1)\, du + \sqrt{t^3}\cot(t + 1)$

    (B) $\dfrac{3}{2}\sqrt{t}\displaystyle\int_2^t \cot(u + 1)\, du - \sqrt{t^3}\csc^2(t + 1)$

    (C) $\dfrac{3}{2}\sqrt{t}\,[\cot(t + 1) - \cot 3]$

    (D) $\dfrac{3}{2}\sqrt{t}\cot(t + 1)$

Section 1: Multiple Choice, Part B

A graphing calculator is required for some of the questions in Part B.

29. A particle travels on the x-axis so that its velocity at time t is given by $v(t) = \ln(t^2 + 2) - 3$ for $0 \le t \le 8$. What is the total distance traveled by the particle?

    (A) 7.406   (B) 3.497   (C) 2.535   (D) 0.242

30. Let $f(x) = e^{x+2}$ and $g(x) = 3x - x^2$. At what value of x do the graphs of f and g have perpendicular tangent lines?

    (A) -4.482 (B) -0.576

    (C) 1.485   (D) 1.515

31. If $f(x) = 2 - x^2 + \displaystyle\int_0^x (t - 3)\sin\dfrac{\pi t}{3}\, dt$, which of the following must be true?

    I. $f(x) < 0$ on the interval $0 < x < 3$.

    II. $f'(x) < 0$ on the interval $0 < x < 3$.

    III. $f''(x) < 0$ on the interval $0 < x < 3$.

    (A) **I** only   (B) **I** and **II**

    (C) **II** only   (D) **II** and **III**

32. For a continuous function f, let

$$g(x) = \int_0^x \left(4f(t) - \sqrt{t^5 + 4}\right) dt.\ \text{If}\ f(2) = 3\ \text{and}$$

$$\int_0^2 f(t)\, dt = 13,\ \text{what is}\ g(2) + 2g'(2)?$$

    (A) 52.000   (B) 52.314

    (C) 58.000   (D) 58.314

33. A particle travels along a straight line with a velocity of

$$v(t) = \frac{1}{t - 2}\cos\left(2\pi\sqrt{t}\right)\ \text{feet per second. What is the}$$

    total distance, in feet, traveled by the particle on the interval $[0, 1]$?

    (A) -1.000 (B) -0.079

    (C) 0.452   (D) 1.000

34. A table of values for a continuouos function h over the interval $[0.1, 2.9]$ is shown below. If four equal subintervals are used, what is the trapezoidal approximation of $\displaystyle\int_{0.1}^{2.9} h(x)\, dx$?

x	0.1	0.8	1.5	2.2	2.9
$h(x)$	0.001	0.178	0.882	1.008	2.073

    (A) 1.450   (B) 2.174   (C) 2.900   (D) 4.347

35. Let $g(x) = \ln 2x^2 + \sqrt[5]{x^4 - 15}$ be defined for $x > 0$ and let h be the inverse of g. What is the value of $h'(5)$?

    (A) 0.5178   (B) 0.6698

    (C) 1.4929   (D) 1.9311

36. The density of a metal rod is given by $d(x) = \sqrt{24 - e^x}$ kg/m for $0 \le x \le 3$ meters. What is the average density across the length of the rod?

    (A) 1.979   (B) 4.142   (C) 4.796   (D) 12.426

37. What is the slope of the line normal to the graph of $f(x) = \ln(x^2)e^{-1/x}$ at the point where the graph intersects the line $y = 2 - 2x$?

(A) -5.4366 (B) -1.3591

(C) 0.1839 (D) 0.7358

38. At time $t = 0$, a small cat weighs 5 pounds and grows at the rate of $r(t) = \dfrac{3t^2}{2(t^3 + 1)}$ pounds per month, where t is measured in months. How many pounds did the cat gain from $t = 0$ months to $t = 7$ months?

(A) 2.920   (B) 5.214   (C) 5.502   (D) 7.920

39. At time $t \geq 0$, the position of a particle moving along the x-axis is $x(t) = \sin 2t^2$. What is the velocity of the particle at time $t = 5$?

(A) 0.408   (B) 0.965   (C) 19.299   (D) 48.248

40. Let g be a differentiable function on the interval $[-1, 5]$. Let $f(-1) = 3$ and $f'(x) \leq 7$. What is the greatest possible value for $f(5)$?

(A) 24   (B) 31   (C) 39   (D) 45

41. Let R be the region bounded by the graphs of $y = 1 - \cos^2 x$ and $y = \cos^2 x$ as shown, where R is the base of a solid whose cross sections perpendicular to the x-axis are semicircles. What is the volume of the solid?

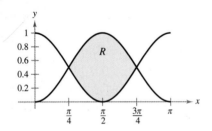

(A) 0.308   (B) 0.393   (C) 0.617   (D) 1.234

42. Let $g(x) = \dfrac{e^x + x^2}{x + 2}$. Which of the following is a critical number of g?

(A) -0.1795 (B) 0.0004

(C) 0.0007   (D) 0.4767

43. The area of a regular octagon is $A = 2(1 + \sqrt{2})s^2$, where s is the length of each side. The perimeter of the octagon is decreasing at a constant rate of 25 centimeters per minute. What is the rate of decrease in the area of the octagon at the instant when the perimeter of the octagon is 192 centimeters?

(A) 181.066   (B) 362.132

(C) 724.264   (D) 2897.056

44. For a twice differentiable function f, let $F(x) = \displaystyle\int_0^x f(t)\, dt$. The table below gives selected values of F, as well as the first two derivatives of F. Find the value of $\displaystyle\int_0^2 [x^2 + f''(x)]\, dx$.

x	$F(x)$	$F'(x)$	$F''(x)$
0	$\frac{4}{3}$	0	-4
2	6	2	$\frac{1}{3}$

(A) $\frac{14}{3}$ (B) 6   (C) 7   (D) $\frac{22}{3}$

45. What is the minimum distance between the graph of $y = x^2 - x$ and the point $(2, -1)$?

(A) 1.000   (B) 1.278   (C) 1.414   (D) 3.000

Section 2: Free Response, Part A

A graphing calculator is required for Part A.

1. The learning curve for the number of parts N a new factory worker produces per day after t days on the job is $N(t) = 30(1.1 - e^{-0.05t})$.

   (a) Find the average rate of change of $N(t)$ over the interval $0 \leq t \leq 30$. Indicate units of measure.

   (b) Find the value of $N'(10)$. Using correct units, interpret the meaning of the value in the context of the problem.

   (c) Find the time t for which the number of parts produced in a day is equal to the average number of parts produced per day in the interval $0 \leq t \leq 30$.

   (d) For $t > 30$, $L(t)$, the linear approximation to A at $t = 30$, is a better model for the number of parts produced per day. Use $L(t)$ to predict the day when the worker produces 33 parts. Show the work that leads to your answer.

2. For $0 \leq t \leq 4$, the velocity of a particle moving along the x-axis is given by $v(t) = [8 \sin(0.5t^2)]/(t - 8)$. The particle is at position $x = 5$ at time $t = 0$.

   (a) Find all times t in the interval $0 < t \leq 4$ at which the particle changes direction. Justify your answer.

   (b) At time $t = 1$, is the particle speeding up or slowing down?

   (c) Evaluate $\displaystyle\int_0^3 v(t)\, dt$ and $\displaystyle\int_0^3 |v(t)|\, dt$. Interpret the meaning of each integral in the context of the problem.

   (d) A second particle moves along the x-axis. Its position is given by $s(t) = t^2 - 2t$ for $0 \leq t \leq 4$. At what time t are the two particles moving with the same velocity?

Section 2: Free Response, Part B

A calculator may not be used for Part B.

3.

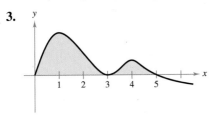

The figure above shows the graph of f', the derivative of a twice-differentiable function f, on the closed interval $[0, 6]$. The graph of f' has horizontal tangent lines at $x = 1$, $x = 3$, and $x = 4$. The areas of the regions between the graph of f' and the x-axis on the intervals $[0, 3]$ and $[3, 5]$ are 9 and 4, respectively. It is known that $f(3) = 6$.

(a) On what open intervals contained in $(0, 6)$ is the graph of f both increasing and concave downward? Give a reason for your answer.

(b) Find all values of x in the open interval $(0, 6)$ for which the function f has a relative maximum. Give a reason for your answer.

(c) Find the x-coordinates of all points of inflection for the graph of f in the interval $[0, 6]$. Give a reason for your answer.

(d) Write an expression for $f(x)$ that involves an integral. Find $f(0)$ and $f(5)$.

4. Consider the differential equation $dy/dx = y - 2x$.

(a) Sketch a slope field for dy/dx at the six points indicated.

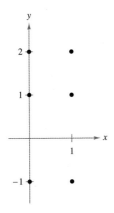

(b) Find d^2y/dx^2 in terms of x and y. Determine the concavity of all of the solution curves for

$$\frac{dy}{dx} = y - 2x$$

in Quadrant IV. Justify your answer.

(c) Let $y = f(x)$ be the particular solution of $dy/dx = y - 2x$ determined by the initial condition $y = 4$ when $x = -2$. Does f have a relative minimum, a relative maximum, or neither at $x = -2$? Justify your answer.

(d) Find the values of m and b for which $y = mx + b$ is a solution of $dy/dx = y - 2x$.

5. Water flows into a tank at a rate modeled by $F(t) = 750e^{-t/3}$ gallons per hour for $0 \le t \le 8$, where t is measured in hours. Water is removed from the tank at a rate modeled by $R(t)$ gallons per hour, where R is differentiable and decreasing on $0 \le t \le 8$. Selected values of $R(t)$ are shown in the table. At time $t = 0$, there are 10,000 gallons of water in the tank.

t (hours)	0	2	4	6	8
$R(t)$ (gallons/hour)	610	442	306	202	130

(a) Use the data in the table to estimate $R'(5)$. Show the work that leads to your answer. Indicate units of measure.

(b) Use a left Riemann sum with the four subintervals of equal length indicated by the table to estimate the total amount of water removed from the tank during the 8 hours. Is this an overestimate or an underestimate? Give a reason for your answer.

(c) Use your answer from part (b) to estimate the amount of water in the tank at the end of 8 hours. Leave your answer in terms of e.

(d) For $0 \le t \le 8$, is there a time t when the rate at which water flowing into the tank is the same as the rate at which water is removed from the tank? Explain your reasoning.

6. A cylindrical tank with a diameter of 4 feet is being filled with water. The rate of change of the height h of the water in the tank with respect to time t is modeled by $dh/dt = \frac{1}{2}\sqrt{h}$, where h is measured in feet and t is measured in minutes. (The volume V of a cylinder with radius r and height h is $V = \pi r^2 h$.)

(a) Find the rate of change of the volume of water in the tank with respect to time when the height of the water is 9 feet. Indicate units of measure.

(b) When the height of the water is 4 feet, is the rate of change of the height of the water with respect to time increasing or decreasing? Explain your reasoning.

(c) At time $t = 0$, the height of the water is 2 feet. Use separation of variables to find a particular expression for h in terms of t.

Section 1: Multiple Choice, Part A

A calculator may not be used for Part A.

1. If $e^{-2x} + \cos 3x^2 - y = 4$, then when $x = 0$, $dy/dx =$

(A) -2. (B) -1. (C) 0. (D) 1.

2. The sum of the infinite series $\displaystyle\sum_{n=1}^{\infty}\left(\frac{1}{(n+2)^2} - \frac{1}{n^2}\right)$ is

(A) $-\frac{5}{4}$. (B) -1. (C) $-\frac{1}{4}$. (D) $\frac{1}{4}$.

3. The position of a particle moving in the xy-plane is given by the parametric equations

$$x(t) = \frac{4}{t^2 - 2} \quad \text{and} \quad y(t) = \frac{-2t}{t+1}.$$

An equation of the line tangent to the path of the particle at $t = 1$ is

(A) $y = -x - 5$. (B) $y = -\dfrac{x}{16} - \dfrac{5}{4}$.

(C) $y = \dfrac{x}{16} - \dfrac{3}{4}$. (D) $y = 16x + 63$.

4. If $f''(x) = x^3(x-2)^2\sqrt{x+1}$, then the graph of f has inflection points when $x =$

(A) 0 only. (B) 2 only.

(C) 0 and 2 only. (D) -1, 0, and 2.

5. Let h be the function defined by

$$h(x) = \int_0^x \sqrt{\cos 4t}\, dt.$$

Which integral represents the length of the graph of h on the interval $\left[-\dfrac{\pi}{8}, \dfrac{\pi}{8}\right]$?

(A) $\sqrt{2}\displaystyle\int_{-\pi/8}^{\pi/8} \sin 2x\, dx$

(B) $\sqrt{2}\displaystyle\int_{-\pi/8}^{\pi/8} \cos 2x\, dx$

(C) $2\displaystyle\int_{-\pi/8}^{\pi/8} \cos 2x\, dx$

(D) $\displaystyle\int_{-\pi/8}^{\pi/8} \sqrt{\cos 4x}\, dx$

6. Which of the following series converge?

I. $\displaystyle\sum_{k=1}^{\infty}\left(\frac{\pi}{3}\right)^k$ **II.** $\displaystyle\sum_{k=1}^{\infty}\left(\frac{\pi}{3k}\right)^k$ **III.** $\displaystyle\sum_{k=1}^{\infty}\left(\frac{\pi k}{3}\right)^k$

(A) I and II only (B) II only

(C) II and III only (D) III only

7. Let f be the function given by $f(x) = e^{-x^2}$. If four subintervals of equal length are used, what is the value of the Midpoint Riemann Sum approximation for $\displaystyle\int_{2.2}^{3.2} f(x)\, dx$?

(A) $0.25(e^{-(2.2)^2} + e^{-(2.45)^2} + e^{-(2.7)^2} + e^{-(2.95)^2})$

(B) $0.125(e^{-(2.2)^2} + 2e^{-(2.45)^2} + 2e^{-(2.7)^2} + 2e^{-(2.95)^2}$
$\qquad + e^{-(3.2)^2})$

(C) $0.25(e^{-(2.325)^2} + e^{-(2.575)^2} + e^{-(2.825)^2} + e^{-(3.075)^2})$

(D) $0.25(e^{-(2.45)^2} + e^{-(2.7)^2} + e^{-(2.95)^2} + e^{-(3.2)^2})$

8. $\displaystyle\int \frac{5x^3 - 4x^2 - 3x - 2}{x - 1}\, dx =$

(A) $\frac{5}{3}x^3 + \frac{1}{2}x^2 - 2x - 4\ln(x-1) + C$

(B) $5x^2 + x - 2 - 4\ln(x-1) + C$

(C) $\frac{5}{3}x^3 + \frac{1}{2}x^2 - 2x + C$

(D) $\frac{1}{6}(5x^3 + x^2 - 12x) - 4\ln(x-1) + C$

9. For what values of p does $\displaystyle\int_0^{\infty} e^{px}\, dx$ diverge?

(A) $p < -1$ (B) $-1 < p \le 0$

(C) $-1 < p < 1$ (D) $p \ge 0$

10. At time $t \ge 0$, a particle moving in the xy-plane has a velocity vector given by

$$\mathbf{v}(t) = \left\langle \ln(t+3), \frac{7t}{2t^2 + 6}\right\rangle.$$

A position vector of this particle could be

(A) $\langle \ln(t+3) - t + 2, 7\ln(t^2 + 3) + 4\rangle$.

(B) $\langle (t+3)\ln(t+3) - 3, \frac{7}{4}\ln(t^2 + 3)\rangle$.

(C) $\langle (t+3)\ln(t+3) - t + 2, \frac{7}{4}\ln(t^2 + 3)\rangle$.

(D) $\langle t\ln(t+3) - t + 1, \frac{7}{4}\ln(t^2 + 3) - 1\rangle$.

11. What is the average value of y for the part of the curve $y = -2x^2 + 8x$ which is in the first quadrant?

(A) $-\frac{16}{3}$ (B) $\frac{4}{3}$ (C) $\frac{16}{3}$ (D) $\frac{32}{3}$

12. What is the coefficient of x^2 in the Maclaurin Series for $f(x) = \ln(e^x + x)$?

(A) -3 (B) $-\frac{3}{2}$ (C) 0 (D) 2

13. If $f(x) = \displaystyle\int_0^x t^2 e^t\, dt$, then $f'(x) =$

(A) $e^x(x^2 - 2x + 2) - 2$.

(B) $e^x(x^2 - 2x + 2)$.

(C) $e^x(x^2 + 2x)$.

(D) $e^x x^2$.

14. Let g be the function given by

$$g(x) = \int_0^x \sin(-t^2)\, dt.$$

Which of the following must be true on the interval $0 < x < \dfrac{\pi}{3}$?

(A) g is increasing, and the graph of g is concave upward.

(B) g is increasing, and the graph of g is concave downward.

(C) g is decreasing, and the graph of g is concave upward.

(D) g is decreasing, and the graph of g is concave downward.

15. What is the sum of the series $\displaystyle\sum_{k=1}^{\infty} \dfrac{(-1)^{k-3}}{2^{k+5}}$?

(A) $-\dfrac{1}{96}$ (B) $-\dfrac{1}{32}$ (C) $\dfrac{1}{32}$ (D) $\dfrac{1}{96}$

16. $\displaystyle\lim_{x \to 1} \dfrac{xe^{2x} - (e^x)^2}{2x^2 - x - 1}$ is

(A) $\dfrac{e^2}{3}$.   (B) $\dfrac{2e^2}{3}$.   (C) 0.   (D) nonexistent.

17. The figure below shows the graph of the polar curves

$$r = 3 + 2\cos 5\theta$$

and

$$r = 1.$$

What is the area of the region that is shaded from $\theta = -\dfrac{\pi}{5}$ to $\theta = \dfrac{\pi}{5}$?

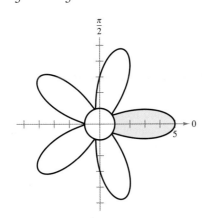

(A) $\dfrac{9\pi}{5}$ (B) 2π (C) $\dfrac{11\pi}{5}$ (D) 4π

18. A solid is obtained by revolving the region in the figure enclosed by the graph of

$$y = e^{-x^2 + x + 2}\sqrt{1 - 2x}$$

and the line

$$y = -\dfrac{2\sqrt{3}}{3}x + \dfrac{\sqrt{3}}{3}$$

about the x-axis. What is the volume of this solid?

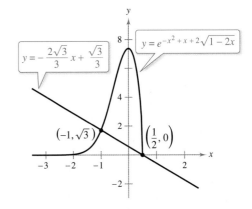

(A) $\dfrac{\pi}{2}\left(e^{9/2} - 4\right)$ (B) $\dfrac{\pi}{2}\left(4 - e^{9/2}\right)$

(C) $\dfrac{\pi}{2}\left(e^{9/2} - 2\right)$ (D) $\pi\left(e^{9/2} - 2\right)$

19. Which of the following is the Maclaurin series for $\sin x^2$?

(A) $x^2 - \dfrac{x^6}{3!} + \dfrac{x^{10}}{5!} - \dfrac{x^{14}}{7!} + \cdots$

(B) $x^2 - \dfrac{x^6}{(3!)^2} + \dfrac{x^{10}}{(5!)^2} - \dfrac{x^{14}}{(7!)^2} + \cdots$

(C) $x^2 - \dfrac{x^6}{3} + \dfrac{x^{10}}{5} - \dfrac{x^{14}}{7} + \cdots$

(D) $x^2 - \dfrac{x^6}{9} + \dfrac{x^{10}}{25} - \dfrac{x^{14}}{49} + \cdots$

20. Let g be the function given by $g(x) = \displaystyle\int_0^{x^2} te^{-(t+1)^2}\, dt$.

The function g has a real point of inflection at $x =$

(A) 0.   (B) $-\dfrac{\sqrt{2}}{2}, \dfrac{\sqrt{2}}{2}$.

(C) $-\dfrac{\sqrt{2}}{2}, 0, \dfrac{\sqrt{2}}{2}$.   (D) $-\sqrt{2}, 0, \sqrt{2}$.

21. In a closed population of healthy mice, three mice infected with a disease are introduced. The rate of change of the number of infected mice follows the model

$$\frac{dP}{dt} = 2P\left(1 - \frac{P}{4}\right)$$

where $P(t)$ is the number of infected mice and t is the number of days after the infected mice were introduced. With a step size of 0.5, use Euler's Method to approximate the number of infected mice after one day.

(A) 3   (B) 4   (C) 6   (D) 7

22. Selected values of a function f and its first three derivatives are indicated in the table below. What is the third-degree Maclaurin polynomial for f?

x	$f(x)$	$f'(x)$	$f''(x)$	$f'''(x)$
0	-4	1	3	-3
1	-1	-5	0	4

(A) $-1 - 5x + \frac{2}{3}x^2$ (B) $-4 + x + 3x^2 - 3x^3$
(C) $-4 + x + \frac{3}{2}x^2 - x^3$ (D) $-4 + x + \frac{3}{2}x^2 - \frac{1}{2}x^3$

23. The volume of a cylindrical container is to be k cubic inches. If a minimum amount of material is to be used to construct the container, what must the area of the bottom of the container be in square inches?

(A) $\sqrt[3]{\frac{\pi k^2}{2}}$ (B) $\sqrt[3]{\frac{\pi k^2}{4}}$

(C) $\sqrt[3]{\left(\frac{\pi k}{2}\right)^2}$ (D) $\sqrt[3]{\pi k^2}$

24. If $\frac{dy}{dt} = kyt^3$ and k is a nonzero constant, then y could be

(A) $y = \frac{kt^4}{4} + 5.$ (B) $y = 8e^{kt^4/4}.$

(C) $y = e^{kt^4/4} + 3.$ (D) $y = \frac{4}{kt^4 + 4}.$

25. $\displaystyle\int \frac{e^{2x}}{(e^x + 1)^2}\, dx =$

(A) $\ln(e^x + 1) - \dfrac{1}{e^x + 1} + C$

(B) $\ln(e^x + 1) - \dfrac{1}{(e^x + 1)^2} + C$

(C) $\ln(e^x + 1) + \dfrac{1}{e^x + 1} + C$

(D) $\dfrac{1}{e^x + 1} + C$

26. What is the radius of convergence of the power series
$$\sum_{k=1}^{\infty} \frac{(-1)^k(x - 2)^{2k}}{2^{k+5}k^2}?$$

(A) $\dfrac{1}{2}$ (B) $\dfrac{\sqrt{2}}{2}$ (C) $\sqrt{2}$ (D) 2

27. $\displaystyle\int_0^1 3xe^{2x}\, dx =$

(A) $\frac{3}{4}(e + 1)$ (B) $\frac{3}{4}(e^2 + 1)$
(C) $\frac{3}{2}(e + 1)$ (D) $\frac{3}{2}(e^2 + 1)$

28. Which of the following series converges?

I. $\displaystyle\sum_{k=1}^{\infty}\left(\frac{1}{5k + 3} - \frac{1}{5k + 1}\right)$

II. $\displaystyle\sum_{k=1}^{\infty}\left(\frac{1}{5k + 3} - \frac{1}{k + 1}\right)$

III. $\displaystyle\sum_{k=1}^{\infty}\left(\frac{1}{k + 3} - \frac{1}{k + 1}\right)$

(A) I only   (B) I and II only
(C) II only   (D) I and III only

Section 1: Multiple Choice, Part B

A calculator is required for some of the questions in Part B.

29. A particle moves in the xy-plane so that its position at any time t is given by

$$x(t) = \frac{t + 1}{\ln(t + 2)}$$

and

$$y(t) = 2t\sin\frac{t^2}{3}.$$

Find the speed of the particle when $t = 2$.

(A) 0.1035   (B) 1.7965
(C) 8.7131   (D) 9.6604

30. Water is poured into an inverted conical tank at the rate of 0.01 cubic meters per minute. The top radius of the inverted conical tank is two-thirds the height of the tank. What is the rate of change in the radius of the water in the tank when the water is 2 meters high?

$$\left(\text{The volume of a cone is } V = \frac{1}{3}\pi r^2 h.\right)$$

(A) 0.00024   (B) 0.00035
(C) 0.00119   (D) 0.00179

31. The graph of a twice differentiable function f is shown. Which of the following is true?

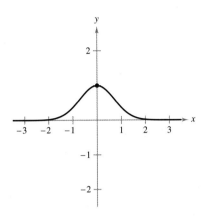

(A) $f(0) < f'(0) < f''(0)$

(B) $f'(0) < f''(0) < f(0)$

(C) $f''(0) < f(0) < f'(0)$

(D) $f''(0) < f'(0) < f(0)$

32. Find the area enclosed by the graphs of $\arccos y = (x - 1)^2$ and $y = (\ln x)^2$?

(A) 0.739   (B) 0.931   (C) 1.179   (D) 1.627

33. Let g be a twice differentiable function. The table gives selected values of g as well as the first two derivatives of g. Use a second-degree Taylor polynomial for the function g about $x = 1$ to approximate

$$\int_{0.2}^{1.3} e^x g(x)\, dx.$$

x	$g(x)$	$g'(x)$	$g''(x)$
1	4	-2	3

(A) 4.959   (B) 10.873   (C) 10.964   (D) 11.397

34. What is the volume of a solid obtained by revolving the curve $y = e^{\sin(x)} + 1$ from $x = \pi/6$ to $x = 9\pi/4$ about the x-axis?

(A) 47.065   (B) 94.129

(C) 121.354   (D) 242.708

35. Let f be a differentiable function on the interval $[36, 42]$. Let $f(36) = 377$ and $f'(x) \geq -14$. What is the least possible value of $f(42)$?

(A) -461 (B) -293 (C) 293   (D) 461

36. What is the area of the region enclosed by the graphs of $r = 1 + \cos 2\theta$ and $r = 2 \cos \theta - \sqrt{4 \cos^2 \theta - 3}$?

(A) 0.298   (B) 0.728   (C) 1.078   (D) 2.157

37. Gravel is poured onto a pile at a rate of

$$g(t) = \frac{25x + 25}{x^2 + 2x + 2}$$

cubic meters per minute, where t is the number of minutes since the pour process began. If the pile contains 3 cubic meters of gravel when the process began, how much gravel, to the nearest cubic meter, is in the pile after 14 minutes?

(A) 35   (B) 62   (C) 73   (D) 101

38. A particle moves along a straight line so that its position at time $t \geq 0$ is given by $s(t) = -5t + \int_0^t (2u)^{u+1}\, du$. Let a denote the average velocity of the particle over the interval $[0, 4]$ and let b denote the speed of the particle at $t = 2$. Find a/b.

(A) 0.024   (B) 0.026   (C) 39.172   (D) 42.407

39. Let g be a twice differentiable function of x. The table gives selected values of the first two derivatives of g. At what value of x is g a local minimum?

x	1	2	3	4	5	6	7	8
$g'(x)$	6	0	-4	-1	0	-1	0	7
$g''(x)$	-2	-3	-2	-1	0	1	4	6

(A) 2   (B) 4   (C) 5   (D) 7

40. Use the particular solution that satisfies $\dfrac{dy}{dx} = \dfrac{2x^2 y}{3}$ with the initial condition $y(0) = 5$ to find $y(0.3)$.

(A) 5.006   (B) 5.030   (C) 5.277   (D) 16.601

41. For $a_n = -\dfrac{1}{2n + 1}$, $\displaystyle\lim_{n \to \infty} a_n = 0$. Which of the following statements is true?

(A) The nth-term test for divergence is inconclusive. By the limit comparison test, $\displaystyle\sum_{n=1}^{\infty} a_n$ diverges.

(B) The nth-term test for divergence is inconclusive. By the alternating series test, $\displaystyle\sum_{n=1}^{\infty} a_n$ converges.

(C) By the nth-term test for divergence, $\displaystyle\sum_{n=1}^{\infty} a_n$ diverges.

(D) By the nth-term test for divergence, $\displaystyle\sum_{n=1}^{\infty} a_n$ converges.

42. Which of the following equations is a particular solution of $dy/dx = \sqrt{1 - y^2}$ with the initial condition $(0, -1/7)$?

(A) $y = \sin(x - 0.1433)$

(B) $y = \sin(x - 1.427)$

(C) $y = \sin(x - 1.714)$

(D) $y = \sin(x - 6.141)$

43. A particle travels along a straight line with a velocity of $v(t) = (5/4)^t \sin(t/2)$ feet per second. On what intervals is the acceleration of the particle increasing on $0 < t < 20$?

(A) $0 < t < 1.679$ and $7.962 < t < 14.245$

(B) $1.679 < t < 7.962$ and $14.245 < t < 20$

(C) $0 < t < 3.981$ and $10.264 < t < 16.547$

(D) $3.981 < t < 10.264$ and $16.547 < t < 20$

44. A particle moves along a straight line with a velocity of $v(t) = t^3 - 8t^2 + 6t - [5t/(t + 1)]$ feet per second. Find the total distance, in feet, traveled by the particle over $0 \le t \le 8$ seconds.

(A) -178.35 (B) 178.35

(C) 183.53 (D) 208.71

45. The table gives values of the twice differentiable function f and its derivative f' at selected values of x.

x	1	6
$f(x)$	3	18
$f'(x)$	0	6

If $\int_1^6 f(x)\,dx = 40$, what is the value of $\dfrac{1}{2}\int_1^6 x^2 f''(x)\,dx$?

(A) -36 (B) 43   (C) 72   (D) 86

Section 2: Free Response, Part A

A graphing calculator is required for Part A.

1. On a given workday, the rate, in tons per hour, of sand poured into a tank is modeled by $S(t) = 1500e^{-t^3/110}$, where t is measured in hours. During the hours of operation, $0 \le t \le 8$, sand is removed from the tank at a rate of 500 tons per hour.

(a) Find $S'(2)$. Using correct units, interpret your answer in the context of the problem.

(b) Find the total amount of sand poured into the tank during this 8-hour workday.

(c) Find the time t for which the rate of sand poured into the tank is equal to the average rate of sand poured into the tank.

(d) Is the amount of sand in the tank increasing or decreasing at $t = 5$ hours? Justify your answer.

2. At time t, a particle moving along a curve in the xy-plane has position $(x(t), y(t))$, where $dx/dt = t^2 + \cos 4t^2$. The graph of y is shown below. At $t = 0$, the particle is at position $(4, 0)$.

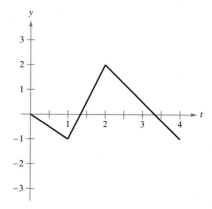

(a) Find the position of the particle at $t = 3$.

(b) At what time on $1 < t < 2$ is the particle at a point on the curve at which the line tangent to the curve has a slope of 3?

(c) Find the speed of the particle at $t = 1.5$.

(d) Find the total distance traveled by the particle from $t = 1$ to $t = 4$.

Section 2: Free Response, Part B

No calculator is allowed for Part B.

3. The number of megabytes of a video game that a computer has downloaded at time t (in seconds) is given by a differentiable function G, where $0 \le t \le 12$. Values of $G(t)$ are shown in the table at various times t.

t (seconds)	0	2	4	6	8	10	12
$G(t)$ (megabytes)	0	6.3	12.5	14.8	16.5	20.9	27.1

(a) Use the data in the table to approximate $G'(9)$. Show the computations that lead to your answer and indicate units of measure.

(b) For $4 \le t \le 8$, is there a time t at which $G'(t) = 1$? Justify your answer.

(c) Use a midpoint sum with three subintervals of equal length indicated by the data in the table to approximate the value of $\dfrac{1}{12}\displaystyle\int_0^{12} G(t)\,dt$. Using correct units, explain the meaning of $\dfrac{1}{12}\displaystyle\int_0^{12} G(t)\,dt$ in the context of the problem.

(d) A short video is also being downloaded. The number of megabytes of the video downloaded at time t (in seconds) is modeled by $V(t) = 32 - 32e^{-0.11t}$. Using this model, find the download rate at $t = 10$.

4. Consider the differential equation $dy/dx = 3x - y/2$.

(a) Find d^2y/dx^2 in terms of x and y. Determine the concavity of all solution curves for the given differential equation in Quadrant II. Give a reason for your answer.

(b) Find the values of the constants m and b for which $y = mx + b$ is a solution to the differential equation.

(c) Let $y = f(x)$ be the particular solution to the differential equation with the initial condition $f(0) = 3$.

(i) Does f have a relative minimum, a relative maximum, or neither at $x = 0$? Justify your answer.

(ii) Use Euler's Method, starting at $x = 0$ with two steps of equal size, to approximate $f(1)$.

5. The graphs of the polar curves $r = 5$ and $r = 2 + 6 \sin \theta$ are shown below. The curves intersect at $\theta = \pi/6$ and $\theta = 5\pi/6$.

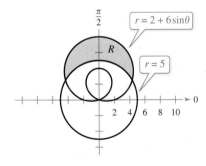

(a) Let R be the shaded region that is inside the graph of $r = 2 + 6 \sin \theta$ and outside the graph of $r = 5$, as shown. Write an expression involving an integral for the area of R.

(b) Find the slope of the line tangent to the graph of $r = 2 + 6 \sin \theta$ at $\theta = \pi$.

(c) A particle moves along the portion of the curve

$$r = 2 + 6 \sin \theta$$

for $0 < \theta < \pi/2$ in such a way that the distance between the particle and the origin increases at a constant rate of 2 units per second. Find the rate at which the angle θ changes with respect to time at the instant when the position of the particle corresponds to $\theta = \pi/3$. Indicate units of measure.

6. A function f has derivatives of all orders that satisfy the following conditions:

$$f(0) = 0$$

and

$$f^{(n)}(0) = -\left(\frac{(-1)^{n+2} - 1}{2}\right)^{n(n+1)/2}$$

for all $n \geq 1$.

(a) Write the first five nonzero terms and the general term of the Maclaurin series for f.

(b) Determine the interval of convergence of the Maclaurin series for f. Show the work that leads to your answer.

(c) Let $P_5(x)$ be the fifth-degree Taylor polynomial for f at $x = 0$. Use the alternating series error bound to find an upper bound for

$$\left| P_5\!\left(\frac{1}{4}\right) - f\!\left(\frac{1}{4}\right) \right|.$$

Appendices

*Available at the text-specific website www.cengage.com

Appendix A: Proofs of Selected Theorems

The text version of Appendix A, Proofs of Selected Theorems, is available at *cengage.com.* Also, to enhance your study of calculus, each proof is available in video format at *LarsonCalculusforAP.com.* At the website, you can watch videos of Bruce Edwards explaining each proof in the text and in Appendix A. To access a video, visit the website at *LarsonCalculusforAP.com* or scan the code near the proof or the proof's reference.

---

136   Chapter 2   Differentiation

The Power Rule

Before proving the next rule, it is important to review the procedure for expanding a binomial.

$(x + \Delta x)^2 = x^2 + 2x\Delta x + (\Delta x)^2$

$(x + \Delta x)^3 = x^3 + 3x^2\Delta x + 3x(\Delta x)^2 + (\Delta x)^3$

$(x + \Delta x)^4 = x^4 + 4x^3\Delta x + 6x^2(\Delta x)^2 + 4x(\Delta x)^3 + (\Delta x)^4$

$(x + \Delta x)^5 = x^5 + 5x^4\Delta x + 10x^3(\Delta x)^2 + 10x^2(\Delta x)^3 + 5x(\Delta x)^4 + (\Delta x)^5$

The general binomial expansion for a positive integer n is

$$(x + \Delta x)^n = x^n + nx^{n-1}(\Delta x) + \underbrace{\frac{n(n-1)x^{n-2}}{2}(\Delta x)^2 + \cdots + (\Delta x)^n}_{(\Delta x)^2 \text{ is a factor of these terms.}}$$

This binomial expansion is used in proving a special case of the Power Rule.

> **Theorem 2.3   The Power Rule**
>
> If n is a rational number, then the function $f(x) = x^n$ is differentiable and
>
> $$\frac{d}{dx}[x^n] = nx^{n-1}.$$
>
> For f to be differentiable at $x = 0$, n must be a number such that x^{n-1} is defined on an interval containing 0.

Justification

From Example 7 in Section 2.1, you know that the function $f(x) = x^{1/3}$ is defined at $x = 0$ but is not differentiable at $x = 0$. This is because $x^{-2/3}$ is not defined on an interval containing 0.

Proof   If n is a positive integer greater than 1, then the binomial expansion produces

$$\frac{d}{dx}[x^n] = \lim_{\Delta x \to 0}\frac{(x + \Delta x)^n - x^n}{\Delta x}$$

$$= \lim_{\Delta x \to 0}\frac{x^n + nx^{n-1}(\Delta x) + \frac{n(n-1)x^{n-2}}{2}(\Delta x)^2 + \cdots + (\Delta x)^n - x^n}{\Delta x}$$

$$= \lim_{\Delta x \to 0}\left[nx^{n-1} + \frac{n(n-1)x^{n-2}}{2}(\Delta x) + \cdots + (\Delta x)^{n-1}\right]$$

$$= nx^{n-1} + 0 + \cdots + 0$$

$$= nx^{n-1}.$$

This proves the case for which n is a positive integer greater than 1. It is l[eft to] prove the case for $n = 1$. Example 7 in Section 2.3 proves the case for [which n is a] negative integer. The cases for which n is rational and n is irrational a[re left as an] exercise. (See Section 2.5, Exercise 82.)

When using the Power Rule, the case for which $n = 1$ is best tho[ught of as a] separate differentiation rule. That is,

$$\frac{d}{dx}[x] = 1.$$ Power Rule when $n = 1$

This rule is consistent with the fact that the slope of the line $y = x$ is 1, [see] Figure 2.15.

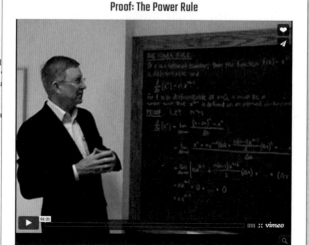

Proof: The Power Rule

**Bruce Edwards's Proof of the Power Rule
at *LarsonCalculusforAP.com***

Appendix B: Integration Tables

Forms Involving u^n

1. $\displaystyle\int u^n\,du = \frac{u^{n+1}}{n+1} + C,\ n \neq -1$

2. $\displaystyle\int \frac{1}{u}\,du = \ln|u| + C$

Forms Involving $a + bu$

3. $\displaystyle\int \frac{u}{a+bu}\,du = \frac{1}{b^2}\big(bu - a\ln|a+bu|\big) + C$

4. $\displaystyle\int \frac{u}{(a+bu)^2}\,du = \frac{1}{b^2}\left(\frac{a}{a+bu} + \ln|a+bu|\right) + C$

5. $\displaystyle\int \frac{u}{(a+bu)^n}\,du = \frac{1}{b^2}\left[\frac{-1}{(n-2)(a+bu)^{n-2}} + \frac{a}{(n-1)(a+bu)^{n-1}}\right] + C,\ n \neq 1, 2$

6. $\displaystyle\int \frac{u^2}{a+bu}\,du = \frac{1}{b^3}\left[-\frac{bu}{2}(2a-bu) + a^2\ln|a+bu|\right] + C$

7. $\displaystyle\int \frac{u^2}{(a+bu)^2}\,du = \frac{1}{b^3}\left(bu - \frac{a^2}{a+bu} - 2a\ln|a+bu|\right) + C$

8. $\displaystyle\int \frac{u^2}{(a+bu)^3}\,du = \frac{1}{b^3}\left[\frac{2a}{a+bu} - \frac{a^2}{2(a+bu)^2} + \ln|a+bu|\right] + C$

9. $\displaystyle\int \frac{u^2}{(a+bu)^n}\,du = \frac{1}{b^3}\left[\frac{-1}{(n-3)(a+bu)^{n-3}} + \frac{2a}{(n-2)(a+bu)^{n-2}} - \frac{a^2}{(n-1)(a+bu)^{n-1}}\right] + C,\ n \neq 1, 2, 3$

10. $\displaystyle\int \frac{1}{u(a+bu)}\,du = \frac{1}{a}\ln\left|\frac{u}{a+bu}\right| + C$

11. $\displaystyle\int \frac{1}{u(a+bu)^2}\,du = \frac{1}{a}\left(\frac{1}{a+bu} + \frac{1}{a}\ln\left|\frac{u}{a+bu}\right|\right) + C$

12. $\displaystyle\int \frac{1}{u^2(a+bu)}\,du = -\frac{1}{a}\left(\frac{1}{u} + \frac{b}{a}\ln\left|\frac{u}{a+bu}\right|\right) + C$

13. $\displaystyle\int \frac{1}{u^2(a+bu)^2}\,du = -\frac{1}{a^2}\left[\frac{a+2bu}{u(a+bu)} + \frac{2b}{a}\ln\left|\frac{u}{a+bu}\right|\right] + C$

Forms Involving $a + bu + cu^2,\ b^2 \neq 4ac$

14. $\displaystyle\int \frac{1}{a+bu+cu^2}\,du = \begin{cases} \dfrac{2}{\sqrt{4ac-b^2}}\arctan\dfrac{2cu+b}{\sqrt{4ac-b^2}} + C, & b^2 < 4ac \\[2ex] \dfrac{1}{\sqrt{b^2-4ac}}\ln\left|\dfrac{2cu+b-\sqrt{b^2-4ac}}{2cu+b+\sqrt{b^2-4ac}}\right| + C, & b^2 > 4ac \end{cases}$

15. $\displaystyle\int \frac{u}{a+bu+cu^2}\,du = \frac{1}{2c}\left(\ln|a+bu+cu^2| - b\int \frac{1}{a+bu+cu^2}\,du\right)$

Forms Involving $\sqrt{a+bu}$

16. $\displaystyle\int u^n\sqrt{a+bu}\,du = \frac{2}{b(2n+3)}\left[u^n(a+bu)^{3/2} - na\int u^{n-1}\sqrt{a+bu}\,du\right]$

17. $\displaystyle\int \frac{1}{u\sqrt{a+bu}}\,du = \begin{cases} \dfrac{1}{\sqrt{a}}\ln\left|\dfrac{\sqrt{a+bu}-\sqrt{a}}{\sqrt{a+bu}+\sqrt{a}}\right| + C, & a > 0 \\[2ex] \dfrac{2}{\sqrt{-a}}\arctan\sqrt{\dfrac{a+bu}{-a}} + C, & a < 0 \end{cases}$

18. $\displaystyle\int \frac{1}{u^n\sqrt{a+bu}}\,du = \frac{-1}{a(n-1)}\left[\frac{\sqrt{a+bu}}{u^{n-1}} + \frac{(2n-3)b}{2}\int \frac{1}{u^{n-1}\sqrt{a+bu}}\,du\right],\ n \neq 1$

19. $\displaystyle\int \frac{\sqrt{a+bu}}{u}\,du = 2\sqrt{a+bu} + a\int \frac{1}{u\sqrt{a+bu}}\,du$

20. $\displaystyle\int \frac{\sqrt{a+bu}}{u^n}\,du = \frac{-1}{a(n-1)}\left[\frac{(a+bu)^{3/2}}{u^{n-1}} + \frac{(2n-5)b}{2}\int \frac{\sqrt{a+bu}}{u^{n-1}}\,du\right], \ n \neq 1$

21. $\displaystyle\int \frac{u}{\sqrt{a+bu}}\,du = \frac{-2(2a-bu)}{3b^2}\sqrt{a+bu} + C$

22. $\displaystyle\int \frac{u^n}{\sqrt{a+bu}}\,du = \frac{2}{(2n+1)b}\left(u^n\sqrt{a+bu} - na\int \frac{u^{n-1}}{\sqrt{a+bu}}\,du\right)$

Forms Involving $a^2 \pm u^2,\ a > 0$

23. $\displaystyle\int \frac{1}{a^2+u^2}\,du = \frac{1}{a}\arctan \frac{u}{a} + C$

24. $\displaystyle\int \frac{1}{u^2-a^2}\,du = -\int \frac{1}{a^2-u^2}\,du = \frac{1}{2a}\ln\left|\frac{u-a}{u+a}\right| + C$

25. $\displaystyle\int \frac{1}{(a^2\pm u^2)^n}\,du = \frac{1}{2a^2(n-1)}\left[\frac{u}{(a^2\pm u^2)^{n-1}} + (2n-3)\int \frac{1}{(a^2\pm u^2)^{n-1}}\,du\right], \ n \neq 1$

Forms Involving $\sqrt{u^2 \pm a^2},\ a > 0$

26. $\displaystyle\int \sqrt{u^2\pm a^2}\,du = \frac{1}{2}\left(u\sqrt{u^2\pm a^2} \pm a^2\ln\left|u+\sqrt{u^2\pm a^2}\right|\right) + C$

27. $\displaystyle\int u^2\sqrt{u^2\pm a^2}\,du = \frac{1}{8}\left[u(2u^2\pm a^2)\sqrt{u^2\pm a^2} - a^4\ln\left|u+\sqrt{u^2\pm a^2}\right|\right] + C$

28. $\displaystyle\int \frac{\sqrt{u^2+a^2}}{u}\,du = \sqrt{u^2+a^2} - a\ln\left|\frac{a+\sqrt{u^2+a^2}}{u}\right| + C$

29. $\displaystyle\int \frac{\sqrt{u^2-a^2}}{u}\,du = \sqrt{u^2-a^2} - a\,\text{arcsec}\,\frac{|u|}{a} + C$

30. $\displaystyle\int \frac{\sqrt{u^2\pm a^2}}{u^2}\,du = \frac{-\sqrt{u^2\pm a^2}}{u} + \ln\left|u+\sqrt{u^2\pm a^2}\right| + C$

31. $\displaystyle\int \frac{1}{\sqrt{u^2\pm a^2}}\,du = \ln\left|u+\sqrt{u^2\pm a^2}\right| + C$

32. $\displaystyle\int \frac{1}{u\sqrt{u^2+a^2}}\,du = \frac{-1}{a}\ln\left|\frac{a+\sqrt{u^2+a^2}}{u}\right| + C$

33. $\displaystyle\int \frac{1}{u\sqrt{u^2-a^2}}\,du = \frac{1}{a}\,\text{arcsec}\,\frac{|u|}{a} + C$

34. $\displaystyle\int \frac{u^2}{\sqrt{u^2\pm a^2}}\,du = \frac{1}{2}\left(u\sqrt{u^2\pm a^2} \mp a^2\ln\left|u+\sqrt{u^2\pm a^2}\right|\right) + C$

35. $\displaystyle\int \frac{1}{u^2\sqrt{u^2\pm a^2}}\,du = \mp \frac{\sqrt{u^2\pm a^2}}{a^2u} + C$

36. $\displaystyle\int \frac{1}{(u^2\pm a^2)^{3/2}}\,du = \frac{\pm u}{a^2\sqrt{u^2\pm a^2}} + C$

Forms Involving $\sqrt{a^2 - u^2},\ a > 0$

37. $\displaystyle\int \sqrt{a^2-u^2}\,du = \frac{1}{2}\left(u\sqrt{a^2-u^2} + a^2\arcsin\frac{u}{a}\right) + C$

38. $\displaystyle\int u^2\sqrt{a^2-u^2}\,du = \frac{1}{8}\left[u(2u^2-a^2)\sqrt{a^2-u^2} + a^4\arcsin\frac{u}{a}\right] + C$

39. $\displaystyle\int \frac{\sqrt{a^2 - u^2}}{u}\, du = \sqrt{a^2 - u^2} - a \ln\left|\frac{a + \sqrt{a^2 - u^2}}{u}\right| + C$

40. $\displaystyle\int \frac{\sqrt{a^2 - u^2}}{u^2}\, du = \frac{-\sqrt{a^2 - u^2}}{u} - \arcsin\frac{u}{a} + C$

41. $\displaystyle\int \frac{1}{\sqrt{a^2 - u^2}}\, du = \arcsin\frac{u}{a} + C$

42. $\displaystyle\int \frac{1}{u\sqrt{a^2 - u^2}}\, du = \frac{-1}{a} \ln\left|\frac{a + \sqrt{a^2 - u^2}}{u}\right| + C$

43. $\displaystyle\int \frac{u^2}{\sqrt{a^2 - u^2}}\, du = \frac{1}{2}\left(-u\sqrt{a^2 - u^2} + a^2 \arcsin\frac{u}{a}\right) + C$

44. $\displaystyle\int \frac{1}{u^2\sqrt{a^2 - u^2}}\, du = \frac{-\sqrt{a^2 - u^2}}{a^2 u} + C$

45. $\displaystyle\int \frac{1}{(a^2 - u^2)^{3/2}}\, du = \frac{u}{a^2\sqrt{a^2 - u^2}} + C$

Forms Involving sin *u or* cos *u*

46. $\displaystyle\int \sin u\, du = -\cos u + C$

47. $\displaystyle\int \cos u\, du = \sin u + C$

48. $\displaystyle\int \sin^2 u\, du = \frac{1}{2}(u - \sin u \cos u) + C$

49. $\displaystyle\int \cos^2 u\, du = \frac{1}{2}(u + \sin u \cos u) + C$

50. $\displaystyle\int \sin^n u\, du = -\frac{\sin^{n-1} u \cos u}{n} + \frac{n-1}{n}\int \sin^{n-2} u\, du$

51. $\displaystyle\int \cos^n u\, du = \frac{\cos^{n-1} u \sin u}{n} + \frac{n-1}{n}\int \cos^{n-2} u\, du$

52. $\displaystyle\int u \sin u\, du = \sin u - u \cos u + C$

53. $\displaystyle\int u \cos u\, du = \cos u + u \sin u + C$

54. $\displaystyle\int u^n \sin u\, du = -u^n \cos u + n\int u^{n-1} \cos u\, du$

55. $\displaystyle\int u^n \cos u\, du = u^n \sin u - n\int u^{n-1} \sin u\, du$

56. $\displaystyle\int \frac{1}{1 \pm \sin u}\, du = \tan u \mp \sec u + C$

57. $\displaystyle\int \frac{1}{1 \pm \cos u}\, du = -\cot u \pm \csc u + C$

58. $\displaystyle\int \frac{1}{\sin u \cos u}\, du = \ln|\tan u| + C$

Forms Involving tan *u,* cot *u,* sec *u, or* csc *u*

59. $\displaystyle\int \tan u\, du = -\ln|\cos u| + C$

60. $\displaystyle\int \cot u\, du = \ln|\sin u| + C$

61. $\displaystyle\int \sec u\, du = \ln|\sec u + \tan u| + C$

62. $\displaystyle\int \csc u\, du = \ln|\csc u - \cot u| + C \quad \text{or} \quad \int \csc u\, du = -\ln|\csc u + \cot u| + C$

63. $\displaystyle\int \tan^2 u\, du = -u + \tan u + C$

64. $\displaystyle\int \cot^2 u\, du = -u - \cot u + C$

65. $\displaystyle\int \sec^2 u\, du = \tan u + C$

66. $\displaystyle\int \csc^2 u\, du = -\cot u + C$

67. $\displaystyle\int \tan^n u\, du = \frac{\tan^{n-1} u}{n-1} - \int \tan^{n-2} u\, du, \ n \neq 1$

68. $\displaystyle\int \cot^n u\, du = -\frac{\cot^{n-1} u}{n-1} - \int (\cot^{n-2} u)\, du, \ n \neq 1$

69. $\displaystyle\int \sec^n u\, du = \frac{\sec^{n-2} u \tan u}{n-1} + \frac{n-2}{n-1}\int \sec^{n-2} u\, du, \ n \neq 1$

70. $\displaystyle\int \csc^n u\, du - -\frac{\csc^{n-2} u \cot u}{n-1} + \frac{n-2}{n-1}\int \csc^{n-2} u\, du, \ n \neq 1$

71. $\displaystyle\int \frac{1}{1 \pm \tan u}\, du = \frac{1}{2}\left(u \pm \ln|\cos u \pm \sin u|\right) + C$

72. $\displaystyle\int \frac{1}{1 \pm \cot u}\, du = \frac{1}{2}\left(u \mp \ln|\sin u \pm \cos u|\right) + C$

73. $\displaystyle\int \frac{1}{1 \pm \sec u}\, du = u + \cot u \mp \csc u + C$

74. $\displaystyle\int \frac{1}{1 \pm \csc u}\, du = u - \tan u \pm \sec u + C$

Forms Involving Inverse Trigonometric Functions

75. $\displaystyle\int \arcsin u\, du = u \arcsin u + \sqrt{1 - u^2} + C$

76. $\displaystyle\int \arccos u\, du = u \arccos u - \sqrt{1 - u^2} + C$

77. $\displaystyle\int \arctan u\, du = u \arctan u - \ln\sqrt{1 + u^2} + C$

78. $\displaystyle\int \operatorname{arccot} u\, du = u \operatorname{arccot} u + \ln\sqrt{1 + u^2} + C$

79. $\displaystyle\int \operatorname{arcsec} u\, du = u \operatorname{arcsec} u - \ln\left|u + \sqrt{u^2 - 1}\right| + C$

80. $\displaystyle\int \operatorname{arccsc} u\, du = u \operatorname{arccsc} u + \ln\left|u + \sqrt{u^2 - 1}\right| + C$

Forms Involving e^u

81. $\displaystyle\int e^u\, du = e^u + C$

82. $\displaystyle\int u e^u\, du = (u - 1)e^u + C$

83. $\displaystyle\int u^n e^u\, du = u^n e^u - n\int u^{n-1} e^u\, du$

84. $\displaystyle\int \frac{1}{1 + e^u}\, du = u - \ln(1 + e^u) + C$

85. $\displaystyle\int e^{au} \sin bu\, du = \frac{e^{au}}{a^2 + b^2}(a \sin bu - b \cos bu) + C$

86. $\displaystyle\int e^{au} \cos bu\, du = \frac{e^{au}}{a^2 + b^2}(a \cos bu + b \sin bu) + C$

Forms Involving $\ln u$

87. $\displaystyle\int \ln u\, du = u(-1 + \ln u) + C$

88. $\displaystyle\int u \ln u\, du = \frac{u^2}{4}(-1 + 2 \ln u) + C$

89. $\displaystyle\int u^n \ln u\, du = \frac{u^{n+1}}{(n + 1)^2}[-1 + (n + 1) \ln u] + C, \; n \neq -1$

90. $\displaystyle\int (\ln u)^2\, du = u[2 - 2 \ln u + (\ln u)^2] + C$

91. $\displaystyle\int (\ln u)^n\, du = u(\ln u)^n - n\int (\ln u)^{n-1}\, du$

Appendix C: Precalculus Review

C.1   Real Numbers and the Real Number Line

▶ Represent and classify real numbers.
▶ Order real numbers and use inequalities.
▶ Find the absolute values of real numbers and find the distance between two real numbers.

Real Numbers and the Real Number Line

Real numbers can be represented by a coordinate system called the **real number line** or *x*-axis. (See Figure C.1.) The real number corresponding to a point on the real number line is the **coordinate** of the point. As Figure C.1 shows, it is customary to identify those points whose coordinates are integers.

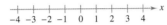

The real number line
Figure C.1

The point on the real number line corresponding to zero is the **origin** and is denoted by 0. The **positive direction** (to the right) is denoted by an arrowhead and is the direction of increasing values of *x*. Numbers to the right of the origin are **positive.** Numbers to the left of the origin are **negative.** The term **nonnegative** describes a number that is either positive or zero. The term **nonpositive** describes a number that is either negative or zero.

Each point on the real number line corresponds to one and only one real number, and each real number corresponds to one and only one point on the real number line. This type of relationship is called a **one-to-one correspondence.**

Each of the four points in Figure C.2 corresponds to a **rational number**—one that can be written as the ratio of two integers. $\left(\text{Note that } 4.5 = \frac{9}{2} \text{ and } -2.6 = -\frac{13}{5}.\right)$ Rational numbers can be represented either by *terminating decimals* such as $\frac{2}{5} = 0.4$ or by *repeating decimals* such as $\frac{1}{3} = 0.333\ldots = 0.\overline{3}$.

Real numbers that are not rational are **irrational.** Irrational numbers cannot be represented as terminating or repeating decimals. In computations, irrational numbers are represented by decimal approximations. Here are three familiar examples.

$$\sqrt{2} \approx 1.414213562$$
$$\pi \approx 3.141592654$$
$$e \approx 2.718281828$$

(See Figure C.3.)

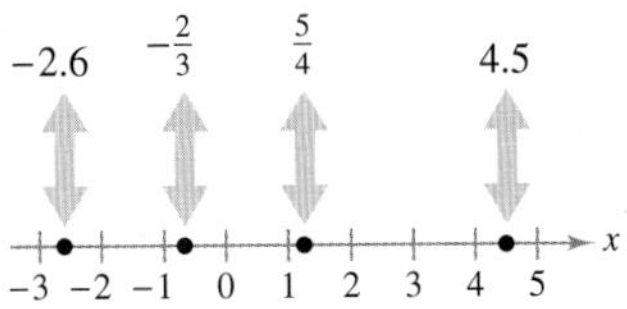

Rational numbers
Figure C.2

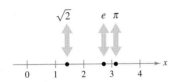

Irrational numbers
Figure C.3

Order and Inequalities

One important property of real numbers is that they are **ordered.** For two real numbers a and b, a is **less than** b when $b - a$ is positive. This order is denoted by the **inequality**

$$a < b.$$

This relationship can also be described by saying that b is **greater than** a and writing $b > a$. If three real numbers a, b, and c are ordered such that $a < b$ and $b < c$, then b is **between** a and c and $a < b < c$.

Geometrically, $a < b$ if and only if a lies to the *left* of b on the real number line. (See Figure C.4.) For example, $1 < 2$ because 1 lies to the left of 2 on the real number line.

Several properties used in working with inequalities are listed below. Similar properties are obtained when $<$ is replaced by $\leq$ and $>$ is replaced by $\geq$. (The symbols $\leq$ and $\geq$ mean **less than or equal to** and **greater than or equal to,** respectively.)

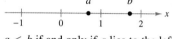

$a < b$ if and only if a lies to the left of b.

Figure C.4

Properties of Inequalities

Let a, b, c, d, and k be real numbers.

1. If $a < b$ and $b < c$, then $a < c$.   Transitive Property

2. If $a < b$ and $c < d$, then $a + c < b + d$.   Add inequalities.

3. If $a < b$, then $a + k < b + k$.   Add a constant.

4. If $a < b$ and $k > 0$, then $ak < bk$.   Multiply by a positive constant.

5. If $a < b$ and $k < 0$, then $ak > bk$.   Multiply by a negative constant.

Note that you *reverse the inequality* when you multiply the inequality by a negative number. For example, if $x < 3$, then $-4x > -12$. This also applies to division by a negative number. So, if $-2x > 4$, then $x < -2$.

A **set** is a collection of elements. Two common sets are the set of real numbers and the set of points on the real number line. Many problems in calculus involve **subsets** of one of these two sets. In such cases, it is convenient to use **set notation** of the form $\{x : \text{condition on } x\}$, which is read as follows.

The set of all x such that a certain condition is true.

$$\{ \quad x \quad : \quad \text{condition on } x\}$$

For example, you can describe the set of positive real numbers as

$$\{x : x > 0\}. \qquad \text{Set of positive real numbers}$$

Similarly, you can describe the set of nonnegative real numbers as

$$\{x : x \geq 0\}. \qquad \text{Set of nonnegative real numbers}$$

The **union** of two sets A and B, denoted by $A \cup B$, is the set of elements that are members of A *or* B *or both.* The **intersection** of two sets A and B, denoted by $A \cap B$, is the set of elements that are members of A *and* B. Two sets are **disjoint** when they have no elements in common.

The most commonly used subsets are **intervals** on the real number line. For example, the **open** interval

$$(a, b) = \{x \colon a < x < b\} \qquad \text{Open interval}$$

is the set of all real numbers greater than a and less than b, where a and b are the **endpoints** of the interval. Note that the endpoints are not included in an open interval. Intervals that include their endpoints are **closed** and are denoted by

$$[a, b] = \{x \colon a \leq x \leq b\}. \qquad \text{Closed interval}$$

The nine basic types of intervals on the real number line are shown in the table below. The first four are **bounded intervals** and the remaining five are **unbounded intervals.** Unbounded intervals are also classified as open or closed. The intervals $(-\infty, b)$ and (a, ∞) are open, the intervals $(-\infty, b]$ and $[a, \infty)$ are closed, and the interval $(-\infty, \infty)$ is considered to be both open *and* closed.

Intervals on the Real Number Line

	Interval Notation	Set Notation	Graph
Bounded open interval	(a, b)	$\{x \colon a < x < b\}$	
Bounded closed interval	$[a, b]$	$\{x \colon a \leq x \leq b\}$	
Bounded intervals (neither open nor closed)	$[a, b)$	$\{x \colon a \leq x < b\}$	
	$(a, b]$	$\{x \colon a < x \leq b\}$	
Unbounded open intervals	$(-\infty, b)$	$\{x \colon x < b\}$	
	(a, ∞)	$\{x \colon x > a\}$	
Unbounded closed intervals	$(-\infty, b]$	$\{x \colon x \leq b\}$	
	$[a, \infty)$	$\{x \colon x \geq a\}$	
Entire real line	$(-\infty, \infty)$	$\{x \colon x \text{ is a real number}\}$	

Note that the symbols ∞ and $-\infty$ refer to positive and negative infinity, respectively. These symbols do not denote real numbers. They simply enable you to describe unbounded conditions more concisely. For instance, the interval $[a, \infty)$ is unbounded to the right because it includes *all* real numbers that are greater than or equal to a.

EXAMPLE 1 Liquid and Gaseous States of Water

Describe the intervals on the real number line that correspond to the temperatures x (in degrees Celsius) of water in

a. a liquid state.   **b.** a gaseous state.

Solution

a. Water is in a liquid state at temperatures greater than 0°C and less than 100°C, as shown in Figure C.5(a).

$$(0, 100) = \{x: \ 0 < x < 100\}$$

b. Water is in a gaseous state (steam) at temperatures greater than or equal to 100°C, as shown in Figure C.5(b).

$$[100, \infty) = \{x: \ x \geq 100\}$$

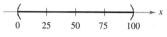

(a) Temperature range of water (in degrees Celsius)

(b) Temperature range of steam (in degrees Celsius)

Figure C.5

If a real number a is a **solution** of an inequality, then the inequality is **satisfied** (is true) when a is substituted for x. The set of all solutions is the **solution set** of the inequality.

EXAMPLE 2   Solving an Inequality

Solve $2x - 5 < 7$.

Solution

$2x - 5 < 7$	Write original inequality.
$2x - 5 + 5 < 7 + 5$	Add 5 to each side.
$2x < 12$	Simplify.
$\dfrac{2x}{2} < \dfrac{12}{2}$	Divide each side by 2.
$x < 6$	Simplify.

The solution set is $(-\infty, 6)$.

In Example 2, all five inequalities listed as steps in the solution are called **equivalent** because they have the same solution set.

Once you have solved an inequality, check some x-values in your solution set to verify that they satisfy the original inequality. You should also check some values outside your solution set to verify that they *do not* satisfy the inequality. For example, Figure C.6 shows that when $x = 0$ or $x = 5$ the inequality $2x - 5 < 7$ is satisfied, but when $x = 7$ the inequality $2x - 5 < 7$ is not satisfied.

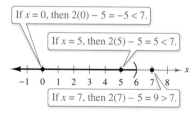

If $x = 0$, then $2(0) - 5 = -5 < 7$.

If $x = 5$, then $2(5) - 5 = 5 < 7$.

If $x = 7$, then $2(7) - 5 = 9 > 7$.

Checking solutions of $2x - 5 < 7$

Figure C.6

Solving a Double Inequality

Solve $-3 \le 2 - 5x \le 12$.

Solution

$-3 \le 2 - 5x$	≤ 12		Write original inequality.
$-3 - 2 \le 2 - 5x - 2$	$\le 12 - 2$		Subtract 2 from each part.
$-5 \le \quad -5x$	≤ 10		Simplify.
$\dfrac{-5}{-5} \ge \dfrac{-5x}{-5}$	$\ge \dfrac{10}{-5}$		Divide each part by -5 and reverse both inequalities.
$1 \ge \quad x$	≥ -2		Simplify.

The solution set is $[-2, 1]$, as shown in Figure C.7.

Solution set of $-3 \le 2 - 5x \le 12$

Figure C.7

The inequalities in Examples 2 and 3 are **linear inequalities**—that is, they involve first-degree polynomials. To solve inequalities involving polynomials of higher degree, use the fact that a polynomial can change signs *only* at its real **zeros** (the x-values that make the polynomial equal to zero). Between two consecutive real zeros, a polynomial must be either entirely positive or entirely negative. This means that when the real zeros of a polynomial are put in order, they divide the real number line into **test intervals** in which the polynomial has no sign changes. So, if a polynomial has the factored form

$$(x - r_1)(x - r_2) \cdots (x - r_n), \qquad r_1 < r_2 < r_3 < \cdots < r_n$$

then the test intervals are

$$(-\infty, r_1), \quad (r_1, r_2), \quad \ldots, \quad (r_{n-1}, r_n), \quad \text{and} \quad (r_n, \infty).$$

To determine the sign of the polynomial in each test interval, you need to test only *one value* from the interval.

Solving a Quadratic Inequality

Solve $x^2 < x + 6$.

Solution

$x^2 < x + 6$	Write original inequality.
$x^2 - x - 6 < 0$	Write in general form.
$(x - 3)(x + 2) < 0$	Factor.

The polynomial $x^2 - x - 6$ has $x = -2$ and $x = 3$ as its zeros. So, you can solve the inequality by testing the sign of $x^2 - x - 6$ in each of the test intervals $(-\infty, -2)$, $(-2, 3)$, and $(3, \infty)$. To test an interval, choose any number in the interval and determine the sign of $x^2 - x - 6$. After doing this, you will find that the polynomial is positive for all real numbers in the first and third intervals and negative for all real numbers in the second interval. The solution of the original inequality is therefore $(-2, 3)$, as shown in Figure C.8.

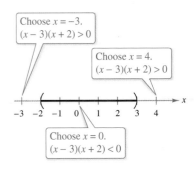

Choose $x = -3$.
$(x - 3)(x + 2) > 0$

Choose $x = 4$.
$(x - 3)(x + 2) > 0$

Choose $x = 0$.
$(x - 3)(x + 2) < 0$

Testing intervals

Figure C.8

Absolute Value and Distance

If a is a real number, then the **absolute value** of a is

$$|a| = \begin{cases} a, & a \geq 0 \\ -a, & a < 0 \end{cases}.$$

The absolute value of a number cannot be negative. For example, let $a = -4$. Then, because $-4 < 0$, you have

$$|a| = |-4| = -(-4) = 4.$$

Remember that the symbol $-a$ does not necessarily mean that $-a$ is negative.

Operations with Absolute Value

Let a and b be real numbers and let n be a positive integer.

1. $|ab| = |a|\,|b|$ **2.** $\left|\dfrac{a}{b}\right| = \dfrac{|a|}{|b|}$, $b \neq 0$

3. $|a| = \sqrt{a^2}$ **4.** $|a^n| = |a|^n$

Remark

You are asked to prove these properties in Exercises 73, 75, 76, and 77.

Properties of Inequalities and Absolute Value

Let a and b be real numbers and let k be a positive real number.

1. $-|a| \leq a \leq |a|$

2. $|a| \leq k$ if and only if $-k \leq a \leq k$.

3. $|a| \geq k$ if and only if $a \leq -k$ or $a \geq k$.

4. *Triangle Inequality:* $|a + b| \leq |a| + |b|$

Properties 2 and 3 are also true when $\leq$ is replaced by $<$ and $\geq$ is replaced by $>$.

EXAMPLE 5   Solving an Absolute Value Inequality

Solve $|x - 3| \leq 2$.

Solution

Using the second property of inequalities and absolute value, you can rewrite the original inequality as a double inequality.

$$-2 \leq x - 3 \quad\ \leq 2 \qquad \text{Write as double inequality.}$$
$$-2 + 3 \leq x - 3 + 3 \leq 2 + 3 \qquad \text{Add 3 to each part.}$$
$$1 \leq x \quad\quad\ \leq 5 \qquad \text{Simplify.}$$

The solution set is $[1, 5]$, as shown in Figure C.9.

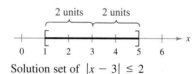

Solution set of $|x - 3| \leq 2$

Figure C.9

EXAMPLE 6   A Two-Interval Solution Set

Solve $|x + 2| > 3$.

Solution

Using the third property of inequalities and absolute value, you can rewrite the original inequality as two linear inequalities.

$$x + 2 < -3 \quad \text{or} \quad x + 2 > 3$$
$$x < -5 \qquad\qquad x > 1$$

The solution set is the union of the disjoint intervals $(-\infty, -5)$ and $(1, \infty)$, as shown in Figure C.10.

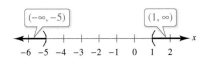

Solution set of $|x + 2| > 3$
Figure C.10

Examples 5 and 6 illustrate the general results shown in Figure C.11. Note that for $d > 0$, the solution set for the inequality $|x - a| \le d$ is a *single* interval, whereas the solution set for the inequality $|x - a| \ge d$ is the union of *two* disjoint intervals.

The **distance between two points** a and b on the real number line is given by

$$d = |a - b| = |b - a|.$$

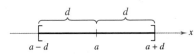

Solution set of $|x - a| \le d$

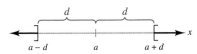

Solution set of $|x - a| \ge d$
Figure C.11

The **directed distance from a to b** is $b - a$ and the **directed distance from b to a** is $a - b$, as shown in Figure C.12.

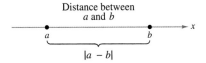
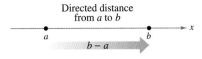
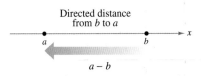

Figure C.12

EXAMPLE 7   Distance on the Real Number Line

a. The distance between -3 and 4 is

$$|4 - (-3)| = |7| = 7 \quad \text{or} \quad |-3 - 4| = |-7| = 7.$$

(See Figure C.13.)

b. The directed distance from -3 to 4 is

$$4 - (-3) = 7.$$

c. The directed distance from 4 to -3 is

$$-3 - 4 = -7.$$

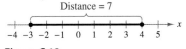

Figure C.13

The **midpoint** of an interval with endpoints a and b is the average value of a and b. That is,

$$\text{Midpoint of interval } (a, b) = \frac{a + b}{2}.$$

To show that this is the midpoint, you need only show that $(a + b)/2$ is equidistant from a and b.

C.1   Exercises

See *CalcChat.com* for tutorial help and worked-out solutions to odd-numbered exercises.

Rational or Irrational?   In Exercises 1–10, determine whether the real number is rational or irrational.

1. 0.22

2. -317

3. $-\pi$

4. $3\sqrt{2} - 1$

5. $4.3\overline{451}$

6. $\frac{22}{7}$

7. $\sqrt[3]{64}$

8. 3.141592

9. $4\frac{5}{8}$

10. $\left(\sqrt{2}\right)^3$

Repeating Decimal   In Exercises 11–14, write the repeating decimal as a ratio of two integers in simplest form using the method in the following example. If $x = 0.6363\ldots$, then $100x = 63.6363\ldots$. Subtracting the first equation from the second produces $99x = 63$ or $x = \frac{63}{99} = \frac{7}{11}$.

11. $0.\overline{48}$

12. $0.5\overline{34}$

13. $0.\overline{297}$

14. $0.\overline{9900}$

15. **Using Properties of Inequalities**   Given $a < b$, determine which of the following are true.

(a) $a + 2 < b + 2$

(b) $5b < 5a$

(c) $5 - a > 5 - b$

(d) $\dfrac{1}{a} < \dfrac{1}{b}$

(e) $(a - b)(b - a) > 0$

(f) $a^2 < b^2$

16. **Intervals and Graphs on the Real Number Line**   Complete the table with the appropriate interval notation, set notation, or graph on the real number line.

Interval Notation	Set Notation	Graph
$(-\infty, -4]$		
	$\left\{x\colon 3 \le x \le \frac{11}{2}\right\}$	
$(-1, 7)$		

Analyzing an Inequality   In Exercises 17–20, verbally describe the subset of real numbers represented by the inequality. Sketch the subset on the real number line, and state whether the interval is bounded or unbounded.

17. $-4 < x < 2$

18. $x \ge 4$

19. $x \le 5$

20. $0 \le x < 8$

Using Inequality and Interval Notation   In Exercises 21–24, use inequality and interval notation to describe the set.

21. y is at least -6.

22. q is nonnegative.

23. The percent increase r in school taxes is expected to be greater than 2% and no more than 4.5%.

24. The temperature T is forecast to be above 90°F today.

Solving an Inequality   In Exercises 25–44, solve the inequality and graph the solution on the real number line.

25. $3x - 1 \ge 0$

26. $3x + 1 \ge 2x + 2$

27. $-4 < 2x - 3 < 4$

28. $0 \le x + 3 < 5$

29. $\dfrac{x}{2} + \dfrac{x}{3} > 5$

30. $x > \dfrac{1}{x}$

31. $|x| < 1$

32. $\dfrac{x}{3} - \dfrac{x}{4} \ge 2$

33. $\left|\dfrac{x - 3}{2}\right| \ge 5$

34. $\left|\dfrac{x}{2}\right| > 3$

35. $|x - a| < b, b > 0$

36. $|x + 2| < 5$

37. $|2x + 1| < 5$

38. $|3x + 1| \ge 4$

39. $\left|1 - \dfrac{2}{3}x\right| < 1$

40. $|9 - 2x| < 1$

41. $x^2 \le 3 - 2x$

42. $x^4 - x \le 0$

43. $x^2 + x - 1 \le 5$

44. $2x^2 + 1 < 9x - 3$

Distance on the Real Number Line   In Exercises 45–48, find the directed distance from a to b, the directed distance from b to a, and the distance between a and b.

45.

46.

47. (a) $a = 126, b = 75$

(b) $a = -126, b = -75$

48. (a) $a = 9.34, b = -5.65$

(b) $a = \frac{16}{5}, b = \frac{122}{75}$

Finding the Midpoint   In Exercises 49–52, find the midpoint of the interval.

49.

50.

51. (a) $[7, 21]$

(b) $[8.6, 11.4]$

52. (a) $[-6.85, 9.35]$

(b) $[-4.6, -1.3]$

Using Absolute Value Notation   In Exercises 53–58, use absolute value notation to define the interval or pair of intervals on the real number line.

53. (a) All numbers that are at most 10 units from 12

  (b) All numbers that are at least 10 units from 12

54. (a) y is at most two units from a.

  (b) y is less than δ units from c.

55.

56.

57.

$a = 0$ $b = 4$

58.

$a = 20$ $b = 24$

59. Profit   The revenue R from selling x units of a product is

$$R = 128.75x$$

and the cost C of producing x units is

$$C = 88x + 965.$$

To make a (positive) profit, R must be greater than C. For what values of x will the product return a profit?

60. Fleet Costs   A utility company has a fleet of vans. The annual operating cost C (in dollars) of each van is estimated to be

$$C = 0.58m + 5200$$

where m is measured in miles. Describe the values of m for which the annual operating cost of a van is less than \$15,000.

61. Fair Coin   To determine whether a coin is fair (has an equal probability of landing tails up or heads up), you toss the coin 100 times and record the number of heads x. The coin is declared unfair when

$$\left| \frac{x - 50}{5} \right| \geq 1.645.$$

For what values of x will the coin be declared unfair?

62. Daily Production   The estimated daily oil production p at a refinery is

$$|p - 2{,}250{,}000| < 125{,}000$$

where p is measured in barrels. Determine the high and low production levels.

Which Number Is Greater?   In Exercises 63 and 64, determine which of the two real numbers is greater.

63. (a) π or $\frac{22}{7}$

  (b) π or $\frac{355}{113}$

64. (a) $\frac{338}{189}$ or $\frac{270}{151}$

  (b) $\frac{73}{81}$ or $\frac{6427}{7132}$

65. Approximation—Powers of 10   Light travels at the speed of 2.998×10^8 meters per second. Which best estimates the distance in meters that light travels in a year?

  (a) 9.5×10^5

  (b) 9.5×10^{15}

  (c) 9.5×10^{12}

  (d) 9.6×10^{16}

66. Writing   The accuracy of an approximation of a number is related to how many significant digits there are in the approximation. Write a definition of significant digits and illustrate the concept with examples.

True or False?   In Exercises 67–72, determine whether the statement is true or false. If it is false, explain why or give an example that shows it is false.

67. The reciprocal of any nonzero integer is an integer.

68. The reciprocal of any nonzero rational number is a rational number.

69. Every real number is either rational or irrational.

70. The absolute value of any real number is positive.

71. If $x < 0$, then $\sqrt{x^2} = -x$.

72. If a and b are two distinct real numbers, then $a < b$ or $a > b$.

Proof   In Exercises 73–80, prove the property.

73. $|ab| = |a||b|$

74. $|a - b| = |b - a|$

  [*Hint*: $(a - b) = (-1)(b - a)$]

75. $\left| \dfrac{a}{b} \right| = \dfrac{|a|}{|b|}, \quad b \neq 0$

76. $|a| = \sqrt{a^2}$

77. $|a^n| = |a|^n, \quad n = 1, 2, 3, \ldots$

78. $-|a| \leq a \leq |a|$

79. $|a| \leq k$ if and only if $-k \leq a \leq k, \quad k > 0$.

80. $|a| \geq k$ if and only if $a \leq -k$ or $a \geq k, \quad k > 0$.

81. Proof   Find an example for which $|a - b| > |a| - |b|$, and an example for which $|a - b| = |a| - |b|$. Then prove that $|a - b| \geq |a| - |b|$ for all real numbers a and b.

82. Maximum and Minimum   Show that the maximum of two real numbers a and b is given by the formula

$$\max(a, b) = \tfrac{1}{2}\big(a + b + |a - b|\big).$$

Derive a similar formula for $\min(a, b)$.

C.2   The Cartesian Plane

▶ Understand the Cartesian plane.
▶ Use the Distance Formula to find the distance between two points and use the Midpoint Formula to find the midpoint of a line segment.
▶ Find equations of circles and sketch the graphs of circles.

The Cartesian Plane

Just as you can represent real numbers by points on a real number line, you can represent ordered pairs of real numbers by points in a plane called the **rectangular coordinate system,** or the **Cartesian plane,** after the French mathematician René Descartes.

The Cartesian plane is formed by using two real number lines intersecting at right angles, as shown in Figure C.14. The horizontal real number line is usually called the ***x*-axis,** and the vertical real number line is usually called the ***y*-axis.** The point of intersection of these two axes is the **origin.** The two axes divide the plane into four parts called **quadrants.**

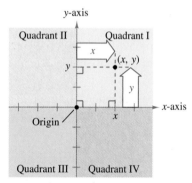

The Cartesian plane
Figure C.14

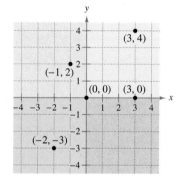

Points represented by ordered pairs
Figure C.15

Each point in the plane is identified by an **ordered pair** (x, y) of real numbers x and y called the **coordinates** of the point. The number x represents the directed distance from the y-axis to the point, and the number y represents the directed distance from the x-axis to the point. (See Figure C.14.) For the point (x, y), the first coordinate is the ***x*-coordinate** or **abscissa,** and the second coordinate is the ***y*-coordinate** or **ordinate.** For example, Figure C.15 shows the locations of the points $(-1, 2)$, $(3, 4)$, $(0, 0)$, $(3, 0)$, and $(-2, -3)$ in the Cartesian plane. The signs of the coordinates of a point determine the quadrant in which the point lies. For instance, if $x > 0$ and $y < 0$, then the point (x, y) lies in Quadrant IV.

Note that an ordered pair (a, b) is used to denote either a point in the plane *or* an open interval on the real number line. This, however, should not be confusing—the nature of the problem should clarify whether a point in the plane or an open interval is being discussed.

The Distance and Midpoint Formulas

Recall from the **Pythagorean Theorem** that, in a right triangle, the hypotenuse c and sides a and b are related by $a^2 + b^2 = c^2$. Conversely, if $a^2 + b^2 = c^2$, then the triangle is a right triangle. (See Figure C.16.)

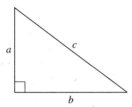

The Pythagorean Theorem:
$a^2 + b^2 = c^2$
Figure C.16

Now, consider the problem of determining the distance d between the two points (x_1, y_1) and (x_2, y_2) in the plane. If the points lie on a horizontal line, then $y_1 = y_2$ and the distance between the points is $|x_2 - x_1|$. If the points lie on a vertical line, then $x_1 = x_2$ and the distance between the points is $|y_2 - y_1|$. When the two points do not lie on a horizontal or vertical line, they can be used to form a right triangle, as shown in Figure C.17. The length of the vertical side of the triangle is $|y_2 - y_1|$, and the length of the horizontal side is $|x_2 - x_1|$. By the Pythagorean Theorem, it follows that

$$d^2 = |x_2 - x_1|^2 + |y_2 - y_1|^2$$
$$d = \sqrt{|x_2 - x_1|^2 + |y_2 - y_1|^2}.$$

Replacing $|x_2 - x_1|^2$ and $|y_2 - y_1|^2$ by the equivalent expressions $(x_2 - x_1)^2$ and $(y_2 - y_1)^2$ produces the **Distance Formula.**

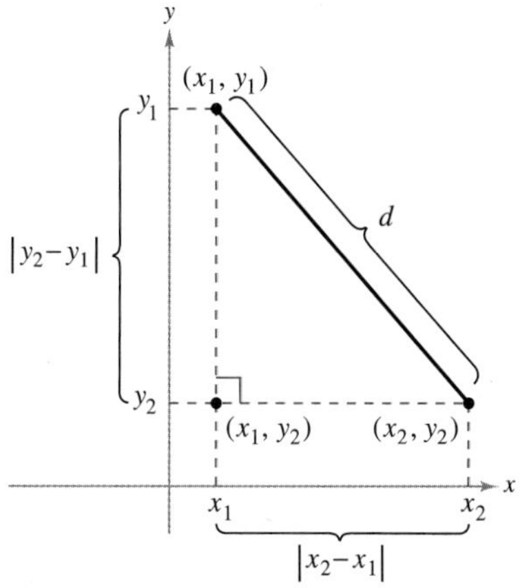

> ### Distance Formula
>
> The distance d between the points (x_1, y_1) and (x_2, y_2) in the plane is given by
> $$d = \sqrt{(x_2 - x_1)^2 + (y_2 - y_1)^2}.$$

The distance between two points
Figure C.17

EXAMPLE 1 Finding the Distance Between Two Points

Find the distance between the points $(-2, 1)$ and $(3, 4)$.

Solution

$$
\begin{aligned}
d &= \sqrt{(x_2 - x_1)^2 + (y_2 - y_1)^2} && \text{Distance Formula} \\
&= \sqrt{[3 - (-2)]^2 + (4 - 1)^2} && \text{Substitute for } x_1, y_1, x_2, \text{ and } y_2. \\
&= \sqrt{5^2 + 3^2} \\
&= \sqrt{25 + 9} \\
&= \sqrt{34} \\
&\approx 5.83
\end{aligned}
$$

EXAMPLE 2   Verifying a Right Triangle

Verify that the points $(2, 1)$, $(4, 0)$, and $(5, 7)$ form the vertices of a right triangle.

Solution

Figure C.18 shows the triangle formed by the three points. The lengths of the three sides are as follows.

$$d_1 = \sqrt{(5-2)^2 + (7-1)^2} = \sqrt{9+36} = \sqrt{45}$$

$$d_2 = \sqrt{(4-2)^2 + (0-1)^2} = \sqrt{4+1} = \sqrt{5}$$

$$d_3 = \sqrt{(5-4)^2 + (7-0)^2} = \sqrt{1+49} = \sqrt{50}$$

Because

$$d_1^2 + d_2^2 = 45 + 5 = 50 \qquad \text{Sum of squares of sides}$$

and

$$d_3^2 = 50 \qquad \text{Square of hypotenuse}$$

you can apply the Pythagorean Theorem to conclude that the triangle is a right triangle.

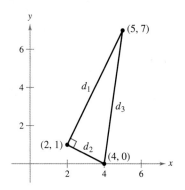

Verifying a right triangle
Figure C.18

EXAMPLE 3   Using the Distance Formula

Find x such that the distance between $(x, 3)$ and $(2, -1)$ is 5.

Solution

Using the Distance Formula, you can write the following.

$$5 = \sqrt{(x-2)^2 + [3-(-1)]^2} \qquad \text{Distance Formula}$$

$$25 = (x^2 - 4x + 4) + 16 \qquad \text{Square each side.}$$

$$0 = x^2 - 4x - 5 \qquad \text{Write in general form.}$$

$$0 = (x-5)(x+1) \qquad \text{Factor.}$$

So, $x = 5$ or $x = -1$, and you can conclude that there are two solutions. That is, each of the points $(5, 3)$ and $(-1, 3)$ lies five units from the point $(2, -1)$, as shown in Figure C.19.

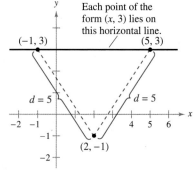

Figure C.19

The coordinates of the **midpoint** of the line segment joining two points can be found by "averaging" the x-coordinates of the two points and "averaging" the y-coordinates of the two points. That is, the midpoint of the line segment joining the points (x_1, y_1) and (x_2, y_2) in the plane is

$$\left(\frac{x_1 + x_2}{2}, \frac{y_1 + y_2}{2} \right). \qquad \text{Midpoint Formula}$$

For instance, the midpoint of the line segment joining the points $(-5, -3)$ and $(9, 3)$ is

$$\left(\frac{-5+9}{2}, \frac{-3+3}{2} \right) = (2, 0)$$

as shown in Figure C.20.

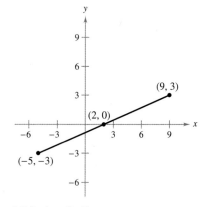

Midpoint of a line segment
Figure C.20

Equations of Circles

A **circle** can be defined as the set of all points in a plane that are equidistant from a fixed point. The fixed point is the **center** of the circle, and the distance between the center and a point on the circle is the **radius.** (See Figure C.21.)

You can use the Distance Formula to write an equation for the circle with center (h, k) and radius r. Let (x, y) be any point on the circle. Then the distance between (x, y) and the center (h, k) is given by

$$\sqrt{(x - h)^2 + (y - k)^2} = r.$$

By squaring each side of this equation, you obtain the **standard form of the equation of a circle.**

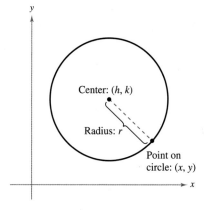

Definition of a circle
Figure C.21

> ### Standard Form of the Equation of a Circle
>
> The point (x, y) lies on the circle of radius r and center (h, k) if and only if
>
> $$(x - h)^2 + (y - k)^2 = r^2.$$

The standard form of the equation of a circle with center at the origin, $(h, k) = (0, 0)$ is

$$x^2 + y^2 = r^2.$$

If $r = 1$, then the circle is called the **unit circle.**

EXAMPLE 4   Writing the Equation of a Circle

The point $(3, 4)$ lies on a circle whose center is at $(-1, 2)$, as shown in Figure C.22. Write the standard form of the equation of this circle.

Solution

The radius of the circle is the distance between $(-1, 2)$ and $(3, 4)$.

$$r = \sqrt{[3 - (-1)]^2 + (4 - 2)^2} = \sqrt{16 + 4} = \sqrt{20}$$

You can write the standard form of the equation of this circle as

$$[x - (-1)]^2 + (y - 2)^2 = \left(\sqrt{20}\right)^2$$
$$(x + 1)^2 + (y - 2)^2 = 20. \qquad \text{Write in standard form.}$$

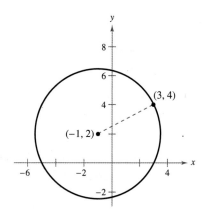

Figure C.22

By squaring and simplifying, the equation $(x - h)^2 + (y - k)^2 = r^2$ can be written in the following **general form of the equation of a circle.**

$$Ax^2 + Ay^2 + Dx + Ey + F = 0, \quad A \neq 0$$

To convert such an equation to the standard form

$$(x - h)^2 + (y - k)^2 = p$$

you can use a process called **completing the square.** If $p > 0$, then the graph of the equation is a circle. If $p = 0$, then the graph is the single point (h, k). If $p < 0$, then the equation has no graph.

EXAMPLE 5   Completing the Square

Sketch the graph of the circle whose general equation is

$$4x^2 + 4y^2 + 20x - 16y + 37 = 0.$$

Solution

To complete the square, first divide by 4 so that the coefficients of x^2 and y^2 are both 1.

$$4x^2 + 4y^2 + 20x - 16y + 37 = 0 \qquad \text{Write original equation.}$$

$$x^2 + y^2 + 5x - 4y + \frac{37}{4} = 0 \qquad \text{Divide by 4.}$$

$$(x^2 + 5x + \quad) + (y^2 - 4y + \quad) = -\frac{37}{4} \qquad \text{Group terms.}$$

$$\left(x^2 + 5x + \frac{25}{4}\right) + (y^2 - 4y + 4) = -\frac{37}{4} + \frac{25}{4} + 4 \qquad \text{Complete the square by adding } \left(\frac{5}{2}\right)^2 = \frac{25}{4} \text{ and } \left(\frac{4}{2}\right)^2 = 4 \text{ to each side.}$$

$$\underbrace{\qquad}_{(\text{half})^2} \qquad \underbrace{\qquad}_{(\text{half})^2}$$

$$\left(x + \frac{5}{2}\right)^2 + (y - 2)^2 = 1 \qquad \text{Write in standard form.}$$

Note that you complete the square by adding the square of half the coefficient of x *and* the square of half the coefficient of y to each side of the equation. The circle is centered at $\left(-\frac{5}{2}, 2\right)$ and its radius is 1, as shown in Figure C.23.

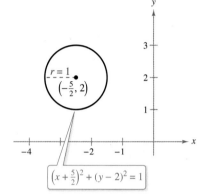

A circle with a radius of 1 and center at $\left(-\frac{5}{2}, 2\right)$

Figure C.23

You have now reviewed some fundamental concepts of *analytic geometry*. Because these concepts are in common use today, it is easy to overlook their revolutionary nature. At the time analytic geometry was being developed by Pierre de Fermat and René Descartes, the two major branches of mathematics—geometry and algebra—were largely independent of each other. Circles belonged to geometry and equations belonged to algebra. The coordination of the points on a circle and the solutions of an equation belongs to what is now called analytic geometry.

It is important to become skilled in analytic geometry so that you can move easily between geometry and algebra. For instance, in Example 4, you were given a geometric description of a circle and were asked to find an algebraic equation for the circle. So, you were moving from geometry to algebra. Similarly, in Example 5, you were given an algebraic equation and asked to sketch a geometric picture. In this case, you were moving from algebra to geometry. These two examples illustrate the two most common problems in analytic geometry.

1. Given a graph, find its equation.

   Geometry ⟹ Algebra

2. Given an equation, find its graph.

   Algebra ⟹ Geometry

Using the Distance and Midpoint Formulas In Exercises 1–6, (a) plot the points, (b) find the distance between the points, and (c) find the midpoint of the line segment joining the points.

1. $(2, 1), (4, 5)$
2. $(-3, 2), (3, -2)$
3. $\left(\frac{1}{2}, 1\right), \left(-\frac{3}{2}, -5\right)$
4. $\left(\frac{2}{3}, -\frac{1}{3}\right), \left(\frac{5}{6}, 1\right)$
5. $\left(1, \sqrt{3}\right), (-1, 1)$
6. $(-2, -4), \left(0, \sqrt{2}\right)$

Locating a Point In Exercises 7–10, determine the quadrant(s) in which (x, y) is located so that the condition(s) is (are) satisfied.

7. $x = -2$ and $y > 0$
8. $y < -2$
9. $xy > 0$
10. $(x, -y)$ is in Quadrant II.

Vertices of a Polygon In Exercises 11–14, show that the points are the vertices of the polygon. (A rhombus is a quadrilateral whose sides are all the same length.)

	Vertices		Polygon
11.	$(4, 0), (2, 1), (-1, -5)$		Right triangle
12.	$(1, -3), (3, 2), (-2, 4)$		Isosceles triangle
13.	$(0, 0), (1, 2), (2, 1), (3, 3)$		Rhombus
14.	$(0, 1), (3, 7), (4, 4), (1, -2)$		Parallelogram

15. **Number of Stores** The table shows the number y of Target stores for each year x from 2009 through 2018. Select reasonable scales on the coordinate axes and plot the points (x, y). (*Source:* Target Corp.)

Year, x	2009	2010	2011	2012	2013
Number, y	1740	1750	1763	1778	1917

Year, x	2014	2015	2016	2017	2018
Number, y	1790	1792	1802	1822	1844

16. **Conjecture** Plot the points $(2, 1), (-3, 5),$ and $(7, -3)$ in a rectangular coordinate system. Then change the sign of the x-coordinate of each point and plot the three new points in the same rectangular coordinate system. What conjecture can you make about the location of a point when the sign of the x-coordinate is changed? Repeat the exercise for the case in which the signs of the y-coordinates are changed.

Collinear Points In Exercises 17–20, use the Distance Formula to determine whether the points lie on the same line.

17. $(0, -4), (2, 0), (3, 2)$
18. $(0, 4), (10, -10), (-5, 11)$
19. $(-2, 1), (-1, 0), (2, -2)$
20. $(-1, 1), (3, 3), (5, 5)$

Using the Distance Formula In Exercises 21 and 22, find x such that the distance between the points is 5.

21. $(0, 0), (x, -4)$
22. $(2, -1), (x, 2)$

Using the Distance Formula In Exercises 23 and 24, find y such that the distance between the points is 8.

23. $(0, 0), (3, y)$
24. $(5, 1), (5, y)$

25. **Using the Midpoint Formula** Use the Midpoint Formula to find the three points that divide the line segment joining (x_1, y_1) and (x_2, y_2) into four equal parts.

26. **Using the Midpoint Formula** Use the result of Exercise 25 to find the points that divide the line segment joining the given points into four equal parts.

(a) $(1, -2), (4, -1)$ (b) $(-2, -3), (0, 0)$

Matching In Exercises 27–30, match the equation with its graph. [The graphs are labeled (a), (b), (c), and (d).]

(a)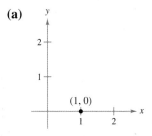

(b)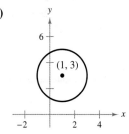

(c)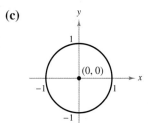

(d)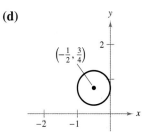

27. $x^2 + y^2 = 1$
28. $(x - 1)^2 + (y - 3)^2 = 4$
29. $(x - 1)^2 + y^2 = 0$
30. $\left(x + \frac{1}{2}\right)^2 + \left(y - \frac{3}{4}\right)^2 = \frac{1}{4}$

Writing the Equation of a Circle **In Exercises 31–38, write the standard form of the equation of the circle.**

31. Center: $(0, 0)$
    Radius: 3

32. Center: $(0, 0)$
    Radius: 5

33. Center: $(2, -1)$
    Radius: 4

34. Center: $(-4, 3)$
    Radius: $\frac{5}{8}$

35. Center: $(-1, 2)$
    Point on circle: $(0, 0)$

36. Center: $(3, -2)$
    Point on circle: $(-4, 1)$

37. Endpoints of a diameter: $(2, 5), (4, -1)$

38. Endpoints of a diameter: $(1, 3), (-1, -2)$

39. **Satellite Communication** Write the standard form of the equation for the path of a communications satellite in a circular orbit 22,000 miles above Earth. (Assume that the radius of Earth is 4000 miles.)

40. **Building Design** A circular air duct of diameter D is fit firmly into the right-angle corner where a basement wall meets the floor (see figure). Find the diameter of the largest water pipe that can be run in the right-angle corner behind the air duct.

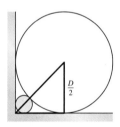

Writing the Equation of a Circle **In Exercises 41–48, write the standard form of the equation of the circle and sketch its graph.**

41. $x^2 + y^2 - 2x + 6y + 6 = 0$

42. $x^2 + y^2 - 2x + 6y - 15 = 0$

43. $x^2 + y^2 + 4x - 8y + 19 = 0$

44. $x^2 + y^2 - 4x + 2y + 3 = 0$

45. $3x^2 + 3y^2 - 6y - 1 = 0$

46. $2x^2 + 2y^2 - 2x - 2y - 3 = 0$

47. $144x^2 + 144y^2 + 96x - 720y + 835 = 0$

48. $16x^2 + 16y^2 + 16x + 40y - 7 = 0$

Graphing a Circle **In Exercises 49 and 50, use a graphing utility to graph the equation. Use a *square* setting. (*Hint:* It may be necessary to solve the equation for y and graph the resulting two equations.)**

49. $4x^2 + 4y^2 - 4x + 24y - 63 = 0$

50. $x^2 + y^2 - 8x - 6y - 11 = 0$

Sketching a Graph of an Inequality **In Exercises 51 and 52, sketch the set of all points satisfying the inequality. Use a graphing utility to verify your result.**

51. $x^2 + y^2 - 4x + 2y + 1 \le 0$

52. $x^2 + y^2 - 10x - 2y + 25 > 0$

53. **Proof** Prove that
$$\left(\frac{2x_1 + x_2}{3}, \frac{2y_1 + y_2}{3} \right)$$
is one of the points of trisection of the line segment joining (x_1, y_1) and (x_2, y_2). Find the midpoint of the line segment joining
$$\left(\frac{2x_1 + x_2}{3}, \frac{2y_1 + y_2}{3} \right)$$
and (x_2, y_2) to find the second point of trisection.

54. **Finding Points of Trisection** Use the results of Exercise 53 to find the points of trisection of the line segment joining each pair of points.
    (a) $(1, -2), (4, 1)$
    (b) $(-2, -3), (0, 0)$

True or False? **In Exercises 55–58, determine whether the statement is true or false. If it is false, explain why or give an example that shows it is false.**

55. If $ab < 0$, then the point (a, b) lies in either Quadrant II or Quadrant IV.

56. The distance between the points $(a + b, a)$ and $(a - b, a)$ is $2b$.

57. If the distance between two points is zero, then the two points must coincide.

58. If $ab = 0$, then the point (a, b) lies on the x-axis or on the y-axis.

Proof **In Exercises 59–62, prove the statement.**

59. The line segments joining the midpoints of the opposite sides of a quadrilateral bisect each other.

60. The perpendicular bisector of a chord of a circle passes through the center of the circle.

61. An angle inscribed in a semicircle is a right angle.

62. The midpoint of the line segment joining the points (x_1, y_1) and (x_2, y_2) is
$$\left(\frac{x_1 + x_2}{2}, \frac{y_1 + y_2}{2} \right).$$

C.3 Review of Trigonometric Functions

▶ Describe angles and use degree measure.
▶ Use radian measure.
▶ Understand the definitions of the six trigonometric functions.
▶ Evaluate trigonometric functions.
▶ Solve trigonometric equations.
▶ Graph trigonometric functions.

Angles and Degree Measure

An **angle** has three parts: an **initial ray** (or side), a **terminal ray,** and a **vertex** (the point of intersection of the two rays), as shown in Figure C.24(a). An angle is in **standard position** when its initial ray coincides with the positive x-axis and its vertex is at the origin, as shown in Figure C.24(b).

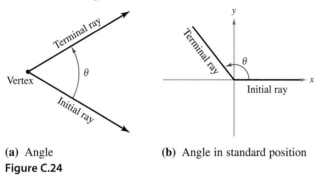

(a) Angle   (b) Angle in standard position
Figure C.24

It is assumed that you are familiar with the degree measure of an angle.* It is common practice to use θ (the lowercase Greek letter theta) to represent both an angle and its measure. Angles between $0°$ and $90°$ are **acute,** and angles between $90°$ and $180°$ are **obtuse.**

Positive angles are measured *counterclockwise*, and negative angles are measured *clockwise*. For instance, Figure C.25 shows an angle whose measure is $-45°$. You cannot assign a measure to an angle by simply knowing where its initial and terminal rays are located. To measure an angle, you must also know how the terminal ray was revolved. For example, Figure C.25 shows that the angle measuring $-45°$ has the same terminal ray as the angle measuring $315°$. Such angles are **coterminal.** In general, if θ is any angle, then $\theta + n(360°)$, where n is a nonzero integer, is coterminal with θ.

An angle that is larger than $360°$ is one whose terminal ray has been revolved more than one full revolution counterclockwise, as shown in Figure C.26(a). You can form an angle whose measure is less than $-360°$ by revolving a terminal ray more than one full revolution clockwise, as shown in Figure C.26(b).

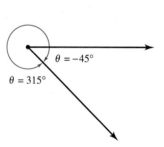

Coterminal angles
Figure C.25

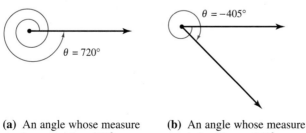

(a) An angle whose measure
    is greater than $360°$
(b) An angle whose measure
    is less than $-360°$
Figure C.26

---

*For a more complete review of trigonometry, see *Precalculus with Limits,* 4th edition or *Precalculus with Limits: A Graphing Approach,* 8th edition, both by Ron Larson and Paul Battaglia (Boston, Massachusetts: Cengage, 2018 and 2020, respectively).

Radian Measure

To assign a radian measure to an angle θ, consider θ to be a central angle of a circle of radius 1, as shown in Figure C.27. The **radian measure** of θ is then defined to be the length of the arc of the sector. Because the circumference of a circle is $2\pi r$, the circumference of a **unit circle** (of radius 1) is 2π. This implies that the radian measure of an angle measuring $360°$ is 2π. In other words, $360° = 2\pi$ radians.

Using radian measure for θ, the **length** s of a circular arc of radius r is $s = r\theta$, as shown in Figure C.28.

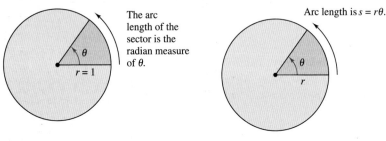

Unit circle	Circle of radius r
Figure C.27	**Figure C.28**

You should know the conversions of the common angles shown in Figure C.29. For other angles, use the fact that $180°$ is equal to π radians.

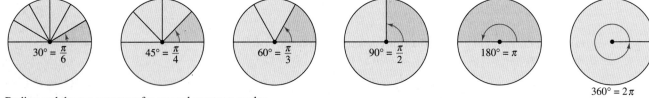

Radian and degree measures for several common angles
Figure C.29

EXAMPLE 1   Conversions Between Degrees and Radians

a. $40° = (40 \text{ deg})\left(\dfrac{\pi \text{ rad}}{180 \text{ deg}}\right) = \dfrac{2\pi}{9}$ radian

b. $540° = (540 \text{ deg})\left(\dfrac{\pi \text{ rad}}{180 \text{ deg}}\right) = 3\pi$ radians

c. $-270° = (-270 \text{ deg})\left(\dfrac{\pi \text{ rad}}{180 \text{ deg}}\right) = -\dfrac{3\pi}{2}$ radians

d. $-\dfrac{\pi}{2}$ radians $= \left(-\dfrac{\pi}{2} \text{ rad}\right)\left(\dfrac{180 \text{ deg}}{\pi \text{ rad}}\right) = -90°$

e. 2 radians $= (2 \text{ rad})\left(\dfrac{180 \text{ deg}}{\pi \text{ rad}}\right) = \left(\dfrac{360}{\pi}\right)° \approx 114.59°$

f. $\dfrac{9\pi}{2}$ radians $= \left(\dfrac{9\pi}{2} \text{ rad}\right)\left(\dfrac{180 \text{ deg}}{\pi \text{ rad}}\right) = 810°$

Technology

Most graphing utilities have both *degree* and *radian* modes. You should learn how to use your graphing utility to convert from degrees to radians, and vice versa. Use a graphing utility to verify the results of Example 1.

The Trigonometric Functions

There are two common approaches to the study of trigonometry. In one, the trigonometric functions are defined as ratios of two sides of a right triangle. In the other, these functions are defined in terms of a point on the terminal side of an angle in standard position. The six trigonometric functions, **sine, cosine, tangent, cotangent, secant,** and **cosecant** (abbreviated as sin, cos, tan, cot, sec, and csc, respectively), are defined below from both viewpoints.

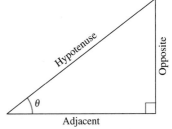

Sides of a right triangle
Figure C.30

Definition of the Six Trigonometric Functions

Right triangle definitions, where $0 < \theta < \dfrac{\pi}{2}$ *(See Figure C.30.)*

$$\sin \theta = \frac{\text{opposite}}{\text{hypotenuse}} \qquad \cos \theta = \frac{\text{adjacent}}{\text{hypotenuse}} \qquad \tan \theta = \frac{\text{opposite}}{\text{adjacent}}$$

$$\csc \theta = \frac{\text{hypotenuse}}{\text{opposite}} \qquad \sec \theta = \frac{\text{hypotenuse}}{\text{adjacent}} \qquad \cot \theta = \frac{\text{adjacent}}{\text{opposite}}$$

Circular function definitions, where θ *is any angle (See Figure C.31.)*

$$\sin \theta = \frac{y}{r} \qquad \cos \theta = \frac{x}{r} \qquad \tan \theta = \frac{y}{x}, \quad x \neq 0$$

$$\csc \theta = \frac{r}{y}, \quad y \neq 0 \qquad \sec \theta = \frac{r}{x}, \quad x \neq 0 \qquad \cot \theta = \frac{x}{y}, \quad y \neq 0$$

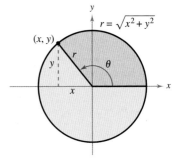

An angle in standard position
Figure C.31

The trigonometric identities listed below are direct consequences of the definitions. [Note that ϕ is the lowercase Greek letter phi, and $\sin^2 \theta$ is used to represent $(\sin \theta)^2$.]

Trigonometric Identities

Pythagorean Identities

$$\sin^2 \theta + \cos^2 \theta = 1$$
$$1 + \tan^2 \theta = \sec^2 \theta$$
$$1 + \cot^2 \theta = \csc^2 \theta$$

Even/Odd Identities

$$\sin(-\theta) = -\sin \theta$$
$$\cos(-\theta) = \cos \theta$$
$$\tan(-\theta) = -\tan \theta$$

$$\csc(-\theta) = -\csc \theta$$
$$\sec(-\theta) = \sec \theta$$
$$\cot(-\theta) = -\cot \theta$$

Sum and Difference Formulas

$$\sin(\theta \pm \phi) = \sin \theta \cos \phi \pm \cos \theta \sin \phi$$
$$\cos(\theta \pm \phi) = \cos \theta \cos \phi \mp \sin \theta \sin \phi$$
$$\tan(\theta \pm \phi) = \frac{\tan \theta \pm \tan \phi}{1 \mp \tan \theta \tan \phi}$$

Power-Reducing Formulas

$$\sin^2 \theta = \frac{1 - \cos 2\theta}{2}$$

$$\cos^2 \theta = \frac{1 + \cos 2\theta}{2}$$

$$\tan^2 \theta = \frac{1 - \cos 2\theta}{1 + \cos 2\theta}$$

Double-Angle Formulas

$$\sin 2\theta = 2 \sin \theta \cos \theta$$
$$\cos 2\theta = 2 \cos^2 \theta - 1$$
$$= 1 - 2 \sin^2 \theta$$
$$= \cos^2 \theta - \sin^2 \theta$$
$$\tan 2\theta = \frac{2 \tan \theta}{1 - \tan^2 \theta}$$

Law of Cosines

$$a^2 = b^2 + c^2 - 2bc \cos A$$

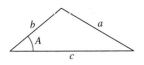

Reciprocal Identities

$$\csc \theta = \frac{1}{\sin \theta}$$

$$\sec \theta = \frac{1}{\cos \theta}$$

$$\cot \theta = \frac{1}{\tan \theta}$$

Quotient Identities

$$\tan \theta = \frac{\sin \theta}{\cos \theta}$$

$$\cot \theta = \frac{\cos \theta}{\sin \theta}$$

Evaluating Trigonometric Functions

There are two ways to evaluate trigonometric functions: (1) decimal approximations with a graphing utility and (2) exact evaluations using trigonometric identities and formulas from geometry. When using a graphing utility to evaluate a trigonometric function, remember to set the graphing utility to the appropriate mode—*degree* mode or *radian* mode.

EXAMPLE 2   Exact Evaluation of Trigonometric Functions

Evaluate the sine, cosine, and tangent of $\dfrac{\pi}{3}$.

Solution

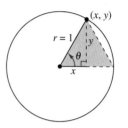

Because $60° = \pi/3$ radians, you can draw an equilateral triangle with sides of length 1 and θ as one of its angles, as shown in Figure C.32. Because the altitude of this triangle bisects its base, you know that $x = \frac{1}{2}$. Using the Pythagorean Theorem, you obtain

$$y = \sqrt{r^2 - x^2} = \sqrt{1 - \left(\frac{1}{2}\right)^2} = \sqrt{\frac{3}{4}} = \frac{\sqrt{3}}{2}.$$

Now, knowing the values of x, y, and r, you can write the following.

$$\sin \frac{\pi}{3} = \frac{y}{r} = \frac{\sqrt{3}/2}{1} = \frac{\sqrt{3}}{2}$$

$$\cos \frac{\pi}{3} = \frac{x}{r} = \frac{1/2}{1} = \frac{1}{2}$$

$$\tan \frac{\pi}{3} = \frac{y}{x} = \frac{\sqrt{3}/2}{1/2} = \sqrt{3}$$

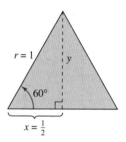

Figure C.32

Note that all angles in this text are measured in radians unless stated otherwise. For example, when sin 3 is written, the sine of 3 radians is meant, and when sin 3° is written, the sine of 3 degrees is meant.

The degree and radian measures of several common angles are shown in the table below, along with the corresponding values of the sine, cosine, and tangent. (See Figure C.33.)

Common First-Quadrant Angles

Degrees	0	30°	45°	60°	90°
Radians	0	$\dfrac{\pi}{6}$	$\dfrac{\pi}{4}$	$\dfrac{\pi}{3}$	$\dfrac{\pi}{2}$
$\sin \theta$	0	$\dfrac{1}{2}$	$\dfrac{\sqrt{2}}{2}$	$\dfrac{\sqrt{3}}{2}$	1
$\cos \theta$	1	$\dfrac{\sqrt{3}}{2}$	$\dfrac{\sqrt{2}}{2}$	$\dfrac{1}{2}$	0
$\tan \theta$	0	$\dfrac{\sqrt{3}}{3}$	1	$\sqrt{3}$	Undefined

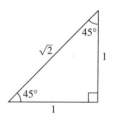

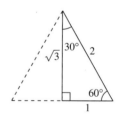

Common angles
Figure C.33

The quadrant signs for the sine, cosine, and tangent functions are shown in Figure C.34. To extend the use of the table on the preceding page to angles in quadrants other than the first quadrant, you can use the concept of a **reference angle** (see Figure C.35), with the appropriate quadrant sign. For instance, the reference angle for $3\pi/4$ is $\pi/4$, and because the sine is positive in Quadrant II, you can write

$$\sin \frac{3\pi}{4} = \sin \frac{\pi}{4} = \frac{\sqrt{2}}{2}.$$

Similarly, because the reference angle for $330°$ is $30°$, and the tangent is negative in Quadrant IV, you can write

$$\tan 330° = -\tan 30° = -\frac{\sqrt{3}}{3}.$$

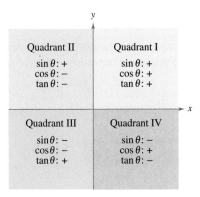

Quadrant signs for trigonometric functions

Figure C.34

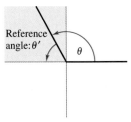

Quadrant II
$\theta' = \pi - \theta$ (radians)
$\theta' = 180° - \theta$ (degrees)

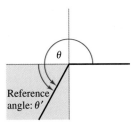

Quadrant III
$\theta' = \theta - \pi$ (radians)
$\theta' = \theta - 180°$ (degrees)

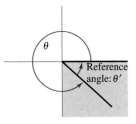

Quadrant IV
$\theta' = 2\pi - \theta$ (radians)
$\theta' = 360° - \theta$ (degrees)

Figure C.35

EXAMPLE 3   Trigonometric Identities and Calculators

Evaluate each trigonometric expression.

a. $\sin\left(-\dfrac{\pi}{3}\right)$ **b.** $\sec 60°$ **c.** $\cos(1.2)$

Solution

a. Using the odd identity $\sin(-\theta) = -\sin \theta$, you can write

$$\sin\left(-\frac{\pi}{3}\right) = -\sin \frac{\pi}{3} = -\frac{\sqrt{3}}{2}.$$

b. Using the reciprocal identity $\sec \theta = 1/\cos \theta$, you can write

$$\sec 60° = \frac{1}{\cos 60°} = \frac{1}{1/2} = 2.$$

c. Using a calculator, you obtain

$$\cos(1.2) \approx 0.3624.$$

Remember that 1.2 is given in *radian* measure. Consequently, your calculator must be set in *radian* mode.

Solving Trigonometric Equations

How would you solve the equation $\sin \theta = 0$? You know that $\theta = 0$ is one solution, but this is not the only solution. Any one of the following values of θ is also a solution.

$$\ldots, -3\pi, -2\pi, -\pi, 0, \pi, 2\pi, 3\pi, \ldots$$

You can write this infinite solution set as $\{n\pi: n \text{ is an integer}\}$.

EXAMPLE 4   Solving a Trigonometric Equation

Solve the equation

$$\sin \theta = -\frac{\sqrt{3}}{2}.$$

Solution

To solve the equation, you should consider that the sine function is negative in Quadrants III and IV and that

$$\sin \frac{\pi}{3} = \frac{\sqrt{3}}{2}.$$

So, you are seeking values of θ in the third and fourth quadrants that have a reference angle of $\pi/3$. In the interval $[0, 2\pi]$, the two angles fitting these criteria are

$$\theta = \pi + \frac{\pi}{3} = \frac{4\pi}{3} \quad \text{and} \quad \theta = 2\pi - \frac{\pi}{3} = \frac{5\pi}{3}.$$

By adding integer multiples of 2π to each of these solutions, you obtain the following general solution.

$$\theta = \frac{4\pi}{3} + 2n\pi \quad \text{or} \quad \theta = \frac{5\pi}{3} + 2n\pi, \quad \text{where } n \text{ is an integer.}$$

See Figure C.36.

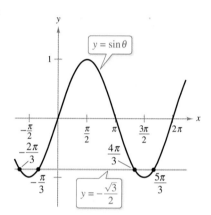

Solution points of $\sin \theta = -\dfrac{\sqrt{3}}{2}$

Figure C.36

EXAMPLE 5   Solving a Trigonometric Equation

Solve $\cos 2\theta = 2 - 3 \sin \theta$, where $0 \le \theta \le 2\pi$.

Solution

Using the double-angle formula $\cos 2\theta = 1 - 2 \sin^2 \theta$, you can rewrite the equation as follows.

$\cos 2\theta = 2 - 3 \sin \theta$	Write original equation.
$1 - 2 \sin^2 \theta = 2 - 3 \sin \theta$	Double-angle formula
$0 = 2 \sin^2 \theta - 3 \sin \theta + 1$	Quadratic form
$0 = (2 \sin \theta - 1)(\sin \theta - 1)$	Factor.

If $2 \sin \theta - 1 = 0$, then $\sin \theta = 1/2$ and $\theta = \pi/6$ or $\theta = 5\pi/6$. If $\sin \theta - 1 = 0$, then $\sin \theta = 1$ and $\theta = \pi/2$. So, for $0 \le \theta \le 2\pi$, the solutions are

$$\theta = \frac{\pi}{6}, \quad \frac{5\pi}{6}, \quad \text{or} \quad \frac{\pi}{2}.$$

Graphs of Trigonometric Functions

A function f is **periodic** when there exists a positive real number p such that $f(x + p) = f(x)$ for all x in the domain of f. The least such positive value of p is the **period** of f. The sine, cosine, secant, and cosecant functions each have a period of 2π, and the other two trigonometric functions, tangent and cotangent, have a period of π, as shown in Figure C.37.

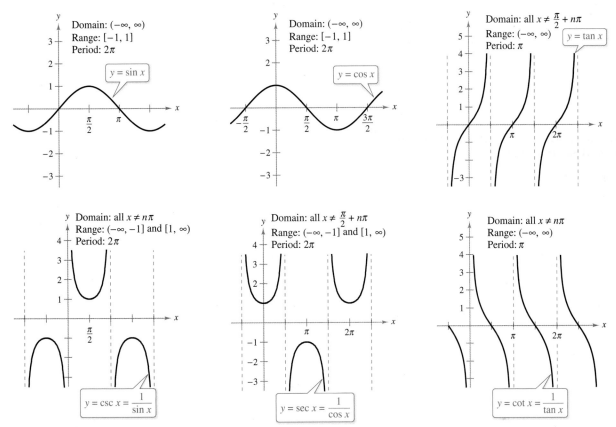

The graphs of the six trigonometric functions

Figure C.37

Note in Figure C.37 that the maximum value of $\sin x$ and $\cos x$ is 1 and the minimum value is -1. The graphs of the functions $y = a \sin bx$ and $y = a \cos bx$ oscillate between $-a$ and a, and so have an **amplitude** of $|a|$. Furthermore, because $bx = 0$ when $x = 0$ and $bx = 2\pi$ when $x = 2\pi/b$, it follows that the functions $y = a \sin bx$ and $y = a \cos bx$ each have a period of $2\pi/|b|$. The table below summarizes the amplitudes and periods of some types of trigonometric functions.

Technology

To use a graphing utility to produce the graphs shown in Figure C.37, make sure you set the graphing utility to *radian* mode.

Function	Period	Amplitude
$y = a \sin bx$ or $y = a \cos bx$	$\dfrac{2\pi}{\|b\|}$	$\|a\|$
$y = a \tan bx$ or $y = a \cot bx$	$\dfrac{\pi}{\|b\|}$	Not applicable
$y = a \sec bx$ or $y = a \csc bx$	$\dfrac{2\pi}{\|b\|}$	Not applicable

EXAMPLE 6   Sketching the Graph of a Trigonometric Function

Sketch the graph of $f(x) = 3 \cos 2x$.

Solution

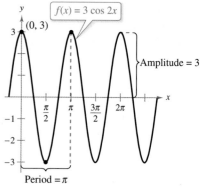

The graph of $f(x) = 3 \cos 2x$ has an amplitude of 3 and a period of $2\pi/2 = \pi$. Using the basic shape of the graph of the cosine function, sketch one period of the function on the interval $[0, \pi]$, using the following pattern.

Maximum: $(0, 3)$

Minimum: $\left(\dfrac{\pi}{2}, -3\right)$

Maximum: $(\pi, 3)$

By continuing this pattern, you can sketch several cycles of the graph, as shown in Figure C.38.

Figure C.38

Horizontal shifts, vertical shifts, and reflections can be applied to the graphs of trigonometric functions, as illustrated in Example 7.

EXAMPLE 7   Shifts of Graphs of Trigonometric Functions

Sketch the graph of each function.

a. $f(x) = \sin\left(x + \dfrac{\pi}{2}\right)$

b. $f(x) = 2 + \sin x$

c. $f(x) = 2 + \sin\left(x - \dfrac{\pi}{4}\right)$

Solution

a. To sketch the graph of $f(x) = \sin(x + \pi/2)$, shift the graph of $y = \sin x$ to the left $\pi/2$ units, as shown in Figure C.39(a).

b. To sketch the graph of $f(x) = 2 + \sin x$, shift the graph of $y = \sin x$ upward two units, as shown in Figure C.39(b).

c. To sketch the graph of $f(x) = 2 + \sin(x - \pi/4)$, shift the graph of $y = \sin x$ upward two units and to the right $\pi/4$ units, as shown in Figure C.39(c).

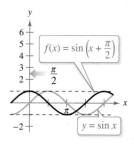 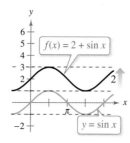 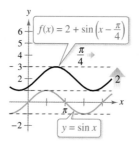

(a) Horizontal shift to the left   **(b)** Vertical shift upward   **(c)** Horizontal and vertical shifts

Transformations of the graph of $y = \sin x$

Figure C.39

C.3 Exercises

Coterminal Angles in Degrees In Exercises 1 and 2, determine two coterminal angles in degree measure (one positive and one negative) for each angle.

1. (a) $\theta = 36°$

(b) $\theta = -120°$

2. (a) $\theta = 300°$

(b) $\theta = -420°$

Coterminal Angles in Radians In Exercises 3 and 4, determine two coterminal angles in radian measure (one positive and one negative) for each angle.

3. (a) $\theta = \frac{\pi}{9}$

(b) 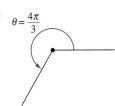 $\theta = \frac{4\pi}{3}$

4. (a) 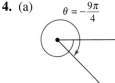 $\theta = -\frac{9\pi}{4}$

(b) 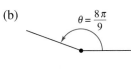 $\theta = \frac{8\pi}{9}$

Degrees to Radians In Exercises 5 and 6, rewrite each angle in radian measure as a multiple of π and as a decimal accurate to three decimal places.

5. (a) $30°$ (b) $150°$ (c) $-135°$ (d) $-36°$

6. (a) $-240°$ (b) $405°$ (c) $-20°$ (d) $144°$

Radians to Degrees In Exercises 7 and 8, rewrite each angle in degree measure.

7. (a) $3\pi/2$ (b) $7\pi/6$ (c) $-7\pi/12$ (d) -2.367

8. (a) $7\pi/3$ (b) $-11\pi/30$ (c) $11\pi/6$ (d) 0.438

9. Completing a Table Let r represent the radius of a circle, θ the central angle (measured in radians), and s the length of the arc subtended by the angle. Use the relationship $s = r\theta$ to complete the table.

r	8 ft	15 in.	85 cm		
s	12 ft			96 in.	8642 mi
θ		1.6	$\frac{3\pi}{4}$	4	$\frac{2\pi}{3}$

10. Angular Speed A car is moving at the rate of 50 miles per hour, and the diameter of its wheels is 2.5 feet.

(a) Find the number of revolutions per minute that the wheels are rotating.

(b) Find the angular speed of the wheels in radians per minute.

Finding the Six Trigonometric Functions In Exercises 11 and 12, determine all six trigonometric functions for the angle θ.

11. (a)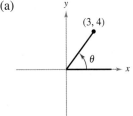

(b)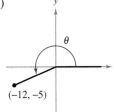

12. (a)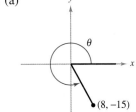

(b)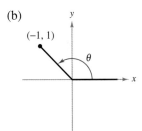

Determining a Quadrant In Exercises 13 and 14, determine the quadrant in which θ lies.

13. (a) $\sin \theta < 0$ and $\cos \theta < 0$

(b) $\sec \theta > 0$ and $\cot \theta < 0$

14. (a) $\sin \theta > 0$ and $\cos \theta < 0$

(b) $\csc \theta < 0$ and $\tan \theta > 0$

Evaluating a Trigonometric Function In Exercises 15–18, evaluate the trigonometric function.

15. $\sin \theta = \frac{1}{2}$

$\cos \theta = $ ▮

16. $\sin \theta = \frac{1}{3}$

$\tan \theta = $ ▮

17. $\cos \theta = \frac{4}{5}$

$\cot \theta = $ ▮

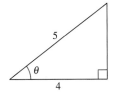

18. $\sec \theta = \frac{13}{5}$

$\csc \theta = $ ▮

Evaluating Trigonometric Functions **In Exercises 19–22, evaluate the sine, cosine, and tangent of each angle *without* using a calculator.**

19. (a) $60°$
    (b) $120°$
    (c) $\dfrac{\pi}{4}$
    (d) $\dfrac{5\pi}{4}$

20. (a) $30°$
    (b) $150°$
    (c) $\dfrac{2\pi}{3}$
    (d) $\dfrac{5\pi}{3}$

21. (a) $225°$
    (b) $-225°$
    (c) 0
    (d) π

22. (a) $90°$
    (b) $630°$
    (c) $\dfrac{11\pi}{6}$
    (d) $-\dfrac{5\pi}{6}$

Evaluating Trigonometric Functions **In Exercises 23–26, use a calculator to evaluate each trigonometric function. Round your answers to four decimal places.**

23. (a) $\sin 10°$
    (b) $\csc 10°$

24. (a) $\cos 200°$
    (b) $\sec 200°$

25. (a) $\tan \dfrac{\pi}{9}$
    (b) $\tan \dfrac{10\pi}{9}$

26. (a) $\cot(1.5)$
    (b) $\cot(1.5 + \pi)$

Solving a Trigonometric Equation **In Exercises 27–30, find two solutions of each equation. Give your answers in radians $(0 \le \theta < 2\pi)$. Do not use a calculator.**

27. (a) $\cos \theta = \dfrac{\sqrt{2}}{2}$
    (b) $\cos \theta = -\dfrac{\sqrt{2}}{2}$

28. (a) $\sin \theta = \dfrac{\sqrt{3}}{2}$
    (b) $\sin \theta = -\dfrac{1}{2}$

29. (a) $\tan \theta = 1$
    (b) $\cot \theta = -\sqrt{3}$

30. (a) $\sec \theta = 2$
    (b) $\sec \theta = -2$

Solving a Trigonometric Equation **In Exercises 31–38, solve the equation for θ $(0 \le \theta < 2\pi)$.**

31. $2 \sin^2 \theta = 1$
32. $\tan^2 \theta = 3$
33. $\tan^2 \theta - \tan \theta = 0$
34. $2 \cos^2 \theta - \cos \theta = 1$
35. $\sec \theta \csc \theta = 2 \csc \theta$
36. $\sin \theta = \cos \theta$
37. $\cos^2 \theta + \sin \theta = 1$
38. $\cos 2\theta + \frac{3}{4} = \cos^2 \theta$

39. **Airplane Ascent** An airplane leaves the runway climbing at an angle of $18°$ with a speed of 275 feet per second (see figure). Find the altitude a of the plane after 1 minute.

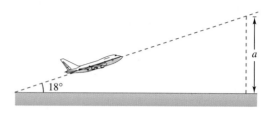

40. **Height of a Mountain** While traveling across flat land, you notice a mountain directly in front of you. Its angle of elevation (to the peak) is $3.5°$. After you drive 13 miles closer to the mountain, the angle of elevation is $9°$. Approximate the height of the mountain.

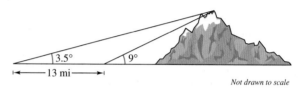

Not drawn to scale

Period and Amplitude **In Exercises 41–44, determine the period and amplitude of each function.**

41. (a) $y = 2 \sin 2x$ (b) $y = \frac{1}{2} \sin \pi x$

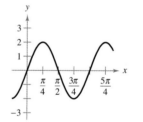
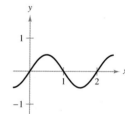

42. (a) $y = \dfrac{3}{2} \cos \dfrac{x}{2}$ (b) $y = -2 \sin \dfrac{x}{3}$

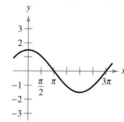
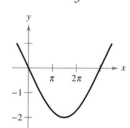

43. $y = 3 \sin 4\pi x$

44. $y = \dfrac{2}{3} \cos \dfrac{\pi x}{10}$

Period **In Exercises 45–48, find the period of the function.**

45. $y = 5 \tan 2x$
46. $y = 7 \cot 2\pi x$
47. $y = \sec 5x$
48. $y = \csc 4x$

Communicating In Exercises 49 and 50, use a graphing utility to graph each function f in the same viewing window for $c = -2$, $c = -1$, $c = 1$, and $c = 2$. Give a written description of the change in the graph caused by changing c.

49. (a) $f(x) = c \sin x$

(b) $f(x) = \cos(cx)$

(c) $f(x) = \cos(\pi x - c)$

50. (a) $f(x) = \sin x + c$

(b) $f(x) = -\sin(2\pi x - c)$

(c) $f(x) = c \cos x$

Sketching the Graph of a Trigonometric Function In Exercises 51–62, sketch the graph of the function.

51. $y = \sin \dfrac{x}{2}$

52. $y = \tan 2x$

53. $y = 2 \tan x$

54. $y = \csc \dfrac{x}{2}$

55. $y = \csc 2\pi x$

56. $y = 2 \cos 2x$

57. $y = 2 \sec 2x$

58. $y = -\sin \dfrac{2\pi x}{3}$

59. $y = \sin(x + \pi)$

60. $y = \cos\left(x - \dfrac{\pi}{3}\right)$

61. $y = 1 + \cos\left(x - \dfrac{\pi}{2}\right)$

62. $y = 1 + \sin\left(x + \dfrac{\pi}{2}\right)$

Graphical Reasoning In Exercises 63 and 64, find a, b, and c such that the graph of the function matches the graph in the figure.

63. $y = a \cos(bx - c)$ **64.** $y = a \sin(bx - c)$

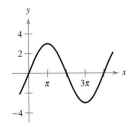

65. Think About It Sketch the graphs of $f(x) = \sin x$, $g(x) = |\sin x|$, and $h(x) = \sin(|x|)$. In general, how are the graphs of $|f(x)|$ and $f(|x|)$ related to the graph of f?

66. Think About It A Ferris wheel has a radius of 50 feet. The model for the height h of the Ferris wheel car is $h = 51 + 50 \sin 8\pi t$, where t is measured in minutes. This model yields a height of 51 feet when $t = 0$. Write a new model so that the height of the car is 1 foot when $t = 0$.

67. Sales The monthly sales S (in thousands of units) of a seasonal product are modeled by

$$S = 58.3 + 32.5 \cos \frac{\pi t}{6}$$

where t is the time (in months), with $t = 1$ corresponding to January. Use a graphing utility to graph the model for S and determine the months when sales exceed 75,000 units.

68. Investigation Two trigonometric functions f and g have a period of 2, and their graphs intersect at $x = 5.35$.

(a) Give one smaller and one larger positive value of x at which the functions have the same value.

(b) Determine one negative value of x at which the graphs intersect.

(c) Is it true that $f(13.35) = g(-4.65)$? Give a reason for your answer.

Pattern Recognition In Exercises 69 and 70, use a graphing utility to compare the graph of f with the given graph. Try to improve the approximation by adding a term to $f(x)$. Use a graphing utility to verify that your new approximation is better than the original. Can you find other terms to add to make the approximation even better? What is the pattern? (In Exercise 69, sine terms can be used to improve the approximation, and in Exercise 70, cosine terms can be used.)

69. $f(x) = \dfrac{4}{\pi}\left(\sin \pi x + \dfrac{1}{3}\sin 3\pi x\right)$

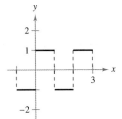

70. $f(x) = \dfrac{1}{2} - \dfrac{4}{\pi^2}\left(\cos \pi x + \dfrac{1}{9}\cos 3\pi x\right)$

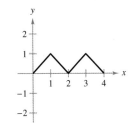

Appendix D: Algebra Review

Chapter P   Algebra Review

Evaluating Algebraic Expressions

Much of the algebra in Chapter P involves evaluating algebraic expressions. To evaluate an algebraic expression, substitute for each variable, then use the *order of operations*.

Order of Operations

1. Perform operations inside grouping symbols or absolute value symbols, starting with the innermost symbol.
2. Evaluate all exponential expressions.
3. Perform all multiplications and divisions from left to right.
4. Perform all additions and subtractions from left to right.

Technology

Most graphing utilities use the same order of operations listed here.

EXAMPLE 1   Evaluating Algebraic Expressions

a. Evaluate $6 - a + 4(3 - b)$ when $a = 5$ and $b = 9$.

$$6 - a + 4(3 - b) = 6 - 5 + 4(3 - 9) \qquad \text{Substitute 5 for } a \text{ and 9 for } b.$$
$$= 6 - 5 + 4(-6) \qquad \text{Subtract inside parentheses.}$$
$$= 6 - 5 + (-24) \qquad \text{Multiply.}$$
$$= 1 + (-24) \qquad \text{Subtract.}$$
$$= -23 \qquad \text{Add.}$$

b. Evaluate $2w^3 + w^2 - 5$ when $w = -3$.

$$2w^3 + w^2 - 5 = 2(-3)^3 + (-3)^2 - 5 \qquad \text{Substitute } -3 \text{ for } w.$$
$$= 2(-27) + 9 - 5 \qquad \text{Evaluate exponential expressions.}$$
$$= -54 + 9 - 5 \qquad \text{Multiply.}$$
$$= -45 - 5 \qquad \text{Add.}$$
$$= -50 \qquad \text{Subtract.}$$

c. Evaluate $x^2 + 8x$ when $x = a - 2$.

$$x^2 + 8x = (a - 2)^2 + 8(a - 2) \qquad \text{Substitute } a - 2 \text{ for } x.$$
$$= a^2 - 4a + 4 + 8(a - 2) \qquad \text{Evaluate exponential expression.}$$
$$= a^2 - 4a + 4 + 8a - 16 \qquad \text{Multiply.}$$
$$= a^2 + 4a - 12 \qquad \text{Simplify.}$$

d. Evaluate $\dfrac{-x^3 + 5x^2 - x}{5}$ when $x = 5b$.

$$\frac{-x^3 + 5x^2 - x}{5} = \frac{-(5b)^3 + 5(5b)^2 - 5b}{5} \qquad \text{Substitute } 5b \text{ for } x.$$
$$= \frac{-125b^3 + 5(25b^2) - 5b}{5} \qquad \text{Evaluate exponential expressions.}$$
$$= \frac{-125b^3 + 125b^2 - 5b}{5} \qquad \text{Multiply.}$$
$$= -25b^3 + 25b^2 - b \qquad \text{Divide.}$$

Solving Quadratic Equations

Recall from algebra that there are several ways to solve quadratic equations, such as taking the square root of each side, factoring, and the Quadratic Formula.

To solve a quadratic equation by taking the square root of each side, you must be able to write the equation in the form $u^2 = d$, where $d > 0$ and u is an algebraic expression [see Example 2(a)].

Before solving a quadratic equation by factoring or the Quadratic Formula, write the equation in general form. A quadratic equation in x is an equation that can be written in the *general form* $ax^2 + bx + c = 0$, where a, b, and c are real numbers, with $a \neq 0$. For a review of factoring, see Example 2(b), the next page, or the algebra page at the end of the text, which also lists the Quadratic Formula [see Example 2(c)].

EXAMPLE 2   Solving Quadratic Equations

Solve each equation.

a. $2x^2 = 10$ **b.** $x^2 - 11 = -3x + 7$ **c.** $2x^2 + 3x = 8$

Solution

a.
$$2x^2 = 10 \qquad \text{Write original equation.}$$
$$x^2 = 5 \qquad \text{Divide each side by 2.}$$
$$x = \pm\sqrt{5} \qquad \text{Take the square root of each side.}$$

b.
$$x^2 - 11 = -3x + 7 \qquad \text{Write original equation.}$$
$$x^2 + 3x - 18 = 0 \qquad \text{Write in general form.}$$
$$(x - 3)(x + 6) = 0 \qquad \text{Factor.}$$
$$x - 3 = 0 \quad\Longrightarrow\quad x = 3 \qquad \text{Set first factor equal to zero.}$$
$$x + 6 = 0 \quad\Longrightarrow\quad x = -6 \qquad \text{Set second factor equal to zero.}$$

c.
$$2x^2 + 3x = 8 \qquad \text{Write original equation.}$$
$$2x^2 + 3x - 8 = 0 \qquad \text{Write in general form.}$$
$$x = \frac{-b \pm \sqrt{b^2 - 4ac}}{2a} \qquad \text{Quadratic Formula}$$
$$x = \frac{-3 \pm \sqrt{3^2 - 4(2)(-8)}}{2(2)} \qquad \text{Substitute 2 for } a, \text{ 3 for } b, \text{ and } -8 \text{ for } c.$$
$$x = \frac{-3 \pm \sqrt{73}}{4} \qquad \text{Simplify.}$$

The solutions are $x = \dfrac{-3 + \sqrt{73}}{4} \approx 1.386$ and $x = \dfrac{-3 - \sqrt{73}}{4} \approx -2.886$. ∎

> **Remark**
>
> When using the Quadratic Formula, remember that *before* applying the formula, you must first write the quadratic equation in general form. You can solve any quadratic equation using the Quadratic Formula.

Rewriting Equations

To rewrite an equation in two variables, solve for one variable in terms of the other variable.

EXAMPLE 3   Rewriting an Equation

Solve $4x - 3y = 15$ for y.

Solution
$$4x - 3y = 15 \qquad \text{Write original equation.}$$
$$-3y = 15 - 4x \qquad \text{Subtract } 4x \text{ from each side.}$$
$$y = -5 + \frac{4}{3}x \qquad \text{Divide each side by } -3. \qquad ∎$$

Chapter 1   Algebra Review

Factoring Expressions

Some of the algebra in Chapter 1 involves factoring different types of polynomials. Remember that a factorable polynomial is *completely factored* when each of its factors is prime. (If a polynomial does not factor using integer coefficients, then it is *prime* or *irreducible over the integers*. For example, the polynomial $x^2 - 3$ is irreducible over the integers.) Below are some of the special forms that can help you factor efficiently.

Factoring Special Polynomial Forms

Difference of Two Squares: $u^2 - v^2 = (u + v)(u - v)$

Perfect Square Trinomial: $u^2 + 2uv + v^2 = (u + v)^2$

   $u^2 - 2uv + v^2 = (u - v)^2$

Sum of Two Cubes: $u^3 + v^3 = (u + v)(u^2 - uv + v^2)$

Difference of Two Cubes: $u^3 - v^3 = (u - v)(u^2 + uv + v^2)$

EXAMPLE 1   Completely Factoring Expressions

Completely factor each expression.

a. $45x^2 - 20$

b. $-4y^2 + 48y - 144$

c. $27p^3 - 1$

d. $3z^2 + 19z - 14$

e. $16w^3 + 250$

Solution

a. $45x^2 - 20 = 5(9x^2 - 4)$ 5 is a common factor.

    $= 5[(3x)^2 - 2^2]$ Write as difference of two squares.

    $= 5(3x + 2)(3x - 2)$ Factor.

b. $-4y^2 + 48y - 144 = -4(y^2 - 12y + 36)$ -4 is a common factor.

    $= -4[y^2 - 2(y)(6) + 6^2]$ Rewrite in $u^2 - 2uv + v^2$ form.

    $= -4(y - 6)^2$ Factor.

> **Remark**
>
> The first step in completely factoring a polynomial is to remove (factor out) any common factors.

c. $27p^3 - 1 = (3p)^3 - 1^3$ Write as difference of two cubes.

    $= (3p - 1)(9p^2 + 3p + 1)$ Factor.

d. To factor the trinomial $3z^2 + 19z - 14$, list the possible factorizations.

   $(3z - 1)(z + 14)$ $(3z + 1)(z - 14)$

   $(3z - 2)(z + 7)$ $(3z + 2)(z - 7)$

   $(3z - 7)(z + 2)$ $(3z + 7)(z - 2)$

   $(3z - 14)(z + 1)$ $(3z + 14)(z - 1)$

Determine which factorization has outer (O) and inner (I) products that add up to $19z$.

   $3z^2 + 19z - 14 = (3z - 2)(z + 7)$ $O + I = 21z - 2z = 19z$

> **Remark**
>
> Factoring some trinomials can involve trial and error. Once you find the factored form, however, you can check your answer by multiplying the factors to see whether you obtain the original trinomial.

e. $16w^3 + 250 = 2(8w^3 + 125)$ 2 is a common factor.

    $= 2[(2w)^3 + 5^3]$ Write as sum of two cubes.

    $= 2(2w + 5)(4w^2 - 10w + 25)$ Factor.

Rationalization Techniques

When working with quotients involving radicals, it is often convenient to move the radical expression from the denominator to the numerator, or vice versa. To do this, multiply the fraction by an appropriate form of 1 to eliminate the radical from the denominator or numerator. For example, you can move $\sqrt{2}$ from the denominator to the numerator in the quotient below by multiplying by $\sqrt{2}/\sqrt{2}$.

Radical in Denominator   *Rationalize*   *Radical in Numerator*

$$\frac{1}{\sqrt{2}} \quad\Longrightarrow\quad \frac{1}{\sqrt{2}}\left(\frac{\sqrt{2}}{\sqrt{2}}\right) \quad\Longrightarrow\quad \frac{\sqrt{2}}{2}$$

This process is called **rationalizing the denominator**. A similar process is used to **rationalize the numerator**.

Rationalizing Techniques

1. When the denominator is $\sqrt{a}$, multiply by $\dfrac{\sqrt{a}}{\sqrt{a}}$.

2. When the denominator is $\sqrt{a} - \sqrt{b}$, multiply by $\dfrac{\sqrt{a} + \sqrt{b}}{\sqrt{a} + \sqrt{b}}$.

3. When the denominator is $\sqrt{a} + \sqrt{b}$, multiply by $\dfrac{\sqrt{a} - \sqrt{b}}{\sqrt{a} - \sqrt{b}}$.

The same guidelines apply to rationalizing numerators.

Remark
Remember that $\sqrt{a} + \sqrt{b}$ and $\sqrt{a} - \sqrt{b}$ are called *conjugates*.

EXAMPLE 2   Rationalizing Denominators and Numerators

Rationalize the denominator or numerator.

a. $\dfrac{3}{\sqrt{12}}$ **b.** $\dfrac{\sqrt{x + 1}}{2}$

c. $\dfrac{1}{\sqrt{5} + \sqrt{2}}$ **d.** $\dfrac{1}{\sqrt{x} - \sqrt{x + 1}}$

Solution

a. $\dfrac{3}{\sqrt{12}} = \dfrac{3}{2\sqrt{3}} = \dfrac{3}{2\sqrt{3}}\left(\dfrac{\sqrt{3}}{\sqrt{3}}\right) = \dfrac{3\sqrt{3}}{2(3)} = \dfrac{\sqrt{3}}{2}$

b. $\dfrac{\sqrt{x + 1}}{2} = \dfrac{\sqrt{x + 1}}{2}\left(\dfrac{\sqrt{x + 1}}{\sqrt{x + 1}}\right) = \dfrac{x + 1}{2\sqrt{x + 1}}$

c. $\dfrac{1}{\sqrt{5} + \sqrt{2}} = \dfrac{1}{\sqrt{5} + \sqrt{2}}\left(\dfrac{\sqrt{5} - \sqrt{2}}{\sqrt{5} - \sqrt{2}}\right)$

$\qquad = \dfrac{\sqrt{5} - \sqrt{2}}{5 - 2}$

$\qquad = \dfrac{\sqrt{5} - \sqrt{2}}{3}$

d. $\dfrac{1}{\sqrt{x} - \sqrt{x + 1}} = \dfrac{1}{\sqrt{x} - \sqrt{x + 1}}\left(\dfrac{\sqrt{x} + \sqrt{x + 1}}{\sqrt{x} + \sqrt{x + 1}}\right)$

$\qquad = \dfrac{\sqrt{x} + \sqrt{x + 1}}{x - (x + 1)}$

$\qquad = -\sqrt{x} - \sqrt{x + 1}$

Chapter 2   Algebra Review

Simplifying Algebraic Expressions

To be successful in using derivatives, you must be good at simplifying algebraic expressions. Here are some helpful simplification techniques.

1. Combine *like terms*. This may involve expanding an expression by multiplying factors.

2. Divide out *common factors* in the numerator and denominator of an expression.

3. Factor an expression.

4. Rationalize a denominator.

5. Add, subtract, multiply, or divide fractions.

Technology

Symbolic algebra systems can simplify algebraic expressions. If you have access to such a system, try using it to simplify the expressions in this Algebra Review.

EXAMPLE 1   Simplifying Fractional Expressions

a. $\dfrac{[3(x + \Delta x) + 5] - (3x + 5)}{\Delta x} = \dfrac{3x + 3\Delta x + 5 - 3x - 5}{\Delta x}$ Multiply factors and remove parentheses.

$\qquad\qquad\qquad = \dfrac{3\Delta x}{\Delta x}$ Combine like terms.

$\qquad\qquad\qquad = 3, \quad \Delta x \neq 0$ Divide out common factor.

b. $\dfrac{(x + \Delta x)^2 - x^2}{\Delta x} = \dfrac{x^2 + 2x(\Delta x) + (\Delta x)^2 - x^2}{\Delta x}$ Expand terms.

$\qquad\qquad\qquad = \dfrac{2x(\Delta x) + (\Delta x)^2}{\Delta x}$ Combine like terms.

$\qquad\qquad\qquad = \dfrac{\Delta x(2x + \Delta x)}{\Delta x}$ Factor.

$\qquad\qquad\qquad = 2x + \Delta x, \quad \Delta x \neq 0$ Divide out common factor.

c. $\dfrac{(x^2 - 1)(-2 - 2x) - (3 - 2x - x^2)(2)}{(x^2 - 1)^2}$

$\qquad = \dfrac{(-2x^2 - 2x^3 + 2 + 2x) - (6 - 4x - 2x^2)}{(x^2 - 1)^2}$ Multiply factors.

$\qquad = \dfrac{-2x^2 - 2x^3 + 2 + 2x - 6 + 4x + 2x^2}{(x^2 - 1)^2}$ Remove parentheses.

$\qquad = \dfrac{-2x^3 + 6x - 4}{(x^2 - 1)^2}$ Combine like terms.

d. $2\left(\dfrac{2x + 1}{3x}\right)\left[\dfrac{3x(2) - (2x + 1)(3)}{(3x)^2}\right]$

$\qquad = 2\left(\dfrac{2x + 1}{3x}\right)\left[\dfrac{6x - (6x + 3)}{(3x)^2}\right]$ Multiply factors.

$\qquad = \dfrac{2(2x + 1)(6x - 6x - 3)}{(3x)^3}$ Multiply fractions and remove parentheses.

$\qquad = \dfrac{2(2x + 1)(-3)}{3(9)x^3}$ Combine like terms and factor.

$\qquad = \dfrac{-2(2x + 1)}{9x^3}$ Divide out common factor.

EXAMPLE 2   **Simplifying Expressions with Powers**

Simplify each expression.

a. $(2x + 1)^2(6x + 1) + (3x^2 + x)(2)(2x + 1)(2)$

b. $(-1)(3x^2 - 2x)^{-2}(6x - 2)$

c. $(x)\left(\frac{1}{2}\right)(2x + 3)^{-1/2}(2) + (2x + 3)^{1/2}(1)$

d. $\dfrac{x^2\left(\frac{1}{2}\right)(x^2 + 1)^{-1/2}(2x) - (x^2 + 1)^{1/2}(2x)}{x^4}$

Solution

a. $(2x + 1)^2(6x + 1) + (3x^2 + x)(2)(2x + 1)(2)$

$= (2x + 1)[(2x + 1)(6x + 1) + (3x^2 + x)(2)(2)]$ ⟶ Factor.

$= (2x + 1)[12x^2 + 8x + 1 + (12x^2 + 4x)]$ ⟶ Multiply factors.

$= (2x + 1)(12x^2 + 8x + 1 + 12x^2 + 4x)$ ⟶ Remove parentheses.

$= (2x + 1)(24x^2 + 12x + 1)$ ⟶ Combine like terms.

b. $(-1)(3x^2 - 2x)^{-2}(6x - 2)$

$= \dfrac{(-1)(6x - 2)}{(3x^2 - 2x)^2}$ ⟶ Rewrite as a fraction.

$= \dfrac{(-1)(2)(3x - 1)}{(3x^2 - 2x)^2}$ ⟶ Factor.

$= \dfrac{-2(3x - 1)}{(3x^2 - 2x)^2}$ ⟶ Multiply factors.

c. $(x)\left(\frac{1}{2}\right)(2x + 3)^{-1/2}(2) + (2x + 3)^{1/2}(1)$

$= (2x + 3)^{-1/2}[x + (2x + 3)]$ ⟶ Factor.

$= \dfrac{x + 2x + 3}{(2x + 3)^{1/2}}$ ⟶ Rewrite as a fraction.

$= \dfrac{3(x + 1)}{(2x + 3)^{1/2}}$ ⟶ Combine like terms and factor.

d. $\dfrac{x^2\left(\frac{1}{2}\right)(x^2 + 1)^{-1/2}(2x) - (x^2 + 1)^{1/2}(2x)}{x^4}$

$= \dfrac{(x^3)(x^2 + 1)^{-1/2} - (x^2 + 1)^{1/2}(2x)}{x^4}$ ⟶ Multiply factors.

$= \dfrac{(x^2 + 1)^{-1/2}(x)[x^2 - (x^2 + 1)(2)]}{x^4}$ ⟶ Factor.

$= \dfrac{x[x^2 - (2x^2 + 2)]}{(x^2 + 1)^{1/2}x^4}$ ⟶ Write with positive exponents.

$= \dfrac{x^2 - 2x^2 - 2}{(x^2 + 1)^{1/2}x^3}$ ⟶ Divide out common factor and remove parentheses.

$= \dfrac{-x^2 - 2}{(x^2 + 1)^{1/2}x^3}$ ⟶ Combine like terms.

> **Remark**
>
> All of the expressions in this Algebra Review are derivatives. Can you see what the original function is for each expression? Explain your reasoning.

Chapter 3   Algebra Review

Solving Equations

Much of the algebra in Chapter 3 involves simplifying algebraic expressions (see pages A38 and A39) and solving algebraic equations. On these two pages, you can review some of the more complicated techniques for solving equations.

When solving an equation, remember that your basic goal is to isolate the variable on one side of the equation. To do this, you use inverse operations. For instance,

- to isolate x in the equation $x - 2 = 0$, you add 2 to each side of the equation, because *addition* is the inverse operation of *subtraction*.
- to isolate x in the equation $\sqrt{x} = 2$, you square each side of the equation, because *squaring* is the inverse operation of *taking the square root*.

EXAMPLE 1   Solving Equations

Solve each equation.

a. $12x^2(x - 1) = 0$

b. $\frac{10}{3}x^{1/3}(x^{1/3} - 2) = 0$

c. $12x(x - 2) = 0$

d. $15x^2(1 - x^2) = 0$

e. $2x(2x^2 - 3) = 0$

Solution

a. $12x^2(x - 1) = 0$ Example 2, page 215

$\quad 12x^2 = 0 \implies x = 0$ Set first factor equal to 0.

$\quad x - 1 = 0 \implies x = 1$ Set second factor equal to 0.

b. $\frac{10}{3}x^{1/3}(x^{1/3} - 2) = 0$ Example 4, page 248

$\quad \frac{10}{3}x^{1/3} = 0 \implies x = 0$ Set first factor equal to 0.

$\quad x^{1/3} - 2 = 0 \implies x = 8$ Set second factor equal to 0.

c. $12x(x - 2) = 0$ Example 3, page 240

$\quad 12x = 0 \implies x = 0$ Set first factor equal to 0.

$\quad x - 2 = 0 \implies x = 2$ Set second factor equal to 0.

d. $15x^2(1 - x^2) = 0$ Example 4, page 241

$\quad 15x^2 = 0 \implies x = 0$ Set first factor equal to 0.

$\quad 1 - x^2 = 0 \implies x = \pm 1$ Set second factor equal to 0.

e. $2x(2x^2 - 3) = 0$ Example 2, page 259

$\quad 2x = 0 \implies x = 0$ Set first factor equal to 0.

$\quad 2x^2 - 3 = 0 \implies x = \pm\sqrt{\dfrac{3}{2}}$ Set second factor equal to 0.

> **Remark**
>
> To isolate x in the equation $x^{1/3} - 2 = 0$, first add 2 to each side. Then, in the equation $x^{1/3} = 2$, cube each side of the equation because *cubing* is the inverse operation of *taking the cube root*.

EXAMPLE 2 **Solving Equations**

Solve each equation.

a. $2\left(\dfrac{x^{1/3} - 1}{x^{1/3}}\right) = 0$

b. $\dfrac{4}{x^2} = 1$

c. $2 - \dfrac{72}{x^2} = 0$

d. $\dfrac{2(\pi + 4)x - 8}{\pi} = 0$

Solution

a. $2\left(\dfrac{x^{1/3} - 1}{x^{1/3}}\right) = 0$ Example 3, page 216

$\dfrac{x^{1/3} - 1}{x^{1/3}} = 0$ Divide each side by 2.

$x^{1/3} - 1 = 0, \ x \neq 0$ Multiply each side by $x^{1/3}$.

$x^{1/3} = 1$ Add 1 to each side.

$x = 1$ Cube each side.

b. $\dfrac{4}{x^2} = 1$ Example 3, page 223

$4 = x^2, \ x \neq 0$ Multiply each side by x^2.

$\pm 2 = x$ Take the square root of each side.

c. $2 - \dfrac{72}{x^2} = 0$ Example 3, page 259

$-\dfrac{72}{x^2} = -2$ Subtract 2 from each side.

$36 = x^2, \ x \neq 0$ Simplify.

$\pm 6 = x$ Take the square root of each side.

d. $\dfrac{2(\pi + 4)x - 8}{\pi} = 0$ Example 5, page 261

$2(\pi + 4)x - 8 = 0$ Multiply each side by π.

$2(\pi + 4)x = 8$ Add 8 to each side.

$x = \dfrac{8}{2(\pi + 4)}$ Divide each side by $2(\pi + 4)$.

$x = \dfrac{4}{\pi + 4}$ Simplify.

$x \approx 0.56$ Use a calculator.

> **Remark**
>
> Because this is a cube root instead of a square root, you cube each side of the equation, because *cubing* is the inverse operation of *taking the cube root*.

Chapter 4   Algebra Review

Simplifying and "Unsimplifying" Expressions

Integration techniques involve many different algebraic skills. It is often helpful to write an expression in its simplest form, but in Chapter 4, you have seen that the reverse is often true. That is, to fit an integrand to an integration formula, it often helps to "unsimplify" the expression. To do this, you use the same algebraic rules, but your goal is different. Study the examples in this Algebra Review. Be sure you understand the algebra used in each step.

EXAMPLE 1   Simplifying Algebraic Expressions

Simplify each expression.

a. $\dfrac{8}{n^3}\left\{ \dfrac{n(n+1)(2n+1)}{6} - 2\left[\dfrac{n(n+1)}{2} \right] + n \right\}$ Example 4, page 295

b. $\dfrac{1}{n^3}\left\{ 2\left[\dfrac{n(n+1)(2n+1)}{6} \right] - \dfrac{n(n+1)}{2} \right\}$ Example 1, page 302

c. $\dfrac{6}{n}\left\{ -2n + \dfrac{3}{n}\left[\dfrac{n(n+1)}{2} \right] \right\}$ Example 2, page 305

Solution

a. $\dfrac{8}{n^3}\left\{ \dfrac{n(n+1)(2n+1)}{6} - 2\left[\dfrac{n(n+1)}{2} \right] + n \right\} = \dfrac{8}{n^3}\left\{ \dfrac{n(2n^2+3n+1)}{6} - 2\left[\dfrac{n^2+n}{2} \right] + n \right\}$

$$= \dfrac{8}{n^3}\left\{ \dfrac{2n^3+3n^2+n}{6} - n^2 - n + n \right\}$$

$$= \dfrac{8}{n^3}\left(\dfrac{2n^3+3n^2+n-6n^2}{6} \right)$$

$$= \dfrac{8}{n^3}\left(\dfrac{2n^3-3n^2+n}{6} \right)$$

$$= \dfrac{4}{3n^3}(2n^3-3n^2+n)$$

b. $\dfrac{1}{n^3}\left\{ 2\left[\dfrac{n(n+1)(2n+1)}{6} \right] - \dfrac{n(n+1)}{2} \right\} = \dfrac{1}{n^3}\left[2\left(\dfrac{2n^3+3n^2+n}{6} \right) - \dfrac{n^2+n}{2} \right]$

$$= \dfrac{1}{n^3}\left(\dfrac{4n^3+6n^2+2n}{6} - \dfrac{3n^2+3n}{6} \right)$$

$$= \dfrac{1}{n^3}\left(\dfrac{4n^3+3n^2-n}{6} \right)$$

$$= \dfrac{4n^3+3n^2-n}{6n^3}$$

c. $\dfrac{6}{n}\left\{ -2n + \dfrac{3}{n}\left[\dfrac{n(n+1)}{2} \right] \right\} = \dfrac{6}{n}\left[-2n + \dfrac{3}{n}\left(\dfrac{n^2+n}{2} \right) \right]$

$$= \dfrac{6}{n}\left(-2n + \dfrac{3n^2+3n}{2n} \right)$$

$$= \dfrac{6}{n}\left(-2n + \dfrac{3}{2}n + \dfrac{3}{2} \right)$$

$$= -12 + 9 + \dfrac{9}{n}$$

| EXAMPLE 2 | Rewriting Algebraic Expressions |

Rewrite each algebraic expression as indicated in the example.

a. $\dfrac{x+1}{\sqrt{x}}$

Example 5, page 284

b. $\dfrac{x^3 + 3}{x^2}$

Example 7(c), page 284

c. $\sqrt[3]{x}(x-4)$

Example 7(d), page 284

Solution

a. $\dfrac{x+1}{\sqrt{x}} = \dfrac{x}{\sqrt{x}} + \dfrac{1}{\sqrt{x}}$

Rewrite as two fractions.

$\qquad = \dfrac{x^1}{x^{1/2}} + \dfrac{1}{x^{1/2}}$

Rewrite with rational exponents.

$\qquad = x^{1-1/2} + x^{-1/2}$

Properties of exponents

$\qquad = x^{1/2} + x^{-1/2}$

Simplify exponent.

b. $\dfrac{x^3 + 3}{x^2} = \dfrac{x^3}{x^2} + \dfrac{3}{x^2}$

Rewrite as two fractions.

$\qquad = x + 3x^{-2}$

Properties of exponents

c. $\sqrt[3]{x}(x-4) = x^{1/3}(x-4)$

Rewrite with rational exponents.

$\qquad = x^{1/3+1} - 4x^{1/3}$

Properties of exponents and Distributive Property

$\qquad = x^{4/3} - 4x^{1/3}$

Simplify.

| EXAMPLE 3 | Solving a Rational Inequality |

Solve the rational inequality

$$\frac{1}{12n^2} \le \frac{1}{100}$$

Example 9, page 311

for n, where n is a positive integer.

Solution

$\dfrac{1}{12n^2} \le \dfrac{1}{100}$

Write original inequality.

$\dfrac{100}{12n^2} \le 1$

Multiply each side by 100.

$\dfrac{100}{12} \le n^2$

Multiply each side by n^2 $(n > 0)$.

$\dfrac{25}{3} \le n^2$

Simplify.

$\sqrt{\dfrac{25}{3}} \le n$

Take positive square root of each side $(n > 0)$.

Because n is a positive integer and $\sqrt{25/3} \approx 2.89$, n must be 3 or more. You can check this result using a graphing utility. Let $y_1 = 1/(12x^2)$ and $y_2 = 1/100$. Then use the *intersect* feature (see figure) to determine that $x \approx 2.89$. So, the solution found algebraically is correct.

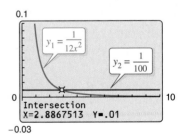

Chapter 5 Algebra Review

Solving Equations

To solve for the constants in the general solution of a differential equation, you will need to use algebraic skills. For instance, to solve for C in the differential equation

$$y = 200e^{-Ce^{-kt}}$$

you must know how to solve an exponential equation, as shown in Example 3.

EXAMPLE 1   Solving for C

Solve the exponential equation $N = 650 - Ce^{-kt}$ for C when $N = 300$ and $t = 0$.

Solution

$N = 650 - Ce^{-kt}$	Example 4, page 389
$300 = 650 - Ce^{-k(0)}$	Substitute 300 for N and 0 for t.
$300 = 650 - C$	$e^{-k(0)} = e^0 = 1$
$350 = C$	Solve for C.

EXAMPLE 2   Solving for C

Solve the exponential equation $y = 1 - Ce^{-kt}$ for C when $y = 0$ and $t = 0$.

Solution

$y = 1 - Ce^{-kt}$	Example 5, page 390
$0 = 1 - Ce^{-k(0)}$	Substitute 0 for y and 0 for t.
$0 = 1 - C$	$e^{-k(0)} = e^0 = 1$
$C = 1$	Add C to each side.

EXAMPLE 3   Solving for C

Solve the exponential equation $y = 200e^{-Ce^{-kt}}$ for C when $y = 20$ and $t = 0$.

Solution

$y = 200e^{-Ce^{-kt}}$	Example 7, page 392
$20 = 200e^{-Ce^{-k(0)}}$	Substitute 20 for y and 0 for t.
$20 = 200e^{-C}$	$e^{-k(0)} = e^0 = 1$
$\dfrac{1}{10} = e^{-C}$	Divide each side by 200.
$\dfrac{1}{10} = \dfrac{1}{e^C}$	Definition of negative exponent
$e^C = 10$	Cross-multiply.
$\ln e^C = \ln 10$	Take natural log of each side.
$C = \ln 10$	Apply the property $\ln e^a = a$.
$C \approx 2.3026$	Approximate.

EXAMPLE 4   Solving for k

Solve each exponential equation for k using the given values.

a. $N = 650 - 350e^{-kt}$ when $N = 500$ and $t = 2$ Example 4, page 389

b. $y = 1 - e^{-kt}$ when $y = 0.5$ and $t = 1$ Example 5, page 390

c. $y = 200e^{-2.3026e^{-kt}}$ when $y = 40$ and $t = 3$ Example 7, page 392

Solution

a.

$N = 650 - 350e^{-kt}$	Write original equation.
$500 = 650 - 350e^{-k(2)}$	Substitute 500 for N and 2 for t.
$-150 = -350e^{-2k}$	Subtract 650 from each side.
$\dfrac{3}{7} = e^{-2k}$	Divide each side by -350.
$\ln \dfrac{3}{7} = \ln e^{-2k}$	Take natural log of each side.
$\ln \dfrac{3}{7} = -2k$	Apply the property $\ln e^a = a$.
$-\dfrac{1}{2}\ln \dfrac{3}{7} = k$	Multiply each side by $-\frac{1}{2}$.
$0.4236 \approx k$	Approximate.

b.

$y = 1 - e^{-kt}$	Write original equation.
$0.5 = 1 - e^{-k(1)}$	Substitute 0.5 for y and 1 for t.
$-0.5 = -e^{-k}$	Subtract 1 from each side.
$0.5 = e^{-k}$	Divide each side by -1.
$\ln 0.5 = \ln e^{-k}$	Take natural log of each side.
$\ln 0.5 = -k$	Apply the property $\ln e^a = a$.
$-\ln 0.5 = k$	Multiply each side by -1.
$0.693 \approx k$	Approximate.

c.

$y = 200e^{-2.3026e^{-kt}}$	Write original equation.
$40 = 200e^{-2.3026e^{-k(3)}}$	Substitute 40 for y and 3 for t.
$\dfrac{1}{5} = e^{-2.3026e^{-3k}}$	Divide each side by 200.
$\ln \dfrac{1}{5} = -2.3026e^{-3k}$	Take natural log of each side.
$\dfrac{\ln(1/5)}{-2.3026} = e^{-3k}$	Divide each side by -2.3026.
$\ln \left[\dfrac{\ln(1/5)}{-2.3026} \right] = \ln e^{-3k}$	Take natural log of each side.
$\ln \left[\dfrac{\ln(1/5)}{-2.3026} \right] = -3k$	Apply the property $\ln e^a = a$.
$-\dfrac{1}{3}\ln \left[\dfrac{\ln(1/5)}{-2.3026} \right] = k$	Multiply each side by $-\frac{1}{3}$.
$0.1194 \approx k$	Approximate.

Chapter 6   Algebra Review

EXAMPLE 1   Solving an Equation

Solve $3x^3 - x^2 - 10x = -x^2 + 2$.

Solution

$3x^3 - x^2 - 10x = -x^2 + 2x$	Example 4, page 413
$3x^3 - 12x = 0$	Write in general form.
$3x(x^2 - 4) = 0$	Factor out $3x$.
$3x(x - 2)(x + 2) = 0$	Factor.
$3x = 0 \implies x = 0$	Set first factor equal to 0.
$x - 2 = 0 \implies x = 2$	Set second factor equal to 0.
$x + 2 = 0 \implies x = -2$	Set third factor equal to 0.

Remark

A polynomial equation of degree n is in general form when all nonzero terms are arranged in descending order by power on one side of the equation and 0 is on the other side.

EXAMPLE 2   Finding Points of Intersection

Find all points of intersection of the graphs of

$$x = 3 - y^2 \quad \text{and} \quad x = y + 1. \qquad \text{Example 5, page 414}$$

Solution

Both equations are already solved for x, so equate x-values and solve for y.

$3 - y^2 = y + 1$	Equate x-values.
$0 = y^2 + y - 2$	Write in general form.
$0 = (y - 1)(y + 2)$	Factor.
$y - 1 = 0 \implies y = 1$	Set first factor equal to 0.
$y + 2 = 0 \implies y = -2$	Set second factor equal to 0.

The corresponding values of x are found by substituting $y = 1$ and $y = -2$ into either of the original equations. Doing this produces two points of intersection, $(2, 1)$ and $(-1, -2)$.

EXAMPLE 3   Simplifying Expressions

a.
$[R(y)]^2 - [r(y)]^2 = 1^2 - \left(\sqrt{y - 1}\right)^2$	Example 4, page 424
$= 1 - (y - 1)$	Evaluate exponential expressions.
$= 2 - y$	Simplify.

b.
$[R(x)]^2 - [r(x)]^2 = \left(\sqrt{25 - x^2}\right)^2 - (3)^2$	Example 5, page 425
$= 25 - x^2 - 9$	Evaluate exponential expressions.
$= 16 - x^2$	Simplify.

EXAMPLE 4   Simplifying Expressions

Simplify each expression.

a. $1 + \left[\dfrac{1}{2}\left(x^2 - \dfrac{1}{x^2}\right)\right]^2$ Example 2, page 442

b. $1 + \left[\dfrac{3}{2}(y - 1)^{1/2}\right]^2$ Example 3, page 442

Solution

a. $1 + \left[\dfrac{1}{2}\left(x^2 - \dfrac{1}{x^2}\right)\right]^2 = 1 + \left(\dfrac{1}{2}x^2 - \dfrac{1}{2x^2}\right)^2$ Distributive Property

$\qquad\qquad = 1 + \dfrac{1}{4}x^4 - \dfrac{2x^2}{4x^2} + \dfrac{1}{4x^4}$ Evaluate exponential expression.

$\qquad\qquad = 1 + \dfrac{1}{4}x^4 - \dfrac{1}{2} + \dfrac{1}{4x^4}$ Divide out common factor.

$\qquad\qquad = \dfrac{1}{4}x^4 + \dfrac{1}{2} + \dfrac{1}{4x^4}$ Combine like terms.

$\qquad\qquad = \dfrac{1}{4}\left(x^4 + 2 + \dfrac{1}{x^4}\right)$ Factor.

b. $1 + \left[\dfrac{3}{2}(y - 1)^{1/2}\right]^2 = 1 + \dfrac{9}{4}(y - 1)$ Evaluate exponential expression.

$\qquad\qquad = 1 + \dfrac{9}{4}y - \dfrac{9}{4}$ Distributive Property

$\qquad\qquad = \dfrac{9}{4}y - \dfrac{5}{4}$ Combine like terms.

EXAMPLE 5   Using Similar Triangles

Use similar triangles and the figure to show that

$$b' = \dfrac{b}{h}(h - y).$$ Example 7, page 426

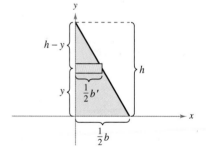

Solution

In the figure at the right, note that the triangle with base $\frac{1}{2}b'$ and height $h - y$ is similar to the triangle with base $\frac{1}{2}b$ and height h. So, their corresponding side lengths are proportional.

$\dfrac{\frac{1}{2}b'}{\frac{1}{2}b} = \dfrac{h - y}{h}$ Write a proportion.

$\dfrac{b'}{b} = \dfrac{h - y}{h}$ Simplify.

$b' = b\left(\dfrac{h - y}{h}\right)$ Multiply each side by b.

$b' = \dfrac{b}{h}(h - y)$ Rewrite.

Chapter 7   Algebra Review

EXAMPLE 1   Using Long Division

Use long division to rewrite the expression $\dfrac{4x^2}{x^2 + 9}$.   Example 1(c), page 456

Solution

Divide $4x^2$ by $x^2 + 9$.

$$
\begin{array}{r}
4 \\
x^2 + 9 \overline{)\, 4x^2 + 0x + 0 } \\
\underline{4x^2 + 36} \\
-36
\end{array}
$$

Insert $0x$ and 0 for the missing terms.

Multiply 4 by $x^2 + 9$.

Subtract.

So, $\dfrac{4x^2}{x^2 + 9} = 4 + \dfrac{-36}{x^2 + 9}$.

EXAMPLE 2   Simplifying Expressions

Simplify each expression.

a. $-\sqrt{3}\left[(0 - \pi) - \left(-\dfrac{1}{\sqrt{3}} - \dfrac{5\pi}{6}\right)\right]$ Page 485

b. $\ln\left|\dfrac{x - 2}{2} + \dfrac{\sqrt{(x - 2)^2 - 4}}{2}\right| + C$ Example 5, page 486

Solution

a. $-\sqrt{3}\left[\left(0 - \pi - \left(-\dfrac{1}{\sqrt{3}} - \dfrac{5\pi}{6}\right)\right)\right]$ Rewrite.

$\quad = -\sqrt{3}\left(-\pi + \dfrac{1}{\sqrt{3}} + \dfrac{5\pi}{6}\right)$ Rewrite.

$\quad = \sqrt{3}\pi - 1 - \dfrac{5\sqrt{3}\pi}{6}$ Distributive Property

$\quad = -1 + \dfrac{6\sqrt{3}\pi}{6} - \dfrac{5\sqrt{3}\pi}{6}$ Rewrite using a common denominator.

$\quad = -1 + \dfrac{\sqrt{3}\pi}{6}$ Simplify.

b. $\ln\left|\dfrac{x - 2}{2} + \dfrac{\sqrt{(x - 2)^2 - 4}}{2}\right| + C$

$\quad = \ln\left|\dfrac{x - 2 + \sqrt{(x - 2)^2 - 4}}{2}\right| + C$ Rewrite.

$\quad = \ln\left|x - 2 + \sqrt{(x - 2)^2 - 4}\right| - \ln 2 + C$ Property of logarithms

$\quad = \ln\left|x - 2 + \sqrt{x^2 - 4x}\right| - \ln 2 + C$ Rewrite radicand.

$\quad = \ln\left|x - 2 + \sqrt{x^2 - 4x}\right| + C_1$ $C_1 = C - \ln 2$

EXAMPLE 3   Solving for a Variable

Solve $\dfrac{x^2}{a^2} + \dfrac{y^2}{b^2} = 1$ for y when $x > 0$ and $y > 0$.

Solution

$$\dfrac{x^2}{a^2} + \dfrac{y^2}{b^2} = 1 \qquad\qquad \text{Example 7, page 487}$$

$$\dfrac{y^2}{b^2} = 1 - \dfrac{x^2}{a^2} \qquad\qquad \text{Subtract } \dfrac{x^2}{a^2} \text{ from each side.}$$

$$y^2 = b^2\!\left(1 - \dfrac{x^2}{a^2}\right) \qquad\qquad \text{Multiply each side by } b^2.$$

$$y = \sqrt{b^2\!\left(1 - \dfrac{x^2}{a^2}\right)} \qquad\qquad \begin{array}{l}\text{Take positive square root}\\ \text{of each side } (y > 0).\end{array}$$

$$y = b\sqrt{1 - \dfrac{x^2}{a^2}} \qquad\qquad \text{Simplify.}$$

$$y = b\sqrt{1 - \left(\dfrac{x}{a}\right)^2} \qquad\qquad \text{Property of exponents}$$

EXAMPLE 4   Rewriting an Integral

Show that the integral for the total area A of the ellipse in Example 7 on page 487 can be rewritten as shown.

$$A = 4\int_0^a b\sqrt{1 - \left(\dfrac{x}{a}\right)^2}\, dx$$

$$= \dfrac{4b}{a}\int_0^a \sqrt{a^2 - x^2}\, dx$$

Solution

$$A = 4\int_0^a b\sqrt{1 - \left(\dfrac{x}{a}\right)^2}\, dx \qquad\qquad \text{Example 7, page 487}$$

$$= 4\int_0^a b\sqrt{1 - \dfrac{x^2}{a^2}}\, dx \qquad\qquad \text{Property of exponents}$$

$$= 4\int_0^a b\sqrt{\dfrac{a^2 - x^2}{a^2}}\, dx \qquad\qquad \text{Rewrite using a common denominator.}$$

$$= 4\int_0^a \dfrac{b}{a}\sqrt{a^2 - x^2}\, dx \qquad\qquad \text{Simplify.}$$

$$= \dfrac{4b}{a}\int_0^a \sqrt{a^2 - x^2}\, dx \qquad\qquad \text{Constant Multiple Rule}$$

EXAMPLE 5   Evaluating an Expression

Find $\displaystyle\lim_{b\to\infty}\,(-e^{-b} + 1).$ $\qquad\qquad$ Example 2(a), page 518

Solution

$$\lim_{b\to\infty}\,(-e^{-b} + 1) = \lim_{b\to\infty}\,(-e^{-b}) + \lim_{b\to\infty} 1 \qquad\qquad \text{Property of limits}$$

$$= \lim_{b\to\infty}\left(-\dfrac{1}{e^{b}}\right) + \lim_{b\to\infty} 1 \qquad\qquad \text{Property of exponents}$$

$$= 0 + 1 \qquad\qquad \text{Evaluate limits.}$$

$$= 1 \qquad\qquad \text{Simplify.}$$

Chapter 8   Algebra Review

EXAMPLE 1   Simplifying Factorial Expressions

Simplify each expression.

a. $\dfrac{8!}{2! \cdot 6!}$ **b.** $\dfrac{2! \cdot 6!}{3! \cdot 5!}$ **c.** $\dfrac{n!}{(n-1)!}$

d. $\dfrac{(2n+2)!}{(2n+4)!}$ **e.** $\dfrac{x^{n+1}}{(n+1)!} \div \dfrac{x^n}{n!}$ **f.** $\dfrac{2^{n+1}x^{n+1}}{(n+1)!} \div \dfrac{2^n x^n}{n!}$

Solution

a. $\dfrac{8!}{2! \cdot 6!} = \dfrac{1 \cdot 2 \cdot 3 \cdot 4 \cdot 5 \cdot 6 \cdot 7 \cdot 8}{1 \cdot 2 \cdot 1 \cdot 2 \cdot 3 \cdot 4 \cdot 5 \cdot 6}$ Factor.

$= \dfrac{7 \cdot 8}{1 \cdot 2}$ Divide out common factors.

$= \dfrac{56}{2}$ Multiply.

$= 28$ Divide.

b. $\dfrac{2! \cdot 6!}{3! \cdot 5!} = \dfrac{1 \cdot 2 \cdot 1 \cdot 2 \cdot 3 \cdot 4 \cdot 5 \cdot 6}{1 \cdot 2 \cdot 3 \cdot 1 \cdot 2 \cdot 3 \cdot 4 \cdot 5}$ Factor.

$= \dfrac{6}{3}$ Divide out common factors.

$= 2$ Divide.

c. $\dfrac{n!}{(n-1)!} = \dfrac{1 \cdot 2 \cdot 3 \cdots (n-1) \cdot n}{1 \cdot 2 \cdot 3 \cdots (n-1)}$ Factor.

$= n$ Divide out common factors.

d. $\dfrac{(2n+2)!}{(2n+4)!} = \dfrac{(2n+2)!}{(2n+2)!(2n+3)(2n+4)}$ Factor.

$= \dfrac{1}{(2n+3)(2n+4)}$ Divide out common factors.

e. $\dfrac{x^{n+1}}{(n+1)!} \div \dfrac{x^n}{n!} = \dfrac{x^{n+1}}{(n+1)!} \cdot \dfrac{n!}{x^n}$ Multiply by reciprocal.

$= \dfrac{x \cdot x^n}{n!(n+1)} \cdot \dfrac{n!}{x^n}$ Factor.

$= \dfrac{x}{n+1}$ Divide out common factors.

f. $\dfrac{2^{n+1}x^{n+1}}{(n+1)!} \div \dfrac{2^n x^n}{n!} = \dfrac{2^{n+1}x^{n+1}}{(n+1)!} \cdot \dfrac{n!}{2^n x^n}$ Multiply by reciprocal.

$= \dfrac{2 \cdot 2^n \cdot x \cdot x^n}{n!(n+1)} \cdot \dfrac{n!}{2^n x^n}$ Factor.

$= \dfrac{2x}{n+1}$ Divide out common factors.

EXAMPLE 2   Partial Fraction Decomposition

Write the partial fraction decomposition of each expression.

a. $\dfrac{2}{4n^2 - 1}$ **b.** $\dfrac{3x - 1}{x^2 - 1}$

Solution

a. Because $4n^2 - 1 = (2n - 1)(2n + 1)$, you should include one partial fraction for each factor and write

$$\frac{2}{4n^2 - 1} = \frac{A}{2n - 1} + \frac{B}{2n + 1}.$$ Example 2, page 547

Multiplying by the least common denominator $(2n - 1)(2n + 1)$ yields the basic equation

$$2 = A(2n + 1) + B(2n - 1).$$ Basic equation

To solve for A, let $n = \frac{1}{2}$.

$$2 = A\left[2\left(\tfrac{1}{2}\right) + 1\right] + B\left[2\left(\tfrac{1}{2}\right) - 1\right]$$ Let $n = \frac{1}{2}$ in basic equation.

$$2 = A(2) + B(0)$$ Simplify.

$$1 = A$$ Solve for A.

To solve B, let $n = -\frac{1}{2}$.

$$2 = A\left[2\left(-\tfrac{1}{2}\right) + 1\right] + B\left[2\left(-\tfrac{1}{2}\right) - 1\right]$$ Let $n = -\frac{1}{2}$ in basic equation.

$$2 = A(0) + B(-2)$$ Simplify.

$$-1 = B$$ Solve for B.

So, the decomposition is $\dfrac{2}{4n^2 - 1} = \dfrac{1}{2n - 1} - \dfrac{1}{2n + 1}$.

b. Because $x^2 - 1 = (x + 1)(x - 1)$, you should include one partial fraction for each factor and write

$$\frac{3x - 1}{x^2 - 1} = \frac{A}{x + 1} + \frac{B}{x - 1}.$$ Example 3, page 609

Multiplying by the least common denominator $(x + 1)(x - 1)$ yields the basic equation

$$3x - 1 = A(x - 1) + B(x + 1).$$ Basic equation

To solve for A, let $x = -1$.

$$3(-1) - 1 = A(-1 - 1) + B(-1 + 1)$$ Let $x = -1$ in basic equation.

$$-3 - 1 = A(-2) + B(0)$$ Simplify.

$$2 = A$$ Solve for A.

To solve for B, let $x = 1$.

$$3(1) - 1 = A(1 - 1) + B(1 + 1)$$ Let $x = 1$ in basic equation.

$$3 - 1 = A(0) + B(2)$$ Simplify.

$$1 = B$$ Solve for B.

So, the decomposition is $\dfrac{3x - 1}{x^2 - 1} = \dfrac{2}{x + 1} + \dfrac{1}{x - 1}$.

Chapter 9 Algebra Review

EXAMPLE 1 Rewriting an Integral

Show that the integral for the circumference C of the ellipse in Example 5 on page 638 can be rewritten as shown.

$$C = 4\int_0^{\pi/2} \sqrt{a^2 - (a^2 - b^2)\sin^2 \theta} \, d\theta$$

$$= 4a\int_0^{\pi/2} \sqrt{1 - e^2 \sin^2 \theta} \, d\theta$$

Solution

For an ellipse, $e = c/a$ and $c^2 = a^2 - b^2$. So,

$$e^2 = \frac{a^2 - b^2}{a^2}$$

which implies that $a^2 - b^2 = a^2 e^2$, and you can rewrite the integral as

$$C = 4\int_0^{\pi/2} \sqrt{a^2 - (a^2 - b^2)\sin^2 \theta} \, d\theta \qquad \text{Example 5, page 638}$$

$$= 4\int_0^{\pi/2} \sqrt{a^2 - a^2 e^2 \sin^2 \theta} \, d\theta \qquad a^2 - b^2 = a^2 e^2$$

$$= 4\int_0^{\pi/2} \sqrt{a^2(1 - e^2 \sin^2 \theta)} \, d\theta \qquad \text{Factor.}$$

$$= 4\int_0^{\pi/2} a\sqrt{1 - e^2 \sin^2 \theta} \, d\theta \qquad \text{Simplify.}$$

$$= 4a\int_0^{\pi/2} \sqrt{1 - e^2 \sin^2 \theta} \, d\theta. \qquad \text{Constant Multiple Rule}$$

EXAMPLE 2 Simplifying an Expression

Simplify the expression $y = \dfrac{t}{t + 1}$, where $t = \dfrac{1 - x^2}{x^2}$.

Solution

$$y = \frac{t}{t + 1} \qquad \text{Example 2, page 648}$$

$$y = \frac{\dfrac{1 - x^2}{x^2}}{\dfrac{1 - x^2}{x^2} + 1} \qquad \text{Substitute } (1 - x^2)/x^2 \text{ for } t.$$

$$y = \frac{\dfrac{1 - x^2}{x^2}}{\dfrac{1 - x^2 + x^2}{x^2}} \qquad \text{Write denominator using LCD.}$$

$$y = \frac{\dfrac{1 - x^2}{x^2}}{\dfrac{1}{x^2}} \qquad \text{Simplify denominator.}$$

$$y = \frac{1 - x^2}{x^2} \cdot \frac{x^2}{1} \qquad \text{Invert divisor and multiply.}$$

$$y = 1 - x^2 \qquad \text{Simplify.}$$

EXAMPLE 3   Finding Values of *t*

The graph of $x = 2t - \pi \sin t$ and $y = 2 - \pi \cos t$ crosses itself at the point $(0, 2)$, as shown in the figure at the right. At what value(s) of *t* does the graph cross itself? (See Example 3, page 657.)

Solution

Begin by solving for *t* in the equation for *y* when $y = 2$.

$$y = 2 - \pi \cos t \qquad \text{Write equation for } y.$$
$$2 = 2 - \pi \cos t \qquad \text{Substitute 2 for } y.$$
$$0 = -\pi \cos t \qquad \text{Subtract 2 from each side.}$$
$$0 = \cos t \qquad \text{Divide each side by } -\pi.$$

The general solution is

$$t = \frac{\pi}{2} + n\pi$$

where *n* is an integer. Because of the difficulty in solving for *t* in the equation for *x*, you can use the *table* feature of a graphing utility. Set the graphing utility in *parametric* mode and look for values of *x* and *y* where $(x, y) = (0, 2)$, as shown below. Note that the table starts at $-7\pi/2 \approx -11$ and increments the value of *t* by π.

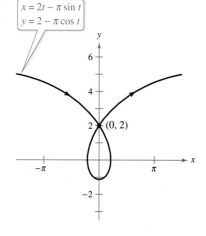

$(x, y) = (0, 2)$ when $t \approx -1.571 \approx -\pi/2$

$(x, y) = (0, 2)$ when $t \approx 1.571 \approx \pi/2$

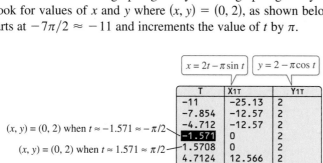

So, the graph crosses itself when $t = \pm\pi/2$.

EXAMPLE 4   Finding an Angle

Find the angle θ in Quadrant II that has a reference angle of $\theta' = 67.4°$. (See Example 4, page 685.) For a review of reference angles, see Appendix C.3.

Solution

Because the angle lies in Quadrant II, use the formula $\theta' = 180° - \theta$.

$$\theta' = 180° - \theta \qquad \text{Quadrant II reference angle formula}$$
$$67.4° = 180° - \theta \qquad \text{Substitute 67.4° for } \theta'.$$
$$-112.6° = -\theta \qquad \text{Subtract 180° from each side.}$$
$$112.6° = \theta \qquad \text{Divide each side by } -1.$$

So, the angle is $\theta = 112.6°$, as shown in the figure.

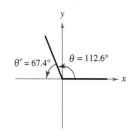

Answers to Odd-Numbered Exercises and Exams

Chapter P

Section P.1 *(page 10)*

1. b   **2.** d   **3.** a   **4.** c

5. 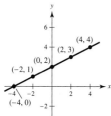   **7.**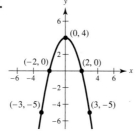

9. 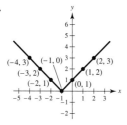   **11.**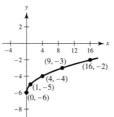

13. 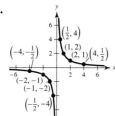   **15.**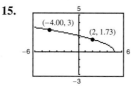

17. $(0, -3), \left(\frac{3}{4}, 0\right)$ **19.** $(0, -2), (-2, 0), (1, 0)$

21. $(0, 0), (4, 0), (-4, 0)$ **23.** $(0, 2), (4, 0)$ **25.** $(0, 0)$

27. y-axis symmetry   **29.** x-axis symmetry

31. Origin symmetry   **33.** No symmetry

35. Origin symmetry   **37.** y-axis symmetry

39. 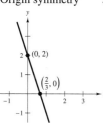   **41.**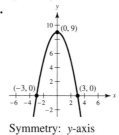

Symmetry: none   Symmetry: y-axis

43. 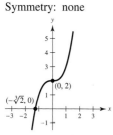   **45.**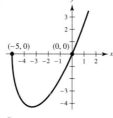

Symmetry: none   Symmetry: none

47. 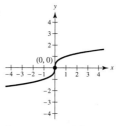   **49.**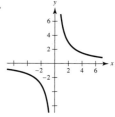

Symmetry: origin   Intercepts: none
Symmetry: origin

51. 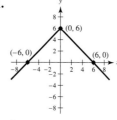   **53.**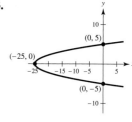

Symmetry: y-axis   Symmetry: x-axis

55.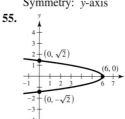

Symmetry: x-axis

57. $(3, 5)$ **59.** $(-4, -1), (1, 14)$ **61.** $(-2, 2), \left(-3, \sqrt{3}\right)$

63. x should be replaced by $-x$, not y by $-y$; $y^2 + 1 = -x$

65. (a)   (b) Sample answer:

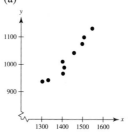   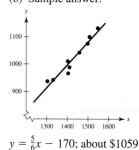

Yes $y = \frac{5}{6}x - 170$; about \$1059

67. (a) $d = 0.066F$

(b)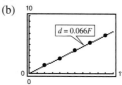

The model fits the data well; $|r|$ is close to 1.

(c) 3.63 cm

69. (a) $y = 0.004t^2 + 0.35t + 1.9$

(b)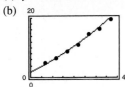

The model is a good fit for the data.

(c) About $28.7 trillion

71. 5200 units

73. (a) $S = 180.89x^2 - 205.79x + 272$

(b)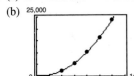

(c) About 583.98 lb   (d) About 4 times greater

(e) About 4.37 times greater; No; Answers will vary.

75. (a) $y = -1.806x^3 + 14.58x^2 + 16.4x + 10$

(b) 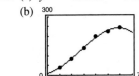   (c) 214 hp

77. (a) Amplitude: 0.35; Period: 0.5

(b) $y = 0.35 \sin 4\pi t + 2$

(c)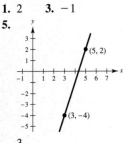

The model appears to fit the data well.

79. (a) 4   (b) $-\frac{1}{8}$ (c) All real numbers   (d) 1

81. Sample answer: $y = (x + 3)(x - 5)(x - 6)$

83. (a) Yes; If (x, y) is on the graph, then $(x, -y)$ and $(-x, -y)$ are on the graph.

(b) Yes; If (x, y) is on the graph, then $(-x, -y)$ is on the graph. Reflecting both points in the same axis produces both $(x, -y)$ and $(-x, y)$.

85. False; $(-3, -4)$ is not on the graph of $x = y^2 - 13$.

Section P.2   *(page 20)*

1. 2   **3.** -1

5.    **7.**

3   m is undefined.

9.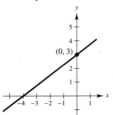

2

11.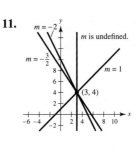

13. Sample answer: $(0, 2), (1, 2), (5, 2)$

15. Sample answer: $(0, 10), (2, 4), (3, 1)$

17. $3x - 4y + 12 = 0$ **19.** $x = 0$

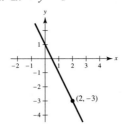

21. $2x + y = 1$

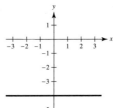

23. (a) $\frac{1}{3}$ (b) $10\sqrt{10}$ ft   **25.** $m = 4, (0, -3)$

27. $m = -5, (0, 20)$ **29.** m is undefined, no y-intercept

31. 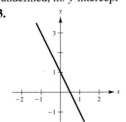   **33.**

35. 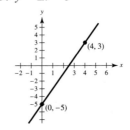   **37.**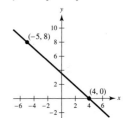

39. $y = 2x - 5$ **41.** $y = -\frac{8}{9}x + \frac{32}{9}$

43. $x = 6$

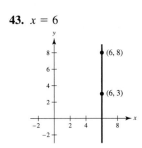

45. $y = \frac{11}{2}x + \frac{3}{4}$

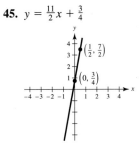

47. $y = \dfrac{(c - b)}{a}x + b$ **49.** $3x + 2y - 6 = 0$

51. $x + y - 1 = 0$ **53.** $x + 2y - 5 = 0$

55. (a) $x + 7 = 0$ **57.** (a) $x + y + 1 = 0$
(b) $y + 2 = 0$ (b) $x - y + 5 = 0$

59. (a) $2x - y - 3 = 0$ **61.** (a) $5x - 3y - 34 = 0$
(b) $x + 2y - 4 = 0$ (b) $3x + 5y = 0$

63. x and y were substituted incorrectly; $y - 4 = -\frac{5}{2}(x - (-1))$,
so $y = -\frac{5}{2}x + \frac{3}{2}$

65. $V = 250t - 400$ **67.** $V = -1600t + 31,600$

69. Not collinear

71. $\left(0, \dfrac{-a^2 + b^2 + c^2}{2c}\right)$

Find the midpoints and slopes of each side, then write equations
of the perpendicular bisectors and find the intersection point.

73. (a) When $a = 0$ and $b \neq 0$; when $b = 0$ and $a \neq 0$
(b) Sample answer: $a = -5$ and $b = 8$
(c) Sample answer: $a = 5$ and $b = 2$ (d) $a = \frac{5}{2}$ and $b = 3$

75. (a) Current job: $W_1 = 0.07s + 2000$
New job offer: $W_2 = 0.05s + 2300$

(b)

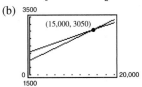

You will make more money at the job offer until you sell
$15,000. When your sales exceed $15,000, your current
job will pay you more.

(c) No; You will make more money at your current job.

77. (a) $x = -\frac{1}{15}p + 102$

(b)

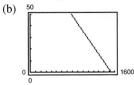

45 units

(c) 49 units

79. $5x + 12y - 169 = 0$ **81.** Answers will vary.

83. $\dfrac{5\sqrt{2}}{2}$ **85.** $2\sqrt{2}$ **87.** True   **89.** True

Section P.3   *(page 31)*

1. (a) -2 (b) 13 (c) $3b - 2$ (d) $3x - 5$

3. (a) 0 (b) -1 (c) $\dfrac{\sqrt{3}}{2}$ (d) 0

5. $3x^2 + 3x\,\Delta x + (\Delta x)^2,\ \Delta x \neq 0$

7. $-\dfrac{1}{x - 1 + \sqrt{x - 1}},\ x \neq 2$

9. Domain: $(-\infty, \infty)$; Range: $(-\infty, \infty)$

11. Domain: $(-\infty, \infty)$; Range: $[0, \infty)$

13. Domain: $(-\infty, \infty)$; Range: $(-\infty, \infty)$

15. Domain: $[0, \infty)$; Range: $[0, \infty)$

17. Domain: $[-4, 4]$; Range: $[0, 4]$

19. Domain: $(-\infty, \infty)$; Range: $[-3, 3]$

21. Domain: all $t \neq 4n + 2$, n is an integer
Range: $(-\infty, -1] \cup [1, \infty)$

23. Domain: $(-\infty, 0) \cup (0, \infty)$; Range: $(-\infty, 0) \cup (0, \infty)$

25. $[0, 1]$ **27.** All $x \neq 2\pi n$, n is an integer

29. $(-\infty, -3) \cup (-3, \infty)$

31. (a) -2 (b) 3 (c) 7 (d) $2t^2 + 5$
Domain: $(-\infty, \infty)$; Range: $(-\infty, 1) \cup [3, \infty)$

33. (a) 4 (b) 0 (c) -2 (d) $-b^2$
Domain: $(-\infty, \infty)$; Range: $(-\infty, 0] \cup [1, \infty)$

35. Not a function   **37.** Function

39. Not a function   **41.** Not a function

43. Horizontal shift two units to the right; $y = \sqrt{x - 2}$

45. Horizontal shift two units to the right and a vertical shift
one unit downward; $y = (x - 2)^2 - 1$

47. d   **48.** b   **49.** c   **50.** a   **51.** e   **52.** g

53. (a)

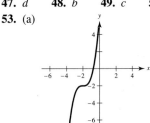

(b)

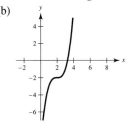

(c)

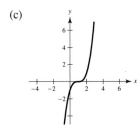

(d)

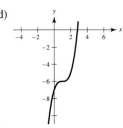

(e)

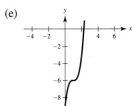

(f)

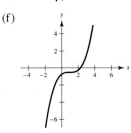

(g)

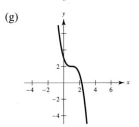

(h)

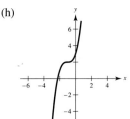

55. (a) $-x - 1$ (b) $5x - 9$
(c) $-6x^2 + 23x - 20$ (d) $\dfrac{2x - 5}{4 - 3x}$

57. (a) 0   (b) 0   (c) -1 (d) $\sqrt{15}$
    (e) $\sqrt{x^2 - 1}$ (f) $x - 1, x \geq 0$

59. $(f \circ g)(x) = \dfrac{3}{x^2 - 1}$; Domain: $(-\infty, -1) \cup (-1, 1) \cup (1, \infty)$

   $(g \circ f)(x) = \dfrac{9 - x^2}{x^2}$; Domain: $(-\infty, 0) \cup (0, \infty)$

   No

61. $(f \circ g)(x) = \cos^2 x - 1$; Domain: $(-\infty, \infty)$
    $(g \circ f)(x) = \cos(x^2 - 1)$; Domain: $(-\infty, \infty)$
    No

63. (a) 4   (b) -2
    (c) Undefined; -5 is not in the domain of g.
    (d) 3   (e) 2
    (f) Undefined; -4 is not in the domain of f.

65. Sample answer: $h(x) = 4x, g(x) = x - 4, f(x) = \sqrt{x}$

67. -16 should be $+16$; $f(p - 4) = p^2 - 5p - 1$

69. (a) $\left(\frac{3}{2}, 4\right)$ (b) $\left(\frac{3}{2}, -4\right)$

71. f is even; g is neither; h is odd   **73.** Even; $x = -2, 0, 2$

75. Odd; $x = 0, x = \dfrac{\pi}{2} + n\pi$, n is an integer

77. $f(x) = -5x - 6, -2 \leq x \leq 0$

79. $f(x) = -\sqrt{-x}, x \leq 0$

81. (a) $T(4) = 16°C$; $T(15) \approx 23°C$
    (b) The changes in temperature occur 1 hour later.
    (c) The temperatures are $1°$ lower.

83. The student travels $\frac{1}{2}$ mile per minute during the first 4 minutes, is stationary for the next 2 minutes, and travels 1 mile per minute during the final 4 minutes.

85. Sample answer: **87.** Sample answer:

89. 25

91. (a) Sample answer:

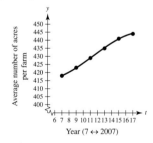

    (b) 438 acres/farm

93. $f(x) = \begin{cases} -2x + 2, & x < 0 \\ 2, & 0 \leq x \leq 2 \\ 2x - 2, & x > 2 \end{cases}$

95–97. Proofs   **99.** $L = \sqrt{a^2 + \left(\dfrac{2a}{a - 3}\right)^2}$

101. False; If $f(x) = x^2$, then $f(-3) = f(3) = 9$, but $-3 \neq 3$.

103. False; $f(x) = 0$ is symmetric with respect to the x-axis.

Section P.4   *(page 42)*

1. (a) $f(g(x)) = 5\left(\dfrac{x - 1}{5}\right) + 1 = x$

   $g(f(x)) = \dfrac{(5x + 1) - 1}{5} = x$

    (b) Sample answer: $f(1) = 6, g(6) = 1$
    (c)

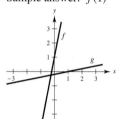

3. (a) $f(g(x)) = \left(\sqrt[3]{x}\right)^3 = x$; $g(f(x)) = \sqrt[3]{x^3} = x$
    (b) Sample answer: $f(2) = 8, g(8) = 2$
    (c)

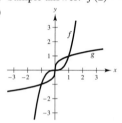

5. (a) $f(g(x)) = \sqrt{(x^2 + 4) - 4} = x, x \geq 0$
    $g(f(x)) = \left(\sqrt{x - 4}\right)^2 + 4 = x, x \geq 4$
    (b) Sample answer: $f(5) = 1, g(1) = 5$
    (c)

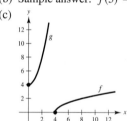

7. (a) $f(g(x)) = \dfrac{1}{1/x} = x, x \neq 0$; $g(f(x)) = \dfrac{1}{1/x} = x, x \neq 0$
    (b) Sample answer: $f\left(\frac{1}{7}\right) = 7, g(7) = \frac{1}{7}$
    (c)

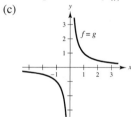

9. c   **10.** b   **11.** a   **12.** d

13.

x	3	5	7	9	11	13
$f^{-1}(x)$	-1	0	1	2	3	4

15. One-to-one

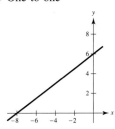

17. Not one-to-one

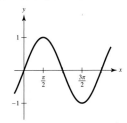

19.

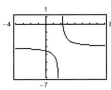

One-to-one

21.

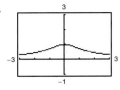

Not one-to-one

23.

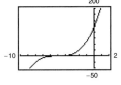

One-to-one

25. One-to-one   **27.** One-to-one   **29.** Not one-to-one

31. (a) $f^{-1}(x) = \dfrac{x+3}{2}$

(b)

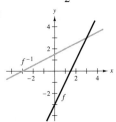

(c) The graph of f^{-1} is a reflection of the graph of f in the line $y = x$.

(d) Domain of f and f^{-1}: $(-\infty, \infty)$
Range of f and f^{-1}: $(-\infty, \infty)$

33. (a) $f^{-1}(x) = x^{1/5}$

(b)

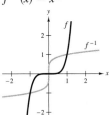

(c) The graph of f^{-1} is a reflection of the graph of f in the line $y = x$.

(d) Domain of f and f^{-1}: $(-\infty, \infty)$
Range of f and f^{-1}: $(-\infty, \infty)$

35. (a) $f^{-1}(x) = x^2, \ x \geq 0$

(b)

(c) The graph of f^{-1} is a reflection of the graph of f in the line $y = x$.

(d) Domain of f and f^{-1}: $[0, \infty)$
Range of f and f^{-1}: $[0, \infty)$

37. (a) $f^{-1}(x) = \sqrt{4 - x^2}, \ 0 \leq x \leq 2$

(b)

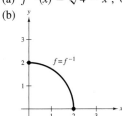

(c) The graph of f^{-1} is a reflection of the graph of f in the line $y = x$.

(d) Domain of f and f^{-1}: $[0, 2]$
Range of f and f^{-1}: $[0, 2]$

39. (a) $f^{-1}(x) = x^3 + 1$

(b)

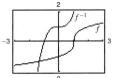

(c) The graph of f^{-1} is a reflection of the graph of f in the line $y = x$.

(d) Domain of f and f^{-1}: $(-\infty, \infty)$
Range of f and f^{-1}: $(-\infty, \infty)$

41. (a) $f^{-1}(x) = x^{3/2}, \ x \geq 0$

(b)

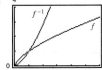

(c) The graph of f^{-1} is a reflection of the graph of f in the line $y = x$.

(d) Domain of f and f^{-1}: $[0, \infty)$
Range of f and f^{-1}: $[0, \infty)$

CHAPTER P

43. (a) $f^{-1}(x) = \dfrac{2x}{1-x}$

(b)

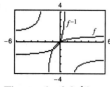

(c) The graph of f^{-1} is a reflection of the graph of f in the line $y = x$.

(d) Domain of f: $(-\infty, -2) \cup (-2, \infty)$
Range of f: $(-\infty, 1) \cup (1, \infty)$
Domain of f^{-1}: $(-\infty, 1) \cup (1, \infty)$
Range of f^{-1}: $(-\infty, -2) \cup (-2, \infty)$

45. (a) $f^{-1}(x) = \left(\dfrac{2}{x-1}\right)^2, \ x > 1$

(b)

(c) The graph of f^{-1} is a reflection of the graph of f in the line $y = x$.

(d) Domain of f: $(0, \infty)$
Range of f: $(1, \infty)$
Domain of f^{-1}: $(1, \infty)$
Range of f^{-1}: $(0, \infty)$

47. When dividing by -1, y^3 should be $-y^3$; $f^{-1}(x) = -x^3 + 5$

49.

x	0	1	2	4
$f(x)$	1	2	3	4

x	1	2	3	4
$f^{-1}(x)$	0	1	2	4

51. (a) $y = -0.35x + 80$

(b) $y = \frac{20}{7}(80 - x)$

x: total cost

y: number of pounds of the less expensive commodity

(c) $[62.5, 80]$; The total cost will be between \$62.50 and \$80.00.

(d) 20 lb

53. One-to-one; $f^{-1}(x) = x^2 + 2, \ x \geq 0$ **55.** Not one-to-one

57. One-to-one; $f^{-1}(x) = \dfrac{x-b}{a}, \ a \neq 0$

59–63. Answers will vary.

65. Sample answer: $x \geq 3$; $f^{-1}(x) = \sqrt{x} + 3$

67. (a)

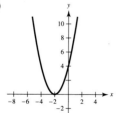

(b) Sample answer: $[-2, \infty)$

(c) $f^{-1}(x) = \sqrt{x} - 2$ (d) $[0, \infty)$

69. (a)

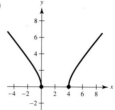

(b) Sample answer: $[4, \infty)$

(c) $f^{-1}(x) = 2 + \sqrt{x^2 + 4}$ (d) $[0, \infty)$

71. (a)

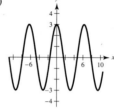

(b) Sample answer: $[0, \pi]$

(c) $f^{-1}(x) = \arccos \dfrac{x}{3}$ (d) $[-3, 3]$

73. 1   **75.** $\dfrac{\pi}{6}$ **77.** 2   **79.** $(g^{-1} \circ f^{-1})(x) = \dfrac{x+1}{2}$

81. $(f \circ g)^{-1}(x) = \dfrac{x+1}{2}$ **83.** 32   **85.** 408

87.

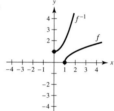

89. (a) One-to-one   (b) $[-2, 2]$ (c) $f^{-1}(2) = -4$

91. (a)

x	-1	-0.8	-0.6	-0.4	-0.2
y	-1.57	-0.93	-0.64	-0.41	-0.20

x	0	0.2	0.4	0.6	0.8	1
y	0	0.20	0.41	0.64	0.93	1.57

(b)   (c)

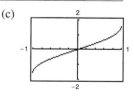

(d) Intercept: $(0, 0)$; Symmetry: origin

93. $\left(-\dfrac{\sqrt{2}}{2}, \dfrac{3\pi}{4}\right), \left(\dfrac{1}{2}, \dfrac{\pi}{3}\right), \left(\dfrac{\sqrt{3}}{2}, \dfrac{\pi}{6}\right)$

95. $\dfrac{\pi}{6}$ **97.** 0   **99.** $\dfrac{\pi}{6}$ **101.** $-\dfrac{\pi}{4}$ **103.** 2.21

105. 0.80   **107.** -0.4 **109.** x **111.** $\dfrac{\sqrt{1-x^2}}{x}$

113. $\dfrac{1}{x}$ **115.** $\sqrt{1-4x^2}$ **117.** $\dfrac{\sqrt{x^2-1}}{|x|}$

119. (a) $\frac{3}{5}$ (b) $\frac{5}{3}$ **121.** (a) $-\sqrt{3}$ (b) $-\frac{13}{5}$

123. $x = \frac{1}{4}(\sin\frac{1}{2} + \pi) \approx 0.905$ **125.** $x = \frac{1}{3}$

127. The tangent function is not one-to-one.

129. 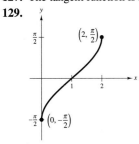   **131.**

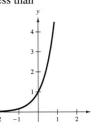

133–135. Proofs   **137.** True

139. (a)–(c) Answers will vary.

141. (a)–(c) Answers will vary.

Section P.5   *(page 51)*

1. (a) 125   (b) 9   (c) $\frac{1}{9}$ (d) $\frac{1}{3}$

3. (a) 3125   (b) $\dfrac{1}{5}$ (c) $\dfrac{1}{5^x}$ (d) 2^{2x}

5. (a) e^7 (b) e^{12} (c) $\dfrac{1}{e^6}$ (d) 1

7. $x = 4$ **9.** $x = 4$ **11.** $x = -5$ **13.** $x = -2$

15. $x = 2$ **17.** $x = 16$ **19.** $x = 2$ **21.** $x = -\frac{5}{2}$

23. Less than

25.   **27.**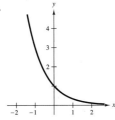

29. 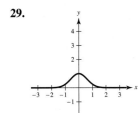   **31.**

33. 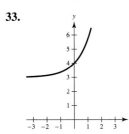   **35.**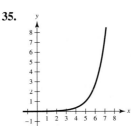

37.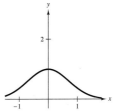

39. $(-\infty, \infty)$ **41.** $(-\infty, 0]$ **43.** $(-\infty, \infty)$

45. (a) 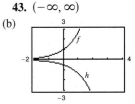   (b)

Horizontal shift two units   Reflection in the x-axis
to the right   and vertical shrink

(c)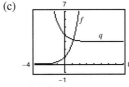

Reflection in the y-axis and vertical shift three units upward

47. c   **48.** d   **49.** a   **50.** b   **51.** $y = 2(3^x)$

53. $\ln 1 = 0$ **55.** $e^{1.6094 \cdots} = 5$

57. 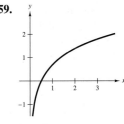   **59.**

$(0, \infty)$ $(0, \infty)$

61. 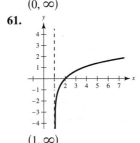   **63.**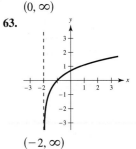

$(1, \infty)$ $(-2, \infty)$

65. $g(x) = -e^x - 8$ **67.** $g(x) = \ln(x - 5) - 1$

69. 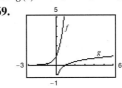   **71.**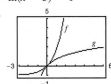

73. (a) $f^{-1}(x) = \dfrac{\ln x + 1}{4}$

(b) 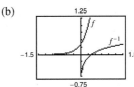   (c) Answers will vary.

75. (a) $f^{-1}(x) = e^{x/2} + 1$

(b) 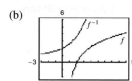   (c) Answers will vary.

77. x^2 **79.** $5x + 2$ **81.** $-1 + 2x$

83. (a) 1.7917   (b) -0.4055 (c) 4.3944   (d) 0.5493

85. $\ln x - \ln 5$ **87.** $\ln x + \ln y - \ln z$

89. $\ln x + \frac{1}{2}\ln(x^2 + 16)$ **91.** $\frac{1}{2}\ln(x - 1) - \frac{1}{2}\ln x$

93. $2 + \ln 3$ **95.** $\ln 7x$ **97.** $\ln \dfrac{x - 2}{x + 2}$

99. $\ln \sqrt[3]{\dfrac{x(x + 3)^2}{x^2 - 1}}$ **101.** $\ln \dfrac{9}{\sqrt{x^2 + 1}}$

103. The expression should not be negative; e^6

105. (a) $x = 4$ (b) $x = \frac{1}{3}(2 + e^3) \approx 7.362$

107. (a) $x = e^2 \approx 7.389$ (b) $x = \ln 8 - 2 \approx 0.079$

109. $x > \ln 6$ **111.** $\dfrac{1}{e^2} < x < 1$

113. (a)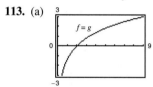

(b) Answers will vary.

115. $f(x) = e^x$ and $g(x) = \ln x$ are inverses functions.

117. (a) False; $y = 0$ when $x = 1$ (b) True; $2^y = x$

(c) True; $y = \log_2 x$

(d) False; The points are not collinear.

119. $\beta = 10 \log_{10} I + 160$

121. False; $\ln x + \ln 25 = \ln 25x \neq \ln(x + 25)$

123.

$(-0.7899, 0.2429)$, $(1.6242, 18.3615)$, and $(6, 46{,}656)$; f

125. $y = 0.25 \ln x - 0.00003$

127. $10! = 3{,}628{,}800$; $10! \approx 3{,}598{,}696$

129. Proof

131. (a) 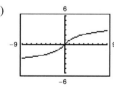   (b) Answers will vary.

(c) $f^{-1}(x) = \dfrac{e^{2x} - 1}{2e^x}$

$(-\infty, \infty)$

Review Exercises for Chapter P   *(page 54)*

1. $\left(\frac{8}{5}, 0\right)$, $(0, -8)$ **3.** $(3, 0)$, $\left(0, \frac{3}{4}\right)$ **5.** No symmetry

7. x-axis symmetry, y-axis symmetry, and origin symmetry

9.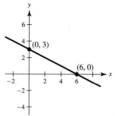

Symmetry: none

11.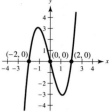

Symmetry: origin

13.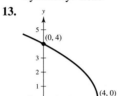

Symmetry: none

15. $(-2, 3)$, $(3, 8)$

17. (a) $y = -1.4x + 66$

(b)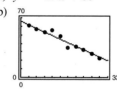

The model is a good fit; $r \approx -0.9745$

19.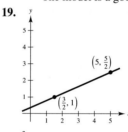

$\dfrac{3}{7}$

21. $y = \frac{7}{4}x - \frac{41}{4}$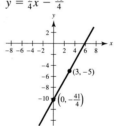

23. $y = -\frac{2}{3}x - 2$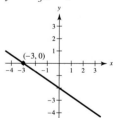

25. 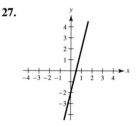   **27.**

29. $y = \frac{1}{4}x$

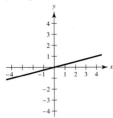

31. (a) $5x - 3y + 30 = 0$ (b) $4x - 3y + 27 = 0$
(c) $x = -3$

33. (a) 4   (b) 29   (c) -11 (d) $5t + 9$

35. $8x + 4\Delta x,\ \Delta x \neq 0$

37. Domain: $(-\infty, \infty)$ **39.** Domain: $(-\infty, \infty)$
Range: $[3, \infty)$ Range: $(-\infty, 0]$

41. (a) 1   (b) 2   (c) 1   (d) $x^4 + 2x^2 + 1$
Domain: $(-\infty, \infty)$; Range: $(-\infty, \infty)$

43.   **45.**

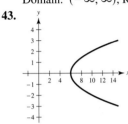

Not a function   Function

47. $g(x) = -x^3 + 3x^2 + 1$

49. (a) $6 - 11x$ (b) $13x + 4$ (c) $-12x^2 - 59x + 5$
(d) $\dfrac{x + 5}{1 - 12x}$

51. $(f \circ g) = x^3$; Domain: $(-\infty, \infty)$
$(g \circ f) = x\sqrt[3]{x^6 + 3x^3 + 3}$; Domain: $(-\infty, \infty)$
No

53. Neither; $x = 0, 5$ **55.** Even; $x = \dfrac{\pi}{2} + n\pi$, n is an integer

57. (a) $f^{-1}(x) = 2x + 6$

(b)   (c) Answers will vary.

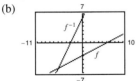

(d) Domain of f and f^{-1}: $(-\infty, \infty)$
Range of f and f^{-1}: $(-\infty, \infty)$

59. (a) $f^{-1}(x) = x^2 - 1$, $x \geq 0$

(b)   (c) Answers will vary.

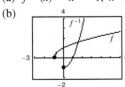

(d) Domain of f: $[-1, \infty)$
Range of f: $[0, \infty)$
Domain of f^{-1}: $[0, \infty)$
Range of f^{-1}: $[-1, \infty)$

61. (a) $f^{-1}(x) = x^3 - 1$

(b)   (c) Answers will vary.

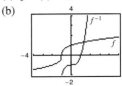

(d) Domain of f and f^{-1}: $(-\infty, \infty)$
Range of f and f^{-1}: $(-\infty, \infty)$

63. (a) $f^{-1}(x) = e^{2x}$

(b)   (c) Answers will vary.

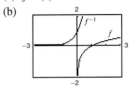

(d) Domain of f: $(0, \infty)$
Range of f: $(-\infty, \infty)$
Domain of f^{-1}: $(-\infty, \infty)$
Range of f^{-1}: $(0, \infty)$

65. Not one-to-one   **67.** One-to-one; $f^{-1}(x) = \sqrt[3]{x^3 + 3}$

69. $\dfrac{\sqrt{3}}{2}$ **71.** $x = \dfrac{1}{3}(2 + \cos 2) \approx 0.5280$ **73.** $x = \dfrac{1}{2}$

75.   **77.**

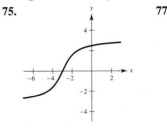 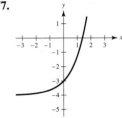

$(-\infty, \infty)$ $(-\infty, \infty)$

79.   **81.**

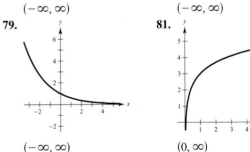

$(-\infty, \infty)$ $(0, \infty)$

83. $\frac{1}{5}[\ln(2x + 1) + \ln(2x - 1) - \ln(4x^2 + 1)]$

85. $x = \frac{19}{6} \approx 3.167$ **87.** $x = e^4 - 1 \approx 53.598$

Chapter 1

Section 1.1   *(page 63)*

1. Precalculus; 300 ft

3. Calculus; the rate is not constant; about 0.16

5. Precalculus; 10 units²

7. Calculus; the region is not a polygon or a circle; 18 units²

9. Precalculus; 27 units²   **11.** 24 units³

13. (a)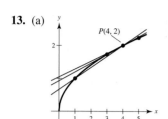

(b) $\frac{1}{3}$; about 0.2679; about 0.2361

(c) 0.25; Use a point closer to (4, 2).

15. Finding the slope of the tangent line at a point

17. About 10.417 units²; about 9.145 units²; Use more rectangles.

19. (a) About 5.66 units **(b)** About 6.11 units

(c) Four segments; the segments are closer to the curve.

21. Sum the areas of several rectangular regions with heights of $y = f(x)$.

23. B

Section 1.2   *(page 72)*

1.

x	3.9	3.99	3.999	4
$f(x)$	0.3448	0.3344	0.3334	?

x	4.001	4.01	4.1
$f(x)$	0.3332	0.3322	0.3226

$\frac{1}{3}$

3.

x	−0.1	−0.01	−0.001	0
$f(x)$	0.9983	0.99998	1.0000	?

x	0.001	0.01	0.1
$f(x)$	1.0000	0.99998	0.9983

1

5.

x	−0.1	−0.01	−0.001	0
$f(x)$	0.9516	0.9950	0.9995	?

x	0.001	0.01	0.1
$f(x)$	1.0005	1.0050	1.0517

1

7.

x	0.9	0.99	0.999	1
$f(x)$	0.2564	0.2506	0.2501	?

x	1.001	1.01	1.1
$f(x)$	0.2499	0.2494	0.2439

$\frac{1}{4}$

9.

x	−0.1	−0.01	−0.001	0
$f(x)$	1.9867	1.9999	2.0000	?

x	0.001	0.01	0.1
$f(x)$	2.0000	1.9999	1.9867

2

11.

x	−6.1	−6.01	−6.001	−6
$f(x)$	−0.1248	−0.1250	−0.1250	?

x	−5.999	−5.99	−5.9
$f(x)$	−0.1250	−0.1250	−0.1252

$-\frac{1}{8}$

13.

x	−0.1	−0.01	−0.001	0
$f(x)$	−2000	-2.0×10^6	-2.0×10^9	?

x	0.001	0.01	0.1
$f(x)$	2.0×10^9	2.0×10^6	2000

Does not exist; $f(x)$ increases and decreases without bound as $x \to 0$.

15.

x	−0.1	−0.01	−0.001	0
$f(x)$	3.99982	4	4	?

x	0.001	0.01	0.1
$f(x)$	0	0	0.00018

Does not exist; $f(x)$ approaches 4 from the left and 0 from the right as $x \to 0$.

17. 1   **19.** 2

21. Does not exist; $f(x)$ approaches −1 from the left and 1 from the right as $x \to 2$.

23. Does not exist; $f(x)$ increases and decreases without bound as $x \to \dfrac{\pi}{2}$.

25. (a) 3   **(b)** 3   **(c)** 2

(d) Does not exist; $f(x)$ approaches 3.5 from the left and 1 from the right as $x \to 1$.

(e) Does not exist; The graph has a hole at $x = 4$.

(f) 2

27.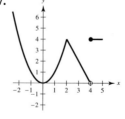

$c \neq 4$

29. Sample answer: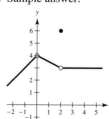

31. 0.4   **33.** $\frac{1}{11}$ **35.** 8; $\frac{1}{300}$ **37.** 1; $\frac{1}{500}$ **39.** 6; Proof

41. −3; Proof   **43.** 3; Proof   **45.** 0; Proof

47. 10; Proof   **49.** 2; Proof

51.

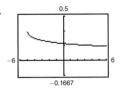

$\frac{1}{6}$

Domain: $[-5, 4) \cup (4, \infty)$

No; The graph does not show the hole at $x = 4$; Use the graph to identify asymptotes and intervals, use the function to identify holes and endpoints.

53. (a)

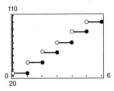

(b)

t	3	3.3	3.4	3.5	3.6	3.7	4
C	55	70	70	?	70	70	70

70

(c)

t	2	2.5	2.9	3	3.1	3.5	4
C	40	55	55	?	70	70	70

No; $C(t)$ approaches 55 from the left and 70 from the right as $t \to 3$.

55. As the graph of the function approaches 8 on the horizontal axis, the graph approaches 25 on the vertical axis.

57. $f(x)$ approaches different numbers from the left and right.

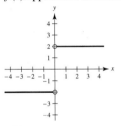

$f(x)$ increases or decreases without bound.

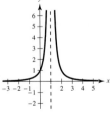

$f(x)$ oscillates between two different numbers.

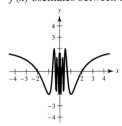

59. (a) $\frac{3}{\pi}$ cm   (b) $\frac{5.9}{2\pi}$ cm to $\frac{6.1}{2\pi}$ cm

(c) When the radius is within $\frac{1}{20\pi}$ centimeter of $\frac{3}{\pi}$ centimeter, the circumference is within 0.1 centimeter of 6 centimeters.

61. e

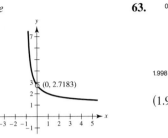

63.

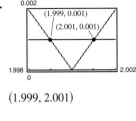

$(1.999, 2.001)$

65. False; The existence or nonexistence of $f(x)$ at $x = c$ has no bearing on the existence of the limit of $f(x)$ as $x \to c$.

67. False; See Exercise 19.

69. Yes; As x approaches 0.25 from either side, $\sqrt{x}$ becomes arbitrarily close to 0.5.

71. $\lim_{x \to 0} \frac{\sin nx}{x} = n$ **73–75.** Proofs   **77.** B   **79.** B

Section 1.3   *(page 84)*

1. 6   **3.** 4   **5.** 49

7. (a) 6   (b) 8   (c) 12   (d) 3

9. (a) 256   (b) 4   (c) 48   (d) 64   **11.** -1

13. 0   **15.** 7   **17.** $\sqrt{14} \approx 3.742$ **19.** 125

21. $\frac{3}{5}$ **23.** $\frac{1}{5}$ **25.** 7   **27.** (a) 4   (b) 64   (c) 64

29. (a) 3   (b) 2   (c) 2

31. The functions are multiplied, not composited;
$\lim_{x \to 4} g(x)f(x) = g(4)f(4)$

33. 1   **35.** $\frac{1}{2}$ **37.** 1   **39.** $\frac{1}{2}$ **41.** -1

43. 1   **45.** $\ln 3 + e$ **47.** $g(x) = -x^3 - 4; 4$

49. $g(x) = x - 1; -2$ **51.** $g(x) = \frac{\ln(x + 6)}{x - 4}; -\frac{\ln 2}{8}$

53. -1 **55.** -6 **57.** $\frac{5}{6}$ **59.** $\frac{1}{6}$ **61.** $\frac{\sqrt{5}}{10}$

63. $-\frac{1}{9}$ **65.** 2   **67.** $2x - 2$ **69.** 3   **71.** $-\frac{1}{(x + 3)^2}$

73. $\frac{1}{5}$ **75.** 0   **77.** 0   **79.** 0   **81.** 0

83. 1   **85.** $\frac{3}{2}$

87.

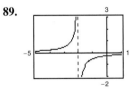

About 0.354; $\frac{\sqrt{2}}{4}$

89.

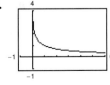

$-0.25; -\frac{1}{4}$

91.

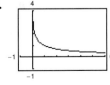

3; 3

93.

1; 1

95. 4

97. 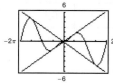   **99.**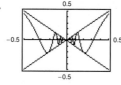

0   0

101. False; The limit does not exist.   **103.** True

105. (a) Two functions that agree at all but one point have the same limits at every point.

(b) Sample answer: $f(x) = \dfrac{x^2 - 1}{x - 1}$, $g(x) = x + 1$

107.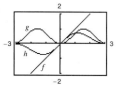

The magnitude of g is less than the magnitude of f; Answers will vary.

109. -64 ft/sec   **111.** -29.4 m/sec

113. Sample answer: $f(x) = 1/x$, $g(x) = -1/x$

115–119. Proofs   **121.** Proof   **123.** B   **125.** C

Section 1.4   *(page 96)*

1. (a) 1   (b) 1   (c) 1; Continuous on $(-\infty, \infty)$

3. (a) 3   (b) 3   (c) 3; Discontinuity at $x = -3$

5. (a) -3 (b) 3   (c) Does not exist;
Discontinuity at $x = 2$

7. $\frac{1}{16}$ **9.** $\frac{1}{8}$

11. Does not exist; The function decreases without bound as $x \to -7^-$.

13. -1 **15.** $-\dfrac{1}{x^2}$ **17.** $\dfrac{5}{2}$

19. Does not exist; The function increases and decreases without bound as $x \to \pi$.

21. 16   **23.** Does not exist; $\lim\limits_{x \to 2^-} f(x) \neq \lim\limits_{x \to 2^+} f(x)$

25. Does not exist; The function decreases without bound as $x \to 4^+$.

27. $\ln 8$ **29.** Discontinuities at $x = \pm 2$

31. Discontinuity at $x = 1$ **33.** Continuous on $[-7, 7]$

35. Continuous on $[-1, 4]$

37. $\dfrac{1}{0} \neq 0$; The limit does not exist.   **39.** 0; none

41. None   **43.** ± 2; none   **45.** None   **47.** $-2, 5; -2$

49. -9; none   **51.** None   **53.** 2; none   **55.** None

57. 0; none   **59.** $n\pi$, n is an integer; none

61. n, n is an integer; none   **63.** $a = 2$

65. $a = -1$, $b = 1$ **67.** $a = -1$

69. Continuous on $(-\infty, \infty)$ **71.** Discontinuities at $x = \pm 1$

73. 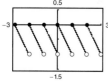   **75.**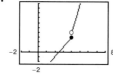

n, n is an integer   4

77. $(-\infty, 4) \cup (4, \infty)$ **79.** $[0, \infty)$

81. $\ldots, (-6, -2), (-2, 2), (2, 6), \ldots$ **83.** $(-\infty, \infty)$

85. 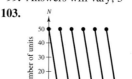   **87.**

Yes; No; Answers will vary.   Yes; No; Answers will vary.

89. f is continuous on $[1, 2]$, $f(1) = 37/12$, and $f(2) = -8/3$.

91. h is continuous on $[0, \pi/2]$, $h(0) = -2$, and $h(\pi/2) \approx 0.9119$.

93. 0.68, 0.6823   **95.** 0.56, 0.5636   **97.** 0.79, 0.7921

99. Answers will vary; 3   **101.** Answers will vary; 2

103.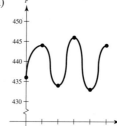

Discontinuities at $2n$, n is a positive integer; every two months

105. (a) The limit does not exist at $x = c$.

(b) The function is not defined at $x = c$.

(c) The limit exists, but it is not equal to the value of the function at $x = c$.

(d) The limit does not exist at $x = c$.

107. Yes; No; Sample answer: $f(x) = x$, $g(x) = x^2 - 1$

109. True   **111.** True   **113.** Proof

115. Answers will vary.   **117.** $\left(-1 \pm \sqrt{5}\right)/2$

119. (a)

(b) No; The frequency is oscillating.

121. The functions differ by 1 for noninteger values of x.

123–125. Proofs   **127.** A

129. (a) $a = -1$; $b = 1$

(b)

(c) 1

Section 1.5   *(page 105)*

1. $\lim\limits_{x \to -2^-} f(x) = \infty$; $\lim\limits_{x \to -2^+} f(x) = \infty$

3. $\lim\limits_{x \to -2^-} f(x) = \infty$; $\lim\limits_{x \to -2^+} f(x) = -\infty$

5. $\lim\limits_{x \to 4^-} f(x) = -\infty$; $\lim\limits_{x \to 4^+} f(x) = \infty$

7. $\lim\limits_{x\to 4^-} f(x) = \infty$; $\lim\limits_{x\to 4^+} f(x) = \infty$

9.

x	-3.5	-3.1	-3.01	-3.001	-3
$f(x)$	0.31	1.64	16.6	167	?

x	-2.999	-2.99	-2.9	-2.5
$f(x)$	-167	-16.7	-1.69	-0.36

$\lim\limits_{x\to -3^-} f(x) = \infty$; $\lim\limits_{x\to -3^+} f(x) = -\infty$

11.

x	-3.5	-3.1	-3.01	-3.001	-3
$f(x)$	3.8	16	151	1501	?

x	-2.999	-2.99	-2.9	-2.5
$f(x)$	-1499	-149	-14	-2.3

$\lim\limits_{x\to -3^-} f(x) = \infty$; $\lim\limits_{x\to -3^+} f(x) = -\infty$

13.

x	-3.5	-3.1	-3.01	-3.001	-3
$f(x)$	1.414	6.392	63.665	636.620	?

x	-2.999	-2.99	-2.9	-2.5
$f(x)$	-636.620	-63.665	-6.392	-1.414

$\lim\limits_{x\to -3^-} f(x) = \infty$; $\lim\limits_{x\to -3^+} f(x) = -\infty$

15. $x = 0$ **17.** $x = \pm 2$ **19.** $x = -3, x = 0$
21. $x = -2, x = 1$ **23.** None **25.** $x = 1$
27. $t = -2$ **29.** $x = 0$ **31.** $x = n$, n is an integer
33. $t = n\pi$, n is a nonzero integer
35. Removable discontinuity **37.** Vertical asymptote
39. ∞ **41.** $-\infty$ **43.** ∞ **45.** $-\infty$ **47.** 0
49. ∞ **51.** ∞ **53.** $-\infty$ **55.** $-\infty$ **57.** $-\infty$
59. ∞ **61.** $-\infty$ **63.** $-\infty$ **65.** ∞
67. $(x + 5)$ should be divided out of the numerator and denominator; So, the graph of h has a vertical asymptote at $x = 5$ and a removable discontinuity at $x = -5$.
69. Answers will vary; No
71. Sample answer: Use a table.
73. (a)

x	1	0.5	0.2	0.1
$f(x)$	0.1585	0.0411	0.0067	0.0017

x	0.01	0.001	0.0001
$f(x)$	0	0	0

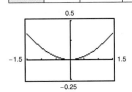

0

(b)

x	1	0.5	0.2	0.1
$f(x)$	0.1585	0.0823	0.0333	0.0167

x	0.01	0.001	0.0001
$f(x)$	0.0017	0	0

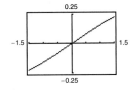

0

(c)

x	1	0.5	0.2	0.1
$f(x)$	0.1585	0.1646	0.1663	0.1666

x	0.01	0.001	0.0001
$f(x)$	0.1667	0.1667	0.1667

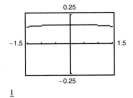

$\frac{1}{6}$

(d)

x	1	0.5	0.2	0.1
$f(x)$	0.1585	0.3292	0.8317	1.6658

x	0.01	0.001	0.0001
$f(x)$	16.67	166.7	1667.0

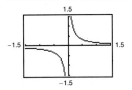

∞

(e)

x	1	0.5	0.2	0.1
$f(x)$	0.1585	0.6584	4.1583	16.6583

x	0.01	0.001	0.0001
$f(x)$	1666.7	1.67×10^5	1.67×10^7

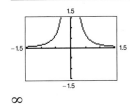

∞

(f)

x	1	0.5	0.2	0.1
$f(x)$	0.1585	1.3168	20.7917	166.58

x	0.01	0.001	0.0001
$f(x)$	1.67×10^5	1.67×10^8	1.67×10^{11}

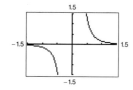

∞

∞

75. (a) $\frac{7}{12}$ ft/sec   (b) $\frac{3}{2}$ ft/sec

(c) ∞; As the distance of the base from the house approaches the length of the ladder, the rate increases without bound.

77. True   **79.** False; Let $f(x) = \tan x$.

81. Sample answer: Let $f(x) = \dfrac{1}{x^2}$, $g(x) = \dfrac{1}{x^4}$, and $c = 0$.

83–85. Proofs   **87.** A   **89.** D

Section 1.6 (page 115)

1. f   **2.** c   **3.** d   **4.** a   **5.** b   **6.** e

7. 12   **9.** 0   **11.** 0   **13.** 2   **15.** $\frac{4}{3}$

17. (a) ∞ (b) 5   (c) 0   **19.** (a) 0   (b) 1   (c) ∞

21. (a) 0   (b) $-\frac{2}{3}$ (c) $-\infty$ **23.** $\frac{2}{3}$ **25.** 0   **27.** 0

29. -1 **31.** -2 **33.** $\frac{1}{2}$ **35.** ∞ **37.** 0   **39.** 0

41. 2   **43.** 0   **45.** $-\dfrac{\pi}{2}$

47. -5 should be divided by x^3; $\dfrac{5}{6}$

49. 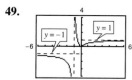   **51.**

53. $\lim\limits_{t \to \infty} N(t) = \infty$; $\lim\limits_{t \to \infty} E(t) = c$ **55.** 100%

57. (a)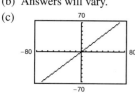

(b) Answers will vary.

(c)

$y = x$

59. 1   **61.** 0   **63.** $\frac{1}{6}$

65.

x	10^0	10^1	10^2	10^3
$f(x)$	1.000	0.513	0.501	0.500

x	10^4	10^5	10^6
$f(x)$	0.500	0.500	0.500

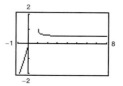

$\frac{1}{2}$

67.

x	10^0	10^1	10^2	10^3
$f(x)$	0.479	0.500	0.500	0.500

x	10^4	10^5	10^6
$f(x)$	0.500	0.500	0.500

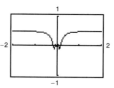

$\frac{1}{2}$

69. (a) As x increases without bound, $f(x)$ approaches 4.

(b) As x decreases without bound, $f(x)$ approaches 2.

71. (a)

(b) Answers will vary.

73. (a) $L = 2$; $K = 2$

(b) $x_1 = \sqrt{\dfrac{4 - 2\varepsilon}{\varepsilon}}$, $x_2 = -\sqrt{\dfrac{4 - 2\varepsilon}{\varepsilon}}$

(c) $x_1 = M$ (d) $x_2 = N$

75. (a) $M \geq \dfrac{5\sqrt{33}}{11}$ (b) $M \geq \dfrac{29\sqrt{177}}{59}$

77–79. Proofs

81. (a) $d(m) = \dfrac{|3m + 3|}{\sqrt{m^2 + 1}}$

(b)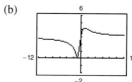

(c) $\lim\limits_{m \to \infty} d(m) = 3$

$\lim\limits_{m \to -\infty} d(m) = 3$

As the slope gets steeper, the distance approaches 3.

83. C   **85.** A

Review Exercises for Chapter 1   *(page 118)*

1. Calculus; The graph is not a line; about 8.3 units

3.

x	2.9	2.99	2.999	3
$f(x)$	-0.9091	-0.9901	-0.9990	?

x	3.001	3.01	3.1
$f(x)$	-1.0010	-1.0101	-1.1111

-1

5. (a) 4   (b) 5   **7.** 5; Proof   **9.** -3; Proof   **11.** 36

13. -2 **15.** $\frac{3}{2}$ **17.** $-\frac{1}{4}$ **19.** $\frac{1}{2}$ **21.** -1 **23.** 0

25. 1   **27.** $\dfrac{\sqrt{3}}{2}$ **29.** -3 **31.** -5

33. 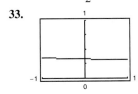   **35.**

$\frac{1}{3}$ 0

37. -39.2 m/sec

39. (a) $(-\infty, 0] \cup [1, \infty)$ (b) 0   (c) 0

41. $\frac{1}{12}$ **43.** $\frac{1}{6}$ **45.** 3   **47.** 0   **49.** None

51. $\pm 1, 0; 0$ **53.** $(-\infty, \infty)$ **55.** $[4, \infty)$

57. $(n, n + 1)$, n is an integer   **59.** $(-\infty, 1) \cup (1, \infty)$

61. f is continuous on $[0, 1]$, $f(0) = -2$ and $f(1) = 1$.

63. $x = \pm 3$ **65.** $x = \frac{1}{2}$ **67.** $x = \pm 5$ **69.** $-\infty$

71. $\frac{1}{12}$ **73.** $-\infty$ **75.** $\frac{4}{5}$ **77.** $-\infty$

79. (a) \$14,117.65; \$80,000.00; \$720,000.00

(b) ∞; No matter how much the company spends, the company will never be able to remove 100% of the pollutants.

81. 8   **83.** $\frac{3}{5}$ **85.** $-\infty$ **87.** 6

89. 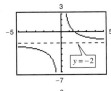   **91.**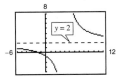

93.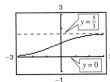

AP® Exam Practice Questions   *(page 120)*

1. B   **2.** D   **3.** A   **4.** B   **5.** D   **6.** C   **7.** C

8. B   **9.** C   **10.** C

---

11. (a) s is continuous on $[1, 2]$, $s(1) = 393.1$ and $s(2) = 378.4$.

(b) 9 sec

(c) $\displaystyle \lim_{x \to 3} \frac{s(t) - s(3)}{t - 3}$

$\displaystyle = \lim_{x \to 3} \frac{(-4.9t^2 + 398) - (-4.9(3)^2 + 398)}{t - 3}$

$\displaystyle = \lim_{x \to 3} \frac{-4.9(t^2 - 9)}{t - 3}$

$\displaystyle = \lim_{x \to 3} -4.9(t + 3)$

$= -29.4$ m/sec

12. (a) 8   (b) 12

(c) $y = 0$, $y = 10$;

$\displaystyle \lim_{x \to \infty} \frac{10}{1 + \frac{1}{4}e^{-x}} = \frac{10}{1 + 0} = 10$

$\displaystyle \lim_{x \to -\infty} \frac{10}{1 + \frac{1}{4}e^{-x}} = \lim_{x \to -\infty} \frac{10e^x}{e^x + \frac{1}{4}} = \frac{0}{0 + \frac{1}{4}} = 0$

13. (a) $-3, -\dfrac{1}{2}$ (b) $\displaystyle \lim_{x \to -3} \frac{x^2 + 5x + 6}{2x^2 + 7x + 3} = \lim_{x \to -3} \frac{x + 2}{2x + 1} = \frac{1}{5}$

(c) $x = -\dfrac{1}{2}$

(d) $y = \dfrac{1}{2}$; $\displaystyle \lim_{x \to \infty} \frac{x^2 + 5x + 6}{2x^2 + 7x + 3} = \lim_{x \to \infty} \frac{1 + \dfrac{5}{x} + \dfrac{6}{x^2}}{2 + \dfrac{7}{x} + \dfrac{3}{x^2}} = \frac{1}{2}$

14. (a) $\dfrac{1}{e^2}$ (b) $f(0) = 1$, $\displaystyle \lim_{x \to 0^-} f(x) = 1$, and $\displaystyle \lim_{x \to 0^+} f(x) = 1$.

(c) 0

15. (a) 6; $\displaystyle \lim_{x \to 1} (f(x) + 4) = \lim_{x \to 1} f(x) + \lim_{x \to 1} 4 = 6$

(b) 5; $\displaystyle \lim_{x \to 3^-} \frac{5}{g(x)} = \frac{5}{1} = 5$

(c) 0; $\displaystyle \lim_{x \to 2} (f(x)g(x)) = 2 \cdot 0 = 0$

(d) -2;

$\displaystyle \lim_{x \to 3} \frac{f(x)}{g(x) - 1} = \lim_{x \to 3} \frac{(-2x + 6)}{(x - 2) - 1} = \lim_{x \to 3} \frac{-2x + 6}{x - 3} = -2$

16. (a) 172; $T(x)$ is continuous on $[0, 10)$, so $\displaystyle \lim_{x \to 4} T(x) = T(4)$.

(b) $-2°$F/min

(c) $(6, 8)$; $T(x)$ is continuous, $T(6) > 166.5°$F, and $T(8) < 166.5°$F.

(d) -2

17. (a) $a = 2, b = 3$ (b) 9   (c) 5

Chapter 2

Section 2.1   *(page 132)*

1. $m_1 = 0$, $m_2 = \frac{5}{2}$

3.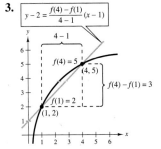

5. $m = -5$ **7.** $m = 8$ **9.** $m = 3$ **11.** 0

13. -5 **15.** $2x$ **17.** $3x^2 - 12$ **19.** $-\dfrac{1}{(x-1)^2}$

21. (a) $y = -2x + 2$ **23.** (a) $y = 12x - 16$

    (b)–(c)   (b)–(c)

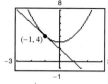 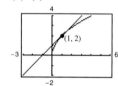 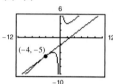

25. (a) $y = x + 1$ **27.** (a) $y = \frac{3}{4}x - 2$

    (b)–(c)   (b)–(c)

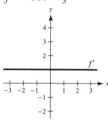 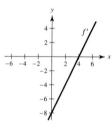

29. $y = -x + 1$ **31.** $y = 3x - 2,\ y = 3x + 2$

33. $\frac{7}{5}$ **35.** $-\frac{1}{5}$

37.   **39.**

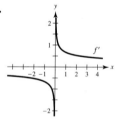 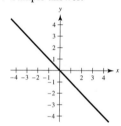

The slope of the graph of   The slope of the graph of
f is 1 for all x-values. f is negative for $x < 4$,
                                    positive for $x > 4$, and 0
                                    at $x = 4$.

41.   **43.** Sample answer:

The slope of the graph of
f is negative for $x < 0$
and positive for $x > 0$. The   Use a line with $m < 0$.
slope is undefined at $x = 0$.

45. $g(4) = 5;\ g'(4) = -\frac{5}{3}$ **47.** $f(x) = 5 - 3x;\ c = 1$

49. $f(x) = -x^2;\ c = 6$

51. $f(x) = -3x + 2$

53. $y = 2x + 1;\ y = -2x + 9$

55. No; Sample answer: $f(x) = x^3$ is symmetric with respect to the origin, but $f'(x) = 3x^2$ is not.

57. (a)

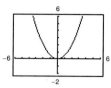

$f'(0) = 0,\ f'\!\left(\frac{1}{2}\right) = \frac{1}{2},\ f'(1) = 1,\ f'(2) = 2,\ f'(3) = 3$

  (b) $f'\!\left(-\frac{1}{2}\right) = -\frac{1}{2},\ f'(-1) = -1,\ f'(-2) = -2,$
      $f'(-3) = -3$

  (c)   (d) $f'(x) = x$

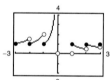

59. $f(2) = 4;\ f(2.1) = 3.99;\ f'(2) \approx -0.1$ **61.** 6

63. 4   **65.** Does not exist   **67.** Does not exist

69. Does not exist   **71.** $x \ne \pm 2$ **73.** $x \ne -4$

75.   **77.**

 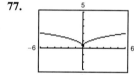

$x \ne 5$ $x \ne 0$

79. Left: -1; Right: 1; no   **81.** Left: 0; Right: 0; yes

83. Yes

85.

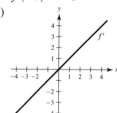

$x \ne n,\ n$ is an integer

87. B   **89.** D

Section 2.2   (page 144)

1. (a) $\dfrac{1}{2}$ (b) 3   **3.** 0   **5.** $7x^6$ **7.** $-\dfrac{5}{x^6}$ **9.** $\dfrac{1}{5x^{4/5}}$

11. 1   **13.** $-6t + 2$ **15.** $2x + 12x^2$ **17.** $6x^2 + 12x$

19. $\dfrac{\pi}{2}\cos\theta + \sin\theta$ **21.** $2x + \dfrac{1}{2}\sin x$ **23.** $4x^3 - 12e^x$

25. $\dfrac{1}{2}e^x - 3\cos x$ **27.** $y = \dfrac{2}{7}x^{-4};\ y' = -\dfrac{8}{7}x^{-5};\ y' = -\dfrac{8}{7x^5}$

29. $y = \dfrac{6}{125}x^{-3};\ y' = -\dfrac{18}{125}x^{-4};\ y' = -\dfrac{18}{125x^4}$

31. $y = x^{-1/2};\ y' = -\dfrac{1}{2}x^{-3/2};\ y' = -\dfrac{1}{2x^{3/2}}$

33. -2 **35.** 8   **37.** 3   **39.** $\dfrac{3}{4}$ **41.** $2t + \dfrac{6}{t^4}$

43. $6x + 4$ **45.** $1 - \dfrac{6}{x^3}$ **47.** $3x^2 + 1$

49. $\dfrac{1}{2x^{1/2}} - \dfrac{4}{3x^{2/3}}$ **51.** $\dfrac{5}{2\sqrt{x}} - 6\sin x$ **53.** $\dfrac{-2}{x^3} - 3e^x$

55. $\dfrac{7}{4}x^{3/4}$ should be $\dfrac{7}{4}x^{-3/4};\ \dfrac{dy}{dx} = -\dfrac{21}{16x^{7/4}}.$

57. (a) $y = 2x - 2$
(b)–(c)
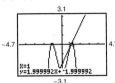

59. (a) $y = \frac{1}{4}x - 4$
(b)–(c)
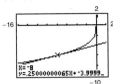

(c)
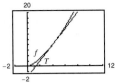
The accuracy decreases.

(d)

Δx	-3	-2	-1	-0.5	-0.1	0
$f(4 + \Delta x)$	1	2.828	5.196	6.548	7.702	8
$T(4 + \Delta x)$	-1	2	5	6.5	7.7	8

Δx	0.1	0.5	1	2	3
$f(4 + \Delta x)$	8.302	9.546	11.180	14.697	18.520
$T(4 + \Delta x)$	8.3	9.5	11	14	17

61. (a) $y = 2x + 1$
(b)–(c)
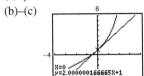

63. $(-1, 2), (0, 3), (1, 2)$ **65.** None
67. $(\ln 4, -4\ln 4 + 4)$ **69.** (π, π)
71. Sample answer:

73. $k = -8$ **75.** $k = 3$ **77.** $k = \frac{4}{27}$ **79.** $g'(x) = f'(x)$
81.
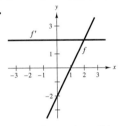

If f is linear, then f' is constant.
83. $y = 2x - 1; y = 4x - 4$
85. $f'(x) = 3 + \cos x \geq 2$ for all x.   **87.** $x - 4y + 4 = 0$
89.
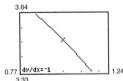

$-1; -1;$ They are the same.
91. (a)
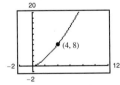

Sample answer: $(3.9, 7.7019), S(x) = 2.981x - 3.924$
(b) $T(x) = 3x - 4$
The secant line approaches the tangent line as you choose points closer to $(4, 8)$.

93. They are the same.
95. The average rate is between $f'(1)$ and $f'(2)$.
97. The average rate is between $g'(0)$ and $g'(1)$.
99. (a) -48 ft/sec
(b) $s'(1) = -32$ ft/sec; $s'(2) = -64$ ft/sec
(c) About 9.226 sec   (d) About -295.242 ft/sec
101. 71 m/sec; 22 m/sec
103.
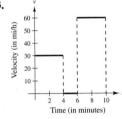
105.
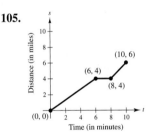

107. 108 cm³/cm
109. (a) $R(v) = 0.417v - 0.02$
(b) $B(v) = 0.0056v^2 + 0.001v + 0.04$
(c) $T(v) = 0.0056v^2 + 0.418v + 0.02$
(d)
(e) $T'(v) = 0.0112v + 0.418$
$T'(40) = 0.866$
$T'(80) = 1.314$
$T'(100) = 1.538$
Answers will vary.
(f) Stopping distance increases at an increasing rate.
111. $y = 2x^2 - 3x + 1$
113. $9x + y = 0, 9x + 4y + 27 = 0$ **115.** $a = \frac{1}{3}, b = -\frac{4}{3}$
117. $f_1(x): x \neq n\pi$, where n is an integer
$f_2(x): x \neq 0$
119. C   **121.** C

Section 2.3 *(page 155)*

1. $-20x + 17$ **3.** $\dfrac{1 - 5t^2}{2\sqrt{t}}$ **5.** $e^x(\cos x - \sin x)$
7. $-\dfrac{5}{(x - 5)^2}$ **9.** $\dfrac{1 - 5x^3}{2\sqrt{x}(x^3 + 1)^2}$ **11.** $\dfrac{\cos x - \sin x}{e^x}$

13. $f'(x) = 15x^4 + 8x^3 + 21x^2 + 16x - 20$
$f'(0) = -20$

15. $f'(x) = \dfrac{x^2 - 6x + 4}{(x - 3)^2}$
$f'(1) = -\dfrac{1}{4}$

17. $f'(x) = \cos x - x \sin x$
$f'\left(\dfrac{\pi}{4}\right) = \dfrac{\sqrt{2}}{8}(4 - \pi)$

19. $f'(x) = e^x(\cos x + \sin x)$
$f'(0) = 1$

21. $\dfrac{d}{dx}[f(x)g(x)] = f(x)g'(x) + f'(x)g(x)$, not

$f(x)g'(x) + g'(x)f(x); \dfrac{d}{dx}\left[\sqrt{x}(x^2 + 1)\right] = \dfrac{5x^2 + 1}{2\sqrt{x}}$

23. -11 **25.** $-\dfrac{1}{9}$

27. $f'(x) = 12x - 3$; Answers will vary.

29. $f'(x) = 6x^2 - 2x - 11$; Answers will vary.

31. $y = \dfrac{1}{3}x^3 + 2x; y' = x^2 + 2; y' = x^2 + 2$

33. $y = \dfrac{6}{7}x^{-2}; y' = -\dfrac{12}{7}x^{-3}; y' = -\dfrac{12}{7x^3}$

35. $y = 4x^{1/2}; y' = 2x^{-1/2}; y' = \dfrac{2}{\sqrt{x}}$

37. $\dfrac{3}{(x + 1)^2}$ **39.** $\dfrac{x^2 + 6x - 3}{(x + 3)^2}$ **41.** $\dfrac{3x + 1}{2x^{3/2}}$

43. $6s^2(s^3 - 2)$ **45.** $-\dfrac{2x^2 - 2x + 3}{x^2(x - 3)^2}$

47. $\dfrac{4s^2(3s^2 + 13s + 15)}{(s + 2)^2}$

49. $10x^4 - 8x^3 - 21x^2 - 10x - 30$ **51.** $-\dfrac{4c^2x}{(x^2 - c^2)^2}$

53. $t(t \cos t + 2 \sin t)$ **55.** $-\dfrac{t \sin t + \cos t}{t^2}$

57. $-e^x + \sec^2 x$ **59.** $\dfrac{3}{2}(\sec x)(\tan x - \sec x)$

61. $\cos x \cot^2 x$ **63.** $x(x \sec^2 x + 2 \tan x)$

65. $2x \cos x + 2 \sin x + x^2 e^x + 2xe^x$

67. $\dfrac{e^x(2x - 1)}{8x^{3/2}}$ **69.** $\dfrac{2x^2 + 8x - 1}{(x + 2)^2}$

71. $\dfrac{1 - \sin \theta + \theta \cos \theta}{(1 - \sin \theta)^2}$ **73.** $-4\sqrt{3}$ **75.** $\dfrac{1}{\pi^2}$

77. (a) $y = -3x - 1$
(b)–(c)

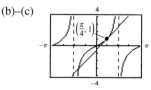

81. (a) $y = 2x - \dfrac{\pi}{2} + 1$
(b)–(c)

83. (a) $y = ex - e$
(b)–(c)

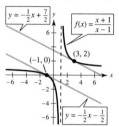

85. $(0, 0), (2, 4)$ **87.** $(3, 8e^{-3})$

89. $y = -\dfrac{1}{2}x + \dfrac{7}{2}, y = -\dfrac{1}{2}x - \dfrac{1}{2}$

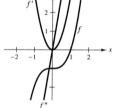

91. $f(x) + 2 = g(x)$ **93.** (a) 1   (b) $-\dfrac{1}{3}$

95. $\dfrac{18t + 5}{2\sqrt{t}}$ cm²/sec

97. $P'(1) \approx 37.68$ bacteria/h; $P'(2) \approx 31.55$ bacteria/h;
$P'(3) \approx 23.56$ bacteria/h

99. 2   **101.** $\dfrac{3}{\sqrt{x}}$ **103.** $\dfrac{2}{(x - 1)^3}$

105. $2 \cos x - x \sin x$ **107.** $\dfrac{e^x}{x^3}(x^2 - 2x + 2)$

109. $6x + \dfrac{6}{25x^{8/5}}$ **111.** $\sin x$

113. $n - 1$ or less; The degree decreases by 1 each time, so $f^{(n-1)}$ is a constant function.

115.

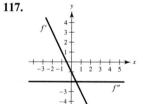

It appears that f is cubic, so f' would be quadratic and f'' would be linear.

117.   **119.**

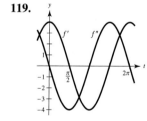

121. The particle moves 4 meters in one direction, then moves 4 meters back; $t = \dfrac{\pi}{2}$

123. (a) -12 in.   (b) -2 in./sec
(c) 8 in./sec   (d) 2 in./sec²

125. (a)–(c) Proofs

127.

t	0	1	2	3	4
$s(t)$	0	57.75	99	123.75	132
$v(t)$	66	49.5	33	16.5	0
$a(t)$	-16.5	-16.5	-16.5	-16.5	-16.5

The average velocity on $[0, 1]$ is 57.75, on $[1, 2]$ is 41.25, on $[2, 3]$ is 24.75, and on $[3, 4]$ is 8.25.

129. $f^{(n)}(x) = n!$

131. (a) $f''(x) = g(x)h''(x) + 2g'(x)h'(x) + g''(x)h(x)$
$f'''(x) = g(x)h'''(x) + 3g'(x)h''(x)$
$\qquad\qquad + 3g''(x)h'(x) + g'''(x)h(x)$
$f^{(4)}(x) = g(x)h^{(4)}(x) + 4g'(x)h'''(x) + 6g''(x)h''(x)$
$\qquad\qquad + 4g'''(x)h'(x) + g^{(4)}(x)h(x)$

(b) $f^{(n)}(x) = g(x)h^{(n)}(x) + \dfrac{n!}{1!(n-1)!}g'(x)h^{(n-1)}(x)$
$\qquad\qquad + \dfrac{n!}{2!(n-2)!}g''(x)h^{(n-2)}(x)$
$\qquad\qquad + \cdots + \dfrac{n!}{(n-1)!1!}g^{(n-1)}(x)h'(x)$
$\qquad\qquad + g^{(n)}(x)h(x)$

133. $n = 1$: $f'(x) = x \cos x + \sin x$
$n = 2$: $f'(x) = x^2 \cos x + 2x \sin x$
$n = 3$: $f'(x) = x^3 \cos x + 3x^2 \sin x$
$n = 4$: $f'(x) = x^4 \cos x + 4x^3 \sin x$
General rule: $f'(x) = x^n \cos x + nx^{(n-1)} \sin x$

135. True   **137.** True   **139.** $f'(x) = 2|x|$; No
141. Proof   **143.** C   **145.** B

Section 2.4   (page 169)

1. $u = 6x - 5$; $y = u^4$ **3.** $u = \csc x$; $y = u^3$
5. $u = -2x$; $y = e^u$ **7.** $6(2x - 7)^2$ **9.** $216x(9x^2 + 4)^3$
11. $-\dfrac{1}{2\sqrt{5-t}}$ **13.** $\dfrac{4x}{\sqrt[3]{(6x^2+1)^2}}$ **15.** $\dfrac{-3x}{\sqrt[4]{(9-x^2)}}$
17. $-\dfrac{1}{(x-2)^2}$ **19.** $-\dfrac{4}{(2t-3)^3}$ **21.** $-\dfrac{3}{2\sqrt{(3x+5)^3}}$
23. $2x(x^2 - 2)^3(5x^2 - 2)$ **25.** $\dfrac{1-2x^2}{\sqrt{1-x^2}}$
27. $\dfrac{1}{\sqrt{(x^2+1)^3}}$ **29.** $-\dfrac{2(x+5)(x^2+10x-2)}{(x^2+2)^3}$
31. $-\dfrac{9(1-2v)^2}{(1+v)^4}$
33. $20x(x^2 + 3)^9 + 2(x^2 + 3)^5 + 20x^2(x^2 + 3)^4 + 2x$
35. $\dfrac{1 - 3x^2 - 4x^{3/2}}{2\sqrt{x}(x^2+1)^2}$

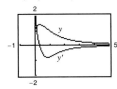

y has a horizontal tangent line.

37. $-\dfrac{\sqrt{\dfrac{x+1}{x}}}{2x(x+1)}$

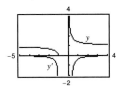

y' has no zeros.

39. $-\dfrac{\pi x \sin \pi x + \cos \pi x + 1}{x^2}$

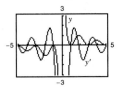

y has a horizontal tangent line.

41. $15 \sec^2 3x$ **43.** $\sin(4 - x)$ **45.** $2e^{2x}$ **47.** $\dfrac{e^{\sqrt{x}}}{2\sqrt{x}}$
49. $2(\sin 2)x$ **51.** $8 \sec^2 x \tan x$ **53.** $10 \tan 5\theta \sec^2 5\theta$
55. $\dfrac{1}{2} \sin 4\theta$ **57.** $\dfrac{6\pi \sin(\pi t - 1)}{\cos^3(\pi t - 1)}$
59. $\dfrac{1}{2\sqrt{x}} + 2x \cos(2x)^2$ **61.** $2[\cos(\tan 2x)]\sec^2 2x$
63. $2 \cos 4x$ **65.** $\dfrac{-1 - \cos^2 x}{\sin^3 x}$
67. $3(e^{-t} + e^t)^2(e^t - e^{-t})$ **69.** $2x$ **71.** $-\dfrac{2(e^x - e^{-x})}{(e^x + e^{-x})^2}$
73. $x^2 e^x$ **75.** $e^{-x}\left(\dfrac{1}{x} - \ln x\right)$ **77.** $2e^x \cos x$ **79.** $\dfrac{2}{x}$
81. $x + 2x \ln x$ **83.** $\dfrac{2x^2 - 1}{x(x^2 - 1)}$ **85.** $\dfrac{1 - x^2}{x(x^2 + 1)}$
87. $\dfrac{1 - 2\ln t}{t^3}$ **89.** $\dfrac{1}{1 - x^2}$ **91.** $\cot x$
93. $-\tan x + \dfrac{\sin x}{\cos x - 1}$ **95.** $\dfrac{3 \cos x}{(\sin x - 1)(\sin x + 2)}$
97. $\dfrac{\sqrt{x^2 + 1}}{x^2}$
99. Chain Rule wasn't used; $y' = -\dfrac{1}{2}(1 - x)^{-1/2}$
101. The derivative of e^{3x} is $3e^{3x}$; $y' = e^{3x}\dfrac{(3x - 1)}{x^2}$
103. (a) 1; same   (b) 2; same   **105.** 4   **107.** 3
109. $\dfrac{x + 4}{\sqrt{x^2 + 8x}}$; $\dfrac{5}{3}$ **111.** $-\dfrac{21x^2}{(x^3 - 6)^2}$; $-\dfrac{3}{7}$
113. $-\dfrac{17}{(t - 1)^2}$; -17 **115.** $-9 \tan 3x \sec^3 3x$; 0
117. (a) $y = \dfrac{28}{11}x + \dfrac{9}{11}$
(b)–(c)

119. (a) $y = 8x - 8\pi$
(b)–(c)

121. (a) $y = 4x + (1 - \pi) = 0$

(b)–(c)

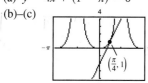

123. (a) $y = -\frac{1}{2}x + 4$

(b)–(c)

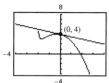

125. $y = -\frac{3}{4}x + \frac{25}{4}$

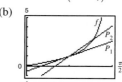

127. $\left(\frac{\pi}{6}, \frac{3\sqrt{3}}{2}\right), \left(\frac{5\pi}{6}, -\frac{3\sqrt{3}}{2}\right), \left(\frac{3\pi}{2}, 0\right)$ **129.** $2940(2 - 7x)^2$

131. $\dfrac{50}{(5x - 12)^3}$ **133.** $2(\cos x^2 - 2x^2 \sin x^2)$

135. $4e^{-2x}(3x - 1)$ **137.** 18   **139.** 0

141. $(\ln 5)5^x$ **143.** $(2 \ln 4)4^{2x-3}$ **145.** $2^t t(2 + t \ln 2)$

147. $-2^{-\theta}[(\ln 2)\cos \pi\theta + \pi \sin \pi\theta]$ **149.** $\dfrac{\sec^2 x}{(\ln 5) \tan x}$

151. $\dfrac{3x + 4}{2x(x + 1)\ln 10}$ **153.** $\dfrac{8(1 - \ln t)}{t^2 \ln 5}$

155.

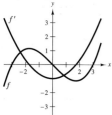

The zeros of f' correspond to the points where the graph of f has horizontal tangents.

157. $g'(x) = 3f'(3x)$ **159.** 24   **161.** $\frac{4}{3}$

163. (a) $\frac{1}{2}$ (b) Does not exist; g is not differentiable at 6.

165. (a) About 1.461   (b) About -1.016

167. 0.25 ft, 4 ft/sec

169. (a) $T'(35) \approx 1.692$

$T'(70) \approx 0.967$

At a pressure of 35 pounds per square inch, the temperature changes about 1.692 degrees Fahrenheit per pound per square inch. At a pressure of 70 pounds per square inch, the temperature changes about 0.967 degree Fahrenheit per pound per square inch.

(b) $T'(35) \approx 1.669°\text{F}/(\text{lb}/\text{in.}^2)$

$T'(70) \approx 0.973°\text{F}/(\text{lb}/\text{in.}^2)$

They are about the same.

171. (a) $V = 10,000(t + 1)^{-1/2}$ (b) $-\$1767.77/\text{year}$

(c) $-\$625/\text{year}$

173. (a) 0 bacteria/day   (b) About 177.8 bacteria/day

(c) About 44.4 bacteria/day   (d) About 10.8 bacteria/day

(e) About 3.3 bacteria/day

(f) The population is growing more slowly over time.

175. (a) $f'(x) = \beta \cos \beta x$

$f''(x) = -\beta^2 \sin \beta x$

$f'''(x) = -\beta^3 \cos \beta x$

$f^{(4)}(x) = \beta^4 \sin \beta x$

(b) $-\beta^2 \sin \beta x + \beta^2(\sin \beta x) = 0$

(c) $f^{(2k)}(x) = (-1)^k \beta^{2k} \sin \beta x$

$f^{(2k-1)}(x) = (-1)^{k+1}\beta^{2k-1} \cos \beta x$

177. (a) 0   (b) $\frac{5}{8}$ **179.** (a)–(b) Answers will vary.

181. $5\left(\dfrac{5x - 3}{|5x - 3|}\right)$ **183.** $-|x| \sin x + \dfrac{x}{|x|} \cos x$

185. True   **187.** True

189. (a) $P_1(x) = 2\left(x - \dfrac{\pi}{4}\right) + 1$

$P_2(x) = 2\left(x - \dfrac{\pi}{4}\right)^2 + 2\left(x - \dfrac{\pi}{4}\right) + 1$

(b)

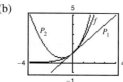

(c) P_2

(d) The accuracy decreases.

191. (a) $P_1(x) = x + 1$

$P_2(x) = \frac{1}{2}x^2 + x + 1$

(b)

(c) P_2

(d) The accuracy decreases.

193. D

195. (a) 108   (b) $y = 108x - 81$ (c) $(0, 1)$

(d) $12(2x^2 + 1)(10x^2 + 1)$

Section 2.5   *(page 180)*

1. $-\dfrac{x}{y}$ **3.** $-\sqrt{\dfrac{y}{x}}$ **5.** $\dfrac{y - 3x^2}{2y - x}$ **7.** $\dfrac{y\sqrt{3} - 2\sqrt{xy}}{2\sqrt{xy} - x\sqrt{3}}$

9. $\dfrac{10 - e^y}{xe^y + 3}$ **11.** $\dfrac{\cos x}{4 \sin 2y}$ **13.** $-\dfrac{\cot x \csc x + \tan y + 1}{x \sec^2 y}$

15. $\dfrac{y \cos xy}{1 - x \cos xy}$ **17.** $\dfrac{2xy}{3 - 2y^2}$ **19.** $\dfrac{y(1 - 6x^2)}{1 + y}$

21. The derivative of $-5y^2$ is $-10y\dfrac{dy}{dx}$; $\dfrac{dy}{dx} = \dfrac{8x + 7}{10y}$

23. (a) $y = \pm\sqrt{64 - x^2}$

(b)

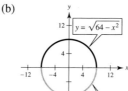

(c) $y' = \mp\dfrac{x}{\sqrt{64 - x^2}}$ (d) $y' = -\dfrac{x}{y}$

25. (a) $y = \pm\dfrac{\sqrt{x^2 + 16}}{4}$

(b)

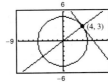

(c) $y' = \pm\dfrac{x}{4\sqrt{x^2 + 16}}$ (d) $y' = \dfrac{x}{16y}$

27. $-\dfrac{y}{x}; -\dfrac{1}{6}$ **29.** $\dfrac{98x}{y(x^2 + 49)^2}$; Undefined

31. $\dfrac{\cot y}{x}; \dfrac{1}{2\sqrt{3}}$ **33.** $\dfrac{1 - 3ye^{xy}}{3xe^{xy}}; \dfrac{1}{9}$ **35.** $-\dfrac{1}{2}$

37. $y = -x + 7$ **39.** $y = \dfrac{\sqrt{3}}{6}x + \dfrac{8\sqrt{3}}{3}$

41. $y = -\dfrac{9}{16}x + \dfrac{9}{4}$ **43.** $y = x - 1$

45. (a) $y = -2x + 4$ (b) Answers will vary.

47. $\cos^2 y; -\dfrac{\pi}{2} < y < \dfrac{\pi}{2}; \dfrac{dy}{dx} = \dfrac{1}{1 + x^2}$ **49.** $-\dfrac{4}{y^3}$

51. $\dfrac{6x^2y + 2y - 20x}{(x^2 - 1)^2}$ **53.** $\dfrac{x \sin x + 2 \cos x + 14y}{7x^2}$

55. At $(4, 3)$:

Tangent line: $y = -\dfrac{4}{3}x + \dfrac{25}{3}$

Normal line: $y = \dfrac{3}{4}x$

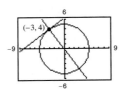

At $(-3, 4)$:

Tangent line: $y = \dfrac{3}{4}x + \dfrac{25}{4}$

Normal line: $y = -\dfrac{4}{3}x$

57. Answers will vary.

59. Horizontal tangents: $(-4, 0), (-4, 10)$

Vertical tangents: $(0, 5), (-8, 5)$

61. $\dfrac{2x^2 + 1}{\sqrt{x^2 + 1}}$ **63.** $\dfrac{3x^3 + 15x^2 - 8x}{2(x + 1)^3\sqrt{3x - 2}}$

65. $\dfrac{(2x^2 + 2x - 1)\sqrt{x - 1}}{(x + 1)^{3/2}}$ **67.** $5x^{(5/x)-2}(1 - \ln x)$

69. $(x - 2)^{x+1}\left[\dfrac{x + 1}{x - 2} + \ln(x - 2)\right]$ **71.** $\dfrac{2x^{\ln x}(\ln x)}{x}$

73.

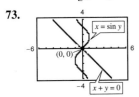

At $(0, 0)$, slopes are ± 1.

75. Sample answer:

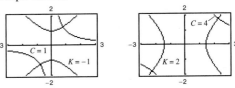

77. Sample answers: $xy = 2$, $yx^2 + x = 2$; $x^2 + y^3 + y = 4$, $xy^3 + y^2 = 2$

79. (a) True   (b) False; $\dfrac{d}{dy}[\cos y^2] = -2y \sin y^2$

(c) False; $\dfrac{d}{dx}[\tan y^2] = 2y \sec^2(y^2)\dfrac{dy}{dx}$

81. $(6, -8)$ and $(-6, 8)$

83. $y = -\dfrac{2}{\sqrt{7}}x + \dfrac{8}{\sqrt{7}}; y = \dfrac{2}{\sqrt{7}}x - \dfrac{8}{\sqrt{7}}$

85. B

87. (a) $-\dfrac{x + 3}{4y - 4}$ (b) $(-1, 1), (-5, 1)$ (c) $(-3, 0), (-3, 2)$

Section 2.6   *(page 187)*

1. $\dfrac{1}{27}$ **3.** $\dfrac{1}{5}$ **5.** $\dfrac{2\sqrt{3}}{3}$ **7.** -2 **9.** $\dfrac{1}{13}$

11. $f'(4) = -2, (f^{-1})'(-3) = -\dfrac{1}{2}$

13. $f'(5) = \dfrac{1}{2}, (f^{-1})'(1) = 2$ **15.** $\dfrac{1}{\sqrt{1 - (x + 1)^2}}$

17. $-\dfrac{3}{\sqrt{4 - x^2}}$ **19.** $\dfrac{e^x}{1 + e^{2x}}$

21. $\dfrac{4x - \sqrt{1 - 16x^2} \arcsin 4x}{x^2\sqrt{1 - 16x^2}}$

23. $e^{5x}\left[5 \arcsin x + \dfrac{1}{\sqrt{1 - x^2}}\right]$ **25.** $-\dfrac{3}{1 + 9x^2}$

27. $-\dfrac{t}{\sqrt{1 - t^2}}$ **29.** 0 **31.** $2 \arccos x$ **33.** $\dfrac{1}{1 - x^4}$

35. $\arcsin x$ **37.** $\dfrac{x^2}{\sqrt{16 - x^2}}$ **39.** $\dfrac{2}{(1 + x^2)^2}$

41. Chain Rule wasn't used for $4x$ in e^{4x};

$\dfrac{d}{dx}[\arcsin e^{4x}] = \dfrac{4e^{4x}}{\sqrt{1 - e^{8x}}}$

43. $y = \dfrac{1}{2}x + \dfrac{1}{2} - \dfrac{\pi}{4}$ **45.** $y = 3\sqrt{2}x + \dfrac{\pi}{4} - 1$

47. $y = \dfrac{1}{3}\left(4\sqrt{3}x - 2\sqrt{3} + \pi\right)$ **49.** $y = \sqrt{2}x + \dfrac{\pi}{4} - 1$

51. $y = (2\pi - 4)x + 4$

53. $y = -2x + \left(\dfrac{\pi}{6} + \sqrt{3}\right); y = -2x + \left(\dfrac{5\pi}{6} - \sqrt{3}\right)$

55. $P_1(x) = x; P_2(x) = x$

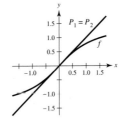

57. $P_1(x) = \dfrac{\pi}{6} + \dfrac{2\sqrt{3}}{3}\left(x - \dfrac{1}{2}\right)$

$P_2(x) = \dfrac{\pi}{6} + \dfrac{2\sqrt{3}}{3}\left(x - \dfrac{1}{2}\right) + \dfrac{2\sqrt{3}}{9}\left(x - \dfrac{1}{2}\right)^2$

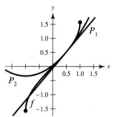

59. $-\dfrac{1}{11}$ **61.** $\dfrac{\pi + 2}{\pi}$ **63.** $y = -\dfrac{2\pi}{\pi + 8}x + 1 - \dfrac{\pi^2}{2\pi + 16}$

65. $y = -x + \sqrt{2}$

67. (a)   (b) Proof

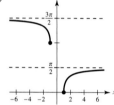

69. $y = x$; j and k are inverses of each other.

71. (a) $\theta = \operatorname{arccot}\dfrac{x}{5}$

(b) $x = 10$: 16 rad/h; $x = 3$: about 58.824 rad/h

73. (a) $h(t) = -16t^2 + 256$; $t = 4$ sec

(b) $t = 1$: about -0.0520 rad/sec;

$t = 2$: about -0.1116 rad/sec

75. About 0.015 rad/sec **77.** Proof **79.** True

81. True **83.** Proof **85.** B **87.** C

Section 2.7 *(page 195)*

1. (a) $\dfrac{3}{4}$ (b) 20 **3.** (a) -12 (b) $-\dfrac{5}{2}$

5. (a) -8 cm/sec (b) 0 cm/sec (c) 8 cm/sec

7. (a) 12 ft/sec (b) 6 ft/sec (c) 3 ft/sec

9. Yes; No; $\dfrac{dy}{dt} = a\dfrac{dx}{dt}$

11. dx and dy should be switched; $\dfrac{dx}{dt} = \dfrac{3}{4}$

13. 80π cm²/min

15. (a) $r = 9$: 972π in.³/min; $r = 36$: $15{,}552\pi$ in.³/min

(b) $\dfrac{dV}{dt} = 4\pi r^2 \dfrac{dr}{dt}$

17. (a) 72 cm³/sec (b) 1800 cm³/sec **19.** $\dfrac{8}{405\pi}$ ft/min

21. (a) 12.5% (b) $\dfrac{1}{144}$ m/min

23. (a) $-\dfrac{7}{12}$ ft/sec; $-\dfrac{3}{2}$ ft/sec; $-\dfrac{48}{7}$ ft/sec

(b) $\dfrac{527}{24}$ ft²/sec (c) $\dfrac{1}{12}$ rad/sec

25. Rate of vertical change: $\dfrac{1}{5}$ m/sec

Rate of horizontal change: $-\dfrac{\sqrt{3}}{15}$ m/sec

27. (a) -750 mi/h (b) 30 min

29. $-\dfrac{50}{\sqrt{85}} \approx -5.42$ ft/sec

31. (a) $\dfrac{25}{3}$ ft/sec (b) $\dfrac{10}{3}$ ft/sec

33. (a) 12 sec (b) $\dfrac{\sqrt{3}}{2}$ m (c) $\dfrac{\sqrt{5}\pi}{120}$ m/sec

35. $\dfrac{1}{25}$ rad/sec

37. (a) $r(f) = -0.0243f^3 + 1.258f^2 - 21.87f + 130.8$

(b) About -0.1 million/year

39. (a) $\dfrac{dx}{dt} = -600\pi \sin\theta$

(b)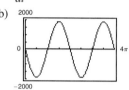

(c) $\theta = \dfrac{\pi}{2} + n\pi$ (or $90° + n \cdot 180°$); $\theta = n\pi$ (or $n \cdot 180°$)

(d) $\theta = 30°$: -300π cm/sec; $\theta = 60°$: $-300\sqrt{3}\pi$ cm/sec

41. (a) Answers will vary. (b) $\theta = \dfrac{\pi}{6}$: $\dfrac{\sqrt{3}s^2}{8}$; $\theta = \dfrac{\pi}{3}$: $\dfrac{s^2}{8}$

43. About -0.1808 ft/sec² **45.** B

47. (a) $-\dfrac{3\pi}{10}$ ft²/h (b) $-\dfrac{3\pi}{5}$ ft²/h

Section 2.8 *(page 202)*

1. About 2.2361 **3.** About 1.5708 **5.** -1.260

7. 0.682 **9.** 1.250 **11.** 0.567 **13.** 1.935

15. 0.900, 1.100, 1.900

17. The fraction should be $\dfrac{f(x_n)}{f'(x_n)}$, not $\dfrac{f'(x_n)}{f(x_n)}$;

$x_{n+1} = x_n - \dfrac{x_n^3 + 5x_n + 1}{3x_n^2 + 5}$

19. (a)

(b) About 1.347 (c) About 2.532

(d)

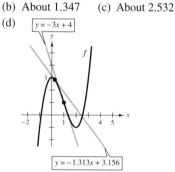

The x-intercept of the tangent line may approximate another zero of the function.

21. 0.567 **23.** 4.493 **25.** $f'(x_1) = 0$

27. 0.74 **29.** 1.12

31. The values would be identical; If $f(x_n) = 0$,

$$x_n - \frac{f(x_n)}{f'(x_n)} = x_n.$$

33. If all the coefficients are positive, then any zeros must be less than or equal to 0.

35. \$384,364   **37.** Proof

39. (a) Answers will vary.   (b) $\sqrt{5} \approx 2.236$; $\sqrt{7} \approx 2.646$

41. True   **43.** 0.217   **45.** A

Review Exercises for Chapter 2   *(page 204)*

1. $f'(x) = 0$ **3.** $f'(x) = 2x - 4$ **5.** 5   **7.** $x \neq 3$

9. $x > 1$ **11.** 0   **13.** $3x^2 - 30x$ **15.** $\dfrac{2}{x^{1/2}} + \dfrac{2}{x^{2/3}}$

17. $-\dfrac{3}{t^3}$ **19.** $4 - 5\cos\theta$ **21.** $-3\sin t - 4e^t$

23. -1 **25.** 2

27. (a) 50 (vibrations/sec)/lb
 (b) About 33.33 (vibrations/sec)/lb

29. (a) $s(t) = -16t^2 - 30t + 600$; $v(t) = -32t - 30$
 (b) -94 ft/sec
 (c) $v'(1) = -62$ ft/sec; $v'(3) = -126$ ft/sec
 (d) About 5.258 sec   (e) About -198.256 ft/sec

31. $\dfrac{\cos x}{2\sqrt{x}} - \sqrt{x}\sin x$ **33.** $-\dfrac{x^2 + 1}{(x^2 - 1)^2}$

35. $\dfrac{4x^3\cos x + x^4\sin x}{\cos^2 x}$ **37.** $3x^2\sec x\tan x + 6x\sec x$

39. $4xe^x + 4e^x + \csc^2 x$ **41.** $4(5x^3 - 15x^2 - 11x - 8)$

43. $5x\cos x + (3 - x^2)\sin x$ **45.** $y = \frac{1}{2}x + 3$

47. $y = 4x + 10$ **49.** $y = -8x + 1$ **51.** $-48t$

53. $\dfrac{225}{4}\sqrt{x}$ **55.** $6\sec^2\theta\tan\theta$

57. (a) $h = r(\csc\theta - 1)$ (b) $-7920\sqrt{3}$ mi/rad

59. $28(7x + 3)^3$ **61.** $-\dfrac{2x}{(x^2 + 4)^2}$ **63.** $-45\sin(9x + 1)$

65. $\sin^2 x$ **67.** $(6x + 1)^4(36x + 1)$ **69.** $\dfrac{3}{(x^2 + 1)^{3/2}}$

71. $\frac{1}{4}te^{t/4}(t + 8)$ **73.** $\dfrac{e^{2x} - e^{-2x}}{\sqrt{e^{2x} + e^{-2x}}}$ **75.** $\dfrac{x(2 - x)}{e^x}$

77. $\dfrac{1}{2x}$ **79.** $\dfrac{1 + 2\ln x}{2\sqrt{\ln x}}$ **81.** $\dfrac{x}{(a + bx)^2}$ **83.** $\dfrac{1}{x(a + bx)}$

85. $y = 2x - 1$ **87.** $y = 6$ **89.** $y = \frac{5}{2}$

91. $384(8x + 5)$ **93.** $\dfrac{16 - 8x}{(x + 1)^4}$ **95.** $2\csc^2 x\cot x$

97. (a) About $-18.667°$F/h   (b) About $-7.284°$F/h
 (c) About $-3.240°$F/h   (d) About $-0.747°$F/h
 As the time increases, the rate of change of the temperature decreases.

99. About 0.04224 cm/sec^2

101. (a)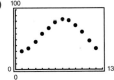

$T(t) = 57.1 + 27.3\sin(0.49t - 1.90)$

(b)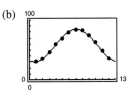

The model is a good fit.

(c) $T'(t) = 13.377\cos(0.49t - 1.90)$

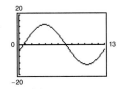

(d) March–May, Oct.–Nov.; Dec.–Feb., June–Aug.; Yes; Answers will vary.

103. $\dfrac{x}{y}$ **105.** $\dfrac{y(y^2 - 3x^2)}{x(x^2 - 3y^2)}$ **107.** $\dfrac{y\sin x + \sin y}{\cos x - x\cos y}$

109. $y = -6x + 28$ **111.** $y = -\frac{1}{2}x + 5$

113. Tangent line: $y = -3x + 10$
 Normal line: $y = \frac{1}{3}x$

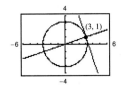

115. Tangent line: $y = -\dfrac{1}{e}x$
 Normal line: $y = ex - e^2 - 1$

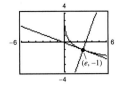

117. $\dfrac{x^3 + 2x^2 + 4}{(x + 1)^2\sqrt{x^2 + 4}}$, $x > 0$ **119.** $\dfrac{1}{3(\sqrt[3]{-3})^2} \approx 0.160$

121. $\dfrac{3}{4}$ **123.** $\dfrac{1}{(1 + x^2)^{3/2}}$ **125.** $\dfrac{x}{|x|\sqrt{x^2 - 1}} + \operatorname{arcsec} x$

127. (a) $2\sqrt{2}$ units/sec   (b) 4 units/sec   (c) 8 units/sec

129. 450π km/h   **131.** About 84.9797 mi/h

133. -0.347, -1.532, 1.879

135. 1.202   **137.** About -0.755

AP® Exam Practice Questions   *(page 208)*

1. D   **2.** A   **3.** D   **4.** A   **5.** C   **6.** A   **7.** B
8. C   **9.** B   **10.** D   **11.** C   **12.** B   **13.** D

14. (a) $v'(t) = -2.45\sin 0.7t$; The acceleration of the particle
 (b) The position of the particle   (c) About 0.859
 (d) Yes; $v(t) = 0$ when $t = \frac{10}{7}\cos^{-1}\left(-\frac{4}{7}\right)$

15. (a) $-\frac{1}{25}$ (b) -14 (c) $\frac{7}{4}$

16. (a) (i) $(0, 1)$, $(4.4, 5)$; The velocity is positive.
  (ii) $(2, 4.4)$; The velocity is negative.
  (iii) $(1, 2)$; The velocity is 0.
 (b) (i) -2 ft/sec^2
  (ii) 5 ft/sec^2

17. (a) $x = \dfrac{\pi}{2}, \dfrac{3\pi}{2}$; $\tan x$ and $\sec^2 x$ are undefined at these values.

   (b) $k = 0$

Chapter 3

Section 3.1   *(page 217)*

1. 0   **3.** 0   **5.** Does not exist

7. 2, absolute maximum and relative maximum

9. 1, absolute maximum and relative maximum

   2, absolute minimum and relative minimum

   3, absolute maximum and relative maximum

11. $\dfrac{3}{4}$ **13.** $\dfrac{8}{3}$ **15.** $\dfrac{\pi}{3}, \pi, \dfrac{5\pi}{3}$ **17.** $\dfrac{1}{5}$ **19.** 0

21. Minimum: $(-1, -3)$; Maximum: $(2, 0)$

23. Minimum: $(-3, -13)$; Maximum: $(0, 5)$

25. Minimum: $\left(-1, -\frac{5}{2}\right)$; Maximum: $(2, 2)$

27. Minimum: $(0, 0)$; Maximum: $(-1, 5)$

29. Minima: $(1, -6)$ and $(-2, -6)$; Maximum: $(0, 0)$

31. Minimum: $(-1, -1)$; Maximum: $(3, 3)$

33. Minimum value is -1 for $-1 \le x < 0$; Maximum: $(3, 3)$

35. Minimum: $\left(\dfrac{3\pi}{2}, -1\right)$; Maximum: $\left(\dfrac{5\pi}{6}, \dfrac{1}{2}\right)$

37. Minimum: $(\pi, -3)$; Maxima: $(0, 3)$ and $(2\pi, 3)$

39. Minimum: $(0, 0)$; Maximum: $(-2, \arctan 4)$

41. Minimum: $(2, 5e^2 - e^4)$; Maximum: $\left(\ln \frac{5}{2}, \frac{25}{4}\right)$

43. Minima: $(0, 0)$ and $(\pi, 0)$; Maximum: $\left(\dfrac{3\pi}{4}, \dfrac{\sqrt{2}}{2}e^{3\pi/4}\right)$

45. $x = 0$ is a critical number but not a relative extremum; $x = -\frac{3}{2}$ and $x = 3$

47. (a) Minimum: $(0, -3)$; Maximum: $(2, 1)$

   (b) Minimum: $(0, -3)$ (c) Maximum: $(2, 1)$

   (d) No extrema

49.

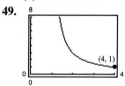

Minimum: $(4, 1)$

51.

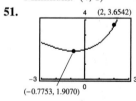

Minimum: $(-0.7753, 1.9070)$

Maximum: $(2, 3.6562)$

53. (a)

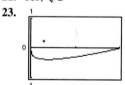

   (b) $\dfrac{4 - 2x}{\sqrt{3 - x}}$ (c) 2; Maximum: $\left(2, \frac{8}{3}\right)$; They are the same.

55. (a)

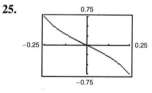

   (b) $\dfrac{x^2 - 2x + (2x^2 + 4x - 6)\ln(x + 3)}{x + 3}$

   (c) About 1.0863; Minimum: $(1.0863, -1.3972)$; They are the same.

57. About 1.47   **59.** 1

61. f is continuous on $\left[0, \dfrac{\pi}{4}\right]$ but not on $[0, \pi]$.

63. (a) Yes; The value is defined.

   (b) No; The value is not reached.

65. No; $f(-2)$ is not defined.

67. 12 amps; No; P is decreasing for $I > 12$.

69. $\operatorname{arcsec}\sqrt{3} \approx 0.9553$ rad   **71.** Answers will vary.

73. False; $f(-a) = f(a)$, so $f(-a)$ is also a relative minimum.

75. D

77. (a) $\dfrac{4(1 - 3\ln x)}{x^4}$ (b) $y = -8e^{-4}x + 12e^{-3}$

   (c) $e^{1/3}$; relative maximum   (d) $-\infty$

Section 3.2   *(page 224)*

1. f is not continuous on $[-1, 1]$.

3. f is not differentiable on $(0, 2)$.

5. $(2, 0), (-1, 0)$; $f'\left(\frac{1}{2}\right) = 0$ **7.** $(0, 0), (-4, 0)$; $f'\left(-\frac{8}{3}\right) = 0$

9. Yes; $\dfrac{3}{2}$ **11.** Yes; $\dfrac{6 - \sqrt{3}}{3}$; $\dfrac{6 + \sqrt{3}}{3}$

13. No; Not differentiable at $x = 0$ **15.** Yes; $-2 + \sqrt{5}$

17. Yes; $\dfrac{\pi}{2}$; $\dfrac{3\pi}{2}$ **19.** No; Not continuous on $[0, \pi]$

21. Yes; $\sqrt{2}$

23.

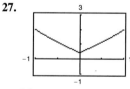

Yes; $\dfrac{\sqrt{3}}{9}$

25.

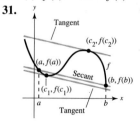

No

27.

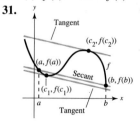

No

29. (a) $f(1) = 38 = f(2)$ (b) 0; $t = \frac{3}{2}$ sec

31.

33. Not continuous on $[0, 6]$

35. (a) $x + y - 3 = 0$ (b) -1

(c) $\left(\frac{1}{2}, \frac{19}{4}\right); 4x + 4y - 21 = 0$

(d)

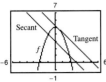

37. Yes; $\dfrac{\sqrt{21}}{3}$ **39.** Yes; $\dfrac{1}{\sqrt{3}}; -\dfrac{1}{\sqrt{3}}$

41. No; Not continuous on $[-3, 3]$

43. No; Not differentiable on $[-1, 3]$ **45.** Yes; $\dfrac{\pi}{2}$

47. No; Not continuous on $[0, \pi]$ **49.** Yes; $\dfrac{4}{e}$

51. (a)–(c)

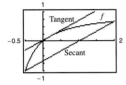

53. (a)–(c)

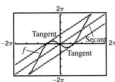

(b) $y = \frac{2}{3}(x - 1)$

(c) $y = \frac{1}{3}\left(2x + 5 - 2\sqrt{6}\right)$

(b) $y = x$

(c) $y = x + 2; y = x - 2$

55. (a)–(c)

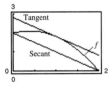

(b) $y = -x + 2$

(c) $y = -x + 2.8161$

57. (a) 12.4 m/sec   (b) 2 sec

59. No; Sample answer: Let $f(x) = x^2$ on $[-1, 2]$.

61. No; f is not continuous on $[0, 1]$.

63. The average rate of change is $-222°$F/h and temperature is continuous.

65. Proof

67. Sample answer:

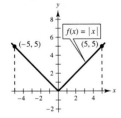

69–71. Proofs

73. $f(x) = 4$; Constant functions have derivatives of 0.

75. $f(x) = x^2 + 2$; Quadratic functions have linear derivatives.

77–79. Proofs   **81.** B   **83.** A

Section 3.3   *(page 233)*

1. (a) $(0, 6)$ (b) $(6, 8)$

3. Increasing on $(-\infty, -1)$; Decreasing on $(-1, \infty)$

5. Increasing on $(-1, 0)$ and $(1, \infty)$
Decreasing on $(-\infty, -1)$ and $(0, 1)$

7. Increasing on $(-\infty, -1)$; Decreasing on $(-1, \infty)$

9. Increasing on $(-\infty, 3)$; Decreasing on $(3, \infty)$

11. Increasing on $(-\infty, 4)$ and $(4, \infty)$

13. Increasing on $\left(0, \dfrac{\pi}{2}\right)$ and $\left(\dfrac{3\pi}{2}, 2\pi\right)$; Decreasing on $\left(\dfrac{\pi}{2}, \dfrac{3\pi}{2}\right)$

15. Increasing on $\left(-2\sqrt{2}, 2\sqrt{2}\right)$
Decreasing on $\left(-4, -2\sqrt{2}\right)$ and $\left(2\sqrt{2}, 4\right)$

17. Increasing on $\left(-\frac{1}{4}\ln 3, \infty\right)$; Decreasing on $\left(-\infty, -\frac{1}{4}\ln 3\right)$

19. Increasing on $\left(\dfrac{2}{\sqrt{e}}, \infty\right)$; Decreasing on $\left(0, \dfrac{2}{\sqrt{e}}\right)$

21. (a) 0   (b) Increasing on $(0, \infty)$; Decreasing on $(-\infty, 0)$
(c) Relative minimum: $(0, -25)$

23. (a) 1   (b) Increasing on $(-\infty, 1)$; Decreasing on $(1, \infty)$
(c) Relative maximum: $(1, 5)$

25. (a) $-2, 1$
(b) Increasing on $(-\infty, -2)$ and $(1, \infty)$
Decreasing on $(-2, 1)$
(c) Relative maximum: $(-2, 20)$
Relative minimum: $(1, -7)$

27. (a) $-\frac{5}{3}, 1$
(b) Increasing on $\left(-\frac{5}{3}, 1\right)$
Decreasing on $\left(-\infty, -\frac{5}{3}\right)$ and $(1, \infty)$
(c) Relative minimum: $\left(-\frac{5}{3}, -\frac{256}{27}\right)$
Relative maximum: $(1, 0)$

29. (a) ± 1
(b) Increasing on $(-\infty, -1)$ and $(1, \infty)$
Decreasing on $(-1, 1)$
(c) Relative maximum: $\left(-1, \frac{4}{5}\right)$; Relative minimum: $\left(1, -\frac{4}{5}\right)$

31. (a) 0   (b) Increasing on $(-\infty, \infty)$
(c) No relative extrema

33. (a) -2
(b) Increasing on $(-2, \infty)$; Decreasing on $(-\infty, -2)$
(c) Relative minimum: $(-2, 0)$

35. (a) 5   (b) Increasing on $(-\infty, 5)$; Decreasing on $(5, \infty)$
(c) Relative maximum: $(5, 5)$

37. (a) $\pm\dfrac{\sqrt{2}}{2}$
(b) Increasing on $\left(-\infty, -\dfrac{\sqrt{2}}{2}\right)$ and $\left(\dfrac{\sqrt{2}}{2}, \infty\right)$
Decreasing on $\left(-\dfrac{\sqrt{2}}{2}, 0\right)$ and $\left(0, \dfrac{\sqrt{2}}{2}\right)$
(c) Relative maximum: $\left(-\dfrac{\sqrt{2}}{2}, -2\sqrt{2}\right)$
Relative minimum: $\left(\dfrac{\sqrt{2}}{2}, 2\sqrt{2}\right)$

39. (a) 0
(b) Increasing on $(-\infty, -3)$ and $(-3, 0)$
Decreasing on $(0, 3)$ and $(3, \infty)$
(c) Relative maximum: $(0, 0)$

41. (a) 0
(b) Increasing on $(-\infty, 0)$; Decreasing on $(0, \infty)$
(c) Relative maximum: $(0, 4)$

43. (a) $0, 1, 3$
   (b) Increasing on $(-\infty, 0)$ and $(1, 3)$
       Decreasing on $(0, 1)$ and $(3, \infty)$
   (c) Relative maxima: $(0, 6)$ and $(3, 9)$
       Relative minimum: $(1, 5)$

45. (a) 2 (b) Increasing on $(-\infty, 2)$; Decreasing on $(2, \infty)$
   (c) Relative maximum: $(2, e^{-1})$

47. (a) 0 (b) Decreasing on $[-1, 1]$ (c) None

49. (a) $\dfrac{1}{\ln 3}$

   (b) Increasing on $\left(-\infty, \dfrac{1}{\ln 3}\right)$; Decreasing on $\left(\dfrac{1}{\ln 3}, \infty\right)$

   (c) Relative maximum: $\left(\dfrac{1}{\ln 3}, \dfrac{3^{-1/\ln 3}}{\ln 3}\right)$ or $\left(\dfrac{1}{\ln 3}, \dfrac{1}{e \ln 3}\right)$

51. (a) $\dfrac{1}{\ln 4}$

   (b) Increasing on $\left(\dfrac{1}{\ln 4}, \infty\right)$; Decreasing on $\left(0, \dfrac{1}{\ln 4}\right)$

   (c) Relative minimum: $\left(\dfrac{1}{\ln 4}, \dfrac{\ln(\ln 4) + 1}{\ln 4}\right)$

53. (a) None   (b) Increasing on $(-\infty, \infty)$ (c) None
55. (a) None   (b) Increasing on $(-\infty, 2)$ and $(2, \infty)$
   (c) None

57. $f'(x)$ does not change signs at $x = 4$; $(4, f(4))$ is not a relative extremum of f.

59. (a) Increasing on $\left(\dfrac{\pi}{3}, \dfrac{5\pi}{3}\right)$

       Decreasing on $\left(0, \dfrac{\pi}{3}\right)$ and $\left(\dfrac{5\pi}{3}, 2\pi\right)$

   (b) Relative maximum: $\left(\dfrac{5\pi}{3}, \dfrac{5\pi}{3} + \sqrt{3}\right)$

       Relative minimum: $\left(\dfrac{\pi}{3}, \dfrac{\pi}{3} - \sqrt{3}\right)$

61. (a) Increasing on $\left(0, \dfrac{\pi}{4}\right)$ and $\left(\dfrac{5\pi}{4}, 2\pi\right)$

       Decreasing on $\left(\dfrac{\pi}{4}, \dfrac{5\pi}{4}\right)$

   (b) Relative maximum: $\left(\dfrac{\pi}{4}, \sqrt{2}\right)$

       Relative minimum: $\left(\dfrac{5\pi}{4}, -\sqrt{2}\right)$

63. (a) Increasing on $\left(0, \dfrac{\pi}{2}\right)$, $\left(\dfrac{7\pi}{6}, \dfrac{3\pi}{2}\right)$, and $\left(\dfrac{11\pi}{6}, 2\pi\right)$

       Decreasing on $\left(\dfrac{\pi}{2}, \dfrac{7\pi}{6}\right)$ and $\left(\dfrac{3\pi}{2}, \dfrac{11\pi}{6}\right)$

   (b) Relative maxima: $\left(\dfrac{\pi}{2}, 2\right)$, $\left(\dfrac{3\pi}{2}, 0\right)$

       Relative minima: $\left(\dfrac{7\pi}{6}, -\dfrac{1}{4}\right)$, $\left(\dfrac{11\pi}{6}, -\dfrac{1}{4}\right)$

65. (a) Increasing on $\left(\dfrac{\pi}{4}, \dfrac{\pi}{2}\right)$, $\left(\dfrac{3\pi}{4}, \pi\right)$, $\left(\dfrac{5\pi}{4}, \dfrac{3\pi}{2}\right)$, and $\left(\dfrac{7\pi}{4}, 2\pi\right)$

       Decreasing on $\left(0, \dfrac{\pi}{4}\right)$, $\left(\dfrac{\pi}{2}, \dfrac{3\pi}{4}\right)$, $\left(\pi, \dfrac{5\pi}{4}\right)$, and $\left(\dfrac{3\pi}{2}, \dfrac{7\pi}{4}\right)$

   (b) Relative maxima: $\left(\dfrac{\pi}{2}, 1\right)$, $(\pi, 1)$, $\left(\dfrac{3\pi}{2}, 1\right)$

       Relative minima: $\left(\dfrac{\pi}{4}, 0\right)$, $\left(\dfrac{3\pi}{4}, 0\right)$, $\left(\dfrac{5\pi}{4}, 0\right)$, $\left(\dfrac{7\pi}{4}, 0\right)$

67. (a) $\dfrac{2(9 - 2x^2)}{\sqrt{9 - x^2}}$

   (b) 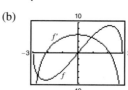   (c) $\pm\dfrac{3\sqrt{2}}{2}$

   (d) $f' > 0$ on $\left(-\dfrac{3\sqrt{2}}{2}, \dfrac{3\sqrt{2}}{2}\right)$;

       $f' < 0$ on $\left(-3, -\dfrac{3\sqrt{2}}{2}\right)$, $\left(\dfrac{3\sqrt{2}}{2}, 3\right)$;

       f is increasing when f' is positive and decreasing when f' is negative.

69. (a) $t(t \cos t + 2 \sin t)$
   (b)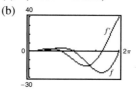

   (c) About 2.2889, about 5.0870
   (d) $f' > 0$ on $(0, 2.2889)$, $(5.0870, 2\pi)$
       $f' < 0$ on $(2.2889, 5.0870)$
       f is increasing when f' is positive and decreasing when f' is negative.

71. (a) $e^x(\sin 2x + 2 \cos 2x)$
   (b)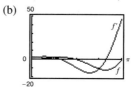

   (c) About 1.0172, about 2.5880
   (d) $f' > 0$ on $(0, 1.0172)$ and $(2.5880, \pi)$
       $f' < 0$ on $(1.0172, 2.5880)$
       f is increasing when f' is positive and decreasing when f' is negative.

73. 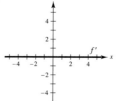   **75.**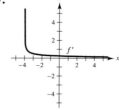

77. 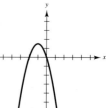   **79.** Sample answer:

81. $<$; $g'(0) = f'(0)$ **83.** $<$; $g'(-6) = -f'(-6)$
85. $>$; $g'(0) = f'(-10)$

87. No; Sample answer: f could be increasing (or decreasing) on both sides of c .

89. Sample answer:

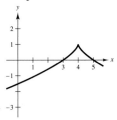

91. (a) Sample answer:

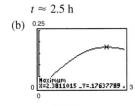

(b) About -0.40 , about 0.48

(c) Relative maximum:
$(0.48, 1.25)$
Relative minimum:
$(-0.40, 0.75)$

93. (a)

t	0	0.5	1	1.5	2	2.5	3
$C(t)$	0	0.055	0.107	0.148	0.171	0.176	0.167

$t \approx 2.5$ h

(b)

```
0.25




0 |_____| 3
  Maximum
  X=2.3811015  Y=.17637789
0
```

$t \approx 2.38$ h

(c) $t = \dfrac{3\sqrt[3]{4}}{2}$

95. $r = \dfrac{2R}{3}$

97. (a) $v(t) = 4t - 8$ (b) $v > 0$ on $(2, \infty)$; $v < 0$ on $(0, 2)$
(c) $t = 2$

99. (a) $v(t) = 2(t - 1)e^{(t-1)^2}$
(b) $v > 0$ on $(1, \infty)$; $v < 0$ on $(0, 1)$ (c) $t = 1$

101. Answers will vary.   **103.** True

105. False; Sample answer: Let $f(x) = x^3$.

107. False; Sample answer: Let $f(x) = \sin x$.

109–113. Proofs   **115.** D

117. (a) $0; \infty$ (b) $-1 \pm \sqrt{2}$
(c) Increasing on $\left(-\infty, -1 - \sqrt{2}\right)$ and $\left(-1 + \sqrt{2}, \infty\right)$
Decreasing on $\left(-1 - \sqrt{2}, -1 + \sqrt{2}\right)$
(d) Relative maximum: $\left(-1 - \sqrt{2}, 0.4318\right)$
Relative minimum: $\left(-1 + \sqrt{2}, -1.2536\right)$

Section 3.4   *(page 242)*

1. Concave upward: $(-\infty, \infty)$

3. Concave upward: $(-\infty, 2)$; Concave downward: $(2, \infty)$

5. Concave upward: $(-\infty, -2), (2, \infty)$
Concave downward: $(-2, 2)$

7. Concave upward: $(-\infty, -1), (1, \infty)$
Concave downward: $(-1, 1)$

9. Concave upward: $(-2, \infty)$; Concave downward: $(-\infty, -2)$

11. Concave upward: $\left(-\dfrac{\pi}{2}, 0\right)$; Concave downward: $\left(0, \dfrac{\pi}{2}\right)$

13. $(3, 0)$; Concave downward: $(-\infty, 3)$;
Concave upward: $(3, \infty)$

15. $(-2, -8), (0, 0)$; Concave upward: $(-\infty, -2), (0, \infty)$;
Concave downward: $(-2, 0)$

17. None; Concave upward: $(-3, \infty)$

19. $\left(-\dfrac{\sqrt{3}}{3}, 3\right), \left(\dfrac{\sqrt{3}}{3}, 3\right)$
Concave upward: $\left(-\infty, -\dfrac{\sqrt{3}}{3}\right), \left(\dfrac{\sqrt{3}}{3}, \infty\right)$
Concave downward: $\left(-\dfrac{\sqrt{3}}{3}, \dfrac{\sqrt{3}}{3}\right)$

21. None; Concave downward: $(-4, 4)$

23. $(2\pi, 0)$; Concave upward: $(2\pi, 4\pi)$;
Concave downward: $(0, 2\pi)$

25. $(\pi, 0) \, (1.823, 1.452), (4.46, -1.452)$
Concave upward: $(1.823, \pi), (4.46, 2\pi)$
Concave downward: $(0, 1.823), (\pi, 4.46)$

27. $(\pi, 0)$; Concave upward: $\left(0, \dfrac{\pi}{2}\right), \left(\pi, \dfrac{3\pi}{2}\right)$;
Concave downward: $\left(\dfrac{\pi}{2}, \pi\right), \left(\dfrac{3\pi}{2}, 2\pi\right)$

29. $\left(\dfrac{3}{2}, e^{-2}\right)$; Concave upward: $(-\infty, 0), \left(0, \dfrac{3}{2}\right)$;
Concave downward: $\left(\dfrac{3}{2}, \infty\right)$

31. None; Concave upward: $(0, \infty)$

33. $\left(\left(-\dfrac{1}{5}\right)^{5/8}, \arcsin \dfrac{\sqrt{5}}{5}\right), \left(\left(\dfrac{1}{5}\right)^{5/8}, \arcsin \dfrac{\sqrt{5}}{5}\right)$
Concave upward: $\left(-1, -\left(\dfrac{1}{5}\right)^{5/8}\right), \left(\left(\dfrac{1}{5}\right)^{5/8}, 1\right)$
Concave downward: $\left(-\left(\dfrac{1}{5}\right)^{5/8}, 0\right), \left(0, \left(\dfrac{1}{5}\right)^{5/8}\right)$

35. Relative maximum: $\left(\dfrac{5}{2}, \dfrac{25}{2}\right)$

37. Relative maximum: $(-3, 9)$; Relative minimum: $\left(-\dfrac{1}{3}, -\dfrac{13}{27}\right)$

39. Relative minimum: $(3, -25)$

41. Relative minimum: $(0, -3)$

43. Relative maximum: $(-2, -4)$; Relative minimum: $(2, 4)$

45. No relative extrema   **47.** Relative minimum: $\left(\dfrac{1}{4}, \dfrac{1}{2} + \ln 4\right)$

49. Relative minimum: (e, e) **51.** Relative minimum: $(0, 1)$

53. Relative maximum: $(2, 4e^{-2})$; Relative minimum: $(0, 0)$

55. Relative maximum: $\left(\dfrac{1}{\ln 4}, \dfrac{4e^{-1}}{\ln 2}\right)$

57. Relative maximum: $(1.272, -0.606)$
Relative minimum: $(-1.272, 3.747)$

59. No; Sample answer: f could be concave upward (or downward) on both sides of c .

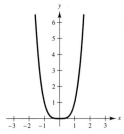

61. Sample answer:

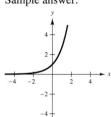

63. Sample answer:

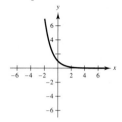

65. Sample answer:

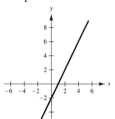

67. Sample answer:

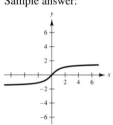

69. (a)

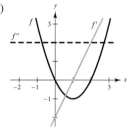

(b)

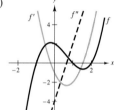

71.

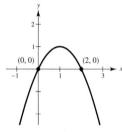

73. Sample answer:

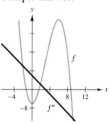

75. (a)

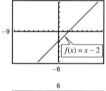

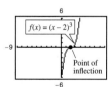

$f(x) = (x - 2)^n$ has a point of inflection at $(2, 0)$ if n is odd and $n \geq 3$.

(b) Answers will vary.

77. (a) $f(x) = \frac{1}{32}x^3 + \frac{3}{16}x^2$ (b) 2 mi west of the runway

79. 100 units; Answers will vary.

81.

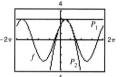

The values of f, P_1, and P_2 and their first derivatives are equal when $x = \pi/4$. The approximations worsen as you move away from $x = \pi/4$.

83.

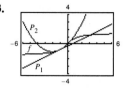

The values of f, P_1, and P_2 and their first derivatives are equal when $x = -1$. The approximations worsen as you move away from $x = -1$.

85.

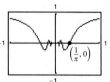

Answers will vary.

87. True

89. False; There can be at most $(n - 2)$ points of inflection.

91. Proof   **93.** A

Section 3.5   *(page 253)*

1.

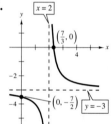

3.

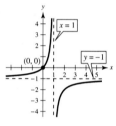

5.

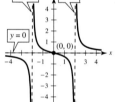

7.

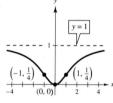

9.

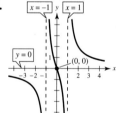

11.

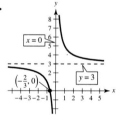

13.

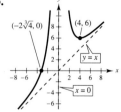

15.

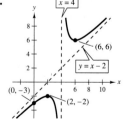

17.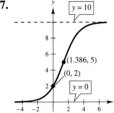

19.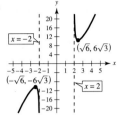

21.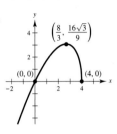

23.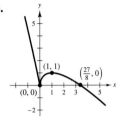

25.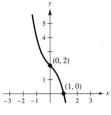

27.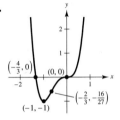

29.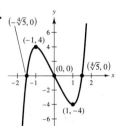

31.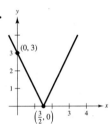

33.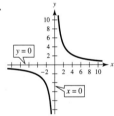

35. The graph does not show the whole curve; The graph of f does not have a vertical asymptote.

37.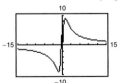

Minimum: $(-1.096, -9.046)$

Maximum: $(1.096, 9.046)$

Points of inflection: $(-1.835, -7.858), (1.835, 7.858)$

Vertical asymptote: $x = 0$

Horizontal asymptote: $y = 0$

39.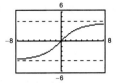

Point of inflection: $(0, 0)$

Horizontal asymptotes:

$y = \pm 4$

41.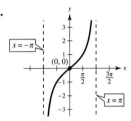

43.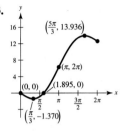

45.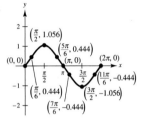

47.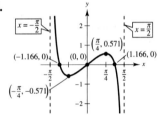

49.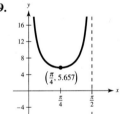

51.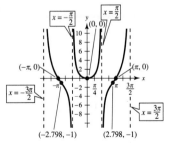

53.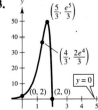

55.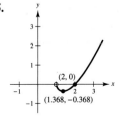

57.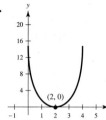

59.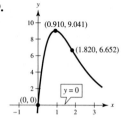

81. (a) Concave downward: $(-\infty, -2)$ and $(6, \infty)$
Concave upward: $(-2, 6)$
(b) f' is decreasing on $(-\infty, -2)$ and $(6, \infty)$. f' is increasing on $(-2, 6)$.
(c) $x = -2, x = 6$

83. (a) Concave upward: $(\pi, 2\pi)$; Concave downward: $(0, \pi)$
(b) f' is increasing on $(\pi, 2\pi)$. f' is decreasing on $(0, \pi)$.
(c) $x = \pi$

61.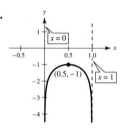

85.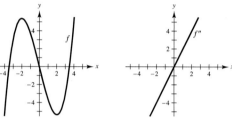

63. f is decreasing on $(2, 8)$.

65.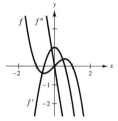

The zeros of f' correspond to the points where the graph of f has horizontal tangents. The zero of f'' corresponds to the point where the graph of f' has a horizontal tangent.

87.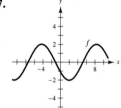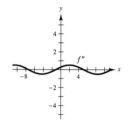

67.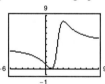

Yes

69.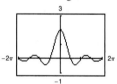

Yes

89. (a)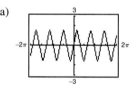

(b) Origin symmetry   (c) Yes; 2
(d) Relative maximum: $\left(\frac{1}{2}, \tan 1\right)$
Relative minimum: $\left(-\frac{1}{2}, -\tan 1\right)$
(e) Concave downward

71.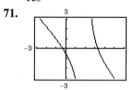

$y = -x + 1$;
Answers will vary.

73.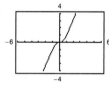

$y = 2x$;
Answers will vary.

75. $y = 4x, y = -4x$

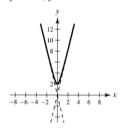

91. (a) x_0, x_2, x_4 (b) x_2, x_3 (c) x_1 (d) x_1 (e) x_2, x_3
93. (a) Yes; $g'(x) > 0$, $f(x) > 0$, and $f'(x) = g'(x)f(x)$, so $f'(x) > 0$.
(b) No; Sample answer: Let $f(x) = x^2 + 1$.
95. Sample answer: The graph has a vertical asymptote at $x = b$. If a and b are both positive or both negative, then the graph of f approaches ∞ as x approaches b, and the graph has a minimum at $x = -b$. If a and b have opposite signs, then the graph of f approaches $-\infty$ as x approaches b, and the graph has a maximum at $x = -b$.

97.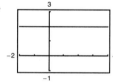

The rational function is not reduced to lowest terms.
99. C   **101.** D

77. Sample answer: $y = \dfrac{1}{x - 3}$

79. (a) $(-3, -1)$ (b) $(-7, -1)$
(c) Relative maximum: $x = -3$; Relative minimum: $x = 1$
(d) $x = -1$

Section 3.6   *(page 262)*

1. (a) and (b)

First Number, x	Second Number	Product, P
10	$110 - 10$	$10(110 - 10) = 1000$
20	$110 - 20$	$20(110 - 20) = 1800$
30	$110 - 30$	$30(110 - 30) = 2400$
40	$110 - 40$	$40(110 - 40) = 2800$
50	$110 - 50$	$50(110 - 50) = 3000$
60	$110 - 60$	$60(110 - 60) = 3000$
70	$110 - 70$	$70(110 - 70) = 2800$
80	$110 - 80$	$80(110 - 80) = 2400$
90	$110 - 90$	$90(110 - 90) = 1800$
100	$110 - 100$	$100(110 - 100) = 1000$

The maximum is attained near $x = 50$ and 60.

(c) $P = x(110 - x)$

(d)
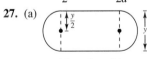

(e) 55; 55 and 55

3. 14 and 14   **5.** 21 and 7   **7.** 54 and 27

9. $\ell = w = 20$ m   **11.** $\ell = w = 7$ ft   **13.** $(1, 1)$

15. $\left(\dfrac{7}{2}, \sqrt{\dfrac{7}{2}}\right)$ **17.** $\left(-3 - \dfrac{\sqrt{38}}{2}, \dfrac{1}{2}\right), \left(-3 + \dfrac{\sqrt{38}}{2}, \dfrac{1}{2}\right)$

19. $\left(2 + \sqrt{30}\right)$ in. $\times \left(2 + \sqrt{30}\right)$ in.   **21.** 700 m $\times$ 350 m

23. Rectangular portion: $\dfrac{16}{\pi + 4}$ ft $\times \dfrac{32}{\pi + 4}$ ft

25. Width: $\dfrac{c}{2}$; Length: $\dfrac{c}{2d}$

27. (a)
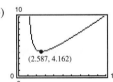

(b)

Length, x	Width, y	Area, xy
10	$\dfrac{2}{\pi}(100 - 10)$	$(10)\left(\dfrac{2}{\pi}\right)(100 - 10) \approx 573$
20	$\dfrac{2}{\pi}(100 - 20)$	$(20)\left(\dfrac{2}{\pi}\right)(100 - 20) \approx 1019$
30	$\dfrac{2}{\pi}(100 - 30)$	$(30)\left(\dfrac{2}{\pi}\right)(100 - 30) \approx 1337$
40	$\dfrac{2}{\pi}(100 - 40)$	$(40)\left(\dfrac{2}{\pi}\right)(100 - 40) \approx 1528$
50	$\dfrac{2}{\pi}(100 - 50)$	$(50)\left(\dfrac{2}{\pi}\right)(100 - 50) \approx 1592$
60	$\dfrac{2}{\pi}(100 - 60)$	$(60)\left(\dfrac{2}{\pi}\right)(100 - 60) \approx 1528$

The maximum area of the rectangle is approximately 1592 square meters.

(c) $A = \dfrac{2}{\pi}(100x - x^2), \quad 0 < x < 100$

(d) 50; About 1592 m^2

(e)
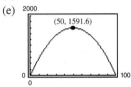

29. No; $S = x + \dfrac{100}{x}$ does not have a maximum.

31. $\sqrt[3]{\dfrac{21}{2\pi}} \approx 1.50$ cm

33. Side of triangle: $\dfrac{30}{9 + 4\sqrt{3}}$; Side of square: $\dfrac{10\sqrt{3}}{9 + 4\sqrt{3}}$

35. (a) $L = \sqrt{x^2 + 4 + \dfrac{8}{x - 1} + \dfrac{4}{(x - 1)^2}}, \quad x > 1$

(b)

Minimum when $x \approx 2.587$

(c) $(0, 0), (2, 0), (0, 4)$

37. (a) 18 in. $\times$ 18 in. $\times$ 36 in.   (b) $r = \dfrac{36}{\pi}$ in.; $h = 36$ in.

39. $w = \dfrac{20\sqrt{3}}{3}$ in.; $h = \dfrac{20\sqrt{6}}{3}$ in.

CHAPTER 3

41.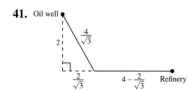

The path of the pipe should go underwater from the oil well to the coast following the hypotenuse of a right triangle with leg lengths of 2 kilometers and $\dfrac{2}{\sqrt{3}}$ kilometers for a distance of $\dfrac{4}{\sqrt{3}}$ kilometers. Then the pipe should go down the coast to the refinery for a distance of $\left(4 - \dfrac{2}{\sqrt{3}}\right)$ kilometers.

43. 18.35 elk/month; $t \approx 4.16$ months

45. About 1.153 radians or 66°

47.

(a) Origin to y-intercept: 2; Origin to x-intercept: $\dfrac{\pi}{2}$

(b) $d = \sqrt{x^2 + (2 - 2\sin x)^2}$

(c) Minimum distance is 0.9795 when $x \approx 0.7967$.

49. Answers will vary. **51.** $y = \dfrac{64}{141}x$; About 6.1 mi

53. $y = \dfrac{3}{10}x$; About 4.50 mi

55. (a) $V = \dfrac{\pi}{3}r^2\sqrt{36 - r^2}$ (b) $r = 2\sqrt{6}; h = 2\sqrt{3}$

Section 3.7 *(page 272)*

1. $T(x) = 4x - 4$

x	1.9	1.99	2	2.01	2.1
$f(x)$	3.610	3.960	4	4.040	4.410
$T(x)$	3.600	3.960	4	4.040	4.400

3. $T(x) = 80x - 128$

x	1.9	1.99	2	2.01	2.1
$f(x)$	24.761	31.208	32	32.808	40.841
$T(x)$	24.000	31.200	32	32.800	40.000

5. $T(x) = (\cos 2)(x - 2) + \sin 2$

x	1.9	1.99	2	2.01	2.1
$f(x)$	0.946	0.913	0.909	0.905	0.863
$T(x)$	0.951	0.913	0.909	0.905	0.868

7. $T(x) = 9(\ln 3)x - 18 \ln 3 + 9$

x	1.9	1.99	2	2.01	2.1
$f(x)$	8.064	8.902	9	9.099	10.045
$T(x)$	8.011	8.901	9	9.099	9.989

9. $y - f(0) = f'(0)(x - 0)$

$y - 2 = \dfrac{1}{4}x$

$y = 2 + \dfrac{x}{4}$

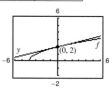

11. $\Delta y = 0.1655; dy = 0.15$

13. $\Delta y \approx -0.053018, dy = -0.053$ **15.** $6x\,dx$

17. $(x \sec^2 x + \tan x)\,dx$ **19.** $-\dfrac{3}{(2x - 1)^2}\,dx$

21. $-\dfrac{x}{\sqrt{9 - x^2}}\,dx$ **23.** $(3 - \sin 2x)\,dx$

25. $\dfrac{x}{x^2 - 4}\,dx$ **27.** $\left(\arcsin x + \dfrac{x}{\sqrt{1 - x^2}}\right)dx$

29. (a) 0.9 (b) 1.04 **31.** dx is missing; $dy = \dfrac{x}{\sqrt{x^2 - 4}}\,dx$

33. (a) 8.035 (b) 7.95 **35.** (a) $\pm\dfrac{5}{8}$ in.^{2} (b) 0.625%

37. (a) ± 20.25 in.^{3} (b) ± 5.4 in.^{2} (c) 0.6%, 0.4%

39. 4.5 ft; About 5.54% **41.** About -2.65%

43. About 9.97; They are about the same.

45. About 4.998; They are about the same.

47. The accuracy increases. Graphs will vary. **49.** True

51. False; Sample answer: Let $f(x) = \sqrt{x}$, $x = 1$, and $\Delta x = dx = 3$.

53. B

55. (a) $P' = \dfrac{1}{4}e^{-x/400}(400 - x)$ (b) 400 units

(c) \$503; about 5.83%

Review Exercises for Chapter 3 *(page 274)*

1. Maximum: $(0, 0)$ **3.** Maximum: $(4, 0)$
Minimum: $\left(-\dfrac{5}{2}, -\dfrac{25}{4}\right)$ Minimum: $(0, -2)$

5. Maximum: $\left(3, \dfrac{2}{3}\right)$ **7.** Maximum: $(2\pi, 17.57)$
Minimum: $\left(-3, -\dfrac{2}{3}\right)$ Minimum: $(2.73, 0.88)$

9. No; $f(0) \neq f(4)$ **11.** Yes; $\pm\dfrac{\pi}{4}, \pm\dfrac{3\pi}{4}$ **13.** Yes; $\dfrac{2744}{729}$

15. No; Not differentiable on $[2, 6]$ **17.** Yes; 0

19. No; f has a discontinuity at $x = 0$.

21. Increasing on $\left(-\dfrac{3}{2}, \infty\right)$; Decreasing on $\left(-\infty, -\dfrac{3}{2}\right)$

23. Increasing on $(1, \infty)$; Decreasing on $(0, 1)$

25. Increasing on $\left(0, \dfrac{\pi}{2}\right), \left(\pi, \dfrac{3\pi}{2}\right)$; Decreasing on $\left(\dfrac{\pi}{2}, \pi\right), \left(\dfrac{3\pi}{2}, 2\pi\right)$

27. Increasing on $\left(-\infty, 2 - \dfrac{1}{\ln 2}\right)$; Decreasing on $\left(2 - \dfrac{1}{\ln 2}, \infty\right)$

29. (a) $0, \dfrac{10}{3}$

(b) Increasing on $(-\infty, 0), \left(\dfrac{10}{3}, \infty\right)$; Decreasing on $\left(0, \dfrac{10}{3}\right)$

(c) Relative maximum: $(0, 0)$; Relative minimum: $\left(\dfrac{10}{3}, -\dfrac{500}{27}\right)$

31. (a) -8

(b) Increasing on $(-8, 0)$; Decreasing on $(-\infty, -8), (0, \infty)$

(c) Relative minimum: $\left(-8, -\frac{1}{16}\right)$

33. (a) $\dfrac{3\pi}{4}, \dfrac{7\pi}{4}$

(b) Increasing on $\left(\dfrac{3\pi}{4}, \dfrac{7\pi}{4}\right)$; Decreasing on $\left(0, \dfrac{3\pi}{4}\right), \left(\dfrac{7\pi}{4}, 2\pi\right)$

(c) Relative minimum: $\left(\dfrac{3\pi}{4}, -\sqrt{2}\right)$

Relative maximum: $\left(\dfrac{7\pi}{4}, \sqrt{2}\right)$

35. (a) $-2, 0$

(b) Increasing on $(-\infty, -2), (0, \infty)$; Decreasing on $(-2, 0)$

(c) Relative maximum: $\left(-2, \dfrac{4}{e^2}\right)$; Relative minimum: $(0, 0)$

37. $(3, -54)$; Concave upward: $(3, \infty)$;
Concave downward: $(-\infty, 3)$

39. None; Concave upward: $(-5, \infty)$

41. $\left(\dfrac{\pi}{2}, \dfrac{\pi}{2}\right), \left(\dfrac{3\pi}{2}, \dfrac{3\pi}{2}\right)$; Concave upward: $\left(\dfrac{\pi}{2}, \dfrac{3\pi}{2}\right)$;

Concave downward: $\left(0, \dfrac{\pi}{2}\right), \left(\dfrac{3\pi}{2}, 2\pi\right)$

43. Relative minimum: $(-9, 0)$

45. Relative maximum: $(-4, 68)$; Relative minimum: $\left(\frac{1}{3}, -\frac{361}{27}\right)$

47. Relative minimum: (e, e)

49.

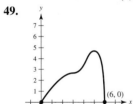

51. (a) Concave downward on $(0, 25)$

(b)

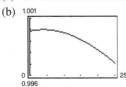

(c) About 1

53.

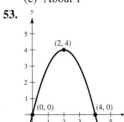

55.

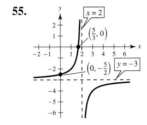

57.

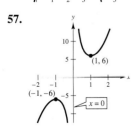

59.

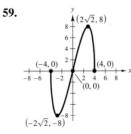

61.

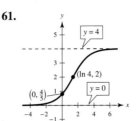

63. $x = 50$ ft, $y = \frac{200}{3}$ ft   **65.** About 12.7 ft

67. $\dfrac{32\pi r^3}{81}$ units^3 **69.** $\Delta y = 0.03005$; $dy = 0.03$

71. $(1 + x \sin x - \cos x)\, dx$

73. (a) $\pm 8.1\pi$ cm^3 (b) $\pm 1.8\pi$ cm^2

AP® Exam Practice Questions   *(page 276)*

1. B   **2.** D   **3.** B   **4.** C   **5.** D   **6.** A   **7.** A

8. (a) Relative maximum: $(-0.7108, 1.4729)$
Relative minimum: $(0.7108, 0.5271)$

(b) $y = \dfrac{3\pi^2}{8}x - \dfrac{\pi^3}{8}$

(c) $f(1.5) \approx 1.6759$; underestimate; $f'\left(\dfrac{\pi}{2}\right) > f'(1.5)$

9. (a) $(-\infty, 4)$; $f'(x) > 0$

(b) Yes; It goes from increasing to decreasing and $f(x)$ is continuous.

(c) $x = 4$; At this value $f''(x)$ changes sign.

(d) No; $f(x)$ is not differentiable on $(3, 5)$.

(e) Sample answer:

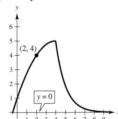

10. (a) $2\pi + 1$; Critical number: $x = \dfrac{\pi}{4}$,

$f(\pi) = 2\pi + 1 > f\left(\dfrac{\pi}{4}\right) > f(0)$

(b) $f(x)$ is continuous on $[0, \pi]$ and differentiable on $(0, \pi)$;

$x = \dfrac{\pi}{2}$

11. (a) $(0, 2)$

(b) $(-2, -0.8), (1.3, \infty)$; $f(x)$ is concave downward when $f'(x)$ is decreasing.

(c) Negative; $f'(x)$ is negative, so the slope of $f(x)$ is negative there.

12. (a) $(-\infty, 0), (0, \infty)$

(b) None; $f''(x) > 0$ for all real x.

(c) No; It does not change concavity.

13. (a) $f'(-1) = -\dfrac{2}{3}; f''(-1) = -\dfrac{1}{3}$

   (b) $x = -3; f'(x)$ changes from positive to negative, so f has a relative maximum at $x = -3$.

   (c) $x = -4, x = 0,$ and $x = 1; f''(0)$ and $f''(1)$ are undefined, and $f''(-4) = 0.$

   (d) Decreasing; $g'(x) = f'(x) + 2 \sin x \cos x,$ so

   $$g'\left(-\frac{\pi}{4}\right) = f'\left(-\frac{\pi}{4}\right) - 1. \ f'\left(-\frac{\pi}{4}\right) \text{ is negative, so } g'\left(-\frac{\pi}{4}\right)$$

   is negative and g is decreasing at $x = -\dfrac{\pi}{4}.$

Chapter 4

Section 4.1   *(page 287)*

1. Answers will vary.   **3.** $y = 3t^3 + C$

5. $y = \dfrac{2}{5}x^{5/2} + C$ **7.** $\displaystyle\int x^{1/3}\,dx; \dfrac{x^{4/3}}{4/3} + C; \dfrac{3}{4}x^{4/3} + C$

9. $\displaystyle\int x^{-3/2}\,dx; \dfrac{x^{-1/2}}{-1/2} + C; -\dfrac{2}{\sqrt{x}} + C$

11. $\dfrac{3}{4}x^4 - 2x^3 + 2x + C$ **13.** $\dfrac{2}{5}x^{5/2} + x^2 + x + C$

15. $\dfrac{3}{5}x^{5/3} + C$ **17.** $-\dfrac{1}{4x^4} + C$ **19.** $\dfrac{2}{3}x^{3/2} + 12x^{1/2} + C$

21. $x^3 + \dfrac{1}{2}x^2 - 2x + C$ **23.** $5 \sin x - 4 \cos x + C$

25. $-2 \cos x - 5e^x + C$ **27.** $\tan y + C$

29. $x^2 - \dfrac{4^x}{\ln 4} + C$ **31.** $-\tan \theta + C$

33. $\dfrac{1}{2}x^2 - 5 \ln|x| + C$

35. $\displaystyle\int -4x^{-2}\,dx = \dfrac{4}{x} + C; \dfrac{3x^2}{2} + \dfrac{4}{x} + C$

37. Sample answer:

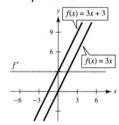

39. $f(x) = 3x^2 + 8$ **41.** $f(\theta) = \sin \theta + 1$

43. $f(x) = x^2 + x + 4$ **45.** $f(x) = -4\sqrt{x} + 3x$

47. $f(s) = 2e^s - 3s + 3$ **49.** None

51.

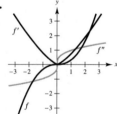

53. (a) $h(t) = \dfrac{3}{4}t^2 + 5t + 12$ (b) 69 cm   **55.** 62.25 ft

57. (a) About 2.562 sec   (b) About -65.970 ft/sec

59. About 62.3 m/sec   **61.** 320 m; -32 m/sec

63. (a) $v(t) = 3t^2 - 12t + 9; a(t) = 6t - 12$

   (b) $(0, 1), (3, 5)$ (c) -3

65. $a(t) = -\dfrac{1}{2t^{3/2}}; x(t) = 2\sqrt{t} + 2$

67. (a) 1.18 m/sec^2 (b) 190 m

69. $f(x) = \dfrac{x^3}{3} - 9x + 19$

71. $f(x) = \begin{cases} -x + 1, & 0 \le x < 2 \\ 2x - 5, & 2 \le x < 3 \\ 1, & 3 \le x \le 4 \end{cases}$

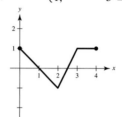

73. True   **75.** D

77. (a) No; $\dfrac{dP}{dt}$ is not always positive.   (b) $t = 1.4$

   (c) $P = 5t^4 - 15t^{7/3} + 8000;$ 54,768 people

Section 4.2   *(page 299)*

1. 75   **3.** $\dfrac{158}{85}$ **5.** $7c$ **7.** $\displaystyle\sum_{i=1}^{11} \dfrac{1}{5i}$

9. $\displaystyle\sum_{j=1}^{6}\left[7\left(\dfrac{j}{6}\right) + 5\right]$ **11.** $\dfrac{2}{n}\displaystyle\sum_{i=1}^{n}\left[\left(\dfrac{2i}{n}\right)^3 - \dfrac{2i}{n}\right]$ **13.** 84

15. 1200   **17.** 2470   **19.** 12,040

21. $\dfrac{n + 2}{n}$ **23.** $2 - \dfrac{2}{n^2}$

$n = 10$: 1.2	$n = 10$: 1.98
$n = 100$: 1.02	$n = 100$: 1.9998
$n = 1000$: 1.002	$n = 1000$: 1.999998
$n = 10{,}000$: 1.0002	$n = 10{,}000$: 1.99999998

25. An extra factor of n was included; $\displaystyle\sum_{i=1}^{n} 4i = 2n^2 + 2n$

27. 13; 15   **29.** 55; 74.5   **31.** About 0.7908; about 1.1835

33. About 0.768; about 0.518   **35.** About 0.746; about 0.646

37. 12.5; 16.5   **39.** $24 + \dfrac{24}{n}; 24 - \dfrac{24}{n}$

41. $\dfrac{5}{3} + \dfrac{5}{2n} + \dfrac{5}{6n^2}; \dfrac{5}{3} - \dfrac{5}{2n} + \dfrac{5}{6n^2}$

43. (a)

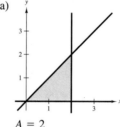

   $A = 2$

   (b)–(d) Answers will vary.

   (e) $s(5) = 1.6, S(5) = 2.4, s(10) = 1.8, S(10) = 2.2,$
   $s(50) = 1.96, S(50) = 2.04, s(100) = 1.98,$
   $S(100) = 2.02$

   (f) Answers will vary.

45. $\dfrac{12(n + 1)}{n}; 12$ **47.** $\dfrac{1}{6}\left(\dfrac{2n^3 - 3n^2 + n}{n^3}\right); \dfrac{1}{3}$

49. $\dfrac{3n + 1}{n}; 3$

51. $A = 3$

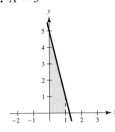

53. $A = \frac{7}{3}$

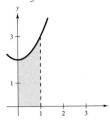

55. $A = 54$

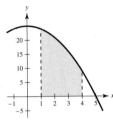

57. $A = 34$

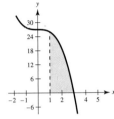

59. $A = \frac{2}{3}$

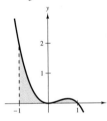

61. $A = 8$

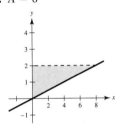

63. $A = \frac{125}{3}$

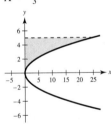

65. $A = \frac{44}{3}$

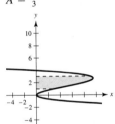

67. $\frac{69}{8}$ **69.** About 0.345   **71.** About 4.0786

73. True   **75.** Underestimate

77. (a)

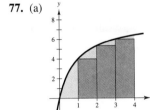

$s(4) = \frac{46}{3}$

(b)

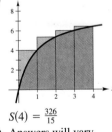

$S(4) = \frac{326}{15}$

(c)

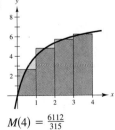

$M(4) = \frac{6112}{315}$

(d) Answers will vary.

(e)

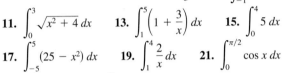

n	4	8	20	100	200
$s(n)$	15.333	17.368	18.459	18.995	19.060
$S(n)$	21.733	20.568	19.739	19.251	19.188
$M(n)$	19.403	19.201	19.137	19.125	19.125

(f) Because f is an increasing function, $s(n)$ is always increasing and $S(n)$ is always decreasing. Because f is also concave down, using the Midpoint Rule produces an overestimate.

79. Suppose there are n rows and $n + 1$ columns. The stars on the left total $1 + 2 + \cdots + n$, as do the stars on the right. There are $n(n + 1)$ stars in total. So, $2[1 + 2 + \cdots + n] = n(n + 1)$ and $1 + 2 + \cdots + n = [n(n + 1)]/2$.

81. B   **83.** B

Section 4.3 *(page 312)*

1. $2\sqrt{3}$ **3.** 32   **5.** 0   **7.** $\frac{10}{3}$ **9.** $\int_{-1}^{5} (3x + 10)\, dx$

11. $\int_{0}^{3} \sqrt{x^2 + 4}\, dx$ **13.** $\int_{1}^{5} \left(1 + \frac{3}{x}\right) dx$ **15.** $\int_{0}^{4} 5\, dx$

17. $\int_{-5}^{5} (25 - x^2)\, dx$ **19.** $\int_{1}^{4} \frac{2}{x}\, dx$ **21.** $\int_{0}^{\pi/2} \cos x\, dx$

23. $\int_{0}^{1} 3\, dy$ **25.** $\int_{0}^{2} y^3\, dy$

27.

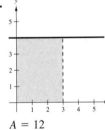

$A = 12$

29.

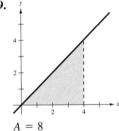

$A = 8$

31.

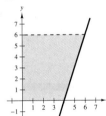

$A = 30$

33.

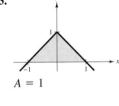

$A = 1$

35.

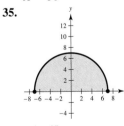

$A = \frac{49\pi}{2}$

37.

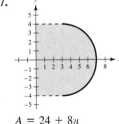

$A = 24 + 8\pi$

39. (a) 13   (b) -10 (c) 0   (d) -13 **41.** -6

43. 48   **45.** 12   **47.** Not possible   **49.** 16

CHAPTER 4

51. Lower: -48; right
Upper: 88; left

53. (a) $-\pi$ (b) 4 (c) $-(1 + 2\pi)$ (d) $3 - 2\pi$
(e) $5 + 2\pi$ (f) $23 - 2\pi$

55. (a) $x = 0$ (b) -1 **57.** (a) $x = -2$ (b) $-\frac{27}{2}$

59. (a) $x = 2$ (b) 12 **61.** 2.7500 **63.** 4.2500

65. 12.6640 **67.** 0.9871

69. 1.282; They are about the same.

71. 1.397; They are about the same.

73. 0.3415; They are about the same.

75. 0.5495; They are about the same.

77. -0.0975; They are about the same.

79. 1.684; They are about the same.

81. 1.500 **83.** $\frac{1}{4}$ **85.** $n = 366$ **87.** $n = 77$

89. The middle three terms should each have a coefficient of 2;

$$\frac{\pi}{8}\left(\cos 0 + 2\cos\frac{\pi}{8} + 2\cos\frac{\pi}{4} + 2\cos\frac{3\pi}{8} + \cos\frac{\pi}{2}\right)$$

91.

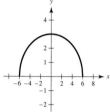

(a) Overestimate (b) Underestimate
(c) Underestimate

93. (a) No; The intervals are not of equal width.
(b) 12.45
(c) $y = -1.25603x^3 + 3.7287x^2 - 0.513x + 4.29$; 12.473;
The results are about the same.

95. (a) The x-values and limits are shifted two units to the right,
so the values are the same.
(b) $f(-x) = f(x)$, so the value is doubled.
(c) $f(-x) = -f(x)$, so the value is 0.

97. No; $f(x) = \dfrac{1}{x - 4}$ is not continuous on $[3, 5]$.

99. $a = -2, b = 8$

101. Sample answer:
$a = \pi, b = 2\pi$
$$\int_{\pi}^{2\pi} \sin x \, dx < 0$$

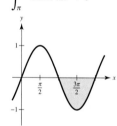

103. False; The partitions do not have to be of equal width.

105. 272

107. No; No matter how small the subintervals, the number of
both rational and irrational numbers within each subinterval
is infinite, and $f(c_i) = 0$ or $f(c_i) = 1$.

109. Proof

111. $a = -1, b = 1$; $1 - x^2$ is positive between -1 and 1.

113. $\frac{1}{3}$ **115.** A

117. (a)

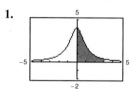

(b) No; f has a nonremovable
discontinuity at $x = 2$.

(c) Yes; Sample answer: Use triangles to represent the three
different regions. So,

$$\int_{0}^{4} f(x)\,dx \approx -\frac{1}{2}(0.75)(6) + \frac{1}{2}(1.25)(2) - \frac{1}{2}(2)(4) = -5.$$

Section 4.4 (page 326)

1.

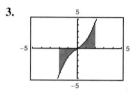

3.

Positive   Zero

5. -2 **7.** $-\frac{28}{3}$ **9.** $\frac{1}{3}$ **11.** $\frac{1}{2}$ **13.** -4

15. $-\dfrac{27}{20}$ **17.** $\dfrac{25}{2}$ **19.** $\dfrac{64}{3}$ **21.** $-7\pi + 2$ **23.** $\dfrac{\pi}{4}$

25. $\dfrac{2\sqrt{3}}{3}$ **27.** $\dfrac{3}{\ln 2} + 12$ **29.** $\dfrac{1}{6}$ **31.** 1 **33.** $\dfrac{52}{3}$

35. 20 **37.** 4 **39.** $\dfrac{3\sqrt[3]{2}}{2} \approx 1.8899$

41. $\dfrac{3}{\ln 4} \approx 2.1640$ **43.** $\pm\arccos\dfrac{\sqrt{\pi}}{2} \approx \pm 0.4817$

45. $\dfrac{8}{3}$; $x = \pm\dfrac{2\sqrt{3}}{3} \approx \pm 1.1547$

47. $2(e - e^{-1}) \approx 4.7008$; $x = \ln\left(\dfrac{e - e^{-1}}{2}\right) \approx 0.1614$

49. $\dfrac{2}{\pi}$; $x \approx 0.690, x \approx 2.451$

51. $F(x) = 2x^2 - 7x$
$F(2) = -6$
$F(5) = 15$
$F(8) = 72$

53. $F(x) = -\dfrac{20}{x} + 20$
$F(2) = 10$
$F(5) = 16$
$F(8) = \frac{35}{2}$

55. $F(x) = \sin x + 1$
$F(0) = 1$
$F\left(\dfrac{\pi}{4}\right) = \dfrac{\sqrt{2}}{2} + 1$
$F\left(\dfrac{\pi}{2}\right) = 2$

57. (a) $\dfrac{1}{2}x^2 + 2x$ (b) $\dfrac{d}{dx}\left[\dfrac{1}{2}x^2 + 2x\right] = x + 2$

59. (a) $\dfrac{3}{4}x^{4/3} - 12$ (b) $\dfrac{d}{dx}\left[\dfrac{3}{4}x^{4/3} - 12\right] = x^{1/3}$

61. (a) $\tan x - 1$ (b) $\dfrac{d}{dx}[\tan x - 1] = \sec^2 x$

63. $x^2 - 2x$ **65.** $\sqrt{x^3 + 1}$ **67.** $\sqrt{x}\csc x$ **69.** 8

71. $(\cos x)\sqrt{\sin x}$ **73.** $3x^2 \sin x^6$

75. There is a discontinuity at $x = 0$; Not possible

77. (a) $F(x) = 500 \sec^2 x$ (b) $\dfrac{1500\sqrt{3}}{\pi} \approx 827$ N

79. About 0.5318 L

81.

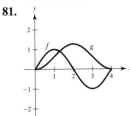

g has a relative maximum at $x = 2$.

83. (a) $g(0) = 0$, $g(2) \approx 7$, $g(4) \approx 9$, $g(6) \approx 8$, $g(8) \approx 5$

(b) Increasing: $(0, 4)$; Decreasing: $(4, 8)$

(c) A maximum occurs at $x = 4$.

(d)

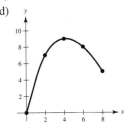

85. True   **87.** Answers will vary.   **89.** D

91. (a) 3.5 ft/sec^2

(b) $\displaystyle\int_{20}^{50} v(t)\, dt \approx 4100$ ft; This represents the net distance covered by the train.

(c) $\displaystyle\int_{20}^{50} v'(t)\, dt = 90$ ft/sec; This represents the change in the velocity of the train.

(d) 126.7 ft/sec

Section 4.5   *(page 332)*

1. About 540 ft   **3.** 8190 L

5. (a) $\frac{3}{2}$ ft to the right   (b) $\frac{113}{10}$ ft   **7.** (a) 0 ft   (b) $\frac{63}{2}$ ft

9. (a) 2 ft to the right   (b) 2 ft   **11.** 28 units

13. Displacement was found, not total distance traveled;

$\displaystyle\int_0^4 |\sin t|\, dt \approx 2.3464$ inches

15. -44.1 m   **17.** \$4587.36

19. The particle is always moving in the same direction on an interval.

21. The rate of oil produced in gallons per hour; the net change in oil produced from hour 5 to hour 12

23. True   **25.** C

27. (a) 2   (b) $2 < t < 4$; $v(t) < 0$ on $(2, 4)$

(c) $\frac{44}{3}$ (d) $t = 4$; $s(t)$ has a minimum at $t = 4$.

Section 4.6   *(page 343)*

1. $5x^2 + 1$; $10x\, dx$ **3.** $\tan x$; $\sec^2 x\, dx$

5. $\frac{1}{5}(1 + 6x)^5 + C$ **7.** $\frac{2}{3}(25 - x^2)^{3/2} + C$

9. $\frac{1}{12}(x^4 + 3)^3 + C$ **11.** $\frac{1}{30}(2x^3 - 1)^5 + C$

13. $\frac{1}{3}(t^2 + 2)^{3/2} + C$ **15.** $-\frac{15}{8}(1 - x^2)^{4/3} + C$

17. $\dfrac{1}{4(1 - x^2)^2} + C$ **19.** $-\dfrac{3}{(1 + x^3)} + C$

21. $-\sqrt{1 - x^2} + C$ **23.** $-\dfrac{1}{4}\left(1 + \dfrac{1}{t}\right)^4 + C$

25. $\sqrt{x^2 + 6x} + C$ **27.** $2x^2 - 4\sqrt{16 - x^2} + C$

29. $-\dfrac{1}{2(x^2 + 2x - 3)} + C$ **31.** $-\cos \pi x + C$

33. $-2\cos\sqrt{x} + C$

35. $\frac{1}{4}\sin^2 2x + C$ or $-\frac{1}{4}\cos^2 2x + C_1$ or $-\frac{1}{8}\cos 4x + C_2$

37. $\frac{1}{2}\tan^2 x + C$ or $\frac{1}{2}\sec^2 x + C_1$ **39.** $e^{9x} + C$

41. $\frac{1}{2}e^{x^2 + 2x} + C$ **43.** $-\frac{5}{2}e^{-2x} + e^{-x} + C$

45. $\dfrac{1}{\pi}e^{\sin \pi x} + C$ **47.** $-\tan(e^{-x}) + C$

49. $\dfrac{2}{\ln 3}(3^{x/2}) + C$ **51.** $f(x) = 2\cos\dfrac{x}{2} + 4$

53. $f(x) = -8e^{-x/4} + 9$ **55.** $f(x) = \frac{1}{12}(4x^2 - 10)^3 - 8$

57. $\frac{2}{9}(3x + 5)^{3/2} + C$ **59.** $\frac{2}{5}(x + 6)^{5/2} - 4(x + 6)^{3/2} + C$

61. $-\frac{2}{3}(1 - x)^{3/2} + \frac{4}{5}(1 - x)^{5/2} - \frac{2}{7}(1 - x)^{7/2} + C$

63. $\frac{1}{20}(2x - 1)^{5/2} + \frac{1}{6}(2x - 1)^{3/2} - \frac{3}{4}(2x - 1)^{1/2} + C$

65. $-x - 1 - 2\sqrt{x + 1} + C$ or $-\left(x + 2\sqrt{x + 1}\right) + C_1$

67. $-\dfrac{1}{12}\cos^3 4x + C$ **69.** 0   **71.** 2   **73.** $\dfrac{e^2 - 1}{2e^2}$

75. $\frac{96}{5}$ **77.** $\frac{164}{3}$ **79.** $\frac{972}{7}$

81. A factor of $\frac{1}{2}$ is missing; $\frac{1}{4}(x^2 + 1)^2 + C$

83. $\frac{1209}{28}$ **85.** $2(\sqrt{3} - 1)$

87. $e^5 - 1 \approx 147.413$

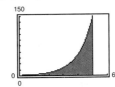

89. $2(1 - e^{-3/2}) \approx 1.554$

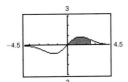

91. $\frac{272}{15}$ **93.** 0

95. (a) $\frac{64}{3}$ (b) $\frac{128}{3}$ (c) $-\frac{64}{3}$ (d) 64

97. $\displaystyle\int_{-3}^{3} (x^3 - 3x)\, dx + \int_{-3}^{3} (4x^2 - 6)\, dx$; 36

99. $du = -2x\, dx$ so $\int x(5 - x^2)^3\, dx = -\frac{1}{2}\int u^3\, du$.

101. (a) $\displaystyle\int x^2\sqrt{x^3 + 1}\, dx$ (b) $\displaystyle\int \tan 3x \sec^2 3x\, dx$

(c) $\displaystyle\int e^{4x - 3}\, dx$

The integrals can be evaluated using a change of variables.

103. \$340,000

105. (a) 102,352 units   (b) 102,352 units   (c) 74,500 units

107. (a) About 35.3%   (b) $b \approx 58.6\%$

CHAPTER 4

109. (a)

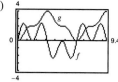

(b) f is positive at the beginning and generally has more positive sections than negative ones.

(c) The points of inflection of g.

(d) No; Some zeros correspond to inflection points of g.

(e)

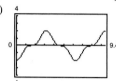

The graph of h is that of g shifted 2 units downward.

111. Proof   **113.** True   **115.** Answers will vary.
117. B   **119.** D

Section 4.7   *(page 353)*

1. $3 \ln|x| + C$ **3.** $-\ln|7 - x| + C$

5. $\frac{2}{3} \ln|3x + 5| + C$ **7.** $-\frac{1}{2} \ln|-x^2 + 1| + C$

9. $\ln|x^4 + 3x| + C$ **11.** $3x^2 - 4 \ln|x| + C$

13. $\frac{1}{3} \ln|x^3 + 3x^2 + 9x| + C$

15. $\frac{1}{2}x^2 - 4x + 6 \ln|x + 1| + C$

17. $-\frac{1}{3}x^3 - 5 \ln|3 - x| + C$

19. $\frac{1}{3}x^3 - 2x + \ln\sqrt{x^2 + 2} + C$ **21.** $-\frac{2}{3} \ln|1 - 3\sqrt{x}| + C$

23. $2 \ln|x - 1| - \dfrac{2}{x - 1} + C$ **25.** $\frac{1}{3}(\ln x)^3 + C$

27. $\sqrt{2x} - \ln|1 + \sqrt{2x}| + C$

29. $x + 6\sqrt{x} + 18 \ln|\sqrt{x} - 3| + C$ **31.** $3 \ln\left|\sin\frac{\theta}{3}\right| + C$

33. $-\frac{1}{2} \ln|\csc 2x + \cot 2x| + C$

35. $4 \tan\frac{\theta}{4} + 4 \ln\left|\cos\frac{\theta}{4}\right| + C$ **37.** $\ln|1 + \sin t| + C$

39. $-\ln|\csc x + \cot x| - \ln|\tan x + \sec x| + C$

41. $\ln|\cos(e^{-x})| + C$

43. $(x + 3)$ should be inside absolute value bars;
$\dfrac{x^2}{2} - 8x + 18 \ln|x + 3| + C$

45. $y = -3 \ln|2 - x| + C$ **47.** $y = \frac{1}{2}[\ln(1 + t)]^2 + C$

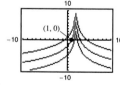 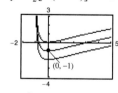

49. $f(x) = -2 \ln x + 3x - 2$ **51.** $\frac{5}{3} \ln 13 \approx 4.275$

53. $-\ln 3 \approx -1.099$ **55.** $\frac{7}{3}$ **57.** $\ln(\sqrt{2} + 1) \approx 0.881$

59. $\ln\left|\dfrac{2 - \sin 2}{1 - \sin 1}\right| \approx 1.929$ **61.** $2[\sqrt{x} - \ln(1 + \sqrt{x})] + C$

63. $\ln(\sqrt{2} + 1) - \dfrac{\sqrt{2}}{2} \approx 0.174$ **65.** $\dfrac{1}{x}$ **67.** $\dfrac{1}{x}$

69. $6 \ln 3$ **71.** $\frac{1}{2} \ln 2$ **73.** $\frac{15}{2} + 8 \ln 2 \approx 13.0452$

75. $\dfrac{12}{\pi} \ln(2 + \sqrt{3}) \approx 5.0304$ **77.** 20.2   **79.** 5.3368

81. (a) *u*-substitution, Power Rule
(b) *u*-substitution, Log Rule
(c) Long division, Log Rule
(d) *u*-substitution, Log Rule

83. d   **85.** $x = 2$ **87.** Proof

89. $-\ln|\cos x| + C = \ln\left|\dfrac{1}{\cos x}\right| + C = \ln|\sec x| + C$

91. $-\dfrac{1}{9}(\ln 7 - \ln 16) \approx 0.0919$ **93.** $\dfrac{1}{e - 1} \approx 0.582$

95. $P(t) = 1000(12 \ln|1 + 0.25t| + 1)$; $P(3) \approx 7715$ bacteria
97. About 4.15 min
99.

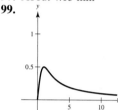

(a) $A = \frac{1}{2} \ln 2 - \frac{1}{4}$
(b) $0 < m < 1$
(c) $A = \frac{1}{2}(m - \ln m - 1)$

101. True   **103.** Proof   **105.** C
107. (a) $f(x) = -3 \ln|x - 2| + \frac{1}{2}x^2 - \frac{1}{2}$
(b) ∞; As x increases without bound, so does $f(x)$.

Section 4.8   *(page 361)*

1. $\arcsin\dfrac{x}{3} + C$ **3.** $\text{arcsec}|2x| + C$

5. $\arcsin(x + 1) + C$ **7.** $\frac{1}{2} \arcsin t^2 + C$

9. $\dfrac{1}{10} \arctan\dfrac{t^2}{5} + C$ **11.** $\dfrac{1}{4} \arctan\dfrac{e^{2x}}{2} + C$

13. $\arcsin\left(\dfrac{\tan x}{5}\right) + C$ **15.** $2 \arcsin\sqrt{x} + C$

17. $\frac{1}{2} \ln(x^2 + 1) - 3 \arctan x + C$

19. $8 \arcsin\dfrac{x - 3}{3} - \sqrt{6x - x^2} + C$ **21.** $\dfrac{\pi}{6}$

23. $\dfrac{\pi}{6}$ **25.** $\dfrac{1}{3} \arctan 3 - \dfrac{\pi}{12} \approx 0.155$

27. $\arctan 5 - \dfrac{\pi}{4} \approx 0.588$ **29.** $\dfrac{\pi}{4}$ **31.** $\dfrac{1}{32}\pi^2 \approx 0.308$

33. $\dfrac{\pi}{2}$ **35.** $\dfrac{\sqrt{2}}{2} \arcsin\left[\dfrac{\sqrt{6}}{6}(x - 2)\right] + C$

37. $\arcsin\dfrac{x + 2}{2} + C$ **39.** $4 - 2\sqrt{3} + \dfrac{1}{6}\pi \approx 1.059$

41. $\frac{1}{2} \arctan(x^2 + 1) + C$

43. $2\sqrt{e^t - 3} - 2\sqrt{3} \arctan\sqrt{\dfrac{e^t - 3}{3}} + C$ **45.** $\dfrac{\pi}{6}$

47. (a) $\arcsin x + C$ (b) $-\sqrt{1 - x^2} + C$
(c) Not possible

49. (a) $\frac{2}{3}(x - 1)^{3/2} + C$ (b) $\frac{2}{5}(x - 1)^{5/2} + \frac{2}{3}(x - 1)^{3/2} + C$
(c) $\frac{2}{3}(x - 1)^{3/2} + 2(x - 1)^{1/2} + C$

51. Answers will vary.
53. No; The functions differ by a constant.
55. The integrals should be subtracted in the first step;
$-\sqrt{1 - x^2} - 5 \arcsin x + C$

57. $\frac{\pi}{3}$ **59.** $\frac{\pi}{8}$ **61.** $y = \arcsin \frac{x}{2} + \pi$

63. False; $\int \frac{dx}{3x\sqrt{9x^2 - 16}} = \frac{1}{12} \operatorname{arcsec} \frac{|3x|}{4} + C$

65. False; $\frac{d}{dx}[\arctan x] = -\frac{d}{dx}[\operatorname{arccot} x]$

67–69. Answers will vary.

71. (a) $F(x)$ represents the average value of $f(x)$ over the interval $[x, x + 2]$. Maximum at $x = -1$

(b) Maximum at $x = -1$; They are the same.

73. (a) Answers will vary. (b) 3.13696 (c) 3.1415927

75. D

77. (a) Yes; $\lim_{x \to 0} g(x)$ exists, and it and $g(0)$ are equal to $\frac{1}{2}$.

(b) $\frac{\pi}{6}$ (c) $\frac{6 + \pi}{6}$

Review Exercises for Chapter 4 *(page 364)*

1. $\frac{4}{3}x^3 + \frac{1}{2}x^2 + 3x + C$ **3.** $\ln|x| - \frac{2}{x^4} + C$

5. $5x - e^x + C$ **7.** $f(x) = -3x^2 + 1$

9. $f(x) = e^{-x} + x + 7$

11. (a) 3 sec; 144 ft (b) $\frac{3}{2}$ sec (c) 108 ft

13. 420 **15.** 60 **17.** 3310

19. $A = 15$ **21.** $A = 12$

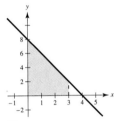 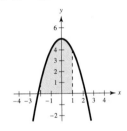

23. $\frac{27}{2}$

25.

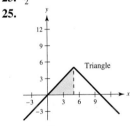

$A = \frac{25}{2}$

27. 17 **29.** 0 **31.** (a) $x = -5$ (b) -56

33. 0.285; They are about the same.

35. 3.432; They are about the same. **37.** 12 **39.** $\frac{422}{5}$

41. $\frac{\sqrt{2} + 2}{2}$ **43.** 30 **45.** $2 \ln 3 \approx 2.1972$

47. $x = \frac{25}{4}$ **49.** (a) $-\frac{15}{2}$ ft (b) $\frac{17}{2}$ ft **51.** $\frac{1160}{27}$ units

53. $\csc^2 x$ **55.** $\frac{1}{30}(3x^2 - 1)^5 + C$ **57.** $\frac{2}{3}\sqrt{x^3 + 3} + C$

59. $\frac{1}{4}\sin^4 x + C$ **61.** $-\frac{1}{4}e^{\cos 4\theta} + C$

63. $\frac{1}{2 \ln 5} 5^{(x+1)^2} + C$ **65.** $\frac{1}{3\pi}(1 + \sec \pi x)^3 + C$

67. $\frac{455}{2}$ **69.** 2 **71.** 2 **73.** $\frac{28\pi}{15}$

75. $\frac{1}{7}\ln|7x - 2| + C$ **77.** $-\ln|1 + \cos x| + C$

79. $3 + \ln 2$ **81.** $\ln(2 + \sqrt{3})$ **83.** $\frac{1}{2}\arctan e^{2x} + C$

85. $\frac{1}{2}\arcsin x^2 + C$ **87.** $\frac{1}{4}\left(\arctan \frac{x}{2}\right)^2 + C$

AP® Exam Practice Questions *(page 366)*

1. B **2.** C **3.** A **4.** A **5.** C
6. D **7.** D **8.** B

9. (a) $-25°$; This represents the total temperature lost from $t = 0$ to $t = 12$.

(b) The average temperature for $0 \le t \le 12$; 49.9°C

(c) $-3.5°C/min$; $C'(4) \approx \frac{C(5) - C(3)}{5 - 3} = -3.5$

(d) 35.1°C

10. (a) 2 in. (b) 0.1938 in./h

(c) $I(t) = 0.002t^3 - 0.06t^2 + 0.87t + 2\cos\frac{\pi t}{12} + 38$

(d) $t \approx 4.2406$ h; 41.6519 in.; $S(t) = M(t)$ when $t \approx 4.2406$ h.

11. (a) $0 \le t \le 4, 8 \le t \le 9$; $v(t) > 0$ on $(0, 4)$ and $(8, 9)$

(b) $\int_0^9 \sin\frac{\pi t}{4} dt$

(c) -0.555; speeding up because $v(t) < 0$ and decreasing

(d) -1.83

12. (a) $F(0) \approx -5.64$; $F'(0) = 3$; $F(4) = -\frac{1}{2}$

(b) None; On $[-3, 4]$, $f(x)$ does not change from negative to positive at any point.

(c) $x = 0$; $f'(x)$ changes sign at $x = 0$. (d) $y = x - \frac{5}{2}$

13. (a) $F(0) = 14.5$; $F(4) = 18.5$

(b) 2 times; $F(0) > 5$, $F(x)$ is decreasing on $(0, 3)$, $F(3) < 5$, $F(x)$ is increasing on $(3, 4)$, $F(4) > 5$

(c) $(3, 4)$; $f(x) > 0$ on $(3, 4)$

Chapter 5

Section 5.1 *(page 375)*

1–11. Answers will vary. **13.** Not a solution
15. Not a solution **17.** Solution **19.** Solution
21. Not a solution **23.** Solution **25.** Not a solution
27. Solution **29.** $y = 3e^{-x/2}$

31.

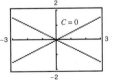 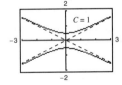

$(-\infty, \infty)$ $(-\infty, \infty)$

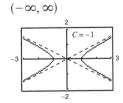 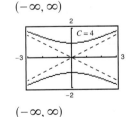

$(-\infty, -1] \cup [1, \infty)$ $(-\infty, \infty)$

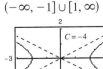
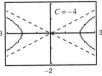

$(-\infty, -2] \cup [2, \infty)$

33. $y = 3e^{-6x}$ **35.** $y = -2x + \frac{1}{2}x^3$

37. $y = 2\sin 3x - \frac{1}{3}\cos 3x$ **39.** $y = 4x^3 + C$

41. $y = 2x^5 - \dfrac{x^4}{2} + C$ **43.** $y = \dfrac{1}{2}\ln(1 + x^2) + C$

45. $y = x - \ln x^2 + C$ **47.** $y = -\frac{1}{2}\cos 2x + C$

49. $y = \frac{2}{5}(x - 6)^{5/2} + 4(x - 6)^{3/2} + C$ **51.** $y = \frac{1}{2}e^{x^2} + C$

53. $y = e^{\sin x} + C$

55.

x	-4	-2	0	2	4	8
y	2	0	4	4	6	8
$\dfrac{dy}{dx}$	-4	Undef.	0	1	$\dfrac{4}{3}$	2

57.

x	-4	-2	0	2	4	8
y	2	0	4	4	6	8
$\dfrac{dy}{dx}$	$-2\sqrt{2}$	-2	0	0	$-2\sqrt{2}$	-8

59. b   **60.** c   **61.** d   **62.** a

63.

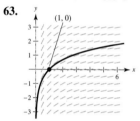

Domain: $(0, \infty)$
As $x \to \infty$, $y \to \infty$.

65. (a)–(b)

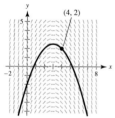

(c) As $x \to \infty$, $y \to -\infty$.
As $x \to -\infty$, $y \to -\infty$.

67. (a)–(b)

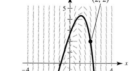

(c) As $x \to \infty$, $y \to -\infty$.
As $x \to -\infty$, $y \to -\infty$.

69. (a)–(b)

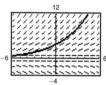

(c) $(-\infty, \infty)$

71. (a)–(b)

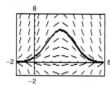

(c) $(-\infty, \infty)$

73.

n	0	1	2	3	4	5	6
x_n	0	0.1	0.2	0.3	0.4	0.5	0.6
y_n	2	2.2	2.43	2.693	2.992	3.332	3.715

n	7	8	9	10
x_n	0.7	0.8	0.9	1.0
y_n	4.146	4.631	5.174	5.781

75.

n	0	1	2	3	4	5	6
x_n	0	0.05	0.1	0.15	0.2	0.25	0.3
y_n	3	2.7	2.438	2.209	2.010	1.839	1.693

n	7	8	9	10
x_n	0.35	0.4	0.45	0.5
y_n	1.569	1.464	1.378	1.308

77.

n	0	1	2	3	4	5	6
x_n	0	0.1	0.2	0.3	0.4	0.5	0.6
y_n	1	1.1	1.212	1.339	1.488	1.670	1.900

n	7	8	9	10
x_n	0.7	0.8	0.9	1.0
y_n	2.213	2.684	3.540	5.958

79.

x	$y(x)$ (exact)	$y(x)$ ($h = 0.2$)	$y(x)$ ($h = 0.1$)
0	3.0000	3.0000	3.0000
0.2	3.6642	3.6000	3.6300
0.4	4.4755	4.3200	4.3923
0.6	5.4664	5.1840	5.3147
0.8	6.6766	6.2208	6.4308
1	8.1548	7.4650	7.7812

The error decreases.

81.

x	$y(x)$ (exact)	$y(x)$ ($h = 0.2$)	$y(x)$ ($h = 0.1$)
0	0.0000	0.0000	0.0000
0.2	0.2200	0.2000	0.2095
0.4	0.4801	0.4360	0.4568
0.6	0.7807	0.7074	0.7418
0.8	1.1231	1.0140	1.0649
1	1.5097	1.3561	1.4273

The error decreases.

83. (a) $y(1) = 112.7141°$; $y(2) = 96.3770°$; $y(3) = 86.5954°$
   (b) $y(1) = 113.2441°$; $y(2) = 97.0158°$; $y(3) = 87.1729°$
   (c) Euler's Method: $y(1) = 112.9828°$; $y(2) = 96.6998°$;
        $y(3) = 86.8863°$
        Exact solution: $y(1) = 113.2441°$; $y(2) = 97.0158°$;
        $y(3) = 87.1729°$
   The approximations are better using $h = 0.05$.

85. $\int \frac{1}{x}\, dx = \ln|x| + C$

87. When the exact solution is a line

89. y'' should be $16e^{-4x}$; Not a solution

91. False; Sample answer: $y = x^3$ is a solution of $xy' - 3y = 0$, but $y = x^3 + 1$ is not a solution.

93. True

95. (a)

x	0	0.2	0.4	0.6	0.8	1
y	4	2.6813	1.7973	1.2048	0.8076	0.5413
y_1	4	2.5600	1.6384	1.0486	0.6711	0.4295
y_2	4	2.4000	1.4400	0.8640	0.5184	0.3110
e_1	0	0.1213	0.1589	0.1562	0.1365	0.1118
e_2	0	0.2813	0.3573	0.3408	0.2892	0.2303
r		0.4312	0.4447	0.4583	0.4720	0.4855

   (b) If h is halved, then the error is approximately halved because r is approximately 0.5.
   (c) The error will again be halved.

97. $k = \pm 4$ **99.** D

101. (a)

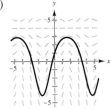

   (b) $y = -3x + 3\pi + 1$; 0.825

Section 5.2   *(page 384)*

1. $y = \frac{1}{2}x^2 + 3x + C$ **3.** $y = Ce^x - 3$
5. $y^2 - 5x^2 = C$ **7.** $y = Ce^{(2x^{3/2})/3}$ **9.** $y = C(1 + x^2)$
11. $\frac{dQ}{dt} = \frac{k}{t^2}$; $Q = -\frac{k}{t} + C$

13. (a) Sample answer: (b) $y = 6 - 6e^{-x^2/2}$

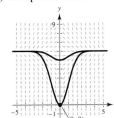   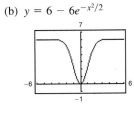

15. $y = \frac{1}{4}t^2 + 10$ **17.** $y = 10e^{-t/2}$

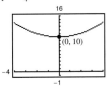   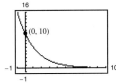

19. $\frac{8192}{5}$ **21.** $y = 2e^{[(1/4)\ln(3/2)]t} \approx 2e^{0.1014t}$
23. $y = 5\left(\frac{5}{2}\right)^{1/4}e^{[(1/4)\ln(2/5)]t} \approx 6.2872e^{-0.2291t}$

25. The x- and y-values of the initial condition were switched; $C = \frac{1}{2}$, $2x^3 - 3y^2 = -3$

27. Quadrants I and III; dy/dx is positive when both x and y are positive (Quadrant I) or when both x and y are negative (Quadrant III).

29. 4.43 g; 1.49 g   **31.** 2.161 g; 1.62 g
33. 12.96 g; 6911 yr   **35.** 76.316 g; 49.471 g   **37.** 95.76%
39. 5.78 yr; $3320.12   **41.** 9.50%; 7.30 yr
43. (a) $P = 2.07e^{-0.011t}$ (b) 1.70 million
   (c) Because $k < 0$, the population is decreasing.
45. (a) $P = 31.58e^{0.032t}$ (b) 56.18 million
   (c) Because $k > 0$, the population is increasing.
47. (a) 45 bacteria   (b) $y = \frac{625}{14}e^{[(1/2)\ln(14/5)]t} \approx 44.64e^{0.5148t}$
   (c) 2744 bacteria   (d) 12.29 h
49. (a) $N = 100.1596e^{0.2195t}$ (b) 6.3 h
51. Because the population increases by a constant each month, the rate of change from month to month will always be the same. So, the slope is constant, and the model is linear.
53. (a) $y = 1420e^{[\ln(52/71)]t} + 80$ (b) 299.2°F
55. (a) $N = 30 - 30e^{[(1/15)\ln(1/2)]t}$ (b) 39 days
57. False; The half-life of radium is 1599 years.
59. A   **61.** D

Section 5.3   *(page 393)*

1. $y = Ce^{(3/2)t}$ **3.** $y^2 - x^2 = C$ **5.** $y^4 - 2x^2 + 4x = C$
7. $y = \dfrac{C}{(2 + x)^2}$ **9.** $y^2 = C - 8\cos x$
11. $y = -\frac{1}{4}\sqrt{1 - 4x^2} + C$ **13.** $y = Ce^{(\ln x)^2/2}$
15. $y^2 = 4e^x + 32$ **17.** $y = e^{-(x^2 + 2x)/2}$ **19.** $y^2 = 4x^2 + 3$
21. $u = e^{(1 - \cos v^2)/2}$ **23.** $y = \frac{1}{4}\ln(\ln x) + 4$
25. $4y^2 - x^2 = 16$, $x, y > 0$ **27.** $y = 2e^{(x-1)/(2x)}$, $x > 0$
29. $y = Ce^{-x/2}$
31. Sample answer: **33.** Sample answer:

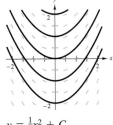   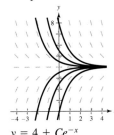

$y = \frac{1}{2}x^2 + C$ $y = 4 + Ce^{-x}$

35. (a) $y = 0.1602$ (b) $y = 5e^{-3x^2}$ (c) $y = 0.2489$
37. (a) $y \approx 3.0318$ (b) $y^3 - 4y = x^2 + 12x - 13$
   (c) $y = 3$

39. The variables were not separated; $-\dfrac{1}{y} = \dfrac{1}{2}x^2 + C$

41. (a) $\dfrac{dy}{dx} = k(y - 4)$ (b) i

43. (a) $\dfrac{dy}{dx} = ky(y - 4)$ (b) iii

45. (a) $w = 1200 - 1140e^{-kt}$
(b) $w = 1200 - 1140e^{-0.8t}$ $w = 1200 - 1140e^{-0.9t}$

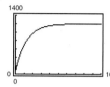   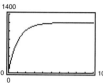

$w = 1200 - 1140e^{-t}$

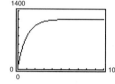

(c) 1.31 yr; 1.16 yr; 1.05 yr   (d) 1200 lb

47. $N = \dfrac{500}{1 + 4e^{-0.2452t}}$ **49.** $y \approx 1 - e^{-1.386t}$

51. $y = \dfrac{360}{8 + 41t}$ **53.** $y = 500e^{-1.6094e^{-0.1451t}}$

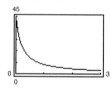   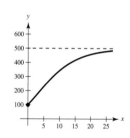

55. 34 beavers

57. (a) $Q = 25e^{-(1/20)t}$ (b) $t \approx 10.2$ min

59. $s = 25 - \dfrac{13\ln(h/2)}{\ln 3}, 2 \le h \le 15$

61. $A = \dfrac{P}{r}(e^{rt} - 1)$ **63.** $23,981,015.77

65. (a)

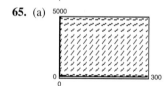

(b) As $t \to \infty, y \to L$.   (c) $y = 5000e^{-2.303e^{-0.02t}}$
(d)

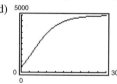

Concave upward on $(0, 41.7)$; concave downward on $(41.7, \infty)$

67. Yes; Rewrite the equation as $\dfrac{dy}{g(y) - h(y)} = f(x)\, dx$.

69. Separable; $\dfrac{1}{y}\, dy = -\dfrac{(1 + x)}{x}\, dx$ **71.** Not separable

73. Separable; $y^5\, dy = \dfrac{1}{x^3}\, dx$

75. (a) $v = 20(1 - e^{-1.386t})$
(b) $s \approx 20t + 14.43(e^{-1.386t} - 1)$

77. False; Sample answer: $y' = \dfrac{x}{y}$ is separable, but $y = 0$ is not a solution.

79. A   **81.** (a) $y = -4e^{-1/x+1/3} + 4$ (b) $-4e^{1/3} + 4$

Section 5.4   *(page 402)*

1. d   **2.** a   **3.** b   **4.** c   **5.** $y(0) = 4$
7. $y(0) = \frac{12}{7}$
9. (a) 0.75   (b) 2100   (c) 70   (d) 4.49 yr
(e) $\dfrac{dP}{dt} = 0.75P\left[1 - \dfrac{P}{2100}\right]$

11. (a) 0.8   (b) 6000   (c) 1.2   (d) 10.65 yr
(e) $\dfrac{dP}{dt} = 0.8P\left[1 - \dfrac{P}{6000}\right]$

13. (a) 3   (b) 100   **15.** (a) 0.1   (b) 250
(c)   (c)

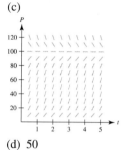   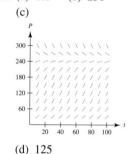

(d) 50   (d) 125

17. $y = \dfrac{36}{1 + 8e^{-t}}$; 34.16; 36.00

19. $y = \dfrac{120}{1 + 14e^{-0.8t}}$; 95.51; 120.0   **21.** $0 \le y(0) \le 3000$

23. For $\dfrac{dy}{dt} = ky\left(1 - \dfrac{y}{L}\right)$, where k and L are positive constants, the slopes are horizontal for $y = 0$ and $y = L$ because $dy/dt = 0$. The slopes are positive for $0 < y < L$ because $dy/dt > 0$. The slopes are negative for $y < 0$ and $y > L$ because $dy/dt < 0$.

25. (a) $P = \dfrac{200}{1 + 7e^{-0.2640t}}$ (b) 70 panthers   (c) 7.37 yr
(d) $\dfrac{dP}{dt} = 0.2640P\left(1 - \dfrac{P}{200}\right)$; 69.25 panthers; They are about the same.
(e) When $P = 100$ panthers; The inflection point is at $P = 100$; 13.2 panthers per year

27. Answers will vary.   **29.** True

31. (a) 5   (b) 5   (c) $P = \dfrac{5}{2}$ (d) $P = \dfrac{5}{1 + \frac{2}{3}e^{-2t}}$

Review Exercises for Chapter 5   *(page 404)*

1. Solution   **3.** $y = \frac{4}{3}x^3 + 7x + C$ **5.** $y = \frac{1}{2}\sin 2x + C$
7. $y = -e^{2-x} + C$
9.

x	-4	-2	0	2	4	8
y	2	0	4	4	6	8
$\dfrac{dy}{dx}$	-10	-4	-4	0	2	8

11. (a)–(b)

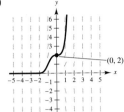

13.

n	0	1	2	3	4	5
x_n	0	0.05	0.1	0.15	0.2	0.25
y_n	4	3.8	3.6125	3.4369	3.2726	3.1190

n	6	7	8	9	10
x_n	0.3	0.35	0.4	0.45	0.5
y_n	2.9756	2.8418	2.7172	2.6038	2.4986

15. $y = -3 - \dfrac{1}{x + C}$ **17.** $y = \dfrac{Ce^x}{(2 + x)^2}$

19. $\dfrac{dy}{dt} = \dfrac{k}{t^3}; y = -\dfrac{k}{2t^2} + C$

21. $y \approx \frac{3}{4}e^{[(1/5)\ln(20/3)]t} \approx \frac{3}{4}e^{0.3794t}$

23. $y = \frac{9}{20}e^{[(1/2)\ln(10/3)]t} \approx \frac{9}{20}e^{0.6020t}$ **25.** About 4.21 g

27. (a) $S \approx 30e^{-1.7918/t}$ (b) 20,965 units

29. $y^2 = 5x^2 + C$ **31.** $y = Ce^{8x^2}$ **33.** $y^4 = 6x^2 - 8$

35. $y^4 = 2x^4 + 1$

37. Sample answer:

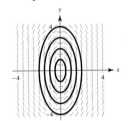

$4x^2 + y^2 = C$

39. About 3.095 g

41. (a) 0.55   (b) 5250   (c) 150   (d) 6.41 yr

(e) $\dfrac{dP}{dt} = 0.55P\left(1 - \dfrac{P}{5250}\right)$

43. $y = \dfrac{21}{1 + \frac{4}{3}e^{-4.2t}}$

45. (a) $P = \dfrac{20,400}{1 + 16e^{-0.553t}}; 4.94$ yr   (b) 17,118 trout

47. $\dfrac{dS}{dt} = k(L - S); S = L(1 - e^{-kt})$

49. $\dfrac{dP}{dn} = kP(L - P); P = \dfrac{CL}{e^{-Lkn} + C}$

AP® Exam Practice Questions   *(page 406)*

1. B   **2.** B   **3.** A   **4.** C   **5.** B   **6.** A   **7.** A

8. (a) $y = 200e^{0.5t}$

(b) $\dfrac{1}{10}\displaystyle\int_0^{10} 200e^{0.5t}\, dt = 40(e^5 - 1) \approx 5896.526$ bacteria

9. (a) $-\frac{5}{8}$

(b) $y = \frac{1}{2}x + \frac{3}{2}; f(1.1) \approx 2.05; 2.05 > f(1.1)$ because $f''(1.1) < 0$.

(c) $f(x) = \sqrt{2\ln|x| + 4}$

10. (a)

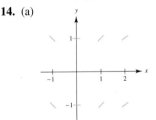

(b) $y < 1$ (c) $f(x) = 1 + e^{(-1/3)x^3}$

(d) $\dfrac{d^2y}{dx^2} = x(2 - x^3)(1 - y);$ neither

11. (a) $y_1 = 2.2, y_2 \approx 2.418; f(1.4) \approx 2.418$

(b) $f(x) = \sqrt{2x^2 + 2};$ Domain: $(-\infty, \infty)$

12. (a) $y_1 = 1.1, y_2 = 1.221; f(1.2) \approx 1.221$

(b) $\dfrac{d^2y}{dx^2} = e^{0.5x^2 - 0.5}(x^2 + 1); 1.221 < f(1.2)$ because $f''(1.2) > 0$.

(c) $f(x) = e^{0.5x^2 - 0.5}$

13. (a) When 200 people have the disease; $\dfrac{dy}{dt}$ is 16 when $y = 200$ and 9 when $y = 100$.

(b) $y = \dfrac{1000}{1 + 9e^{-0.1t}}$ (c) 1000

14. (a)

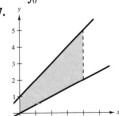

(b) $\dfrac{d^2y}{dx^2} = \dfrac{y^3 - 2x^2}{y^5}$ (c) $y = \sqrt{0.5x^2 + 4}$

Chapter 6

Section 6.1   *(page 416)*

1. $-\displaystyle\int_0^6 (x^2 - 6x)\, dx$ **3.** $\displaystyle\int_0^3 (-2x^2 + 6x)\, dx$

5. $-6\displaystyle\int_0^1 (x^3 - x)\, dx$

7.

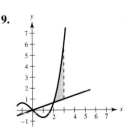

9.

CHAPTER 6

11.

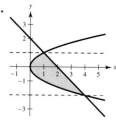

13. Should have subtracted g from f; $\int_0^2 (2x^3 + 2x^2 - 4x)\, dx$

15.

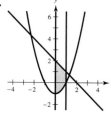

$\frac{13}{6}$

17.

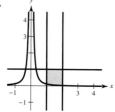

$\frac{17}{18}$

19.

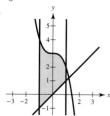

6

21.

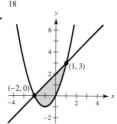

$\frac{9}{2}$

23.

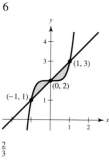

$\frac{2}{3}$

25.

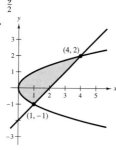

$\frac{9}{2}$

27.

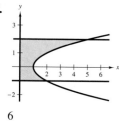

6

29.

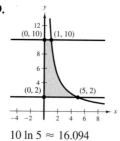

$10 \ln 5 \approx 16.094$

31. (a) $\frac{125}{6}$ (b) $\frac{125}{6}$
  (c) Integrating with respect to y; Answers will vary.

33. (a)

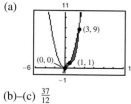

  (b)–(c) $\frac{37}{12}$

35. (a)

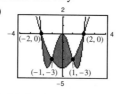

  (b)–(c) 8

37. (a)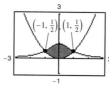

  (b)–(c) $\dfrac{\pi}{2} - \dfrac{1}{3} \approx 1.237$

39. (a)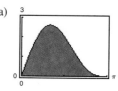

  (b)–(c) 4

41. (a)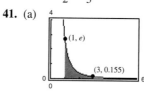

  (b)–(c) About 1.323

43.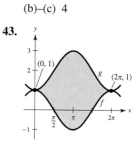

  $4\pi \approx 12.566$

45.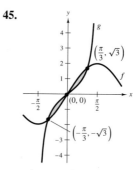

  $2(1 - \ln 2) \approx 0.614$

47.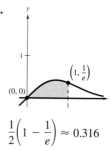

  $\dfrac{1}{2}\left(1 - \dfrac{1}{e}\right) \approx 0.316$

49. (a)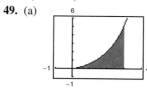

  (b) The function does not have an elementary antiderivative.

  (c) 4.7721

51. (a)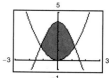

  (b) The intersection points are difficult to find.

  (c) 6.3043

53. $F(x) = \frac{1}{4}x^2 + x$

  (a) $F(0) = 0$

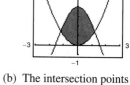

  (b) $F(3) = \frac{21}{4}$

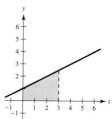

  (c) $F(6) = 15$

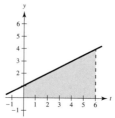

55. $F(\alpha) = \dfrac{2}{\pi}\left(\sin\dfrac{\pi\alpha}{2} + 1\right)$

(a) $F\left(-\dfrac{1}{2}\right) = \dfrac{2 - \sqrt{2}}{\pi} \approx 0.1865$

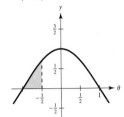

(b) $F(0) = \dfrac{2}{\pi} \approx 0.6366$ (c) $F\left(\dfrac{1}{2}\right) = \dfrac{\sqrt{2} + 2}{\pi} \approx 1.0868$

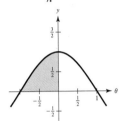 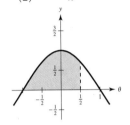

57. 2   **59.** 14   **61.** 16

63. $x^4 - 2x^2 + 1 \le 1 - x^2$ on $[-1, 1]$;

$\displaystyle\int_{-1}^{1}[(1 - x^2) - (x^4 - 2x^2 + 1)]\,dx = \dfrac{4}{15}$

65. (a) $\int_0^5 [v_1(t) - v_2(t)]\,dt = 10$: The first car traveled 10 more meters than the second car between 0 and 5 seconds.

$\int_0^{10} [v_1(t) - v_2(t)]\,dt = 30$: The first car traveled 30 more meters than the second car between 0 and 10 seconds.

$\int_{20}^{30} [v_1(t) - v_2(t)]\,dt = -5$: The second car traveled 5 more meters than the first car between 20 and 30 seconds.

(b) The car with velocity v_1; 30 m

(c) Car 1 is ahead by 8 meters.

(d) No; You do not know the velocity of the cars at any time.

67. $\dfrac{1}{6}$

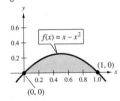

69. $b = 9\left(1 - \dfrac{1}{\sqrt[3]{4}}\right) \approx 3.330$ **71.** $a = 4 - 2\sqrt{2} \approx 1.172$

73. (a) About 6.031 m²   (b) About 12.062 m³

(c) About 60,310 lb

75. $3.44 million   **77.** $\dfrac{\sqrt{3}}{2} + \dfrac{7\pi}{24} + 1 \approx 2.7823$ **79.** True

81. False; Sample answer: Let $f(x) = x$, $g(x) = 2x - x^2$, $a = 0$, and $b = 2$. f and g intersect at $(1, 1)$, $\int_0^2 [x - (2x - x^2)]\,dx = \dfrac{2}{3}$.

83. C   **85.** D

Section 6.2   *(page 427)*

1. $\pi\displaystyle\int_0^1 (-x + 1)^2\,dx = \dfrac{\pi}{3}$ **3.** $\pi\displaystyle\int_1^4 (\sqrt{x})^2\,dx = \dfrac{15\pi}{2}$

5. $\pi\displaystyle\int_0^4 \left(\dfrac{1}{\sqrt{x+1}}\right)^2\,dx = \pi\ln 5$ **7.** $\pi\displaystyle\int_1^3 \left(\dfrac{1}{x}\right)^2\,dx = \dfrac{2\pi}{3}$

9. $\pi\displaystyle\int_0^1 (e^{-x})^2\,dx = \dfrac{\pi}{2}\left(1 - \dfrac{1}{e^2}\right)$ **11.** $\pi\displaystyle\int_0^4 (\sqrt{y})^2\,dy = 8\pi$

13. $\pi\displaystyle\int_0^1 (y^{3/2})^2\,dy = \dfrac{\pi}{4}$ **15.** $\pi\displaystyle\int_0^6 \left[\dfrac{1}{3}(6 - y)\right]^2\,dy = 8\pi$

17. $\pi\displaystyle\int_1^6 \left(\dfrac{y^2 - 1}{5}\right)^2\,dy = \dfrac{170\pi}{3}$ **19.** $\dfrac{64\pi}{3}$ **21.** $\dfrac{19\pi}{6}$

23. $\dfrac{144\pi}{7}$ **25.** $\dfrac{27\pi}{2}$ **27.** $\pi\left(\dfrac{327}{4} - 30\ln 4\right) \approx 126.17$

29. The region was revolved about the x-axis; $\pi\displaystyle\int_0^1 (e^y - 1)^2\,dy$

31. $\dfrac{6\pi}{55}$ **33.** 72π **35.** $\dfrac{32{,}912\pi}{105}$ **37.** 280π

39. $\dfrac{1088\pi}{5}$ **41.** $\dfrac{84\pi}{5}$ **43.** $\dfrac{277\pi}{3}$ **45.** $\dfrac{\pi^2}{2} \approx 4.935$

47. $\dfrac{\pi}{2}(e^2 - 1) \approx 10.036$ **49.** 1.9686   **51.** 15.4115

53. $\dfrac{\pi}{3}$ **55.** $\dfrac{2\pi}{15}$ **57.** $\dfrac{\pi}{2}$ **59.** $\dfrac{\pi}{6}$

61. A sine curve on $\left[0, \dfrac{\pi}{2}\right]$ revolved about the x-axis

63. They are equal; $y = 4x - x^2$ is a horizontal translation of $y = 4 - x^2$.

65. $2\sqrt{2}$ **67.** $V = \dfrac{4}{3}\pi(R^2 - r^2)^{3/2}$

69. Answers will vary.   **71.** $\pi r^2 h\left(1 - \dfrac{h}{H} + \dfrac{h^2}{3H^2}\right)$

73.

![graph from -0.25 to 0.5, 0 to 2]

$\dfrac{\pi}{30}$ m³

75. (a) 60π (b) 100π

77. (a) $V = \pi\left(4b^2 - \dfrac{64}{3}b + \dfrac{512}{15}\right)$

(b)

![graph 0 to 4, 0 to 120]

(c) $b = \dfrac{8}{3} \approx 2.67$

$b \approx 2.67$

79. Proof   **81.** (a) $\dfrac{128}{3}$ (b) $\dfrac{32\sqrt{3}}{3}$ (c) $\dfrac{16\pi}{3}$ (d) $\dfrac{32}{3}$

83. C   **85.** (a) 1.9054   (b) 2.2215   (c) 3.2296

Section 6.3   *(page 436)*

1. $2\pi\displaystyle\int_0^2 x^2\,dx = \dfrac{16\pi}{3}$ **3.** $2\pi\displaystyle\int_0^4 x\sqrt{x}\,dx = \dfrac{128\pi}{5}$

5. $2\pi\displaystyle\int_0^4 x\left(\dfrac{1}{4}x^2\right)\,dx = 32\pi$ **7.** $2\pi\displaystyle\int_0^2 x(4x - 2x^2)\,dx = \dfrac{16\pi}{3}$

9. $2\pi\displaystyle\int_0^2 x(x^2 - 4x + 4)\,dx = \dfrac{8\pi}{3}$

11. $2\pi\displaystyle\int_0^1 x\left(\dfrac{1}{\sqrt{2\pi}}e^{-x^2/2}\right)\,dx = \sqrt{2\pi}\left(1 - \dfrac{1}{\sqrt{e}}\right) \approx 0.986$

13. $2\pi \displaystyle\int_0^2 y(2-y)\,dy = \dfrac{8\pi}{3}$

15. $2\pi \left[\displaystyle\int_0^{1/2} y\,dy + \int_{1/2}^1 y\left(\dfrac{1}{y}-1\right)dy \right] = \dfrac{\pi}{2}$

17. $2\pi \displaystyle\int_0^8 y^{4/3}\,dy = \dfrac{768\pi}{7}$ **19.** $2\pi \displaystyle\int_0^1 y(y^2-3y+2)\,dy = \dfrac{\pi}{2}$

21. 8π **23.** 16π

25. y should be subtracted from 4; $V = 2\pi \displaystyle\int_0^2 (4-y)(4-y^2)\,dy$

27. y^2+1 should be subtracted from 5;

$$V = 2\pi \int_0^2 (4-y)(4-y^2)\,dy$$

29. Shell method; It is much easier to put x in terms of y.

31. (a) $\dfrac{128\pi}{7}$ (b) $\dfrac{64\pi}{5}$ (c) $\dfrac{96\pi}{5}$

33. (a) $\dfrac{\pi a^3}{15}$ (b) $\dfrac{\pi a^3}{15}$ (c) $\dfrac{4\pi a^3}{15}$

35. (a) 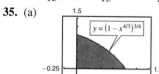   (b) 1.506

37. (a) 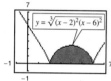   (b) 187.25

39. (a) The rectangles would be vertical.
(b) The rectangles would be horizontal.

41. (a) Both integrals represent the volume of the solid generated by revolving the region bounded by the graphs of $y=\sqrt{x}-1$, $y=0$, and $x=5$ about the x-axis.
(b) Both integrals represent the volume of the solid generated by revolving the region bounded by $y=\dfrac{x}{2}$, $y=0$, and $x=4$ about the y-axis.

43. (a) Region bounded by $y=x^2$, $y=0$, $x=0$, $x=2$
(b) y-axis

45. (a) Region bounded by $y=e^x$, $y=0$, $x=0$, $x=1$
(b) $x=4$

47. (a) Region bounded by $y=\dfrac{4x+5}{2x^2}$, $y=0$, $x=1$, $x=8$
(b) y-axis

49. First bucket; $\dfrac{8\pi}{15}$ cups   **51.** About 94.782 cm³

53. $2\sqrt{4-2\sqrt{3}} \approx 1.464$ **55.** (a) $V=2\pi$ (b) $V=6\pi^2$

57. $4\pi^2$ **59.** $c=2$

61. (a) $R_1(n) = \dfrac{n}{n+1}$; 1

(b) $V=\pi ab^{n+2}\left(\dfrac{n}{n+2}\right)$; $R_2(n)=\dfrac{n}{n+2}$; 1

(c) (i) The region approaches the x-axis from 0 to b.
(ii) The region approaches a $1 \times a$ rectangle.
(iii) The region is unbounded.

63.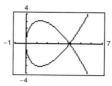

(a) $\dfrac{64\pi}{3}$ (b) $\dfrac{2048\pi}{35}$ (c) $\dfrac{8192\pi}{105}$

65. C

67. (a) About 0.5348   (b) About 4.5888   (c) $V=\dfrac{36\pi}{25}$

Section 6.4   *(page 446)*

1. (a)–(b) 15   **3.** $\frac{2}{3}\left(2\sqrt{2}-1\right) \approx 1.219$ **5.** $\frac{5}{3}$

7. $5\sqrt{5}-2\sqrt{2} \approx 8.352$ **9.** 309.3195

11. $\ln\left(\dfrac{\sqrt{2}+1}{\sqrt{2}-1}\right) \approx 1.763$ **13.** $\dfrac{e^2-1}{2e} \approx 1.175$

15. $\dfrac{20\sqrt{10}-2}{27} \approx 2.268$ **17.** $\dfrac{76}{3}$ **19.** c

21. (a)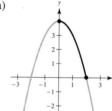

(b) $\displaystyle\int_0^2 \sqrt{1+4x^2}\,dx$

(c) About 4.647

23. (a)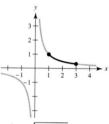

(b) $\displaystyle\int_1^3 \sqrt{1+\dfrac{1}{x^4}}\,dx$

(c) About 2.147

25. (a)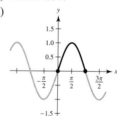

(b) $\displaystyle\int_0^\pi \sqrt{1+\cos^2 x}\,dx$

(c) About 3.820

27. (a)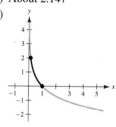

(b) $\displaystyle\int_0^2 \sqrt{1+e^{-2y}}\,dy$

(c) About 2.221

29. (a)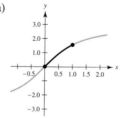

(b) $\displaystyle\int_0^1 \sqrt{1+\left(\dfrac{2}{1+x^2}\right)^2}\,dx$

(c) About 1.871

31. dy/dx should be $\sec^2 x$, not $\sec x$; $s=\displaystyle\int_a^b \sqrt{1+\sec^4 x}\,dx$

33. 47.008 m   **35.** 48

37. $2\pi \displaystyle\int_0^3 3x\sqrt{10}\,dx = 27\sqrt{10}\pi \approx 268.23$

39. $2\pi \int_0^3 \frac{1}{3}x^3\sqrt{1+x^4}\,dx = \frac{\pi}{9}\left(82\sqrt{82}-1\right) \approx 258.85$

41. $2\pi \int_{-1}^1 2\,dx = 8\pi \approx 25.13$

43. $2\pi \int_1^8 x\sqrt{1+\frac{1}{9x^{4/3}}}\,dx = \frac{\pi}{27}\left(145\sqrt{145}-10\sqrt{10}\right) \approx 199.48$

45. $2\pi \int_0^2 x\sqrt{1+\frac{x^2}{4}}\,dx = \frac{\pi}{3}\left(16\sqrt{2}-8\right) \approx 15.318$

47. (a) Distance Formula with representative element

$$\sqrt{(\Delta x_i)^2 + (\Delta y_i)^2} = \sqrt{1+\left(\frac{\Delta y_i}{\Delta x_i}\right)^2}\,\Delta x_i$$

(b) The formula for the lateral surface area of the frustum of a right circular cone, $S = \pi(r_1 + r_2)L$, with representative element

$$2\pi f(d_i)\sqrt{1+\left(\frac{\Delta y_i}{\Delta x_i}\right)^2}\,\Delta x_i$$

49. They have the same value.

51.

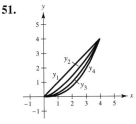

$y_1,\ y_2,\ y_3,\ y_4$

53. 20π **55.** $6\pi\left(3-\sqrt{5}\right) \approx 14.40$

57. (a) About 5208 in.^{3} (b) About 1169 in.^{2}

(c) $r = 0.0040y^3 - 0.142y^2 + 1.23y + 7.9$

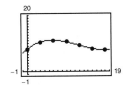

(d) 5279.64 in.^{3}; 1179.5 in.^{2}; They are about the same.

59. (a) $\pi\left(1-\frac{1}{b}\right)$ (b) $2\pi \int_1^b \frac{\sqrt{x^4+1}}{x^3}\,dx$

(c)–(d) Answers will vary.

61. $\frac{2}{3}$ unit; Answers will vary.

63. Answers will vary.   **65.** B   **67.** C

Review Exercises for Chapter 6   *(page 450)*

1. $\int_0^2 (\sin \pi x - x^3 + 4x)\,dx$ **3.** $2\int_0^2 (-2x^3 + 8x)\,dx$

5.

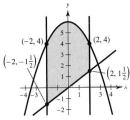

$\dfrac{64}{3}$

7.

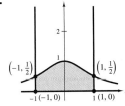

$\dfrac{\pi}{2}$

9.

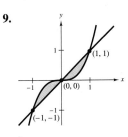

$\dfrac{1}{2}$

11.

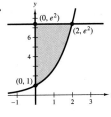

$e^2 + 1$

13.

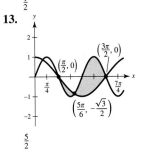

$\dfrac{5}{2}$

15. (a)

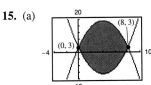

(b) 170.6667

17. (a)

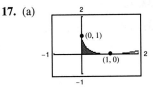

(b) 0.1667

19. R_2; \$1.125 million

21. $F(x) = \frac{4}{3}x^3 + x$

(a) $F(0) = 0$ (b) $F\left(\frac{3}{2}\right) = 6$

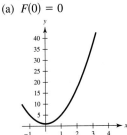

(c) $F(3) = 39$

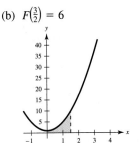

23. $\dfrac{\pi^2}{2}$ **25.** $\dfrac{\pi\sqrt{3}}{3}$ **27.** $2\pi \ln \dfrac{5}{2} \approx 5.757$

29. (a) 9π (b) 18π (c) 9π (d) 36π

31. 64π ft^3 **33.** Answers will vary.   **35.** (a)–(b) 13

37. $\frac{8}{15}\left(1 + 6\sqrt{3}\right) \approx 6.076$ **39.** $100\left(e^{1/2} - e^{-1/2}\right) \approx 104.22$ ft

41. $3 \arcsin \frac{2}{3} \approx 2.1892$ **43.** 15π

45. $2\pi \int_0^8 \left(4 - x^{2/3}\right)^{3/2} \sqrt{\dfrac{4}{x^{2/3}}}\,dx$

AP® Exam Practice Questions *(page 452)*

1. A **2.** C **3.** A **4.** B **5.** D **6.** B
7. A **8.** B **9.** C

10. (a) $\displaystyle\int_1^{10}\left(\frac{y-1}{6}\right)^{2/3}dy = 2\int_0^{1+6k^{3/2}}\left(\frac{y-1}{6}\right)^{2/3}dy$

(b) 6.103   (c) 143.289

11. (a) 1.471   (b) 18.783

(c) $\displaystyle\pi\int_{-2.888703}^{0.58307388}\left[\left(\frac{y+3}{2}\right)^2 - (e^y)^2\right]dy$

12. (a) 1.377   (b) 11.501

(c) $\displaystyle\pi\int_0^{0.5248886}\left[(\sqrt{x}+1)^2 - (-\sqrt{x}+1)^2\right]dx$

$\displaystyle + \pi\int_{0.5248886}^{1.4902161}\left[(\sqrt{x}+1)^2 - (x^2)^2\right]dx$

13. (a)

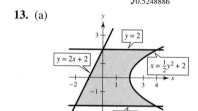

(b) $A = \displaystyle\int_{-2}^{2}\left[\left(\frac{y^2}{2}+2\right) - \left(\frac{y}{2}-1\right)\right]dy$

$= \displaystyle\int_{-2}^{0}\left(\frac{y^2}{2} - \frac{y}{2} + 3\right)dy = \left[\frac{y^3}{6} - \frac{y^2}{4} + 3y\right]_{-2}^{2} = \frac{44}{3}$

14. (a) 2π (b) $\dfrac{16}{5}\pi\sqrt{2}$ (c) $\pi\displaystyle\int_0^{\sqrt{2}}(2-y^2)^2\,dy$ (d) $\dfrac{\sqrt{3}}{2}$

15. (a) 12   (b) $\dfrac{96\pi}{5}$ (c) $\dfrac{16\pi}{7}$

16. (a) $\dfrac{20}{3}$ (b) $\dfrac{736\pi}{15}$ (c) $P = 2\sqrt{5} + 8 + \displaystyle\int_0^2\sqrt{1+4x^2}\,dx$

Chapter 7

Section 7.1 *(page 460)*

1. $\displaystyle\int[f(u) - g(u)]\,du = \int f(u)\,du - \int g(u)\,du;$

$\displaystyle\int\frac{du}{u} = \ln|u| + C, u = x; \int kf(u) = k\int f(u)\,du;$

$\displaystyle\int u^n\,du = \frac{u^{n+1}}{n+1} + C, u = x$

3. $\displaystyle\int u^n\,du = \frac{u^{n+1}}{n+1} + C$ **5.** $\displaystyle\int\frac{du}{u} = \ln|u| + C$
$u = 4 - x^2$ $\qquad u = 1 - 2\sqrt{x}$

7. $\displaystyle\int\sin u\,du = -\cos u + C$ **9.** $\displaystyle\int e^u\,du = e^u + C$
$u = t^2$ $\qquad\qquad u = \sin x$

11. $-\dfrac{7}{6(z-10)^6} + C$ **13.** $\dfrac{1}{2}v^2 - \dfrac{1}{6(3v-1)^2} + C$

15. $\dfrac{1}{6}(t^4+1)^{3/2} + C$ **17.** $-\dfrac{1}{3}\ln|-t^3 + 9t + 1| + C$

19. $\dfrac{1}{2}x^2 + x + \ln|x-1| + C$ **21.** $\ln(1+e^x) + C$

23. $\dfrac{x}{15}(48x^4 + 200x^2 + 375) + C$ **25.** $\dfrac{1}{4\pi}\sin 2\pi x^2 + C$

27. $\sec\theta + \sin\theta + C$ **29.** $2\ln(1+e^x) + C$

31. $-\dfrac{1}{\ln(\sin y)} + C$ **33.** $-\ln|\csc\alpha + \cot\alpha| + \ln|\sin\alpha| + C$

35. $-\dfrac{1}{4}\arcsin(4t+1) + C$ **37.** $\dfrac{1}{2}\ln\left|\cos\dfrac{2}{t}\right| + C$

39. $6\arcsin\left(\dfrac{x-5}{5}\right) + C$ **41.** $\dfrac{1}{4}\arctan\left(\dfrac{2x+1}{8}\right) + C$

43. (a) Sample answer: (b) $\dfrac{1}{2}\arcsin t^2 - \dfrac{1}{2}$

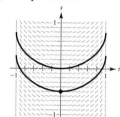 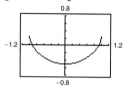

45. $y = 16x - 4e^{2x} + \dfrac{1}{4}e^{4x} + C$ **47.** $r = 10\arcsin e^t + C$

49. $y = \dfrac{1}{2}\arctan\left(\dfrac{\tan x}{2}\right) + C$

51. The integrand fits the Arcsecant Rule, not the Power Rule;
$\displaystyle\int\frac{1}{2x\sqrt{x^2-16}}\,dx = \frac{1}{8}\operatorname{arcsec}\frac{x}{4} + C$

53. $\dfrac{1}{4}\ln 2 + \dfrac{1}{2}\ln(1+\sqrt{2}) \approx 0.614$

55. $\dfrac{1}{2}(1 - e^{-1}) \approx 0.316$ **57.** 8   **59.** $\dfrac{\pi}{18} \approx 0.175$

61. $\dfrac{8}{3} + \ln 9 \approx 4.864$ **63.** $\dfrac{240}{\ln 3} \approx 218.457$

65. $\dfrac{18\sqrt{6}}{5} \approx 8.82$ **67.** $\dfrac{4}{3} \approx 1.333$

69. $\displaystyle\int\sec u\tan u\,du = \sec u + C; u = x^2 + 1$

71. $\displaystyle\int\frac{du}{a^2+u^2} = \frac{1}{a}\arctan\frac{u}{a} + C; u = x, a = 1$

73. $a = \sqrt{2},\ b = \dfrac{\pi}{4};\ -\dfrac{1}{\sqrt{2}}\ln\left|\csc\left(x+\dfrac{\pi}{4}\right) + \cot\left(x+\dfrac{\pi}{4}\right)\right| + C$

75. $a = \dfrac{1}{2}$

77. (a) $e^{x+C_1} = e^x \cdot e^{C_1} = Ce^x, C = e^{C_1}$
(b) $\sec^2 x + C_1 = (\tan^2 x + 1) + C_1 = \tan^2 x + C$

79. a   **81.** $\dfrac{1}{3}\arctan 3 \approx 0.416$

83. (a) $\pi(1 - e^{-1}) \approx 1.986$ (b) $b = \sqrt{\ln\left(\dfrac{3\pi}{3\pi-4}\right)} \approx 0.743$

85. $\ln(\sqrt{2}+1) \approx 0.8814$ **87.** $\dfrac{8\pi}{3}(10\sqrt{10} - 1) \approx 256.545$

89. (a)   (b)

(c)

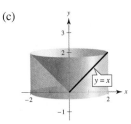

91. About 1.0320

93. (a) $\frac{1}{3}(\sin x)(\cos^2 x + 2)$

   (b) $\frac{1}{15}(\sin x)(3 \cos^4 x + 4 \cos^2 x + 8)$

   (c) $\frac{1}{35}(\sin x)(5 \cos^6 x + 6 \cos^4 x + 8 \cos^2 x + 16)$

   (d) Write $\cos^{15} x$ as $(1 - \sin^2 x)^7 \cos x$ and expand $(1 - \sin^2 x)^7$.

95. B   **97.** C

Section 7.2   *(page 469)*

1. $u = x,\ dv = e^{9x}\,dx$ **3.** $u = (\ln x)^2,\ dv = dx$

5. $u = x,\ dv = \sec^2 x\,dx$ **7.** $u = \arcsin 4x,\ dv = x^3\,dx$

9. $\frac{1}{16}x^4(4 \ln x - 1) + C$ **11.** $\frac{1}{64}e^{8x}(8x - 1) + C$

13. $\frac{1}{9} \sin 3x - \frac{1}{3}x \cos 3x + C$ **15.** $\frac{e^{4x}}{16}(4x - 1) + C$

17. $e^x(x^3 - 3x^2 + 6x - 6) + C$

19. $\frac{1}{4}[2(t^2 - 1) \ln|t + 1| - t^2 + 2t] + C$ **21.** $\frac{1}{3}(\ln x)^3 + C$

23. $\frac{e^{2x}}{4(2x + 1)} + C$ **25.** $\frac{2}{15}(x - 5)^{3/2}(3x + 10) + C$

27. $-x \cot x + \ln|\sin x| + C$ **29.** $x \ln 2x - x + C$

31. $x \arctan x - \frac{1}{2}\ln(1 + x^2) + C$

33. $(6x - x^3) \cos x + (3x^2 - 6) \sin x + C$

35. $-\frac{3}{34}e^{-3x} \sin 5x - \frac{5}{34}e^{-3x} \cos 5x + C$

37. The constant of integration is missing.
$$\int x \sin x\,dx = -x \cos x + \sin x + C$$

39. $y = 2x \ln x - 2x + C$

41. $y = \frac{2}{625}\sqrt{3 + 5t}(25t^2 - 20t + 24) + C$

43. (a) Sample answer: (b) $2\sqrt{y} - \cos x - x \sin x = 3$

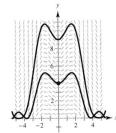 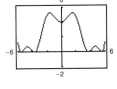

45. $y = \frac{1}{2}xe^{2x} - \frac{1}{4}e^{2x} + \frac{17}{4}$ **47.** $y^2 = \frac{1}{4}x^2 \ln x^3 - \frac{3}{8}x^2 + \frac{35}{8}$

49. $2e^{3/2} + 4 \approx 12.963$ **51.** $\frac{\pi}{8} - \frac{1}{4} \approx 0.143$

53. $\frac{\pi - 3\sqrt{3} + 6}{6} \approx 0.658$

55. $\frac{1}{2}[e(\sin 1 - \cos 1) + 1] \approx 0.909$

57. $8 \text{ arcsec } 4 + \frac{\sqrt{3}}{2} - \frac{\sqrt{15}}{2} - \frac{2\pi}{3} \approx 7.380$

59. $\frac{e^{2x}}{4}(2x^2 - 2x + 1) + C$

61. $(3x^2 - 6) \sin x - (x^3 - 6x) \cos x + C$

63. $-(x + 2)^2 \cos x + 2(x + 2) \sin x + 2 \cos x + C$

65. $2(\sin \sqrt{x} - \sqrt{x} \cos \sqrt{x}) + C$

67. $\frac{e^{x^2}}{2}(x^4 - 2x^2 + 2) + C$

69. (a)–(b) $\frac{1}{3}\sqrt{4 + x^2}(x^2 - 8) + C$ **71.** Product Rule

73. $\frac{x^2}{2} \sin x - \int \frac{x^2}{2} \cos x\,dx$ has a more complicated integral.

75. (a) No; Use substitution.

   (b) Yes; $u = \ln x,\ dv = x^8\,dx$; The integrand is the product of an algebraic function and a transcendental function.

   (c) Yes; $u = x^2,\ dv = e^{-3x}\,dx$; The integrand is the product of an algebraic function and a transcendental function.

   (d) No; Use substitution.   (e) No; Use substitution.

   (f) No; Use substitution.

77. $n = 0$: $x(\ln x - 1) + C$

   $n = 1$: $\frac{1}{4}x^2(2 \ln x - 1) + C$

   $n = 2$: $\frac{1}{9}x^3(3 \ln x - 1) + C$

   $n = 3$: $\frac{1}{16}x^4(4 \ln x - 1) + C$

   $\int x^n \ln x\,dx = \frac{x^{n+1}}{(n + 1)^2}[(n + 1)\ln x - 1] + C$

   $n = 4$: $\frac{1}{25}x^5(5 \ln x - 1) + C$

79–83. Proofs   **85.** $-x^2 \cos x + 2x \sin x + 2 \cos x + C$

87. $\frac{1}{36}x^6(6 \ln x - 1) + C$

89. $\frac{e^{-3x}(-3 \sin 4x - 4 \cos 4x)}{25} + C$

91.   **93.**

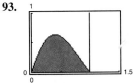

   $2 - \frac{8}{e^3} \approx 1.602$ $\frac{\pi}{1 + \pi^2}\left(\frac{1}{e} + 1\right) \approx 0.395$

95. (a) $3.2 \ln 2 - 0.2 \approx 2.018$

   (b) $7.2 \ln 3 - 3.2 \ln 2 - 1 \approx 4.692$

   (c) $12.8 \ln 4 - 7.2 \ln 3 - 1.8 \approx 8.035$

97. \$771,721.44   **99.** Answers will vary.

101. $b_n = \frac{8h}{(n\pi)^2} \sin \frac{n\pi}{2}$

103. (a) π (b) 3π (c) 5π

   $A = (2n + 1)\pi$

105. The graph of $y = x \sin x$ is below the graph of $y = x$ on $\left[0, \frac{\pi}{2}\right]$.

107. (a) 1   (b) $\pi(e - 2) \approx 2.257$ (c) $\frac{\pi}{2}(e^2 + 1) \approx 13.177$

109. (a) $\frac{3}{2} - \frac{2}{e} \approx 0.764$ (b) 4.009

   (c) $\sqrt{2} + e^{-1} + 1 + \int_0^1 \sqrt{1 + e^{-2x}(x - 1)^2}\,dx$

Section 7.3   *(page 479)*

1. $-\frac{1}{6}\cos^6 x + C$ **3.** $\frac{1}{16}\sin^8 2x + C$

5. $-\frac{1}{3}\cos^3 x + \frac{1}{5}\cos^5 x + C$

7. $-\frac{1}{3}(\cos 2\theta)^{3/2} + \frac{1}{7}(\cos 2\theta)^{7/2} + C$

9. $\frac{3x}{8} + \frac{1}{12} \sin 6x + \frac{1}{96} \sin 12x + C$

11. $x^2 + x \sin 2x + \dfrac{1}{2} \cos 2x + C$ **13.** $\dfrac{2}{3}$ **15.** $\dfrac{231\pi}{2048}$

17. $\dfrac{3\pi}{16}$ **19.** $\dfrac{1}{4} \ln|\sec 4x + \tan 4x| + C$

21. $\dfrac{1}{2\pi}\left(\sec \pi x \tan \pi x + \ln|\sec \pi x + \tan \pi x|\right) + C$

23. $\dfrac{1}{2} \tan^4 \dfrac{x}{2} - \tan^2 \dfrac{x}{2} - 2 \ln\left|\cos \dfrac{x}{2}\right| + C$

25. $\dfrac{1}{2}\left(\dfrac{\sec^5 2t}{5} - \dfrac{\sec^3 2t}{3}\right) + C$ **27.** $\dfrac{1}{24} \sec^6 4x + C$

29. $\dfrac{1}{7} \sec^7 x - \dfrac{1}{5} \sec^5 x + C$

31. $\ln|\sec x + \tan x| - \sin x + C$

33. $r = \dfrac{1}{32\pi}\left[12\pi\theta - 8 \sin(2\pi\theta) + 4 \sin(4\pi\theta)\right] + C$

35. $y = \dfrac{1}{9} \sec^3 3x - \dfrac{1}{3} \sec 3x + C$

37. (a) Sample answer: (b) $y = \dfrac{1}{2}x - \dfrac{1}{4} \sin 2x$

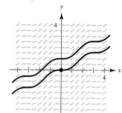 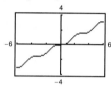

39.

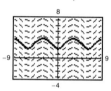

41. $\dfrac{1}{8} \sin 4x + \dfrac{1}{16} \sin 8x + C$

43. $-\dfrac{1}{10} \cos 5t - \dfrac{1}{26} \cos 13t + C$ **45.** $\dfrac{1}{4} \sin 2\theta - \dfrac{1}{8} \sin 4\theta + C$

47. $-\dfrac{1}{8} \csc^4 2x + \dfrac{1}{4} \csc^2 2x + \dfrac{1}{2} \ln|\sin 2x| + C$

49. $-\dfrac{1}{25} \cot^5 5x - \dfrac{2}{15} \cot^3 5x - \dfrac{1}{5} \cot 5x + C$

51. $\ln|\csc x - \cot x| + \cos x + C$ **53.** $t - 2 \tan t + C$

55. $\sin^2 x = 1 - \cos^2 x$, not $1 + \cos^2 x$; $-\ln|\cos x| + \dfrac{\cos^2 x}{2} + C$

57. $\dfrac{1}{3}$ **59.** 1

61. $2\pi\left(1 - \dfrac{\pi}{4}\right) \approx 1.348$ **63.** (a) $-\dfrac{1}{8\pi}$ (b) $\dfrac{7}{8\pi}$

65. π **67.** $3(1 - \ln 2)$ **69.** $\dfrac{\pi}{4}$ **71.** 4

73. (a) $\dfrac{1}{18} \tan^6 3x + \dfrac{1}{12} \tan^4 3x + C_1$, $\dfrac{1}{18} \sec^6 3x - \dfrac{1}{12} \sec^4 3x + C_2$

(b) 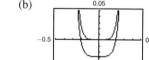   (c) Answers will vary.

75. (a) $\dfrac{1}{2} \sin^2 x + C$ (b) $-\dfrac{1}{2} \cos^2 x + C$

(c) $\dfrac{1}{2} \sin^2 x + C$ (d) $-\dfrac{1}{4} \cos 2x + C$

The answers are the same or differ by a constant.

77–79. Answers will vary.

81. $-\dfrac{1}{15}(\cos x)(3 \sin^4 x + 4 \sin^2 x + 8) + C$

83. $\dfrac{5}{6\pi}\left(\tan \dfrac{2\pi x}{5}\right)\left(\sec^2 \dfrac{2\pi x}{5} + 2\right) + C$

85. (a) $H(t) \approx 57.54 - 23.06 \cos \dfrac{\pi t}{6} - 2.89 \sin \dfrac{\pi t}{6}$

$L(t) \approx 42.03 - 21.01 \cos \dfrac{\pi t}{6} - 4.41 \sin \dfrac{\pi t}{6}$

(b)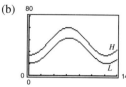

May

87. Answers will vary.   **89.** B

Section 7.4   *(page 488)*

1. $x = 3 \tan \theta$ **3.** $x = 5 \sin \theta$

5. $4 \ln\left|\dfrac{4 - \sqrt{16 - x^2}}{x}\right| + \sqrt{16 - x^2} + C$

7. $\dfrac{1}{4} \ln\left|\dfrac{x + 4}{\sqrt{16 - x^2}}\right| + C$ **9.** $\dfrac{1}{3}(1 + x^2)^{3/2} + C$

11. $\dfrac{1}{2}\left(\arctan x + \dfrac{x}{1 + x^2}\right) + C$ **13.** $\ln\left|x + \sqrt{x^2 - 25}\right| + C$

15. $\dfrac{1}{15}(x^2 - 25)^{3/2}(3x^2 + 50) + C$

17. $\dfrac{3}{2} \arcsin(x - 1) - \dfrac{1}{2}\sqrt{2x - x^2}(x + 3) + C$

19. $\sqrt{x^2 + 6x + 12} - 3 \ln\left|\sqrt{x^2 + 6x + 12} + x + 3\right| + C$

21. $\dfrac{x\sqrt{36 - x^2}}{2} + 18 \arcsin \dfrac{x}{6} + C$

23. $x\sqrt{25 + 3x^2} + \dfrac{25\sqrt{3}}{3} \ln\left|\sqrt{3}x + \sqrt{25 + 3x^2}\right| + C$

25. $4 \arcsin \dfrac{x}{2} + x\sqrt{4 - x^2} + C$ **27.** $\arcsin \dfrac{x}{4} + C$

29. $-\dfrac{(1 - x^2)^{3/2}}{3x^3} + C$ **31.** $-\dfrac{1}{3} \ln\left|\dfrac{\sqrt{4x^2 + 9} + 3}{2x}\right| + C$

33. $\dfrac{1}{3(16 - x^2)^{3/2}} + C$ **35.** $\dfrac{1}{2}\left(\arcsin e^x + e^x\sqrt{1 - e^{2x}}\right) + C$

37. $\dfrac{1}{4}\left(\dfrac{x}{x^2 + 2} + \dfrac{\sqrt{2}}{2} \arctan \dfrac{\sqrt{2}x}{2}\right) + C$

39. $x \operatorname{arcsec} 2x - \dfrac{1}{2} \ln\left|2x + \sqrt{4x^2 - 1}\right| + C$

41. (a)–(b) $\sqrt{3} - \dfrac{\pi}{3} \approx 0.685$

43. (a)–(b) $9(2 - \sqrt{2}) \approx 5.272$

45. (a)–(b) $-\dfrac{9}{2} \ln\left(\dfrac{2\sqrt{7}}{3} - \dfrac{4\sqrt{3}}{3} - \dfrac{\sqrt{21}}{3} + \dfrac{8}{3}\right) + 9\sqrt{3} - 2\sqrt{7}$

≈ 12.644

47. (a) $u = a \sin \theta$; The radical simplifies to $a \cos \theta$, where $-\dfrac{\pi}{2} \le \theta \le \dfrac{\pi}{2}$.

(b) $u = a \tan \theta$; The radical simplifies to $a \sec \theta$, where $-\dfrac{\pi}{2} < \theta < \dfrac{\pi}{2}$.

(c) $u = a \sec \theta$; The radical simplifies to $\tan \theta$ if $u > a$ and $-\tan \theta$ if $u < -a$, where $0 \le \theta < \dfrac{\pi}{2}$ or $\dfrac{\pi}{2} < \theta \le \pi$.

49. (a) $\dfrac{1}{2} \ln(x^2 + 9) + C$; The answers are equivalent.

(b) $x - 3 \arctan \dfrac{x}{3} + C$; The answers are equivalent.

51. True   **53.** False; $\displaystyle\int_0^{\sqrt{3}} \dfrac{dx}{(1 + x^2)^{3/2}} = \displaystyle\int_0^{\pi/3} \cos \theta \, d\theta$

55. $\frac{1}{2}a^2\pi - a^2\arcsin\frac{h}{a} - h\sqrt{a^2-h^2}$ 57. $6\pi^2$

59. $\frac{1}{2}\left[4\sqrt{17} + \ln(4+\sqrt{17})\right] \approx 9.2936$

61. $\ln\left[\frac{5(\sqrt{2}+1)}{\sqrt{26}+1}\right] + \sqrt{26} - \sqrt{2} \approx 4.3675$

63. Answers will vary.

65. $\frac{\pi}{32}\left[102\sqrt{2} - \ln(3+2\sqrt{2})\right] \approx 13.989$

67. Answers will vary.   69. $12 + \frac{9\pi}{2} - 25\arcsin\frac{3}{5} \approx 10.050$

71. D

73. (a) Geometric formula: $A \approx 0.09806$
    Integral: $A \approx 0.09902$
   (b) Geometric formula: $A \approx 0.01495$
    Integral: $A \approx 0.01516$
   (c) 0.08386

Section 7.5   (page 498)

1. $\frac{A}{x} + \frac{B}{x-8}$ 3. $\frac{A}{x} + \frac{Bx+C}{x^2+10}$ 5. $\frac{1}{6}\ln\left|\frac{x-3}{x+3}\right| + C$

7. $\ln\left|\frac{x-1}{x+4}\right| + C$ 9. $5\ln|x-2| - \ln|x+2| - 3\ln|x| + C$

11. $\frac{1}{2}x^2 + 2x + \frac{5}{6}\ln|x-4| + \frac{1}{6}\ln|x+2| + C$

13. $\frac{1}{x} + \ln|x^4+x^3| + C$

15. $\frac{1}{4}\ln|x+2| + \frac{3}{4}\ln|x-2| - \frac{2}{x-2} + C$

17. $2\ln|x^2+1| - \ln|x| + \arctan x + C$

19. $\frac{1}{6}\left(\ln\left|\frac{x-2}{x+2}\right| + \sqrt{2}\arctan\frac{x}{\sqrt{2}}\right) + C$

21. $\ln|x+1| + \sqrt{2}\arctan\left(\frac{x-1}{\sqrt{2}}\right) + C$ 23. $\ln 3 \approx 1.099$

25. $\frac{1}{2}\ln\frac{8}{5} - \frac{\pi}{4} + \arctan 2 \approx 0.557$

27. Need to multiply by $\frac{1}{2}$ when integrating first integral;
$\frac{2}{7}\ln|2x-1| + \frac{12}{7}\ln|x+3| + C$

29. $\frac{1}{4}\ln\left|\frac{\tan x-2}{\tan x+2}\right| + C$ 31. $\frac{1}{5}\ln\left|\frac{e^x-1}{e^x+4}\right| + C$

33. $2\sqrt{x} + 2\ln\left|\frac{\sqrt{x}-2}{\sqrt{x}+2}\right| + C$

35–37. Answers will vary.

39. Substitution; The integrand fits the Log Rule.

41. Substitution; The integrand fits the Arctangent Rule.

43. $225\pi\left(\frac{1}{45} + \frac{\ln 5}{108}\right) \approx 26.242$ 45. $x = \frac{n\left[e^{(n+1)kt}-1\right]}{n+e^{(n+1)kt}}$

47. 4.90 or \$490,000   49. $\frac{\pi}{8}$ 51. A

Section 7.6   (page 504)

1. $-\frac{1}{2}x(10-x) + 25\ln|5+x| + C$ 3. $-\frac{\sqrt{1-x^2}}{x} + C$

5. $\frac{1}{24}(3x + \sin 3x \cos 3x + 2\cos^3 3x \sin 3x) + C$

7. $-2\left(\cot\sqrt{x} + \csc\sqrt{x}\right) + C$ 9. $x - \frac{1}{2}\ln(1+e^{2x}) + C$

11. $\frac{1}{169}x^{13}(13\ln x - 1) + C$

13. (a)–(b) $x\left(\ln\frac{x}{3} - 1\right) + C$ 15. (a)–(b) $\frac{1}{x} + \ln\left|\frac{x-1}{x}\right| + C$

17. $\frac{1}{2}\left[(x^2+1)\operatorname{arccsc}(x^2+1) + \ln(x^2+1 + \sqrt{x^4+2x^2})\right] + C$

19. $\frac{\sqrt{x^4-1}}{x^2} + C$ 21. $\frac{4}{25}\left(\ln|2-5x| + \frac{2}{2-5x}\right) + C$

23. $e^x\arccos e^x - \sqrt{1-e^{2x}} + C$

25. $\frac{1}{2}(x^2 + \cot x^2 + \csc x^2) + C$

27. $\frac{\sqrt{2}}{2}\arctan\left(\frac{1+\sin\theta}{\sqrt{2}}\right) + C$ 29. $-\frac{\sqrt{2+9x^2}}{2x} + C$

31. $\frac{1}{4}\left(2\ln|x| - 3\ln\left|3 + 2\ln|x|\right|\right) + C$

33. $\frac{3x-10}{2(x^2-6x+10)} + \frac{3}{2}\arctan(x-3) + C$

35. $\frac{1}{2}\ln\left|x^2-3 + \sqrt{x^4-6x^2+5}\right| + C$

37. $\frac{2}{1+e^x} - \frac{1}{2(1+e^x)^2} + \ln|1+e^x| + C$

39. a and u were reversed; $\int\frac{1}{x^2+9}\,dx = \frac{1}{3}\arctan\frac{x}{3} + C$

41. $\frac{2}{3}(2-\sqrt{2})$ 43. $\frac{32}{5}\ln 2 - \frac{31}{25}$ 45. $\frac{\pi}{2}$

47. $\frac{\pi^3}{8} - 3\pi + 6$ 49–51. Answers will vary.

53. $\frac{1}{\sqrt{5}}\ln\left|\frac{2\tan(\theta/2)-3-\sqrt{5}}{2\tan(\theta/2)-3+\sqrt{5}}\right| + C$ 55. $2\sqrt{2} - 2$

57. $\frac{1}{2}\ln(3-2\cos\theta) + C$ 59. $-2\cos\sqrt{\theta} + C$

61. About 0.0722

63. A reduction formula reduces an integral to the sum of a function and a simpler integral; Sample answer: See Formulas 50 and 54.

65. $11,840\ln(3+\sqrt{10}) \approx 21,530.4$ lb

67. $32\pi^2$ 69. B   71. A

Section 7.7   (page 513)

1.

x	-0.1	-0.01	-0.001	0.001	0.01	0.1
$f(x)$	1.3177	1.3332	1.3333	1.3333	1.3332	1.3177

$\frac{4}{3}$

3.

x	1	10	10^2	10^3	10^4	10^5
$f(x)$	0.9900	90,483.7	3.7×10^9	4.5×10^{10}	0	0

0

5. (a)–(b) $\frac{3}{8}$ 7. (a)–(b) $\frac{1}{8}$ 9. (a)–(b) 0

11. (a)–(b) $\frac{5}{3}$ 13. 0   15. ∞ 17. $\frac{25}{4}$ 19. $\frac{3}{5}$

21. $\frac{7}{6}$ 23. $-\frac{1}{4}$ 25. ∞ 27. 0   29. 1   31. -7

33. 0   35. 0   37. ∞ 39. $\frac{5}{9}$ 41. 0   43. ∞

45. (a) Not indeterminate   47. (a) $0 \cdot \infty$
   (b) ∞ (b) 1
   (c) 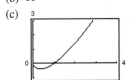   (c)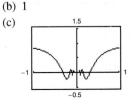

49. (a) Not indeterminate

(b) 0

(c)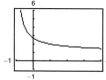

51. (a) ∞^0

(b) 1

(c)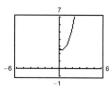

53. (a) 1^∞

(b) e

(c)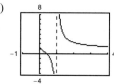

55. (a) 0^0

(b) 3

(c)

57. (a) 0^0

(b) 1

(c)

59. (a) $\infty - \infty$

(b) $\frac{5}{4}$

(c)

61. (a) $\infty - \infty$

(b) ∞

(c)

63. Sample answers:

(a) $f(x) = x^2 - 25, g(x) = x - 5$

(b) $f(x) = (x - 5)^2, g(x) = x^2 - 25$

(c) $f(x) = x^2 - 25, g(x) = (x - 5)^3$

Explanations will vary.

65. (a) Yes; $\frac{0}{0}$ (b) No; $\frac{0}{-1}$ (c) Yes; $\frac{\infty}{\infty}$ (d) Yes; $\frac{0}{0}$

(e) No; $\frac{-1}{0}$ (f) Yes; $\frac{0}{0}$

67.

x	10	10^2	10^4	10^6	10^8	10^{10}
$\dfrac{(\ln x)^4}{x}$	2.811	4.498	0.720	0.036	0.001	0.000

69. $g' > f'$ **71.** $f' > h'$ **73.** $f' > h'$

75. Horizontal asymptote: $y = 1$

Relative maximum: $(e, e^{1/e})$

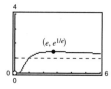

77. Horizontal asymptote: $y = 0$

Relative maximum: $\left(1, \dfrac{2}{e}\right)$

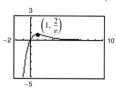

79. Limit is not of the form $\dfrac{0}{0}$ or $\dfrac{\infty}{\infty}$; $\lim\limits_{x \to \infty} \dfrac{e^{-x}}{1 + e^{-x}} = 0$

81. (a) Applying L'Hôpital's Rule twice results in the original limit.

(b) 1

(c)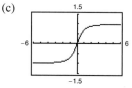

1; They are the same.

83. 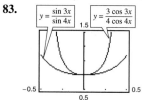 As $x \to 0$, the graphs get closer together. By L'Hôpital's Rule,

$$\lim_{x \to 0} \frac{\sin 3x}{\sin 4x} = \lim_{x \to 0} \frac{3 \cos 3x}{4 \cos 4x} = \frac{3}{4}.$$

85. $v = 32t + v_0$ **87.** Answers will vary.

89. $c = \dfrac{2}{3}$ **91.** $c = \dfrac{\pi}{4}$

93. False. A limit of the form $\dfrac{\infty}{0}$ is equal to ∞ (or $-\infty$).

95. True **97.** True **99.** $\frac{3}{4}$ **101.** $\frac{4}{3}$

103. $a = 1, b = \pm 2$ **105.** (a)–(b) Answers will vary.

107. Proof **109.** $\dfrac{m}{n}$

111. (a)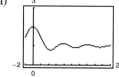

(b) $\lim\limits_{x \to \infty} h(x) = 1$ (c) No; $\sin x$ oscillates as $x \to \infty$.

113. B **115.** C

Section 7.8 *(page 524)*

1. Improper; infinite limit of integration

3. Improper; infinite discontinuity at $x = -5$

5. Not improper; The discontinuity at $x = 2$ is removable.

7. Not improper; continuous on $[0, \pi]$

9. Infinite discontinuity at $x = 0$; converges; 4

11. Infinite discontinuity at $x = 1$; diverges

13. Infinite discontinuity at $x = 0$; Answers will vary.

15. Infinite limit of integration; Answers will vary.

17. Converges; $\frac{1}{2}$ **19.** Diverges **21.** Diverges

23. Converges; 2 **25.** Converges; $\dfrac{1}{2(\ln 4)^2}$ **27.** Diverges

29. Converges; $\dfrac{\pi}{2}$ **31.** Diverges   **33.** Diverges

35. Diverges   **37.** Converges; $-\dfrac{1}{4}$ **39.** Diverges

41. Converges; $\dfrac{\pi}{3}$ **43.** Converges; $\ln 3$ **45.** Diverges

47. Converges; $\dfrac{2\pi\sqrt{6}}{3}$ **49.** $p > 1$ **51.** Answers will vary.

53. Diverges   **55.** Converges   **57.** Converges

59. Diverges   **61.** Converges   **63.** Converge

65. $\dfrac{7}{8}$ **67.** π **69.** (a) 1   (b) $\dfrac{\pi}{2}$ (c) 2π

71.   Perimeter $= 162$

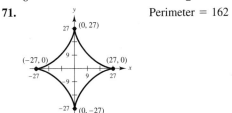

73. $8\pi\left[\dfrac{(\ln 2)^2}{3} - \dfrac{2\ln 2}{9} + \dfrac{2}{27}\right] \approx 2.0155$

75. (a) Answers will vary.   (b) $P = 43.53\%$ (c) $E(x) = 7$

77. (a) \$245,317.31   (b) \$282,419.99   (c) \$450,000.00

79. $P = \dfrac{2\pi NI\left(\sqrt{r^2 + c^2} - c\right)}{kr\sqrt{r^2 + c^2}}$

81. False; Sample answer: Let $f(x) = \dfrac{1}{x + 1}$.   **83.** True

85. (a) and (b) Answers will vary.

(c) The definition of the improper integral $\displaystyle\int_{-\infty}^{\infty} f(x)\,dx$ is not

$\displaystyle\lim_{a\to\infty}\int_{-a}^{a} f(x)\,dx.$

87. $\dfrac{1}{s}, s > 0$ **89.** $\dfrac{2}{s^3}, s > 0$ **91.** $\dfrac{s}{s^2 + a^2}, s > 0$

93. Answers will vary.

95. (a)

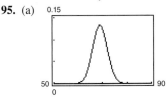

(b) About 0.1587

(c) 0.1587; The area to the right of $x = 69$ is 0.5.

97. (a) $\Gamma(1) = 1, \Gamma(2) = 1, \Gamma(3) = 2$ (b) Answers will vary.

(c) $\Gamma(n) = (n - 1)!$

99. $c = 1; \ln 2$ **101.** D   **103.** B

Review Exercises for Chapter 7   *(page 528)*

1. $(x^2 + 9)^{3/2} + C$ **3.** $-3\cot\left(\dfrac{x + 6}{3}\right) + C$

5. $\dfrac{1}{2} + \ln 2 \approx 1.1931$ **7.** $100\arcsin\dfrac{x}{10} + C$

9. $\dfrac{1}{32}e^{4x}(8x^2 - 4x + 1) + C$

11. $\dfrac{1}{13}e^{2x}(2\sin 3x - 3\cos 3x) + C$

13. $\dfrac{1}{2}x^2\sin 2x + \dfrac{1}{2}x\cos 2x - \dfrac{1}{4}\sin 2x + C$

15. $\dfrac{1}{8}\left[(4x^2 - 1)\arcsin 2x + 2x\sqrt{1 - 4x^2}\right] + C$

17. $\dfrac{1}{7}\sin^7 x + C$

19. $\dfrac{1}{3\pi}[\sin(\pi x - 1)][2 + \cos^2(\pi x - 1)] + C$

21. $\dfrac{2}{3}\left(\tan^3\dfrac{x}{2} + 3\tan\dfrac{x}{2}\right) + C$

23. $\dfrac{1}{6}\tan^3 x^2 - \dfrac{1}{2}\tan x^2 + \dfrac{x^2}{2} + C$ **25.** $\tan\theta + \sec\theta + C$

27. $\dfrac{3\pi}{16} + \dfrac{1}{2} \approx 1.0890$ **29.** $\dfrac{3\sqrt{4 - x^2}}{x} + C$

31. $\dfrac{1}{3}(x^2 + 169)^{1/2}(x^2 - 338) + C$ **33.** $256 - 62\sqrt{17}$

35. (a)–(c) $\dfrac{1}{3}\sqrt{4 + x^2}(x^2 - 8) + C$

37. $2\ln|x + 2| - \ln|x - 3| + C$

39. $x + 2\ln|x - 1| + \dfrac{1}{1 - x} + C$

41. $\dfrac{1}{2}\ln|e^x - 1| - \ln|e^x + 1| + \dfrac{1}{2}\ln|e^x + 3| + C$

43. $\dfrac{1}{25}\left(\dfrac{4}{4 + 5x} + \ln|4 + 5x|\right) + C$ **45.** $1 - \dfrac{\sqrt{2}}{2}$

47. $\dfrac{1}{2}\ln|x^2 + 4x + 8| - \arctan\left(1 + \dfrac{x}{2}\right) + C$

49. Answers will vary.   **51.** $\dfrac{1}{8}(\sin 2\theta - 2\theta\cos 2\theta) + C$

53. $\dfrac{4}{3}[x^{3/4} - 3x^{1/4} + 3\arctan(x^{1/4})] + C$

55. $2\sqrt{1 - \cos x} + C$ **57.** $(\sin x)\ln(\sin x) - \sin x + C$

59. $\dfrac{5}{2}\ln\left|\dfrac{x - 5}{x + 5}\right| + C$ **61.** $x\ln|x^2 + x| - 2x + \ln|x + 1| + C$

63. $\dfrac{1}{5}$ **65.** $\dfrac{1}{2}(\ln 4)^2 \approx 0.961$

67. $\pi^2 - 4\sin 2 - 2\cos 2 - 6 \approx 1.065$ **69.** $\dfrac{128}{15}$

71. 3.82   **73.** 0   **75.** ∞ **77.** 0

79. $1000e^{0.09} \approx 1094.17$ **81.** Converges; $\dfrac{32}{3}$

83. Diverges   **85.** Converges; 1   **87.** Converges; $\dfrac{\pi}{4}$

89. (a) \$6,321,205.59   (b) \$10,000,000

91. (a) 0.5551   (b) 0.0808

AP® Exam Practice Questions   *(page 530)*

1. A   **2.** D   **3.** A   **4.** D   **5.** A   **6.** A   **7.** C

8. A   **9.** B   **10.** C   **11.** B

12. (a) π (b) 4.401

(c)

$\displaystyle\int_0^{1.6693678}(-2x + 5 - x\sin x)\,dx = 2\int_0^k(-2x + 5 - x\sin x)\,dx$

13. (a) $10 - 15e^{-2/3} \approx 2.299$

(b) $-\displaystyle\int_0^{0.61344435}\left(te^{-t/3} - \dfrac{1}{2}\right)dt + \int_{0.61344435}^2\left(te^{-t/3} - \dfrac{1}{2}\right)dt$

(c) Neither; because $a(3) = 0$, the particle's speed is not changing at $t = 3$.

14. (a) $y = \dfrac{1}{e}x + 3$

(b) Concave downward on $(1, 5)$ because $f''(x) < 0$ on $(1, 5)$

(c) $f(x) = -\dfrac{1}{2(\ln x)^2} + \dfrac{9}{2}$

15. (a) $\displaystyle\lim_{x\to 1^-}f(x) = \lim_{x\to 1^+}f(x) = f(1) = \dfrac{1}{4}$

(b) $f'(x) = \begin{cases} 2\tan(x - 1)\sec^2(x - 1), & x \le 1 \\ \dfrac{-3x^2 + 4x\sqrt{x} - 1}{2\sqrt{x}(x^2 - 1)^2}, & x > 1 \end{cases}$

(c) $\dfrac{1}{4}\left(\dfrac{1}{2}\ln 5 - \ln 3 + \arctan 2 + \dfrac{1}{2}\ln 2 - \dfrac{\pi}{4} + \tan 1 - \dfrac{3}{4}\right)$

CHAPTER 7

16. (a) $T = 0.1 \ln|R| - 0.1 \ln|5 - R| + 0.1 \ln \frac{2}{3}$ (b) $R = \frac{5}{2}$

17. (a) $\lim\limits_{x\to\infty} xe^{-x} = \lim\limits_{x\to\infty} \dfrac{x}{e^x} = \lim\limits_{x\to\infty} \dfrac{1}{e^x} = 0$

Horizontal asymptote: $y = 0$

  (b) Maximum value is $g(1) = e^{-1}$ because $g(x)$ is increasing on $(-\infty, 1)$ and decreasing on $(1, \infty)$.

  (c) $2e^{-1}$

18. (a) Diverges; $\displaystyle\int_0^3 g'(x)\, dx = \int_0^2 \frac{1}{(x-2)^2}\, dx + \int_2^3 \frac{1}{(x-2)^2}\, dx.$

$\displaystyle\int_0^2 \frac{1}{(x-2)^2}\, dx$ diverges, so $\displaystyle\int_0^3 g'(x)\, dx$ diverges.

  (b) Infinite discontinuity at $x = 2$ (c) $\frac{1}{2}$

19. (a) $\lim\limits_{x\to 0} \dfrac{f(x) + 2}{\tan x} = \lim\limits_{x\to 0} \dfrac{f'(x)}{\sec^2 x} = (-2)^2[4(0) + 1] = 4$

  (b) $-\dfrac{1}{2}$ (c) $y = -\left(2x^2 + x + \dfrac{1}{2}\right)^{-1}$

Chapter 8

Section 8.1 *(page 542)*

1. $1, 5, 9, 13, 17$ **3.** $-3, 9, -27, 81, -243$

5. $1, 0, -1, 0, 1$ **7.** $2, -1, \frac{2}{3}, -\frac{1}{2}, \frac{2}{5}$ **9.** $3, 4, 6, 10, 18$

11. c   **12.** a   **13.** d   **14.** b

15. $-1, -4$; Subtract 3 from preceding term.

17. $80, 160$; Multiply the preceding term by 2.

19. $n + 1$ **21.** $\dfrac{1}{2n(2n+1)}$ **23.** 1   **25.** 2   **27.** 1

29. Dividing the numerator and exponent by n does not produce an equivalent expression; $\lim\limits_{n\to\infty} \dfrac{n+4}{e^n} = 0$

31.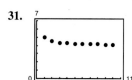

Converges to 4

33.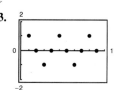

Diverges

35. Converges; 0   **37.** Diverges   **39.** Converges; 5

41. Converges; 0   **43.** Diverges   **45.** Converges; 0

47. Converges; 1   **49.** Converges; 0

51. Sample answer: $a_n = -4 + 6n$; Diverges

53. Sample answer: $a_n = \dfrac{(-1)^{n-1}}{n^2}$; Converges

55. Sample answer: $a_n = \dfrac{n+1}{n+2}$; Converges

57. Sample answer: $a_n = \dfrac{1}{n!}$; Converges

59. Monotonic, bounded   **61.** Not monotonic, bounded

63. Monotonic, bounded   **65.** Not monotonic, not bounded

67. (a) Answers will vary.   **69.** (a) Answers will vary.

  (b)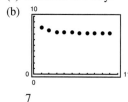

7

  (b)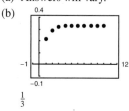

$\frac{1}{3}$

71. (a) No; $\lim\limits_{n\to\infty} A_n$ does not exist.

  (b) $A_1 = \$10,045.83$, $A_2 = \$10,091.88$, $A_3 = \$10,138.13$, $A_4 = \$10,184.60$, $A_5 = \$10,231.28$, $A_6 = \$10,278.17$, $A_7 = \$10,325.28$, $A_8 = \$10,372.60$, $A_9 = \$10,420.14$, $A_{10} = \$10,467.90$

73. $\{a_n\}$ is bounded and monotonic; $2 \le \lim\limits_{n\to\infty} a_n \le 4$.

75. Sample answer: $10 - \dfrac{1}{n}$

77. Does not exist; If a limit exists, then the limit is unique.

79. (a) $\$4,500,000,000(0.8)^n$

  (b) $n = 1$: $\$3,600,000,000$; $n = 2$: $\$2,880,000,000$; $n = 3$: $\$2,304,000,000$; $n = 4$: $\$1,843,200,000$

  (c) Converges to 0

81. False; Sample answer: Let $a_n = \dfrac{1}{n^2 + 1}$ and $b_n = \dfrac{1}{n}$.

83. True

85. (a) $1, 1, 2, 3, 5, 8, 13, 21, 34, 55, 89, 144$

  (b) $1, 2, 1.5, 1.6667, 1.6, 1.6250, 1.6154, 1.6190, 1.6176, 1.6182$

  (c) Answers will vary.   (d) $\rho = \dfrac{1 + \sqrt{5}}{2} \approx 1.6108$

87. Answers will vary.

89. (a) Answers will vary.

  (b)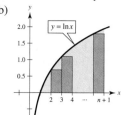

  (c) and (d) Answers will vary.

  (e) $\dfrac{\sqrt[20]{20!}}{20} \approx 0.4152$; $\dfrac{\sqrt[50]{50!}}{50} \approx 0.3897$; $\dfrac{\sqrt[100]{100!}}{100} \approx 0.3799$

91. Proof   **93.** Proof   **95.** D

Section 8.2 *(page 551)*

1. $1, 1.25, 1.3611, 1.4236, 1.4636$

3. $3, -1.5, 5.25, -4.875, 10.3125$

5. $3, 4.5, 5.25, 5.625, 5.8125$ **7.** Geometric series: $r = \frac{5}{2} > 1$

9. $\lim\limits_{n\to\infty} a_n = 1 \ne 0$ **11.** $\lim\limits_{n\to\infty} a_n = 1 \ne 0$

13. $\lim\limits_{n\to\infty} a_n = \frac{1}{4} \ne 0$ **15.** Geometric series: $r = \frac{5}{6} < 1$

17. Geometric series: $r = 0.9 < 1$

19. Telescoping series: $a_n = \dfrac{1}{n} - \dfrac{1}{n+1}$

21. (a) $\frac{11}{3}$

  (b)

n	5	10	20	50	100
S_n	2.7976	3.1643	3.3936	3.5513	3.6078

  (c)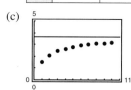

  (d) The terms of the series decrease in magnitude slowly. So, the sequence of partial sums approaches the sum slowly.

23. (a) 20

(b)

n	5	10	20	50	100
S_n	8.1902	13.0264	17.5685	19.8969	19.9995

(c)

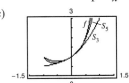

(d) The terms of the series decrease in magnitude slowly. So, the sequence of partial sums approaches the sum slowly.

25. 12   **27.** 3   **29.** 32   **31.** $\dfrac{1}{2}$ **33.** $\dfrac{\sin 1}{1 - \sin 1}$

35. Used $|r|$ instead of r; Sum $= \dfrac{4}{7}$

37. (a) $\displaystyle\sum_{n=0}^{\infty} \dfrac{4}{10}\left(\dfrac{1}{10}\right)^n$ (b) $\dfrac{4}{9}$

39. (a) $\displaystyle\sum_{n=0}^{\infty} \dfrac{2}{100}\left(\dfrac{1}{100}\right)^n$ (b) $\dfrac{2}{99}$ **41.** Diverges

43. Diverges   **45.** Converges; $\dfrac{3}{2}$ **47.** Diverges

49. Diverges   **51.** Diverges   **53.** Diverges

55. $\displaystyle\lim_{n\to\infty} a_n = 5$ means that the limit of the sequence $\{a_n\}$ is 5.

$\displaystyle\sum_{n=1}^{\infty} a_n = 5$ means that the limit of the partial sums is 5.

57. The series in (a) and (b) are the same. The series in (c) is different unless $a_1 = a_2 = \cdots = a$ is constant.

59. $-\dfrac{1}{4} < x < \dfrac{1}{4}$; $\dfrac{4x}{1 - 4x}$ **61.** $0 < x < 2$; $\dfrac{x-1}{2-x}$

63. $-1 < x < 1$; $\dfrac{1}{1 + x}$

65. (a) x (b) $f(x) = \dfrac{1}{1 - x}$, $|x| < 1$

(c)

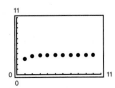

Answers will vary.

67. $\dfrac{1}{n(n + 1)} < 0.0001$ when $n = 100$.

$\left(\dfrac{1}{8}\right)^n < 0.0001$ when $n = 5$.

The second series converges at a faster rate.

69. $160{,}000(1 - 0.95^n)$ units

71. (a) $a_n = 248.184(1.0926)^n$

(b) $\displaystyle\sum_{n=0}^{\infty} 248.184(1.0926)^n$; Diverges because $r = 1.0926 > 1$

(c) Model: \$8470 million
    Actual: \$8476 million
    The sum using the model is slightly less than the actual amount.

73. $\displaystyle\sum_{i=0}^{\infty} 500(0.75)^i$; \$2000 million   **75.** 152.42 ft

77. (a) 126 in.^{2} (b) 128 in.^{2}

79. $\dfrac{1}{8}$; $\displaystyle\sum_{n=0}^{\infty} \dfrac{1}{2}\left(\dfrac{1}{2}\right)^n = \dfrac{1/2}{1 - 1/2} = 1$

81. (a) $\displaystyle\sum_{n=1}^{\infty}\left(\dfrac{1}{2}\right)^n = -1 + \displaystyle\sum_{n=0}^{\infty}\left(\dfrac{1}{2}\right)^n = -1 + \dfrac{1}{1 - 1/2} = 1$

(b) No   (c) 2

83. False; Sample answer: $\displaystyle\lim_{n\to\infty}\dfrac{1}{n} = 0$, but $\displaystyle\sum_{n=1}^{\infty}\dfrac{1}{n}$ diverges.

85. False; $\displaystyle\sum_{n=1}^{\infty} ar^n = \dfrac{a}{1 - r} - a$; The formula requires that the geometric series begins with $n = 0$.

87. True   **89.** (a)–(b) Answers will vary.   **91.** Proof

93. B   **95.** B

Section 8.3 *(page 559)*

1. Diverges   **3.** Converges   **5.** Converges

7. Converges   **9.** Diverges   **11.** Diverges

13. Converges   **15.** Converges   **17.** Converges

19. Diverges   **21.** Converges   **23.** Diverges

25. $f(x)$ is not positive for $x \geq 1$.

27. $f(x)$ is not decreasing for $x \geq 1$.   **29.** Converges

31. Diverges   **33.** Diverges   **35.** Converges

37. Converges   **39.** $p = \dfrac{3}{5}$, not 5; The series diverges.

41. (a)

n	5	10	20	50	100
S_n	3.7488	3.75	3.75	3.75	3.75

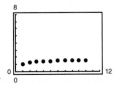

(b)

n	5	10	20	50	100
S_n	1.4636	1.5498	1.5962	1.6251	1.635

The partial sums in part (b) approach the sum slower than the series in part (a).

43. If f is positive, continuous, and decreasing for $x \geq 1$ and $a_n = f(n)$, then $\displaystyle\sum_{n=1}^{\infty} a_n$ and $\displaystyle\int_1^{\infty} f(x)\, dx$ either both converge or both diverge. Sample answer: $\displaystyle\sum_{n=1}^{\infty}\dfrac{1}{n^2 + 1}$ converges because $\displaystyle\int_1^{\infty}\dfrac{1}{x^2 + 1}\, dx$ converges.

CHAPTER 8

45. (a) 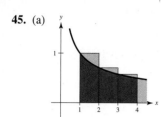   Diverges; The area under the rectangles is greater than the area under the curve and the integral diverges.

(b) 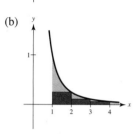   Converges; The area under the rectangles is less than the area under the curve and the integral converges.

47. $p > 1$ **49.** $p > 1$ **51.** $p < 2$ **53.** Proof
55. $S_8 \approx 0.9597$ **57.** $S_4 \approx 0.4049$
$R_8 \approx 0.1244$ $R_4 \approx 5.6 \times 10^{-8}$
59. $N \geq 7$ **61.** $N \geq 16$

63. (a) $\displaystyle\sum_{n=2}^{\infty} \frac{1}{n^{1.1}}$ converges by the p-Series Test because $1.1 > 1$.

$\displaystyle\sum_{n=2}^{\infty} \frac{1}{n \ln n}$ diverges by the Integral Test because $\displaystyle\int_{2}^{\infty} \frac{1}{x \ln x}\,dx$ diverges.

(b) $\displaystyle\sum_{n=2}^{\infty} \frac{1}{n^{1.1}} = 0.4665 + 0.2987 + 0.2176 + 0.1703$

$+ 0.1393 + \cdots$

$\displaystyle\sum_{n=2}^{\infty} \frac{1}{n \ln n} = 0.7213 + 0.3034 + 0.1803 + 0.1243$

$+ 0.0930 + \cdots$

(c) $n \geq 3.431 \times 10^{15}$

65. $x > 1$ **67.** Diverges   **69.** Converges
71. Converges   **73.** Diverges   **75.** Diverges
77. Diverges   **79.** A   **81.** D

Section 8.4   *(page 566)*

1. (a)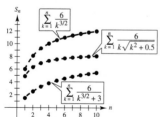

$\displaystyle\sum_{n=1}^{\infty} \frac{6}{n^{3/2}}$ is a p-series; Converges

(b) The magnitudes of the terms of the p-series are greater than the magnitudes of the terms of the other two series. The series converge.

(c) The smaller the magnitudes of the terms, the slower the convergence of the series.

3. Diverges   **5.** Converges   **7.** Diverges
9. Diverges   **11.** Converges   **13.** Converges
15. Diverges   **17.** Converges   **19.** Converges
21. Converges   **23.** Diverges
25. Diverges; p-Series Test
27. Converges; Direct Comparison Test
29. Diverges; nth-Term Test   **31.** Converges; Integral Test
33. The nth terms do not have the same magnitude; Compare with

$$\sum_{n=1}^{\infty} \frac{1}{n^{3/2}}.$$

35. $\displaystyle\lim_{n\to\infty} \frac{a_n}{1/n} = \lim_{n\to\infty} na_n$; $\displaystyle\lim_{n\to\infty} na_n \neq 0$, but is finite. The series diverges by the Limit Comparison Test.
37. Converges   **39.** Diverges   **41.** Answers will vary.
43. Diverges   **45.** Converges
47. No; The test only determines convergence or divergence.
49. Convergence or divergence is dependent on the form of the general term for the series and not necessarily on the magnitudes of the terms.
51. (a) Because the degree of the numerator is two less than the degree of the denominator, the series converges.

(b)

n	5	10	20	50	100
S_n	1.1839	1.2087	1.2212	1.2287	1.2312

(c) 0.1226   (d) 0.0277

53. False; Sample answer: Let $a_n = \dfrac{1}{n^3}$ and $b_n = \dfrac{1}{n^2}$.   **55.** True

57. True   **59.** Proof   **61.** Sample answer: $\displaystyle\sum_{n=1}^{\infty} \frac{1}{n^2}, \sum_{n=1}^{\infty} \frac{1}{n^3}$

63. Proof   **65.** Answers will vary.   **67.** Proof

69. $\dfrac{\ln n}{n^{3/2}} < \dfrac{1}{n^{5/4}}$ for $n > 5504$. Because $\displaystyle\sum_{n=1}^{\infty} \frac{1}{n^{5/4}}$ is a convergent p-series, $\displaystyle\sum_{n=1}^{\infty} \frac{\ln n}{n^{3/2}}$ converges by direct comparison.

71. B

Section 8.5   *(page 575)*

1. (a)

n	1	2	3	4	5
S_n	1	0.6667	0.8667	0.7238	0.8349

n	6	7	8	9	10
S_n	0.7440	0.8209	0.7543	0.8131	0.7605

(b)

(c) The points are on alternate sides of $y = \dfrac{\pi}{4}$; decreases

(d) The distance is eventually less than the magnitude of the next term of the series.

3. (a)

n	1	2	3	4	5
S_n	1	0.75	0.8611	0.7986	0.8386

n	6	7	8	9	10
S_n	0.8108	0.8312	0.8156	0.8280	0.8180

(b)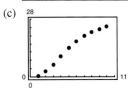

(c) The points are on alternate sides of $y = \dfrac{\pi^2}{12}$; decreases

(d) The distance is eventually less than the magnitude of the next term of the series.

5. Converges **7.** Converges **9.** Converges
11. Diverges **13.** Converges **15.** Diverges
17. Diverges **19.** Converges **21.** Converges
23. Converges **25.** Converges **27.** $1.8264 \le S \le 1.8403$
29. $1.7938 \le S \le 1.8054$ **31.** 10 **33.** 7 **35.** 7
37. Converges absolutely **39.** Converges absolutely
41. Converges conditionally **43.** Diverges
45. Converges conditionally **47.** Converges absolutely
49. Converges absolutely **51.** Converges conditionally
53. Converges absolutely
55. Overestimate; the next term is negative.
57. $|S - S_N| = |R_N| \le a_{N+1}$
59. (a) No; Sample answer: Let $a_n = \dfrac{(-1)^n}{n}$.

(b) Yes; If $\sum |a_n|$ converged, then so would $\sum a_n$ by Theorem 8.16.

61. $p > 0$ **63.** Proof; No; Sample answer: Let $a_n = \dfrac{1}{n}$.

65. Sample answer: $\displaystyle\sum_{n=1}^{\infty} \dfrac{1}{n^2}$ converges, and so does $\displaystyle\sum_{n=1}^{\infty} \dfrac{1}{n^4}$.

67. (a) No; $a_{n+1} \le a_n$ is not satisfied for all n. (b) Yes; $\frac{1}{2}$
69. Diverges; p-Series Test **71.** Diverges; nth-Term Test
73. Diverges; Geometric Series Test
75. Converges; Geometric Series Test or Integral Test
77. Converges absolutely; Alternating Series Test

79. The partial sums of the series $\displaystyle\sum_{n=0}^{\infty} (-1)^n$ alternate between 0 and 1, but the series does not converge to either value.

81. A

Section 8.6 *(page 583)*

1–3. Answers will vary. **5.** d **6.** c **7.** f
8. b **9.** a **10.** e **11.** Converges **13.** Diverges
15. Diverges **17.** Diverges **19.** Converges
21. Converges **23.** Diverges **25.** Converges
27. Converges **29.** Diverges **31.** Converges
33. Converges **35.** Converges **37.** Diverges
39. Converges **41.** Diverges **43.** Converges
45. Converges **47.** Converges
49. Converges; Alternating Series **51.** Converges; p-Series
53. Diverges; Sample answer: nth-Term

55. Diverges; Sample answer: nth-Term
57. Converges; Limit Comparison
59. Converges; Sample answer: Direct Comparison
61. Converges; Direct Comparison
63. Converges; Sample answer: Ratio **65.** a and c
67. a and b **69.** $\displaystyle\sum_{n=0}^{\infty} \dfrac{n+1}{7^{n+1}}$ **71.** (a) 9 (b) -0.7769

73. Diverges; $\displaystyle\lim_{n\to\infty} \left| \dfrac{a_{n+1}}{a_n} \right| > 1$

75. Converges; $\displaystyle\lim_{n\to\infty} \left| \dfrac{a_{n+1}}{a_n} \right| < 1$ **77.** Diverges; $\displaystyle\lim_{n\to\infty} a_n \ne 0$

79. Converges **81.** Converges **83.** $(-3, 3)$
85. $(-2, 0]$ **87.** $x = 0$
89. (a) Answers will vary.

(b)

n	5	10	15	20
S_n	13.7813	24.2363	25.8468	25.9897

n	25	30
S_n	25.9994	26.0000

(c)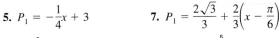

(d) 26

91. The more rapidly the terms of the series approach 0, the more rapidly the sequence of partial sums approaches the sum of the series.

93. Nothing; $\displaystyle\lim_{n\to\infty} \dfrac{a_{n+1}}{a_n} = 1$ **95.** Proof

97–101. Answers will vary.
103. (a) Diverges (b) Converges (c) Converges
(d) Converges for all integers $x \ge 2$
105. B

Section 8.7 *(page 594)*

1. d **2.** c **3.** a **4.** b

5. $P_1 = -\dfrac{1}{4}x + 3$ **7.** $P_1 = \dfrac{2\sqrt{3}}{3} + \dfrac{2}{3}\left(x - \dfrac{\pi}{6}\right)$

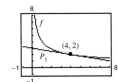 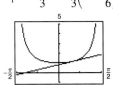

9. (a)

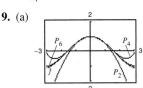

(b) $f^{(2)}(0) = -1 = P_2^{(2)}(0)$
$f^{(4)}(0) = 1 = P_4^{(4)}(0)$
$f^{(6)}(0) = -1 = P_6^{(6)}(0)$
(c) $f^{(n)}(0) = P_n^{(n)}(0)$

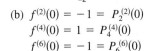

11. $1 + 4x + 8x^2 + \frac{32}{3}x^3 + \frac{32}{3}x^4$ **13.** $x - \frac{1}{6}x^3 + \frac{1}{120}x^5$

15. $x + x^2 + \frac{1}{2}x^3 + \frac{1}{6}x^4$ **17.** $1 + x + x^2 + x^3 + x^4 + x^5$

19. $1 + \frac{1}{2}x^2$ **21.** $2 - 2(x - 1) + 2(x - 1)^2 - 2(x - 1)^3$

23. $2 + \frac{1}{4}(x - 4) - \frac{1}{64}(x - 4)^2 + \frac{1}{512}(x - 4)^3$

25. $\ln 2 + \frac{1}{2}(x - 2) - \frac{1}{8}(x - 2)^2 + \frac{1}{24}(x - 2)^3 - \frac{1}{64}(x - 2)^4$

27. $f'''(1)$ should be divided by 3!, not 3;

$$P_3(x) = \pi(x - 1) + \frac{\pi^3}{3}(x - 1)^3$$

29. 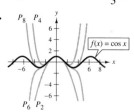 **31.**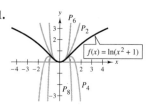

33. (a)

x	0.00	0.25	0.50
$\sin x$	0.0000	0.2474	0.4794
$P_1(x)$	0.0000	0.2500	0.5000
$P_3(x)$	0.0000	0.2474	0.4792
$P_5(x)$	0.0000	0.2474	0.4794

x	0.75	1.00
$\sin x$	0.6816	0.8415
$P_1(x)$	0.7500	1.0000
$P_3(x)$	0.6797	0.8333
$P_5(x)$	0.6817	0.8417

(b)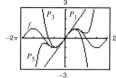

(c) As the distance increases, the accuracy decreases.

35. $f(x) = \arcsin x$

(a) $P_3(x) = x + \dfrac{x^3}{6}$

(b)

x	-0.75	-0.50	-0.25	0
$f(x)$	-0.848	-0.524	-0.253	0
$P_3(x)$	-0.820	-0.521	-0.253	0

x	0.25	0.50	0.75
$f(x)$	0.253	0.524	0.848
$P_3(x)$	0.253	0.521	0.820

(c)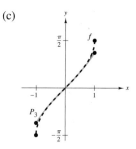

37. 2.7083 **39.** 0.7419

41. $R_4(x) \le \dfrac{(0.3)^5}{5!} \approx 2.03 \times 10^{-5}; 0.000001$

43. $R_3(x) \le 7.82 \times 10^{-3}; 0.00085$ **45.** 3 **47.** 5

49. 2 **51.** $-0.3936 < x < 0$

53. The graphs of the approximating polynomial P and the elementary function f both pass through the point $(c, f(c))$, and the slope of the graph of P is the same as the slope of the graph of f at the point $(c, f(c))$. If P is of degree n, then the first n derivatives of f and P agree at c. This allows the graph of P to resemble the graph of f near the point $(c, f(c))$.

55. $f(x) = e^x$: $P_4(x) = 1 + x + \frac{1}{2}x^2 + \frac{1}{6}x^3 + \frac{1}{24}x^4$

$g(x) = e^{2x}$: $Q_4(x) = 1 + 2x + 2x^2 + \frac{4}{3}x^3 + \frac{2}{3}x^4$

Replace x with $2x$.

57. (a) $P_6(x) = \dfrac{1}{\sqrt{2\pi}} - \dfrac{1}{2\sqrt{2\pi}}x^2 + \dfrac{1}{8\sqrt{2\pi}}x^4 - \dfrac{1}{48\sqrt{2\pi}}x^6$

(b) 0.6800

(c) 0.6803; Yes; The values are about the same.

59. (a) $Q_2(x) = -1 + \dfrac{\pi^2(x + 2)^2}{32}$

(b) $R_2(x) = -1 + \dfrac{\pi^2(x - 6)^2}{32}$

(c) No; Horizontal translations are possible only at $x = -2 + 8n$ (where n is an integer) because the period of f is 8.

61. Proof **63.** B

Section 8.8 (page 604)

1. 0 **3.** -5 **5.** $R = 1$ **7.** $R = \frac{1}{4}$ **9.** $R = 0$

11. $R = \infty$ **13.** $(-4, 4)$ **15.** $(-1, 1]$ **17.** $(-\infty, \infty)$

19. $x = 0$ **21.** $(-7, 5)$ **23.** $(-5, 13]$ **25.** $(0, 2]$

27. $[-6, 0]$ **29.** $\left(-\frac{1}{2}, \frac{1}{2}\right)$ **31.** $(-\infty, \infty)$ **33.** $(-1, 1)$

35. $x = 3$ **37.** $R = c$ **39.** $(-k, k)$ **41.** $(-1, 1)$

43. (a) $\displaystyle\sum_{n=1}^{\infty} 4n(4x)^{n-1}$ (b) $\displaystyle\sum_{n=2}^{\infty} 16n(n - 1)(4x)^{n-2}$

(c) $C + \displaystyle\sum_{n=0}^{\infty} \dfrac{(4x)^{n+1}}{4(n + 1)}$

45. (a) $\displaystyle\sum_{n=1}^{\infty} \dfrac{(-1)^{n+1}(n + 1)(x - 3)^n}{n3^n}$

(b) $\displaystyle\sum_{n=1}^{\infty} \dfrac{(-1)^{n+1}(n + 1)(x - 3)^{n-1}}{3^n}$

(c) $C + \displaystyle\sum_{n=1}^{\infty} \dfrac{(-1)^{n+1}(x - 3)^{n+2}}{n(n + 2)3^n}$

47. (a) $(-3, 3)$ (b) $(-3, 3)$ (c) $(-3, 3)$ (d) $[-3, 3)$

49. (a) $(0, 2]$ (b) $(0, 2)$ (c) $(0, 2)$ (d) $[0, 2]$

51. The interval of convergence of a power series is the set of all values of x for which the series converges. The radius of convergence is half the length of this interval.

53. A single point, an interval, or the entire real number line

55. Sample answers:

$\sum_{n=1}^{\infty} \frac{x^n}{n}$ converges for $-1 \le x < 1$. At $x = -1$, the convergence is conditional because $\sum \frac{1}{n}$ diverges. $\sum_{n=1}^{\infty} \frac{x^n}{n^2}$ converges for $-1 \le x \le 1$. At $x = \pm 1$, the convergence is absolute.

57. Sample answer: $\sum_{n=1}^{\infty} \frac{1}{n^2}\left(\frac{x-2}{5}\right)^n$; Answers will vary.

59. (a) $(-\infty, \infty)$; $(-\infty, \infty)$ (b) Answers will vary.
(c) $f(x) = \sin x$; $g(x) = \cos x$

61–65. Answers will vary.

67. (a)–(b) Answers will vary.
(c)
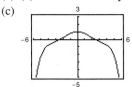
(d) 0.92

69. (a) $\frac{8}{3}$ (b) $\frac{8}{13}$
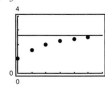
(c) The alternating series converges more rapidly. The partial sums in part (a) approach the sum from below. The partial sums in part (b) are on alternate sides of $y = \frac{8}{13}$.
(d)

M	10	100	1000	10,000
N	5	14	24	35

71. False; Sample answer: $\sum_{n=1}^{\infty} \frac{(-1)^n x^n}{n 2^n}$ converges for $x = 2$ but diverges for $x = -2$.

73. True   **75–77.** Proofs   **79.** C

Section 8.9   *(page 612)*

1. (a)–(b) $\sum_{n=0}^{\infty} \frac{x^n}{4^{n+1}}$ **3.** (a)–(b) $\sum_{n=0}^{\infty} \frac{3(-1)^n x^n}{4^{n+1}}$

5. $f(x) = \sum_{n=0}^{\infty} \left(\frac{x}{2}\right)^n$ **7.** $\sum_{n=0}^{\infty} \frac{(x-1)^n}{5^{n+1}}$; $(-4, 6)$

9. $\sum_{n=0}^{\infty} (3x)^n$; $\left(\frac{1}{3}, \frac{1}{3}\right)$ **11.** $\sum_{n=0}^{\infty} \frac{(-2)^n(x-2)^n}{3^n}$; $\left(\frac{1}{2}, \frac{7}{2}\right)$

13. $4\sum_{n=0}^{\infty} \frac{(-3)^n(x-3)^n}{11^{n+1}}$; $\left(3, \frac{20}{3}\right)$

15. $\sum_{n=0}^{\infty} \left[\frac{1}{(-3)^n} - 1\right]x^n$; $(-1, 1)$ **17.** $2\sum_{n=0}^{\infty} x^{2n}$; $(-1, 1)$

19. $2\sum_{n=0}^{\infty} x^{2n}$; $(-1, 1)$ **21.** $\sum_{n=0}^{\infty} (-1)^{n+1}(n+1)x^n$; $(-1, 1)$

23. $\sum_{n=0}^{\infty} \frac{(-1)^n x^{n+1}}{n+1}$; $(-1, 1]$ **25.** $\sum_{n=0}^{\infty} (-1)^n x^{2n}$; $(-1, 1)$

27. $\sum_{n=0}^{\infty} (-1)^n (2x)^{2n}$; $\left(-\frac{1}{2}, \frac{1}{2}\right)$

29.
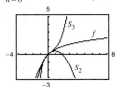

x	0.0	0.2	0.4	0.6	0.8	1.0
S_2	0.000	0.180	0.320	0.420	0.480	0.500
$\ln(x+1)$	0.000	0.182	0.336	0.470	0.588	0.693
S_3	0.000	0.183	0.341	0.492	0.651	0.833

31. (a)
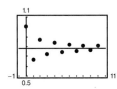
(b) $\ln x$, $0 < x \le 2$, $R = 1$
(c) -0.6931
(d) $\ln(0.5)$; The error is approximately 0.

33. 0.245   **35.** 0.125   **37.** $\sum_{n=1}^{\infty} nx^{n-1}$; $(-1, 1)$

39. $\sum_{n=0}^{\infty} (2n+1)x^n$; $(-1, 1)$

41. $E(n) = 2$; Because the probability of obtaining a head on a single roll is $\frac{1}{2}$, it is expected that, on average, a head will be obtained in two tosses.

43. Proof   **45.** (a) Answers will vary.   (b) 3.1401

47. 0.4055; $\ln(x+1)$; Let $x = \frac{1}{2}$.

49. 0.3365; $\ln(x+1)$; Let $x = \frac{2}{5}$.

51. 0.4636; $\arctan x$; Let $x = \frac{1}{2}$.

53. $\sum_{n=0}^{\infty} (-1)^n \frac{1}{2n+1}$; The terms approach 0 at a much slower rate.

55. The series converges for $|x+1| < 4$, which is the interval $(-5, 3)$, and perhaps also at the endpoints;
$\frac{d}{dx}\left[\sum_{n=0}^{\infty} \frac{a_n x^{n+1}}{n+1}\right] = \sum_{n=1}^{\infty} a_n x^n$

57. (a) $|x| < 5$ (b) $\frac{2}{25}$ (c) $\frac{1}{5}, \frac{1}{5^2}, \frac{1}{5^3}, \frac{1}{5^n}$ (d) 0.25

Section 8.10   *(page 623)*

1. $\sum_{n=0}^{\infty} \frac{(2x)^n}{n!}$ **3.** $\frac{\sqrt{2}}{2}\sum_{n=0}^{\infty} \frac{(-1)^{n(n+1)/2}[x - (\pi/4)]^n}{n!}$

5. $\sum_{n=0}^{\infty} (-1)^n (x-1)^n$ **7.** $\sum_{n=0}^{\infty} \frac{(-1)^n (x-1)^{n+1}}{n+1}$

9. $\sum_{n=0}^{\infty} \frac{(-1)^n (3x)^{2n+1}}{(2n+1)!}$ **11.** $1 + \frac{x^2}{2!} + \frac{5x^4}{4!} + \cdots$

13. Proof   **15.** $\sum_{n=0}^{\infty} \frac{(-1)^n(n+3)!}{3!n!}x^n$

17. $1 + \sum_{n=1}^{\infty} \dfrac{1 \cdot 3 \cdot 5 \cdots (2n-1)x^{2n}}{2^n n!}$

19. $1 + \dfrac{1}{4}x + \sum_{n=2}^{\infty} \dfrac{(-1)^{n+1}3 \cdot 7 \cdot 11 \cdots (4n-5)}{4^n n!}x^n$

21. $\sum_{n=0}^{\infty} \dfrac{x^{2n}}{2^n n!}$ **23.** $2\sum_{n=1}^{\infty} \dfrac{(-1)^{n-1}x^n}{n}$ **25.** $\sum_{n=0}^{\infty} \dfrac{(-1)^n(5x)^{2n+1}}{(2n+1)!}$

27. $\sum_{n=0}^{\infty} \dfrac{(-1)^n(5x)^{2n+1}}{2n+1}$ **29.** $\sum_{n=0}^{\infty} \dfrac{(-1)^n x^{3n}}{(2n)!}$ **31.** $3 + 4\sum_{n=0}^{\infty} \dfrac{x^{3n}}{n!}$

33. $-7x$ should be substituted in for x in the series; $\sum_{n=0}^{\infty} \dfrac{(-7x)^n}{n!}$

35. $\sum_{n=0}^{\infty} \dfrac{(-1)^n x^{2n+2}}{(2n+1)!}$ **37.** $\begin{cases} \sum_{n=0}^{\infty} \dfrac{(-1)^n x^{2n}}{(2n+1)!}, & x \neq 0 \\ 1, & x = 0 \end{cases}$

39. Answers will vary.

41. $P(x) = x + x^2 + \dfrac{1}{3}x^3 - \dfrac{1}{30}x^5$

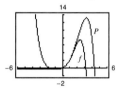

43. $P(x) = x - \dfrac{x^2}{2} - \dfrac{x^3}{6} + \dfrac{3x^5}{40}$

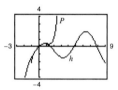

45. $P(x) = x - x^2 + \dfrac{5}{6}x^3 - \dfrac{5}{6}x^4$

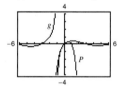

47. $\sum_{n=0}^{\infty} \dfrac{(-1)^{n+1}x^{2n+3}}{(2n+3)(n+1)!}$ **49.** Answers will vary; 0.6931

51. Answers will vary; 7.3891 **53.** 0 **55.** 1

57. 0.8992 **59.** 0.9461 **61.** 0.48725 **63.** 0.201

65. 0.7040 **67.** 0.3412

69. Use the half-angle formula $\cos^2 x = \frac{1}{2}(1 + \cos 2x)$; square the series for $\cos x$; use the definition of Maclaurin series; Answers will vary.

71. $\dfrac{1}{4}\sin(x+3)$; $\sin x = \sum_{n=0}^{\infty} \dfrac{(-1)^n x^{2n+1}}{(2n+1)!}$

73. Answers will vary.

75. (a)

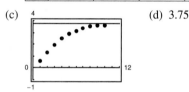

(b) Answers will vary. (c) $\sum_{n=0}^{\infty} 0x^n$; No

77. 56 **79.** 0.0708 **81.** $\sum_{n=0}^{\infty} \binom{k}{n} x^n$ **83.** Proof

85. A **87.** B

Review Exercises for Chapter 8 *(page 626)*

1.

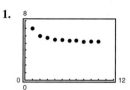

Converges to 5

3. Diverges **5.** Diverges **7.** Converges; 0

9. Converges; 0 **11.** $\frac{6}{7}$ **13.** 5.5

15. (a) $\sum_{n=0}^{\infty} \left(\dfrac{7}{100}\right)\left(\dfrac{1}{10}\right)^n$ (b) $\dfrac{7}{90}$ **17.** Diverges

19. Diverges **21.** $45\frac{1}{3}$ meters **23.** Diverges

25. Converges **27.** Diverges **29.** Diverges

31. Diverges **33.** Diverges **35.** Converges absolutely

37. Converges conditionally **39.** Diverges

41. Diverges **43.** Converges **45.** Diverges

47. (a) Answers will vary.

(b)

n	5	10	15	20	25
S_n	2.8752	3.6366	3.7377	3.7488	3.7499

(c) [graph] (d) 3.75

49. $P_4(x) = 1 + \dfrac{1}{3}x + \dfrac{1}{18}x^2 + \dfrac{1}{162}x^3 + \dfrac{1}{1944}x^4$

51. $P_3(x) = 1 - 3x + \dfrac{9}{2}x^2 - \dfrac{9}{2}x^3$ **53.** 5 **55.** $\left(-\frac{4}{3}, \frac{4}{3}\right)$

57. $[1, 3]$ **59.** $x = 2$

61. (a) $(-5, 5)$ (b) $(-5, 5)$ (c) $(-5, 5)$ (d) $(-5, 5)$

63. $\sum_{n=0}^{\infty} \dfrac{2x^n}{3^{n+1}}$ **65.** $2\sum_{n=0}^{\infty} \dfrac{(x-1)^n}{3^n}$; $(-2, 4)$

67. 0.2231; $\ln(x+1)$; Let $x = \frac{1}{4}$. **69.** 1.6487; e^x; Let $x = \frac{1}{2}$.

71. 0.7859; $\cos x$; Let $x = \frac{2}{3}$.

73. $\dfrac{\sqrt{2}}{2}\sum_{n=0}^{\infty} \dfrac{(-1)^{n(n+1)/2}[x - (3\pi/4)]^n}{n!}$

75. $-\sum_{n=0}^{\infty} (x+1)^n$, $-2 < x < 0$

77. $1 + \dfrac{x}{5} + \sum_{n=2}^{\infty} \dfrac{(-1)^{n+1}4 \cdot 9 \cdot 14 \cdots (5n-6)x^n}{5^n n!}$

79. (a)–(c) $1 + 2x + 2x^2 + \dfrac{4}{3}x^3$ **81.** $\sum_{n=0}^{\infty} \dfrac{(6x)^n}{n!}$

AP® Exam Practice Questions *(page 628)*

1. C **2.** B **3.** C **4.** C **5.** C **6.** B **7.** C

8. (a) $P_1(x) = 50 + \dfrac{160}{3}(x-3)$; 55.33;

The approximation is less than the actual value of $g(3.1)$.

(b) $P_3(x) = 50 + \dfrac{160}{3}(x-3) + \dfrac{141}{8}(x-3)^2 + \dfrac{21}{6}(x-3)^3$; 55.51308

(c) Proof

9. (a) $x - x^2 + \dfrac{x^3}{2!} - \dfrac{x^4}{3!} + \cdots + \dfrac{(-1)^n x^{n+1}}{n!} + \cdots$ (b) $\dfrac{1}{2}$

(c) $\dfrac{x^2}{2} - \dfrac{x^3}{3} + \dfrac{x^4}{8} + \cdots + \dfrac{(-1)^{n+2}x^{n+2}}{(n+2)n!} + \cdots$; 0.01753

(d) Proof

10. (a) $1 - \dfrac{x^4}{2!} + \dfrac{x^8}{4!} - \dfrac{x^{12}}{6!} + \cdots + \dfrac{(-1)^n x^{4n}}{(2n)!} + \cdots$

(b) $R = \infty$ (c) 0.54167; Proof

11. (a) $f'(0) = 0$; $f''(0) = -2$; There is a relative maximum at $x = 0$, determined by the Second Derivative Test.

(b) Yes; $\dfrac{1}{4!} < 0.1$ (c) Answers will vary.

12. (a) $(0, 2]$

When $x = 0$, f is a harmonic series, which diverges. When $x = 2$, f is an alternating harmonic series, which converges.

(b) $1, -(x - 1), (x - 1)^2, (-1)^n(x - 1)^n$

(c) $\dfrac{1}{x}$ (d) $\dfrac{3x^2}{1 + x^3}$

13. (a) $y = 4x - 5$; 4.6; less; $g'(x) > 4$ on $(2, 2.4)$

(b) $\displaystyle\int_2^{2.4} g'(x)\, dx = 2.6$; $g(2.4) \approx 5.6$ (c) 5.2

(d) $g(2) + g'(2)(x - 2) + \dfrac{g''(2)}{2}(x - 2)^2$; 6.2;

Answers will vary.

Chapter 9

Section 9.1   *(page 642)*

1. c   **2.** a   **3.** d   **4.** b

5. Vertex: $(0, 0)$
Focus: $(-2, 0)$
Directrix: $x = 2$

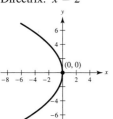

7. Vertex: $(-5, 3)$
Focus: $\left(-\dfrac{21}{4}, 3\right)$
Directrix: $x = -\dfrac{19}{4}$

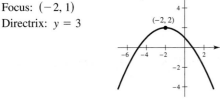

9. Vertex: $(-2, 2)$
Focus: $(-2, 1)$
Directrix: $y = 3$

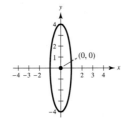

11. $(y - 4)^2 = 4(-2)(x - 5)$ **13.** $(x - 0)^2 = 4(8)(y - 5)$

15. $(x - 0)^2 = 4\left(-\dfrac{1}{4}\right)(y - 4)$ **17.** $\left(x - \dfrac{7}{5}\right)^2 = 4\left(\dfrac{3}{20}\right)\left(y + \dfrac{4}{15}\right)$

19. $2\ln\left(1 + \sqrt{2}\right) + 2\sqrt{2} \approx 4.5912$

21. $\dfrac{1}{2}\ln\left(4 + \sqrt{17}\right) + 2\sqrt{17} \approx 9.2936$

23. Center: $(0, 0)$
Foci: $\left(0, \pm\sqrt{15}\right)$
Vertices: $(0, \pm 4)$
$e = \dfrac{\sqrt{15}}{4}$

25. Center: $(3, 1)$
Foci: $(3, 1 + 3) = (3, 4)$,
$\quad\quad (3, 1 - 3) = (3, -2)$
Vertices: $(3, 6), (3, -4)$
$e = \dfrac{3}{5}$

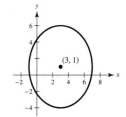

27. Center: $(-2, 3)$
Foci: $\left(-2, 3 \pm \sqrt{5}\right)$
Vertices: $(-2, 6), (-2, 0)$
$e = \dfrac{\sqrt{5}}{3}$

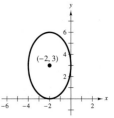

29. $\dfrac{x^2}{36} + \dfrac{y^2}{11} = 1$ **31.** $\dfrac{(x - 3)^2}{9} + \dfrac{(y - 5)^2}{16} = 1$

33. $\dfrac{x^2}{16} + \dfrac{7y^2}{16} = 1$

35. The equation should have been divided by 9;
$\dfrac{(x - 2)^2}{3} + \dfrac{(y + 1)^2}{9} = 1$

37. (a)–(b) 15.87 units

39. Center: $(0, 0)$
Foci: $\left(\pm\sqrt{41}, 0\right)$
Vertices: $(\pm 5, 0)$
$e = \dfrac{\sqrt{41}}{5}$

Asymptotes: $y = \pm\dfrac{b}{a}x = \pm\dfrac{4}{5}x$

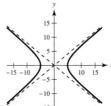

41. Center: $(2, -3)$
Foci: $\left(2 \pm \sqrt{10}, -3\right)$
Vertices: $(1, -3), (3, -3)$
$e = \sqrt{10}$
Asymptotes: $y = -3 \pm 3(x - 2)$

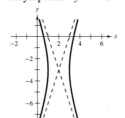

43. Center: $(-1, 1)$
Foci: $\left(-1 \pm \sqrt{7}, 1\right)$
Vertices: $\left(-1 \pm \sqrt{3}, 1\right)$
$e = \dfrac{\sqrt{21}}{3}$
Asymptotes: $y = 1 \pm \dfrac{2\sqrt{3}}{3}(x + 1)$

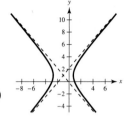

45. $\dfrac{x^2}{1} - \dfrac{y^2}{25} = 1$ **47.** $\dfrac{y^2}{9} - \dfrac{(x - 2)^2}{9/4} = 1$

49. $\dfrac{y^2}{4} - \dfrac{x^2}{12} = 1$ **51.** $\dfrac{(x - 3)^2}{9} - \dfrac{(y - 2)^2}{4} = 1$

53. (a) $\left(6, \sqrt{3}\right)$: $2x - 3\sqrt{3}y - 3 = 0$
$\left(6, -\sqrt{3}\right)$: $2x + 3\sqrt{3}y - 3 = 0$
(b) $\left(6, \sqrt{3}\right)$: $9x + 2\sqrt{3}y - 60 = 0$
$\left(6, -\sqrt{3}\right)$: $9x - 2\sqrt{3}y - 60 = 0$

55. Ellipse   **57.** Parabola   **59.** Circle   **61.** Hyperbola
63. $\frac{9}{4}$ m   **65.** (a) Proof   (b) $(3, -3)$ **67.** 15.536 ft^2
69. Least distance $\approx 147{,}101{,}680$ km
Greatest distance $\approx 152{,}098{,}320$ km
71. Answers will vary.
73. (a) 2π

(b) Volume $= \dfrac{8\pi}{3}$

Surface area $= \dfrac{2\pi\left(9 + 4\sqrt{3}\pi\right)}{9} \approx 21.48$

(c) Volume $= \dfrac{16\pi}{3}$

Surface area $= \dfrac{4\pi\left[6 + \sqrt{3}\ln\left(2 + \sqrt{3}\right)\right]}{3} \approx 34.69$

75. 40   **77.** $x \approx 110.3$ mi
79. As p increases, the graph becomes wider.

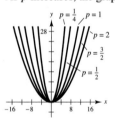

81. The circumference is $C = 4\displaystyle\int_0^{\pi/2} \sqrt{a^2 - (a^2 - b^2)\sin^2\theta}\, d\theta$
and $0 \le \sin^2\theta \le 1$.

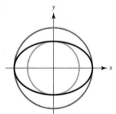

83. (a) Ellipse   (b) Hyperbola
(c) Eliminate the x^2-term or y^2-term.
85. False; The parabola is equidistant from the directrix and focus and therefore cannot intersect the directrix.

87. True   **89.** True   **91.** $\dfrac{(x - 6)^2}{9} - \dfrac{(y - 2)^2}{7} = 1$
93. Proof   **95.** A

Section 9.2   *(page 652)*

1.

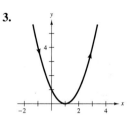

$3x - 2y + 11 = 0$

3.

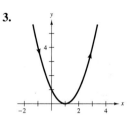

$y = (x - 1)^2$

5.

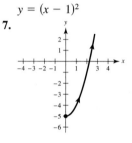

$x = \dfrac{y^3}{64} - \dfrac{y}{4}$

7.

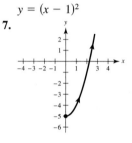

$y = x^2 - 5,\ x \ge 0$

9.

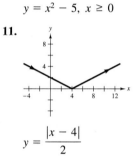

$y = \dfrac{x + 3}{x}$

11.

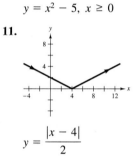

$y = \dfrac{|x - 4|}{2}$

13.

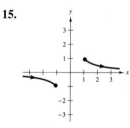

$y = x^3 + 1,\ x > 0$

15.

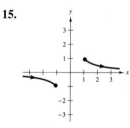

$y = \dfrac{1}{x},\ |x| \ge 1,\ |y| \le 1$

17.

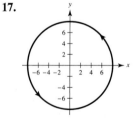

$x^2 + y^2 = 64$

19. -2 should have been distributed instead of 2; $y = -2x + 13$

21.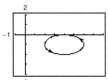
23.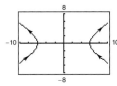

$$\frac{(x-4)^2}{4} + \frac{(y+1)^2}{1} = 1 \qquad \frac{x^2}{36} - \frac{y^2}{16} = 1$$

25.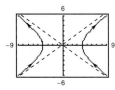
27.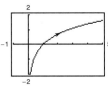

$$\frac{x^2}{16} - \frac{y^2}{9} = 1 \qquad y = \ln x$$

29. The graphs are the same. The orientations are reversed. They are both smooth.

31. By eliminating the parameters in (a)–(d), you get $y = 2x + 1$. They differ from each other in orientation and in restricted domains. These curves are all smooth except for (b).

33. $y - y_1 = m(x - x_1)$ **35.** $\dfrac{(x-h)^2}{a^2} + \dfrac{(y-k)^2}{b^2} = 1$

37. Sample answer: $x = 4t, y = -7t$
39. Sample answer: $x = 1 + 2\cos\theta, y = 1 + 2\sin\theta$
41. Sample answer: $x = 2 + 5\cos\theta, y = 4\sin\theta$
43. Sample answer: $x = \tan\theta, y = 2\sec\theta$
45. Sample answer: $x = t, y = 6t - 5; x = t + 1, y = 6t + 1$
47. Sample answer: $x = t, y = t^3; x = \tan t, y = \tan^3 t$
49. $x = t + 3, y = 2t + 1$ **51.** $x = t, y = t^2$

53.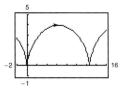
55.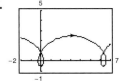

Not smooth at $\theta = 2n\pi$ Smooth everywhere

57.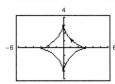
59.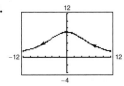

Not smooth at $\theta = \frac{1}{2}n\pi$ Smooth everywhere

61. For $-1 \le t \le 0$, the orientation is right to left along $y = x^2$, $0 \le x \le 1$.
For $0 \le t \le 1$, the orientation is left to right along $y = x^2$, $0 \le x \le 1$.

63. No; $\cos\theta = \cos(-\theta)$ and $\sin^2\theta = \sin^2(-\theta)$, so the parameter was not changed.

65. Different parametric representations can be used to represent various speeds at which objects travel along a given path.

67. d; $(4, 0)$ is on the graph.   **68.** a; $(0, 2)$ is on the graph.
69. b; $(1, 0)$ is on the graph.
70. e; The graph is undefined when $\theta = 0$.
71. $x = a\theta - b\sin\theta; y = a - b\cos\theta$
73. False; The graph of the parametric equations is only a portion of the line $y = x$ when $x \ge 0$.

75. True
77. (a) $x = \left(\frac{440}{3}\cos\theta\right)t; y = 3 + \left(\frac{440}{3}\sin\theta\right)t - 16t^2$

(b)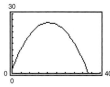
(c)

Not a home run   Home run

(d) $19.4°$
79. C   **81.** A

Section 9.3   *(page 659)*

1. $-\dfrac{3}{t}$ **3.** $-\dfrac{1}{2}\csc 2\theta$

5. $\dfrac{dy}{dx} = -\dfrac{1}{2}, \dfrac{d^2y}{dx^2} = 0$

At $t = 0, \dfrac{dy}{dx} = -\dfrac{1}{2}, \dfrac{d^2y}{dx^2} = 0$; Neither concave upward nor concave downward

7. $\dfrac{dy}{dx} = 8t\sqrt{t - 1}, \dfrac{d^2y}{dx^2} = 24t - 16$

At $t = 5, \dfrac{dy}{dx} = 80, \dfrac{d^2y}{dx^2} = 104$; Concave upward

9. $\dfrac{dy}{dx} = -\cot\theta, \dfrac{d^2y}{dx^2} = -\dfrac{(\csc\theta)^3}{4}$

At $\theta = \dfrac{\pi}{4}, \dfrac{dy}{dx} = -1, \dfrac{d^2y}{dx^2} = -\dfrac{\sqrt{2}}{2}$; Concave downward

11. $\dfrac{dy}{dx} = 2\csc\theta, \dfrac{d^2y}{dx^2} = -2\cot^3\theta$

At $\theta = \dfrac{\pi}{6}, \dfrac{dy}{dx} = 4, \dfrac{d^2y}{dx^2} = -6\sqrt{3}$; Concave downward

13. $\dfrac{dy}{dx} = -\tan\theta, \dfrac{d^2y}{dx^2} = \dfrac{1}{3}\sec^4\theta\csc\theta$

At $\theta = \dfrac{\pi}{4}, \dfrac{dy}{dx} = -1, \dfrac{d^2y}{dx^2} = \dfrac{4\sqrt{2}}{3}$; Concave upward

15. The derivatives are substituted in the wrong places; $\dfrac{dy}{dx} = 3t$

17. $\left(-\dfrac{2}{\sqrt{3}}, \dfrac{3}{2}\right)$: $3\sqrt{3}x - 8y + 18 = 0$

$(0, 2)$: $y - 2 = 0$

$\left(2\sqrt{3}, \dfrac{1}{2}\right)$: $\sqrt{3}x + 8y - 10 = 0$

19. $(0, 0)$: $2y - x = 0$
$(-3, -1)$: $y + 1 = 0$
$(-3, 3)$: $2x - y + 9 = 0$

21. (a) and (d)

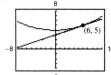

(b) $\dfrac{dx}{dt} = 6, \dfrac{dy}{dt} = 2, \dfrac{dy}{dx} = \dfrac{1}{3}$ (c) $y = \dfrac{1}{3}x + 3$

CHAPTER 9

23. (a) and (d)

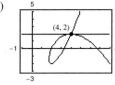

(b) $\dfrac{dx}{dt} = -3, \dfrac{dy}{dt} = 0, \dfrac{dy}{dx} = 0$ (c) $y = 2$

25. $y = \pm\frac{3}{4}x$ **27.** $y = 1, y = 3x - 5$

29. Horizontal: $(-1, \pi), (1, -2\pi)$

Vertical: $\left(\dfrac{\pi}{2}, 1\right), \left(-\dfrac{3\pi}{2}, -1\right)\left(\dfrac{5\pi}{2}, 1\right)$

31. Horizontal: $(6, 0)$ **33.** Horizontal: $(18, -3)$

Vertical: None   Vertical: $(2, 1)$

35. Horizontal: $(0, 3), (0, -3)$ **37.** Horizontal: $(5, -1), (5, -3)$

Vertical: $(3, 0), (-3, 0)$ Vertical: $(8, -2), (2, -2)$

39. Horizontal: None

Vertical: $(1, 0), (-1, 0)$

41. Concave downward: $-\infty < t < 0$

Concave upward: $0 < t < \infty$

43. Concave upward: $0 < t < \infty$

45. Concave downward: $0 < t < \dfrac{\pi}{2}$

Concave upward: $\dfrac{\pi}{2} < t < \pi$

47. 14   **49.** $\sqrt{2}\left(1 - e^{-\pi/2}\right) \approx 1.12$

51. $\frac{1}{12}\left[\ln\left(\sqrt{37} + 6\right) + 6\sqrt{37}\right] \approx 3.249$ **53.** $6a$ **55.** $8a$

57. (a)

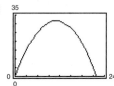

(b) 219.2 ft

(c) 230.8 ft; The arc length is greater.

59. (a)

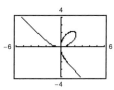

(b) About 6.557

$(0, 0), \left(\dfrac{4\sqrt[3]{2}}{3}, \dfrac{4\sqrt[3]{4}}{3}\right)$

61. (a)

 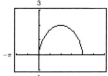 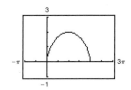

(b) The average speed of the particle on the second path is twice the average speed of the particle on the first path.

(c) 4π

63. $y - g(t_1) = \dfrac{g'(t_1)}{f'(t_1)}(x - f(t_1))$

65. If the curve is traced out only once on $[a, b]$ and does not intersect itself on (a, b), then the arc length is $\displaystyle\int_a^b \sqrt{[f'(t)]^2 + [g'(t)]^2} \, dt$.

67. Sample answer: Let $x = t + 1$ and $y = -e^t$.

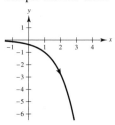

69. $\dfrac{3\pi}{2}$ **71.** d   **72.** b   **73.** f   **74.** c   **75.** a

76. e   **77.** 189   **79.** 2

81. (a) $\dfrac{dy}{dx} = \dfrac{\sin\theta}{1 - \cos\theta}; \dfrac{d^2y}{dx^2} = -\dfrac{1}{a(\cos\theta - 1)^2}$

(b) $y = \left(2 + \sqrt{3}\right)\left[x - a\left(\dfrac{\pi}{6} - \dfrac{1}{2}\right)\right] + a\left(1 - \dfrac{\sqrt{3}}{2}\right)$

(c) $(a(2n + 1)\pi, 2a)$

(d) Concave downward on $(0, 2\pi), (2\pi, 4\pi)$, etc.

(e) $s = 8a$

83. Answers will vary.   **85.** True

87. False; Both dx/dt and dy/dt are zero when $t = 0$. By eliminating the parameter, you have $y = x^{2/3}$, which does not have a horizontal tangent at the origin.

89. B

91. (a) $y - 3 = -\dfrac{\sin 4}{8 - 5\cos 4}(x + 1)$

(b) $t \approx 1.11051$; down; $y'(1.11051) < 0$

(c) $4 - \cos 4 \approx 4.6536$ (d) 26.6561

Section 9.4   *(page 670)*

1.

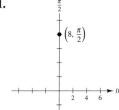

$(0, 8)$

3.

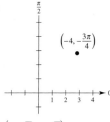

$\left(2\sqrt{2}, 2\sqrt{2}\right)$

5.

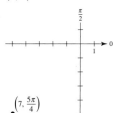

$\left(-\dfrac{7\sqrt{2}}{2}, -\dfrac{7\sqrt{2}}{2}\right)$

7.

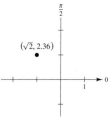

$(-1.0038, 0.9962)$

9.

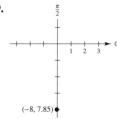

$(-0.0319, -7.9999)$

11.

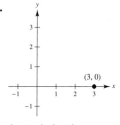

$(-3, \pi), (3, 0)$

13.

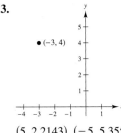

$(5, 2.2143), (-5, 5.3559)$

15.

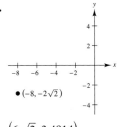

$\left(6\sqrt{2}, 3.4814\right),$
$\left(-6\sqrt{2}, 0.3398\right)$

17.

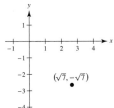

$\left(\sqrt{14}, \dfrac{7\pi}{4}\right), \left(-\sqrt{14}, \dfrac{3\pi}{4}\right)$

19.

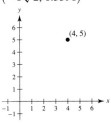

$\left(\sqrt{41}, 0.8961\right),$
$\left(-\sqrt{41}, 4.0376\right)$

21. (x, y) is in Quadrant II, so $\theta = \dfrac{3\pi}{4}$; $(r, \theta) = \left(3, \dfrac{3\pi}{4}\right)$

23. $r = 3$

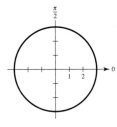

25. $r = a$

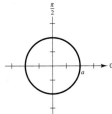

27. $r = 8 \csc \theta$

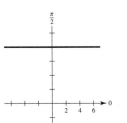

29. $r = -\dfrac{2}{3\cos\theta - \sin\theta}$

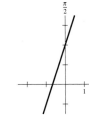

31. $r = 9\csc^2\theta \cos\theta$

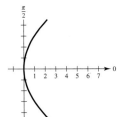

33. $x^2 + y^2 = 16$

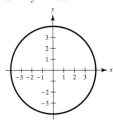

35. $x^2 + \left(y - \dfrac{3}{2}\right)^2 = \dfrac{9}{4}$

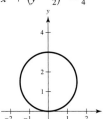

37. $y(x^2 + y^2) = x$

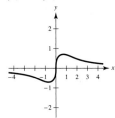

39. $x - 3 = 0$

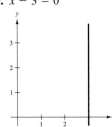

41. $y = x^2$

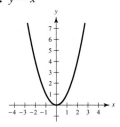

43.

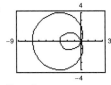

Sample answer:
$0 \le \theta < 2\pi$

45.

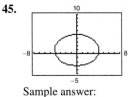

Sample answer:
$0 \le \theta < 2\pi$

47.

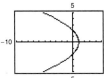

Sample answer:
$-\pi < \theta < \pi$

49.

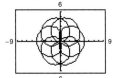

Sample answer:
$-4\pi \le \theta < 4\pi$

51.

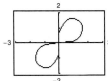

Sample answer: $0 \le \theta < \dfrac{\pi}{2}$

53. $(x - h)^2 + (y - k)^2 = h^2 + k^2$
Radius: $\sqrt{h^2 + k^2}$
Center: (h, k)

55. (a)

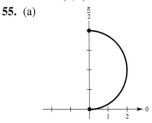

(b)

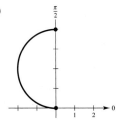

(c)

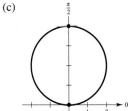

CHAPTER 9

57. $\sqrt{17}$ **59.** 5.6

61. $\dfrac{dy}{dx} = \dfrac{2(\cos\theta)(3\sin\theta + 1)}{6\cos^2\theta - 2\sin\theta - 3}$

$(2, \pi)$: $\dfrac{dy}{dx} = -\dfrac{2}{3}$

$\left(-1, \dfrac{3\pi}{2}\right)$: $\dfrac{dy}{dx} = 0$

$\left(3.5, \dfrac{\pi}{6}\right)$: $\dfrac{dy}{dx} = 5\sqrt{3}$

63. (a) and (b)

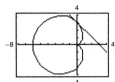

(c) $\dfrac{dy}{dx} = -1$

65. (a) and (b)

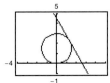

(c) $\dfrac{dy}{dx} = -\sqrt{3}$

67. $\left(5, \dfrac{\pi}{2}\right), \left(1, \dfrac{3\pi}{2}\right)$

69. Horizontal: $\left(2, \dfrac{3\pi}{2}\right), \left(\dfrac{1}{2}, \dfrac{\pi}{6}\right), \left(\dfrac{1}{2}, \dfrac{5\pi}{6}\right)$

Vertical: $\left(\dfrac{3}{2}, \dfrac{7\pi}{6}\right), \left(\dfrac{3}{2}, \dfrac{11\pi}{6}\right)$

71.

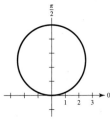

$\theta = 0$

73.

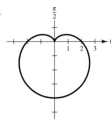

$\theta = \dfrac{\pi}{2}$

75.

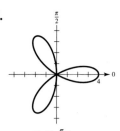

$\theta = \dfrac{\pi}{6}, \dfrac{\pi}{2}, \dfrac{5\pi}{6}$

77.

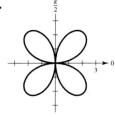

$\theta = 0, \dfrac{\pi}{2}$

79.

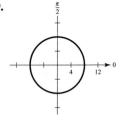

81.

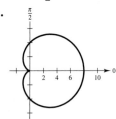

83.

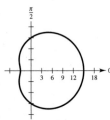

85.

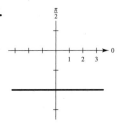

87.

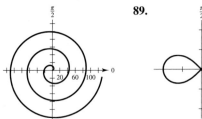

89.

91. The rectangular coordinate system is a collection of points of the form (x, y), where x is the directed distance from the y-axis to the point and y is the directed distance from the x-axis to the point. Every point has a unique representation.

The polar coordinate system is a collection of points of the form (r, θ), where r is the directed distance from the origin O to a point P and θ is the directed angle, measured counterclockwise, from the polar axis to the segment $\overline{OP}$. Polar coordinates do not have unique representations.

93. Slope of tangent line to graph of $r = f(\theta)$ at (r, θ) is

$$\dfrac{dy}{dx} = \dfrac{f(\theta)\cos\theta + f'(\theta)\sin\theta}{-f(\theta)\sin\theta + f'(\theta)\cos\theta}.$$

If $f(\alpha) = 0$ and $f'(\alpha) \neq 0$, then $\theta = \alpha$ is tangent at the pole.

95. Answers will vary.

97. (a) $r = 2 - \sin\left(\theta - \dfrac{\pi}{4}\right)$ (b) $r = 2 + \cos\theta$

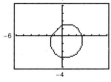

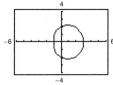

(c) $r = 2 + \sin\theta$ (d) $r = 2 - \cos\theta$

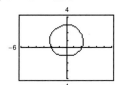

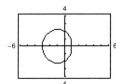

99. $\psi = \dfrac{\pi}{2}$ **101.** $\psi = \dfrac{\pi}{3}$

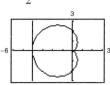

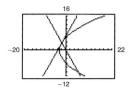

103. True

105. (a) $-\dfrac{1}{3}$ (b) $y = -\dfrac{1}{3}x - \dfrac{5}{3}$

(c) $\theta \approx 2.42, 3.86$; $x = \dfrac{5\cos\theta}{3 - \cos\theta}$

Section 9.5 *(page 678)*

1. $8\displaystyle\int_0^{\pi/2} \sin^2\theta\, d\theta$ **3.** $\dfrac{1}{2}\displaystyle\int_{\pi/2}^{3\pi/2} (3 - 2\sin\theta)^2\, d\theta$

5. The interior is traced twice from 0 to 2π;

$$A = \dfrac{1}{2}\int_0^\pi (\sin\theta)^2\, d\theta$$

7. 9π **9.** $\dfrac{\pi}{3}$ **11.** $\dfrac{\pi}{4}$ **13.** $\dfrac{97\pi}{4} - 60$ **15.** $\dfrac{33\pi}{2}$

17. 4

19.

21.

$\dfrac{2\pi - 3\sqrt{3}}{2}$ $\dfrac{1}{2}\left(2\pi - 3\sqrt{3}\right)$

23.

25.

$\pi + 3\sqrt{3}$ $9\pi + 27\sqrt{3}$

27. $\left(1, \dfrac{\pi}{2}\right), \left(1, \dfrac{3\pi}{2}\right), (0, 0)$

29. $\left(\dfrac{2 - \sqrt{2}}{2}, \dfrac{3\pi}{4}\right), \left(\dfrac{2 + \sqrt{2}}{2}, \dfrac{7\pi}{4}\right), (0, 0)$

31. $\left(\dfrac{3}{2}, \dfrac{\pi}{6}\right), \left(\dfrac{3}{2}, \dfrac{5\pi}{6}\right), (0, 0)$ **33.** $(2, 4), (-2, -4)$

35.

$(0, 0), (0.935, 0.363),$
$(0.535, -1.006)$

The graphs reach the pole at different times (θ-values).

37. 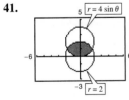   **39.**

$\dfrac{4}{3}\left(4\pi - 3\sqrt{3}\right)$ $11\pi - 24$

41. 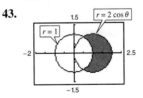   **43.**

$\dfrac{2}{3}\left(4\pi - 3\sqrt{3}\right)$ $\dfrac{\pi}{3} + \dfrac{\sqrt{3}}{2}$

45. $\dfrac{5a^2\pi}{4}$ **47.** $\dfrac{a^2}{2}(\pi - 2)$

49. (a) $(x^2 + y^2)^{3/2} = ax^2$

(b)

(c) $\dfrac{15\pi}{2}$

51. The area enclosed by the function is $\pi a^2/4$ if n is odd and is $\pi a^2/2$ if n is even.

53. $\dfrac{4\pi}{3}$ **55.** 4π **57.** 8

59. 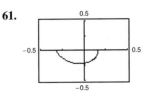   **61.**

About 4.16   About 0.71

63.

About 4.39

65. (a)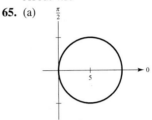

(b) $0 \le \theta < \pi$ (c) and (d) 25π

67. Sample answer: $f(\theta) = \cos^2 \theta + 1, g(\theta) = -\dfrac{3}{2}$

69. (a) 16π

(b)

θ	0.2	0.4	0.6	0.8	1.0	1.2	1.4
A	6.32	12.14	17.06	20.80	23.27	24.60	25.08

(c) and (d) $\dfrac{1}{4}$ of area: $\theta \approx 0.42$

$\dfrac{1}{2}$ of area: $\theta \approx 1.57 = \dfrac{\pi}{2}$

$\dfrac{3}{4}$ of area: $\theta \approx 2.73$

(e) No; The sector is the same fraction of the total area for any radius.

71. $\dfrac{\pi}{2}$ **73.** About 9.3655

75. Answers will vary.   **77.** A

Section 9.6   *(page 686)*

1. $\mathbf{u} = \mathbf{v} = \langle 2, 4 \rangle$ **3.** $\mathbf{u} = \mathbf{v} = \langle 6, -5 \rangle$

5. (a) $\langle 4, 2 \rangle$ **7.** (a) and (c)

(b)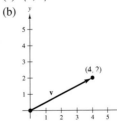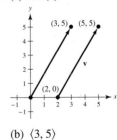

(b) $\langle 3, 5 \rangle$

9. (a) and (c)

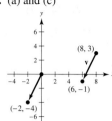

(b) $\langle -2, -4 \rangle$

11. (a) and (c)

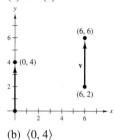

(b) $\langle 0, 4 \rangle$

13. (a) and (c)

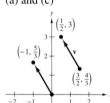

(b) $\langle -1, \frac{5}{3} \rangle$

15. The coordinates were subtracted in the wrong order; $\langle 4, 7 \rangle$

17. 4   **19.** $\sqrt{26}$ **21.** 17

23. (a) $\langle 6, 10 \rangle$ (b) $\langle -9, -15 \rangle$

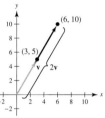

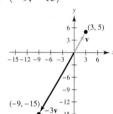

(c) $\langle \frac{21}{2}, \frac{35}{2} \rangle$ (d) $\langle 2, \frac{10}{3} \rangle$

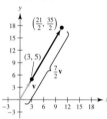

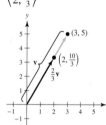

25. (a) $\langle \frac{8}{3}, 6 \rangle$ (b) $\langle 6, -15 \rangle$
(c) $\langle -2, -14 \rangle$ (d) $\langle 18, -7 \rangle$

27.

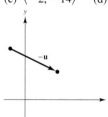

29.

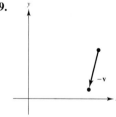

31.

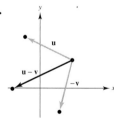

33. $(3, 5)$ **35.** $\left\langle \dfrac{\sqrt{17}}{17}, \dfrac{4\sqrt{17}}{17} \right\rangle$ **37.** $\left\langle \dfrac{3\sqrt{34}}{34}, \dfrac{5\sqrt{34}}{34} \right\rangle$

39. (a) $\sqrt{2}$ (b) $\sqrt{5}$ (c) 1   (d) 1   (e) 1   (f) 1

41. (a) $\dfrac{\sqrt{5}}{2}$ (b) $\sqrt{13}$ (c) $\dfrac{\sqrt{85}}{2}$ (d) 1   (e) 1   (f) 1

43. $\langle 0, 6 \rangle$ **45.** $\langle -\sqrt{5}, 2\sqrt{5} \rangle$ **47.** $\langle 3, 0 \rangle$

49. $\langle -\sqrt{3}, 1 \rangle$ **51.** $\left\langle \dfrac{2 + 3\sqrt{2}}{2}, \dfrac{3\sqrt{2}}{2} \right\rangle$

53. $\langle 2\cos 4 + \cos 2, 2\sin 4 + \sin 2 \rangle$

55. (a) $\theta = 0°$ (b) $\theta = 180°$ **57.** $a = \frac{7}{3}, b = \frac{14}{3}$

59. $a = 3, b = 1$ **61.** $a = 2, b = 10$

63. (a) $\pm \dfrac{1}{\sqrt{37}} \langle 1, 6 \rangle$ **65.** (a) $\pm \dfrac{1}{\sqrt{10}} \langle 1, 3 \rangle$

(b) $\pm \dfrac{1}{\sqrt{37}} \langle -6, 1 \rangle$ (b) $\pm \dfrac{1}{\sqrt{10}} \langle 3, -1 \rangle$

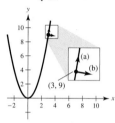

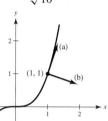

67. (a) $\pm \dfrac{1}{\sqrt{5}} \langle 1, 2 \rangle$

(b) $\pm \dfrac{1}{\sqrt{5}} \langle -2, 1 \rangle$

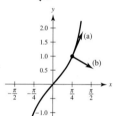

69. $\left\langle -\dfrac{\sqrt{2}}{2}, \dfrac{\sqrt{2}}{2} \right\rangle$ **71.** $(-4, -1), (6, 5), (10, 3)$

73. $\overrightarrow{CB}$: 1958.1 lb; $\overrightarrow{CA}$: 2638.2 lb   **75.** 71.3°; 228.5 lb

77. 10.7°; 584.6 lb   **79.** 84.46° north of east; 336.35 mi/h

81. 38.34° north of west; 882.9 km/h

83. Proof   **85.** $x^2 + y^2 = 25$ **87.** C

Section 9.7   *(page 695)*

1. $(-\infty, -1) \cup (-1, \infty)$ **3.** $(0, \infty)$ **5.** $[0, \infty)$

7. (a) $\langle \frac{1}{2}, 0 \rangle$ (b) $\langle 0, 1 \rangle$ (c) $\langle \frac{1}{2}(s + 1)^2, -s \rangle$
(d) $\langle 2\Delta t + \frac{1}{2}(\Delta t)^2, -\Delta t \rangle$

9. c   **10.** b   **11.** d   **12.** a

13.

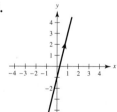

15.

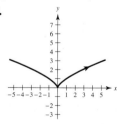

17.

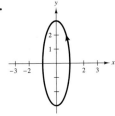

19.

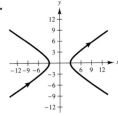

21. Sample answer: $\mathbf{r}(t) = \langle t, t + 7 \rangle$

23. Sample answer: $\mathbf{r}(t) = \langle t, (t - 2)^2 \rangle$

25. Sample answer: $\mathbf{r}(t) = \langle 5 \cos t, 5 \sin t \rangle$

27. Sample answer: $\mathbf{r}(t) = \langle 4 \sec t, 2 \tan t \rangle$

29. $\langle \pi, -1 \rangle$ **31.** $\langle 0, 3 \rangle$ **33.** $\langle 0, 0 \rangle$

35. $(-\infty, 0) \cup (0, \infty)$ **37.** $(0, 5]$

39. $\left[0, \dfrac{\pi}{2} \right) \cup \left(-\dfrac{\pi}{2} + n\pi, \dfrac{\pi}{2} + n\pi \right)$, n is a positive integer

41. $\mathbf{r}'(t) = \langle 2t, 1 \rangle$

$\mathbf{r}(2) = \langle 4, 2 \rangle$

$\mathbf{r}'(2) = \langle 4, 1 \rangle$

43. $\mathbf{r}'(t) = \langle -\sin t, \cos t \rangle$

$\mathbf{r}\left(\dfrac{\pi}{2} \right) = \langle 0, 1 \rangle$

$\mathbf{r}'\left(\dfrac{\pi}{2} \right) = \langle -1, 0 \rangle$

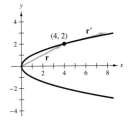

$\mathbf{r}'(2)$ is tangent to the

curve at $t = 2$.

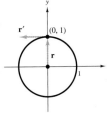

$\mathbf{r}'\left(\dfrac{\pi}{2} \right)$ is tangent to the

curve at $t = \dfrac{\pi}{2}$.

45. $\mathbf{r}'(t) = \langle e^t, 2e^{2t} \rangle$

$\mathbf{r}(0) = \langle 1, 1 \rangle$

$\mathbf{r}'(0) = \langle 1, 2 \rangle$

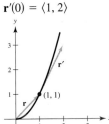

$\mathbf{r}'(0)$ is tangent to the curve at $t = 0$.

47. $\langle 3t^2, -3 \rangle$ **49.** $\left\langle \dfrac{3}{t}, \dfrac{1}{\sqrt{2t}} \right\rangle$ **51.** $\langle 2 \sin t, \sin t + t \cos t \rangle$

53. $\langle 6t, 1 \rangle$ **55.** $\langle -4 \cos t, -4 \sin t \rangle$ **57.** $\left\langle 9e^{-3t}, -\dfrac{1}{4t^{3/2}} \right\rangle$

59. (a) $\langle 3, 2t \rangle$ (b) $\langle 16, 8t \rangle$ (c) $\langle 7, 4t \rangle$

(d) $\langle 5, 4t \rangle$ (e) $\langle 40t, 15t^2 \rangle$ (f) $\langle 6, 8t \rangle$

61. (a) $\left\langle 1, \dfrac{1}{t} \right\rangle$ (b) $\langle 4e^t, 12t^2 \rangle$ (c) $\left\langle 1 + e^t, 3t^2 + \dfrac{1}{t} \right\rangle$

(d) $\left\langle 3 - e^t, \dfrac{3}{t} - 3t^2 \right\rangle$ (e) $\langle 5te^t + 5e^t, 20t^3 \rangle$ (f) $\left\langle 2, \dfrac{1}{t} \right\rangle$

63. $\langle t^2, t \rangle + \mathbf{C}$ **65.** $\left\langle \ln|t|, -\dfrac{2}{5}t^{5/2} \right\rangle + \mathbf{C}$

67. $\left\langle \dfrac{3}{8}(2t + 8)^{4/3}, \sec t \right\rangle + \mathbf{C}$

69. $\left\langle \ln\left| \dfrac{1}{3}(t + \sqrt{9 + t^2}) \right|, \arcsin \dfrac{t}{3} \right\rangle + \mathbf{C}$ **71.** $\langle 4, -3 \rangle$

73. $\langle a, a \rangle$ **75.** $\langle e^2 - 1, -e^2 - 1 \rangle$ **77.** $\langle 2e^{2t}, 3(e^t - 1) \rangle$

79. $\left\langle \dfrac{2 - e^{-t^2}}{2}, e^{-t} - 2 \right\rangle$ **81.** $\langle t, -16t^2 + 6t \rangle$

83. A vector-valued function $\mathbf{r}$ is continuous at $t = a$ if the limit of $\mathbf{r}(t)$ exists as $t \to a$ and $\lim\limits_{t \to a} \mathbf{r}(t) = \mathbf{r}(a)$. Sample answer:

$$\mathbf{r}(t) = \begin{cases} \langle 1, 1 \rangle, & t \geq 2 \\ \langle -1, 1 \rangle, & t < 2 \end{cases}$$

85. They are similar, but for a vector you integrate each component and then add a constant vector $\mathbf{C}$.

87–89. Proofs

91. (a)

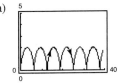

The curve is a cycloid.

(b) For $\|\mathbf{r}'(t)\|$, the minimum is 0 and the maximum is 2. For $\|\mathbf{r}''(t)\|$, the minimum and maximum are both 1.

93. Proof   **95.** True

97. False; The definite integral is a vector, not a real number.

99. D

Section 9.8   *(page 702)*

1. (a) $\mathbf{v}(t) = \langle 3, 1 \rangle$, $\|\mathbf{v}(t)\| = \sqrt{10}$, $\mathbf{a}(t) = \langle 0, 0 \rangle$

(b) $\mathbf{v}(1) = \langle 3, 1 \rangle$, $\mathbf{a}(1) = \langle 0, 0 \rangle$

(c)

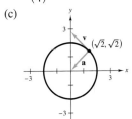

3. (a) $\mathbf{v}(t) = \langle 2t, 1 \rangle$, $\|\mathbf{v}(t)\| = \sqrt{4t^2 + 1}$, $\mathbf{a}(t) = \langle 2, 0 \rangle$

(b) $\mathbf{v}(2) = \langle 4, 1 \rangle$, $\mathbf{a}(2) = \langle 2, 0 \rangle$

(c)

5. (a) $\mathbf{v}(t) = \langle -2 \sin t, 2 \cos t \rangle$, $\|\mathbf{v}(t)\| = 2$,

$\mathbf{a}(t) = \langle -2 \cos t, -2 \sin t \rangle$

(b) $\mathbf{v}\left(\dfrac{\pi}{4} \right) = \langle -\sqrt{2}, \sqrt{2} \rangle$, $\mathbf{a}\left(\dfrac{\pi}{4} \right) = \langle -\sqrt{2}, -\sqrt{2} \rangle$

(c)

7. (a) $\mathbf{v}(t) = \langle 2 - \cos t, \sin t \rangle$, $\|\mathbf{v}(t)\| = \sqrt{5 - 4 \cos t}$,
$\mathbf{a}(t) = \langle \sin t, \cos t \rangle$

(b) $\mathbf{v}\left(\dfrac{3\pi}{2}\right) = \langle 2, -1 \rangle$, $\mathbf{a}\left(\dfrac{3\pi}{2}\right) = \langle -1, 0 \rangle$

(c)

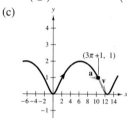

9. (a) $\langle 13, 8 \rangle$ (b) $3\sqrt{10}$ (c) $\langle 3t + 4, t + 5 \rangle$
11. (a) $\langle 13, 4 \rangle$ (b) 9.747 (c) $\langle t^2 + 4, t + 1 \rangle$
13. (a) $\langle 29, 12 \rangle$ (b) 28.728 (c) $\langle t^3 + 2, t^2 + 3 \rangle$

15. $\mathbf{v}(t) = \langle 2t, 3t + 4 \rangle$, $\mathbf{r}(t) = \left\langle t^2, \dfrac{3t^2}{2} + 4t \right\rangle$, $\mathbf{r}(2) = \langle 4, 14 \rangle$

17. $\mathbf{v}(t) = \left\langle 2t^2 + 5, \dfrac{t^3}{3} \right\rangle$, $\mathbf{r}(t) = \left\langle \dfrac{2}{3}t^3 + 5t + 4, \dfrac{t^4}{12} + 2 \right\rangle$,
$\mathbf{r}(2) = \left\langle \dfrac{58}{3}, \dfrac{10}{3} \right\rangle$

19. (a)

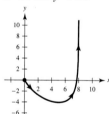

(b) $t = 3$ (c) 14.394
21. (a) $t \geq 0; t \geq 4$

(b) $\mathbf{r}(t) = \langle -8e^{-t/4} + 8, t - 5 \ln(t + 1) \rangle$
$\mathbf{a}(t) = \left\langle -\dfrac{1}{2}e^{-t/4}, \dfrac{5}{(t + 1)^2} \right\rangle$

(c) The particle is moving to the right for $t \geq 0$, but it never
reaches the line $x = 8$. The particle is moving down on the
interval $0 < t < 4$ and up on the interval $t > 4$. As $t \to \infty$,
$x \to 8$ and $y \to \infty$.

23. The initial condition was forgotten; $\langle \ln 4, e^3 \rangle$
25. $\mathbf{v}(t) = \langle b(\omega - \omega \cos \omega t), b\omega \sin \omega t \rangle$
$\mathbf{a}(t) = \langle b\omega^2 \sin \omega t, b\omega^2 \cos \omega t \rangle$

(a) $t = 0, \dfrac{2\pi}{w}, \dfrac{4\pi}{w}, \ldots$ (b) $t = \dfrac{\pi}{w}, \dfrac{3\pi}{w}, \ldots$

27. $\mathbf{v}(t) = \langle -b\omega \sin \omega t, b\omega \cos \omega t \rangle$
29. $\mathbf{a}(t) = \langle -b\omega^2 \cos \omega t, -b\omega^2 \sin \omega t \rangle$

$\mathbf{a}(t)$ is a negative multiple of a unit vector from $(0, 0)$ to
$(\cos \omega t, \sin \omega t)$. So, $\mathbf{a}(t)$ is directed toward the origin.
31. The particle could be changing direction.
33. No. This is true for uniform circular motion only.

35. (a) $\mathbf{v}(t) = \langle -6 \sin t, 3 \cos t \rangle$
$\|\mathbf{v}(t)\| = 3\sqrt{3 \sin^2 t + 1}$
$\mathbf{a}(t) = \langle -6 \cos t, -3 \sin t \rangle$

(b) $\|\mathbf{v}(0)\| = 3$, $\left\| \mathbf{v}\left(\dfrac{\pi}{4}\right) \right\| = \dfrac{3}{2}\sqrt{10}$, $\left\| \mathbf{v}\left(\dfrac{\pi}{2}\right) \right\| = 6$,
$\left\| \mathbf{v}\left(\dfrac{2\pi}{3}\right) \right\| = \dfrac{3}{2}\sqrt{13}$, $\|\mathbf{v}(\pi)\| = 3$

(c)

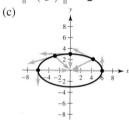

(d) The speed is increasing when the angle between $\mathbf{v}$ and $\mathbf{a}$ is
in the interval $\left[0, \dfrac{\pi}{2} \right)$. The speed is decreasing when the
angle is in the interval $\left(\dfrac{\pi}{2}, \pi \right]$.

37. B

Review Exercises for Chapter 9   *(page 704)*

1. e   **2.** c   **3.** b   **4.** d   **5.** a   **6.** f
7. Circle
Center: $\left(\dfrac{1}{2}, -\dfrac{3}{4} \right)$
Radius: 1

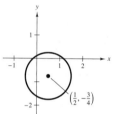

9. Hyperbola
Center: $(-4, 3)$
Vertices: $\left(-4 \pm \sqrt{2}, 3 \right)$
Foci: $\left(-4 \pm \sqrt{5}, 3 \right)$
$e = \dfrac{\sqrt{10}}{2}$
Asymptotes:
$$y = 3 \pm \sqrt{\dfrac{3}{2}}(x + 4)$$

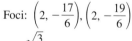

11. Ellipse
Center: $(2, -3)$
Vertices: $\left(2, -3 \pm \dfrac{\sqrt{2}}{2} \right)$
Foci: $\left(2, -\dfrac{17}{6} \right), \left(2, -\dfrac{19}{6} \right)$
$e = \dfrac{\sqrt{3}}{3}$

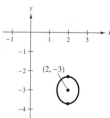

13. Parabola
Vertex: $(3, -1)$
Directrix: $y = -3$
Focus: $(3, 1)$

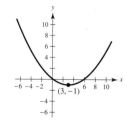

15. $(y - 2)^2 = 4(3)x$ **17.** $\dfrac{x^2}{36} + \dfrac{(y-1)^2}{20} = 1$

19. $\dfrac{(x-3)^2}{5} + \dfrac{(y-4)^2}{9} = 1$ **21.** $\dfrac{y^2}{64} - \dfrac{x^2}{16} = 1$

23. $\dfrac{x^2}{49} - \dfrac{(y+1)^2}{32} = 1$

25. (a) $(0, 50)$ (b) About 38,294.49

27.

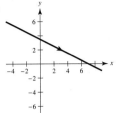

$x + 2y - 7 = 0$

29.

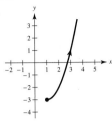

$y = (x - 1)^2 - 3,\, x \geq 1$

31.

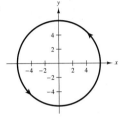

$x^2 + y^2 = 36$

33.

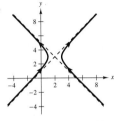

$(x - 2)^2 - (y - 3)^2 = 1$

35. Sample answers: $x = t,\, y = 4t + 3;\ x = t + 1,\, y = 4t + 7$

37.

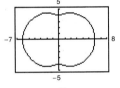

39. $\dfrac{dy}{dx} = -6,\ \dfrac{d^2y}{dx^2} = 0$

At $t = -1,\ \dfrac{dy}{dx} = -6,\ \dfrac{d^2y}{dx^2} = 0$;

Neither concave upward nor concave downward

41. $\dfrac{dy}{dx} = \dfrac{1}{8t^{3/2}},\ \dfrac{d^2y}{dx^2} = -\dfrac{3}{64t^{7/2}}$

At $t = 1,\ \dfrac{dy}{dx} = \dfrac{1}{8},\ \dfrac{d^2y}{dx^2} = -\dfrac{3}{64}$; Concave downward

43. $\dfrac{dy}{dx} = -4\cot\theta,\ \dfrac{d^2y}{dx^2} = -4\csc^3\theta$

At $\theta = \dfrac{\pi}{6},\ \dfrac{dy}{dx} = -4\sqrt{3},\ \dfrac{d^2y}{dx^2} = -32$; Concave downward

45. $\dfrac{dy}{dx} = -4\tan\theta,\ \dfrac{d^2y}{dx^2} = \dfrac{4}{3}\sec^4\theta\csc\theta$

At $\theta = \dfrac{\pi}{3},\ \dfrac{dy}{dx} = -4\sqrt{3},\ \dfrac{d^2y}{dx^2} = \dfrac{128\sqrt{3}}{9}$; Concave upward

47. (a) and (d)

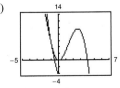

(b) $\dfrac{dx}{dt} = -1,\ \dfrac{dy}{dt} = 11,\ \dfrac{dy}{dx} = -11$ (c) $y = -11x - 6$

49. Horizontal: $(5, 0)$
Vertical: None

51. Horizontal: $(2, 2), (2, 0)$
Vertical: $(4, 1), (0, 1)$

53. $\dfrac{1}{54}(145^{3/2} - 1) \approx 32.3154$ **55.** 3π

57.

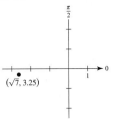

$(0, -5)$

59.

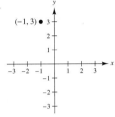

$(-2.6302, -0.2863)$

61.

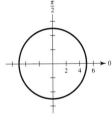

$\left(4\sqrt{2}, \dfrac{7\pi}{4}\right), \left(-4\sqrt{2}, \dfrac{3\pi}{4}\right)$

63.

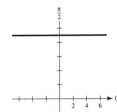

$\left(\sqrt{10}, 1.89\right), \left(-\sqrt{10}, 5.03\right)$

65. $r = 5$

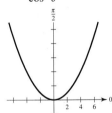

67. $r = \dfrac{9}{\sin\theta}$

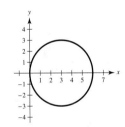

69. $r = \dfrac{4\sin\theta}{\cos^2\theta}$

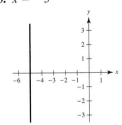

71. $(x - 3)^2 + y^2 = 9$

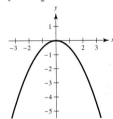

73. $x = -5$

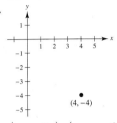

75. $y = -\dfrac{1}{2}x^2$

77.

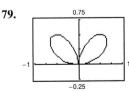

Sample answer:
$0 \leq \theta < 2\pi$

79.

Sample answer:
$0 \leq \theta < \pi$

81. Horizontal: $\left(\frac{3}{2}, \frac{2\pi}{3}\right), \left(\frac{3}{2}, \frac{4\pi}{3}\right)$

Vertical: $(0, 0), \left(\frac{1}{2}, \frac{\pi}{3}\right), \left(\frac{1}{2}, \frac{5\pi}{3}\right)$

83.

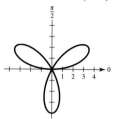

85.

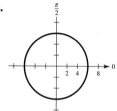

$\theta = 0, \frac{\pi}{3}, \frac{2\pi}{3}$

87.

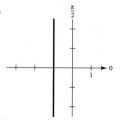

89.

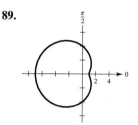

91.

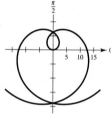

93.

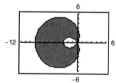

95. $\frac{9\pi}{20}$ **97.** $\frac{75\pi}{2}$

99. $\left(1 + \frac{\sqrt{2}}{2}, \frac{3\pi}{4}\right), \left(1 - \frac{\sqrt{2}}{2}, \frac{7\pi}{4}\right), (0, 0)$

101.

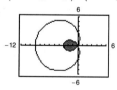

$\frac{18\pi - 27\sqrt{3}}{2}$

103.

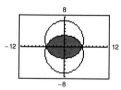

$9\pi + 27\sqrt{3}$

105.

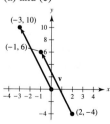

$27\pi - 40$

107. $\frac{5\pi}{2}$

109. (a) and (c)

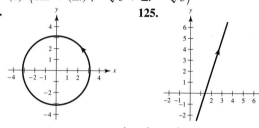

(b) $\langle -3, 10 \rangle$

111. (a) $\langle 12, -4 \rangle$ (b) $\langle 4, \frac{1}{2} \rangle$ (c) $\langle -5, -2 \rangle$ (d) $\langle 31, -3 \rangle$

113. (a) $\sqrt{5}$ (b) $\sqrt{10}$ (c) 1   **115.** $\langle 4, 4\sqrt{3} \rangle$

117. (a) $(-\infty, 0) \cup (0, \infty)$ (b) $(-\infty, 0) \cup (0, \infty)$

119. (a) $(0, \infty)$ (b) $(0, \infty)$

121. (a) $\langle 0, -\sqrt{2} \rangle$ (b) $\langle 4, 0 \rangle$

(c) $\langle (c - 1)^2, -\sqrt{c + 1} \rangle$

(d) $\langle 2\Delta t + (\Delta t)^2, -\sqrt{3 + \Delta t} - \sqrt{3} \rangle$

123.

125.

127. Sample answer: $\mathbf{r}(t) = \langle t, -\frac{3}{4}t + 3 \rangle$ **129.** $\langle 6, 1 \rangle$

131. $\langle 0, \frac{1}{2} \rangle$ **133.** $\langle -18t, 2t^{-1/3} \rangle$

135. $\langle -\pi \sin \pi t, 2 \sec t \tan t \rangle$ **137.** $\langle 2, -6 \rangle$

139. $\langle 64e^{-8t}, 8 \rangle$

141. (a) $\langle 3, 1 \rangle$ (b) $\langle 5, 10t \rangle$ (c) $\langle 4, 2t + 1 \rangle$

(d) $\langle -5, 2t - 2 \rangle$ (e) $\langle 18t, 6t - 3 \rangle$ (f) $\langle 3, 18t \rangle$

143. $\langle t, 4t^2 \rangle + \mathbf{C}$ **145.** $\langle 2t^{3/2}, 2 \ln t \rangle + \mathbf{C}$ **147.** $\langle \frac{32}{3}, 0 \rangle$

149. $\langle 2(e - 1), -2 \rangle$ **151.** $\langle t^2 + 1, e^t + 2 \rangle$

153. (a) $\mathbf{v}(t) = \langle 2t, 1 \rangle, \|\mathbf{v}(t)\| = \sqrt{4t^2 + 1}, \mathbf{a}(t) = \langle 2, 0 \rangle$

(b) $\mathbf{v}(1) = \langle 2, 1 \rangle, \mathbf{a}(1) = \langle 2, 0 \rangle$

155. (a) $\mathbf{v}(t) = \left\langle \frac{1}{2\sqrt{t}}, 5 \right\rangle, \|\mathbf{v}(t)\| = \sqrt{\frac{1}{4t} + 25},$

$\mathbf{a}(t) = \left\langle -\frac{1}{4t^{3/2}}, 0 \right\rangle$

(b) $\mathbf{v}(4) = \left\langle \frac{1}{4}, 5 \right\rangle, \mathbf{a}(4) = \left\langle -\frac{1}{32}, 0 \right\rangle$

157. (a) $\mathbf{v}(t) = \langle 1, -\sec^2 t \rangle, \|\mathbf{v}(t)\| = \sqrt{1 + \sec^4 t},$

$\mathbf{a}(t) = \langle 0, -2 \tan t \sec^2 t \rangle$

(b) $\mathbf{v}(0) = \langle 1, -1 \rangle, \mathbf{a}(0) = \langle 0, 0 \rangle$

159. (a) $(12, 5)$ (b) 16.3052 (c) $\langle 2t^2 + 3t - 2, 4t - 3 \rangle$

161. $\mathbf{v}(t) = \langle 0, 8t + 3 \rangle, \mathbf{r}(t) = \langle 1, 4t^2 + 3t + 5 \rangle, \mathbf{r}(4) = (1, 81)$

163. $\mathbf{v}(t) = \langle \sin t, -3 \cos t \rangle, \mathbf{r}(t) = \langle -\cos t, -3 \sin t \rangle,$

$\mathbf{r}(4) = \langle -\cos 4, -3 \sin 4 \rangle$

AP® Exam Practice Questions *(page 708)*

1. B   **2.** C   **3.** B   **4.** B   **5.** B   **6.** D   **7.** B

8. (a) 12.165 (b) 59.725 (c) 45.131

(d) $\langle -2.216, -0.334 \rangle$

9. (a) $\mathbf{a}(2) = \langle \frac{27}{32}, -8 \rangle$; Speed = 5.2926

(b) 13.0279 (c) $y = -3.5427x + 48.1535$

(d) The particle is never at rest on its domain.

10. (a) 13.338 (b) $\theta \approx 2.936$ radians; $x \approx -4.79$

(c) -11.2391; The particle is moving to the left on the rectangular coordinate system.

11. (a) 14.1969

(b) $-\sqrt{3}$; The particle is moving closer to the origin of the polar coordinate system.

(c) $-2\sqrt{3}$; The particle is moving to the left on the rectangular coordinate system.

12. (a) $\dfrac{1}{2}\displaystyle\int_0^{\pi/6}(1-2\sin\theta)^2\,d\theta$

    (b) $\dfrac{dx}{dt}=2\sin^2\theta-2\cos^2\theta-\sin\theta$

        $\dfrac{dy}{dt}=\cos\theta-4\sin\theta\cos\theta$

    (c) For $\theta=\pi$, $r=1$, $x=-1$, $y=0$, and $\dfrac{dy}{dx}=\dfrac{1}{2}$.

        $y-0=\dfrac{1}{2}[x-(-1)]$

        So, the tangent line is $y=\dfrac{1}{2}x+\dfrac{1}{2}$.

13. (a) dx/dt is positive at point B because the particle is moving to the right. dy/dt is positive at point B because the particle is moving upward.

    (b) $t=27^{1/6}$; There is a cusp at C.

    (c) $y(27^{1/6})=3$; The y-coordinate when $t=0$ is 0, so $y(t)=-\left(t^3-3\sqrt3\right)^{2/3}+3$.

    (d) $\dfrac{dy}{dt}\approx-\dfrac{2}{3}(1.837)$; Speed $\approx\dfrac{1.837\sqrt{13}}{3}$

AP® Practice Exam: Calculus AB
(page 711)

Section 1

1. A	**2.** B	**3.** D	**4.** B	**5.** D	**6.** D	**7.** C
8. C	**9.** B	**10.** A	**11.** D	**12.** A	**13.** D	
14. A	**15.** C	**16.** C	**17.** B	**18.** A	**19.** B	
20. B	**21.** C	**22.** B	**23.** D	**24.** C	**25.** B	
26. C	**27.** D	**28.** A	**29.** A	**30.** D	**31.** D	
32. D	**33.** C	**34.** B	**35.** B	**36.** B	**37.** B	
38. A	**39.** C	**40.** D	**41.** A	**42.** A	**43.** C	
44. C	**45.** C					

Section 2

1. (a) 0.777 parts/day

    (b) $N'(10)\approx0.910$; After 10 days on the job, the worker's production increases by 0.910 parts per day.

    (c) $t\approx13.159$ (d) $t\approx50.000$

2. (a) $t\approx2.507$, $t\approx3.545$; $v(t)$ changes from negative to positive at $t\approx2.507$. $v(t)$ changes from positive to negative at $t\approx3.545$.

    (b) Speeding up

    (c) $\displaystyle\int_0^3 v(t)\,dt\approx-1.154$ is the displacement of the particle over the time interval $0\le t\le4$.

        $\displaystyle\int_0^3 |v(t)|\,dt\approx2.017$ is the total distance traveled by the particle over the time interval $0\le t\le3$.

    (d) $t\approx0.817$

3. (a) $1<t<3$ and $4<t<5$; f' is positive and decreasing on those intervals.

    (b) $x=5$; $f'(x)$ changes from positive to negative at $x=5$.

    (c) $x=1$, $x=3$, $x=4$; f' changes from increasing to decreasing at $x=1$ and $x=4$. f' changes from decreasing to increasing at $x=3$.

    (d) $f(x)=6+\displaystyle\int_3^x f'(t)\,dt$

        $f(0)=-3$

        $f(5)=10$

4. (a)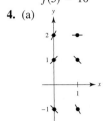

    (b) $\dfrac{d^2y}{dx^2}=y-2x-2$; concave downward; In Quadrant IV, $x>0$ and $y<0$, so $y-2x-2<0$.

    (c) Neither; For $(-2,4)$, $dy/dx=4-2(-2)=8\ne0$.

    (d) $m=2$, $b=2$

5. (a) $R'(5)\approx-52$ gal/h^2

    (b) $\displaystyle\int_0^8 R(t)\,dt\approx3120$ gal

        This is an overestimate because R is a decreasing function.

    (c) $9130-\dfrac{2250}{e^{8/3}}$ gal

    (d) Yes; $F(0)-R(0)>0$, $F(8)-R(8)<0$, and $F(t)-R(t)$ is continuous. So, the Intermediate Value Theorem guarantees at least one time t in $0\le t\le8$ for which $F(t)-R(t)=0$.

6. (a) 6π ft^3/min

    (b) Increasing; The rate of change of dh/dt is positive for all time $t>0$.

    (c) $h=\left(\tfrac{1}{4}t+\sqrt2\right)^2$

AP® Practice Exam: Calculus BC
(page 716)

Section 1

1. A	**2.** A	**3.** C	**4.** A	**5.** B	**6.** B	**7.** C
8. A	**9.** D	**10.** C	**11.** C	**12.** B	**13.** D	
14. D	**15.** D	**16.** A	**17.** B	**18.** A	**19.** A	
20. B	**21.** B	**22.** D	**23.** B	**24.** B	**25.** C	
26. C	**27.** B	**28.** D	**29.** D	**30.** C	**31.** D	
32. C	**33.** C	**34.** C	**35.** C	**36.** C	**37.** B	
38. D	**39.** D	**40.** B	**41.** A	**42.** A	**43.** A	
44. D	**45.** B					

Section 2

1. (a) $S'(2)\approx-152.158$, which means that the rate at which the sand is poured into the tank is decreasing by 152.158 tons per hour per hour at time $t=2$ hours.

    (b) $\displaystyle\int_0^8 S(t)\,dt\approx6410.673$ tons   (c) $t\approx4.101$ h

    (d) Decreasing; $S(5)\approx481.476<500$, which means that at time $t=5$, the rate at which sand is poured into the tank is less than the rate at which sand is removed from the tank.

2. (a) $(13.272, 0.5)$ (b) $t \approx 1.069$ (c) 3.285
(d) 22.911

3. (a) $G'(9) \approx 2.2$ MB/sec
(b) Yes; G is differentiable $\Rightarrow$ G is continuous (on the closed interval)
$$\frac{G(8) - G(4)}{8 - 4} = \frac{16.5 - 12.5}{4} = 1$$
Therefore, by the Mean Value Theorem, there is at least one time t, $4 \le t \le 8$, for which $G'(t) = 1$.

(c) $\frac{1}{12}\int_0^{12} G(t)\, dt \approx 14$ MB, which is the average number of megabytes downloaded over the time interval $0 \le t \le 12$ seconds.

(d) $V'(10) = \frac{3.52}{e^{1.1}}$ MB/sec

4. (a) $\frac{d^2y}{dx^2} = 3 - \frac{3}{2}x + \frac{1}{4}y$; concave upward; In Quadrant II, $x < 0$ and $y > 0$, so $3 - \frac{3}{2}x + \frac{1}{4}y > 0$.

(b) $m = 6, b = -12$

(c) (i) Neither; For $(0, 3)$, $\frac{dy}{dx} = 3(0) - \frac{3}{2} = -\frac{3}{2} \ne 0$.
(ii) $f(1) \approx \frac{39}{16}$

5. (a) Area $= \frac{1}{2}\int_{\pi/6}^{5\pi/6} [(2 + 6\sin\theta)^2 - 5^2]\, d\theta$
(b) $-\frac{1}{3}$ (c) $\frac{2}{3}$ rad/sec

6. (a) $x - \frac{x^3}{3!} + \frac{x^5}{5!} - \frac{x^7}{7!} + \frac{x^9}{9!} - \cdots + (-1)^{n+1}\frac{x^{2n-1}}{(2n-1)!} + \cdots$
(b) $-\infty < x < \infty$ (c) $\frac{1}{4^{11}11!}$

Appendix C

Appendix C.1   *(page A14)*

1. Rational   **3.** Irrational   **5.** Rational   **7.** Rational
9. Rational   **11.** $\frac{16}{33}$ **13.** $\frac{11}{37}$
15. (a) True   (b) False   (c) True   (d) False
(e) False   (f) False
17. x is greater than -4 and less than 2.

The interval is bounded.
19. x is no more than 5.

The interval is unbounded.
21. $y \ge -6$; $[-6, \infty)$ **23.** $0.02 < r \le 0.045$; $(0.02, 0.045]$
25. $x \ge \frac{1}{3}$ **27.** $-\frac{1}{2} < x < \frac{7}{2}$

29. $x > 6$ **31.** $-1 < x < 1$

33. $x \ge 13, x \le -7$

35. $a - b < x < a + b$

37. $-3 < x < 2$ **39.** $0 < x < 3$

41. $-3 \le x \le 1$ **43.** $-3 \le x \le 2$

45. $4; -4; 4$ **47.** (a) $-51; 51; 51$ (b) $51; -51; 51$
49. 1   **51.** (a) 14   (b) 10
53. (a) $|x - 12| \le 10$ (b) $|x - 12| \ge 10$ **55.** $|x| \le 2$
55. $|x| \le 2$ **57.** $|x - 2| > 2$ **59.** $x \ge 24$ units
61. $x \le 41$ or $x \ge 59$ **63.** (a) $\frac{22}{7}$ (b) $\frac{355}{113}$ **65.** b
67. False; Sample answer: The reciprocal of 2 is $\frac{1}{2}$.
69. True   **71.** True   **73–79.** Proofs
81. Sample answer:
$|-3 - 1| > |-3| - |1|$; $|3 - 1| = |3| - |1|$; Proof

Appendix C.2   *(page A21)*

1. (a)   **3.** (a)

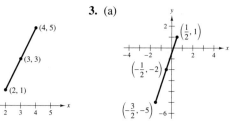

(b) $2\sqrt{5}$ (c) $(3, 3)$ (b) $2\sqrt{10}$ (c) $\left(-\frac{1}{2}, -2\right)$
5. (a)

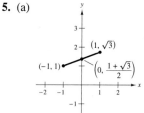

(b) $\sqrt{8 - 2\sqrt{3}}$ (c) $\left(0, \frac{1 + \sqrt{3}}{2}\right)$

7. Quadrant II   **9.** Quadrants I or III
11. Right triangle:
$d_1 = \sqrt{45}$
$d_2 = \sqrt{5}$
$d_3 = \sqrt{50}$
$(d_1)^2 + (d_2)^2 = (d_3)^2$
13. Rhombus: $d_1 = d_2 = d_3 = d_4 = \sqrt{5}$
15.

17. Collinear   **19.** Not collinear   **21.** $x = \pm 3$

23. $y = \pm\sqrt{55}$

25. $\left(\dfrac{3x_1 + x_2}{4}, \dfrac{3y_1 + y_2}{4}\right), \left(\dfrac{x_1 + x_2}{2}, \dfrac{y_1 + y_2}{2}\right),$
$\left(\dfrac{x_1 + 3x_2}{4}, \dfrac{y_1 + 3y_2}{4}\right)$

27. c   **28.** b   **29.** a   **30.** d   **31.** $x^2 + y^2 = 9$

33. $(x - 2)^2 + (y + 1)^2 = 16$ **35.** $(x + 1)^2 + (y - 2)^2 = 5$

37. $(x - 3)^2 + (y - 2)^2 = 10$ **39.** $x^2 + y^2 = 26{,}000^2$

41. $(x - 1)^2 + (y + 3)^2 = 4$ **43.** $(x + 2)^2 + (y - 4)^2 = 1$

 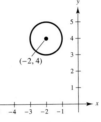

45. $x^2 + (y - 1)^2 = \dfrac{4}{3}$ **47.** $\left(x + \dfrac{1}{3}\right)^2 + \left(y - \dfrac{5}{2}\right)^2 = \dfrac{9}{16}$

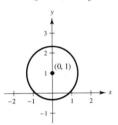 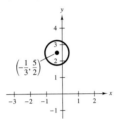

49. 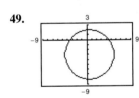   **51.**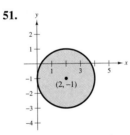

53. Proof   **55.** True   **57.** True   **59–61.** Proofs

Appendix C.3 *(page A31)*

1. (a) $396°, -324°$ (b) $240°, -480°$

3. (a) $\dfrac{19\pi}{9}, -\dfrac{17\pi}{9}$ (b) $\dfrac{10\pi}{3}, -\dfrac{2\pi}{3}$

5. (a) $\dfrac{\pi}{6}; 0.524$ (b) $\dfrac{5\pi}{6}; 2.618$

(c) $-\dfrac{3\pi}{4}; -2.356$ (d) $-\dfrac{\pi}{5}; -0.628$

7. (a) $270°$ (b) $210°$ (c) $-105°$ (d) $-151.1°$

9.

r	8 ft	15 in.	85 cm	24 in.	$\dfrac{12{,}963}{\pi}$ mi
s	12 ft	24 in.	63.75π cm	96 in.	8642 mi
θ	1.5	1.6	$\dfrac{3\pi}{4}$	4	$\dfrac{2\pi}{3}$

11. (a) $\sin\theta = \dfrac{4}{5}$ $\csc\theta = \dfrac{5}{4}$ (b) $\sin\theta = -\dfrac{5}{13}$ $\csc\theta = -\dfrac{13}{5}$
$\cos\theta = \dfrac{3}{5}$ $\sec\theta = \dfrac{5}{3}$ $\cos\theta = -\dfrac{12}{13}$ $\sec\theta = -\dfrac{13}{12}$
$\tan\theta = \dfrac{4}{3}$ $\cot\theta = \dfrac{3}{4}$ $\tan\theta = \dfrac{5}{12}$ $\cot\theta = \dfrac{12}{5}$

13. (a) Quadrant III   (b) Quadrant IV

15. $\dfrac{\sqrt{3}}{2}$ **17.** $\dfrac{4}{3}$

19. (a) $\sin 60° = \dfrac{\sqrt{3}}{2}$ (b) $\sin 120° = \dfrac{\sqrt{3}}{2}$
$\cos 60° = \dfrac{1}{2}$ $\cos 120° = -\dfrac{1}{2}$
$\tan 60° = \sqrt{3}$ $\tan 120° = -\sqrt{3}$

(c) $\sin\dfrac{\pi}{4} = \dfrac{\sqrt{2}}{2}$ (d) $\sin\dfrac{5\pi}{4} = -\dfrac{\sqrt{2}}{2}$
$\cos\dfrac{\pi}{4} = \dfrac{\sqrt{2}}{2}$ $\cos\dfrac{5\pi}{4} = -\dfrac{\sqrt{2}}{2}$
$\tan\dfrac{\pi}{4} = 1$ $\tan\dfrac{5\pi}{4} = 1$

21. (a) $\sin 225° = -\dfrac{\sqrt{2}}{2}$ (b) $\sin(-225°) = \dfrac{\sqrt{2}}{2}$
$\cos 225° = -\dfrac{\sqrt{2}}{2}$ $\cos(-225°) = -\dfrac{\sqrt{2}}{2}$
$\tan 225° = 1$ $\tan(-225°) = -1$

(c) $\sin 0 = 0$ (d) $\sin\pi = 0$
$\cos 0 = 1$ $\cos\pi = -1$
$\tan 0 = 0$ $\tan\pi = 0$

23. (a) 0.1736   (b) 5.759   **25.** (a) 0.3640   (b) 0.3640

27. (a) $\theta = \dfrac{\pi}{4}, \dfrac{7\pi}{4}$ (b) $\theta = \dfrac{3\pi}{4}, \dfrac{5\pi}{4}$

29. (a) $\theta = \dfrac{\pi}{4}, \dfrac{5\pi}{4}$ (b) $\theta = \dfrac{5\pi}{6}, \dfrac{11\pi}{6}$

31. $\theta = \dfrac{\pi}{4}, \dfrac{3\pi}{4}, \dfrac{5\pi}{4}, \dfrac{7\pi}{4}$ **33.** $\theta = 0, \dfrac{\pi}{4}, \pi, \dfrac{5\pi}{4}$

35. $\theta = \dfrac{\pi}{3}, \dfrac{5\pi}{3}$ **37.** $\theta = 0, \dfrac{\pi}{2}, \pi$ **39.** 5099 ft

41. (a) Period: π; Amplitude: 2   (b) Period: 2; Amplitude: $\dfrac{1}{2}$

43. Period: $\dfrac{1}{2}$; Amplitude: 3   **45.** Period: $\dfrac{\pi}{2}$

47. Period: $\dfrac{2\pi}{5}$

49. (a) 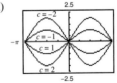   (b)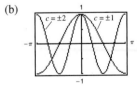

Change in amplitude   Change in period

(c)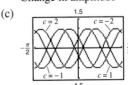

Horizontal translation

51. 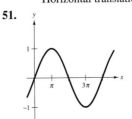   **53.**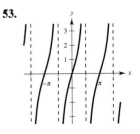

55.

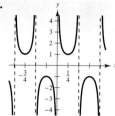

57.

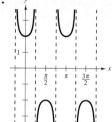

59.

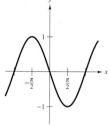

61.

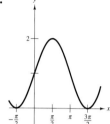

63. $a = 3$, $b = \dfrac{1}{2}$, $c = \dfrac{\pi}{2}$

65.

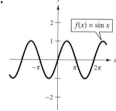

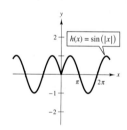

The graph of $|f(x)|$ will reflect any parts of the graph of $f(x)$ below the x-axis about the x-axis. The graph of $f(|x|)$ will reflect the part of the graph of $f(x)$ right of the y-axis about the y-axis.

67.

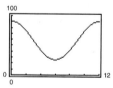

January, November, December

69. $f(x) = \dfrac{4}{\pi}\left(\sin \pi x + \dfrac{1}{3}\sin 3\pi x + \dfrac{1}{5}\sin 5\pi x + \cdots\right)$

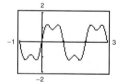

Index of Applications

Index

ALGEBRA

Factors and Zeros of Polynomials

Let $p(x) = a_n x^n + a_{n-1} x^{n-1} + \cdots + a_1 x + a_0$ be a polynomial. If $p(a) = 0$, then a is a *zero* of the polynomial and a solution of the equation $p(x) = 0$. Furthermore, $(x - a)$ is a *factor* of the polynomial.

Fundamental Theorem of Algebra

An *n*th degree polynomial has n (not necessarily distinct) zeros. Although all of these zeros may be imaginary, a real polynomial of odd degree must have at least one real zero.

Quadratic Formula

If $p(x) = ax^2 + bx + c$, and $0 \le b^2 - 4ac$, then the real zeros of p are $x = \left(-b \pm \sqrt{b^2 - 4ac}\right)/2a$.

Special Factors

$$x^2 - a^2 = (x - a)(x + a) \qquad\qquad x^3 - a^3 = (x - a)(x^2 + ax + a^2)$$
$$x^3 + a^3 = (x + a)(x^2 - ax + a^2) \qquad\qquad x^4 - a^4 = (x - a)(x + a)(x^2 + a^2)$$

Binomial Theorem

$$(x + y)^2 = x^2 + 2xy + y^2 \qquad\qquad (x - y)^2 = x^2 - 2xy + y^2$$
$$(x + y)^3 = x^3 + 3x^2 y + 3xy^2 + y^3 \qquad\qquad (x - y)^3 = x^3 - 3x^2 y + 3xy^2 - y^3$$
$$(x + y)^4 = x^4 + 4x^3 y + 6x^2 y^2 + 4xy^3 + y^4 \qquad (x - y)^4 = x^4 - 4x^3 y + 6x^2 y^2 - 4xy^3 + y^4$$
$$(x + y)^n = x^n + nx^{n-1} y + \frac{n(n - 1)}{2!} x^{n-2} y^2 + \cdots + nxy^{n-1} + y^n$$
$$(x - y)^n = x^n - nx^{n-1} y + \frac{n(n - 1)}{2!} x^{n-2} y^2 - \cdots \pm nxy^{n-1} \mp y^n$$

Rational Zero Theorem

If $p(x) = a_n x^n + a_{n-1} x^{n-1} + \cdots + a_1 x + a_0$ has integer coefficients, then every *rational zero* of p is of the form $x = r/s$, where r is a factor of a_0 and s is a factor of a_n.

Factoring by Grouping

$$acx^3 + adx^2 + bcx + bd = ax^2(cx + d) + b(cx + d) = (ax^2 + b)(cx + d)$$

Arithmetic Operations

$$ab + ac = a(b + c) \qquad \frac{a}{b} + \frac{c}{d} = \frac{ad + bc}{bd} \qquad \frac{a + b}{c} = \frac{a}{c} + \frac{b}{c}$$

$$\frac{\left(\dfrac{a}{b}\right)}{\left(\dfrac{c}{d}\right)} = \left(\frac{a}{b}\right)\left(\frac{d}{c}\right) = \frac{ad}{bc} \qquad \frac{\left(\dfrac{a}{b}\right)}{c} = \frac{a}{bc} \qquad \frac{a}{\left(\dfrac{b}{c}\right)} = \frac{ac}{b}$$

$$a\left(\frac{b}{c}\right) = \frac{ab}{c} \qquad \frac{a - b}{c - d} = \frac{b - a}{d - c} \qquad \frac{ab + ac}{a} = b + c$$

Exponents and Radicals

$$a^0 = 1, \quad a \ne 0 \qquad (ab)^x = a^x b^x \qquad a^x a^y = a^{x+y} \qquad \sqrt{a} = a^{1/2} \qquad \frac{a^x}{a^y} = a^{x-y} \qquad \sqrt[n]{a} = a^{1/n}$$

$$\left(\frac{a}{b}\right)^x = \frac{a^x}{b^x} \qquad \sqrt[n]{a^m} = a^{m/n} \qquad a^{-x} = \frac{1}{a^x} \qquad \sqrt[n]{ab} = \sqrt[n]{a}\,\sqrt[n]{b} \qquad (a^x)^y = a^{xy} \qquad \sqrt[n]{\frac{a}{b}} = \frac{\sqrt[n]{a}}{\sqrt[n]{b}}$$